**RUGBY
FOOTBALL
UNION**

THE
OFFICIAL
RFU
CLUB
DIRECTORY
2001-2002

RUGBY
FOOTBALL
UNION

THE
OFFICIAL
RFU
CLUB
DIRECTORY
2001-2002

ALL RFU
AFFILIATED CLUBS
INCLUDED

EDITOR & STATISTICIAN
STEPHEN MCCORMACK

Queen Anne Press

First published in Great Britain in 2001 by
Queen Anne Press
a division of Lennard Associates Limited
Mackerye End, Harpenden
Hertfordshire AL5 5DR

© Tony Williams Publications Ltd.
Helland, North Curry, Taunton TA3 6DU

A CIP catalogue record for this book
is available from the British Library

ISBN 1 85291 640 0

The publishers wish to confirm that the views expressed in articles and reviews in this publication are not necessarily those of the Rugby Football Union, any sponsor or indeed agencies employed by the RFU or sponsors.

Compiled, typeset and designed by
Tony Williams Publications Ltd.
Helland, North Curry, Taunton TA3 6DU

Printed and bound in Great Britain by
Butler & Tanner, Frome & London

FOREWORD

BY FRANCIS BARON
CHIEF EXECUTIVE

**RUGBY
FOOTBALL
UNION**

Covering every club affiliated to the Rugby Football Union, this Official RFU Club Directory is an essential reference book for club rugby in England and the most comprehensive guide available.

I can thoroughly recommend it as the Club Directory continues to prove an invaluable handbook for the entire game, from players to referees and coaches to supporters.

Everything is included: contact information, directions to grounds, club colours for all levels of the game. Anyone heading off on a Saturday for an away game only needs to turn to the index and there will be no more heading the wrong way down highways and byways as kick-off approaches.

I am happy to recommend the Directory and delighted to wish everyone involved with rugby union in England an enjoyable and successful season.

SEASON 2000-2001 ended with the English rugby union family still together - if only just, according to speculation. Talk of breakaways and splits evolved into a July peace agreement which saw the Premiership clubs sign up to an eight-year agreement.

The deal included automatic one-up one-down movement for at least the next two seasons on a topic that fires argument like no other in the English game. For the moment, the league competition still embraces nearly 1,000 clubs from plc Leicester to the amateur ways of Old Rubberduckians. The "seamless game" created in 1987 is still intact.

There are some very persuasive economic arguments why the elitists should wind up the drawbridge, though it must be remembered that only five of the present 12 clubs in the Zurich Premiership - Bath, Leicester, Harlequins, Gloucester and Wasps - have remained untouched by life outside the top division. Officials at Bristol, Leeds, London Irish, Newcastle, Northampton, Saracens and Sale should remember tortuous fortunes that include three near cases of bankruptcy and being beholden to the whims of rich men.

English professional rugby has progressed positively in many ways over the last five years. The improved standards of fitness and quality of play is a testimony to the players and coaches. However, the most disturbing fact is that the clubs have not recognised that their biggest potential supporter base lies among the junior clubs. Too few have gone out to build a bridge that straddles the whole game. In the days of falling numbers playing recreational rugby, the top clubs must realise, and accept, their role in fostering the sport. An emphasis on the elite is all well and good, but without proper nourishment of grassroots (excuse the cliché) then the whole tree will fall.

Having delivered the sermon, let's pay tribute to Leicester, the champion club. That glorious last-minute try by Leon Lloyd to pip Stade Francais will be forever replayed as the crowning moment of a triple-winning season. Whether it be a spring day in Paris or a murky winter's afternoon at Welford Road, 2000-2001 will be remembered as the season of the Tiger.

Week-in, week-out Leicester were a bound ahead of opponents, gaining them a title haul of Heineken Cup, Zurich Premiership and play-off that is unlikely to be matched. In sober moments, even the most one-eyed Tiger might agree.

Leicester have set the standards in England to an extent that they have become the equivalent of Manchester United. Such success - three consecutive Premiership titles - makes them the 'team to beat.'

How manager Dean Richards and chief coach John Wells combine Neil Back, Josh Kronfeld, Martin Corry and Lewis Moody into a new back-row is akin to Alex Ferguson trying to mix the likes of David Beckham and Juan Veron.

The beauty of sport is that as one season ends another appears on the horizon. No sooner had Leicester returned from the Parc des Princes than Richards was completing his plotting and planning for a new campaign. Indeed, he had

> **An emphasis on the elite is all well and good, but without proper nourishment of grassroots (excuse the cliché) then the whole tree will fall**

already made crucial decisions in the agreements to sign Kronfeld, the former All Black flanker, and Rod Kafer, the Australian centre.

Kronfeld and Kafer will need no telling that Leicester's success is based on the team ethic. "Do it our way, or get out," is the gist of Richards' philosophy. So far it has proved a winning way. Based on a group of players from his own days as No 8 and captain, he has proved adept at evolving a team that no longer relies on forward moves led by Back, Corry and Martin Johnson. To beat Stade Francais by three tries to nil showed Leicester to be the best, most consistent side in Europe.

Leicester gained that status by winning crucial games when the TV spotlight was focused on other games. Club professionals are growing accustomed to playing Premiership matches on weekends dominated by showpiece autumn internationals at Twickenham.

Yet despite the loss of Johnson, Corry, Back and Austin Healey, Leicester emerged from the autumn of 2000 with the Premiership virtually in the bag. After a memorable 31-28 success against Gloucester (one of seven Premiership matches won by seven points or less) on the first weekend in December, the Tigers led second-placed Wasps by six points to prompt thoughts of a third title. By New Year, the prize was virtually secured after a dropped goal from Andy Goode stopped Bath at the Rec.

Leicester grew in strength as the season headed towards the spring. Comfortable victories over London Irish, Northampton and Bath in the inaugural play-off competition highlighted how opponents had lost form and impetus. Surely, some team will mount a prolonged challenge in season 2001-2002?

And for those who forget then remember that Leicester did lose to Saracens and Bristol before starting out on their unbeaten run of 12 Premiership games. That early-season blip also featured a tricky evening at Welford Road when Rotherham, the Premiership newcomers, competed on equal terms.

Despite a resilient pack, Rotherham did not possess the match-winning speed to make a lasting impression. Two wins out of 22 was a disappointing return for a club that have risen like no other on the English league ladder.

The most startling aspect of Rotherham's rise and fall is that they possessed a squad 20-30 points better than the one Leeds put out to win the Second Division. It's a massive leap, but one several clubs are still trying to take. Mention ring-fenced leagues to the likes of Worcester, Bracknell, Rosslyn Park, Stourbridge or Sedgley Park and you will be met by fierce denunciations of the idea. For some the dream is still alive.

Rob Wildman (Daily Telegraph)

British Lions, England and Leicester Tigers captain Martin Johnson turned in one of the greatest ever seasons by a player last season.

July this year.

We decided it was worth documenting and opposite have listed all his matches – it makes for impressive reading.

His season started way back in August 2000 when the Zurich Premiership kicked off and Leicester picked up two points in a narrow win at Loftus Road against London Wasps.

From then on till Christmas Johnson played rugby every week and in one week played twice – 19 consecutive weeks.

He had January off due to his suspension for an incident involving Saracens's Australian outside half Duncan McRea.

During the season he finished on the losing side just five times in his 41 matches. After losing to Pontypridd, in October 2000, Johnson went eight months without playing on the losing side in a match – in total that was 28 matches before the Lions lost the second test in

Overall record:

Started	38	matches
Came on as a replacement	3	matches
Total appearances	41	
Won	35	(including 28 consecutive matches)
Drawn	1	
Lost	5	

He played 19 consecutive weeks from the start of the season – plus a mid week match.
He did not play in January due to a suspension for an incident against Saracens during their Tetley's Bitter Cup match.

Record by Competition

Zurich Premiership –	Won 14	Drawn 1	Lost 2
Heineken Cup –	Won 5		Lost 1
Zurich Play-offs –	Won 3		
Tetley's Bitter Cup –	Won 3		
England –	Won 7		
British Lions –	Won 3		Lost 2

Stephen McCormack

2000

Aug 19	Leicester beat London Wasps 24-22 (A)	Zurich Premiership
Aug 27	Leicester beat Newcastle 25-22 (A)	Zurich Premiership
Sept 2	Leicester beat Northampton 33-19 (H)	Zurich Premiership
Sept 6	Leicester beat Rotherham 26-18 (H)	Zurich Premiership
Sept 10	Leicester lost to Saracens 9-17 (A)	Zurich Premiership
Sept 16	Leicester beat London Irish 33-20 (H)	Zurich Premiership
Sept 23	Leicester lost to Bristol 20-24 (A)	Zurich Premiership
Sept 30	Leicester drew with Sale 17-17 (A)	Zurich Premiership
Oct 7	Leicester beat Pau 46-18 (H)	Heineken Cup
Oct 15	Leicester beat Glasgow Caledonians 33-21 (A)	Heineken Cup
Oct 20	Leicester lost to Pontypridd 11-18 (A)	Heineken Cup
Oct 28	Leicester beat Pontypridd 27-19 (H)	Heineken Cup
Nov 4	Leicester beat Otley 83-11 (H) Replacement	Tetley's Bitter Cup
Nov 11	Leicester beat Gloucester 25-13 (A)	Tetley's Bitter Cup
Nov 18	England beat Australia 22-19 (H)	Cook Cup
Nov 25	England beat Argentina 19-0 (H)	International
Dec 2	England beat South Africa 25-17	International
Dec 9	Leicester beat Saracens 41-24 (H)	Tetley's Bitter Cup
Dec 16	Leicester beat Bath 27-19 (H)	Zurich Premiership
Dec 26	Leicester beat Rotherham 27-9 (A)	Zurich Premiership

2001

Feb 3	England beat Wales 44-15 (A)	Six Nations
Feb 6	Leicester beat Bristol 17-10 (H) Replacement	Zurich Premiership
Feb 10	Leicester beat London Irish 28-9 (A)	Zurich Premiership
Feb 17	England beat Italy 80-23 (H)	Six Nations
Feb 24	Leicester beat Saracens 56-15 (H)	Zurich Premiership
Mar 3	England beat Scotland 43-3 (H)	Six Nations
Mar 6	Leicester beat Sale 24-12 (H)	Zurich Premiership
Mar 12	Leicester beat Northampton 12-9 (A)	Zurich Premiership
Mar 17	Leicester beat Newcastle 51-7 (H)	Zurich Premiership
Mar 21	Leicester beat Gloucester 19-15 (N)	Heineken Cup
Apr 7	England beat France 48-19 (H)	Six Nations
Apr. 14	Leicester beat Harlequins 37-5 (H)	Zurich Premiership
Apr 28	Leicester beat London Irish 24-11 (H)	Zurich Play-offs
May 5	Leicester beat Northampton 17-13 (H) Replacement	Zurich Play-offs
May 13	Leicester beat Bath 22-10 (N)	Zurich Play-offs
May 20	Leicester beat Stade Francais 34-30 (N)	Heineken Cup
Jun 16	British Lions beat Queensland 42-8 (A)	
Jun 23	British Lions beat New South Wales 41-24 (A)	
Jun 30	British Lions beat Australia 29-13 (A)	
Jul 7	British Lions lost to Australia 14-35 (A)	
Jul 14	British Lions lost to Australia 23-29 (A)	

TETLEY'S BITTER CUP SECTION

Tetley's Bitter Cup 2000-01

First Round

(Saturday 23rd September)

Darlington 32 Aspatria 15
Darlington MP 38 Broughton Park 14
Dorchester 24 Staines 21
Dunstabilians 26 Dudley Kingswinford 34
Gloucester OB 17 Cheltenham 29
Gordano 31 Camborne 22
Halifax 18 Tynedale 19
Havant 31 Harlow 17
Launceston 26 Truro 20
Leicester Lions 28 Scunthorpe 14
Liverpool St H 33 Driffield 28
Longton 29 Hinckley 15
Norwich 3 Westcombe Park 7
Old Colfeians 39 Basingstoke 3
Selby 14 West Park St Helens 20
Swanage & Wareham 18 Amersham & Chiltern 12
Weston 15 Barnstaple 46
Whitchurch 22 Spalding 9
Wimbledon 10 Haywards Heath 38
Worthing 8 Cheshunt 9

Second Round

(Saturday 7th October)

Barking 24 Tabard 8
Blackheath 9 Swanage & Wareham 7
Bracknell 45 Dorchester 0
Camberley 28 Barnstaple 26
Cheshunt 18 Clifton 12
Darlington MP 21 West Park St Helens 3
Fylde 16 Whitchurch 11
Havant 13 Penzance & Newlyn 32
Launceston 40 Gordano 10
Liverpool St Helens 23 Nuneaton 7
New Brighton 40 Leicester Lions 17
Newbury 45 Haywards Heath 21
Nottingham 19 Morley 23
Old Colfeians 17 North Walsham 21
Plymouth 54 Westcombe Park 6
Preston Grasshoppers 49 Bedford Athletic 19
Reading 49 Cheltenham 8
Redruth 10 Esher 14
Rosslyn Park 30 Lydney 3
Rugby Lions 16 Harrogate 15
Sandal 14 Tynedale 15
Sedgley Park 17 Kendal 9
Stourbridge 13 Doncaster 9
Walsall 17 Dudley Kingswinford 21
Wharfedale 28 Darlington 17
West Hartlepool 8 Longton 15

London One side Old Colfeians beat last year's London One Champions Basingstoke comfortably. They won by 36 points which was the biggest winning margin in the first round. Other teams knocking out National League sides were Darlington and Barnstaple.
Darlington with home advantage took care of Aspatria whilst Barnstaple make the second round after narrowly losing to National Three South side Redruth last season.
In the big Midlands One match Leicester Lions beat Scunthorpe, but by the end of the season it was Scunthorpe who had come good and won the Midlands One title from Leicester Lions.
Darlington Mowden Park, who were the shock team last season making the fifth round before going out to Harlequins, were comfortably home winners against Broughton Park, who they did the double over last season in the league.

Sedgley Park kept up their excellent cup record and yet again beat a side from above them in the league structure. This time they dispatched Kendal who were Three North Champions last season.
Longton from Midlands One beat National Two side West Hartlepool away from home.
Cheshunt from London Two North beat Clifton from National Three South.

Third round

(Saturday 21st October)

Barking 17 Rosslyn Park 29

Bedford 45 Sedgley Park 15

Birmingham & Solihull 29 Orrell 25

Bracknell 33 Cheshunt 3

Coventry 30 Preston Grasshoppers 19

Darlington MP 27 North Walsham 10

Esher 38 Camberley 24

Exeter 29 Stourbridge 15

Fylde 10 Manchester 33

Leeds Tykes 100 Morley 0

Liverpool St Helens 17 Rugby Lions 48

London Welsh 44 Blackheath 3

Moseley 6 Worcester 34

New Brighton 15 Newbury 11

Otley 26 Henley Hawks 24

Penzance & Newlyn 22 Wakefield 26

Plymouth 21 Wharfedale 11

Reading 31 Launceston 25

Tynedale 23 Longton 11

Waterloo 57 Dudley Kingswinford 27

Three South leaders Plymouth beat Wharfedale from the league above at home 21-11.
Leeds Tykes ran up 100 points as they beat near neighbours Morley 100-0 at Headingley.
Three North side New Brighton put out National Two side Newbury at home 15-11, thanks to five Paul Brett penalties.
North One side Darlington Mowden Park were at it again as they knocked out National Three South side North Walsham 27-10 at home to continue their amazing Cup success over the last two years.
In the three all National One matches Worcester won at Moseley, whilst Birmingham & Solihull and Otley had home wins against Orrell and Henley Hawks respectively.

Fourth Round

(Saturday 4th November)

Bath 18 Gloucester 24
Bedford 24 Saracens 54
Birmingham & Solihull 16 Darlington MP 10
Bristol 22 Wasps 17
Esher 26 Waterloo 27
Exeter 12 London Irish 57
Leicester 83 Otley 11
Northampton 73 Leeds Tykes 35
Plymouth Albion 8 Harlequins 36
Rosslyn Park 13 Newcastle Falcons 25
Rugby Lions 26 Manchester 38
Tynedale 12 Worcester 76
Wakefield 31 Bracknell 23

(Sunday 5th November)

New Brighton 17 London Welsh 32
Reading 27 Rotherham 46
Sale 37 Coventry 19

Bath went out in a West Country derby to Gloucester in a closely contested match for the second season running. This time, though Gloucester won at the Recreation Ground, a rare feat for them in recent times.
Holders Wasps were beaten at the first hurdle in their defence of the title at Bristol.
There were no instances of teams from lower leagues beating teams from above in this round.
Esher gave Waterloo a run for their money before going down by a single point 26-27.
In Leicester's 83-11 win against Otley second half replacement Perry Freshwater, playing hooker, grabbed a hat trick of tries. Andy Goode, playing at full back, converted nine of Leicester's tries and scored a try in a 23 point haul.
Another player kicking nine conversion was former England international Paul Grayson as Northampton ran in 11 tries against Leeds Tykes.
Top scorer of the day, though, was the Worcester full back Sateki Tuipulotu who scored four tries and kicked eight conversions in a 36 point haulas Worcester beat Tynedale 76-12.

Fifth Round

Saturday 11th November

Gloucester 13 Leicester 25
Harleqins 38 Manchester 8
London Welsh 10 London Irish 33
Northampton 47 Birmingham & Solihull 14
Wakefield 23 Waterloo 35

Sunday 12th November

Newcastle 32 Bristol 16
Sale 20 Rotherham 12
Saracens 42 Worcester 13

In the four matches between Zurich Premiership sides and teams from the National One it was the Premiership sides who came out on top.
In the all National One clash Waterloo managed a good win at Wakefield to advance to the quarter-finals, the only side still left in the competition from outside the Premiership..
In the big clash of the round Leicester went to Kingsholm and came away with an excellent victory.

Quarter Finals

Saturday 8th Decmber

Harlequins 11 Northampton 6
Leicester 41 Saracens24

Sunday 9th December

Newcastle 33 London Irish 29
Sale 59 Waterloo 12

Despite their poor league form Harlequins continue to do well in the Cup competitions. The match against Northampton was a close affair and a try from Steve White-Cooper in the second half proved the difference.
Leicester were comfortable winners over Saracens with four tries and 21 points from Tim Stimpson's boot.
Jonny Wilkinson played an influential role for the Falcons scoring 23 points as they narrowly beat London Irish.
Sale were comfortable winners aginst Waterloo, the only non Premiership side left in the competition, Steven Hanley grabbing a hat trick.

Semi- Finals

Saturday 6th January

Newcastle Falcons 37 Sale Sharks 25

Attendance: 6,257
Referee: R Goodliffe (Yorkshire)

NEWCASTLE: D Walder: M Stephenson (rep H Charlton 59-61), J Noon (rep R Cook 55), T May, V Tuigamala, J Wilkinson, G Armstrong: I Peel (rep G Graham 52), R Nesdale, M Hurter, S Grimes, G Wier, R Arnold (sin bin 40-50), A Mower, R Beattie (J Jenner 39).
SALE: V Going: S Hanley, M Shaw, M Deane(rep D Harris 56), J Robinson, C Hodgson (rep N Little 52), B Redpath: A Black (rep D Bell 41), J Clark (rep B Jackman 39), J Thiel (rep A Black 77), G Manson-Bishop, A Whittle, P Anglesea, R Appleyard, A Perelini.
Scoring sequence: (Newcastle first) 0-3, 3-3, 10-3, 13-3, 16-3, 23-3, 23-10 (half time), 26-10, 26-13, 31-13, 34-13, 34-20, 34-25, 37-25.
Scorers: Newcastle: Tries: May (27, 56), Beattie(14). Conversions: Wilkinson 2. Pens: Wilkinson 6 (11, 21, 25, 41, 60, 71)
Sale: Tries: Hodgson (36), Bell (66), Hanley (69). Conversions: Hodgson, Little. Penalty goals Hodgson 2 (7, 51)

Newcastle kept up their excellent record in semi finals as they made it five wins out of six.

Saturday 6th January

NEC Harlequins 22 Leicester Tigers 18

Attendance: 8,500
Referee: B Campsall (Yorkshire)

HARLEQUINS: R O'Neill: N Greenstock (rep N Woods 64), N Burrows, W Greenwood, B Daniel, C Chalmers, M Powell: J Leonard, K Wood, J Dawson (rep B Starr 59), G Morgan, S White-Cooper, R Winters (rep R Jenkins 64), D Wilson, E Peters.
LEICESTER: T Stimpson (rep G Gelderbloom 45-55): G Murphy, L Lloyd, P Howard, F Tuilagi, A Goode, A Healey: G Rowntree (rep P Freshwater 59), D West, D Garforth (rep R Nebbett 9-14), M Corry, B Kay, P Gustard (rep L Moody 15), N Back, W Johnson (rep A Balding 42-53, 69).
Scoring sequence: (Harlequins first): 5-0, 5-5, 5-12, 8-12, 8-15, 15-15 (half time), 22-15, 22-18.
SCORERS: Harlequins: Tries: Wood (9), Greenwood (40), Wilson (44). Cons: Chalmers 2 Pens: Chalmers (36).
Leicestern: Tries: Murphy (19), Goode (23). Con: Stimpson. Pens: Stimpson 2 (38, 63).

Harlequins reached their fifth Cup final in a tight match that was in the balance right till the end. They did out score Leicester three tries to two, but their goal kicking nearly let them down.

FINAL

Saturday 24th Febuary

NEC Harlequins 27 Newcastle Falcons 30

Attendance: 71,000
Referee: Ed Morrison (Bristol)

HARLEQUINS: R O'Neill: N Greenstock, W Greenwood, N Burrows, B Daniel (rep B Gollings 67), P Burke, M Powell: J Leonard, K Wood, J Dawson (rep B Starr 66), G Morgan (rep A Codling 79), S White-Cooper, P Sanderson, D Wilson (rep R Jenkins 63), R Winters.
NEWCASTLE: D Walder: M Stephenson, J Noon, T May, V Tuigamala, J Wilkinson, G Armstrong: M Ward (rep I Peel 49), R Nesdale, M Hurter, S Grimes, G Weir (rep H Vyvyan 50), R Devonshire (rep R Arnold 57), A Mower, J Jenner..

Scoring sequence:
(Harlequins first): 0-7, 3-7, 8-7, 11-7, 11-10, 14-10 (half time), 17-10, 17-13, 20-13, 20-18, 27-18, 27-23, 27-30.

SCORERS:
Harlequins: Tries: Wilson (15), Burke (70). Cons: Burke. Pens: Burke 5 (13, 28, 40, 43, 62).
Newcastle: Try: May (9,65), Jenner (72), Walder (80). Cons: Wilkinson 2. Pens: Wilkinson 2 (33, 46).

Newcastle won the Cup for a third time, but the first time since way back in 1977, when they were known as Gosforth.
For Harlequins it was a third final loss in five appearances. Paul Burke set a new record scoring 22 points in the final and still ended up on the losing side. Nick Greenstock became the third player to pick up losers medals for two different sides in the final.

TETLEY'S BITTER CUP
INDIVIDUAL MEDALLISTS
(asterisk signifys an appearance as a substitute)*

ACKERMAN, RA	Lon. Welsh	L - 85
ACKFORD, PJ	Harlequins	W - 88, 91 L - 92
ADCASTER, SD	Moseley	W - 82
ADEBAYO, AA	Bath	W - 90, 94, 95, 96
ADEY, GJ	Leicester	W - 79, 80, 81 L - 78
AKENHEAD, R	Moseley	L - 79
ALEXANDER, JR	Harlequins	L - 93
ALLEN, M	Northampton	L - 00
ALSTON, P	Northampton	L - 91
ANDERSON, TR	Gosforth	L - 81
ANDERSON, PG	Rosslyn Park	L - 75
ANDREW, CR	Wasps	L - 87, 95
ARCHER, G	Newcastle	L - 99
ARCHER, JS	Gosforth	W - 77 L - 81
ARMSTRONG, G	Newcastle	W - 01.L - 99
ARNOLD, R	Newcastle	W - 01.L - 99
ASHURST, N	Sale	L - 97
ASTLEY, KJ	Moseley	L - 79
AYRE, B	Moseley	L - 79
BACK, NA	Leicester	W - 93, 97 L - 94, 96
BAILEY, MD	Wasps	L - 86, 87
BAILWARD, CJ	Bedford	W - 75
BAINBRIDGE, S	Gosforth	L - 81
BAKER, SJW	Gloucester	W - 82
BALCOMBE, P	Wasps	L - "86
BALDWIN, D	Sale	L - 97
BALDWIN, G	Northampton	L - 91
BALL, I	Waterloo	L - 77
BARKER, RG	Leicester	L - 78
BARKER, N	Bedford	W - 75
BARLOW, RL	Rosslyn Park	L - 75
BARNES, S	Bath	W - 86, 87, 89, 90, 92, 94
	BristoL	W - 83 L - 84
BARNWELL, RC	Coventry	W - 74
	Leicester	W - 79, 80, 81 L - 83
BARTON, J	Coventry	W - 73
BATEMAN, A	Northampton	L - 00
BATES, SM	Wasps	L - 86, 87, 95
BATES, I	Leicester	W - 93 L - *83, 89
BAXENDALE, J	Sale	L - 97
BAYLISS, JA	Gloucester	W - 72
BAZALGETTE, MB	Rosslyn Park	L - 75
BEAL, N	Northampton	L - 00
BEALE, JD	Moseley	L - 79
BEATTIE, R	Newcastle	L - 99
BEIM, T	Sale	L - 97
BELL, JAH	Gosforth	L - 81
BELL, TP	Harlequins	W - 88
BELL, DE	Lon. Scot	L - 74
BENNETT, WN	Bedford	W - 75
BERINGER, GG	Lon. Irish	L - 80
BESS, G	Bath	W - 85, "87
BIGGAR, AG	Lon. Scot	L - 74
BIGGAR, MA	Lon. Scot	L - 74
BILLINGHAM, MF	Waterloo	L - 77
BLACK, A	Wasps	L - *98

BLACKHURST, F	Waterloo	L - 77
BLACKMORE, AG	Bristol	L - 88
BLAKEWAY, PJ	Gloucester	W - 82
BOGIRA, MK	Bristol	W - 83
BONNER, J	Wasps	L - 86, 87
BOOTH, MH	Gloucester	W - 72
BOWRING, K	Lon. Welsh	L - 85
BOYLE, LS	Leicester	L - 94
BOYLE, SB	Gloucester	W - 78 82
BRACKEN, K	Saracens	W - 98
BRADLEY, B	Lon. Welsh	L - 85
BRAIN, J	Gloucester	L - 90
BRAY, KA	Harlequins	L - 93
BREAKEY, RW	Gosforth	W - 76, 77 L - 81
BREEZE, J	Gloucester	L - 90
BRINN, A	Gloucester	W - 72
BRITTEN, JK	Gosforth	W - 76, 77
BRODERICK, JM	Coventry	W - 73, 74
BULPITT, MA	Rosslyn Park	L - 76
BURKE, P	Harlequins	L - 01
BURROWS, N	Harlequins	L - 01
BURTON, MA	Gloucester	W - 72, 78
BURWELL, T	Leicester	W - 79, 80
BUTLAND, R	Bath	W - 95
BUTLER, JL	Gosforth	L - 81
BUTLER, PE	Gloucester	W - 78
BYRNE, L	Rosslyn Park	L - *76
CALLARD, JEB	Bath	W - 90, 94, 95, 96
CARDUS, RM	Wasps	L - 86
CARDWELL, R	Coventry	W - 74
CARFOOT, DJ	Waterloo	L - 77
CARLING, WDC	Harlequins	W - 88, 91 L - 92, 93
CARR, JF	Bristol	W - 83 L - 84, 88
CARTMELL, J	Newcastle	L - *99
CASKIE, D	Gloucester	L - 90
CATT, MJ	Bath	W - 94, 96
CHADWICK, R	Bedford	W - 75
CHALLINOR, AP	Harlequins	L - 92, 93
CHIDGEY, DL	Bristol	L - 84
CHILCOTT, GJ	Bath	W - 84, 85, 86, 87, 89, 90, 92
CHILDS, G	Wasps	L - 95
CHRISTOPHERSON, SF	Waterloo	L - 77
CHUTER, G	Saracens	W - 98
CLARKE, BB	Bath	W - 92, 94, 95
CLEWS, RJ	Gloucester	W - 72, 78
COCKERILL, R	Leicester	W - 93, 97 L - 94, 96
CODD, RA	Rosslyn Park	L - 75
CODLING, A	Harlequins	L - 01*
COHEN, B	Northampton	L - 00
COKER, T	Harlequins	W - 91
COLLINGS, P	Bristol	L - 88
COLLINS, J	Lon. Welsh	L - 85
CONDON, HC	Lon. Irish	L - 80
CONSTABLE, R	Saracens	W - 98
CONNOR, L	Waterloo	L - 77
COOPER, MJ	Moseley	W - 82 L - 79
CORLESS, TF	Moseley	W - 82
CORLESS BJ	Coventry	W - 74
	Moseley	L - 79
CORSTORPHINE, AE	Lon. Scot	L - 74

COWLING, RJ	Leicester	W - 79, 80, 81		FISHER, CD	Waterloo	L - 77
	Gloucester	W - 72		FLETT, MA	Waterloo	L - 77
COWMAN, AR	Coventry	W - 73, 74		FLUSKEY, S	Rosslyn Park	L - 76
COX, GNJ	Moseley	W - 82 L - 79		FORD, P	Gloucester	W - 82
CREED, RN	Coventry	W - 73		FORFAR, DJ	Leicester	L - 78
CRERAR, RD	Lon. Scot	L - 74		FOUHY, D	Lon. Welsh	L - 85
CRONIN, DF	Bath	W - 89, 90		Foulkes-ARNOLD, M	Leicester	L - 83, 89
CUE, PC	Bristol	L - 84		FOULKS, D	Coventry	W - 74
CUNNINGHAM, R	Gosforth	L - 81		FOWLIE, DG	Lon. Scot	L - 74
	Bath	W - 84		FRASER, G	Lon. Scot	L - 74
CURTIS, PS	Harlequins	W - 88		FRIDAY, M	Wasps	W-"99 L - 98
CUSWORTH, L	Leicester	W - 79, 80, 81		FRIELL, AAS	Lon. Scot	L - 74
		L - 83, 89		FRY, MJ	Bristol	L - 73
CUTTER, AJ	Gosforth	W - 76, 77		GADD, J	Gloucester	W - 82 L - 90
DALLAGLIO, LBN	Wasps	W-99, 00 L - 95, 98		GALLAGHER, J	Coventry	W - 74
DANDY, MJW	Bristol	L - 73		GARFORTH, DJ	Leicester	W - 93, 97 L - 94, 96
DANIEL, B	Saracens	W - 98		GAYMOND, N	Bath	W - 84, 85
	Harlequins	L - 01		GIFFORD, CJ	Moseley	L - 79
DARNELL, IR	Coventry	W - 73, 74		GILLINGHAM, NK	Leicester	W - 80 L - 83
DAVIDSON, JS	Moseley	W - 82		GITTINGS, WJ	Coventry	W - 73, 74
DAVIES, GH	Wasps	L - 87		DE GLANVILLE, PR	Bath	W - 92, 94, 95, 96
DAVIS, EG	Harlequins	W - 88, 91 L - 92		GLENISTER, RJ	Harlequins	W - 91 L - 93
DAWE, RGR	Bath	W - 86, 87, 89, 90, 92,		GOLLINGS, B	Harlequins	L - 01*
		94, 95, 96		GOMERSALL, A	Wasps	W-99 L - *98
DAWSON, J	Harlequins	L - 01		GOODWIN, JM	Moseley	W - 82
DAWSON, M	Northampton	L - 00		GRAHAM, G	Newcastle	L - 99
DEMMING, R	Bedford	W - 75		GRAU, R	Saracens	W - 98
DENNEY, M	Wasps	W - 99, 00 L - 98		GRAY, JD	Coventry	W - 73
DESBOROUGH, JE	Moseley	W - 82		GRAYSON, P	Northampton	L - 00
DEVONSHIRE, R	Newcastle	W - 01		GREAVES, WH	Moseley	L - 79
DIAMOND, S	Sale	L - 97		GREEN, W	Wasps	W-99, 00 L - 98
DIPROSE, A	Saracens	W - 98		GREENSTOCK, N	Wasps	L - 95
DIX, J	Gloucester	W - 72			Harlequins	L - 01
DIXON, PJ	Gosforth	W - 76, 77		GREENWOOD, M	Wasps	L - 95
DOBLE, SA	Moseley	L - 72		GREENWOOD, W	Leicester	W - 97
DOBSON, I	Leicester	L - 83			Harlequins	L - 01
DODGE, PW	Leicester	W - 79, 80, 81		GREWCOCK, D	Saracens	W - 98
		L - 78, 83, 89		GRIFFIN, SM	Gosforth	W - 76
DOUBLEDAY, RJ	Bristol	W - 83 L - 84, 88		GRIFFITHS, J	Moseley	L - 72
DOUGLAS, MHJL	Lon. Welsh	L - 85		GRIMES, S	Newcastle	W - 01
DUCKHAM, DJ	Coventry	W - 73, 74		GUSCOTT, JC	Bath	W - *85, 87, 89, 90, 92,
DUGGAN, MJ	Leicester	L - 78				95
DUGGAN, IH	Bristol	W - 83 L - 88		GUSTARD, JS	Gosforth	W - 76, 77
DUN, AF	Bristol	L - 88		HAAG, M	Bath	W - 92, 95, 96
DUNN, KA	Wasps	L - 95		HACKNEY, S	Leicester	L - 96
	Gloucester	L - 90		HADLEY, A	Sale	L - 97
DUNSTON, I	Wasps	L - 95		HADLEY, N	Wasps	L - 95
EBSWORTH, M	Lon. Welsh	L - 85		HALL, C	Northampton	L - 91
EDWARDS, NGB	Harlequins	W - 88 L - 92		HALL, BP	Leicester	L - 78
EDWARDS, EF	Bedford	W - 75		HALL, JP	Bath	W - 84, 85, 86, 87, 89,
EGERTON, DW	Bath	W - 87, 89, 90				94
ELKINGTON, D	Northampton	L - 91		HALLIDAY, SJ	Harlequins	W - 91 L - 92
ERSKINE, D	Sale	L - 97			Bath	W - 85, 86, 87, 89, 90
ETHERIDGE, J	Northampton	L - 91		HAMLIN, M	Gloucester	L - 90
EVANS, BJ	Leicester	L - 83, 89		HANCOCK, K	Waterloo	L - 77
EVANS, GW	Coventry	W - 73		HANNAFORD, M	Gloucester	L - 90
FAIRBROTHER, KE	Coventry	W - 73, 74		HANNAFORD, RC	Bristol	L - 73
FALLON, JA	Bath	W - 92		HARDING, RM	Bristol	W - 83 L - 84, 88
FIDLER, JH	Gloucester	W - 78		HARE, WH	Leicester	W - 79, 80, 81
FIELD, R	Moseley	L - 79				L - 78, 89
FINLAN, JF	Moseley	L - 72		HARRIMAN, AT	Harlequins	W - *88, 91
FISHER, RG	Rosslyn Park	L - 75		HARRIS, JC	Leicester	W - 93 L - 94

HATTER, K	Moseley	L - 72	LAM, P	Northampton	L - 00
HAZLERIGG, AG	Leicester	W - 79 L - 78	LANE, DE	Moseley	L - 72
HEALEY, A	Leicester	W - 97	LANGHORN, RS	Harlequins	W - 88, 91 L - 93
HEDLEY, J	Gosforth	W - 77	LAWSON, RD	Moseley	W - 82
HENDERSON, R	Wasps	W - *99, 00 L - 98	LE CHEVALIER	Wasps	W - *00
HESFORD, R	Bristol	W - 83	LEE, MR	Bath	W - 84, 85, 86, 89
HILL, RJ	Bath	W - 84, 85, 86, 87, 89, 90, 92, 94	LEGG, S	Newcastle	L - 99
			LEONARD, J	Harlequins	W - 91 L - 93, 01
HILTON, DIW	Bath	W - 94, 96	LEOPOLD, DA	Lon. Irish	L - 80
HINTON, NP	Rosslyn Park	L - 75, 76	LEOTA, T	Wasps	W - 99, 00 L-"98
HOBLEY, MJ	Harlequins	L - 92	LEWIS, E	Lon. Welsh	L - 85
HOGG, ST	Bristol	W - 83 L - 84, 88	LEWIS, A	Bedford	W - 75
HOLLINS, AJ	Bedford	W - 75	LEWSEY, J	Wasps	W - 99, 00
HOLMES, G	Wasps	L - 86	LIGHT, B	Lon. Welsh	L - 85
HOLT, BC	Coventry	W - 73	LILEY, J	Leicester	W - 93 L - 96
HONE, W	Bristol	L - 88	LINK, G	Rosslyn Park	L - 75
HOOKER, C	Bedford	W - 75	LLOYD, L	Leicester	W - 97
HOPLEY, P	Wasps	L - 95	LLOYD-ROBERTS, G	Rosslyn Park	L - 76
HOPLEY, DP	Wasps	L - 95	LOGAN, K	Wasps	W - *99, 00
HORTON, JP	Bath	W - 84, 85	LONGSTAFF, M	Gloucester	W - 82
HORTON, NE	Moseley	L - 72	LOVETT, MS	Lon. Scot	L - 74
HOWARD, JM	Bedford	W - 75	LOZOWSKI, RAP	Wasps	L - 87
HOWELL, PR	Gloucester	W - 78	LUMSDEN, A	Bath	W - 96
HUGHES, J	Lon. Welsh	L - 85	LUNT, K	Waterloo	L - 77
HUNTER, I	Northampton	L - 91	LUXTON, TC	Harlequins	L - 92
HURTER, M	Newcastle	L - 99. W 01	LYNAGH, M	Sarecens	W - 98
JACKSON, N	Leicester	W - 81	MacKINNON	Northampton	L - *00
JACKSON, GT	Waterloo	L - 77	MacMILLAN, AJ	Gosforth	L - 81
JARDINE, R	Gloucester	W - 78	MADDERSON, CS	Harlequins	L - 93
JARRETT, JS	Gloucester	W - 72	MADSEN, DF	Gosforth	W - 76, 77
JEAVONS, NC	Moseley	W - 82 L - 79	MALLETT, J	Bath	W - *95, 96
JENKINS, R	Harlequins	L - 01*	MALLINDER, J	Sale	L - 97
JENNER, J	Newcastle	W - 01	MALONE, NG	Leicester	W - 97 L - 96
JOHNS, P	Saracens	W - 98	MANNIX, S	Sale	L - 97
JOHNSON, D	Gosforth	L - 81	MANTELL, ND	Rosslyn Park	L - 75, 76
JOHNSON, G	Saracens	W - 98	MARTIN, CR	Bath	W - 84, 85, 86, 87
JOHNSON, SR	Leicester	W - 79, 80, 81 L - 78, 83	MAY, T	Newcastle	W - 01.L - 99
JOHNSON, MO	Leicester	W - 93, 97 L - 94, 96	McDOWELL, NH	Gosforth	L - 81
JOINER, C	Leicester	W - 97	McFADYAN, CW	Moseley	L - 72
JONES, W	Lon. Irish	L - 80	McHARG, AF	Lon. Scot	L - 74
JONES, TW	Lon. Welsh	L - 85	McKAY, DJ	Rosslyn Park	L - 75
JONES, B	Leicester	L - 78	McKENZIE, RA	Lon. Scot	L - 74
JONES, L	Gloucester	W - 82	McKIBBIN, R	Lon. Irish	L - 80
JORDEN, AM	Bedford	W - 75	McKIBBIN, AR	Lon. Irish	L - 80
JOYCE, NJ	Leicester	W - 79, 80, 81 L - 78	MEANWELL, CA	Lon. Irish	L - 80
KARDOONI, A	Leicester	W - 93,* 97 L - 89, 94, 96	MENDEZ, F	Northampton	L - 00
			METCALFE, R	Northampton	L - 00
KEDDIE, RR	Lon. Scot	L - 74	MILLER, E	Leicester	W - 97
KEEN, B	Bedford	W - 75	MILLS, SGF	Gloucester	W - 78, 82
d'A KEITH-ROACH, P	Rosslyn Park	L - 75, 76	MITCHELL, J	Sale	L - 97
KENNEY, S	Leicester	W - 79, 80, 81 L - 78	MITCHELL, S	Wasps	L - 98
KENT, CP	Rosslyn Park	L - 76	MOGG, RR	Gloucester	W - 78, 82 L - 90
KERR, R	Moseley	L - 72	MOIR, C	Northampton	L - 00
KILFORD, WA	Leicester	L - 94	MOLLOY, D	Wasps	W - 99, 00 L - 95, 98
KILLICK, N	Harlequins	L - 93	MOON, RHQB	Harlequins	W - 88
KING, A	Wasps	W - 99, 00 L - 98	MOORE, BC	Harlequins	W - 91 L - 92
KING, S	Moseley	L - *79	MORDELL, R	Rosslyn Park	L - 76
KNIBBS, RA	Bristol	W - 83 L - 84, 88	MORGAN, D	Gloucester	L - 90
KNIGHT, S	Bath	W - *90	MORGAN, G	Harlequins	L - 01
KNIGHT, PM	Bristol	L - 73	MORLEY, AJ	Bristol	W - 83 L - 73, 84
LAIRD, R	Moseley	L - 79	MORRELL, CC	Moseley	L - 72
			MORRIS, D	Sale	L - 97

MORRIS, R	Gloucester	W - 72		PREECE, PS	Coventry	W - 73
MORRIS, R	Moseley	L - 72		PREEDY, M	Gloucester	W - 82 L - 90
MORRISON, JSC	Bath	W - 86, 87, 89		PRESTON, AJ	Gosforth	W - 76
MOSS, P	Northampton	L - 91		PRICE, C	Lon. Welsh	L - 85
MOWER, A	Newcastle	W - 01		PRINGLE, IN	Moseley	L - 72
MOYLES, JL	Rosslyn Park	L - 76		PRITCHARD, P	Gloucester	W - 82
MULLINS, AR	Harlequins	W - 88, 91 L - 92, 93		PROBYN, JA	Wasps	L - 86, 87
MUNDEN, AC	Bristol	L - 73		PULLIN, JV	Bristol	L - 73
MURPHY, BW	Lon. Irish	L - 80		RAFTER, M	Bristol	W - 83 L - 84
NANCEKIVELL, R	Northampton	L - 91		RALSTON, CS	Rosslyn Park	L - 76
NAYLOR, J	Newcastle	L - 99		RAVENSCROFT, S	Saracens	W - 98
NEEDHAM, RJ	Leicester	L - 78		RECARDO, A	Moseley	W - 82
NESDALE, R	Newcastle	W - 01.L - 99		REDFERN, SP	Leicester	W - 79, 80, 81
NEWBERRY, JA	Lon. Irish	L - 80				L - 78, 83, 89
NEWMAN, A	Northampton	L - 00		REDFERN, SB	Leicester	L - 83
NEWTON, M	Leicester	W - 79		REDMAN, NC	Bath	W - 84, 85, 86, 87, 90,
NICHOLLS, MJ	Gloucester	W - 72				92, 94, 95, 96
NICHOLLS, AH	Bristol	L - 73		REED, AI	Bath	W - 94
NICOL, AD	Bath	W - 96			Wasps	W - 00 L - *98
NINNES, BF	Coventry	W - 73, 74		REED, D	Waterloo	L - 77
NOON, J	Newcastle	W - 01		REES, CWF	Lon. Welsh	L - 85
NUTT, DR	Moseley	W - 82 L - 79		REES, D	Sale	L - 97
O'DONNELL, P	Lon. Irish	L - 80		REES, GL	Wasps	W-99 L - 86, 98
O'DRISCOLL, JB	Lon. Irish	L - 80		REES, A	Bath	W - 84
O'GRADY, D	Sale	L - 97		RENDALL, PAG	Wasps	L - 87
O'NEILL, R	Harlequins	L - 01		RICHARDS, D	Leicester	W - 93, "97
OJOMOH, SO	Bath	W - 92, *94, 95, 96				L - 83, 89, 94, 96
OLSEN, M	Saracens	W - *98		RICHARDSON, WP	Leicester	L - 89
OLVER, A	Saracens	W - *98		RIGBY, MA	Wasps	L - 86, 87
OLVER, JC	Northampton	L - 91		RIPLEY, AG	Rosslyn Park	L - 75, 76
	Harlequins	W - 88		ROBERTS, TC	Gosforth	W - 76, 77 L - 81
ORLEDGE, RJ	Bristol	L - 73		ROBINSON, D	Gosforth	W - 76, 77
ORWIN, J	Gloucester	W - 82		ROBINSON, RP	Leicester	L - 96
PACKMAN, F	Northampton	L - 91		ROBINSON, RA	Bath	W - 87, 89, 90, 92, 94,
PAGEL, G	Northampton	L - 00				95, 96
PALMER, JA	Bath	W - 84, 85, 86, 87, 89		RODBER, T	Northampton	L - 91, 00
PALMER, T	Gloucester	W - 72		RODGERS, AJ	Bristol	L - 73
PALMER, DJ	Bristol	W - *83 L - 84, 88		RODGERS, AK	Rosslyn Park	L - 75, 76
PARSLOE, SG	Gloucester	W - 82		ROGERS, DP	Bedford	W - 75
PASCALL, R	Gloucester	L - 90		ROISER, S	Wasps	W - 00 L - 98
PASK, P	Northampton	L - 91		ROLINSON, LJ	Coventry	W - 74
PATRICK, B	Gosforth	W - 76, 77 L - 81		ROLLITT, DM	Bristol	L - 73
PATRICK, HE	Gosforth	W - 76, 77		ROSE, MA	Wasps	L - 86, 87
PEARCE, GS	Northampton	L - 91		ROSSBOROUGH, PA	Coventry	W - 73, 74
PEARN, AFA	Bristol	L - 73		ROWNTREE, GC	Leicester	W - 93, 97 L - 94, 96
PEARS, D	Harlequins	W - 91 L - 92		RUSSELL, S	Lon. Welsh	L - 85
PEEL, I	Newcastle	W - 01*.L - *99		RUSSELL, MP	Harlequins	L - 92, 93
PEGLAR, DJ	Wasps	L - 86, 87		RYAN, D	Wasps	L - 95
PELLOW, R	Wasps	L - 86		SAGOE, FK	Bath	W - 89
PERRY, MH	Moseley	W - 82		SALMON, JLB	Harlequins	W - 88
PETERS, EW	Bath	W - 96		SAMPSON	Wasps	W-99 L - *98
PHILLIPS, CA	Bristol	L - 88		SANDERS, I	Bath	W - 95
PICKERING, DA	Lon. Scot	L - 74		SANDERSON, P	Harlequins	L - 01
PIENNAAR, F	Saracens	W - 98		SARGENT, GAF	Gloucester	W - 78, *82
PINNEGAR, MCF	Wasps	L - 86, 87		SAVILLE, CD	Rosslyn Park	L - 75
POLLEDRI, P	Bristol	W - 83 L - 84		SCELZO, M	Northampton	L - *00
POMPHREY, NJC	Bristol	W - 83 L - 84, 88		SCRASE, L	Wasps	L - 98
POOLE, MD	Leicester	W - 93, 97 L - 94, 96		SCRIVENER, P	Wasps	W-99
POTTER, S	Leicester	W - 93, 97 L - 94, 96		SCRIVENS, N	Gloucester	L - 90
POTTER, MJ	Gloucester	W - 72		SELLA, P	Saracens	W - 98
POUNTNEY, A	Northampton	L - 00		SHAW, M	Newcastle	L - 99
POWELL, M	Harlequins	L - 01		SHAW, S	Wasps	W - 99, 00 L - 98

Name	Club	Result
SHEASBY, CMA	Harlequins	L - 92, 93
SHEEHAN, JM	Lon. Irish	L - 80
SHEPARD, A	Bristol	W - 83 L - 84
SHORROCK,, DW	Moseley	W - 82
SHORT, JJO	Gosforth	W - 76
SHORT, KS	Lon. Irish	L - 80
SHORT, KF	Waterloo	L - 77
SIMMONS, A	Wasps	L - 86, 87
SIMMS, KG	Wasps	L - 87
SIMONETT, JF	Gloucester	W - 78
SIMPSON, PD	Bath	W - 84, 85, 86, *89
SINGER, M	Saracens	W - *98
SKINNER, MG	Harlequins	W - 88, 91
SLEIGHTHOLME, JM	Bath	W - 96
SMITH, A	Sale	L - 97
SMITH, SM	Gosforth	L - 81
SMITH, ST	Wasps	L - 86, 87
SMITH, IR	Leicester	W - 79, 80, 81
		L - 83, 89
SMITH, T	Leicester	L - 89
SMITH, R	Glouceste	W - 72
SMITH, T	Gloucester	L - 90
SMITH, I	Gloucester	L - 90
SMITH, TJ	Moseley	L - 72
SMYTHE, MJ	Lon. Irish	L - 80
SNOW, ACW	Harlequins	L - 93
SOLE, DMB	Bath	W - 87
SPAVEN, JN	Waterloo	L - 77
SPURRELL, RA	Bath	W - 84, 85, 86
STARLING, D	Rosslyn Park	L - 76
STARR, B	Harlequins	L - 01*
STEELE, J	Northampton	L - 91
STEPHENS,EJF	Gloucester	W - 72
STEPHENSON, M	Newcastle	W - 01
STEVENSON, GB	Lon. Scot	L - 74
STEWART, M	Northampton	L - 00
STIFF, PJ	Bristol	L - 84
STRANSKY, J	Leicester	W - 97
STRINGER, NC	Wasps	L - 86
STURNHAM, B	Saracens	W - 98
SUTHERLAND, IS	Moseley	W - 82
SWAIN, MK	Moseley	L - 72, 79
SWATFIELD, RJ	Bristol	L - 73
SWIFT, AH	Bath	W - 86, 87, 89, 90, 92, 94, 95
TAYLOR, PA	Gloucester	W - 82
TEAGUE, MC	Gloucester	W - 82 L - 90
THACKER, T	Leicester	L - 89
THAME, J	Northampton	L - 91
THOMAS, DG	Bristol	L - 88
THOMAS, A	Moseley	L - 79
THOMPSON, AL	Harlequins	W - 88
THOMPSON, GJ	Harlequins	L - 93
THORBURN, CW	Lon. Scot	L - 74
THORNEYCROFT, H	Northampton	L - 91
THRESHER, SE	Harlequins	W - 88, 91
TICKLE, SG	Waterloo	L - 77
TRESEDER, PA	Rosslyn Park	L - 75, 76
TREVASKIS, B	Bath	W - 84, 85, 87
TRICK, DM	Bath	W - 84, 85, 86
TROUGHTON, AH	Bristol	W - 83
TUIGAMALA, V	Newcastle	W - 01.L - 99
UBOGU, VE	Bath	W - 90, 92, 94, 95
UFTON, J	Wasps	L - 95
UNDERWOOD, R	Leicester	W - 93 L - 89, 94, 96
	Newcastle	L - 99
UNDERWOOD, T	Leicester	W - 93 L - 94
UTTLEY, RM	Gosforth	W - 77
VINE, BJ	Gloucester	W - 78
VOLLEY, P	Wasps	W - 00 L - 98
VYVYAN, H	Newcastle	W - 01*
WALDER, D	Newcastle	W - 01
WALKER, R	Coventry	W - 74
WALLACE, P	Saracens	W - 98
WALLACE, R	Saracens	W - *98
WALTER, S	Northampton	L - *00
WALTON, P	Newcastle	L - 99
WARD, B	Northampton	L - *91
WARD, M	Newcastle	W - 01
WARDLOW, CS	Coventry	W - 73
WARREN, DG	Moseley	W - 82
WATERS, F	Wasps	W-99
WATKINS, M	Lon. Welsh	L - 85
WATKINS, JA	Gloucester	W - 72, 78
WATSON-JONES, A	Moseley	L - *79
WATT, DEJ	Bristol	L - 73
WEBB, JM	Bath	W - 92
	Bristol	L - 88
WEBSTER, JG	Moseley	L - 72
WEDDERBURN, MA	Harlequins	L - 92
WEEDON, M	Wasps	W - 99, 00 L - 98
WEIR, D	Newcastle	W - 01.L - 99
WELLS, JM	Leicester	W - 93, 97
		L - 89, 94, 96
WESTON, LE	Rosslyn Park	L - 75, 76
WHEELER, PJ	Leicester	W - 79, 80, 81
		L - 78, 83
WHITE, C	Gosforth	W - 76, 77 L - 81
WHITE, L	Lon. Irish	L - 80
WHITE, M	Wasps	L - 95, *98
WHITE, JC	Moseley	L - 72
WHITE-COOPER, S	Harlequins	L - 01
WILKINSON, J	Newcastle	W - 01.L - 99
WILKINSON, RM	Bedford	W - 75
WILLIAMS, K	Leicester	W - 81
WILLIAMS, CG	Gloucester	W - 78
WILLIAMS, CJ	Bristol	L - 73
WILSON, D	Harlequins	L - 01
WINSTANLEY, P	Sale	L - 97
WINTERBOTTOM, PJ	Harlequins	W - 91 L - 92, 93
WINTERS, R	Harlequins	L - 01
WITHEY, K	Bath	W - 90
WOOD, K	Harlequins	L - 01
WOOD, M	London Wasps	W - 00
WOOD, P	Gloucester	W - *82
WOODWARD, C	Leicester	W - 80, 81 L - 83
WOOLEY, VJ	Gloucester	W - 78
WORSLEY, J	Wasps	W - 99, 00 L - 98
WYATT, D	Bedford	W - 75
YATES, K	Bath	W - 95
YOUNG, M	Gosforth	W - 76, 77 L - 81
YOUNGS, NC	Leicester	L - 83

Year	Winners	Captain	Pts	Tries	Cons	Pens	DG	Runners-up	Captain	Pts	Tries	Cons	Pens	DG	Losing Semi-Finalists
1972	Gloucester	M Nicholls	17	2		1	2	Moseley	J Webster	6			1	1	Coventry, Wilmslow
1973	Coventry	D Duckham	27	4	1	2	1	Bristol	A Nicholls	15			5		Sale, London Welsh
1974	Coventry	D Duckham	26	4	2	2		London Scottish	M Biggar	6				2	Rosslyn Park, Orrell
1975	Bedford	D Rogers	28	5	4			Rosslyn Park	P Keith-Roach	12			4		Coventry, Morpeth
1976	Gosforth	M Young	23	4	2	1		Rosslyn Park	P Keith-Roach	14	2		2		Sale, Wakefield
1977	Gosforth	R Uttley	27	5	2	1		Waterloo	C Fisher	11	2		1		London Welsh, Saracens
1978	Gloucester	J Watkins	6	1	1			Leicester	B Hall	3			1		Harlequins, Coventry
1979	Leicester	P Wheeler	15	1	1	2	1	Moseley	M Cooper	12	1	1	1	1	Wasps, Gosforth
1980	Leicester	P Wheeler	21			4	3	London Irish	J O'Driscoll	9	1	1	1		Rosslyn Park, Harlequins
1981	Leicester	P Wheeler	22	3	2	2		Gosforth	C White	15	1	1	3		London Scottish, Moseley
1982	Gloucester	S Mills	12			4		Moseley	D Nutt	12			3	1	Coventry, Leicester
1983	Bristol	M Rafter	28	4	3	2		Leicester	S Johnson	22	2	1	4		Coventry, London Scottish
1984	Bath	R Spurrell	10	1		2		Bristol	M Rafter	9	1	1	1		Nottingham, Harlequins
1985	Bath	R Spurrell	24	2	2	4		London Welsh	C Rees	15			5		Gloucester, Coventry
1986	Bath	J Palmer	25	4	3	1		Wasps	R Cardus	17	3	1	1		Leicester, London Scottish
1987	Bath	R Hill	19	3	2	1		Wasps	D Pegler	12	1	1	1	1	Orrell, Leicester
1988	Harlequins	J Olver	28	3	2	4		Bristol	N Pomphrey	22	2	1	3	1	Wasps, Moseley
1989	Bath	S Barnes	10	1		2		Leicester	P Dodge	6			2		Gloucester, Harlequins
1990	Bath	S Barnes	48	8	5	2		Gloucester	M Hamlin	6			2		Moseley, Northampton
1991	Harlequins	P Winterbottom	25	4		3		Northampton	G Pearce	13	1		3		Nottingham, Orrell
1992	Bath	A Robinson	15	1	1	2	1	Harlequins	P Winterbottom	12	1	1	2		Gloucester, Leicester
1993	Leicester	J Wells	23	2	2	2	1	Harlequins	P Winterbottom	16	1	1	3		Northampton, Wasps
1994	Bath	J Hall	21	2	1	3		Leicester	D Richards	9			3		Harlequins, Orrell
1995	Bath	P de Glanville	36	5	4	1		Wasps	D Ryan	16	2		2		Harlequins, Leicester
1996	Bath	P de Glanville	16	1	1	2	1	Leicester	D Richards	15	2	1	1		Gloucester, London Irish
1997	Leicester	M Johnson	9			3		Sale	J Mallinder	3			1		Gloucester, Harlequins
1998	Saracens	A Diprose	48	7	5	1		Wasps	L Dallaglio	18	2	1	2		Northampton, Sale
1999	Wasps	M Weedon	29	2	2	4	1	Newcastle	G Armstrong	19	1	1	4		Gloucester, Richmond
2000	Wasps	L Dallaglio	31	4	1	3		Northampton	M Dawson	23	1		6		Bristol, London Irish
2001	Newcastle	G Weir	30	4	2	2		Harlequins	D Wilson	27	2	1	5		Sale, Leicester

TETLEY'S BITTER CUP

FINAL TRIVIA

MOST WINNERS MEDALS

9   Nigel Redman (Bath).
8   Richard Hill (Bath)
     Graham Dawe (Bath).
7   Stuart Barnes (Bristol 1, Bath 6)
     Andy Robinson (Bath)
     Tony Swift (Bath)
     Gareth Chilcott (Bath)
6   Jeremy Guscott (Bath-2 as Rep)
     John Hall (Bath)
     Simon Halliday (Bath 5, Harlequins 1)

MOST LOSERS MEDALS

4   Dean Richards (Leicester)
3   Steve Bates (Wasps)
     Paul Dodge (Leicester)
     Adel Kardooni (Leicester)
     Steve Redfern (Leicester)
     Rory Underwood (Leicester)
     John Wells (Leicester)

WINNERS MEDALS FOR TWO CLUBS

Stuart Barnes (Bristol, Bath)
Roger Barnwell (Coventry, Leicester)
RogerCowling (Gloucester, Leicester)
Andy Reed (Bath, Wasps)

LOSERS MEDALS FOR TWO CLUBS

Kevin Dunn (Gloucester, Wasps)
Tony Underwood (Leicester, Newcastle)
Nick Greenstock (Wasps, Harlequins)

PLAYERS APPEARING FOR TWO CLUBS

Stuart Barnes (Bristol, Bath); Roger Barnwell (Coventry, Leicester); Barrie Corless (Coventry, Moseley); Roger Cowling (Gloucester, Leicester); Rob Cunningham (Gosforth, Bath); Kevin Dunn (Gloucester, Wasps); Simon Halliday (Bath, Harlequins); John Olver (Harlequins, Northampton); Jonathan Webb (Bristol, Bath); Andy Reed (Bath, Wasps); Tony Underwood (Leicester, Newcastle); W Greenwood (Wasps, Harlequins); Will Greenwood (Leicester, Harlequins); B Daniel (Saracens, Harlequins).

PLAYERS SENT OFF

Player	Match	Year	Referee
Nigel Horton	Moseley v Gloucester	1972	Ron Lewis
Bob Mordell	Rosslyn Park v Gosforth	1976	Norman Sanson
John Gadd	Gloucester v Bath	1990	Fred Howard

TETLEY'S BITTER CUP

	Winners	R-up	SF	QF	Years in competition	Played	Won	Drawn	Lost
Bath	10	0	10	13	29	79	60	-	19
Leicester	5	5	16	20	29	100	76	-	24
Gloucester	*3	1	10	17	29	87	60	1	26
Wasps	2	4	9	14	26	72	48	-	24
Harlequins	2	3	12	20	28	88	62	-	26
Newcastle	3	2	6	12	30	80	53	-	27
Coventry	2	0	8	10	30	78	50	-	28
Bristol	1	3	5	12	29	75	47	-	28
Moseley	*1	2	6	12	30	77	47	1	29
Saracens	1	0	2	6	27	60	34	-	26
Bedford	1	0	1	3	29	53	25	-	28
Northampton	-	2	5	11	29	70	41	-	29
Rosslyn Park	-	2	4	7	29	69	40	-	29
London Welsh	-	1	3	9	28	73	45	-	28
London Scottish	-	1	4	6	27	59	32	-	27
Sale	-	1	5	12	28	71	43	-	28
London Irish	-	1	3	7	27	59	32	-	27
Waterloo	-	1	1	6	24	50	26	-	24
Orrell	-	-	4	6	25	50	25	-	25
Nottingham	-	-	2	7	28	59	31	-	28
Wakefield	-	-	1	4	22	51	29	-	22
Wilmslow	-	-	1	2	5	11	6	-	5
Morpeth	-	-	1	1	3	6	3	-	3
Richmond	-	-	-	5	26	59	33	-	26
West Hartlepool	-	-	-	4	21	44	23	-	21
Penryn	-	-	-	2	4	9	5	-	4
Metropolitan Police	-	-	-	2	17	36	19	-	17
Exeter	-	-	-	2	23	56	33	-	23
Liverpool St Helens	-	-	-	2	25	44	19	-	25
Halifax	-	-	-	1	3	6	3	-	3
Manchester	-	-	-	1	7	19	12	-	7
Roundhay	-	-	-	1	7	10	3	-	7
Fylde	-	-	-	1	20	43	23	-	20
Plymouth Albion	-	-	-	1	22	33	11	-	22
Total	31	29	120	240					

ZURICH

PREMIERSHIP

2000-01 Season

CLUBS

LEAGUE TABLE SEASON 2000-01

	P	W	D	L	F	A	PD	Bonus Pts	Tries	Pens	PTS	Last 6 Matches W-D-L
Leicester	22	18	1	3	571	346	225	8	60	64	82	5 -0- 1
London Wasps	22	16	0	6	663	428	235	10	77	56	74	5 -0- 1
Bath	22	14	0	8	680	430	250	14	72	52	70	5 -0- 1
Northampton	22	13	0	9	518	463	55	7	45	74	59	3 -0- 3
Saracens	22	12	0	10	589	501	88	10	63	62	58	3 -0- 3
Newcastle	22	11	0	11	554	568	-14	13	57	56	57	3 -0- 3
Gloucester	22	10	0	12	473	526	-53	8	43	65	48	3 -0- 3
London Irish	22	10	1	11	476	576	-100	3	36	81	45	2 -0- 4
Bristol	22	9	1	12	443	492	-49	6	34	71	44	2 -1- 3
Sale	22	8	1	13	561	622	-61	9	56	68	43	2 -0- 4
NEC Harlequins	22	7	0	15	440	538	-98	10	44	52	38	4 -0- 2
Rotherham	22	2	0	20	335	813	-478	4	29	50	12	0 -0- 6

REVIEW OF THE SEASON

Pictured opposite are two of Champions
Leicester's stalwarts - top Neil Back
and below Darren Garforth

Leicester Tigers took the Premiership title for the third consecutive year finishing eight points clear of second placed London Wasps. They had exactly the same win-loss record as last season suffering just three defeats. After two early season defeats they put together a 12 match-winning run until losing their penultimate match of the season at Gloucester. They kept their impressive home record and were again unbeaten at home for the second successive league campaign. They did not score as many points as the previous season, but they did improve defensively by conceding 80 points fewer. They only other defeats they suffered in the league programme were away matches at Saracens and Bristol.

London Wasps moved up five places on the previous season to finish a highly creditable second. They finished the season strongly and won nine of their last ten matches after losing in mid December to London Irish. Their only defeat after that was an away loss at Bath, going down narrowly 16-13. They lost their first two home matches of the season but after that put together a run of nine successive wins. Where London Wasps really improved last season was defensively where they conceded just 428 compared with 661 from the season before. They had both the leading points and try scorer in the Zurich Premiership with Kenny Logan scoring 282 points and Paul Sampson running in 11 tries.

Bath dropped a place in finishing third, four points behind London Wasps. They won five of the last six matches to retain a top four spot and keep home advantage in the Championship play-offs. They did though lose twice at home with Leicester Tigers and Saracens leaving the Rec with the points. Leicester went on to do the double over Bath, but they did manage an excellent win at Saracens. They were, though, the leading points scorers in the Premiership with 680 and they ran in 72 tries, second only to London Wasps. Some 58 of those tries came from their young and exciting back division, which was 10 more than their counterparts at London Wasps. Bath picked up more bonus points than any other side in the Premiership with 14 - one more than Newcastle Falcons.

Northampton Saints ended the season in fourth place, a one place improvement on the previous season. At Franklin's Garden they had an impressive record with nine wins and only the top two, Leicester Tigers and London Wasps, left with the points; both these sides did the double over the Saints. They were another side who failed to perform on the road, as they would have liked, picking up just four wins and three of those were in a row mid season when they played their best rugby.

Saracens dropped in the league table for the third consecutive season and ended up in 5th place. In finishing fifth and with Harlequins winning the European Shield they have failed to qualify for the Heineken Cup, which is a huge blow to the club and its aspirations. They did well at home with eight wins, but away from Vicarage Road they picked up just four wins. In the run-in at the end of the season they did win four of their last five league matches, but it was not enough to move into a Heineken Cup place. Their cause was not helped with injuries to key players Thomas Castaignede and Duncan McRae.

Newcastle Falcons had their best league campaign since were crowned Champions back in 1997-98 with a sixth place finish. It was a two place improvement on last season. They managed five more wins this season, scored more points and improved defensively. The Falcons picked up 13 bonus points, which was the second highest in the division behind Bath who notched up 14. Newcastle were heavily reliant on their home form with eight of their 11 wins coming at home and just three on the road. Both Gloucester and Leicester Tigers did the double over Newcastle. With some good exciting backs coming through the ranks the future looks bright for Rob Andrew.

Gloucester did not have a good season, dropping four places from their excellent third spot the previous season and missing out on Heineken Cup rugby for the coming season. With big name players like Ian Jones and Jason Little in the side it makes it even more disappointing and both could well have left the club by the start of next season. They got off to a bad start losing four of their opening six matches and were always playing catch up. The Cherry and Whites lost both their games against rivals Bath, but were the only the only team to beat Leicester Tigers in the second half of the season.

London Irish finished in eighth position for the second successive year and again failed to qualify for the Heineken Cup and must again play in the Shield competition. They scored just 34 tries with only Rotherham managing fewer. Defensively they conceded 59 tries including 44 by the opposition backs which was the second highest total behind Rotherham, who allowed the opposition backs in 72 times. At their new home in the Madejski Stadium they won eight matches, drew one and were beaten just twice by Bath and Leicester Tigers. Their season fell flat because away from home they managed to win just twice (and they were early season) and then they lost eight on the bounce.

Bristol had a disappointing season finishing ninth, which was a three place drop on the previous season in their first season back in the top flight. They scored nearly 200 points fewer last season but, despite dropping three places and losing three matches more, they actually conceded fewer improving from 602 to 492. They managed just 34 tries with only Rotherham on 28 scoring fewer. Bristol lost their first three Premiership matches of the season before ending the run with a win against eventual Champions Leicester Tigers. After that success their home form improved, losing just once more at the Memorial Ground against London Wasps in March after stringing together six successive wins including a rare one against Bath.

Sale Sharks moved up a place on the previous season to finish 10th five points ahead of Harlequins. Sale improved their scoring dramatically running up 180 points more than the previous season. The consistent kicking of Nicky Little and Charlie Hodgson helped their cause. Sale started the season with four wins from their first five matches with good wins against Bath, Gloucester and Northampton. After that initial burst of form they were only to win another four games in their remaining 17 league matches. They ended the season as the sixth highest try scorers in the division with 56, of which 21 came from their wingers. Sale have now gone four seasons without a winning campaign.

Harlequins will look to put last season's league campaign behind them as they dropped another place to 11th. With just one side to be relegated they survived, otherwise it could have been an embarrassing end to a season in which they did well in the Cup competitions. They managed just seven wins but did pick up 10 bonus points, which was the joint third highest total in the Premiership. Quins made a dreadful start to the season and in their first 14 matches they managed just two wins, after that they got some form and managed five wins out of six before losing their last two matches to the top two sides. What they would give to turn their Cup form into league form.

New boys **Rotherham** lasted just the one season and by the end of the season were well adrift of the rest finishing with 12 points, 26 behind Harlequins. It is was their first ever season when they lost more games than they won in their national League history, which began back in 1992-93. They managed just two wins against Saracens and London Irish, both these being at Clifton Road whilst away from home they lost all eleven.

2000-01 RECORD REVIEW (Individual Records)

The ALL-TIME RECORDS for MOST POINTS IN A MATCH, MOST POINTS IN A SEASON & MOST TRIES IN A MATCH can be found in the Records Section for this division.

MOST POINTS - IN A MATCH

Newcastle's David Walder in his first full season of senior rugby equalled Niall Woods' record. Walder scored 32 points as Newcastle beat Saracens in November. Two other players came close to the record with both Tim Stimpson and Felipe Contepomi scoring 31 points in a match to move to joint third on the all time list.

The London Wasps left wing Kenny Logan had two big points returns during the season - he scored 29 points against Sale late in the season and 28 points two weeks previously against Rotherham.

Most Points in a Match 2000-01

32	David Walder	Newcastle v Saracens	26.11.00
31	Tim Stimpson	Leicester v Saracens	24.02.01
31	Felipe Contepomi	Bristol v Northampton	16.04.01
29	Jonny Wilkinson	Newcastle v Lon. Wasps	23.09.00
29	Thomas Castaignede	Saracens v Rotherham	24.09.00
29	Kenny Logan	Lon. Wasps v Sale	14.04.01

EVOLUTION OF RECORD - Points in a match

21	Ian Aitchison	Waterloo v Sale	02.01.88
23	Jamie Salmon	Quins v Waterloo	27.02.88
24	Dusty Hare	Leicester v Rosslyn P.	19.11.88
26	John Liley	Leicester v Bedford	23.09.89
27	David Pears	Quins v Bedford	14.10.89
28	Martin Strett	Orrell v Rosslyn P.	21.03.92
31	John Liley	Leicester v Rosslyn P.	21.03.92
32	Niall Woods	Lon. Irish v Harlequins	25.04.98
32	David Walder	Newcastle v Saracens	26.11.00

MOST POINTS - IN A SEASON

London Wasps Kenny Logan topped the scoring list with 282 points. This was some way off the Divisions record of 331 set by John Schuster back in the 1998-99 season. He Did though have the London Wasps record for a season in his sights 291 set by Gareth Rees but just came up short in the end. In April he scored 70 points in three matches and fell just nine points short of the record. The number of playes scoring 200 points dropped again this season with just three achieving the feat. The season before there was four nd the one before that there were ten.

Second place in the scoring went to the Leicester full back Tim Stimpson with 260 whilst the only other player to top the 200 point mark was the former England Outside half Paul Grayson. He totaled 219 which was a new Northampton record beating his own record of 215.

EVOLUTION OF RECORD - Points in a season

126	Dusty Hare	Leicester	1987-88
126	John Liley	Leicester	1989-90
126	Rob Andrew	Wasps	1990-91
202	Jez Harris	Leicester	1993-94
272	John Liley	Leicester	1996-97
291	Gareth Rees	Wasps	1996-97
331	John Schuster	Harlequins	1998-99

MOST TRIES - IN A MATCH

The record set by Ryan Constable was safe and never really challenged last season. The best performance was four tries by the Irish International Geordan Murphy. He ran in four tries as Leicester ran out comfortable winners against Saracens. It was not a good season for tries with only eight onther hat tricks all season.

Of the nine players to score hat tricks five did so against Rotherham. Bath had the most players scoring hat tricks with three players doing so. All three were in the final month of the season.

EVOLUTION OF RECORD - Tries in a match
(Only the first to reach the figure is shown)

3	Peter Shillingford	Moseley v Wasps	05.02.88
4	Gary Hartley	Nottingham v Bedford	18.11.89
5	Kenny Logan	Wasps v Orrell	22.03.97
6	Ryan Constable	Saracens v Bedford	16.04.00

MOST TRIES - IN A SEASON

Nobody came near to breaking the record of 17 tries in a season. In fact nobody made in into the all time top 10. Leading the way was the London Wasps Full back/Right wing Paul Sampson on his return to the club after a spell playing Rugby League. He topped the list with 11 tries from 14 starts. Just one behind was his teammate Kenny Logan and the Sale Sharks winger Steven Hanley. Hanley scored his 10 tries from just 14 starts.

EVOLUTION OF RECORD - Tries in a season

11	Andrew Harriman	Harlequins	1987-88
11	Daren O'Leary	Harlequins	1993-94
14	Daren O'Leary	Harlequins	1995-96
16	Adedayo Adebayo	Bath	1996-97
17	Domonic Chapman	Richmond	1997-98

ALL-TIME RECORDS - Tries in a season

17	Domonic Chapman	Richmond	1997-98
16	Adedayo Adebayo	Bath	1996-97
16	Neil Back	Leicester	1998-99
15	Daren O'Leary	Harlequins	1996-97
15	Iain Balshaw	Bath	1999-00
14	Daren O'Leary	Harlequins	1995-96
14	Tom Beim	Sale	1997-98
13	Steven John	West Hartlepool	1996-97
13	Tom Beim	Sale	1996-97
13	Gary Armstrong	Newcastle	1997-98

MOST DROP GOALS - IN A MATCH

This record was not challenged with nobody managing more than one drop goal in a match.

ALL-TIME RECORDS - Drop Goals in a match

3	John Steele	Northampton v Wasps	23.09.91
3	Jez Harris	Leicester v Wasps	23.11.91
3	Jez Harris	Leicester v Bath	15.04.95
3	Matthew McCarthy	Orrell v W. Hartlepool	07.12.96

MOST CONVERSIONS - IN A MATCH

This record was never seriously challenged. The best return during the season was six conversions in a match by five different players.

EVOLUTION OF RECORD - Conversions in a match

10 Stuart Barnes	Bath v Bedford	13.01.90
13 Rich Butland	Richmond v Bedford	17.05.99

ALL-TIME RECORDS - Conversions in a match

13 Rich Butland	Richmond v Bedford	17.05.99
10 Stuart Barnes	Bath v Bedford	13.01.90
9 Paul Challinor	Quins v W. Hartlepool	23.03.96
8 Martin Strett	Orrell v Rosslyn P.	28.04.90
8 Will Carling	Quins v Orrell	05.10.96
8 Mike Catt	Bath v Sale	26.04.97
8 Niall Woods	Lon. Irish v Harlequins	25.04.98
8 Mike Catt	Bath v London Scottish	16.05.99
8 Alex King	Wasps v Bedford	26.03.00

MOST CONVERSIONS - IN A SEASON

Kenny Logan got within five of the record for most conversions in a season. He kicked 47 conversion from his 18 matches he started but the four matches he missed proved vital and probably cost him the record. It was though enough to put him equal sixth on the on the all time list with Thierry Lacroix.

The next best after Logan last season was Jonny Wilkinson with 34 conversions from 15 matches started in the Premiership.

EVOLUTION OF RECORD - Conversions in a season

15 Dusty Hare	Leicester	1987-88
29 Stuart Barnes	Bath	1989-90
43 Jonathon Callard	Bath	1995-96
51 Jonathon Callard	Bath	1996-97
52 Gavin Johnson	Saracens	1998-99

ALL-TIME RECORDS - Conversions in a season

52 Gavin Johnson	Saracens	1998-99
52 Tim Stimpson	Leicester	1999-00
51 Jonathon Callard	Bath	1996-97
51 Jonny Wilkinson	Newcastle	1998-99
50 Mike Catt	Bath	1998-99
47 Thierry Lacroix	Saracens	1999-00
47 Kenny Logan	London Wasps	2000-01
46 Jarod Cunningham	London Irish	1999-00
45 Gareth Rees	Wasps	1996-97
44 Rob Andrew	Newcastle	1997-98
43 Jonathon Callard	Bath	1995-96
42 Shane Howarth	Sale	1998-99
39 Shane Howarth	Sale	1997-98
39 Joel Stransky	Leicester	1997-98

MOST PENALTIES - IN A MATCH

This was where all the activity was last season. Gloucesters Simon Mannix equaled the record of nine penalties in a match. He did so against Harlequins to equal the record Thierry Lacroix set the previous season. Two other player moved into joint third on the all time list after kicking eight penalties in a match. They were Tim Stimpson in Leicesters home win against Gloucester and Jarrod Cunningham for London Irish against Bristol.

Five other players kicked seven penalties in a match and moved into joint sixth on the all time list. London Irishs new kicking star Barry Everitt achieved this feat twice.

EVOLUTION OF RECORD

6 Dusty Hare	Leicester v Rosslyn P.	19.11.88
7 David Pears	Quins v Rosslyn P.	07.12.91
8 John Liley	Leicester v Bristol	28.10.95
9 Thierry Lacroix	Saracens v Wasps	07.11.99
9 Simon Mannix	Gloucester v Harlequins	23.09.00

ALL-TIME RECORDS

9 Thierry Lacroix	Saracens v Wasps	07.11.99
9 Simon Mannix	Gloucester v Harlequins	23.09.00
8 John Liley	Leicester v Bristol	28.10.95
8 Jarrod Cunningham	London Irish v Bristol	10.09.00
8 Tim Stimpson	Leicester v Gloucester	02.12.00
7 David Pears	Quins v Rosslyn P.	07.12.91
7 Jez Harris	Leicester v Bristol	11.12.93
7 Rob Andrew	Wasps v Orrell	11.12.93
7 Jez Harris	Leicester v Gloucester	29.01.94
7 Mark Tainton	Bristol v Leicester	05.11.94
7 John Liley	Leicester v Bath	07.09.96
7 Simon Mannix	Sale v Northampton	08.03.97
7 Paul Grayson	N'hampton v Richmond	08.03.97
7 Shane Howarth	Sale v Wasps	18.04.98
7 Joel Stransky	Leicester v London Irish	
7 Steven Vile	W Hartlepool v Richmond	
7 Tim Stimpson	Leicester v Newcastle	
7 Tim Stimpson	Leicester v Gloucester	08.04.00
7 Paul Grayson	Northampton v Leicester	29.04.00
7 Nicky Little	Sale v Bath	19.08.00
7 Tim Stimpson	Leicester v Lon. Wasps	18.11.00
7 Barry Everitt	Lon. Irish v Harlequins	19.11.00
7 Kevin Sorrell	Saracens v Harlequins	17.12.00
7 Barry Everitt	London Irish v Bristol	24.02.01

MOST PENALTIES - IN A SEASON

Nobody came near the record of 77 set by Harlequins John Schuster back in 1998-99. Paul Grayson just edged ahead of Tim Stimpson with 58 to 57. It was enough to put Grayson into joint seventh on the all time list and Stimpson joint 11th on the all time list.

EVOLUTION OF RECORD - Penalties in a season

31 Dusty Hare	Leicester	1987-88
31 Michael Corcoran	London Irish	1992-93
41 Jez Harris	Leicester	1993-94
56 Mark Tainton	Bristol	1994-95
64 John Liley	Leicester	1995-96
77 John Schuster	Harlequins	1998-99

ALL-TIME RECORDS - Penalties in a season

77 John Schuster	Harlequins	1998-99
66 Jarod Cunningham	Lon Irish	1999-00
64 John Liley	Leicester	1995-96
63 T Stimpson	Leicester	1999-00
62 Gareth Rees	Wasps	1996-97
62 Simon Mannix	Gloucester	1999-00
58 Mark Mapletoft	Gloucester	1996-97
58 Michael Lynagh	Saracens	1997-98
58 Mark Mapletoft	Gloucester	1997-98
58 Gavin Johnson	Saracens	1998-99
58 Paul Grayson	Northampton	2000-01
57 Gareth Rees	Wasps	1997-98
57 Tim Stimpson	Leicester	2000-01
56 Mark Tainton	Bristol	1994-95

2000-01

ZURICH PREMIERSHIP

MOST POINTS

POINTS			T	C	P	DG
282	Kenny Logan	London Wasps	10	47	46	-
260	Tim Stimpson	Leicester	7	27	57	-
219	Paul Grayson	Northampton	1	20	58	-
198	Jonny Wilkinson	Newcastle	2	34	37	3
182	Barry Everitt	London Irish	1	15	49	-
172	Jon Preston	Bath	-	23	42	-
168	Felipe Contepomi	Bristol	4	17	38	-
163	Nicky Little	Sale	1	19	39	1
157	Simon Mannix	Gloucester	1	16	40	-
141	Charlie Hodgson	Sale	4	17	29	-
139	Mike Umaga	Rotherham	3	14	32	-
138	Matt Perry	Bath	2	25	26	-
133	Thomas Castaignede	Saracens	5	15	25	1
133	Paul Burke	Harlequins	-	17	30	3
111	Jarrod Cunningham	London Irish	-	9	30	1
104	Duncan McRae	Saracens	4	12	17	3
92	David Walder	Newcastle	5	8	17	-
91	Steven Vile	Bristol	2	9	21	-

MOST PENALTIES

58	Paul Grayson	Northampton
57	Tim Stimpson	Leicester
49	Barry Everitt	London Irish
46	Kenny Logan	London Wasps
42	Jon Preston	Bath
40	Simon Mannix	Gloucester
39	Nicky Little	Sale
38	Felipe Contepomi	Bristol
37	Jonny Wilkinson	Newcastle
32	Mike Umaga	Rotherham
30	Paul Burke	Harlequins
29	Charles Hodgson	Sale
26	Matt Perry	Bath
25	Thomas Castaignede	Saracens
21	Steven Vile	Bristol

MOST CONVERSIONS

47	Kenny Logan	London Wasps
34	Jonny Wilkinson	Newcastle
27	Tim Stimpson	Leicester
25	Matt Perry	Bath
23	Jon Preston	Bath
20	Paul Grayson	Northampton
19	Nicky Little	Sale
17	Paul Burke	Harlequins
17	Charles Hodgson	Sale
16	Simon Mannix	Gloucester
15	Thomas Castaignede	Saracens
14	Mike Umaga	Rotherham
12	Duncan McRae	Saracens
12	Byrom Hayward	Gloucester
9	Steven Vile	Bristol

MOST TRIES

11	Paul Sampson	London Wasps
10	Steven Hanley	Sale
10	Kenny Logan	London Wasps
9	Tom Voyce	Bath
9	Ben Cohen	Northampton
8	Neil Back	Leicester
8	Rob Thirlby	Bath
8	Geordan Murphy	Leicester
8	Paul Sackey	London Irish
7	Matt Tindall	Bath
7	Shaun Berne	Bath
7	Mike Catt	Bath
7	Tim Stimpson	Leicester
7	Will Greenwood	Harlequins
7	Gary Armstrong	Newcastle
7	Michael Stephenson	Newcastle
7	Jason Robinson	Sale

MOST DROP GOALS

3	Jonny Wilkinson	Newcastle
3	Paul Burke	Harlequins
3	Duncan McRae	Saracens
2	Jannie de Beer	Saracens
1	Will Greenwood	Harlequins
1	Andy Goode	Leicester
1	Simon Binns	Rotherham
1	Luke SMith	Rotherham
1	Ali Hepher	Northampton
1	Nicky Little	Sale
1	Elton Moncrieff	Gloucester
1	Jarrod Cunningham	London Irish
1	Thomas Castaignede	Saracens

ZURICH
PREMIERSHIP

FIXTURES 2001-02

Away Teams

HOME TEAMS	Bath (1)	Bristol (2)	Gloucester (3)	Leeds Tykes (4)	Leicester Tigers (5)	London Irish (6)	London Wasps (7)	NEC Harlequins (8)	Newcastle Falcons (9)	Northampton (10)	Sale Sharks (11)	Saracens (12)
1 Bath		29.12	8.12	13.04	9.03	11.11	11.05	13.10	9.02	25.11	30.03	15.09
2 Bristol	18.11		27.01	23.09	4.05	16.09	21.10	2.09	31.03	24.02	23.12	2.12
3 Gloucester	4.05	10.11		1.12	15.09	9.02	24.11	9.03	13.10	29.12	1.09	30.03
4 Leeds Tykes	2.09	10.03	11.05		11.11	31.03	30.12	25.11	9.12	10.02	16.09	14.10
5 Leicester Tigers	22.09	8.12	16.03	26.01		11.05	8.09	29.12	23.11	13.04	23.02	20.10
6 London Irish	26.01	16.03	20.10	8.09	1.12		23.02	4.05	13.04	22.09	17.11	22.12
7 London Wasps	2.12	10.02	23.12	18.11	31.03	14.10		16.09	10.03	11.11	5.05	2.09
8 NEC Harlequins	20.10	8.09	23.02	4.05	22.12	1.09	22.09		16.03	26.01	1.12	16.11
9 Newcastle Falcons	23.12	14.10	18.11	21.10	2.09	10.03	27.01	16.09		2.12	31.03	5.05
10 Northampton	8.09	25.11	13.04	16.03	13.10	29.12	8.12	9.11	11.05		9.02	9.03
11 Sale Sharks	23.02	13.04	22.09	22.12	17.11	8.12	16.03	11.05	8.09	20.10		26.01
12 Saracens	17.03	11.05	9.09	24.02	10.02	25.11	14.04	30.12	9.12	23.09	11.11	
	1	2	3	4	5	6	7	8	9	10	11	12

BATH RUGBY

Chief Executive Andrew Brownsword

Coach Jon Callard

Ticket Office Manager Sarah Dade

PR Manager/Press Helen Mercer

Business Developement Ian Bant

Sales Rob Bennett

Bath Rugby,
11 Argyle Street,
Bath BA2 4BQ
01225 325200 (Office)
01225 325201 (Fax)

Jon Callard will look back on his first season in charge at the Rec. as one of laying foundations for a more successful campaign in 2001/2002.

The season ended with a deserved trip to Twickenham in the Zurich Championship Final following some impressive end of season form that yielded six straight wins during March and April. However, a 22-10 loss to Leicester that afternoon served to highlight exactly how far the club has still to come to challenge for future honours.

The start of the season saw an away game to Sale Sharks and a defeat by the narrowest margins, this however did not set the trend and the team went on to win the next four games. The Heineken Cup knockout stages eluded the '98 Champions, going out in the pool stages, but still heads did not go down and a convincing win against Castres away and Newport at home saw them bid farewell to the Heineken European Cup with their heads held high. With five internationals missing due to International duty Bath Rugby fell to Bristol for the first time away from home, and the return match, with a full strength squad proved Bath Rugby the better team.

Bath Rugby then took the bull by the horns and reeled off eleven wins in their final fourteen matches, including Northampton Saints, Newport and in the game of the season, London Wasps in the semi-final of the Championship.

On the international front the club continued to provide players for the home nations. Matt Perry became England's most capped full back against South Africa, whilst Mike Catt won his 50th cap. The sparkling talents of Iain Balshaw (pictured left) ensured the future of English rugby is in good hands, whilst there were debut caps for Steve Borthwick, Ollie Barkley and Tom Voyce (England), Gavin Thomas, Gareth Cooper and Andy Lloyd (Wales) while Mark Regan and Andy Long added to their totals. The Club also provided four British Lions in Catt, Perry, Balshaw and Danny Grewcock.

Bath Rugby are now building on their home grown talent for an exciting squad for the 2001/2002 season. With the likes of Ollie Barkley, England International, yet to play in the first XV at Bath, Tom Voyce, Sam Cox and Andy Lloyd to name just a few of the club's young stars who will grow from the experience of seasoned Internationals such as Mike Catt and new signing Danny Grewcock. With their wealth of talent, Bath Rugby anticipate an exciting 2001/2002 season - not one to miss.

BATH RUGBY

Comp.	Date	H/A	Opponents	Result & Score	Att	15	14	13	12	11
P1	19-Aug	A	Sale	L 32-33	3785	Perry/t	Thirlby/t	Tindall	Maggs	Adebayo
P1	27-Aug	A	London Wasps	W 36-12	4037	Perry	Thirlby	Maggs/t	Tindall/t	Adebayo
P1	2-Sep	H	Harlequins	W 38-22	6958	Perry	Thirlby/t	Maggs	Tindall	Adebayo/t
P1	9-Sep	A	Gloucester	W 22-21	6754	Perry	Thirlby/t(a/t)	Maggs	Tindall	Adebayo
P1	16-Sep	H	Newcastle Falcons	W 19-12	7503	Perry	Balshaw	Tindall/t	Maggs	Adebayo
P1	23-Sep	A	Northanpton Saints	L 13-24	7465	Perry	Balshaw	Tindall	Maggs	Adebayo
P1	30-Sep	H	Saracens	L 21-33	8240	Perry/c3p	Balshaw	Tindall	Maggs	Adebayo/2t
P1	19-Nov	H	Sale	W 34-32	7348	Voyce	Thirlby	Maggs	Guscott	Adebayo
P1	26-Nov	H	Rotherham	W 42-19	7100	Voyce	Thirlby/t	Maggs/t	Guscott	Bellinger
P1	2-Dec	A	Bristol	L 9-16	6335	Voyce	Thirlby	Maggs	Cox	Adebayo
P1	16-Dec	A	Leicester Tigers	L 19-27	14505	Perry/c4p	Balshaw	Maggs	Tindall	Thirlby
P1	23-Dec	H	London Irish	W 56-20	7317	Perry/4c3p	Balshaw/t	Maggs/t	Tindall/t	Thirlby
P1	26-Dec	H	Leicester Tigers	L 16-17	8200	Perry/c3p	Balshaw/t	Maggs	Tindall	Thirlby
P1	30-Dec	A	Saracens	W 31-11	11193	Perry/4cp	Balshaw/t	Maggs	Tindall/2t	Thirlby
P1	6-Jan	H	Northanpton Saints	W 36-13	7802	Perry/4cp	Balshaw/t	Maggs	Tindall/t	Voyce/2t
P1	11-Feb	A	Newcastle Falcons	L 23-24	7319	Perry	Balshaw	Maggs	Tindall/t	Voyce/2t
P1	24-Feb	H	Gloucester	W 50-16	8200	Perry/tc	Balshaw/t	Maggs	Berne/t	Voyce
P1	10-Mar	A	Harlequins	L 22-24	7067	Perry/c5p	Balshaw	Maggs	Berne	Voyce/t
P1	14-Mar	A	London Irish	W 58-13	5303	Perry/c	Thirlby/t	Maggs	Berne/t	Voyce
P1	17-Mar	H	London Wasps	W 16-13	8200	Perry	Thirlby	Maggs	Cox	Voyce
P1	31-Mar	H	Bristol	W 19-16	8200	Perry/c4p	Balshaw	Maggs	Cox	Voyce/t
P1	14-Apr	A	Rotherham	W 68-12	2000	Perry/6c2p	Thirlby/3t	Berne/2t	Cox/t	Voyce/3t
EC	7-Oct	H	Castres	W 25-13	7135	Perry	Balshaw	De Glanville	Tindall	Adebayo
EC	13-Oct	A	Newport	L 17-28	11432	Perry/2cp	Balshaw	De Glanville	Tindall	Adebayo
EC	21-Oct	A	Munster	L 9-31	12500	Perry	Balshaw	De Glanville	Tindall	Maggs
EC	28-Oct	H	Munster	W 18-5	8200	Perry/2p	Balshaw	De Glanville	Tindall	Maggs
EC	13-Jan	A	Castres	W 32-19		Perry/2cp	Balshaw	Maggs	Berne	Voyce/t
EC	23-Jan	H	Newport	W 38-10	6500	Perry/2c	Balshaw	Maggs	Tindall	Voyce
TBC	4-Nov	H	Gloucester	L 18-24	6200	Perry	Balshaw	Berne	Maggs	Adebayo
PO	28-Apr	H	Newcastle Falcons	W 18-9	6840	Perry/c2p	Balshaw	Maggs	Berne/t	Voyce
PO	6-May	A	London Wasps*	W 36-31	8094	Perry/3c	Balshaw/t	Maggs	Berne	Voyce/2t
PO	13-May	N	Leicester Tigers	L 10-22	33500	Perry/cp(b/t)	Balshaw	Maggs	Berne	Voyce

after opponents name indicates a penalty try. Brackets after a player's name indicates he was replaced. eg (a) means he was replaced by replacement code "a" and so on. / after a player or replacement name is followed by any scores he made - eg /t, /c, /p, /dg or any combination of these

LEAGUE DEBUTS

David Barnes, S Bellinger, Sam Cox, Simon Emms, Mark Gabey, Andrew Lloyd, Lee Mears, Tom Voyce.

EVER PRESENT

Most Appearances 21 Steve Borthwick (1), Ben Clarke (1)

PLAYERS USED
29 plus 3 as replacements only

MOST POINTS

Pts	Player	T	C	P	DG
172	J Preston	-	23	42	-
138	M Perry	2	25	26	-
53	S Berne	7	3	4	-
45	T Voyce	9	-	-	-

MATCH FACTS

10	9	1	2	3	4	5	6	7	8
Catt	Preston/2c6p	Barnes	Regan	Mallett	Haag	Borthwick	Thomas	Clarke	Thomas
Catt	Preston/2c4p	Barnes	Regan	Mallett	Haag	Borthwick	Thomas	Clarke/t	Thomas/t
Catt	Preston/3c4p	Barnes	Long	Mallett	Haag	Borthwick	Gardiner	Clarke/t	Thomas/t
Catt	Preston/4p	Barnes	Regan	Mallett	Haag	Borthwick	Gardiner	Clarke	Thomas
Berne	Preston/c4p	Barnes	Regan	Horsman	Haag	Borthwick	Gardiner	Clarke	Thomas
Berne(b/c)	Preston/2p	Barnes	Regan	Mallett	Haag	Borthwick	Gardiner(c/t)	Clarke	Lyle
Berne	Cooper	Barnes	Regan	Mallett	Haag	Borthwick	Clarke	Thomas	Lyle
Berne/t	Preston/2c5p	Barnes	Long	Mallett/t	Haag	Gabey	Gardiner	Clarke/t	Thomas
Berne/t3c2p	Cooper	Barnes	Long	Mallett	Gabey/t	Borthwick	Gardiner	Clarke	Lyle/2t
Berne/2p	Preston/p	Barnes	Long	Mallett	Haag	Borthwick	Thomas	Clarke	Lyle
Catt	Cooper/t	Emms	Regan	Mallett	Haag	Borthwick	Thomas	Clarke	Lyle
Catt/t(e/t)	Cooper/2t(d/2c)	Emms	Regan	Mallett	Haag	Borthwick	Thomas	Clarke	Lyle
Catt	Cooper	Emms	Regan	Mallett	Haag	Borthwick	Thomas	Clarke	Lyle
Catt	Cooper	Emms	Long/t	Mallett	Haag	Borthwick	Thomas	Clarke	Lyle
Catt	Cooper/t	Emms	Long	Mallett	Haag	Borthwick	Thomas	Clarke	Lyle
Catt	Preston/c2p	Barnes	Regan	Emms	Haag	Borthwick	Thomas	Clarke	Lyle
Catt/2t	Preston/3c4p	Emms	Regan	Mallett	Lloyd	Borthwick	Thomas	Clarke/t	Lyle
Catt	Cooper	Emms	Long	Mallett	Lloyd	Borthwick	Thomas	Clarke	Lyle
Catt/3t	Preston/6c3p	Barnes	Regan	Mallett	Haag/t	Borthwick	Thomas/t	Clarke	Lyle
Catt/t	Preston/c3p	Emms	Regan	Mallett	Haag	Borthwick	Thomas	Clarke	Lyle
Catt	Cooper	Emms	Regan	Mallett	Gabey	Borthwick	Thomas	Clarke	Lyle
Catt	Cooper/t	Barnes	Long	Mallett	Gabey	Borthwick	Gardiner	Thomas	Lyle
Preston/c6p	Cooper	Barnes	Regan	Mallett	Haag	Borthwick	Thomas	Clarke	Lyle/t
Preston(e/t)	Cooper/t	Barnes	Regan	Mallett	Haag	Borthwick	Thomas	Clarke	Lyle
Preston/3p	Cooper	Barnes	Regan	Horsman	Haag	Borthwick	Gardiner	Clarke	Lyle
Catt	Cooper(d/4p)	Emms	Regan	Horsman	Haag	Borthwick	Gardiner	Clarke	Lyle
Catt/2t	Cooper/t	Emms	Regan	Mallett	Haag/t	Borthwick	Thomas	Clarke	Lyle
Catt(e/2t)	Cooper/t(d/tc)	Emms(f/t)	Regan	Mallett	Haag	Borthwick	Thomas/t	Clarke	Lyle/c
Catt	Preston/6p	Emms	Regan	Horsman	Haag	Borthwick	Thomas	Clarke	Thomas
Catt	Cooper	Barnes	Long	Mallett	Gabey	Borthwick	Gardiner/t	Lloyd	Lyle
Catt	Cooper	Barnes/t	Long	Mallett	Gabey	Borthwick	Gardiner	Clarke	Lyle/t
Catt	Cooper	Emms	Long	Mallett	Gabey	Borthwick	Gardiner	Clarke	Lyle

REPLACEMENTS

a - I Balshaw	b - R Thirlby	c - G Thomas	d - J Preston	e - S Berne	f - D Barnes

Most replacement appearances: 9 N Thomas, A Long. 8 David Barnes.

Most times replaced: 10 B Clarke. 9 M Regan. 8 S Emms..

2000-01 HIGHLIGHTS

New Zealander Jon Preston topped the Bath scoring list for the second successive season. He also kicked six penalties twice and has done so three times overall. Preston has now sored over 350 points in his three seasons at the club, but he did miss nearly all his first season at the Rec.

Newcomer Tom Voyce topped the try scoring list in his first season with 9 tries.

Veteran second row forward Martin Haag in his final season moved ahead of Nigel Redman as the Bath forward with the most appearances in the league and took the overall record from winger Adedayo Adebayo. Haag finished the season on 167.

Bath set a new record both both most points scored and biggest wuin in an away match when they ran out 68-12 winners at Rotherham in the last league match of the season.

BATH RUGBY

LEAGUE STATISTICS
compiled by Stephen McCormack

SEASON	Division	P	W	D	L	F	A	Pts Diff	Lge Pts	Lge Pos	Most Points	Most Tries
91-92	1	12	10	1	1	277	126	151	21	1	95 Stuart Barnes	8 Tony Swift
92-93	1	12	11	0	1	355	97	258	22	1	122 Jon Webb	7 Stuart Barnes
93-94	1	18	17	0	1	431	181	250	34	1	178 Jon Callard	5 Mike Catt & Ben Clarke
94-95	1	18	12	3	3	373	245	128	27	2	150 Jon Callard	5 Adedayo Adebayo
95-96	1	18	15	1	2	575	276	299	31	1	236 Jon Callard	9 Jeremy Guscott
96-97	1	22	15	1	6	863	411	452	31	2	224 Jon Callard	16 Adedayo Adebayo
97-98	P1	22	13	0	9	575	455	120	26	3	183 Jon Callard	9 Andy Nicol
98-99	P1	26	15	0	11	698	574	124	30	6	294 Mike Catt	14 Jeremy Guscott
99-00	P1	22	15	2	5	690	425	265	43	2	184 Jon Preston	15 Iain Balshaw
00-01	P1	22	14	0	8	680	430	250	70	3	172 Jon Preston	9 Tom Voyce

BIGGEST MARGINS

Home Win 77pts - 84-7 v Sale 26.4.97

Away Win 56pts - 68-12 v Rotherham 14.4.01

Home Defeat 16pts - 13-29 v Saracens 10.4.98

Away Defeat 27pts - 23-50 v Saracens 14.12.97

MOST POINTS

Scored at Home 84 v Sale 26.4.97

Scored Away 68 v Rotherham 14.4.01

Conceded at Home 40 v Wasps 14.9.96

Conceded Away 50 v Saracens 14.12.97

MOST CONSECUTIVE

Appearances 50 Tony Swift 9.9.89-25.9.93

Matches scoring Tries 6 Andy Nicol, Adedayo Adebayo

Matches scoring points 15 Jon Callard

Victories 15

Defeats 6 (2)

MOST TRIES

Scored in a match 14 v Bedford 13.1.90
v Sale 26.4.97

Conceded in a match 7 v London Irish 17.4.99

MOST APPEARANCES

by a forward 157 Martin Haag

by a back 144 Adedayo Adebayo

	MOST IN A SEASON	MOST IN A CAREER	MOST IN A MATCH	
Points	294 MikeCatt 98-99	1177 Jon Callard 89-00	26 Stuart Barnes	v W. Hartlepool 27.3.93 (A)
			Mike Catt	v Sale 26.4.97 (H)
				v London Scot 15.5.99 (H)
Tries	16 Adedayo Adebayo 96-97	67 Jeremy Guscott 85-99	4 Jeremy Guscott	v Bedford 13.1.90 (H)
			Jeremy Guscott	v London Scot 15.5.99 (H)
			Tony Swift	v Bedford 13.1.90 (H)
Conversions	51 Jon Callard 96-97	186 Jon Callard 89-00	10 Stuart Barnes	v Bedford 13.1.90 (H)
Penalties	53 Mike Catt 99-99	228 Jon Callard 89-00	6 Jon Callard	v Harlequins 6.4.96 (H)
			Mike Catt	v Richmond 13.3.99 (A)
			Jon Preston	v Bristol 25.03.00 (H)
Drop Goals	2 Stuart Barnes 87-88 Mike Catt 96-97	9 Stuart Barnes 87-94	1 by eight players	incl. Stuart Barnes (x9)

PLAYING SQUAD

BATH RUGBY

BACKS

	Ht.	Wt.	Birthdate	Birthplace	CLUB	League Apps	Tries	Pts
Matt Perry England, British Lions.	5.10	13.07	27.01.77	Bath	Bath	77(6)	21	253
Adedayo Adebayo England , A.	5.9	14.07	30.11.70	Ibadan	Bath	142(5)	57	279
Jeremy Guscott England , British Lions 8.	6.1	13.10	07.07.65	Bath	Bath	130(2)	67	333
Phil de Glanville England , A.	5.11	13.06	01.10.68	Loughborough	Bath	124(13)	25	121
Shaun Berne Scotland , A.	5.8	13.4	08.01.79		Bath	18(11)	12	85
Mike Catt England , A.	5.10	13.00	17.09.71	Port Elizabeth	Bath	131(1)	38	569
Jon Preston New Zealand	5.10	12.12	15.11.67	Dunedin	Bath	31(4)	1	359
Kevin Maggs England A.	5.11	14.00	03.06.74	Bristol	Bath	59(2)	11	55
Tom Voyce England .	6.0	13.00	05.01.81		Bath	1(4)	9	45
Iain Belshaw England U21 Colts.	6.1	13.02	14.04.79	Lancashire	Bath	60(9)	35	177
Matt Tindall	6.2	14.07	18.10.78	Wakefield	Bath	55(9)	16	80
Gary Cooper	5.7	12.00	07.05.79	Bridgend	Bath	30(7	11	55

FORWARDS

	Ht.	Wt.	Birthdate	Birthplace	CLUB	League Apps	Tries	Pts
Ben Clarke England. Other club: Saracens 22/8/35	6.5	17.7	15.04.68		Bath Richmond	96(1) 63	23 20	108 100
Gavin Thomas	6.1	15.10	22.10.77		Bath	23(14)	1	5
John Mallett England .	6.1	17.10	28.05.70	Lincoln	Bath	76(23)	3	14
Nathan Thomas Wales .	6.3	15.07	22.01.76	Bridgend	Bath	54(14)	5	25
Mark Regan England .	5.1	16.02	28.01.72	Bristol	Bath Bristol	59(15) 66	7 4	35 20
Andrew Long England1.	5.11	15.08	02.09.78	Poole	Bath	22(21)	2	10
Martin Haag England , A, B.	6.5	16.07	28.07.68	Chelmsford	Bath	157(9)	11	53
Angus Gardiner Canterbury .	6.1	15.00	06.01.71	England	Bath	18(5)	1	5
Steve Borthwick	6.6	15.12	12.10.79	Carlisle	Bath	57(1)	-	-
Dan Lyle US Eagles	6.5	17.12	28.07.70	San Diego	Bath	60(4)	11	55

BATH RUGBY

FACT FILE

Founded: 1865
Colours: Blue with black and white
Change colours: Black with white and blue
Website: www.bathrugby.co.uk

GROUND	The Recreation Ground, Bath. BA2 6PW. Telephone: 01225 325200 Fax: 01225 325201 e-mail: enquiries@bathrugby.co.uk Capacity:7,622 + 560 in corporate boxes (8,182) Seated: (covered) 2,044 (uncovered) 3,696 Standing: 1,868
Directions:	Follow signs to Bath City Centre and then signs to the Recreation Ground. Nearest Railway Station: Bath Spa (BR). From station walk up Manvers St. towards centre of town. Turn right into North Parade & left down steps.
Car Parking:	None on ground, unlimited `Park & Ride'.
Admission	Matchdays: Variable depending upon fixture Ticket Office: 01225 460588 Season Tickets: From £85 Junior to £385 covered seating
Club Shop:	1 Argyle Street, Bath BA2 4BA Tel: 01225 311950.
Clubhouse:	Matchdays 12-11 Snacks & bar meals are available. Functions: Capacity 250-300 Contact Dean Quinton 01225 469230
PROGRAMME	Size: A5 Pages: 56 Price: £2.50 Editor: Jennie McMahon 01225 325200
Advertising Rates	Colour (Rates excl. VAT) Page £2,000 1/2 page £1,250

ANYONE WHO'S ANYONE IS IN THE RUGBY STORE TWICKENHAM

ENGLAND RUGBY

THE RUGBY STORE TWICKENHAM

VISIT THE RUGBY STORE TWICKENHAM - OPEN 7 DAYS PER WEEK
Monday to Saturday 10.00am - 5.00pm   Sunday 2.00pm - 5.00pm
Mail Order Hotline 020 8891 4141   Order Online at www.rfu.com

BRISTOL SHOGUNS

Chairman	Malcolm Pearce
Managing Director	Jack Rowell
Directors	John Rushton, John Newman
Commercial Director	Mike Turner
Operations Director	David Winnie
Registered Office	Bristol Rugby Ltd., Unit 4, Eastgate Office Centre, Eastgate Road, Bristol BS5 6XX
	Tel: 0117 311 1460 Fax: 0117 311 1460 Information Line: 08451 220077
Head Coach	Dean Ryan, c/o Bristol Rugby Ltd..
Press & P.R.	Ian & Sandy Bell E-mail: tintinna@aol.com
	Bristol Rugby Press Office, Summerfield, Bristol Rd., Chew Stoke, Somerset. BS40 8UB.
	Tel: 01275 333128 Mobiles: 07050 107918, 07879 898551 Fax: 01275. 332316

During the close season Dean Ryan took over as Head Coach and Director of Rugby, Bob Dwyer, returned to Australia to coach New South Wales Waratahs in the Super 12. Bristol's record points scorer, Mark Tainton, was appointed Backs Coach and the squad was strengthened by the signing of Ben Sturnham from Bath, Leigh Davies from Cardiff and Neil McCarthy from Gloucester.

After an opening day victory away at Rotherham, the early part of the season was disappointing, but things started to look up after the arrival of Argentine fly half Felipe Contepomi. He had the chance to settle into the side during the early European Shield matches and when the Premiership re-started the team had grown in confidence, producing a run of 10 home matches without defeat. That sequence included the memorable first league win over Bath, a rare victory against Leicester and cup success over the holders, Wasps.

Off the field Jack Rowell became Managing Director during the autumn and successful community initiatives, including the introduction of a popular Kids Club, saw an increase in the number of young supporters among a steadily growing fan base.

At one stage European qualification looked a distinct possibility as the team fought its way into mid-table, but a difficult run-in ended those hopes. In the end Bristol were also just edged out of the play offs despite a wonderful performance against Northampton in their last home game when they ran in four tries for the first time in the season. However, that performance plus the arrival of Australian World Cup Winner Jason Little and some talented youngsters has left the club in good heart for the new campaign.

L-R - **Back row:** Andrew Sheridan, Saul Nelson, David Rees, Lee Best, Garath Archer, Scott Morgan, Craig Short, James Ogilvie-Bull, Jamie Mayer, Mark Bennett, Mike McCarrick.   **Middle:** Paul Hull (u21s' coach), Mark Tainton (backs' coach), Matt Salter, Steven Vile, Ben Stunrham, Spencer Brown, Kris Fullman, Eduardo Simone, Alex cadwallader, Alex Brown, Darren Compton, Richard Siveter, Simon Fenn, Donna Sanderson (physio), Paul Johnstone, Keith James (physio), Ellery Hanley (defensive coach), Leigh Davies. **Front:** Ockert Booyse, Neil McCarthy, Jim Brownrigg, Dean Dewdney, Gareth Bowen, Luke Nabaro, Dean Ryan (first team coach), Agustin Pichot, Barry Williams, Gareth Baber, Leighton Gerrard, Adam Vander, Sean Marsden, Mervyn Evans.

BRISTOL

Comp.	Date	H/A	Opponents	Result & Score	Att	15	14	13	12	11
P1	20-Aug	A	Rotherham	W 23-20	3100	Best	Rees	Simone	Davies	Dewdney/t
P1	26-Aug	H	Saracens	L 23-34	4280	Best	Rees	Simone	Davies	Dewdney/t
P1	3-Sep	A	London Wasps	L 17-23	3525	Best/t	Rees	Simone	Davies	Dewdney
P1	6-Sep	H	Sale	L 13-36	3100	Dewdney	Rees	Simone	Mayer/t	Nabaro
P1	10-Sep	H	London Irish	L 26-30	2902	Dewdney	Rees	Simone	Mayer	Brown/t
P1	16-Sep	A	Harlequins	L 25-31	3089	Brown	Rees	Simone	Mayer	Dewdney/t
P1	23-Sep	H	Leicester Tigers	W 24-20	4500	Brown/t	Rees	Simone	Davies	Dewdney
P1	30-Sep	A	Gloucester	L 16-38	6503	Marsden	Rees	Simone	Davies	Brown
P1	18-Nov	H	Rotherham	W 32-21	2380	Best	Rees	Nabaro	Davies	Brown
P1	25-Nov	A	Northanpton Saints	L 6-24	6093	Best	Rees	Nabaro	Davies	Marsden
P1	2-Dec	H	Bath	W 16-9	6335	Best	Rees	Simone	Davies	Nabaro
P1	17-Dec	H	Newcastle Falcons	W 27-14	3687	Best	Rees/t	Simone	Mayer	Nabaro
P1	23-Dec	A	Sale	W 26-25	2631	Best	Rees/t	Nabaro	Mayer	Brown
P1	27-Dec	A	Newcastle Falcons	L 15-23	3738	Best	Rees	Nabaro/2t	Mayer	Brown
P1	6-Jan	H	Gloucester	W 18-9	6781	Best	Rees	Nabaro	Mayer	Brown
P1	6-Feb	A	Leicester Tigers	L 10-17	12332	Best	Nabaro	Simone	Mayer	Brown
P1	11-Feb	H	Harlequins	W 13-9	4600	Best	Nabaro	Simone	Mayer	Brown
P1	24-Feb	A	London Irish	D 26-26	3349	Best	Rees/t	Simone	Mayer/t	Brown
P1	11-Mar	H	London Wasps	L 12-24	5444	Best	Rees	Simone	Mayer	Brown
P1	18-Mar	A	Saracens	L 13-24	12843	Best	Rees	Marsden	Mayer/t	Brown
P1	31-Mar	A	Bath	L 16-19	8200	Best	Rees	Simone	Mayer	Brown
P1	16-Apr	H	Northampton Saints	W 46-16	5315	Best	Rees	Simone/t	Mayer/2t	Brown
ES	7-Oct	H	Mont de Marsan	W 41-24		Marsden	Rees	Nabaro/t	Davies/t	Brown
ES	14-Oct	A	La Rochelle	L 19-34	6500	Marsden	Rees	Simone	Contepomi/p	Nabaro
ES	21-Oct	H	Parma	W 61-14		Marsden/t	Dewdney	Simone/t	Mayer/t(c/t)	Nabaro/t
ES	28-Oct	A	Parma	W 25-12		Marsden	Nabaro	Simone/t	Davies	Brown
ES	13-Jan	A	Mont de Marsan	L 12-24		Marsden	Nabaro	Simone	Davies	Brown
ES	20-Jan	H	La Rochelle*	D 41-41	2105	Marsden	Brown	Simone/t	Mayer	Dewdney
TBC	4-Nov	H	London Wasps	W 22-17	3133	Best	Rees	Simone	Davies	Brown
TBC	12-Nov	A	Newcastle Falcons	L 16-32	2151	Best	Rees	Nabaro	Davies	Dewdney

** after opponents name indicates a penalty try. Brackets after a player's name indicates he was replaced.
eg (a) means he was replaced by replacement code "a" and so on. / after a player or replacement name
is followed by any scores he made - eg /t, /c, /p, /dg or any combination of these*

LEAGUE DEBUTS

Felipe Contepomi, Leigh Davies, Neil McCarthy, Ben Sturnham.

EVER PRESENT
None

Most Appearances
20   David Rees.
19   Adam Vander (1), Paul Johnstone (1).
17   Lee Best, Agustin Pichot.

PLAYERS USED
30 + four as replacements only

MOST POINTS

Pts	Player	T	C	P	DG
168	F Contepomi	4	17	38	-
91	S Vile	2	9	21	-
44	G Bowen	-	4	12	-
25	J Mayer	5	-	-	-

MATCH FACTS

10	9	1	2	3	4	5	6	7	8
Bowen/6p	Pichot	Gerrard	Williams	Crompton	Sheridan	Ryan	Salter	Short	Brownrigg
Bowen/c3p(a/c)	Pichot	Johnstone	McCarthy	Crompton	Sheridan	Ryan	Fenn	Vander/t	Brownrigg
Bowen/2cp	Pichot	Johnstone	Williams	Crompton	Sheridan	Brown(b/t)	Fenn	Vander	Ryan
Bowen/c2p	Pichot	Johnstone	Williams	Fullman	Ryan	Brown	Fenn	Vander	Sturnham
Vile/2c4p	Pichot	Johnstone/t	Williams	Fullman	Ryan	Archer	Salter	Vander	Sturnham
Vile/2t2c2p	Pichot	Johnstone	Williams	Fullman	Ryan	Sheridan	Salter	Vander	Sturnham
Vile/c4p	Pichot/t	Johnstone	Williams	Fullman	Ryan	Sheridan	Fenn	Vander	Sturnham
Vile/c3p	Pichot	Johnstone	Williams/t	Crompton	Ryan	Sheridan	Fenn	Vander	Sturnham
Vile/2c6p	Baber/t	Johnstone	McCarthy	Fullman	Archer	Brown	Short	Vander	Sturnham/t
Vile/2p	Baber	Johnstone	McCarthy	Fullman	Archer	Brown	Salter	Vander	Sturnham
Contepomi/c3p	Pichot/t	Johnstone	McCarthy	Crompton	Archer	Brown	Salter	Vander	Sturnham
Contepomi/t3c2p	Baber/t	Johnstone	McCarthy	Crompton	Archer	Brown	Salter	Vander	Sturnham
Contepomi/2c4p	Baber	Johnstone/t	McCarthy	Crompton	Archer	Brown	Short	Vander	Salter
Contepomi/cp	Baber	Johnstone	Williams	Crompton	Archer	Brown	Fenn	Vander	Brownrigg
Contepomi/6p	Pichot	Gerrard	McCarthy	Crompton	Archer	Brown	Fenn	Short	Salter
Contepomi/tcp	Pichot	Johnstone	McCarthy	Crompton	Archer	Brown	Short	Vander	Salter
Contepomi/c2p	Pichot	Johnstone/t	McCarthy	Crompton	Archer	Brown	Short	Vander	Salter
Contepomi/2c4p	Pichot	Johnstone	McCarthy	Crompton	Archer	Brown	Short	Vander	Salter
Contepomi/4p	Pichot	Johnstone	McCarthy	Crompton	Archer	Brown	Short	Vander	Salter
Contepomi/c2p	Pichot	Gerrard	McCarthy	Crompton	Archer	Brown	Short	Sturnham	Salter
Contepomi/tc3p	Pichot	Johnstone	Williams	Crompton	Archer	Brown	Short	Vander	Salter
Contepomi/t4c6p	Pichot	Johnstone	McCarthy	Crompton	Archer	Brown	Short	Vander	Salter
Vile/2c9p	Pichot	Johnstone	McCarthy	Crompton	Ryan	Brown	McCarrick	Vander	Sturnham
Vile/c3p	Pichot/t	Johnstone	McCarthy	Crompton	Sheridan	Brown	Short	Vander	Sturnham
Contepomi/t7c4p	Baber	Gerrard	McCarthy	Fullman	Ryan	Brown	Short	Vander/t	Sturnham
Contepomi/2c2p	Baber/t	Johnstone	Williams/t	Fullman	Sheridan	Brown	Short	Vander	Sturnham
Contepomi	Baber	Johnstone	Williams	Fullman	Sheridan	Brown	Short	Vander	Sturnham
Vile/c7p(d/p)	Baber	Siviter	Williams/t	Fullman	Sheridan	Archer	Short	McCarrick	Sturnham
Contepomi/tc4pdg	Pichot	Johnstone	McCarthy	Fullman	Archer	Brown	Short	Vander	Sturnham
Vile/tc3p	Baber	Johnstone	McCarthy	Fullman	Archer	Brown	Short	Vander	Sturnham

REPLACEMENTS   a - S Vile   b - J Brownrigg   c - D Rees   d - G Bowen

Most replacement appearances: 13 Andrew Sheridan. 6 Scott Morgan

Most times replaced: 9 Matt Salter. 7 A Brown

2000-01 HIGHLIGHTS

Argentinian International Felipe Contepomi joined mid season and went on to notch 168 points from just 12 matches.

In the late season match against Northampton he scored a club record 31 points.

This eclipsed the previous record of 26 held by Mark Tainton and dating back to 1994.

It is the fourth consecutive season that someone new has topped the Bristol scoring chart.

Leading the try scorers was the Scottish centre Jamie Mayer who finished with five tries.

This is the lowest total since 1995-96 when Martin Corry finished on four tries.

BRISTOL

LEAGUE STATISTICS
compiled by Stephen McCormack

SEASON	Division	P	W	D	L	F	A	Pts Diff	Lge Pts	Lge Pos	Most Points	Most Tries
91-92	1	12	4	0	8	192	174	18	8	10	29 Mark Tainton	5 Pete Stiff
92-93	1	12	6	0	6	148	169	-21	12	6	68 Mark Tainton	3 Derek Eves
93-94	1	18	10	0	8	331	276	55	20	4	161 Mark Tainton	8 A Saveriamutto
94-95	1	18	7	0	11	301	353	-52	14	6	196 Mark Tainton	6 Derek Eves
95-96	1	18	8	0	10	329	421	-92	16	6	120 Mark Tainton	4 Martin Corry
96-97	1	22	8	1	13	432	625	-193	17	9	178 Paul Burke	10 David Tiueti
97-98	P1	22	2	0	20	351	733	-382	4	12r	163 Paul Burke	7 David Tiueti
98-99	P2	26	22	0	4	848	418	430	44	1p	164 Paul Hull	13 A Larkin & L Nabaro
99-00	P1	22	12	1	9	632	602	30	34	6	178 Henry Honiball	9 Spencer Brown
00-01	P1	22	9	1	12	443	492	-49	44	11	168 Felipe Contepomi	5 Jamie Mayer

BIGGEST MARGINS

Home Win 41pts - 55-14 v Fylde 12.9.98
Away Win 38pts - 57-19 v Bedford 28.4.00
Home Defeat 42pts 8-50 v Newcastle 27.12.97
Away Defeat 76pts 0-76 v Sale 9.11.97

MOST CONSECUTIVE

Appearances 81 Derek Eves 11.3.88 - 4.3.95
Matches scoring Tries 4 Luke Nabaro
Matches scoring points 31 Mark Tainton
Victories 8
Defeats 12

MOST POINTS

Scored at Home 58 v Moseley 22.11.98
Scored Away 57 v Bedford 28.4.00
Conceded at Home 50 v Newcastle 27.12.97
Conceded Away 76 v Bath 30.10.96
v Sale 9.11.97

MOST TRIES

Scored in a match 10 v Rugby 28.3.92
Conceded in a match 12 v Sale 9.11.97 (A)

MOST APPEARANCES

by a forward 107(1) Dave Hinkins
by a back 146 (4) Paul Hull

	MOST IN A SEASON	MOST IN A CAREER	MOST IN A MATCH
Points	196 Mark Tainton	637 Mark Tainton 87-97	31 Felipe Contepomi v North'ton 16.4.01 (H)
Tries	13 Adam Larkin 98-99 Luke Nabaro 98-99	28 Paul Hull 87-99	5 Luke Nabaro v Blackheath 13.3.99 (H)
Conversions	35 Paul Hull 98-99	62 Mark Tainton 87-97	5 Jon Webb v Sale 24.10.87 (H) Henry Honiball v Sale 13.11.99 (A)
Penalties	56 Mark Tainton 94-95	165 Mark Tainton 87-97	7 Mark Tainton v Leicester 5.11.94 (H)
Drop Goals	3 Simon Hogg 88-89 Arwel Thomas 95-96	6 Mark Tainton 87-97	2 Simon Hogg v Leicester 9.3.91 (H)

PLAYING SQUAD

BRISTOL

BACKS

	Ht.	Wt.	Birthdate	Birthplace	CLUB	League Apps	Tries	Pts
Luke Nabaro	6.0	14.02	24.04.76	Fiji	Bristol	22	19	95
Felipe Contepomi Argentina					Bristol	12	4	168
Steven Vile	6.0	13.0	16.07.70		Bristol	6(2)	2	91
Spencer Brown England 2, A	5.11	13.05	11.07.73	Eton	Bristol	34(1)	10	50
Dean Dewdney Zimbabwe	5.10	10.10	05.11.74	Zimbabwe	Bristol Clifton	27(9)	9	45
Gareth Baber Wales U-21, Oxford and Swansea Univ.	5.10	12.02	23.05.72	Cardiff	Bristol	41(9)	17	85
Augustin Pichot Argentina	5.9	12.05	22.08.74	Buenos Aires	Bristol Richmond	31	6	30
Jamie Mayer Scotland	5.10	14.06	16.04.77	Edinburgh	Bristol	27(4)	11	55
Eduardo Simone Argentina	6.0	14.0	14.10.74		Bristol	26(4)	2	10
Lee Best	6.3	16.0	16.10.78		Bristol	30	4	205
David Rees England	5.9	13.10	15.10.74	London	Bristol Sale	26 41(3)	5 11	25 55

FORWARDS

	Ht.	Wt.	Birthdate	Birthplace	CLUB	League Apps	Tries	Pts
Neil McCarthy England	5.9	14.6	29.11.73	Slough	Bristol Gloucester	13 27(15)	- 1	- 5
Matthew Salter	6.4	15.0	02.12.76		Bristol	20(3)	-	-
Adam Vander England A. Other club: Rosslyn Park	6.2	15.07	27.01.74	Turners Hill	Bristol Richmond	34(3)	6	30
Dean Ryan England. Other club: Wasps	6.6	17.00	20.06.66	Tuxford	Bristol Newcastle	28	3	15
Ben Sturnham England. Other club: Saracens	6.5	18.5	06.03.74	St Albans	Bristol Bath	10(4)	1	5
Andrew Sheridan	6.5	20.6	01.11.79		Bristol	11(13)	2	10
Barry Williams Wales. Other clubs: Neath	6.0	16.06	06.01.74	Camarthan	Bristol Richmond	28(3)	8	40
Darren Crompton England A. Other clubs: Bath	6.1	17.00	12.09.72	Exeter	Bristol Richmond	26(3)	1	5
John Brownrigg England U-21.	6.6	15.00	04.06.77	Chicester	Bristol	21(22)	3	15
Paul Johnstone Zimbabwe. Other clubs: Clifton	6.0	17.05	16.10.70	Bulawayo (Zim)	Bristol London Scottish	37(3)	8	40
Simon Fenn	6.2	16.00	24.04.71	Manly	Bristol London Scottish	17(2)	-	-
Craig Short	6.1	14.02	26.06.75	Kingswood	Bristol	29(12)	2	10

BRISTOL SHOGUNS

FACT FILE

Founded: 1888

Colours: Dark blue with a broad white band on the front
Change colours: Red with a broad white band

GROUND

Address: Memorial Stadium, Filton Avenue, Horfield, Bristol. BS7 0AQ

Tel: 0117 908 5500   Fax: 0117 907 4682
Club Newsline: 0839 44 66 33   Website: www.bristolrugby.co.uk
Capacity: 12,000   Seated: 2,780 Standing: Enclosure 2,200, Ground 7,020

Directions: M4 to junction 19, M32 to junction 2, then join B4469 towards Horfield. Turn left at 2nd set of traffic lights after `Brunel Ford' and bus garage (on the right) into Filton Ave. Ground is on the left.

Nearest Railway Station: Bristol Parkway or Bristol Temple Meads.

Car Parking: Very limited at the ground. Plenty of street parking nearby

Admission:

Season tickets   Centenary & West Stands: £199   Centenary Family ticket: £425
                West Enclosure: Adult £145, Senior Citizens & under 16s £90
                Club House & Centenary Terraces: Adult £145, Students £90 Senior Citizens £70 & under 16s £50
Matchday   Centenary & West Stands: £16   Centenary Family ticket £48
                West Enclosure: Adults £12, Senior Citizens, Students and under 16s £8
                Club House & Centenary Terraces: Adults £12, Senior Citizens, Students and under 16s £8
                South Stand & Family Enclosure: Adults £10, under 16s free when accompanied by an adult.

Club Shop: Monday - Friday 9.30 - 5.00, Saturday 10 - 3 & matchdays from noon

Clubhouse: Snacks & bar meals available. Contact: Robert Laurence
        Tel: 0117 909 6648. Mob: 07831 463437 Fax: 0117 908 5530
        Corprate Hospitality: Kay Booker,
        Tel: 0117 311 1464 Fax: 0171 311 1460

PROGRAMME

Ian and Sandy Bell
Bristol Rugby Press Office,
Summerfield, Bristol Rd., Chew Stoke,
Somerset. BS40 8UB.
Tel: 01275 333128
Mobile: 07050 107918
Fax: 01275 332316
E-mail: tintinna@aol.com

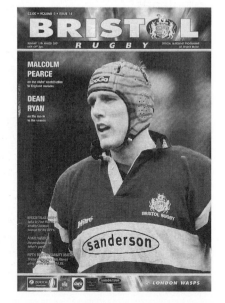

GLOUCESTER RFC

Club Chairman	Tom Walkinshaw	c/o Gloucester Rugby Club,
Managing Director	Ken Nottage	Kingsholm,
Company Secretary	Doug Wadley	Kingsholm Road,
Director of Rugby	Philippe St. Andre	Gloucester GL1 3AX
Commercial Officer	Karen Ellis	Tel: 01452 381087
Media & Marketing Exec.	James Bennett	Ticket Office: 01452 381087
Team Manager	Pete Glanville	Fax: 01452 383321

The 2000-01 season was a like a roller coaster for the Cherry and Whites and their fans. The Gloucester team achieved many fantastic highs, only to have themselves brought back down to earth by some nasty lows. In European competition, Gloucester were a revelation. In their first season of Heineken Cup rugby, they reached the semi-final. Their domestic form however, was a constant cause of consternation for the coaches.

The roots of this problem started in August. An entire first team was on the sidelines recovering from the monumental effort the season before. Gloucester suffered an ignominious start to the season, receiving a drubbing at Saracens on the first day of the season.

At fortress Kingsholm, fortunes were little better as loses followed to both Bath and Sale. New captain Ian Jones stood down to concentrate on his own game, leaving Kingsley Jones, (back from injury), to steer the good ship Gloucester out of these very muddy waters once again.

October brought a change in fortune as both Jason Little and Phil Vickery made their first starts in a rousing win over west-country rivals Bristol. European competition started and the Cherry and Whites enjoyed great success. After beating Llanelli twice, Gloucester topped their group and then beat Cardiff at Kingsholm in January, after being written off buy the press.

At Bath, Gloucester's underdogs triumphed again in the Tetley's Bitter Cup. An expectant Bath crowd saw their team beaten by an unfancied Gloucester XV, who won at the Rec for the first time in twenty-nine years.

After these great cup exploits the return to the league was far less spectacular. Wins against London Irish and Saracens sent the team to Leicester in buoyant mood. They outscored the Champions elect by three tries to one only to lose to a try in the eighty-fourth minute of play.

A win against Newcastle, before Christmas, was to be Gloucester's last win in five subsequent league games. This apparent riches to rags story was hard for all concerned and many fingers outside the club were pointing accusingly.

An end of season rally though, saw Gloucester qualify seventh in the championship. But loses to both Leicester, in the Heineken Cup, and Wasps in the playoffs on consecutive weeks saw Gloucester's season come to a sudden halt.

The up turn in fortunes and spirit towards the end of the season are cause for hope however. With a new coaching team of Philippe Saint-Andre, Laurent Seigne and Andrew Keast expectations are again high for one of the country's most famous clubs.

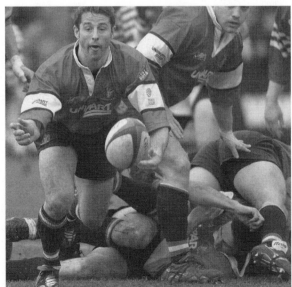

Andy Gomarsall gets the ball out in the game against Sale.
Photo courtesy of Gloucestershire Picture Agency

GLOUCESTER

Comp.	Date	H/A	Opponents	Result & Score	Att	15	14	13	12	11
P1	20-Aug	A	Saracens	L 20-50	7682	Fanolua	Catling	Ewens	Yates/t	Jewell
P1	26-Aug	H	Sale	L 18-19	5500	Fanolua	Jewell	Ewens	Yates	Schisano/t
P1	2-Sep	A	Rotherham	W 29-23	2500	Fanolua	Schisano/3t	Ewens	Yates	Jewell/t
P1	6-Sep	H	Newcastle Falcons	W 19-18	2623	Fanolua	Lougheed	Ewens/t	Yates	Schisano
P1	9-Sep	H	Bath	L 21-22	6754	Fanolua	Lougheed	Ewens	Yates	Schisano
P1	17-Sep	A	London Wasps	L 23-43	4727	Fanolua	Catling	Ewens	Yates/t	Beim/t
P1	23-Sep	A	Harlequins	W 27-23	5428	Catling	Ewens	Fanolua	Yates	Beim
P1	30-Sep	H	Bristol	W 38-16	6503	Catling	Ewens	Little/2t	Yates	Beim
P1	18-Nov	H	Saracens	W 16-15	5909	Catling	Fanolua	Little	Yates	Beim/t
P1	25-Nov	H	London Irish	W 26-6	5618	Catling	Ewens	Little	Yates	Beim/t
P1	2-Dec	A	Leicester Tigers	L 28-31	11989	Catling	Fanolua	Little	Yates/t	Greenslade-Jones
P1	16-Dec	A	Northanpton Saints	L 15-34	7225	Hayward	Catling	Little	Yates	Greenslade-Jones
P1	23-Dec	H	Newcastle Falcons	W 28-13	7455	Catling	Ewens	Fanolua	Little/t	Beim/t
P1	27-Dec	H	Northanpton Saints	L 12-15	9859	Catling	Ewens	Fanolua/tc	Little	Beim
P1	6-Jan	A	Bristol	L 9-18	6781	Catling	Ewens	Fanolua	Yates	Beim
P1	6-Feb	A	Harlequins	L 19-21	4800	Catling	Greenslade-Jones/t	Fanolua	Little	Beim
P1	10-Feb	H	London Wasps	L 3-28	6940	Catling	Greenslade-Jones	Ewens	Little	Beim
P1	24-Feb	A	Bath	L 16-50	8200	Catling/t	Fanolua	Little	Yates	Beim
P1	10-Mar	H	Rotherham*	W 50-17	5850	Catling/t	Ewens	Fanolua	Little/t(e/t)	Beim/t(d/t)
P1	17-Mar	A	Sale	W 24-16	3514	Catling	Ewens	Fanolua	Little/2t	Simpson Daniel
P1	31-Mar	H	Leicester Tigers	W 22-13	7614	Catling	Ewens	Fanolua	Little	Beim
P1	16-Apr	A	London Irish	L 10-35	7131	Goodridge	Todd	Murray	Yates	Greenslade-Jones
EC	6-Oct	A	Llanelli	W 27-20	7000	Catling	Fanolua/2p	Little/t	Yates	Beim
EC	15-Oct	H	Roma	W 52-12	4926	Catling	Schisano/t	Fanolua/3c	Yates	Beim/5t
EC	21-Oct	H	Colomiers*	D 22-22		Catling	Schisano(a/c)	Fanolua	Yates	Beim
EC	28-Oct	A	Colomiers	L 19-30	7000	Catling/t	Fanolua	Little	Yates	Beim
EC	13-Jan	H	Llanelli*	W 28-27	10800	Catling	Fanolua	Little	Yates	Beim
EC	20-Jan	A	Roma	W 38-29	2200	Beim	Fanolua	Little/t	Yates	Ewens/t
EC	27-Jan	H	Cardiff	W 21-15	10800	Catling	Ewens	Fanolua	Little	Beim
EC	21-Mar	N	Leicester Tigers	L 15-19		Hayward	Greenslade-Jones	Fanolua	Little	Simpson Daniel
TBC	4-Nov	A	Bath	W 24-18	6200	Catling	Jewell	Ewens	Fanolua	Beim/t
TBC	11-Nov	H	Leicester Tigers*	L 13-25	5100	Catling	Jewell	Ewens	Fanolua	Beim
PO	29-Apr	A	London Wasps	L 6-18	4986	Goodridge	Greenslade-Jones	Fanolua	Little	Simpson Daniel

** after opponents name indicates a penalty try. Brackets after a player's name indicates he was replaced.
eg (a) means he was replaced by replacement code "a" and so on. / after a player or replacement name
is followed by any scores he made - eg /t, /c, /p, /dg or any combination of these*

LEAGUE DEBUTS

Oliver Azam, Jake Boer, James Forrester, Andy Gomersall,
John Goodridge, H Grigore, Rory Greenslade-Jones, Jason
Little, Dave Lougheed, Duncan Murray, Stephane Sanchez,
Franck Schisano, John Simpson-Daniel, Robert Todd.

EVER PRESENT

None

Most Appearances   19 Junior Paramore (1)
                     18 Ian Jones.

PLAYERS USED

39 plus 3 as replacement only.

MOST POINTS

Pts	Player	T	C	P	DG
157	S Mannix	1	16	40	-
86	B Hayward	1	12	19	-
30	A Gomersall	2	1	6	-
30	J Little	6	-	-	-

MATCH FACTS

10	9	1	2	3	4	5	6	7	8
Mannix(a/2c2p)	Sanders	Powles	Azam	Deacon	Fidler	Jones	Ojomoh	Boer	Paramore
Hayward/c2p	Sanders	Azam	Djoudi	Powles	Cornwell	Jones	Ojomoh	Boer/t	Paramore
Hayward/3cp	Gomersall	Simon	Azam	Powles	Fidler	Jones	Boer	Jones	Paramore
Hayward/3p	Gomersall	Simon	Azam	Powles	Fidler	Cornwell	Ojomoh	Hazell/t	Paramore
Hayward/tp	Gomersall/tc2p	Azam	Fortey	Powles	Fidler	Jones	Boer	Jones	Paramore
Mannix/2c3p	Gomersall	Simon	Azam	Deacon	Eustace	Jones	Boer	Hazell	Paramore
Mannix/9p	Gomersall	Azam	Fortey	Powles	Fidler	Jones	Ojomoh	Jones	Paramore
Mannix/3c4p	Gomersall	Powles(b/t)	Fortey	Vickery/t	Fidler	Jones	Boer	Jones	Paramore
Hayward/c3p	Gomersall	Sanchez	Fortey	Deacon	Eustace	Jones	Boer	Jones	Paramore
Mannix/2c4p	Moncrieff	Woodman	Azam	Deacon	Fidler	Jones	Boer	Jones/t	Paramore
Hayward/2c3p	Gomersall	Woodman	Azam	Deacon/t	Fidler	Jones	Ojomoh	Hazell	Paramore/t
Mannix/4p	Moncrieff/dg	Woodman	Azam	Vickery	Fidler	Jones	Ojomoh	Jones	Paramore
Mannix/2c3p	Gomersall	Woodman	Fortey	Vickery	Fidler	Cornwell/t	Boer	Jones	Paramore
Mannix/t	Gomersall	Woodman	Azam	Deacon	Fidler	Jones	Boer	Jones	Ojomoh
Mannix/3p	Gomersall	Woodman	Fortey	Deacon	Fidler	Jones	Boer	Hazell	Paramore
Hayward/c2p(c/2p)	Gomersall	Woodman	Fortey	Deacon	Fidler	Jones	Boer	Jones	Paramore
Hayward/p	Moncrieff	Woodman	Azam	Vickery	Fidler	Jones	Boer	Hazell	Paramore
Mannix/c3p	Gomersall	Woodman	Azam	Vickery	Eustace	Jones	Boer	Jones	Ojomoh
Mannix/5cp(a/c)	Gomersall	Woodman	Azam	Vickery	Fidler	Cornwell/t	Boer	Jones	Paramore
Mannix/c4p	Gomersall	Woodman	Fortey	Vickery	Fidler	Jones	Boer	Hazell	Paramore
Simpson Daniel	Gomersall/t4p	Woodman	Fortey	Deacon	Fidler	Jones/t	Boer	Hazell	Paramore
Hayward/cp	Moncrieff	Sanchez	Djoudi	Deacon	Eustace	Cornwell	Forrester/t	Grigoire	Ojomoh
Mannix/3p	Gomersall/c	Simon	Azam	Vickery	Eustace	Jones	Ojomoh(f/t)	Jones	Paramore
Little	Moncrieff/2c4p	Powles	Azam	Vickery	Fidler	Eustace	Boer	Jones	Ojomoh
Little	Moncrieff/5p	Simon	Azam	Vickery	Eustace	Jones	Hazell	Jones	Paramore
Mannix/c4p	Gomersall	Vickery	Azam	Deacon	Fidler	Jones	Ojomoh	Jones	Paramore
Mannix/c6p	Moncrieff/dg	Woodman	Azam	Vickery	Fidler	Jones	Boer	Jones	Ojomoh
Mannix/2c8p	Moncrieff	Woodman	Azam	Vickery	Fidler	Cornwell	Boer	Hazell	Ojomoh
Mannix/6p(a/p)	Moncrieff	Woodman	Azam	Vickery	Fidler	Jones	Boer	Jones	Paramore
Mannix/5p	Gomersall	Deacon	Azam	Vickery	Jones	Fidler	Boer	Jones	Paramore
Hayward/t3cp	Moncrieff	Vickery	Fortey	Deacon	Fidler	Cornwell/t	Boer	Hazell	Ojomoh
Hayward/c2p	Gomersall	Vickery	Fortey	Deacon	Fidler	Cornwell	Boer	Hazell	Ojomoh
Mannix/2p	Gomersall	Azam	Fortey	Vickery	Fidler	Jones	Boer	Hazell	Ojomoh

REPLACEMENTS   a - B Hayward   b - O Azam   c - S Mannix   d - J Simpson-Daniel   e - R Todd   f - A Hazell

Most replacement appearances: 9 Adam Eustace. 7 Steve Ojomoh, Ed Pearce, Serge Sanchez.

Most times replaced: 11 Rob Fidler. 10 O Azam

2000-01 HIGHLIGHTS

Simon Mannix topped the scoring list for the second successive time but with only 157 points.
That is the lowest toal since the 1995-96 season when Tim Smith finished top with 79 points.

Gloucester suffered their biggest ever home defeat when going down 28-3 to London Irish in February. The 25 point loss was one worse than when they were beaten 11-35 by Northampton last season.

Jason Little topped the try scorerrs list with six tries, the lowest total to top the scoring charts since Paul Holford managed just 5 in 1995-96.

GLOUCESTER

LEAGUE STATISTICS
compiled by Stephen McCormack

SEASON	Division	P	W	D	L	F	A	Pts Diff	Lge Pts	Lge Pos	Most Points		Most Tries	
91-92	1	12	7	1	4	193	168	25	15	4	81	Tim Smith	5	Simon Morris
92-93	1	12	6	0	6	173	151	22	12	5	71	Tim Smith	3	Tim Smith & Derek Morgan
93-94	1	18	6	2	10	247	356	-109	14	8	82	Tim Smith	3	Paul Holford & Bruce Fenley
94-95	1	18	6	1	11	269	336	-67	13	7	85	Mark Mapletoft	8	Paul Holford
95-96	1	18	6	0	12	275	370	-95	12	8	79	Tim Smith	5	Paul Holford
96-97	1	22	11	1	10	476	589	-113	23	6	269	Mark Mapletoft	7	Mike Lloyd
97-98	P1	22	11	1	10	512	528	-16	23	7	275	Mark Mapletoft	8	Terry Fanolua
98-99	P1	26	9	1	16	554	643	-89	19	10	198	Mark Mapletoft	8	C Catling & P St Andre
99-00	P1	22	15	0	7	628	490	138	40	3	282	Simon Mannix	9	C Catling & E Moncrieff
00-01	P1	22	10	0	12	473	526	-53	48	7	187	Simon Mannix	6	Jason Little

BIGGEST MARGINS

Home Win 54pts - 61-7 v Sale 16.4.88

Away Win 46pts - 49-3 v Orrell 16.11.96

Home Defeat 24pts - 11-35 v Northampton 11.3.00

Away Defeat 56pts - 19-75 v Harlequins 31.8.96

MOST CONSECUTIVE

Appearances 47 Dave Sims 11.4.92-25.3.95

Matches scoring Tries 4 Phillipe St Andre

Matches scoring points 48 Mark Mapletoft

Victories 8

Defeats 7

MOST POINTS

Scored at Home 61 v Sale 16.4.88

Scored Away 49 v Orrell 16.11.96

Conceded at Home 45 v Bath 21.9.96

Conceded Away 75 v Harlequins 31.8.96

MOST TRIES

Scored in a match 11 v Sale 16.4.88

Conceded in a match 11 v Harlequins 31.8.96 v Bath 30.4.97

MOST APPEARANCES

by a forward 130 Dave Sims

by a back 96(1) Chris Catling

	MOST IN A SEASON	MOST IN A CAREER	MOST IN A MATCH
Points	282 Simon Mannix 99-00	848 Mark Mapletoft 94-99	28 Simon Mannix v Northampton 16.5.99 (H)
Tries	9 Elton Moncrieff 99-00 Chris Catling 99-00	23 Chris Catling 96-00	4 Elton Moncrieff v Bedford 15.5.00 (H)
Conversions	36 Simon Mannix 99-00	90 Mark Mapletoft 94-99	7 Simon Mannix v Bedford 16.5.00 (H)
Penalties	62 Simon Mannix 99-00	183 Mark Mapletoft 94-99	9 Simon Mannix v Harlequins 23.9.00 (H)
Drop Goals	6 Martyn Kimber 94-95,95-96	12 Martin Kimber 94-96	2 Martyn Kimber v Bath 4.3.95 (A) Mark Mapletoft v Saracens 5.4.97 (H)

PLAYING SQUAD

GLOUCESTER

BACKS

	Ht.	Wt.	Birthdate	Birthplace	CLUB	League Apps	Tries	Pts
Chris Catling	6.2	13.07	17.06.76	Surrey	Gloucester	97(1)	23	118
Other club: Old Mid Whit 2/2/10					Exeter	6	1	5
Tom Beim	5.11	13.09	01.12.75	Frimley	Gloucester	35(1)	15	75
					Sale	45(1)	31	155
Terry Fanolua Samoa	6.0	14.08	03.07.74	Motoutua	Gloucester	66(1)	13	70
Byrom Hayward	5.8	13.2	02.01.73		Gloucester	19(7)	3	106
Joe Ewens	6.0	13.00	16.12.77	Bristol	Gloucester	31(3)	2	10
Other clubs: Bath 1(1)/-/-					Bedford	21(4(	10	50
Chris Yates	6.1	16.00	13.05.71	Otahuhu	Gloucester	36(3)	8	40
					Sale Sharks	60(7)	19	101
Elton Moncrieff	5.7	12.08	08.06.72	Australia	Gloucester	22	9	60
Ian Sanders	5.9	12.00	22.01.71	Penzance	Gloucester	17(10)	1	5
					Bath	30(4)	3	15
Brian Johnson England A. Army	5.11	12.06	27.07.72	Wegberg	Gloucester	35(4)	9	45
					Newbury	31	35	175
Simon Mannix New Zealand	5.8	13.09	10.08.71	Wellington	Gloucester	50(2)	6	537
					Sale	22	8	198
Richard Jewell	6.0	15.02	11.10.78	Bromsgrove	Gloucester	13(13)	6	30
Andy Hazell	6.0	14.06	25.04.78	Gloucester	Gloucester	10(24)	1	5
Jason Little Australia	6.0	14.7	26.08.70		Gloucester	13	6	30

FORWARDS

	Ht.	Wt.	Birthdate	Birthplace	CLUB	League Apps	Tries	Pts
Serge Simon France	6.1	15.10	03.07.67		Gloucester	7(6)	1	5
Jawad Djoudi Morocco	5.9	14.12	02.01.73		Gloucester	6(14)	-	-
Andy Deacon	6.2	17.00	21.02.65	Glouester	Gloucester	111(12)	8	40
Adey Powles	5.11	17.00	14.03.67	Cowsford	Gloucester	23(17)	-	-
Chris Fortey	6.0	16.07	25.08.75	Gloucester	Gloucester	42(19)	2	10
Phil Vickery England	6.3	19.06	30.04.69	Gloucester	Gloucester	41(11)	2	10
Ian Jones New Zealand.	6.6	16.05	17.04.67	Whangerei	Gloucester	31(1)	3	15
Rob Fidler England , A,	6.5	17.08	21.09.74	Gloucester	Gloucester	108(2)	5	25
Mark Cornwall England Colts.	6.7	17.00	22.02.73	Gloucester	Gloucester	11(12)	3	15
Steve Ojomoh	6.2	15.10	25.05.70	Benin City	Gloucester	61(14)	7	35
England , A, U21, Colts, Schools.					Bath	58(2)	4	20
Ed Pearce	6.6	17.00	02.09.75	Bristol	Gloucester	39(12)	1	5
					Bath	2(1)	-	-
Junior Paramore Western Samoa	6.3	17.00	18.11.68	Apia	Gloucester	23(2)	2	10
					Bedford	48	18	90

GLOUCESTER

FACT FILE

Founded: 1873
Nickname: Cherry & whites

Colours: Cherry & white hoops.
Change colours: Blue and red halves.

GROUND

Address: Kingsholm, Gloucester. GL1 3AX.
Tel: 01452 381087   Ticket Hotline: 01452 422422   Fax: 01452 383321
Website: www.gloucesterrugbyclub.com   email: postbox@gloucesterrugbyclub.com
Capacity: 10,800   Seated:1,498 Standing: Covered 4,350 Uncovered 4,622

Directions: From M5 junction 11 or 11A follow signs for City Centre and then Kingsholm.
Nearest Railway Station: Gloucester. About a 5 minute walk from the ground. Follow signs

Car Parking: 250 spaces at ground, 1,000 at cattle market 5 mins walk

Admission: Season tickets   Premier Grandstand: £330, concessions £270, u16 £165
Grandstand: £270, concessions £210, u16 £135   Ground: £140, concessions £70, u16 £40
Matchday   Grandstand: Adults £22; no concessions
Ground: Adults £15; Concessions £8; u16 £3

Club Shop: 10-4 & matchdays. Contact John Hudson 01452 522978.

Clubhouse: Mon-Sat 6.30-11, Sat matchdays 11-11. Snacks & bar meals available
Function room: Available for hire, capacity 150.

PROGRAMME Size: B5   **Pages**: 48   **Price**: £2
Editor: James bennett 07989 582111; 01452 381087
Advertising Rates   Contact Dunwoody Sports, Newbury 01635 35599

Back row: Andy Gomarsall, Andy Deacon, Chris Fortey, Chris Catling, Rory Greenslade-Jones, Olivier Azam, Kingsley Jones, Franck Schisano, Trevor Woodman, Tom Beim. **Middle**: Ed Archer (conditioning coach), Rob Jewell, Junior Paramore, Jake Boer, Ed Pearce, Mark Cornwell, Richard Ward, Adam Eustace, Steve Ojomoh, Chris Yates, Peter Finch (conditioning coach). **Front**: Ian Sanders, Hervé Gregoire-Mazzocco, Adey Powles, Phil Vickery, Ian Jones (captain), Rob Fidler, Joe Ewens, Robert Todd, Simon Mannix. **On ground**: Elton Moncrieff, Byron Hayward, Stephane Sanchez, Andy Hazell.

Picture by Bruce Seabrook/Gloucestershire Picture Agency

LEEDS TYKES

Chief Executive	Gary Hetherington	c/o Leeds RUFC, The Pavilion, Headingley Stadium, St Michaels Lane, Leeds LS6 3BR 0113 278 6181 (B), 0113 275 4284 (Fax)
Director of Rugby	Phil Davies	c/o Leeds RUFC, Chandos Park, Chandos Avenue, Leeds LS8 1RX 07710 342050 (Mobile), 0113 266 1406 (B), 0113 266 1406 (Fax)
Club Administrator	Mike Bidgood	c/o Leeds RUFC, The Pavilion as above 01423 734953 (H) 0113 278 6181 X 242 (B), 0113 275 4284 (Fax) 07710 342054 (Mobile) E-Mail: mike.bidgood @ leedsrugby.co.uk
Managing Director	David Howes	c/o Leeds RUFC, The Pavilion as above
Fixtures Secretary	Les Jackson	4 Gledhow Wood Avenue, Leeds. LS8 1NY 0113 266 5544 (H,B & Fax) 07989 878523 (Mobile)

When the Leeds club was formed in 1992 it was hoped that a team could eventually reach the top flight. The consolidation began to bear fruit with promotion to the second division for the start of the 1998-99 campaign. After missing out narrowly in 1999-2000 the team was strengthened for last seasons campaign. Following the loss at Worcester in the second game of the season the league quickly looked like a two-horse race at the top and so it proved although Worcester appeared to have the upper hand throughout the first half. In the Tetley Cup the Tykes beat local rivals Morley with a record 100-0 victory. Reality dawned at Northampton where we lost 72-35 but scored 5 tries in the process.

Back to the league and we kept picking up the bonus points through four-try victories as Worcester began to feel the heat. Centre Graham Mackay tore into opposition defences, scoring a try a game. He created space for partner Shaun Woof and wing Chris Hall to also appear on the score sheet in virtually all games. Although the weather disrupted the post Xmas matches the Tykes run continued and the 'decider' arrived on April 1st where 5509 spectators saw the Tykes soundly beat Worcester by 30-13 and only conceded the one try in the 80th minute. It was two penalties apiece at half time but the introduction of Ian Clarke on the hour proved to be the inspired replacement of the year as he made three clean breaks to create the tries and seal the victory.

More bad weather saw a second re-arrangement at Exeter and a mid-week trip proved difficult, but it was not until the final game when the record 23-match unbeaten run was broken at Henley that promotion was secured.

International recognition for England came the way of Ian Clarke and Phil Murphy at U-21 level and Scott Benton and Tom Palmer toured Canada and the USA. Tom made his debut against USA. A fitting reward to an excellent season.

LEEDS TYKES

Comp.	Date	H/A	Opponents	Result & Score	H-	15	14	13	12	11
N1	9-Sep	H	Birmingham & Solihull	W 40-25	734	Hall	Marr	Woof/t	Le Bas/t4c4p	Emmerson
N1	16-Sep	A	Worcester	L 13-40	3002	Benson	Marr	Woof	Le Bas/c2p	Emmerson
N1	23-Sep	A	Orrell	W 24-17	500	Benson	Marr	Woof	Le Bas/c4p	Emmerson
N1	30-Sep	H	Moseley	W 19-16	960	Benson	Marr	Woof/t	Le Bas/c4p	Emmerson
N1	7-Oct	A	Manchester	W 21-9	630	Benson	Stanger	Woof	Le Bas/7p	Emmerson
N1	14-Oct	H	Bedford	W 42-6	1019	Le Bas/t4c3p	Stanger	Woof/t	Mackay	Emmerson/t
N1	28-Oct	A	Coventry	W 34-3	1500	Le Bas/2c	Hall/t	Woof	Stanger	Benson
N1	19-Nov	H	Wakefield	W 32-21	1578	Le Bas/3t2cp	Hall	Mackay	Woof	Stanger
N1	2-Dec	H	Henley Hawks	W 43-7	306	Le Bas/4c	Stanger/t	Mackay/2t	Woof	Hall/2t
N1	9-Dec	A	London Welsh	W 35-12	800	Le Bas/3c3p	Benson	Woof	Mackay/2t	Hall
N1	16-Dec	H	Exeter	W 63-13	657	Benson/4c	Hall/2t	Mackay/t	Woof/2t	Stanger
N1	6-Jan	H	Waterloo	W 45-0		Le Bas/5c	Hall	Mackay/t	Stanger/t	Emmerson
N1	13-Jan	A	Wakefield	W 38-25	600	Le Bas/3c4p	Hall/t	Stanger(b/t)	Mackay/t	Emmerson
N1	20-Jan	H	Otley	W 43-22	1341	Le Bas/t(c/t)	Hall	Woof	Mackay/tc	Benson/4cp
N1	27-Jan	A	Waterloo	W 45-17	320	Benson/6cp	Hall	Woof/t	Mackay/t	Stanger(c/t)
N1	10-Feb	A	Bedford	W 48-3	1255	Le Bas/5cp	Hall/t	Woof/3t	Mackay/t	Benson
N1	17-Feb	A	Otley	W 40-14	850	Le Bas/5c	Hall	Woof/2t	Mackay	Benson
N1	24-Feb	H	Manchester	W 46-13	407	Le Bas/t4cp	Hall/3t	Woof	Mackay	Emmerson/t
N1	4-Mar	H	Coventry	W 68-8	512	Le Bas/t2c	Hall/tc	Woof/2t	Mackay/t	Emmerson/2t
N1	10-Mar	A	Moseley	W 50-23	723	Le Bas/4c	Hall/3tc	Woof	Mackay/2t	Emmerson/2t
N1	17-Mar	H	Orrell	W 81-20	480	Le Bas/t9cp	Woof/2t	Stanger/2t	Mackay/2t(e/t)	Emmerson
N1	1-Apr	H	Worcester	W 30-13	5509	Le Bas/2c3p(f/c)	Hall/t	Woof	Mackay	Emmerson/t
N1	14-Apr	A	Birmingham & Solihull	W 31-20		Le Bas/3c	Hall/t	Stanger/t	Mackay	Emmerson
N1	18-Apr	A	Exeter	W 33-26	1021	Le Bas/3c4p	Hall	Woof/t	Mackay	Emmerson
N1	21-Apr	H	London Welsh	W 55-16	1254	Le Bas/3c3p	Hall(h/t)	Woof/t	Mackay/3t	Emmerson
N1	28-Apr	A	Henley Hawks	L 13-18	840	Le Bas/c2p	Hall	Stanger	Mackay/t	Emmerson
TBC	21-Oct	H	Morley	W 100-0	501	Le Bas/3t10c	Hall/2t	Stanger	Woof/t	Emmerson
TBC	4-Nov	A	Northanpton Saints	L 35-73	3299	Benson/5c	Hall/2t	Woof/t	Stanger	Emmerson/t

** after opponents name indicates a penalty try. Brackets after a player's name indicates he was replaced.
eg (a) means he was replaced by replacement code "a" and so on. / after a player or replacement name
is followed by any scores he made - eg /t, /c, /p, /dg or any combination of these*

LEAGUE DEBUTS

Steve Bachop, Ian Clarke, Dan Crowley, Chris, Hall, Carl Hogg, Andrew Hurdley, Dan Hyde, Gavin Kerr, Graham Mackay, Jeremy Marr, Phil Murphy, Tony Stanger, James Tiffeny, Shaun Wof.

EVER PRESENT

Scot Benton & Mike Shelley.

Most Appearances:

26	Scot Benton, Mike Shelley.
25	Richard Le Bas (1), James Ponton.

PLAYERS USED

26 plus 6 as replacement only.

MOST POINTS

Pts	Player	T	C	P	DG
333	R LeBas	9	72	48	-
97	G Mackay	19	1	-	-
90	S Woof	18	-	-	-
89	C Hall	17	2	-	-
65	S Benton	13	-	-	-

MATCH FACTS

10	9	1	2	3	4	5	6	7	8
Bachop	Benton	Shelley	Luffman	Ozdemir	Jones	Palmer	Hurdley/t	Ponton	Clarke/t
Bachop	Benton	Shelley	Rawlinson	Ozdemir	Jones	Palmer/t	Hyde	Ponton	Clarke
Bachop	Benton/t	Shelley	Rawlinson	Crowley	Jones	Palmer	Hyde	Ponton	Clarke/t
Bachop	Benton	Shelley	Luffman	Crowley	Murphy	Palmer	Hurdley	Ponton	Hyde
Bachop	Benton	Crowley	Luffman	Shelley	Murphy	Palmer	Hurdley	Ponton	Hyde
Bachop	Benton	Crowley	Luffman	Shelley	Murphy	Palmer/t	Hurdley	Ponton	Hyde/t
Bachop/t	Benton/2t	Shelley	Luffman	Johnston	Murphy	Palmer	Hurdley	Ponton/t	Hyde/t
Bachop/t	Benton	Shelley	Luffman	Johnston	Jones	Palmer	Hurdley	Ponton	Hyde/t
Bachop	Benton	Crowley	Luffman/t	Shelley/t	Murphy	Jones	Hurdley	Ponton	Hyde
Bachop/t	Benton	Crowley	Luffman	Shelley	Jones	Palmer/t	Hurdley	Ponton	Hyde
Le Bas/cp	Benton/t(a/t)	Crowley	Luffman	Shelley/t	Palmer	Jones/t	Hurdley	Ponton	Hyde/t
Bachop	Benton/3t	Crowley	Luffman/2t	Shelley	Jones	Palmer	Hyde	Ponton	Clarke
Bachop	Benton	Crowley	Luffman	Shelley	Jones	Hurdley	Tiffany	Ponton	Hyde/t
Bachop	Benton/t	Crowley	Luffman	Shelley/t	Murphy	Jones	Hurdley	Ponton/t	Hyde
Bachop/2t	Benton	Shelley	Luffman	Johnston	Jones	Murphy	Hurdley	Ponton	Hyde(d/t)
Bachop	Benton/t	Shelley	Luffman	Johnston	Jones	Palmer	Hyde	Ponton/t	Clarke
Bachop	Benton	Shelley	Luffman/t	Johnston/t	Jones	Palmer/2t	Hyde	Ponton	Clarke
Bachop	Benton(a/t)	Shelley	Luffman	Kerr	Palmer	Jones	Hyde	Ponton	Clarke/t
Bachop/c	Benton	Shelley	Luffman	Kerr	Palmer/2t	Jones	Hogg	Ponton/2t	Hyde/t
Bachop	Benton/t	Shelley	Luffman	Kerr	Murphy	Palmer	Hogg	Ponton	Clarke
Bachop/3t	Benton	Shelley	Luffman	Kerr	Jones/t	Palmer	Hurdley	Clarke	Hogg
Bachop	Benton	Shelley	Luffman/t	Kerr	Jones	Palmer	Hyde	Ponton	Hogg
Bachop/t	Benton/2t	Shelley	Rawlinson	Kerr	Jones	Murphy	Hogg	Ponton	Clarke
Bachop	Benton/t	Shelley	Luffman/t	Kerr	Jones	Palmer	Hyde	Ponton	Hogg
Bachop	Benton	Shelley	Rawlinson	Kerr	Murphy	Palmer/t	Hurdley/t(g/t)	Ponton	Hogg
Bachop	Benton	Shelley	Luffman	Johnston	Jones	Palmer	Hyde	Ponton	Clarke
Bachop/t	Benton/2t	Shelley	Luffman	Johnston	Murphy	Palmer/2t	Hurdley/t	Ponton/2t	Hyde/2t
Bachop	Benton/t	Shelley	Luffman	Johnston	Jones	Palmer	Hurdley	Ponton	Hyde

REPLACEMENTS

a - C Kendra   b - S Wof   c - C Emmerson   d - I Clarke   e - C Hall
f - J Benson   g - D Hyde   h - T Stanger

Most replacement appearances: 17 Chris Kendra. 14 Ian Clarke. 11 Altan Ozdemir.
Most times replaced: 18 Scot Benton. 17 Mark Luffman.

2000-01 HIGHLIGHTS

Leeds Tykes continued their improvement.
In their third season in the division they finally made the top, but only after a tight tussle against Worcester.

Richard Le Bas led the way rattling up 337 points to beat the club record for points in a season set back in 1997-98 by Sateki Tuipulotu with 322.
In that total Le Bas kicked a record 72 conversions.

They also broke the try scoring record with Graham Mackay running in 19 tries, one clear of Shaun Woof and another clear of Chris Hall. The three were neck and neck but Mackay finished on top, he was also the leading try scorer in the division.

Despite their success they did suffer their worst ever away defeat in league rugby in terms of both highest score against and biggest margin. They were beaten early season by Worcester 40-13.

LEEDS TYKES

LEAGUE STATISTICS
compiled by Stephen McCormack

SEASON	Division	P	W	D	L	F	A	Pts Diff	Lge Pts	Lge Pos	Most Points		Most Tries	
91-92														
92-93	3	11	7	0	4	228	220	8	14		45	Ben Lloyd	7	Chris Thornton
93-94	4	18	7	0	11	243	318	-75	14		97	David Breakwell	3	Penalty Tries
94-95	4	18	8	0	10	335	291	44	16		83	Ralph Bennett	6	Phil Griffin & Chris Thornton
95-96	4	18	9	1	8	312	347	-35	19		67	Colin Stephens	6	Chris Thornton
96-97	3	30	24	0	6	1209	432	777	48		307	Gerry Ainscough	16	Mark Appleson
97-98	JN1	26	21	1	4	858	407	451	43		322	Sateki Tuipulotu	7	Simon Middleton
98-99	P2	26	16	0	10	713	367	336	28*	6	250	Sateki Tuipulotu	10	Simon Middleton Jonathan Scales
99-00	P2	26	22	0	4	794	269	525	44	2	190	Jon Benson	14	Matt Oliver
00-01	N1	26	24	0	2	1032	407	625	116	1p	337	Richard Le Bas	19	Graham Mackay

BIGGEST MARGINS

Home Win	81pts - 84-3 v Walsall 1.3.97
Away Win	75pts - 84-9 v Clifton 12.4.97
Home Defeat	6pts - 20-26 v Liverpool St. Helens 25.3.94
Away Defeat	25pts - 10-35 v Liverpool St H. 15.10.93

MOST POINTS

Scored at Home	84 v Walsall 1.3.97
Scored Away	84 v Clifton 12.4.97
Conceded at Home	26 v Liverpool St. Helens 25.3.94
Conceded Away	35 v Liverpool St Helens 15.10.93

MOST CONSECUTIVE

Appearances	65 Sateki Tuipulotu 7.9.96 - 3.1.99
Matches scoring Tries	7 Simon Middleton
Matches scoring points	46 Sateki Tuipulotu
Victories	11 (twice)
Defeats	5

MOST TRIES

Scored in a match	14 v Redruth 9.1.96 (H) v Walsall 1.3.97 (H)
Conceded in a match	6 v Aspatria 13.4.96 (A)

MOST APPEARANCES

by a forward	96(4) Mike Shelley
by a back	76 (1) Sateki Tuipulotu

	MOST IN A SEASON	MOST IN A CAREER	MOST IN A MATCH	
Points	337 Richard Le Bas 00-01	769 Sateki Tuipulotu 96-99	27 Gerry Ainscough	v Rosslyn Park 14.9.96(H) v Walsall 1.3.97 (H)
Tries	19 Graham Mackay 00-01	29 Sateki Tuipulotu 96-99	5 Simon Middleton	v Otley 24.1.98 (H)
Conversions	72 Richard Le Bas 00-01	135 Sateki Tuipulotu 96-98	9 Gerry Ainscough	v Clifton 7.12.96 (H)
Penalties	53 Sateki Tuipulotu 98-99	118 Sateki Tuipulotu 96-98	7 Sateki Tuipulotu Jon Benson	v Coventry 3.1.99 (A) vManchester 8.4.00 (A)
Drop Goals	5 Colin Stephens 96-97	13 Colin Stephens 95-98	2 Dan Eddie Colin Stephens	v Broughton Park 19.2.94 v Exeter 9.9.95 (H) v Lon. Welsh 19.10.96 (H)

PLAYING SQUAD

LEEDS TYKES

BACKS

	Ht.	Wt.	Birthdate	Birthplace	CLUB	League Apps	Tries	Pts
Jon Benson	5.11	11.10	11.01.76	Durham	Leeds	33(18)	6	116
Chris Hall					Leeds	20(3)	17	89
Tony Stanger					Leeds	12(6)	6	30
Shaun Woof Other club: Waterloo 50(3)/16/80.	6.2	15.0	06.03.77	Liverpool	Leeds Worcester	22(3) 7(6)	18 -	90 -
Graham Mackay					Leeds	20	19	97
Richard LeBas Other club: Moseley 14/3/177	5.10	14.00	26.07.71		Leeds Worcester	34(1) 45(1)	3 13	113 378
Scott Benton England, A. Other club: Morley.	5.11	13.0	08.09.74	Bradford	Leeds Gloucester	51 55(3)	23 8	115 40
Steve Bachop	5.10	13.9	02.04.66	New Zealand	Leeds London Irish	25 32	9 4	47 23

FORWARDS

	Ht.	Wt.	Birthdate	Birthplace	CLUB	League Apps	Tries	Pts
Ian Clarke					Leeds Manchester	11(14) 3	4 -	20 -
Mark Luffman	5.10	14.12	17.08.71	Nottingham	Leeds Otley	110(14) 10	11 1	55 5
Mike Shelley North.	6.0	18.08	13.03.72	Leeds	Leeds W Hartlepool	122(4) 18	20 4	100 20
James Ponton	6.3	14.07	31.07.74	Hexham	Leeds W Hartlepool	50 42(3)	11 5	55 25
Tom Palmer	6.5	16.00	27.03.79		Leeds	51(6)	11	55
Eddie Jones					Leeds	46	9	45
Andrew Hurdley	6.6	16.9	14.02.72	Wollongong	Leeds Wakefield	14(6) 28(3)	2 14	10 89
Rob Rawlinson	6.0	16.00	27.08.76	Littleborough	Leeds	14(13)	-	-
Phil Murphy	6.8	18.0	02.02.76	Hull	Leeds	10(9)	-	-

LEEDS TYKES

FACT FILE

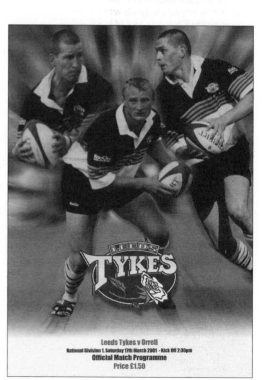

Founded: 1991
Colours: Royal blue, black, gold & white
Change colours: White, royal blue, gold
Nickname: Tykes
Web site: www.leedsrugby.com

GROUND
Address: Headingley Stadium, St Michaels Lane, Headingley, Leeds. LS6 3BR
Tel: 0113 278 6181   Fax: 0113 275 4284   e-mail: mike.bidgood@leedsrugby.co.uk
Capacity: 23,000   Seated: 9,000 Standing: Covered 11,000, Uncovered 3,000

Directions: From East: M62 Junction 29 (M1). Follow signs Leeds M1,junction 43 (A61), Junc 47 leave motorway & follow signs City Centre. From City Centre follow signs Otley, Skipton A660 to leave by Woodhouse Lane. In 2.3 miles turn left, then left again into St Michaels Lane. Ground on right. Nearest Railway Station: Headingley (1/2 mile), Leeds City (2.5 miles)

Car Parking: 450 at ground £1

Admission:
Season   Adult £80, Children £20, OAPs £40
Matchday   Adult £8,   Children £2,   OAPs £4

Club Shop: Open 9-5 Mon-Fri + Matchdays.
Tel 0113 274 0460

Clubhouse: Open during normal licensing hours
Snacks, bar meals & restaurant.
Functions: Capacity 1,200
contact Leeds RUFC

Training Nights: Monday, Tuesday, & Thursday.

PROGRAMME
Full colour
Size: A5
Pages: 36 + cover
Price: £1.50
Editor: Phil Daly
0113 278 6181 x246 (B)
0113 230 7617 (F)
07775 946935 (Mobile)

ADVERTISING RATES
Page £500
1/2 page £300
1/4 page £150

Leeds Tykes v Orrell
National Division 1. Saturday 17th March 2001 - Kick Off 2:30pm
Official Match Programme
Price £1.50

LEICESTER TIGERS

Chief Executive	Peter Wheeler
Chairman	Peter Tom
Operations Director	David Clayton
Company Secretary	Mary Ford
Director of Rugby	Dean Richards
Press Officer	Janet Berry

Leicester Football Club plc,
Aylestone Road,
Leicester LE2 7TR
Tel: 0116 254 1607
Fax: 0116 285 4766

SFMS Ltd, 1A Stamford House, 5 Hill St. Leicester LE10 1DS
Tel: 01455 895470   Fax: 01455 895475

Leicester Tigers look forward to the start of a another new season, not only as English Champions, but also as Champions of Europe thanks to a unique treble that saw them clinch their third successive Premiership title, win the inaugural knockout Zurich Championship and then conquer French champions, Stade Francais, at the famous Parc des Princes in Paris, to lift the biggest prize in northern hemisphere rugby - The Heineken Cup.

Tigers' success on the field has been recognised in the fact that last season 13 players received international caps, the club had five representatives in the British and Irish Lions and club captain Martin Johnson became the only player to captain the Lions on two separate tours. The club also provided international players at many representative levels including England Sevens and Under-19 level and below.

Under the expert guidance of director of rugby Dean Richards, ably assisted by coaches John Wells, Andy Key and last season Pat Howard, Tigers are renowned for nurturing home grown talent. Their Academy set-up is now paying dividends with players such as 21 year old Lewis Moody gaining his first senior cap this summer during England's tour of North America.

Awards were heaped upon both management and players, departing Australian Howard was named Player of the Season, whilst coach John Wells was appointed England 'A' forwards' coach.

But it is not just on the pitch that the Tigers are successful. They have the largest dedicated rugby ground outside Twickenham, the most number of season ticket holders and consistently attract the biggest crowds, with five figure attendances commonplace at Welford Road.

And with the signing of international stars Josh Kronfeld of New Zealand and Rod Kafer from Australia over the summer, the Tigers have signalled their intent for next season of "competing and winning honours at the highest levels of British and European rugby".

© sfms/lfc

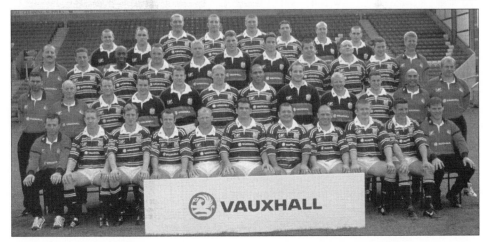

LEICESTER TIGERS

Comp.	Date	H/A	Opponents	Result & Score	Att	15	14	13	12	11
P1	19-Aug	A	London Wasps	W 24-22	6378	Stimpson/3cp	Murphy	Lloyd	Howard	Stanley/t
P1	27-Aug	A	Newcastle Falcons	W 25-22	4298	Stimpson/p	Murphy/tc	Lloyd/t	Howard	Stanley/t
P1	2-Sep	H	Northampton Saints	W 33-19	14278	Murphy/3c4p	Newmarch	Lloyd/t	Howard	Stanley
P1	6-Sep	H	Rotherham	W 26-18	9801	Murphy/c(a/t)	Newmarch	Gelderbloom	Howard	Stanley
P1	10-Sep	A	Saracens	L 9-17	13021	Stimpson/3p	Murphy	Lloyd	Howard	Stanley
P1	16-Sep	H	London Irish	W 33-20	12168	Stimpson/2c3p	Newmarch/t	Lloyd	Howard/t	Stanley/t
P1	23-Sep	A	Bristol	L 20-24	4500	Stimpson/p	Stanley	Lloyd	Howard/t	Newmarch
P1	30-Sep	A	Sale	D 17-17	3407	Stimpson/4p	Murphy/t	Lloyd	Howard	Stanley
P1	18-Nov	H	London Wasps	W 28-13	9300	Stimpson/c7p	Lloyd	Smith	Howard	Stanley
P1	24-Nov	A	Harlequins	W 16-13	4651	Stimpson/tc3p	Tuilagi	Lloyd	Smith	Murphy
P1	2-Dec	H	Gloucester	W 31-28	11989	Stimpson/c8p	Murphy	Lloyd	Howard	Tuilagi/t
P1	16-Dec	H	Bath	W 27-19	14505	Stimpson/c5p	Murphy	Lloyd	Howard/t	Stanley
P1	23-Dec	A	Rotherham	W 27-9	3800	Newmarch	Booth/t3c2p	Smith/t	Gelderbloom	Stanley
P1	26-Dec	A	Bath	W 17-16	8200	Stimpson/3p	Murphy	Smith	Howard	Lloyd
P1	6-Feb	H	Bristol	W 17-10	12332	Stimpson/4p	Tuilagi	Smith	Gelderbloom	Stanley/t
P1	10-Feb	A	London Irish	W 28-9	7591	Stimpson/2t4c	Tuilagi	Smith	Howard	Murphy/t
P1	24-Feb	H	Saracens	W 56-15	14212	Murphy/4t	Tuilagi	Lloyd	Howard	Stimpson/2t6c3p
P1	6-Mar	H	Sale	W 24-12	9000	Stimpson/c4p	Tuilagi	Smith	Gelderbloom	Booth
P1	10-Mar	A	Northampton Saints	W 12-9	9800	Murphy	Stimpson/4p	Lloyd	Howard	Stanley
P1	17-Mar	A	Newcastle Falcons	W 51-7	15009	Stimpson/2t4cp(a/t)Lloyd/t		Smith	Howard	Stanley/t
P1	31-Mar	A	Gloucester	L 13-22	7614	Reeves	Murphy	Gelderbloom	Howard	Stanley/t
P1	14-Apr	H	Harlequins	W 37-5	16006	Murphy/t	Stimpson/3c2p	Lloyd/t	Howard/t	Stanley
EC	7-Oct	H	Pau*	W 46-18	12331	Stimpson/4c5p	Murphy	Lloyd	Howard/t	Stanley
EC	15-Oct	A	Glasgow Caledonians	W 33-21	3900	Stimpson/t3c4p	Murphy	Lloyd/t	Howard	Stanley
EC	20-Oct	A	Pontypridd	L 11-18	4500	Murphy	Stimpson/t2p	Lloyd	Howard	Stanley
EC	28-Oct	H	Pontypridd*	W 27-19	13913	Stimpson/c4p	Murphy	Lloyd	Howard	Tuilagi
EC	13-Jan	A	Pau	W 20-3	6800	Stimpson/3p	Murphy	Lloyd	Howard	Tuilagi
EC	20-Jan	H	Glasgow Caledonians	W 41-26	12260	Stimpson/c5p	Murphy	Smith/t	Howard	Stanley
EC	28-Jan	H	Swansea	W 41-10	14000	Stimpson/3c4p	Tuilagi	Lloyd	Howard	Murphy/2t
EC	21-Mar	N	Gloucester	W 19-15		Murphy	Stimpson/c4p	Lloyd/t	Howard	Stanley
EC	20-May	N	Stade Francais	W 34-30	43000	Stimpson/2c5p	Murphy	Lloyd/2t	Howard	Stanley
TBC	4-Nov	H	Otley	W 83-11	5328	Goode/t9c	Lloyd/t	Gelderbloom	Smith	Tuilagi/3t(e/t)
TBC	11-Nov	A	Gloucester	W 25-13	5100	Stimpson/2c2p	Healey	Smith/t	Howard	Lloyd/2t
TBC	9-Dec	H	Saracens	W 41-24	10007	Stimpson/3c5p	Murphy	Smith	Howard	Tuilagi
TBC	6-Jan	A	Harlequins	L 18-22	8500	Stimpson/c2p	Murphy/t	Lloyd	Howard	Tuilagi
PO	28-Apr	A	London Irish	W 24-11	8112	Murphy	Stimpson/c4p	Lloyd	Howard	Stanley/t
PO	5-May	H	Northampton Saints	W 17-13	12000	Stimpson/2cp	Booth/t	Smith	Howard/t	Stanley
PO	13-May	N	Bath	W 22-10	33500	Stimpson/2cp	Murphy	Lloyd	Howard	Stanley/t

* after opponents name indicates a penalty try. Brackets after a player's name indicates he was replaced.
eg (a) means he was replaced by replacement code "a" and so on. / after a player or replacement name
is followed by any scores he made - eg /t, /c, /p, /dg or any combination of these

LEAGUE DEBUTS

Stephen Booth, Louis Deacon, Glen Gelderbloom, Ali Newmarch, John O'Reilly, P Reeves, Oliver Smith, Winston Stanley, Freddie Tuilagi.

PLAYERS USED

33 + 1 as replacement only.

EVER PRESENT

None

Most Appearances:
18 Tim Stimpson, Pat Howard.
17: Ben Kay, Austin Healey.

MOST POINTS

Pts	Player	T	C	P	DG
260	T Stimpson	7	27	57	-
62	G Murphy	8	5	4	-
40	N Back	8	-	-	-
30	S Booth	3	3	3	-

MATCH FACTS

10	9	1	2	3	4	5	6	7	8
Goode	Healey/2t	Jelley	West	Garforth	Johnson	Kay	Gustard	Back	Corry
Healey	Grindal	Jelley	West/t	Garforth	Johnson	Kay	Gustard	Back	Corry
Healey/t	Grindal	Jelley	West	Garforth	Johnson	Kay	Gustard	Back	Corry/t
Healey/t2c	O'Reilly	Rowntree	Cockerill	Nebbett	Johnson	Deacon	Gustard	Back/2t	Balding
Healey	Grindal	Jelley	West	Garforth	Johnson	Kay	Gustard	Back	Corry
Goode	Healey	Rowntree	West	Garforth	Johnson	Kay	Corry	Back/t	Balding
Goode/tc	Grindal	Rowntree	Cockerill	Garforth	Short	Kay	Gustard/t	Balding	Corry
Goode	Healey	Jelley	West	Garforth	Johnson	Short	Gustard	Back	Corry
Goode	Hamilton/t	Rowntree	Cockerill	Garforth	Deacon	Kay	Gustard	Moody	Johnson
Healey	Hamilton	Rowntree	Cockerill	Garforth	Deacon	Kay	Gustard	Moody	Johnson
Goode	Hamilton	Rowntree	Cockerill	Garforth	Deacon	Kay	Gustard	Moody	Johnson
Goode	Healey	Rowntree/t	West	Garforth	Johnson	Kay	Gustard	Back	Johnson
Healey	Hamilton	Jelley	Cockerill	Nebbett	Johnson/t	Deacon	Johnson	Moody	Corry
Goode/dg	Healey	Rowntree	West	Garforth	Johnson	Kay	Gustard	Back/t	Johnson
Goode	Hamilton	Rowntree	Cockerill	Nebbett	Deacon	Kay	Johnson	Moody	Corry
Healey	Hamilton	Rowntree	West	Garforth	Johnson	Deacon	Johnson	Back/t	Corry
Goode	Healey	Rowntree	West	Garforth/t	Johnson	Kay	Johnson	Moody	Corry
Healey	Hamilton	Rowntree	Cockerill	Garforth	Johnson/t	Kay	Balding/t	Moody	Corry
Goode	Healey	Rowntree	West	Garforth	Johnson	Kay	Johnson	Moody	Corry
Goode/t	Healey	Rowntree	West	Garforth	Johnson	Kay	Johnson	Back/2t	Corry
Booth/p	Grindal	Freshwater	Cockerill/t	Nebbett	Deacon	Corry	Gustard	Moody	Short
Goode	Healey/t	Rowntree	West	Garforth	Johnson	Kay	Corry	Back/t	Johnson
Goode/dg	Hamilton/t	Jelley	West	Garforth	Johnson	Kay	Gustard	Back/t	Corry
Goode	Hamilton	Rowntree	West	Garforth	Johnson	Kay	Gustard	Back/t	Balding
Goode	Hamilton	Rowntree	West	Garforth	Johnson	Kay	Moody	Back	Corry
Healey/tdg	Hamilton	Rowntree	Cockerill	Garforth	Johnson	Kay	Gustard	Back	Corry
Goode/2dg	Healey	Rowntree	West	Garforth	Deacon	Kay	Johnson	Back/t	Corry
Goode	Hamilton/t	Freshwater	West/t(b/t)	Garforth	Deacon	Kay	Johnson	Moody	Corry
Goode/tdg	Healey/t	Rowntree	West	Garforth	Deacon	Kay	Johnson	Back	Corry
Goode	Healey	Rowntree	West	Garforth	Johnson	Kay	Johnson	Back	Corry
Goode	Healey	Rowntree	West	Garforth	Johnson	Kay	Corry	Back/t	Johnson
Healey/t	Grindal(c/t)	Jelley	West(d/3t)	Nebbett	Deacon	Kay	Gustard/t	Short/t	Balding
Goode	Hamilton	Rowntree	West	Garforth	Johnson	Kay	Gustard	Moody	Johnson
Goode	Healey	Rowntree	West/t	Garforth	Johnson	Kay	Johnson	Back/t	Corry(f/2t
Goode/t	Healey	Rowntree	West	Garforth	Corry	Kay	Gustard	Back	Johnson
Goode	Hamilton/t	Freshwater	Chuter	Nebbett	Johnson	Corry	Gustard	Moody	Balding
Goode	Hamilton	Rowntree	Cockerill	Garforth	Deacon	Kay	Short	Back	Johnson
Goode	Healey/t	Rowntree	West	Garforth	Johnson/t	Kay	Johnson	Back	Corry

REPLACEMENTS   a - S Booth   b - R Cockerill   c - J O'Reilly   d - P Freshwater   e - M Johnson   f - A Balding

Most replacement appearances: 13 A Balding. 8 R Cockerill

Most times replaced: 9 D West, W Johnson

2000-01 HIGHLIGHTS

Tim Stimpson continued to rattle up the points and has now scored 601 in the last two league campaigns.

During the season he equalled John Liley's record of 31 points in a match in the home game against Saracens in February.

In December he equalled another Liley record when he slotted over eight penalty goals in the home win against Gloucester.

Geordan Murphy equalled Tony Underwood's record of four tries in a match doing so in the home fixture against Saracens.

Murphy finished joint leading try scorer with Neil Back whose eight tries took him passed 50 in league rugby for the Tigers. Back in Leicester's leading try scorer in league rugby with 55.

Darren Garforth extended his record for appearances to 167(5).

LEICESTER TIGERS

LEAGUE STATISTICS
compiled by Stephen McCormack

SEASON	Division	P	W	D	L	F	A	Pts Diff	Lge Pts	Lge Pos	Most Points		Most Tries	
91-92	1	12	6	1	5	262	216	46	13	6	125	John Liley	9	Rory Underwood
92-93	1	12	9	0	3	220	116	104	18	3	106	John Liley	3	Rory Underwood Nigel Richardson
93-94	1	18	14	0	4	425	210	215	28	2	202	Jez Harris	8	Tony Underwood
94-95	1	18	15	1	2	400	239	161	31	1	181	Jez Harris	5	Steve Hackney
95-96	1	18	15	0	3	476	242	234	30	2	272	John Liley	8	Rory Underwood
96-97	1	22	14	1	7	600	395	205	29	4	195	John Liley	9	Penalty Tries
97-98	1	22	12	2	8	569	449	120	26	4	253	Joel Stransky	9	Will Greenwood
98-99	1	26	22	0	4	771	423	348	44	1	202	Joel Stransky	16	Neil Back
99-00	1	22	18	1	3	687	425	262	51	1	321	Tim Stimpson	10	Dave Lougheed
00-01	1	22	18	1	3	571	346	225	82	1	260	Tim Stimpson	8	Geordan Murphy & Neil Back

BIGGEST MARGINS

Home Win	61pts - 66-5 v Newcastle Gosforth 12.3.94
Away Win	49pts - 54-9 v Harlequins 6.5.00
Home Defeat	10pts - 21-31 v Harlequins 26.11.89
Away Defeat	38pts - 9-47 v Bath 12.4.97

MOST CONSECUTIVE

Appearances	32 Darren Garforth 28.3.92-3.4.94
Matches scoring Tries	4 Geordan Murphy
Matches scoring points	24 John Liley
Victories	13
Defeats	3

MOST POINTS

Scored at Home	72 v West Hartlepool 16.5.99
Scored Away	55 v London Irish 17.5.98
Conceded at Home	31 v Harlequins 26.11.89
Conceded Away	47 v Bath 12.4.97

MOST TRIES

Scored in a match	12 v W Hartlepool 16.5.99
Conceded in a match	7 v Bath 11.1.92

MOST APPEARANCES

by a forward	167 (5) Darren Garforth
by a back	100 (2) John Liley & Stuart Potter 100(3)

	MOST IN A SEASON	MOST IN A CAREER	MOST IN A MATCH	
Points	321 Tim Stimpson 99-00	1070 John Liley 88-97	31 John Liley Tim Stimpson	v Rosslyn P. 21.3.92 (H) v Saracens 24.02.01 (H)
Tries	16 Neil Back 98-99	55 Neil Back 91-01	4 Tony Underwood Geordan Murphy	v Newcastle G. 12.3.94 (H) v Saracens 24.02.01 (H)
Conversions	52 Tim Stimpson 99-00	129 John Liley 88-97	7 John Liley Tim Stimpson	v Rosslyn P. 21.3.92 (H) v Harlequins 6.5.00 (A)
Penalties	64 John Liley 95-96	232 John Liley 88-97	8 John Liley Tim Stimpson	v Bristol 28.10.95 (H) v Gloucester 2.12.00 (H)
Drop Goals	13 Jez Harris 94-95	37 Jez Harris 87-95	3 Jez Harris	v Wasps 23.11.91 (H) v Bath 15.4.95 (H)

PLAYING SQUAD

LEICESTER TIGERS

BACKS

	Ht.	Wt.	Birthdate	Birthplace	CLUB	League Apps	Tries	Pts
Tim Stimpson	6.3	15.13	10.09.73	Liverpool	Leicester	59(3)	14	742
England.Other clubs: W Hartlepool 23/7/203					Newcastle	23(2)	14	138
Leon Lloyd	6.4	14.00	22.09.77	Coventry	Leicester	75(3)	19	95
England U21, Colts.								
Winstan Stanley	6.1	13.2	17.07.74		Leicester	16	6	30
Canada								
Ali Newmarch	6.2	13.10	28.11.78		Leicester	6(1)	1	5
Freddie Tuilagi	5.11	15.0	09.06.71		Leicester	6	1	5
Austin Healey	5.10	13.07	26.10.73	Wallasey	Leicester	31(1)	9	52
England , A, Students, U21. Other club:Waterloo 20/3/18					Orrell	32(1)	4	27
Andy Goode	5.11	13.10	03.04.80		Leicester	18(2)	4	28
Glen Gelderbloom	5.11	13.5	11.12.69		Leicester	5(6)	-	-
Pat Howard	5.10	13.09	14.11.73	Brisbane	Leicester	62(2)	7	37
	Australia.							
Jamie Hamilton	5.9	12.06	01.07.70	Guildford	Leicester	41(18)	5	25
					London Scottish	5(1)	1	5
James Grindal	5.9	13.3	18.08.80		Leicester	10(7)	4	20
Gordean Murphy	6.0	12.07	19.04.78	Dublin	Leicester	44(7)	22	168
Ireland								

FORWARDS

	Ht.	Wt.	Birthdate	Birthplace	CLUB	League Apps	Tries	Pts
Graham Rowntree	6.0	17.05	18.04.71	Stockton on Tees	Leicester	145(14)	3	15
England , A, U21, U18, Colts.								
Darren Garforth	5.10	18.00	09.04.66	Coventry	Leicester	167(4)	6	29
England .					Nuneaton		2	8
Richard Cockerill	5.10	15.10	16.12.70	Rugby	Leicester	129(18)	9	45
England .					Coventry	12	-	-
Dorian West	5.11	16.00	03.10.67	Wrexham	Leicester	33(30)	4	20
England , A.					Nottingham	41	6	30
Martin Johnson	6.7	18.04	09.03.70	Solihull	Leicester	156(1)	10	50
England , A, U21, Colts, U18, British Lions.								
Ben Kay	6.6	17.10	14.12.75	Liverpool	Leicester	30(4)	3	15
England					Waterloo	68(1)	2	10
Ricky Nebbett	5.11	17.00	16.08.77	Kingston	Leicester	10(6)	-	-
					Harlequins	13(6)	1	5
Neil Back	5.10	14.04	16.01.69	Coventry	Leicester	149	55	274
England, A, B, U21, Colts, U18.British Lions					Nottingham			
Martin Corry	6.5	17.00	12.10.73	Birmingham	Leicester	69(4)	7	35
England , A, Emerging, U21, U18. Newcastle 24(1)/7/35					Bristol	29	8	40
Perry Freshwater	6.0	17.05	27.07.73	Wellington	Leicester	9(35)	-	-
Lewis Moody	6.4	15.11	12.06.78	Berkshire	Leicester	45(16)	4	20
Paul Gustard	6.4	17.03	02.02.76	Newcastle OT	Leicester	46(26)	13	65
Will Johnson	6.4	17.04	18.03.74	Solihull	Leicester	24	-	-

LEICESTER TIGERS

FACT FILE

Founded: 1880
Nickname: Tigers
Colours: Dark green with red and white hoops
Change colours: Navy with green and red hoops
Website: www.tigers.co.uk

GROUND	Aylestone Road., Leicester. LE2 7TR	Web site: http://www.tigers.co.uk

Tel: 0116 254 1607   Fax: 0116 285 4766   e-mail: tigers@tigers.co.uk
Capacity: 16,250   Seated: 12,000   Standing: 4,000

Directions: From M1, junction 21. Along the A5460 into Leicester. At the Post House Hotel traffic lights turn right onto B5418 (Braunstone Lane East). After 1 mile turn left at `T' junction traffic lights onto A426 (Aylestone Road). Ground 2 miles on right.

Nearest Railway Station: Leicester (London Road).
The ground is about 3/4 mile walk along Waterloo Way.   (Station Tel. No. 0116 248 1000)

Car Parking: None available at the ground.

Admission :
Season   Standing Adults £139, Juniors £59, Concessions £89.
            Seated Adults £149-289, Juniors £69-209, Concessions £119-239
Matchday   Standing Adults £12-14, Juniors £5, Concessions £10-12.
            Seated Adults £14-27, Juniors £6-18, Concessions £12-25

Club Shop: Yes, manager Sarah Watson, 0116 254 0077

Clubhouse: With six bars and food available.
Functions: Various rooms available.
For details contact Joanna Fairey,
0116 254 1607

PROGRAMME
Size: 170mm x 240mm
Pages: 52   Price: £2.50
Editor: Stuart Farmer, Press Off.
01455 895470

ADVERTISING RATES
On application to
Tracey Branson, c/o Leicester FC

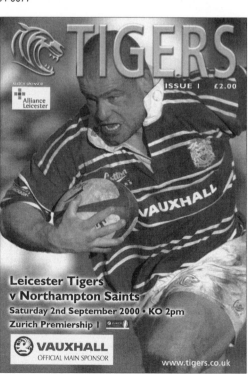

HONOURS

Premiership	98-99, 99-2000, 00-01
Courage League Div. 1	87-88, 94-95 R-up 93-94, 95-96
Pilkington Cup	92-93, 96-97 R-up 88-89, 93-94, 95-96
John Player Cup	78-79, 79-80, 80-81 R-up 77-78, 82-83
European Cup	00-01 R-up 96-97

LONDON IRISH RFC

Media Liaison Officer   Patrick Lennon
Tel: 01753 893050
Fax: 01753 893051
email: mail@patricklennon.com

Chief Executive   Geoff Huckstep

Player Coach   Brendon Venter

Official Photographer   Michael Peel
Tel: 020 8949 5082

Sunbury Administration

Tel: 01932 783034
Fax: 01932 784462
email: lisrmanagement@hotmail.com

Who would have confidently forecast at the end of last season that London Irish would be setting record home attendances in Reading? Very few. Such has been the season of change that the club has experienced. In May 2000, London Irish were forced into an unexpected search for a new playing home. The search ended in Reading at the magnificent Madejski Stadium where 12,037 people, a new club record, came to see the defeat of Northampton Saints on St. Patrick's Day.

There was also much change in the playing squad. A combination of contracts ending, players moving on and the recruitment of new talent saw nineteen comings and goings.

Victory in the plate competition of the Middlesex 7's in mid August paved the way for a successful pre season tour to Kerry. The long Zurich Premiership campaign started on the squad's return to base. A 27-22 win over star-studded Saracens in the first home match at the Madejski provided a good start. A second home victory over Sale Sharks was followed by wins in Reading over French sides, Aurillac and Brive, in the European Shield.

The good home performance continued through Christmas and the New Year. January passed and the home record remained intact. Inevitably, it was the visit of Leicester that brought the sequence to an end on 10th February. That was the first of only two home defeats in the season.

The club's efforts to qualify for the latter stages of the European Shield ended disappointingly with an away defeat at former European champions, Brive.

The Tetley's Bitter Cup campaign started with impressive Fourth and Fifth Round victories over Exeter and London Welsh respectively. However, being drawn away to Newcastle Falcons in the quarter final was always going to be difficult and so it proved, London Irish went down by 33-20 to the eventual winners.

Winter became spring and it was off the field developments that took the headlines. A review of costs and structures resulted in late March in the departure on agreed terms of director of rugby Dick Best and coach Ged Glynn.

The absence through injury of key players impacted on playing performances throughout the season, so there was some satisfaction that a victory over Gloucester in the final match of the Premiership secured eighth place and a position in the quarter-finals of the new Zurich Championship away to Leicester. Despite a brave performance at Welford road, Irish lost to the champions.

L-R - **Back:** Dinos Alexopoulous, Simon Halford, Richard Bates, David Charles, Neal Hatley, Jarrod Cunningham, Richard Kirke, Ben Joyce. **Middle:** Ofisa Tonu'u, Graeme Haley, Mike Worsley, Colin Allen, Ryan Strudwick, Steve Williams, Glenn Delaney, Tabai Matson, Declan Danaher, Matt Oliver, Nnamdi Ezulike, Paul Sackey, Chris Sheasby. **Front:** Rob Hoadley, Kieran Campbell, Rob Hardwick, Adrian Flavin, Eddie Harvey, Conor O'Shea, Justin Bishop, Kieron Dawson, Barry Everitt, Rob Ashforth, Kevin Barrett, Jason Wright.

LONDON IRISH

Comp.	Date	H/A	Opponents	Result & Score	Att	15	14	13	12	11
P1	19-Aug	A	Harlequins	W 22-16	5093	O'Shea	Ezulike	Matson	Wright	Bishop
P1	26-Aug	A	Northanpton Saints	L 10-27	6713	O'Shea/t	Ezulike	Matson	Wright	Bishop
P1	2-Sep	H	Saracens	W 27-22	7312	O'Shea	Sackey/t	Matson	Wright	Bishop
P1	10-Sep	A	Bristol	W 30-26	2902	O'Shea/p	Sackey	Matson	Wright	Bishop
P1	16-Sep	A	Leicester Tigers	L 20-33	12168	O'Shea/p	Sackey/t	Matson	Wright	Bishop
P1	24-Sep	H	Sale	W 28-13	4198	O'Shea/t	Sackey	Matson	Wright	Bishop/t
P1	30-Sep	A	Rotherham	L 18-19	1800	O'Shea	Sackey/t	Bishop	Wright	Ezulike
P1	19-Nov	H	Harlequins	W 21-16	5918	O'Shea	Oliver	Matson	Campbell	Sackey
P1	25-Nov	A	Gloucester	L 6-26	5618	O'Shea	Ezulike	Matson	Wright	Bishop
P1	5-Dec	H	Newcastle Falcons*	W 19-17	4605	Cunningham	Sackey	Oliver	Wright	Bishop
P1	16-Dec	H	London Wasps	W 14-13	5220	Cunningham	Sackey	Matson	Wright	Bishop
P1	23-Dec	A	Bath	L 20-56	7317	Cunningham/c2p	Sackey	Oliver/t	Wright	Bishop
P1	27-Dec	A	London Wasps	L 16-29	5084	Cunningham	Sackey/t	Oliver	Appleford	Ezulike
P1	10-Feb	H	Leicester Tigers	L 9-28	7591	Bishop	Sackey	Appleford	Wright	Ezulike
P1	20-Feb	H	Rotherham	W 54-11	2504	Bishop	Sackey/t	Appleford/t	Wright	Ezulike/t
P1	24-Feb	H	Bristol	D 26-26	3349	Bishop	Sackey	Appleford	Wright/t	Ezulike
P1	11-Mar	A	Saracens*	L 22-35	7913	Cunningham	Sackey	Appleford/t	Oliver	Bishop
P1	14-Mar	H	Bath	L 13-58	5303	Cunningham	Sackey	Appleford	Oliver/t	Bishop
P1	17-Mar	H	Northanpton Saints	W 13-10	12037	Bishop	Sackey/t	Appleford	Wright	Ezulike
P1	1-Apr	A	Newcastle Falcons	L 35-42	5963	Bishop	Sackey/t	Appleford	Wright	Ezulike
P1	10-Apr	A	Sale	L 18-43	2469	Cunningham	Bishop	Appleford	Wright	Ezulike/t
P1	16-Apr	H	Gloucester	W 35-10	7131	Cunningham/p	Sackey/t	Oliver	Hoadley	Ezulike/t
ES	7-Oct	H	Aurillac	W 42-10	2277	Ashworth/3c3p	Sackey	Oliver/t	Wright	Haley
ES	14-Oct	A	Aurillac	W 36-19	4500	Ashworth	Ezulike	Oliver/t	Wright/t	Bishop/t
ES	21-Oct	H	Brive	W 35-8	3182	Ashworth	Ezulike/t	Oliver	Wright	Haley/t
ES	28-Oct	A	Piacenza	W 58-13	300	Ashworth(e/t)	Ezulike/2t	Oliver/t	Wright	Haley/t
ES	14-Jan	A	Brive	L 27-37	3500	Cunningham	Sackey	Bishop	Oliver	Ezulike
ES	21-Jan	H	Piacenza	W 53-19	2754	Cunningham/2t	Sackey/t	Bishop/t	Oliver/2t	Ezulike/t
TBC	4-Nov	A	Exeter	W 57-12	1850	O'Shea/t	Ezulike/2t	Oliver/t	Wright	Bishop
TBC	11-Nov	A	London Welsh	W 33-10	2800	O'Shea	Ezulike/t	Oliver/t	Matson	Sackey/t
TBC	10-Dec	A	Newcastle Falcons	L 20-33	3293	Cunningham	Sackey	Oliver	Wright	Bishop/t
PO	28-Apr	A	Leicester Tigers	L 11-24	8112	Bishop	Sackey	Appleford	Hoadley	Ezulike/t

*after opponents name indicates a penalty try. Brackets after a player's name indicates he was replaced.
eg (a) means he was replaced by replacement code "a" and so on. / after a player or replacement name
is followed by any scores he made - eg /t, /c, /p, /dg or any combination of these

MATCH FACTS

10	9	1	2	3	4	5	6	7	8
Cunningham/c5p	Campbell	Worsley	Kirke/t	Halford	Williams	Strudwick	Halvey	Dawson	Sheasby
Cunningham/cp	Campbell	Worsley	Kirke	Halford	Williams	Strudwick	Halvey	Dawson	Sheasby
Cunningham/c5p	Campbell	Worsley	Kirke	Halford	Williams	Strudwick	Halvey	Dawson/t	Sheasby
Cunningham/8pdg	Campbell	Worsley	Kirke	Halford	Strudwick	Williams	Halvey	Dawson	Sheasby
Cunningham/2cp	Ellis	Worsley	Kirke	Halford	Strudwick	Williams	Halvey/t	Dawson	Sheasby
Cunningham/2c3p	Ellis	Worsley	Kirke	Halford	Strudwick	Delaney	Halvey/t	Dawson	Sheasby
Cunningham/c2p	Ellis/t	Worsley	Kirke	Halford	Strudwick	Delaney	Danagher	Dawson	Sheasby
Everitt/7p	Ton'u	Worsley	Alexopoulous	Hardwick	Williams	Halvey	Fahrenson	Allen	Sheasby
Cunningham/2p	Ton'u	Hatley	Alexopoulous	Hardwick	Delaney	Williams	Halvey	Allen	Bates
Everitt/c4p	Ton'u	Worsley	Alexopoulous	Halford	Fahrenson	Delaney	Halvey	Allen	Bates
Everitt/3p	Ton'u/t	Worsley	Alexopoulous	Hardwick	Fahrenson	Delaney	Bates	Allen	Sheasby
Ashworth/c	Ton'u	Hatley(a/t)	Alexopoulous	Hardwick	Fahrenson	Delaney	Bates	Allen	Sheasby
Everitt/c3p	Ton'u	Worsley	Alexopoulous	Hardwick	Fahrenson	Williams	Halvey	Danagher	Sheasby
Everitt/3p	Ton'u	Hatley	Kirke	Hardwick	Strudwick	Williams	Halvey	Allen	Sheasby
Everitt/6c4p	Ton'u	Worsley(b/t)	Kirke(c/t)	Halford	Strudwick/t	Delaney	Cockle	Allen	Sheasby
Everitt/7p	Ton'u	Worsley	Kirke	Hardwick	Strudwick	Delaney	Cockle	Danagher	Sheasby
Everitt/t2cp	Ton'u	Hatley	Kirke	Halford	Strudwick	Williams	Danagher	Dawson	Bates
Everitt/c2p	Campbell	Worsley	Alexopoulous	Hardwick	Strudwick	Delaney	Cockle	Allen	Bates
Everitt/c2p	Campbell	Hatley	Kirke	Halford	Strudwick	Fahrenson	Halvey	Dawson	Sheasby
Everitt/c6p	Campbell(d/t)	Worsley	Kirke/t	Halford	Strudwick	Fahrenson	Halvey	Dawson	Sheasby
Everitt/c2p	Ton'u	Hatley	Kirke	Halford	Dawson	Strudwick	Fahrenson	Halvey/t	Sheasby
Everitt/c5p	Campbell/t	Worsley	Kirke	Hatley	Strudwick	Delaney	Halvey	Dawson	Danagher
Everitt/4p(e/t)	Campbell	Haley	Alexopoulous	Hardwick	Strudwick	Delaney/t	Bates	Allen	Danagher
Everitt/3c5p	Campbell	Hatley	Alexopoulous	Hardwick	Fahrenson	Delaney	Cockle	Allen	Danagher
Everitt/2c7p	Campbell	Hatley	Alexopoulous	Hardwick	Fahrenson	Delaney	Cockle	Allen	Danagher
Everitt/4c5p	Campbell	Hatley	Alexopoulous	Hardwick	Fahrenson/t(f/t)Williams		Cockle	Allen	Danagher
Everitt/tc5p	Campbell	Hatley	Alexopoulous	Hardwick	Strudwick/t	Fahrenson	Halvey	Allen	Sheasby
Everitt/5cp	Campbell	Hatley	Kirke	Hardwick	Strudwick	Delaney	Cockle	Danagher/t	Sheasby
Everitt/2c2p(g/c)	Campbell/t	Worsley	Kirke	Halford	Strudwick/t	Delaney/t	Halvey/t	Allen/t	Bates
Everitt/2p(g/c)	Ton'u/t	Hatley	Kirke	Halford	Strudwick(h/t)	Fahrenson	Halvey	Allen	Bates
Everitt/2c2p	Ton'u/t	Hatley	Alexopoulous	Hardwick	Fahrenson	Delaney	Halvey	Allen	Bates
Everitt/2p	Campbell	Hatley	Kirke	Halford	Strudwick	Delaney	Halvey	Dawson	Danagher

REPLACEMENTS

a - M Worsley	b - N Hatley	c - D Alexopoulous	d - J Ton'u
e - C O'Shea	f - R Strudwick	g - J Cunningham	h - S Williams

Most replacement appearances: 12 N Hatley. 8 R Hardwick. 7 D Danagher, G Delaney

Most times replaced: 12 M Worsley. 9 S Halford.

2000-01 HIGHLIGHTS

Ben Everitt in his first season of first team rugby topped the points scorers list.

He finished ahead of Jarrod Cunningham who was top last season, and it was Cunningham who kicked during the early season otherwise Everitt could have been challenging the 300 point mark.

It was another newcomer who topped the try scoring list. Right winger Paul Sackey, a summer signing from Bedford, ran in eight tries and was rewarded with a trip on England's tour of Canada and the United States.

Justin Bishop has now appeared in more league matches for London Irish than any other player. His 19 appearances last season took him to 117 as he became the first man to pass the 100 mark for the club.

LONDON IRISH

LEAGUE STATISTICS
compiled by Stephen McCormack

SEASON	Division	P	W	D	L	F	A	Pts Diff	Lge Pts	Lge Pos		Most Points		Most Tries
91-92	1	12	3	3	6	147	237	-90	9	9	71	Michael Corcoran	5	Michael Corcoran
92-93	1	12	6	0	6	175	223	-48	12	7	111	Michael Corcoran	3	Simon Geoghegan
93-94	1	18	4	0	17	217	391	-174	8	9r	75	Michael Corcoran	5	Simon Geoghegan
94-95	2	18	9	0	9	363	381	-18	18	5	164	Michael Corcoran	6	Rob Henderson
95-96	2	18	15	0	3	583	405	178	30	2p	301	Michael Corcoran	10	Conor O'Shea
96-97	1	22	6	0	16	502	749	-247	12	10	189	David Humphreys	8	Conor O'Shea
97-98	1	22	6	0	16	457	673	-216	12	11	237	Niall Woods	8	Conor O'Shea / Niall Woods
98-99	1	26	15	0	11	703	607	96	30	7	215	Niall Woods	12	Niall Woods
99-00	1	22	9	1	12	613	616	-3	25	8	324	Jarod Cunningham	10	Conor O'Shea
00-01	1	22	10	1	11	476	576	-100	45	8	182	Barry Everitt	8	Paul Sackey

BIGGEST MARGINS

Home Win	48pts - 62-14 v Harlequins 25.4.98
	56-8 v Newcastle 2.10.99
Away Win	34pts - 50-16 v Waterloo 23.9.95
Home Defeat	48pts - 16-64 v Bath 11.3.00
Away Defeat	59pts - 7-66 v Harlequins 14.9.96

MOST CONSECUTIVE

Appearances	29 Rob Henderson
Matches scoring Tries	4 Rob Saunders
Matches scoring points	24 Michael Corcoran
Victories	8
Defeats	7

MOST POINTS

Scored at Home	62 v Harlequins 25.4.98
Scored Away	50 v Waterloo 23.9.95
Conceded at Home	65 v Northampton 9.9.95
Conceded Away	66 v Harlequins 14.9.96

MOST TRIES

Scored in a match	8 v Moseley 30.9.95 (H)
	v Harlequins 25.4.98 (H)
Conceded in a match	11 v Harlequins 14.9.96 (A)

MOST APPEARANCES

by a forward	96 (1) Gary Halpin
by a back	117 Justin Bishop

	MOST IN A SEASON	MOST IN A CAREER	MOST IN A MATCH	
Points	324 Jarod Cunningham 99-00	744 Michael Corcoran 89-98	32 Niall Woods	v Harlequins 25.4.98 (H)
Tries	12 Niall Woods 98-99	47 Conor O'Shea 95-00	4 Niall Woods	v Northampton 5.1.99 (A)
Conversions	46 Jarod Cunningham 99-00	65 Michael Corcoran 89-98	8 Niall Woods	v Harlequins 25.4.98 (H)
Penalties	66 Jarod Cunningham 99-00	169 Michael Corcoran 89-98	8 Jarod Cunningham	v Bristol 10.9.00 (H)
Drop Goals	6 Paul Burke 92-93	10 Brian Mullen 88-92	2 Ralph Kuhn	v Lon. Scottish 14.1.89 (H)
			Brian Mullen	v Richmond 8.4.89 (A)
			Ian Aitchison	v Plymouth 13.1.90 (H)
			Paul Burke	v Bristol 24.1.92 (H)

PLAYING SQUAD

LONDON IRISH

BACKS

	Ht.	Wt.	Birthdate	Birthplace	CLUB	League Apps	Tries	Pts
Conor O'Shea Ireland , A, Leinster.	6.2	15.00	21.10.70	Limerick	London Irish	102	55	305
Justin Bishop Ireland, U21.	6.0	13.00	08.11.74	Crawley	London Irish	117(3)	26	130
Barry Everitt	5.8	12.9	09.03.76		London Irish	13(1)	1	182
Junior Tonu'u New Zealand, Auckland Blues	5.10	14.13	03.02.70		London Irish	16(4)	3	15
Nmandi Ezulike	6.0	13.6	16.02.71	Nigeria	London Irish Leicester	12(1) 19(3)	3 7	15 35
Kieran Campbell	5.8	11.08	06.07.69	Hillingdon	London Irish	23(15)	5	25
Paul Sackey	6.1	13.10	08.11.79		London Irish Bedford	18(1) 13(3)	8 9	40 45
Jason Wright	6.2	14.13	08.07.69		London Irish	17	1	5
Kevin Ellis	5.9	13.10	29.04.65		London Irish	3(4)	1	5
Jarod Cunningham	5.11	14.05	07.09.68	New Zealand	London Irish	49(2)	8	578

FORWARDS

	Ht.	Wt.	Birthdate	Birthplace	CLUB	League Apps	Tries	Pts
Simon Halford	6.2	18.3	26.06.69		London Irish	24(7)	-	-
Neil Hatley	6.0	18.07	23.12.69	Chorley	London Irish	39(20)	4	20
Richard Kirke	5.11	16.07	16.04.71	New Zealand	London Irish	49(6)	8	40
Kieran Dawson Ireland .	6.1	15.06	29.01.75	Bangor	London Irish	60(2)	3	15
Ryan Strudwick Natal	6.5	16.09	03.08.73	Natal	London Irish	37	2	10
Steven Williams	6.4	17.9	30.10.70		London Irish	10(2)	-	-
Glenn Delaney Other club: Nottingham 50/7/35	6.6		16.11.73	New Zealand	London Irish Coventry	10(7) 25	- 5	- 25
Michael Worsley Other club: Orrell	6.1	16.10	01.02.76		London Irish Bristol	26(15)	3	15
James Cockle Other club: Moseley 26(2)/2/10.	6.3	16.6	29.10.76	Clifton	London Irish Bedford	3(3) 18(7)	- 1	- 5
Eddie Halvey	6.4	16.4	11.07.70		London Irish	15(2)	3	15
Chris Sheasby England, A, 7s. Other club: Wasps 22(5)/8/40	6.3	16.0	30.11.66	Windsor	London Irish Harlequins	17 93(10)	- 7	- 35
Jeff Fahrenson	6.4	16.11	21.04.68		London Irish	8(1)	-	-

LONDON IRISH

FACT FILE

Founded: 1898

Nickname: The Irish

web site: www.london-irish-rugby.com

Colours: Green/white/green

Change colours: Blue/white/blue

GROUND   Madejski Stadium, Reading, Berkshire RG2 0FL
Capacity: 25,000   - all covered seating

Directions: The ground is directly next to Junction 11 of the M4
Nearest Railway Station: Reading Central

Car Parking   At the stadium

Admission   Matchdays: £1-18
Season Tickets   Adults £199

Club Shop   At the Madejski Stadium

Clubhouse   The Avenue, Sunbury-on-Thames

Sunbury Administration
Tel: 01932 783034   Fax: 01932 784462
email: lisrmanagement@hotmail.com

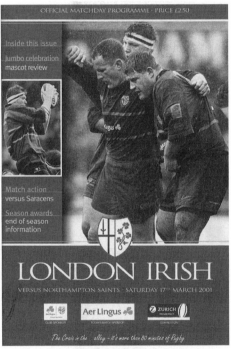

PROGRAMME
Size:A5   Price: £2.50   Pages: 80
Editor: Sian Isaac 01934 783034
Advertising Rates
Colour - Page £2,000 Half £1,200
Spot Colour - Page 1,500 Half £850

Ryan Strudwick, last season's Captain

LONDON WASPS

Chairman	Chris Wright
Director of Rugby	Nigel Melville
Operations Manager	Gloria Sennitt
Academy Director	Rob Smith
Community Development Manager	Toni Smyth

London Wasps Training Ground, Twyford Ave. Sports Ground, Twyford Ave., Acton, London W3 9QA
Tel: 020 8902 4200   Fax: 020 8900 2659

Alex King

Second place in the Zurich Premiership, the semi-finals of the Zurich championship, the leading points scorer, the leading try scorer, three British Lions and seven players on England's tour to North America was not a bad year for London Wasps.

After an early exit from the Heineken Cup and a disappointing defeat in the Tetley's Bitter Cup to end Wasps' two year strangle hold on the competition, it left Nigel Melville's side the chance to focus on league honours.

After a mixed start to the season, in which injuries to captain Lawrence Dallaglio, Trevor Leota and Phil Greening disrupted the team, it wasn't until just before Christmas that Wasps found their consistency.

A 25-6 victory in December to complete the league double over Saracens started a run of seven consecutive wins for Wasps that lifted them to within striking distance of Leicester Tigers. A defeat at Bath ended any hopes of catching the leaders, but the season ended on a high with another four wins and a second place finish in the Zurich Premiership - the club's highest since winning the title in 1996.

The Zurich championships gave Wasps another shot at silverware and a victory at home to Gloucester set up a thrilling home tie against Bath in the semi-finals. The watching Sky TV audience were given a treat as both sides served up a feast of rugby, but it was the West Country side who progressed to the final.

It wasn't just a successful season on the pitch, as the club enjoyed great results behind the scenes. We achieved the biggest gate for a Wasps match as 12,137 enjoyed the visit of Harlequins added more than 10,000 new names to our database of prospective supporters thanks to ticket promotions for our Leicester Tigers, Stade Francais, Saracens and NEC Harlequins games and ended the season with our biggest average attendance.

We also enjoyed our record number of season ticket holders and junior members last season and our community scheme visited more schools than ever before. We were also able to benefit from increased media exposure away from the rugby-related press with appearances on the likes of Live and Kicking, The Big Breakfast, The Priory and Celebrity Auction.

After finishing the season with the country's top points scorer in Kenny Logan, the top try scorer in Paul Sampson, coupled with the emergence of youngsters Joe Beardshaw and Richard Birkett last season, the future looks bright for London Wasps.

LONDON WASPS

Comp.	Date	H/A	Opponents	Result & Score	Att	15	14	13	12	11
P1	19-Aug	H	Leicester Tigers	L 22-24	6378	Ufton	Lewsey/t	Waters	Henderson	Logan/c5p
P1	27-Aug	H	Bath	L 12-36	4037	Lewsey	Roiser	Waters	Denney	Logan/3p
P1	3-Sep	H	Bristol	W 23-17	3525	Lewsey	Roiser	Waters	Denney	Logan/t2c3p
P1	6-Sep	A	Saracens	W 30-24	7312	Lewsey	Roiser	Denney	Henderson/t	Sampson/2t
P1	9-Sep	A	Harlequins	W 31-18	4880	Scrase	Roiser/t	Waters	Henderson/t	Sampson/t
P1	17-Sep	H	Gloucester	W 43-23	4727	Lewsey	Roiser/t	Waters	Denney	Logan/3c4p
P1	23-Sep	A	Newcastle Falcons	L 21-59	4232	Lewsey	Roiser	Waters	Denney	Logan/2t3c
P1	1-Oct	H	Northanpton Saints	W 53-17	4612	Lewsey/t	Roiser	Denney	Henderson	Logan/3c4p
P1	18-Nov	A	Leicester Tigers	L 13-28	9300	Lewsey	Roiser	Waters	Denney	Sampson
P1	26-Nov	H	Sale	W 33-24	3087	Lewsey	Roiser/t	Denney	Henderson/t	Logan/3c4p
P1	2-Dec	A	Rotherham	W 30-15	1770	Sampson/t	Roiser/t	Denney	Waters	Logan/3c3p
P1	16-Dec	A	London Irish	L 13-14	5220	Lewsey	Roiser	Waters	Denney	Logan/c2p
P1	23-Dec	H	Saracens	W 25-6	7835	Lewsey	Sampson	Waters	Denney	Logan/2c2p
P1	27-Dec	H	London Irish	W 29-16	5084	Lewsey	Sampson/t	Waters	Denney	Logan/2c5p
P1	30-Dec	A	Northanpton Saints	W 21-18	9662	Roiser	Sampson/t	Waters	Denney	Logan/cp
P1	10-Feb	A	Gloucester	W 28-3	6940	Sampson	Roiser	Denney	Henderson/t	Logan/2c3p
P1	11-Mar	A	Bristol	W 24-12	5444	Lewsey/t	Sampson	Denney	Henderson	Logan/3cp
P1	17-Mar	A	Bath	L 13-16	8200	Sampson/t	Roiser	Waters	Denney	Scrase/t
P1	28-Mar	H	Newcastle Falcons	W 44-7	3444	Sampson	Roiser	Waters	Denney/t	Logan/t4c2p
P1	1-Apr	H	Rotherham*	W 58-3	4276	Sampson/2t	Roiser/t	Waters	Denney	Logan/3t5cp
P1	10-Apr	H	Harlequins	W 38-19	12137	Sampson/t	Lewsey/t	Waters	Denney	Logan/t4c
P1	14-Apr	A	Sale	W 59-29	3877	Sampson/t	Lewsey	Waters/t	Denney/t	Logan/2t5c3p
EC	7-Oct	A	Swansea	L 28-54	6000	Lewsey/t	Roiser	Denney	Henderson	Logan/2c3p
EC	15-Oct	A	L'Aquila	W 37-10		Lewsey/t	Roiser	Denney	Henderson/2t	Sampson
EC	21-Oct	A	Stade Francais	L 10-40	8000	Lewsey	Roiser	Denney	Henderson	Logan/tcp
EC	29-Oct	H	Stade Francais	L 28-31	8233	Lewsey	Roiser	Waters	Denney/t	Logan/c7p
EC	14-Jan	H	Swansea	W 28-16	6383	Sampson/2t	Roiser	Waters	Henderson	Logan/2c3p
EC	21-Jan	H	L'Aquila	W 42-5	3244	King/t	Roiser	Waters/2t	Denney/t	Logan/t6c
TBC	4-Nov	A	Bristol	L 17-22	3133	Lewsey	Roiser	Denney	Henderson/t	Logan/4p
PO	29-Apr	H	Gloucester	W 18-6	4986	Sampson/t	Lewsey	Waters	Denney	Logan/tc2p
PO	6-May	H	Bath	L 31-36	8094	Lewsey	Roiser/t	Denney	Henderson/t(c/t)	Logan/2c4p

* after opponents name indicates a penalty try.

Brackets after a player's name indicates he was replaced. eg (a) means he was replaced by replacement code "a" and so on. / after a player or replacement name is followed by any scores he made - eg /t, /c, /p, /dg or any combination of these

LEAGUE DEBUTS

Matthew Leek

EVER PRESENT

Will Green, Martyn Wood, Joe Worsley.

Most Appearances:

22:	Will Green, Martyn Wood, Joe Worsley.
21:	Darren Molloy, Paul Volley.

PLAYERS USED

27 plus 1 as replacement only.

MOST POINTS

Pts	Player	T	C	P	DG
282	K Logan	10	46	47	-
55	P Sampson	11	-	-	-
47	A King	6	1	4	1
35	R Henderson	7	-	-	-
30	T Leota	6	-	-	-

MATCH FACTS

10	9	1	2	3	4	5	6	7	8
Leek	Wood	Molloy	Greening	Green	Reed	Shaw	Beardshaw	Volley	Worsley
Leek	Wood	Molloy	Greening	Green	Reed	Shaw/dg	Birkett	Volley	Worsley
Leek	Wood	Molloy	Greening/t	Green	Reed	Shaw	Birkett	Volley	Worsley
Leek/3c3p	Wood	Molloy	Greening	Green	Reed	Shaw	Worsley	Volley	Dallaglio
Leek/c3p	Wood	Molloy	Greening	Green	Reed	Shaw	Worsley/t	Volley	Dallaglio
Henderson/3t	Wood	Molloy	Greening	Green	Reed	Shaw/t	Worsley	Volley	Dallaglio
Leek	Wood/t	Molloy	Greening	Green	Reed	Shaw	Worsley	Volley	Dallaglio
King/2t	Wood	Molloy	Leota/t	Green	Reed/t	Shaw	Worsley	Volley/t	Dallaglio/t
King/c2p	Wood	Le Chevalier	Leota	Green	Beardshaw	Shaw	Birkett	Volley	Worsley/t
King	Wood	Molloy	Leota	Green	Reed	Shaw/t	Birkett	Lock	Worsley
King/t	Wood	Molloy	Leota	Green	Reed	Shaw	Birkett	Volley	Worsley
King	Wood	Molloy	Leota/t	Green	Reed	Beardshaw	Dallaglio	Volley	Worsley
King	Wood	Molloy	Leota/t	Green	Reed/t	Shaw	Worsley	Volley	Dallaglio/t
King	Wood	Molloy	Leota/t	Green	Reed	Shaw	Worsley	Volley	Dallaglio
King/pdg	Wood	Molloy	Leota	Green	Reed	Shaw	Worsley/t	Volley	Dallaglio
King	Wood	Molloy	Macer	Green	Beardshaw	Shaw	Worsley/t	Volley/t	Dallaglio
King	Wood	Molloy	Leota	Green	Beardshaw/t	Birkett	Worsley/t	Volley	Dallaglio
King/p	Wood	Molloy	Greening	Green	Birkett	Shaw	Worsley	Volley	Dallaglio
King/t	Wood(a/t)	Molloy	Leota/t	Green	Birkett	Shaw	Worsley	Volley	Dallaglio/t
King	Wood	Molloy	Greening	Green/t	Birkett	Shaw/t	Worsley	Volley	Dallaglio
King/2t	Wood	Molloy	Leota	Green/t	Birkett	Shaw	Worsley	Volley	Dallaglio
King	Wood	Molloy	Greening(b/t)	Green	Birkett	Shaw	Worsley	Volley/t	Dallaglio/t
King	Wood	Molloy	Leota	Green	Reed	Shaw	Worsley/2t	Volley	Dallaglio
King/cp	Wood/c	Le Chevalier	Leota/t	Green	Reed	Shaw/t	Worsley	Volley/t	Scrivener
King	Wood	Le Chevalier	Leota	Green	Reed	Shaw	Worsley	Volley	Scrivener
Henderson	Wood	Le Chevalier	Greening	Green	Reed	Shaw	Worsley	Volley	Scrivener
King	Wood	Le Chevalier	Leota	Webb	Reed	Shaw/t	Birkett	Worsley	Dallaglio
Leek	Page	Molloy	Leota	Webb	Beardshaw	Scrivener	Birkett	Lock	Dallaglio/t
King	Wood	Le Chevalier	Leota	Green	Reed	Beardshaw	Worsley	Volley	Dallaglio
King	Wood	Molloy	Leota	Green	Birkett	Shaw	Worsley	Volley	Dallaglio
King	Wood	Molloy	Greening	Green	Birkett	Shaw	Worsley	Volley	Dallaglio

REPLACEMENTS   a - H Bijon.   b - T Leota   c - F Waters

Most replacement appearances: 10 J Beardshaw. 9 A Chevalier

Most times replaced: 10 Andy Reed. 8 D Molloy

2000-01 HIGHLIGHTS

Kenny Logan topped the Wasps scoring list for the third straight season.

He just missed out on Gareth Rees's all time record of 291 finishing just nine short.

In that 282 was a record number of conversions, 47 which eclipsed Gareth Rees's record. During the season he passed Rob Andrew's record of career points. Andrew amassed 748 from 1987 to 1996 before leaving for his present position at Newcastle.

In away matches Wasp's set new records for both highest points scored and most points conceded, on each occasion it was 59. Early in the season they were thrashed at Newcastle whilst on the final day of the season they thrashed Sale Sharks.

In the match against Newcastle they equalled the club record for tries conceded in a league match, 6.

LONDON WASPS

LEAGUE STATISTICS
compiled by Stephen McCormack

SEASON	Division	P	W	D	L	F	A	Pts Diff	Lge Pts	Lge Pos	Most Points		Most Tries	
91-92	1	12	6	0	6	177	180	-3	12	7	101	Steve Pilgrim	5	Chris Oti
92-93	1	12	11	0	1	186	118	68	22	2	54	Alan Buzza	4	Phil Hopley & Chris Oti
93-94	1	18	10	1	7	362	340	22	21	3	159	Rob Andrew	5	Damian Hopley
94-95	1	18	13	0	5	470	313	157	26	3	135	Rob Andrew	7	Phil Hopley
95-96	1	18	11	0	7	439	322	117	22	4	91	Guy Gregory	8	Shane Roiser
96-97	1	22	18	1	3	685	406	279	37	1	291	Gareth Rees	11	Kenny Logan
97-98	1	22	8	1	13	490	609	-119	17	9	253	Gareth Rees	5	Mike Friday & Penalty Tries
98-99	1	26	15	1	10	717	506	211	31	5	263	Kenny Logan	8	Kenny Logan
99-00	1	22	11	1	10	640	661	-21	31	7	136	Kenny Logan	9	Josh Lewsey
00-01	1	22	16	0	6	663	428	235	74	2	282	Kenny Logan	11	Paul Sampson

BIGGEST MARGINS

Home Win	57pts - 62-5 v Orrell 22.3.97
Away Win	31pts - 57-26 v Harlequins 17.9.94
Home Defeat	31pts - 3-34 v Harlequins 9.3.96
Away Defeat	32pts - 6-38 v Leicester 12.10.93

MOST CONSECUTIVE

Appearances	36 Richard Kinsey 29.2.92-30.4.94
Matches scoring Tries	4 Kenny Logan
Matches scoring points	25 Gareth Rees
Victories	9
Defeats	4

MOST POINTS

Scored at Home	65 v Orrell 22.3.97
Scored Away	57 v Harlequins 17.9.94
Conceded at Home	34 v Harlequins 9.3.96
Conceded Away	45 v London Irish 17.5.00

MOST TRIES

Scored in a match 9
v Coventry 13.4.88 (H); v Bedford 12.3.90 (A); v Liverpool St H 20.4.91; v Orrell 2.3.97 (H) & v Bedford 26.3.00 (H)

Conceded in a match 6
v Orrell 30.4.94/v Lon Irish17.5.00

MOST APPEARANCES

by a forward	127 Lawrence Dallaglio
by a back	91 Steve Bates 87-96

	MOST IN A SEASON	MOST IN A CAREER	MOST IN A MATCH
Points	291 Gareth Rees 96-97	758 Kenny Logan 96-01	26 Kenny Logan v W Hartlepool 27.9.98 (H)
Tries	11 Kenny Logan 96-97 Paul Sampson 00-01	40 Kenny Logan 96-01	5 Kenny Logan v Orrell 22.3.97 (H)
Conversions	47 Kenny Logan 00-01	82 Rob Andrew 87-96	8 Alex King v Bedford 26.3.00 (H)
Penalties	62 Gareth Rees 96-97	161 Rob Andrew 87-96	7 Rob Andrew v Orrell 11.12.93 (H)
Drop Goals	6 Alex King 96-97	11 Rob Andrew 87-96	2 Jon Ufton v Saracens 23.9.95 (H) Rob Andrew v Sale 30.9.95 (A) Guy Gregory v Leicester 6.4.96 (A)

PLAYING SQUAD

LONDON WASPS

BACKS

	Ht.	Wt.	Birthdate	Birthplace	CLUB	League Apps	Tries	Pts
Paul Sampson England ,	5.10	12.09	12.07.77	Wakefield	Wasps Otley	50(11) 2	26 -	130 -
Matthew Leek	5.9	13.0	25.10.80		Wasps Saracens	6(3) 2(5)	- -	26 10
Jonathan Ufton England u21, Students, Colts.	6.1	13.10	31.01.74	Dulwich	Wasps Old Mid Whit	66(11) 8	9 1	129 75
Shane Roiser England students, London	6.0	12.07	10.09.72	Dubai	Wasps Rosslyn Park	101(8) 42	32 19	160 95
Kenny Logan Scotland .	6.1	14.08	03.04.72	Stirling	Wasps	77(3)	40	758
Mark Denney Other club: Bedford	6.0	15.10	25.01.75		Wasps Bristol	51(4)	9	45
Rob Henderson Ireland .	6.1	16.04	27.10.72	New Malden	Wasps London Irish	56(8) 56	20 22	100 110
Fraser Waters	6.0	13.12	31.03.76		Wasps			
Alex King England, A.	6.0	13.04	17.01.75	Brighton	Wasps Rosslyn Park	88(2) 7	18 2	314 70
Josh Lewsey England	5.10	12.07	30.11.76	Bromley	Wasps Bristol	54(2) 22(3)	16 7	80 46
Martyn Wood England A, u18.	5.9	13.07	25.04.77	Harrogate	Wasps	51(5)	9	45
Laurence Scrase	6.0	12.07	10.09.72	Dubai	Wasps	51(7)	10	50

FORWARDS

	Ht.	Wt.	Birthdate	Birthplace	CLUB	League Apps	Tries	Pts
Darren Molloy	6.2	17.07	31.08.72	Middlesex	Wasps	126(6	1	5
Will Green England .	5.11	17.02	25.10.73	Littlehampton	Waps	106	7	35
Trevor Leota	5.9	17.07	08.02.75	W Samoa	Wasps	50(19)	19	95
Phil Greening England. Other club: Gloucester 36/2/10	5.11	17.00	03.10.75	Gloucester	Wasps Sale	12(3) 19(3)	3 -	15 -
Mark Lock	6.2	15.7	22.09.79		Wasps	2(4)	-	-
Joe Beardshaw Simon Shaw England , A, Students, Colts, U21, U18.	6.5 6.9	17.2 19.08	30.10.76 01.09.73	Norwich Nairobi	Wasps Wasps Bristol	10(12) 67(13) 56	1 6 3	5 30 15
Richard Birkett	6.4	16.5	01/10/79		Wasps	12(5)	-	-
Andy Reed Scotland . Other clubs: Camborne 10(1)/2/8, Plymouth 10/2/8.	6.7	17.10	04.05.69	St Austell	Wasps Bath	61(16) 24	5 -	25 -
Paul Volley	6.1	15.06	02.11.71	Chinnor	Wasps	58(5)	17	85
Lawrence Dallaglio England , A, Emerging, U21, Colts.	6.4	16.04	10.08.72	Sheperd's Bush	Wasps	143(4)	25	125
Peter Schrivener England A, U21, U18, Schools.	6.6	17.12	27.10.73	Harold Wood	Wasps	53(16)	14	70
Joe Worsley England U21, Colts.	6.6	17.00	14.06.77	London	Wasps	67(10)	12	60

LONDON WASPS

FACT FILE

Founded: 1867
Nickname: Wasps
Web site: wasps.co.uk

Colours: Black and gold
Change colours: Gold and black

GROUND

Address: Loftus Road Stadium, South Africa Road, London W12 7PA
Tel: 020 8743 0262   Fax: 020 8740 2525   e-mail: lrtickets@21t_ltd.com
Capacity: 19,159 all seated   15,990 covered   3,196 uncovered

Directions: A40(M) Westway (London-Oxford). Turn south at White City (BBC) into Wood Lane.
Turn right into South Africa Road, ground 200yards on right
London Transport: White City (Central Line). In Wood Lane, turn right, then left into South
Africa Rd. Shepherds Bush (Hammersmith & City Line).
By Bus: 72, 95, 220 to White City Station.

Car Parking: Weekends only, £5 per match

Admission: Season: Adults £156-223, Junior £32, Concessions £77-109
Matchday: Adults £11-£17, Junior & Concessions £5-9

Club Shop: Yes - Loftus Road Stadium 020 8743 0262

Clubhouse: Loftus Road Stadium   Bars & kiosks open on matchdays

PROGRAMME   Size: B5   Pages: 48   Price: £2   Editor: Phil Harris
Advertising   PIA Sport Tel: 01625 35546 Fax: 01635 845811

Paul Sampson

HARLEQUIN FC

NEC
HARLEQUINS
— OF LONDON —

Stoop Memorial Ground,
Langhorn Drive,
Twickenham TW2 7SX.
Tel: 0208 410 6000
Fax: 0208 410 6001

		Telephone	e-mail
Chairman	Christopher Haines		
Chief Executive	Mark Evans	020 8410 6036	marke@quins.co.uk
Managing Director	Tony Copsey	020 8410 6037 07990 571810	tonyc@quins.co.uk
General Manager	Ross Young	020 8410 6042 07790 571802	rossy@quins.co.uk
Team Manager	Mike Scott	01252 311311 07774 651330	mail@harlequins.fsnetco.uk
Press Officer	Nick Melton	020 8410 6045 07990 571807	nickm@quins.co.uk

A 42-33 victory over Narbonne on the 20th May saw Quins finish the season as European Shield Champions, the club's first piece of silverware in ten years. Quins also become the first British side to win the title and end the French domination over the tournament. Victory went some way to eradicate the heart breaking and controversial defeat by Newcastle (30-27) in the Tetley's Bitter Cup Final on 24th February, although Quins did exact revenge by beating Newcastle 17-12 in the Shield semi-final.

Whilst the cup form was impressive, the club had another poor league campaign and finished eleventh in the table. Only two league victories from fourteen matches were enough to force Zinzan Brooke to resign on New Year's Day. Chief Executive Mark Evans took over the coaching duties and had an instant effect. Against all the odds, Quins defeated Leicester Tigers 22-18 in the Tetley's Bitter Cup semi-final at the Stoop on the 6th January, 2001.

Three weeks later Quins recorded another famous victory. A 20-13 win away in Brive booked them their place in the European Shield semi-finals and they became the first British side ever to win a European tie at the Parc Municipal des Sports. Quins' transformation in the second half of the season is highlighted by the fact that they only lost four games out of fifteen in 2001.

The return of Will Greenwood from Leicester proved a crucial signing as he ended the season with thirteen tries to his name. Equally as important was the arrival of Irish fly half Paul Burke from Cardiff, who was a prolific points scorer with the boot, including an individual tally of 22 and 27 points in the Tetley's Bitter Cup and European Shield finals respectively. Arguably, the most significant new arrival at the Stoop was Australian David Wilson, who showed great commitment and leadership skills throughout.

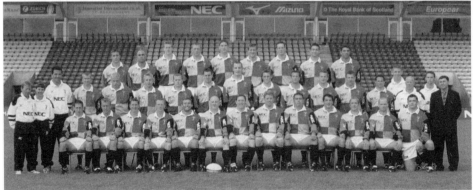

L-R - **Back:** Richard Nias, Brendan Daniel, Jim Evans, Karl Rudzki, Adam Jones, Will Greenwood, Ryan O'Neill, Phil Davies, Pat Sanderson. **Middle:** Chris McCarthy (Kit Manager), Amanda Turner (Physio), Zinzan Brooke (Head Coach), Niall Woods, Jon Dawson, Anthony Morris, Matthew Williams, Jamie Williams, Alex Codling, Matthew Powell, Ed Jennings, Nick Burrows, Bruce Starr, Ben Gollings, Paul Pook (Fitness Advisor), Richard Hill (Asst. Coach), Cameron Steele (Physio), Mike Scott (Team Manager). **Front:** Alex Alesbrook, Steve White-Cooper, Daren O'Leary, Peter Richards, Jason Leonard, Keith Wood, Rory Jenkins, Garrick Morgan, Kevin Nepia, Nick Greenstock, Mark Mapletoft, Paul Burke, Ramin Mathieson.

NEC HARLEQUINS

Comp.	Date	H/A	Opponents	Result & Score	Att	15	14	13	12	11
P1	19-Aug	H	London Irish	L 16-22	5093	O'Neill	O'Leary	Greenwood/t	Greenstock	Daniel
P1	26-Aug	H	Rotherham	W 26-13	2314	O'Neill	O'Leary/t	Greenwood/t	Greenstock/t	Daniel
P1	2-Sep	A	Bath	L 22-38	6958	Mapletoft	Greenstock	Greenwood/2t	Burrows	Gollings
P1	6-Sep	A	Northampton Saints	L 20-27	6645	Mapletoft	Greenstock	Greenwood	Burrows	Gollings/t
P1	9-Sep	H	London Wasps	L 18-31	4880	Mapletoft	O'Neill	Greenwood/t	Burrows	Gollings/2tp
P1	16-Sep	H	Bristol	W 31-25	3089	Mapletoft(a/t)	O'Neill	Greenwood	Burrows	Gollings/2c4p
P1	23-Sep	A	Gloucester	L 23-27	5428	O'Neill	Gollings	Greenwood/t	Burrows/t	Daniel
P1	30-Sep	H	Newcastle Falcons	L 18-20	4445	O'Neill/t	Williams	Greenwood	Greenstock	Gollings
P1	19-Nov	A	London Irish	L 16-21	5919	Williams	Gollings	Burrows	Greenstock/t	Woods/c3p
P1	24-Nov	H	Leicester Tigers	L 13-16	4651	Woods/c2p	Gollings	Burrows	Greenstock	Jennings
P1	2-Dec	A	Sale	L 10-35	2002	Woods/cp	Gollings	Jennings	Burrows	O'Leary
P1	17-Dec	A	Saracens	L 18-26	7681	Williams	Greenstock	Greenwood	Burrows	Woods/6p
P1	23-Dec	H	Northampton Saints	L 25-34	4128	Woods/2c2p	O'Leary(b/t)	Greenwood	Burrows	Daniel/t
P1	27-Dec	H	Saracens	L 14-30	5089	Woods/3p	Gollings	Greenwood	Greenstock	Daniel/t
P1	6-Feb	H	Gloucester	W 21-19	4800	O'Neill	Gollings/t	Burrows	Greenstock	Daniel
P1	11-Feb	A	Bristol	L 9-13	4600	O'Neill	Greenstock	Greenwood/dg	Burrows	Gollings
P1	6-Mar	A	Newcastle Falcons	W 24-22	3620	O'Neill/t	Hackett	Greenwood	Greenstock	Gollings
P1	10-Mar	H	Bath	W 24-22	7067	O'Neill	Jewell	Greenstock	Burrows(c/t)	O'Leary/t
P1	17-Mar	H	Rotherham	W 32-12	2000	O'Neill	Jewell/t	Greenwood	Greenstock	O'Leary/t
P1	31-Mar	H	Sale	W 36-10	5039	Gollings	O'Neill	Jewell	Greenstock	O'Leary/2t
P1	10-Apr	A	London Wasps	L 19-38	12137	Gollings/t	O'Neill	Hackett	Greenstock	O'Leary
P1	14-Apr	A	Leicester Tigers	L 5-37	16006	Gollings	O'Neill	Greenwood	Jewell/t	O'Leary
ES	7-Oct	A	Perigueux	W 23-16	1867	Williams/t	O'Leary	Burrows(e/p)	Greenstock	Gollings/cp
ES	14-Oct	A	Ebbw Vale	W 18-6	2000	O'Neill	Jennings/c2p	Greenwood/t	Greenstock	O'Leary
ES	21-Oct	H	Dax	W 25-3		O'Neill	O'Leary	Greenwood/t	Greenstock	Jennings
ES	28-Oct	A	Dax	L 22-23	5000	O'Neill	O'Leary	Greenwood/t	Greenstock/t	Jennings/t2c
ES	13-Jan	H	Perigueux	W 55-10		O'Neill/t	Woods/2c4p(b/2c)	Greenwood/t	Greenstock	Daniel/t
ES	20-Jan	H	Ebbw Vale	W 45-22	3000	O'Neill	Jennings	Burrows/2t	Greenstock/2t	Gollings/5cp
ES	28-Jan	A	Brive	W 20-13		O'Neill	Greenstock	Greenwood/t	Burrows	Daniel
ES	22-Apr	N	Newcastle Falcons	W 17-12	6000	O'Neill	Gollings	Greenwood	Greenstock	O'Leary
ES	20-May	N	Narbonne	W 42-33	11211	Williams	Gollings/t	Greenwood	Greenstock	O'Leary/t
TBC	4-Nov	A	Plymouth Albion	W 36-8	3500	O'Neill(g/t)	Woods/t4cp	Greenwood	Greenstock	Williams/2t
TBC	11-Nov	H	Manchester	W 38-8	1489	Williams/t	Gollings	Greenwood	Greenstock/2t	Woods/2t4c
TBC	9-Dec	H	Northampton Saints	W 11-6	4406	Williams	O'Neill	Greenwood	Greenstock	Woods/2p
TBC	6-Jan	H	Leicester Tigers	W 22-18	8500	O'Neill	Greenstock	Greenwood/t	Burrows	Daniel
TBC	24-Feb	N	Newcastle Falcons	L 27-30	71000	O'Neill	Greenstock	Greenwood	Burrows	Daniel

*after opponents name indicates a penalty try. Brackets after a player's name indicates he was replaced.
eg (a) means he was replaced by replacement code "a" and so on. / after a player or replacement name
is followed by any scores he made - eg /t, /c, /p, /dg or any combination of these*

LEAGUE DEBUTS

Paul Burke, Nick Burrows, Craig Chalmers, Alex Codling, Andy Dawling, Jon Dawson, Mike Friday, Tani Fuga, S Hackett, Ed Jennings, Rob Jewell, Adam Jones, Mark Mapletoft, R Nias, Ryan O'Neill, Adiian Olver, Eric Peters, J Powell, Matt Powell, Peter Richards, Bruce Starr, David Wilson, Roy Winters, Niall Woods.

EVER PRESENT None

Most Appearances: 18 Steve White-Cooper.
17 Keith Wood.

PLAYERS USED 36 plus 6 as replacements only

MOST POINTS

Pts	Player	T	C	P	DG
133	P Burke	-	17	30	3
61	N Woods	-	5	17	-
38	W Greenwood	7	-	-	1

MATCH FACTS

10	9	1	2	3	4	5	6	7	8
Burke/c2pdg	Richards	Leonard	Wood	Dawson	Morgan	Jones	White-Cooper	Jenkins	Sanderson
Burke/3c	Richards	Leonard	Wood	Starr	Codling	Jones	White-Cooper/t	Jenkins	Sanderson
Burke/4p	Richards	Leonard	Wood	Starr	Codling	Jones	White-Cooper	Jenkins	Sanderson
Burke/2c2p	Richards/t	Leonard	Wood	Starr	Codling	Jones	Jenkins	Dawling	White-Cooper
Burke	Richards	Leonard	Wood	Starr	Morgan	Codling	Nias	Dawling	Jenkins
Burke	Richards	Leonard	Wood/t	Starr	Morgan/t	Jones	Jenkins	Wilson	White-Cooper
Burke/2c3p	Richards	Leonard	Wood	Starr	Morgan	Codling	Jenkins	Wilson	White-Cooper
Burke/c2p	Richards	Leonard	Wood	Starr	Morgan	Jones	White-Cooper/t	Wilson	Winters
Daniel	Richards	Starr	Fuga	Dawson	Morgan	White-Cooper	Jenkins	Wilson	Powell
Lawson	Richards	Starr	Wood	Dawson	Morgan	White-Cooper	Jenkins	Wilson/t	Powell
Chalmers	Powell	Starr	Fuga	Dawson	Morgan	White-Cooper	Jenkins	Wilson	Powell/t
Chalmers	Powell	Leonard	Fuga	Starr	Morgan	White-Cooper	Jenkins	Wilson	Powell
Chalmers	Powell	Starr	Wood	Olver	Morgan	White-Cooper	Jenkins/t	Dawling	Powell
Chalmers	Powell	Leonard	Wood	Olver	Jones	White-Cooper	Jenkins	Winters	Peters
Burke/c2pdg	Powell	Leonard	Wood	Olver	Codling	White-Cooper	Sanderson/t	Wilson	Winters
Burke/2p	Powell	Starr	Fuga	Olver	Morgan	White-Cooper	Jenkins	Sanderson	Winters
Burke/c4p	Powell	Starr	Wood	Olver	Morgan	White-Cooper	Sanderson	Wilson/t	Winters
Burke/c4p	Powell	Leonard	Wood	Olver	Morgan	White-Cooper	Sanderson	Wilson	Winters
Burke/cpdg(d/2c)	Powell	Leonard	Wood/t	Olver	Morgan	Codling	Jenkins	Wilson/t	Winters
Burke/2c4p	Powell	Starr	Wood	Olver	Morgan/t	White-Cooper	Sanderson	Wilson/t	Winters
Burke/2c	Powell	Starr	Fuga	Olver/t	Morgan/t	Richards	Jenkins	Wilson	Winters
Burke	Powell	Leonard	Wood	Dawson	Morgan	Codling	Sanderson	Wilson	Winters
Powell	Friday	Starr	Fuga/t	Mathieson	Morgan	Jones	Sanderson	Wilson	Winters/t
Powell	Friday	Leonard	Matthews/t	Dawson	Morgan	Jones	Jenkins	Wilson	White-Cooper
Burke/c6p	Powell	Leonard	Wood	Dawson	Morgan	White-Cooper	Sanderson	Wilson	Winters
Burke/p	Powell	Leonard	Wood	Dawson	Morgan	White-Cooper	Jenkins	Wilson	Winters
Powell/t	Friday/t	Leonard	Wood/2t	Dawson	Morgan	White-Cooper	Jenkins	Wilson	Winters
Powell(f/c)	Friday	Starr	Wood	Dawson	Morgan	White-Cooper	Sanderson/2t	Wilson	Winters
Burke/2c2p	Powell	Leonard	Wood	Dawson	Morgan	White-Cooper/t	Winters	Wilson	Peters
Chalmers/t3pdg	Powell	Leonard	Fuga	Dawson	Morgan	White-Cooper	Sanderson	Wilson	Winters
Burke/3c6pdg	Powell	Leonard	Wood	Dawson	Morgan	White-Cooper	Sanderson/t	Wilson	Winters
Powell	Richards/t	Hackett	Fuga	Dawson	Codling	Jones	Jenkins	Wilson	White-Cooper
Powell	Richards	Starr	Fuga	Dawson	Codling	Cross	Jenkins/t	Wilson	White-Cooper
Chalmers	Powell	Leonard	Fuga	Starr	Morgan	White-Cooper/t	Jenkins	Wilson	Powell
Chalmers/2cp	Powell	Leonard	Wood/t	Dawson	Morgan	White-Cooper	Winters	Wilson/t	Peters
Burke/tc5p	Powell	Leonard	Wood	Dawson	Morgan	White-Cooper	Sanderson	Wilson/t	Winters

REPLACEMENTS

a - B Daniel   b - B Gollings   c - W Greenwood   d - C Chalmers
e - E Jennings   f - P Burke   g - D O'Leary

Most replacement appearances: 8 - J Dawson. 7 - T Fuga. 6 - E Jennings, A Dawling, M Powell

Most times replaced: 12 B Starr. 8 - R Jenkins.

2000-01 HIGHLIGHTS

Former Irish International Paul Burke topped the points scoring in his first season at the club.

Burke also made big contributions in the two Cup finals that Harlequins reached during the campaign.

During the season winger Daren O'Leary passed Andy Mullins record for most league appearances. O'Leary ended the season on 124 and also extended his try scoring record. He took his total to 65 in what may have been his last season.

Former player Will Greenwood topped the try scoring list on his return to the club from Leicester Tigers. Whilst his total of seven is not great he had a habit of scoring crucial tries in games that mattered.

In the league Quins finished 11th - their lowest ever position.

HARLEQUINS

LEAGUE STATISTICS
compiled by Stephen McCormack

SEASON	Division	P	W	D	L	F	A	Pts Diff	Lge Pts	Lge Pos		Most Points		Most Tries
91-92	1	12	5	1	6	213	207	6	11	8	109	David Pears	4	David Pears
92-93	1	12	5	1	6	197	187	10	11	8	57	Sturat Thresher	3	by 4 players
93-94	1	18	8	0	10	333	287	46	16	6	143	Kent Bray	11	Daren O'Leary
94-95	1	18	6	1	11	275	348	-73	13	8	103	Paul Challinor	4	Peter Mensah
95-96	1	18	13	0	5	524	314	210	26	3	112	Paul Challinor	14	Daren O'Leary
96-97	1	22	15	0	7	745	416	329	30	3	176	Thierry Lacroix	15	Daren O'Leary
97-98	1	22	8	0	14	516	645	-129	16	10	109	Thierry Lacroix	9	Daren O'Leary
98-99	1	26	16	1	9	690	653	37	33	4	331	John Schuster	11	Dan Luger
99-00	1	22	7	0	15	441	687	-246	28	10	84	Rob Liley	7	Brandon Daniel
00-01	1	22	7	0	15	440	538	-98	38	11	133	Paul Burke	7	Will Greenwood

BIGGEST MARGINS

Home Win — 71pts - 89-18 v Orrell 5.10.96
Away Win — 70pts - 91-21 v W. Hartlepool 23.3.96
Home Defeat — 49pts - 5-54 v Leicester 6.5.00
Away Defeat — 58pts - 19-77 v Bath 29.4.00

MOST CONSECUTIVE

Appearances — 42 Andy Mullins 16.11.91-30.4.94
Matches scoring Tries — 5 Daren O'Leary
Matches scoring points — 21 JohnSchuster
Victories — 6 (twice)
Defeats — 5

MOST POINTS

Scored at Home — 89 v Orrell 5.10.96
Scored Away — 91 v West Hartlepool 23.3.96
Conceded at Home — 57 v Wasps 17.9.94
Conceded Away — 77 v Bath 29.4.00

MOST

Scored in a match — 14 v W. Hartlepool 23.3.96
Conceded in a match — 10 v Bath 29.4.00

MOST APPEARANCES

by a forward — 118 (2) Andy Mullins
by a back — 124(5) Daren O'Leary

	MOST IN A SEASON	MOST IN A CAREER	MOST IN A MATCH	
Points	331 John Schuster 98-99	431 David Pears 89-96	28 John Schuster	v Bath 21.11.98 (H)
Tries	15 Daren O'Leary 96-97	65 Daren O'Leary 93-01	4 Daren O'Leary	v Gloucester 31.8.96 (H)
Conversions	36 John Schuster 98-99	57 David Pears 89-96	9 Paul Challinor	v W Hartlepool 23.3.96 (A)
Penalties	77 John Schuster 98-99	83 David Pears 89-96	7 David Pears	v Rosslyn Park 7.12.91 (A)
Drop Goals	7 David Pears 95-96	14 David Pears 89-96	3 David Pears	v Wasps 16.9.95 (H)

PLAYING SQUAD

HARLEQUINS

NEC
HARLEQUINS
······ OF LONDON ······

BACKS

	Ht.	Wt.	Birthdate	Birthplace	CLUB	League Apps	Tries	Pts
Jamie Williams Middlesex U21.	6.1	13.09	16.03.76	Marston(NZ)	Harlequins	36(4)	11	55
Matthew Powell	5.10	13.6	08.05.78	Abergavenny	Harlequins Saracens	13(6)	-	-
Daren O'Leary England A, Emerging, U21.	6.0	13.00	27.06.73	Harold Wood	Harlequins Saracens	125(2) 10	65 3	339 15
Brandon Daniel	6.1	14.04	19.07.77	New Zealand	Harlequins Saracens	20(3) 32(4)	10 16	50 80
Paul Burke Ireland	5.8	13.0	01/05/73	London	Harlequins	16	-	133
Will Greenwood England, A, Students, U21. Waterloo 4/1/5.	6.4	15.00	20.10.72	Blackburn	Harlequins Leicester	39(1) 38(9)	13 19	85 95
Ben Gollings	5.6	12.6	12.05.80		Harlequins	22(1)	10	69
Peter Richards England A	5.10	12.00	10.03.78	Portsmouth	Harlequins London Irish	23(5) 21(7)	2 5	13 25
Mike Friday England Students.	5.8	12.1	25.4.72	Chichester	Harlequins Wasps	(4) 20(17)	- 7	- 35
Nick Greenstock England.	6.3	15.04	03.11.73	Dubai	Harlequins Wasps	32(1) 61(5)	1 20	5 100

FORWARDS

	Ht.	Wt.	Birthdate	Birthplace	CLUB	League Apps	Tries	Pts
Jason Leonard England , B, Colts, British Lions.	5.10	17.02	14.08.68	Barking	Harlequins Saracens	13(3) 19	1	4
Steve White-Cooper	6.4	16.00	15.07.74	Cape Town	Harlequins	35(6)	2	10
David Wilson Australia	6.2	15.2	04.01.67	Brisbane	Harlequins	14	4	20
Pat Sanderson England 3, A, U21, 18, 16	6.4	16.00	06.09.77	Chester	Harlequins Sale	26(4) 31(5)	4 7	20 35
Garrick Morgan Australia, Queensland	6.7	18.02	25.01.70	Sydney	Harlequins	60(1)	9	45
Keith Wood Ireland, British Lions, Munster	6.0	16.10	27.01.72	Limerick	Harlequins	60(8)	11	58
Bruce Starr Queensland Reds	5.11	18.00	05.01.73	Qurindi	Harlequins	16(3)	-	-
Roy Winters	6.4	16.00	13.12.75	Cuckfield	Harlequins Bedford	10(1) 65(9)	- 8	- 40
Rory Jenkins England A, Emerging, Students.	6.2	16.05	29.06.70	Leicester	Harlequins London Irish	112(14) 15	8 1	40 5

HARLEQUINS

FACT FILE

Founded: 1866
Nickname: Quins
Web site: www.quins.co.uk

Colours: Light blue, magenta, chocolate, french grey, light green & black
Change colours: None

GROUND Stoop Memorial Ground, Langhorn Drive, Twickenham. TW2 7SX
Tel: 020 8410 6000   Fax: 020 8410 6001
e-mail: mail@quins.co.uk   Advance Ticket Line: 020 8410 6010
Capacity: 8,500   Seated Covered: 4,600 Uncovered: 2,850   Standing uncovered: 1,050

Directions: Langhorn Drive is off the westbound carriageway of theA316 Chertsey Road, 450 yards west of
RFU roundabout. No entry for vehicles from Craneford Way
Nearest Railway Station: Twickenham (BR). 12 minutes walk, proceed towards RFU ground,
turn left into Court Way, then left into Craneford Way. The ground is at the far end.

Car Parking: Limited amount available @ £5

Admission: Season Tickets (all seated)   each price band reflects different seating areas
£399* / 275* / 220*§ / 125 / 75@   @ Under16s concession £25
* includes membership   § OAPs/Young Adult (16-23) concession £159
Matchday: Adults £25 - 8   OAPs & Students £10 - 5   Under16s £5/2

Club Shop: Mon-Sat 10-4. Closed Wednesday. Contact Angela Lambert 020 8410 6056
Mail order 07000 478467

Clubhouse: Matchdays 12-late, Evening games 18.30-23.00. Colours restuarant. Snacks & light meals available.
Functions: 500-600 seated, 1000 buffet, 2000 bar.
Contact Crown Catering 020 8410 6052 / 6054

PROGRAMME
Size: 170 x 245mm
Pages: 56   Price: £2.50
Editor: Nick Melton 020 8410 6045

Advertising Rates
Contact - Gareth Lloyd 020 8410 6039

David Wilson, Quins' captain

NEWCASTLE FALCONS

Vice President	Harry Sharp
Chairman	Dave Thompson
Director	John Gray
Managing Director	John Parkinson
Director of Rugby	Rob Andrew
Communications & **Media Manager**	Richard Woollam Mobile - 07808 572990
Head of Marketing	Mick Hogan Mobile - 07808 572989
1st Team Coach	Steve Bates

c/o Newcastle R.F.C.
Kingston Park,
Brunton Road,
Kenton Bank Foot,
Newcastle upon Tyne NE13 8AF
Tel: 0191 214 5588
Fax: 0191 286 0824
e-mail:
commercial@newcastle-falcons.co.uk

2001 Tetley's Bitter Cup Champions on a day that saw 71,000 fans pack Twickenham and possibly the biggest day for club rugby in recent times. Rob Andrew claimed that the day was as big a day in his rugby career as there has ever been – and we all know there have been a few. Furthermore, the Kingston Park crowds have been up 61% on last season, a sign surely of things to come. The Falcons also have development plans for Kingston Park that will see Europe's best rugby facilities in Newcastle.

The past season therefore has certainly been one to cherish. The much-publicised Falcons "Young Guns" proved there worth throughout the Zurich Premiership, Tetley's Bitter Cup and the European Shield campaigns. A narrow loss to NEC Harlequins in the semi-final of the European Shield meant missing out on two cup finals in one season, however, the Tetley's Cup victory proved enough to secure European Cup qualification and cap off a memorable season.

Kingston Park once again proved a difficult place for teams to visit and the open style of the Falcons play entertained the crowds. Not only were the youngsters such as Noon, Walder, May and Stephenson outstanding, but also the old guard led by example, highlighted by the fact that Gary Armstrong received the Players Player of the Year Award.

The 2001/02 season brings European Cup rugby to the North East for the first time and the resigning of Pat Lam along with 7 of last years hugely successful Under 21 squad should ensure another fantastic season of rugby in Newcastle. The return from Lions duty of Jonny Wilkinson and the three new caps (Noon, Stephenson and Walder for England) adds experience to young shoulders providing a worrying combination to any opposition.

NEWCASTLE FALCONS

Comp.	Date	H/A	Opponents	Result & Score	Att	15	14	13	12	11
P1	20-Aug	H	Northampton Saints	W 27-21	3245	Massey	Botham	Cook	Leslie	Tuigamala/t
P1	27-Aug	H	Leicester Tigers	L 22-25	4298	Cook	Botham	May	Leslie	Tuigamala
P1	2-Sep	A	Sale	W 27-13	2885	Stephenson	Botham	May	Leslie/2t	Tuigamala
P1	6-Sep	A	Gloucester	L 18-19	2623	Stephenson	Botham	May	Leslie	Taione
P1	10-Sep	H	Rotherham	W 34-19	2735	Cook	Botham/t	May	Leslie/t	Taione
P1	16-Sep	A	Bath	L 12-19	7503	Cook	Botham	Noon	Leslie	Taione
P1	23-Sep	H	London Wasps	W 59-21	4232	Stephenson	Botham/2t	Noon/t	Leslie/t	Tuigamala
P1	30-Sep	A	Harlequins	W 20-18	4445	Stephenson/2t	Botham	Leslie	Noon	Tuigamala
P1	18-Nov	A	Northampton Saints	L 18-26	6734	Stephenson	Botham	Noon	May/t(c/t)	Taione
P1	26-Nov	H	Saracens	W 32-27	5473	Stephenson	Botham	Noon	May	Tuigamala
P1	5-Dec	A	London Irish	L 17-19	4605	Stephenson	Botham	Noon(d/t)	May	Tuigamala
P1	17-Dec	A	Bristol	L 14-27	3687	Stephenson	Taione	Botham	May/t	Tuigamala
P1	23-Dec	A	Gloucester	L 13-28	7455	Walder	Stephenson	Botham	Tuigamala	Cook
P1	27-Dec	H	Bristol	W 23-15	3738	Walder	Stephenson	May	Cook	Tuigamala
P1	11-Feb	H	Bath	W 24-23	7319	Walder/t	Stephenson/t	Botham	May	Tuigamala
P1	6-Mar	H	Harlequins	L 22-24	3620	Massey	Taione	Noon	Botham	Maclure/t
P1	11-Mar	H	Sale	W 48-24	3318	Walder/t	Taione	Noon	May/t	Stephenson/2t
P1	17-Mar	A	Leicester Tigers	L 7-51	15009	Massey	Stephenson	Maclure/t	May	Taione
P1	28-Mar	A	London Wasps	L 7-44	3444	Massey/t	Cook	Noon	Maclure	Taione
P1	1-Apr	A	London Irish	W 42-35	5963	Walder/t	Maclure	Noon	May	Stephenson/t
P1	10-Apr	A	Rotherham	W 39-36	1700	Stephenson/t	Taione	Noon	Tuigamala	Maclure
P1	15-Apr	A	Saracens	L 29-34	10107	Walder/2c	Taione	Stephenson	May	Noon
ES	7-Oct	A	Benetton Treviso	L 15-28	2000	Stephenson	Botham	Noon	Leslie	Taione
ES	15-Oct	H	Cross Keys	W 99-8	2000	Stephenson/2t	Botham/3t	Noon/2t	May/2t	Taione/2t
ES	22-Oct	A	Begles-Bordeaux	W 26-18		Stephenson/t	Botham	Noon	Leslie	Taione/t
ES	29-Oct	H	Begles-Bordeaux*	W 39-15	3000	Stephenson	Botham	Noon	May	Taione
ES	14-Jan	H	Benetton Treviso	W 30-19	2496	Walder	Stephenson	Botham	May	Tuigamala/t
ES	21-Jan	A	Cross Keys	W 25-11	1500	Stephenson	Maclure	Botham	May	Tuigamala
ES	28-Jan	A	Mont de Marsan	W 61-23	2500	Walder/2t2c	Botham/t	Noon/t	May/t	Tuigamala
ES	22-Apr	N	Harlequins	L 12-17	6000	Walder	Stephenson	Noon	May	Taione
TBC	4-Nov	A	Rosslyn Park	W 25-13	1500	Stephenson	Botham/t	Noon/2t	May	Taione
TBC	12-Nov	H	Bristol	W 32-16	2151	Stephenson	Botham	Noon	May	Taione
TBC	10-Dec	H	London Irish	W 33-20	3293	Stephenson	Maclure	Botham/t	May	Tuigamala/t
TBC	6-Jan	H	Sale	W 37-25	6257	Walder	Stephenson	Noon	May/2t	Tuigamala
TBC	24-Feb	N	Harlequins	W 30-27	71000	Walder/t	Stephenson	Noon	May/2t	Tuigamala
PO	28-Apr	A	Bath	L 9-18	6840	Stephenson	Botham	Noon	May	Taione

after opponents name indicates a penalty try. Brackets after a player's name indicates he was replaced. eg (a) means he was replaced by replacement code "a" and so on. / after a player or replacement name is followed by any scores he made - eg /t, /c, /p, /dg or any combination of these

LEAGUE DEBUTS

Christian Balsham, Liam Botham, Ross Cook, Jim Jenner, Andrew Mower, Epeli Taione.

PLAYERS USED

31 plus 2 as replacements only

EVER PRESENT

None

Most Appearances:
20 Dodie Weir (1)
18 Richard Arnold.
17 Gary Armstrong.

MOST POINTS

Pts	Player	T	C	P	DG
198	J Wilkinson	2	34	37	3
92	D Walder	5	8	17	-
49	G Armstrong	7	4	2	-
35	M Stephenson	7	-	-	-

MATCH FACTS

10	9	1	2	3	4	5	6	7	8
Wilkinson/3c2p	Armstrong	Graham	Howe	Hurter	Grimes	Weir	Arnold	Beattie/t	Mower/t
Wilkinson/c5p	Charlton	Graham	Howe	Hurter	Grimes/t	Weir	Arnold	Mower	Beattie
Wilkinson/3c2p	Armstrong	Graham	Nesdale	Hurter	Weir(a/t)	Grimes	Arnold	Mower	Jenner
Wilkinson/6p	Armstrong	Graham	Nesdale	Peel	Weir	Grimes	Arnold	Mower	Jenner
Wilkinson/4c2p	Armstrong	Graham	Nesdale	Peel	Vyvyan	Weir	Arnold	Mower/t	Beattie(b/t)
Wilkinson/3pdg	Armstrong	Graham	Nesdale	Peel	Grimes	Weir	Arnold	Mower	Beattie
Wilkinson/4c6pdg	Armstrong/2t	Graham	Nesdale	Peel	Weir	Grimes	Beattie	Mower	Jenner
Wilkinson/2c2p	Armstrong	Graham	Nesdale	Peel	Grimes	Weir	Arnold	Mower	Jenner
Walder/c2p	Armstrong	Peel	Balshan	Hurter	Vyvyan	Weir	Devonshire	Mower	Jenner
Walder/2t2c6p	Armstrong	Peel	Nesdale	Hurter	Vyvyan	Weir	Arnold	Mower	Beattie
Walder/4p	Charlton	Ward	Nesdale	Graham	Vyvyan	Weir	Arnold	Mower	Beattie
Wilkinson/2pdg	Armstrong	Ward	Nesdale	Hurter	Grimes	Weir	Arnold	Mower	Jenner
Wilkinson/c2p	Armstrong	Peel	Nesdale	Hurter	Grimes	Weir/t	Arnold	Cartmell	Jenner
Wilkinson/2c3p	Armstrong/t	Ward/t	Nesdale	Hurter	Grimes	Weir	Arnold	Mower	Beattie
Wilkinson/t2c	Armstrong/t	Ward	Nesdale	Hurter	Grimes	Weir	Devonshire	Mower	Jenner
Walder/c5p	Charlton	Ward	Howe	Hurter	Grimes	Vyvyan	Arnold	Cartmell	Jenner
Wilkinson/5cp	Armstrong/t	Peel	Howe	Hurter	Grimes/t	Weir/t	Vyvyan	Mower	Jenner
Walder/c	Charlton	Peel	Howe	Hurter	Vyvyan	Weir	Arnold	Cartmell	Jenner
Walder/c	Charlton	Ward	Nesdale	Graham	Rule	Weir	Devonshire	Cartmell	Arnold
Wilkinson/t6c	Armstrong/t	Peel	Nesdale/t	Hurter	Grimes	Vyvyan/t	Arnold	Mower	Jenner
May	Armstrong/t4c2p	Ward	Nesdale	Graham/2t	Grimes	Weir	Arnold	Devonshire	Jenner/t
Wilkinson/cp	Armstrong	Hurter	Nesdale	Ward(e/t)	Weir/t	Grimes/t	Vyvyan/t	Devonshire	Arnold
Wilkinson/tcp	Charlton/t	Ward	Nesdale	Peel	Grimes	Weir	Beattie	Cartmell	Jenner
Walder/t12c	Charlton/t	Ward/t	Nesdale/t	Peel	Vyvyan	Weir	Arnold	Mower	Beattie
Wilkinson/2c4p	Armstrong	Peel	Nesdale	Graham	Grimes	Weir	Arnold	Mower	Beattie
Walder/3c6p	Armstrong	Ward	Nesdale/t	Graham	Vyvyan	Weir/t	Arnold	Mower	Beattie
Wilkinson/3c3p	Armstrong	Ward/t	Nesdale	Hurter(e/t)	Grimes	Weir	Arnold	Mower	Jenner
Walder/c6p	Armstrong/t	Peel	Howe	Graham	Vyvyan	Weir	Arnold	Mower	Jenner
Wilkinson/4c3p(d/t)	Armstrong/t	Ward	Nesdale	Hurter/t	Grimes	Weir	Devonshire	Mower	Jenner
Wilkinson/4p	Armstrong	Ward	Nesdale	Hurter	Grimes	Weir	Vyvyan	Mower	Arnold
Walder/cp	Armstrong	Ward	Nesdale	Hurter	Vyvyan	Weir/t	Devonshire	Mower	Beattie
Wilkinson/2c6p	Armstrong/t	Ward	Howe	Hurter	Vyvyan	Weir	Jenner	Mower/t	Beattie
Wilkinson/t3c4p	Armstrong	Ward	Nesdale	Hurter	Vyvyan	Grimes	Arnold	Mower	Jenner
Wilkinson/2c6p	Armstrong	Peel	Nesdale	Hurter	Weir	Grimes	Arnold	Mower	Beattie/t
Wilkinson/2c2p	Armstrong	Ward	Nesdale	Hurter	Grimes	Weir	Devonshire	Mower	Jenner/t
Walder/3p	Armstrong	Ward	Nesdale	Hurter	Grimes	Weir	Vyvyan	Mower	Arnold

REPLACEMENTS   a - H Vyvyan   b - J Jenner   c - V Tuigamala   d - G Maclure   e - G Graham

Most replacement appearances: 9 - G Graham. 8 - H Vyvyan

Most times replaced: 10 - D Weir. 7 - J Rule.

2000-01 HIGHLIGHTS

England outside half Jonny Wilkinson topped the Newcastle scoring list for the third consecutive season.

He finished just two short of 200 points but in the process passed Rob Andrew as the clubs all time leading points scorer in league rugby.

Scottish international scrum half, Gary Armstrong was again amongs the tries and finished joint top scorer along with new boy on the block Michael Stephenson.

Stephenson's reward for a fine season was a place on the England tour to North America in the summer and he was further awarded with his first full cap.

Armstrong took his career record to 52.

NEWCASTLE FALCONS

LEAGUE STATISTICS
compiled by Stephen McCormack

SEASON	Division	P	W	D	L	F	A	Pts Diff	Lge Pts	Lge Pos	Most Points		Most Tries	
91-92	2	12	7	0	5	371	140	231	14	4	147	David Johnson	10	Peter Walton
92-93	2	12	10	0	2	241	106	135	20	1p	136	David Johnson	6	Ross Wilkinson
93-94	1	18	2	1	15	190	483	-293	5	10r	79	David Johnson	4	Ross Wilkinson
94-95	2	18	8	2	8	373	281	92	18	3	193	Simon Mason	8	Tony Penn
95-96	2	18	5	1	12	348	405	-57	11	8	73	Richard Cramb	4	Mike Brummitt & Gary Armstrong
96-97	2	22	19	1	2	1255	346	909	39	2p	297	Rob Andrew	23	John Bentley
97-98	1	22	19	0	3	645	387	258	38	1	226	Rob Andrew	13	Gary Armstrong
98-99	1	26	14	0	12	719	639	80	28	8	306	Jonny Wilkinson	12	Gary Armstrong
99-00	1	22	6	2	14	377	630	-253	19	9	163	Jonny Wilkinson	3	Four players
00-01	1	22	11	0	11	554	568	-14	57	6	198	Jonny Wilkinson	7	Michael Stephenson Gary Armstrong

BIGGEST MARGINS

Home Win 151pts - 156-5 v Rugby 5.10.96

Away Win 66pts - 75-9 v Moseley 19.10.96

Home Defeat 43pts - 9-52 v Northampton 21.10.95

Away Defeat 61pts - 5-66 v Leicester 12.3.94

MOST CONSECUTIVE

Appearances 44 Neil Frankland 13.1.90-2.10.93

Matches scoring Tries 8 Gary Armstrong

Matches scoring points 22 Rob Andrew

Victories 6

Defeats 12

MOST POINTS

Scored at Home 156 v Rugby 5.10.96

Scored Away 75 v Moseley 19.10.96

Conceded at Home 52 v Northampton 21.10.95

Conceded Away 66 v Leicester 12.3.94

MOST TRIES

Scored in a match 24 v Rugby 5.10.96 (H)

Conceded in a match 10 v Leicester 12.3.94

MOST APPEARANCES

by a forward 148 (2) Richard Arnold

by a back 105 Ross Wilkinson

	MOST IN A SEASON	MOST IN A CAREER	MOST IN A MATCH	
Points	306 Jonny Wilkinson 98-99	575 Rob Andrew 95-99	36 Rob Andrew	v Rugby 5.10.96 (H)
Tries	23 John Bentley 96-97	52 Gary Armstrong 95-00	5 Pat Lam	v Rotherham 4.5.97 (H)
Conversions	95 Rob Andrew 96-97	152 Rob Andrew 95-99	18 Rob Andrew	v Rugby 5.10.96 (H)
Penalties	53 Jonny Wilkinson 98-99	105 David Johnson 87-94	6 David Johnson Rob Andrew Jonny Wilkinson	v Morlet 11.1.92 (H) v Richmond 26.10.97 (H) four times in 2000/01
Drop Goals	4 David Johnson 87-88	10 David Johnson 87-94	2 David Johnson	v Bedford 5.12.87 (A)

PLAYING SQUAD

NEWCASTLE FALCONS

BACKS

	Ht.	Wt.	Birthdate	Birthplace	CLUB	League Apps	Tries	Pts
Michael Stephenson England	6.0	13.0	20.09.80		Newcastle	20	7	35
Va'aiga Tuigamala New Zealand, Western Samoa. RL: Western Samoa	5.10	16.00	04.09.69	Faleasiu	Newcastle Wasps	78(7) 8	32 3	162 15
Jonny Wilkinson England , U21, Colts, Schools.	5.10	12.09	25.05.79	Surrey	Newcastle	62(3)	14	667
Peter Massey Other club: Wakefield 22/7/35	5.11	13.07	03.04.75	Pontefract	Newcastle Moseley	22(8) 11(1)	1 3	21 15
Allen Chilton	5.10	13.0	29.03.79		Newcastle	2(7)		
David Walder England	5.10	13.0	07.05.76		Newcastle	19(2)	5	138
Liam Botham England A. Other club: Cardiff	6.0	15.0	26.08.77		Newcastle W Hartlepool	15	3	15
Tim May	5.10	14.07	05.02.79	London	Newcastle	28	6	30
Jamie Noon	5.10	13.7	09.05.79		Newcastle	29(4)	4	20
Gary Armstrong Scotland	5.8	13.08	30.09.66	Edinburgh	Newcastle	100(2)	59	309
Hall Charlton	5.11	13.02	25.10.79	Durham	Newcastle	10(8)	2	10

FORWARDS

	Ht.	Wt.	Birthdate	Birthplace	CLUB	League Apps	Tries	Pts
Mike Howe	6.0	15.3	06.11.73		Newcastle	10(9)	-	-
Marius Hurter	6.2	17.13	08.10.70	South Africa	Newcastle	48	-	-
George Graham Scotland.	5.7	17.00	19.01.66	Stirling	Newcastle	63(22)	15	75
Ross Nesdale Ireland .	5.10	16.02	30.07.69	Auckland	Newcastle	88	14	70
Micky Ward	5.11	17.0	09.01.79		Newcastle	8(7)	1	5
Dodie Weir Scotland , British Lions.	6.6	17.07	04.07.70	Edinburgh London Scottish	Newcastle 3	105(2) 1	12 4	60
Stuart Grimes Scotland	6.5	16.07	04.04.74	Aberdeen	Newcastle Glasgow Caledonians	26(4)	4	20
Ross Beattie	6.5	17.07	15.11.77	Sittingbourne	Newcastle	34(7)	4	20
Ian Peel	6.0	17.00	24.01.76	Otley	Newcastle	32(14)	-	-
Andrew Mower	6.2	15.1	09.09.75		Newcastle London Irish	16(1)	2	10
Jimmy Cartmell	6.0	13.07	08.01.77	Carlisle	Newcastle	19(12)	3	15
Richard Arnold	6.4	15.12	16.08.65	Taranaki	Newcastle	148(3)	15	69
Hugh Vyvyan	6.6	16.00	08.09.76	Guildford	Newcastle	26(18)	5	25
Jim Jenner Durham	6.4	17.2	27.11.71	Reading	Newcastle Worcester	13(5) 55(11)	2 32	10 160

NEWCASTLE FALCONS

FACT FILE

Founded: 1877
Nickname: The Falcons
Web site: www.newcastle-falcons.co.uk

Colours: Black with gold trim
Change colours: Gold with black trim

GROUND

Address: Kingston Park, Brunton Road, Kenton Bank Foot, Newcastle upon Tyne NE13 AF
Tel: 0191 214 5588   Fax: 0191 271 5213
Capacity: 7,500   Seated: 2,500

Directions: Travelling from North or South on the City by-pass (A1 Western by-pass) take the Newcastle Airport sign and then follow signs for Kingston Park (Rugby Ground) - approx 1 mile.
Nearest Railway Station: Newcastle Central then Metro to Kingston Park (Green Line)

Car Parking: 600 spaces at ground

Admission:
Season	Standing, Adults £110, Concessions £55, Family (2A & 2C): £290.	
	Seated, Adults £200,Concessions £100, Family: £520	(2000-01
Matchday	Standing, Adults £10, Concessions £5, Family: £30.	Prices)
	Seated, Adults £15,Concessions £8, Family: £46.	

Club Shop: Yes, at Kingston Park
Clubhouse: At Kingston Park, open normal licensing hours
4 inside bar facilities, including corporate facilities,
1 outside bar facility and snack bars.
Functions: Capacity 200 - contact Karen Errington 0191 214 2811

PROGRAMME

Size: B2   Pages: 64   Price: £2.50
Editor: Richard Woollam   0191 214 2808

Advertising Rates   Negotiable
Contact Martin Hutton Business Development 0191 214 2830

Gary Armstrong - joint top try scorer

NORTHAMPTON SAINTS

Franklin's Gardens,
Weedon Road,
St. James',
Northampton NN5 5BG

Tel: 01604 751543
Fax: 01604 599110
e-mail: clubinfo@northamptonsaints.co.uk

Chairman	Keith Barwell
Commercial Director	Allan Robson
Communications Manager	Caroline Hayden
Director of Rugby	John Steele
Rugby Administrator	Ros Hargreaves

Northampton Saints made top four of the league to ensure they had a home draw against Saracens in the new Zurich Championship. A momentous 45-17 over Saints' former bogey side led to a semi-final against Midlands rivals Leicester Tigers at Welford Road – somewhere Saints had not won for nine years.

Saints lost the last match of their season by just four points and the intensity of the match was a fitting tribute to Saints' departing heroes – skipper Pat Lam, former captain Tim Rodber, 1995 World Cup medal winner Garry Pagel and Welsh Lion Allan Bateman.

Despite having such a talented international line-up that included those four players, Saints struggled with the first quarter of the season with many players still out injured following the strains of being involved in the league, Tetley's Bitter Cup and Heineken Cup right to the end. A total of 25 players out of a squad of 37 underwent surgery last season. However, it did give some of the club's young Academy players a taste of the Premiership and a dozen players made their debuts.

The reigning European champions made an early exit from the Heineken Cup following defeats by Edinburgh Reivers and Leinster, and were ousted by Harlequins in the quarter-final of the Tetley's Bitter Cup.

In the league though, Saints fortunes were better and the busy Christmas period saw them beat Gloucester at Kingsholm for only the third time in 50 years just two weeks after they beat Saracens in the league for the first time since the game went professional.

At the end of February, Saints were still in the running for the top league spot but defeats at Franklin's Gardens by Tigers and a poor St Patrick's Day performance against London Irish at the Madejski Stadium put a halt to any winning hopes.

A top four place and Heineken Cup qualification became Saints' priority and their victory against Saracens in the last home game of the season made that aim a lot easier.

Next season the club will welcome two new props, Scotland and Lions' Tom Smith and former Birmingham Solihull player, Chris Budgen. The start of 2001/02 will also mark the completion of two new stands at Franklin's Gardens, the Tetley's Stand and South Stand, that will boost capacity by 1,200 and offer fully covered viewing for all of the club's loyal fans.

Northampton Saints' top try scorer last season, Ben Cohen, charges through the Biarritz defence during their Heineken Cup Pool 1 match in January.
Photo:
Action Images/David Field

NORTHAMPTON SAINTS

Comp.	Date	H/A	Opponents	Result & Score	Att	15	14	13	12	11
P1	20-Aug	A	Newcastle Falcons	L 21-27	3245	Bramhall	Moir	Bateman	Allen	Martin/t
P1	26-Aug	H	London Irish	W 27-10	6713	Tucker	Moir	Martin	Allen	Cohen/2t
P1	2-Sep	A	Leicester Tigers	L 19-33	14278	Bramhall	Moir	Bateman	Allen	Cohen
P1	6-Sep	H	Harlequins	W 27-20	6645	Moir/t	Martin	Bateman	Allen	Sleightholme
P1	9-Sep	A	Sale*	L 23-34	1844	Moir	Cohen	Bateman	Allen	Sleightholme
P1	16-Sep	A	Rotherham	W 32-19	2363	Moir	Webster/t	Martin	Bateman	Cohen/t
P1	23-Sep	H	Bath	W 24-13	7465	Tucker/t2cp	Sleightholme	Martin	Bateman	Cohen/t
P1	1-Oct	A	London Wasps*	L 17-53	4612	Webster	Martin/t	Bateman	Kirk	Cohen
P1	18-Nov	H	Newcastle Falcons	W 26-18	6734	Grayson/2c4p	Thorneycroft	Hyndman	Allen	Webster
P1	25-Nov	H	Bristol	W 24-6	6093	Grayson/c4p	Shaw	Hyndman	Allen/t	Webster
P1	3-Dec	A	Saracens	W 30-10	10483	Grayson/c5p	Thorneycroft	Bateman(a/t)	Allen	Martin
P1	16-Dec	H	Gloucester	W 34-15	7225	Shaw	Thorneycroft/t	Martin	Allen/t	Cohen/t
P1	23-Dec	A	Harlequins	W 34-25	4128	Shaw	Martin/t	Bateman	Allen	Cohen/t
P1	27-Dec	A	Gloucester	W 15-12	9859	Grayson/5p	Martin	Bateman	Leslie	Shaw
P1	30-Dec	H	London Wasps	L 18-21	9662	Grayson/6p	Shaw	Bateman	Allen	Cohen
P1	6-Jan	A	Bath	L 13-36	7802	Grayson/c2p	Martin	Bateman	Allen	Cohen
P1	10-Feb	H	Rotherham	W 42-0	8062	Beal	Shaw/t	Bateman	Leslie/t	Cohen/2t
P1	24-Feb	H	Sale	W 32-26	7849	Beal	Shaw	Bateman	Leslie	Cohen/t
P1	10-Mar	H	Leicester Tigers	L 9-12	9800	Beal	Martin	Bateman	Leslie	Cohen
P1	17-Mar	A	London Irish	L 10-13	12037	Beal	Moir	Tucker/t	Allen	Cohen
P1	31-Mar	H	Saracens	W 25-14	9424	Beal	Martin	Bateman/t	Leslie/t	Cohen
P1	16-Apr	A	Bristol	L 16-46	5315	Beal	Martin	Tucker	Leslie	Shaw
EC	7-Oct	A	Biarritz	L 30-37	10000	Vass/t	Webster	Martin	Bateman	Cohen/t
EC	14-Oct	H	Edinburgh Reivers	L 22-23	7057	Grayson/c5p	Martin	Bateman	Allen	Cohen
EC	21-Oct	H	Leinster	L 8-14		Vass	Webster/t	Martin	Allen	Cohen
EC	27-Oct	A	Leinster	L 31-40		Vass	Martin	Bateman/t	Allen	Cohen
EC	13-Jan	A	Biarritz	W 32-24	6019	Beal/t	Martin	Bateman	Allen	Cohen/3t
TBC	19-Jan	H	Edinburgh Reivers		4000	Beal	Martin	Bateman	Allen	Cohen
TBC	4-Nov	H	Leeds Tykes*	W 73-35	3299	Grayson/9c	Thorneycroft/t	Bateman	Allen/t	Cohen/2t(e/t)
TBC	11-Nov	H	Birmingham & Solihull	W 47-14	3280	Grayson/t6c	Thorneycroft/t	Hyndman	Allen/t	Cohen/3t
PO	9-Dec	A	Harlequins	L 6-11	4406	Grayson/2p	Shaw	Martin	Allen	Cohen
PO	28-Apr	H	Saracens	W 45-17	8500	Beal	Martin/t	Bateman	Leslie	Cohen/t
	5-May	A	Leicester Tigers	L 13-17	12000	Beal	Martin/t	Bateman	Leslie	Cohen

* after opponents name indicates a penalty try.

Brackets after a player's name indicates he was replaced. eg (a) means he was replaced by replacement code "a" and so on. / after a player or replacement name is followed by any scores he made - eg /t, /c, /p, /dg or any combination of these

LEAGUE DEBUTS Adrian Blowers, James Brooks, Olivier Brouzet, Robert Hunter, Chris Hyndman, Tom Kirk, John Leslie, Luca Martin, Dan Richmond, Joe Shaw, Mark Soden, Steve Thompson, Kelvin Todd, Ian Vass, Simon Webster.

EVER PRESENT None

Most Appearances 19 Garry Pagel.
18 Budge Pountney, Mattie Stewart, Pat Lam.

PLAYERS USED 38 plus 4 as replacement only

MOST POINTS

Pts	Player	T	C	P	DG
219	P Grayson	1	20	58	-
49	M Dawson	1	7	10	-
45	B Cohen	9	-	-	-
36	A Hepher	3	3	4	1

MATCH FACTS

10	9	1	2	3	4	5	6	7	8
Grayson/c3p	Malone	Pagel/t	Thompson	Scelzo	Brouzet	Rodber	Seely	Pountney	Lam
Grayson/c5p	Malone	Pagel	Thompson	Scelzo	Brouzet	Rodber	Seely	Pountney	Lam
Grayson/c4p	Malone	Stewart	Thompson/t	Scelzo	Brouzet	Phillips	Rodber	Pountney	Lam
Grayson/c5p	Malone	Todd	Brotherstone	Stewart	Newman	Phillips	Seely	Pountney/t	Lam
Grayson/t2c3p	Malone	Todd	Brotherstone	Volland	Newman	Brouzet	Seely	Pountney	Lam
Grayson/3c2p	Malone	Pagel	Brotherstone	Stewart	Phillips/t	Brouzet	Seely	Pountney/t	Lam
Grayson/c	Malone	Pagel	Brotherstone	Stewart	Phillips	Brouzet	Seely	Pountney/t	Lam
Tucker/2cp	Malone	Pagel	Brotherstone	Stewart	Phillips	Brouzet	Hunter	Pountney	Lam
Hepher/t	Malone	Pagel	Thompson	Stewart	Newman/t	Phillips	Rodber	Blowers	Lam
Hepher	Malone	Pagel	Thompson	Stewart	Phillips	Rodber	Blowers	Pountney/t	Lam
Hepher/dg	Malone	Pagel	Brotherstone	Stewart	Newman	Rodber	Blowers	Pountney	Lam/t
Hepher	Dawson/2c5p	Pagel	Brotherstone	Stewart	Brouzet	Rodber	Blowers	Pountney	Lam
Hepher/2t	Dawson/4c2p	Pagel	Brotherstone	Stewart	Brouzet	Rodber	Blowers	Pountney	Lam
Hepher	Dawson	Pagel	Thompson	Stewart	Brouzet	Rodber	Blowers	Pountney	Seely
Hepher	Dawson	Pagel	Brotherstone	Stewart	Brouzet	Rodber	Blowers	Pountney	Lam
Brooks/t	Dawson	Pagel	Thompson	Stewart	Brouzet	Rodber	Blowers	Pountney	Lam
Hepher/2c3p(b/2c)	Malone	Pagel	Thompson	Stewart	Newman	Rodber	Blowers/t	Pountney	Seely
Grayson/c5p	Dawson	Pagel	Thompson	Stewart	Newman	Rodber/t	Blowers	Pountney/t	Lam
Brooks	Dawson/3p	Pagel	Brotherstone	Stewart	Brouzet	Newman	Blowers	Pountney	Lam
Hepher/cp	Dawson	Todd	Richmond	Pagel	Phillips	Brouzet	Rodber	Blowers	Lam
Hepher(b/c2p)	Dawson/tc	Pagel	Richmond	Stewart	Brouzet	Phillips	Rodber	Blowers	Soden
Grayson/c3p	Dawson	Pagel	Thompson/t	Stewart	Brouzet	Phillips	Rodber	Blowers	Soden
Hepher/tcp	Bramhall	Pagel	Brotherstone	Stewart	Phillips(c/t)	Brouzet/t	Rodber	Pountney	Lam
Hepher	Malone	Pagel	Brotherstone	Stewart	Newman	Brouzet	Rodber/t	Pountney	Lam
Hepher	Dawson/p	Pagel	Thompson	Stewart	Phillips	Brouzet	Hunter	Pountney	Lam
Hepher/2c3pdg	Dawson	Pagel	Brotherstone	Stewart	Phillips/t	Brouzet	Thompson	Pountney	Seely/t
Hepher/2cp	Malone	Pagel	Brotherstone	Stewart	Newman	Rodber	Thompson/t	Rennick	Seely
Hepher	Malone	Todd	Brotherstone	Stewart	Newman	Rodber	Thompson	Rennick	Seely
Hepher	Dawson/2t	Pagel	Thompson	Stewart(d/t)	Phillips	Rodber/t	Seely/t	Blowers	Lam
Hepher	Dawson/t	Pagel	Thompson	Todd	Newman	Phillips	Soden	Blowers	Seely
Hepher	Dawson	Pagel	Brotherstone	Stewart	Newman	Rodber	Blowers	Pountney	Lam
Grayson/5c	Dawson/2t	Todd	Thompson/t	Stewart	Newman	Brouzet	Rodber/t	Blowers/t	Soden
Grayson/c2p	Dawson	Pagel	Thompson	Stewart	Newman	Brouzet	Rodber	Soden	Seely

REPLACEMENTS   a - M Shaw   b - P Grayson   c - R Hunter.   d - K Todd   e - S Webster

Most replacement appearances: 8 - J Phillips, R Hunter

Most times replaced: 11 - T Rodber

2000-01 HIGHLIGHTS

Paul Grayson regained the Northampton kicking title and has now finished top on seven of the last eight seasons. He set a new record with 219 points - four more than his previous best.

Grayson kicked 58 penalties and now needs just 17 to reach 300 in the league for Northampton.

England international wing Ben Cohen topped the try scoring list for the second successive season.

Centre Matt Allen did not have one of his better seasons but did edge his club try scoring record to 44.

Tim Rodber ended his career with a club record 143 league appearances.

NORTHAMPTON SAINTS

LEAGUE STATISTICS
compiled by Stephen McCormack

SEASON	Division	P	W	D	L	F	A	Pts Diff	Lge Pts	Lge Pos	Most Points		Most Tries	
91-92	1	12	9	1	2	209	136	73	19	3	110	John Steele	5	Harvey Thorneycroft
92-93	1	12	8	0	4	215	150	65	16	4	52	John Steele	6	Harvey Thorneycroft
93-94	1	18	9		0	305	342	-37	18	5	132	Paul Grayson	2	by seven players
94-95	1	18	6	0	12	267	335	-68	12	10r	189	Paul Grayson	3	Grant Seely & Matt Dawson
95-96	2	18	18	0	0	867	203	664	36	1p	215	Paul Grayson	20	Matt Allen
96-97	1	22	10	0	12	515	477	38	20	8	129	Paul Grayson	7	Jonathon Bell
97-98	1	22	9	1	12	493	472	21	19	8	210	Paul Grayson	7	Matt Allen
98-99	1	26	19	0	7	754	556	198	38	2	156	Paul Grayson	14	Pat Lam
99-00	1	22	13	0	9	551	480	71	35	5	99	Ali Hepher	6	Ben Cohen
00-01	1	22	13	0	9	518	43	55	59	4	219	Paul Grayson	9	Ben Cohen

BIGGEST MARGINS

Home Win	64pts - 69-5 v Waterloo 13.4.95
Away Win	66pts - 69-3 v Waterloo 28.10.95
Home Defeat	47pts - 3-50 v Lon. Scottish 3.10.87
Away Defeat	60pts - 0-60 v Orrell 27.10.90

MOST CONSECUTIVE

Appearances	31 Frank Packman
Matches scoring Tries	4 Ian Hunter
Matches scoring points	18 Paul Grayson
Victories	20
Defeats	6

MOST POINTS

Scored at Home	69 v Waterloo 13.4.96
Scored Away	69 v Waterloo 28.10.95
Conceded at Home	50 v Lon. Scottish 3.10.87
Conceded Away	60 v Orrell 27.10.90

MOST TRIES

Scored in a match	11 v Blackheath 14.10.95 v Waterloo 28.10.95 & 13.4.96
Conceded in a match	11 v Orrell 27.10.90

MOST APPEARANCES

by a forward	143 (2) Tim Rodber
by a back	132 (10) Harvey Thorneycroft

	MOST IN A SEASON	MOST IN A CAREER	MOST IN A MATCH	
Points	219 Paul Grayson 00-01	1335 Paul Grayson 93-01	26 Paul Grayson	v Bristol 2.10.93 (A)
Tries	20 Matt Allen 95-96	44 Matt Allen 94-01	4 Craig Moir	v Waterloo 13.4.96 (H)
Conversions	76 Paul Grayson 95-96	190 Paul Grayson 93-01	7 Paul Grayson	v Lon. Irish 9.9.95 (H) v Lon. Scottish 4.11.95 (H) v Lon. Scottish 27.4.96 (A)
			Michael Dods	v Blackheath 14.10.95 (H)
Penalties	58 Paul Grayson 00-01	283 Paul Grayson 93-01	7 Paul Grayson	v Richmond 21.2.98 (H) v Leicester 29.04.00 (A)
Drop Goals	4 Paul Grayson 96-97	13 Paul Grayson 93-00	3 John Steele	v Wasps 23.3.91 (A)

PLAYING SQUAD

NORTHAMPTON SAINTS

BACKS

	Ht.	Wt.	Birthdate	Birthplace	CLUB	League Apps	Tries	Pts
Mark Tucker					Northampton	10(3)	4	34
Nick Beal England , A.	6.2	13.08	02.12.70	York	Northampton High Wycombe	115	26	191
Craig Moir Wales U21, Schools.	5.10	14.10	25.10.73	Aberdeen	Northampton	82(8)	17	85
Matt Allen England A, U21.	6.2	15.02	28.02.74	Farnborough	Northampton	115(7)	44	220
Luca Martin	6.1	15.7	25.11.73		Northampton	14(2)	3	15
Harvey Thorneycroft England A, Students, U21,Colts.	6.0	15.11	22.02.69	Northampton	Northampton	133(9)	33	158
Jonathan Sleightholme England , A, Emerging, U21.Other club: Wakefield 38/27/127	5.10	13.05	05.08.72	Malton	Northampton Bath	36 39	5 22	25 110
Matt Dawson England , A,U21, U18, British Lions	5.11	12.10	31.10.72	Birkenhead	Northampton	130(2)	32	411
Paul Grayson England , A, Emerging, U21.Other club: Preston ??/5/265	6.0	12.07	30.05.71	Chorley	Northampton Waterloo	115(9) 10	14 1	1335 126
Ben Cohen	6.3	15.00	14.09.78	Northampton	Northampton	58(3)	19	95
Allan Bateman Wales	5.9	14.00	06.03.65	Maesteg	Northampton Richmond	28 55	1 26	5 130
Alastair Hepher	5.11	13.00	03.10.74	Yardley Gobian	Northampton	46(8)	11	359
Domonic Malone	6.0	15.00	12.12.74	Bedford	Northampton	30(6)	6	30
John Bramhall	5.11	12.06	20.05.78	Northampton	Northampton	11(18)	-	-

FORWARDS

	Ht.	Wt.	Birthdate	Birthplace	CLUB	League Apps	Tries	Pts
Martin Scelzo Argentina	6.4	20.2	05.02.76		Northampton	12(6)	-	-
Mattie Stewart Scotland .	5.11	17.00	18.05.73	Dartford	Northampton Blackheath	70(5) 41	1 2	5 10
Olivier Brouzet France	6.7	18.5	22.11.72		Northampton	16(1)	-	-
Matt Volland England U21.	6.0	16.07	30.06.74	Peterborough	Northampton	52(21)	-	-
Dan Richmond	5.11	16.5	12.02.79		Northampton	2(2)	-	-
Jon Phillips England U21, Colts.	6.6	18.07	16.08.72	Peterborough	Northampton	129(21)	8	40
Steve Thompson	6.2	18.7	15.07.78		Northampton	10(6)	2	10
Adrian Blowers New Zealand					Northampton	14	1	5
Budge Pountney Scotland A, England U21, Students.	6.0	14.10	13.11.74	Southampton	Northampton	112(2)	29	145
Tim Rodber England England ,A, B, U21.	6.6	16.07	02.07.65	Richmond	Northampton	143(3)	19	92
Grant Seely England U21, Students.	6.4	18.04	17.01.73	Aylesbury	Northampton	73(21)	29	145
Gary Pagel South Africa, Western Province	6.1	18.04	17.09.66	South Africa	Northampton	75(2)	10	50
Steve Brotherstone Scotland	6.0	17.0	16.04.71		Northampton	10(4)	-	-
Pat Lam Western Samoa	6.1	15.10	29.09.68	W Samoa	Northampton Newcastle	30(1) 31(2)	5 24	25 120

NORTHAMPTON SAINTS
FACT FILE

Founded: 1880
Nickname: The Saints
Web site: www.northamptonsaints.co.uk

Colours: Black, green, gold hoops
Change colours: Black

GROUND

Address: Franklin's Gardens, Weedon Road, Northampton NN5 5BG
Tel: 01604 751543 Fax: 01604 599110
Capacity: 11,000   Seated Covered: 9,000.   Standing: 2,000

Directions: Take junction 16 from the M1, follow signs to St James' and Town Centre,
turn right at Roiss Road or The Franklin's pub.
Nearest Railway Station: Northampton

Car Parking : 1000 spaces, £3.

Admission: Season   Matchday
Adults   £170-£310   £14-£23
Concessions   £85-£310   £9-£23
Juniors   £85-£310   £7-£23

Club Shop: Manager Jo Norman 01604 599111

Clubhouse: Matchday 12-11 Bar meals & restaurant available
Functions: Rooms for up to 700,
contact Nicola Clark 01604 751543

PROGRAMME

Size: A5
Pages: 64
Price: £2.50
Editor: Caroline Hayden 01604 599125
Advertising Rates
Call 01604 751543 for details

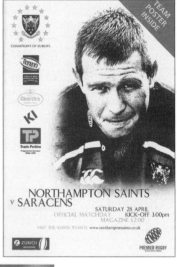

Northampton's new club captain, Budge Pountney, runs at the Wasps defence.

Photo:
Action Images/Aubrey Washington

SALE SHARKS

Chief Executive   Peter Deakin

Rugby Administrator
& Media & PR Manager   Dave Swanton
                             Direct Line: 0161 610 0406
                             email: dave.swanton@salesharks.co.uk

Chairman   Brian Kennedy

c/o Sale Sharks RUFC,
Heywood Road,
Sale M33 3WB
Tel: 0161 283 1861
Fax: 0161 969 4124

The 2000-01 season saw Sale Sharks appoint Alex Sanderson as the youngest skipper in the Zurich Premiership at the age of 20. The biggest pre-season signings were Bryan Redpath (Scotland) and Apollo Perelini who joined the club after helping St. Helens retain their Rugby League Championship.

Bath visited Heywood Road on the opening day of the season and Sale won a thrilling contest 33-32. More success was to follow with a win at Gloucester the following week 19-18. Newcastle Falcons systematically broke down the Sharks at the end of August, but they bounced back with a 36-13 win at Bristol. European Champions Northampton were next to witness the improvement of the Sharks when Sale beat the Saints 34-23.

At the end of September, Leicester Tigers looked to have won the game at Heywood Road, but a Vaughan Going try, Nikki Little conversion and drop goals tied the scores at seventeen all. The down side to Sale's incredible fight back was an injury to skipper Alex Sanderson, who damaged his neck and the required surgery and rehabilitation would keep him out of the game for almost six months.

The European Shield gave little cheer, but on October 17th 2000 Brian Kennedy unveiled his biggest signing when he introduced Jason Robinson to a gathering of media men that filled the Sale clubhouse. Jason made his debut against Coventry in the Tetley's Bitter Cup and crowned an impressive start with a last minute try.

Rotherham visited Heywood Road the following week in the Cup and Sale won a bruising encounter 20-12. The nex two matches at Bath and Wasps saw the Sharks defeated, but they played attractive rugbyon each occason and many believed they were unlucky not to win both games. Steve Hanley scored a second half hat trick of tries.

First Division Waterloo were soundly beaten in the quarter-finals of the cup and the Sharks were mid table and semi- finalists in the cup prior to Christmas. Newcastle beat the Sharks in the semi final although Sale staged a late fight back to bring some respectability to the score at 25-37, but they then bowed out of the European Shield, although they did win 56-31 at Caerphilly in a game that was not for the defensive purists! They also lost five league games on the trot and in Alex Sanderson's come back game he was led off with concussion to add to Sale's problems.

Director of Rugby Adrian Hadley resigned after the Gloucester defeat, Head Coach Glen Ross moved sideways onto player recruitment and two famous Sale old boys, Jim Mallinder and Steve Diamond, were installed as coach and assistant.

Sale stopped the rot with a 36-10 win at Rotherham and, although they lost to Harlequins at the Stoop, they bounced back to defeat London Irish 43-18 on a wet Tuesday night in April. Star of the show was Jason Robinson, who had his best game in Sale colours and he had some British Lions Selection Committee Members sitting in the stand watching his breathtaking display.

Sale went into the last game in eighth place, looking for a play off place, but London Wasps showed they are still a major force in the game when they beat the Sharks 59-29.   Dave Swanton

Apollo Perelini in action against London Wasps.

SALE SHARKS

Comp.	Date	H/A	Opponents	Result & Score	Att	15	14	13	12	11
P1	19-Aug	H	Bath	W 33-32	3785	Going	Moore	Shaw	Deane	Hanley/t
P1	26-Aug	A	Gloucester	W 19-18	5500	Going/t	Moore	Baxendell	Harris	Hanley
P1	2-Sep	H	Newcastle Falcons	L 13-27	2885	Going	Moore	Shaw	Deane	Hanley
P1	6-Sep	A	Bristol	W 36-13	3100	Mallinder	Davidson/t	Baxendell	Harris	Hanley/t
P1	9-Sep	H	Northanpton Saints	W 34-23	1844	Mallinder	Davidson	Deane	Harris	Hanley/2t
P1	16-Sep	H	Saracens	L 6-51	3130	Going	Moore	Deane	Harris	Hanley
P1	24-Sep	A	London Irish	L 13-28	4198	Going	Moore	Deane/t	Harris	Hanley
P1	30-Sep	H	Leicester Tigers	D 17-17	3407	Mallinder	Davidson	Baxendell	Deane	Going/t
P1	19-Nov	A	Bath	L 32-34	7348	Going/2t(a/c)	Moore/t	Baxendell	Harris	Robinson
P1	26-Nov	A	London Wasps	L 24-33	3087	Going	Moore	Baxendell(b/t)	Harris	Robinson
P1	2-Dec	H	Harlequins	W 35-10	2002	Going	Hanley/3t	Shaw	Deane	Robinson/2t
P1	16-Dec	H	Rotherham	W 45-12	2600	Going	Hanley/t	Shaw	Deane	Robinson
P1	23-Dec	H	Bristol	L 25-26	2631	Going/t	Hanley	Shaw	Deane	Robinson
P1	11-Feb	A	Saracens	L 30-44	7115	Going/t	Moore	Shaw	Deane	Robinson
P1	24-Feb	A	Northanpton Saints	L 26-32	7849	Robinson/t	Moore	Baxendell/t	Harris	Hanley
P1	6-Mar	A	Leicester Tigers	L 12-24	9000	Robinson	Moore	Baxendell	Harris	Hanley
P1	11-Mar	A	Newcastle Falcons	L 24-48	3318	Robinson	Moore/t	Baxendell	Harris	Going
P1	17-Mar	H	Gloucester	L 16-24	3514	Robinson/t	Elliott	Baxendell	Harris	Davidson
P1	24-Mar	A	Rotherham	W 39-13	1650	Robinson/t	Elliott/2t	Baxendell/t	Harris	Davidson
P1	31-Mar	A	Harlequins	L 10-36	5039	Robinson	Elliott	Baxendell	Harris	Davidson
P1	10-Apr	H	London Irish	W 43-18	2469	Robinson/t	Hanley/t	Baxendell	Deane	Davidson/2t
P1	14-Apr	H	London Wasps	L 29-59	3877	Robinson/t	Hanley/t	Baxendell	Deane	Davidson/t
ES	7-Oct	A	Auch	L 23-26		Mallinder	Davidson	Shaw	Harris	Going
ES	14-Oct	H	Caerphilly	W 23-14	1500	Going/t	Davidson	Shaw	Deane	Hanley
ES	21-Oct	A	Agen	L 9-44	9000	Mallinder	Davidson	Baxendell	Deane	Hanley
ES	28-Oct	H	Agen	W 28-23	1701	Mallinder	Moore	Baxendell	Deane/t	Davidson
ES	13-Jan	H	Auch	W 39-17	3500	Davidson/tc	Moore	Baxendell	Harris	Elliott/t
ES	20-Jan	A	Caerphilly	W 56-31		Davidson	Moore/2t	Baxendell/t	Harris	Elliott/2t
TBC	5-Nov	H	Coventry	W 37-19		Davidson/t	Moore/t	Baxendell	Deane/t	Robinson/t
TBC	12-Nov	H	Rotherham	W 20-12	2167	Going	Moore/t	Baxendell/t	Shaw	Robinson
TBC	10-Dec	H	Waterloo	W 59-12	2028	Going	Hanley/3t	Shaw/t	Deane/2t	Robinson/t
TBC	6-Jan	A	Newcastle Falcons	L 25-37	6257	Going	Hanley/t	Shaw	Deane	Robinson

* after opponents name indicates a penalty try. Brackets after a player's name indicates he was replaced.
eg (a) means he was replaced by replacement code "a" and so on. / after a player or replacement name
is followed by any scores he made - eg /t, /c, /p, /dg or any combination of these

---

LEAGUE DEBUTS Adam Black, Mel Deane, A Elliott, Vaughan Going, Dan Harris, Charles Hodgson, Bernard Jackman, Scott Lines, Apollo Perelini, Bryan Redpath, Jason Robinson, Norm Rusk, MartinShaw, John Thiel, Andrew Titterell, Richard Wilks.

EVER PRESENT

Most Appearances: 20 Peter Anglesea. 19 Bryan Redpath.

PLAYERS USED 35 plus one as a replacement.

MOST POINTS

Pts	Player	T	C	P	DG
163	N Little	1	19	39	1
141	CHodgson	4	17	29	-
50	S Hanley	10	-	-	-
35	J Robinson	7	-	-	-

MATCH FACTS

10	9	1	2	3	4	5	6	7	8
Little/c7p	Redpath/t	Black	Clark	Thiel	Manson-Bishop	Whittle	Anglesea	Morris	Sanderson
Little/c4p	Hatley	Winstanley	Jackman	Bell	Manson-Bishop	Whittle	Anglesea	Appleyard	Sanderson
Little/c2p	Redpath	Black/t	Clark	Thiel	Manson-Bishop	Whittle	Anglesea	Appleyard	Sanderson
Little/t3c5p	Redpath	Winstanley	Rusk	Thiel	Manson-Bishop	Lines	Anglesea	Morris	Sanderson
Little/4c2p	Redpath	Black	Clark	Thiel	Manson-Bishop/t	Whittle	Anglesea	Morris	Sanderson/t
Little/2p	Redpath	Black	Clark	Thiel	Manson-Bishop	Whittle	Anglesea	Appleyard	Sanderson
Little/p	Redpath	Black	Jackman	Bell	Manson-Bishop	Whittle	Anglesea	Appleyard	Sanderson/t
Little/3pdg	Redpath	Smith	Jackman	Bell	Manson-Bishop	Whittle	Anglesea	Appleyard	Sanderson
Little/2c2p	Hatley	Black	Jackman	Bell	Manson-Bishop/t	Whittle	Anglesea	Lines	Perelini
Little/c4p	Redpath/t	Black	Jackman	Bell	Manson-Bishop	Lines	Anglesea	Wilks	Perelini
Hodgson/c2p(c/c)	Redpath	Black	Jackman	Bell	Manson-Bishop	Whittle	Lines	Anglesea	Perelini
Hodgson/2t2c3p(c/c)	Redpath/t	Black	Jackman	Bell/t	Manson-Bishop	Whittle	Anglesea	Appleyard	Perelini
Hodgson/c4p(c/2p)	Redpath	Black	Jackman	Bell	Manson-Bishop	Fletcher	Anglesea	Appleyard	Perelini
Hodgson/2t3c3p	Redpath	Bell	Titterell	Thiel	Manson-Bishop	Whittle	Lines	Appleyard	Anglesea
Hodgson/2c4p	Redpath	Bell	Titterell	Thiel	Anglesea	Lines	Appleyard	Morris	Perelini
Little/4p	Redpath	Bell	Jackman	Thiel	Manson-Bishop	Lines	Appleyard	Morris	Perelini
Hodgson/cp(c/2c)	Redpath	Bell/t	Jackman	Thiel	Manson-Bishop/t	Lines	Appleyard	Morris	Perelini
Hodgson/c3p	Hatley	Bell	Jackman	Thiel	Lines	Anglesea	Appleyard	Morris	Sanderson
Hodgson/4c2p	Redpath	Black	Jackman	Thiel	Lines/t	Anglesea	Appleyard	Morris	Perelini
Hodgson/p(c/c)	Redpath	Black	Jackman	Thiel	Lines	Anglesea	Appleyard	Morris	Perelini
Hodgson/2c2p(c/p)	Redpath	Black	Titterell/t	Thiel	Baldwin	Lines	Anglesea/t	Sanderson	Perelini
Hodgson/4p(c/c)	Redpath	Black	Titterell	Thiel	Baldwin	Lines	Anglesea	Sanderson	Perelini
Little/c3p(d/c)	Redpath	Winstanley	Jackman	Black	Manson-Bishop/t	Whittle	Lines	Appleyard	Anglesea
Hodgson/3p(c/3p)	Redpath	Black	Rusk	Thiel	Manson-Bishop	Baldwin	Lines	Anglesea	Appleyard
Little/3p	Redpath	Black	Jackman	Thiel	Manson-Bishop	Baldwin	Lines	Anglesea	Appleyard
Little/c7p	Hatley	Bell	Jackman	Black	Manson-Bishop	Whittle	Lines	Wilks	Anglesea
Little/3c2p	Knight/2t	Winstanley	Jackman	Bell	Manson-Bishop	Fletcher	Lines	Morris	Anglesea/t
Hodgson/t5c3p(c/c)	Redpath	Bell	Titterell	Thiel	Manson-Bishop/t	Whittle	Lines	Morris	Anglesea
Little/4c3p	Hatley	Bell	Jackman	Black	Manson-Bishop	Whittle	Lines	Appleyard	Perelini
Little/2c2p	Hatley	Bell	Jackman	Thiel	Lines	Whittle	Anglesea	Appleyard	Perelini
Hodgson/8cp	Redpath	Black/t	Jackman	Bell	Manson-Bishop	Whittle	Lines	Appleyard	Perelini
Hodgson/tc2p(c/c)	Redpath	Black	Clark	Thiel	Manson-Bishop	Whittle	Anglesea	Appleyard	Perelini

REPLACEMENTS a - S Davidson b - Deane c - N Little d - C Hodgson

Most replacement appearances: 10 - N Little. 9 - R Wilks.
Most times replaced: 11 A Black. 9 - C Hodgson, G Manson-Bishop.

2000-01 HIGHLIGHTS

Nicky Little topped the points scorers for the second successive season.

He started the season as first choice but by the end had to settle for a part as a second half replacement for the promising Charles Hodgson.

England's out of favour winger Steven Hanley topped the Sale try scoring list for the third straight season. He scored his 10 tries in just 14 appearances to keep up his exceptional scoring ratio.

In their final league game of the season they suffered their worst ever score against in a home league match. London Wasps scored 59 points to add one to the 58 that Saracens scored back in October 1999.

SALE SHARKS

LEAGUE STATISTICS
compiled by Stephen McCormack

SEASON	Division	P	W	D	L	F	A	Pts Diff	Lge Pts	Lge Pos	Most Points		Most Tries
91-92	2	12	6	0	6	204	209	-5	12	8	79	Matthew Alexander	5 Jim Mallinder
92-93	2	12	7	1	4	237	102	35	15	5	63	Phil Jee	7 Mark Warr
93-94	2	18	13	2	3	438	160	278	28	1	144	Paul Turner	16 Simon Verbickas
94-95	1	18	7	2	9	327	343	+16	16	4	92	Paul Turner	5 Gareth Stocks & Jim Mallender
95-96	1	18	9	1	8	365	371	-6	19	5	167	Rob Liley	6 Jos Baxendall
96-97	1	22	13	2	7	603	525	78	28	5	150	Simon Mannix	13 Tim Beim
97-98	1	22	10	22	10	605	558	47	22	6	227	Shane Howarth	14 Tim Beim
98-99	1	26	9	1	16	604	731	-127	19	11	246	Shane Howarth	12 Steven Hanley
99-00	1	22	7	0	15	381	633	-252	18	11	101	Nicky Little	6 Steven Hanley
00-01	1	22	8	1	13	561	622	-61	43	10	163	Nicky Little	10 Steven Hanley

BIGGEST MARGINS

Home Win 79pts - 88-9 v Otley 12.2.94

Away Win 32pts - 40-8 v Orrell 18.1.97

Home Defeat 46pts - 12-58 v Saracens 29.10.99

Away Defeat 77pts - 7-84 v Bath 26.4.97

MOST CONSECUTIVE

Appearances 39 Phillip Stansfield 22.10.88-14.3.92

Matches scoring Tries 8 Simon Verbickas

Matches scoring points 18 Shane Howarth

Victories 7

Defeats 11

MOST POINTS

Scored at Home 88 v Otley 12.2.94

Scored Away 50 v Bedfordl 14.5.00

Conceded at Home 58 v Saracens 29.10.99

Conceded Away 84 v Bath 26.4.97

MOST TRIES

Scored in a match 14 v Otley 12.2.94 (H)

Conceded in a match 12 v Harlequins 23.4.88 (A)
v Bath 24.4.97 (A)

MOST APPEARANCES

by a forward 149 (15) Dave Baldwin

by a back 165 (2) Jim Mallinder

	MOST IN A SEASON	MOST IN A CAREER	MOST IN A MATCH	
Points	246 Shane Howarth 97-98	473 Shane Howarth 97-99	27 Simon Mannix	v Northampton 9.3.97 (H)
Tries	16 Simon Verbickas 93-94	38 Jim Mallinder 88-00	5 Simon Verbickas	v Otley 12.2.94 (H)
Conversions	42 Shane Howarth 98-99	55 Paul Turner 92-96	9 Paul Turner	v Otley 12.2.94 (H)
Penalties	41 Shane Howarth 97-98	47 Paul Turner 92-96	7 Simon Mannix Shane Howarth Nicky Little	v Northampton 9.3.97 (H) v Wasps 18.4.98 (H) v Bath 19.8.00 (H)
Drop Goals	4 Paul Turner 95-96	13 Paul Turner 92-96	2 David Pears Paul Turner	v Bedford 22.2.89 (H) v Morley 3.10.92 (H) v Wakefield 9.4.94 (A) v Orrell 6.1.96 (H)

PLAYING SQUAD

SALE SHARKS

BACKS

	Ht.	Wt.	Birthdate	Birthplace	CLUB	League Apps	Tries	Pts
Jim Mallinder England 2, A, North, Yorkshire.	6.3	16.00	16.03.66	Halifax	Sale Roundhay	169(2)	38	184
Charles Hodgson	5.10	12.10	12.01.80		Sale	11	4	141
Stephen Hanley England 1,A, U21, 18.	6.3	16.00	11.06.79	Whitehaven	Sale Aspatria	38(1) 21	28 20	140 100
Matt Moore	5.11	13.00	02.04.76	Frimley	Sale	62(2)	20	100
Jos Baxendell England 2, A, North, U21.	6.0	14.04	03.12.71	Manchester	Sale Sheffield	131(2)	22	110
Jason Robinson England, British Lions			30.07.74		Sale	14	7	35
Nicky Little Fiji. North Harbour	6.0	15.0	13.09.76		Sale	25(10)	5	242
Dan Harris Other club: Moseley 33/7/35	5.10	15.0	17.05.77		Sale Bedford	13(4) 26(1)	1 2	5 10
Paul Knight Gloucestershire, U21, Colts	5.11	14.00	26.03.77	Gloucester	Sale	1(11)	2	19
Steven Davidson North colts, Cumbria	6.2	16.00	28.04.76	Whitehaven	Sale Aspatria	34(8)	10	125
Bryan Redpath Scotland.	5.8	13.9	21.07.71		Sale	19(1)	3	15

FORWARDS

	Ht.	Wt.	Birthdate	Birthplace	CLUB	League Apps	Tries	Pts
Duncan Bell England U18.	6.2	18.00	01.10.74	Kings Lynn	Sale	54(22)	4	20
Phil Winstanley North, Lancashire.	5.11	16.10	16.09.68	Orrell	Sale Orrell	42(24) 36(2)	6 3	30 18
Pete Anglesea	6.3	16.6	30.10.71		Sale	62(3)	4	20
Adam Black	6.2	19.0	24.05.75		Sale Bedford	14(7) 14(3)	1 -	5 -
Andy Whittle	6.6	17.4	21.07.75		Sale	19(5)	-	-
Dave Baldwin England A, Barbarians, Yorkshire, North.	6.6	19.04	03.09.65	Ilkley	Sale Wakefield	151(22) 11	15 -	74 -
Bernard Jackman	6.1	17.0	05.05.76		Sale	13(7)	-	-
John Thiel	6.1	17.8	31.05.75		Sale	14(3)	-	-
Alex Sanderson England U16, U18	6.3	15.06	07.10.79	Chester	Sale	44(5)	6	30
Scott Lines	6.5	16.7	28.07.73		Sale Bristol	13(7)	1	5
Apollo Perelini Other clubs: St Helens RL			16.07.69		Sale	12(2)	-	-
Paul Smith	6.1	17.00	28.03.69	Nantwich	Sale	70(1)	-	-
Robert Appleyard	6.2	16.4	09.12.72		Sale	22(5)	-	-
Guy Manson-Bishop Natal, U21, Barbarians	6.7	19.00	03.08.73	Dundee (SA)	Sale	36(3)	5	25

SALE SHARKS

FACT FILE

Founded: 1861

Colours: Royal blue shirt with navy band
Change colours: Black with green band

Web site: www.salesharks.co.uk

GROUND

Address: Heywood Road, Sale, Cheshire M33 3WB
Tel: 0161 283 1861   Fax: 0161 969 4124   email: enquiries@salesharks.co.uk
Capacity: 4,800   Seated: 2,254   Standing: 2,546

Directions: M6 J19, take A556/A56 for approx 8 miles. Turn right into Marsland Rd and Heywood Rd is on the right after 800m. M60 J6, take A6144. Old Hall Rd/Marsland Rd, Heywood Rd on left after 1.5 miles from J6.
Nearest Railway Station: Brooklands Metrolink, left out of station into Marsland Rd. & Heywood Rd is 200m on the right.

Car Parking: None on ground, 100 spaces nearby

Admission:

		Adults	Concessions	Sale Subs	Family
Season	Seated	£169	£100	£75	
	Standing	£ 124	£65	£35	
Matchday	Seated	£17	£12	£9	£38
	Standing	£13	£ 7	£4	£28

Club Shop: 12-5 matchdays, 9-5 weekdays.
0161 610 0407

Clubhouse: Mon-Fri 7-11, Sat 11-11, Sun 12-3
Matchdays 12-11.
Snacks available   Functions: Up to 150
Contact Tracy Grady on 0161 610 0409

MATCHDAY MAGAZINE
Size: B5 Pages: 40 full colour

LEFT: Dave Baldwin, who retired at the end of the season with over 150 league appearances for Sale, leads the side out against London Wasps.

SARACENS FC

SARACENS

Vicarage Road Stadium
Vicarage Road
Watford
Herts. WD1 8ER

Tel: 01923 4475222

Managing Director	Tim Lawler
Commercial Manager	Tom Hill
Office Manager	Jon Salinger
Team Admin. Manager	Hannah Wyatt
Financial Controller	Damian Slevin
	01923 204604
Brand & Media Director	Robin Bye
Media Manager	Matt Jones
	01923 204616
	07713 684429

With Sarries it was a case of plenty of good-hearted effort in a strong league and two cup competitions with nothing tangible to show at the end of the season in terms of top honours, although a Premier position of fifth and a Tetley's Bitter Cup quarter-final place hardly denoted failure.

The Premier campaign was a story of boom followed by bust followed by boom - and so on. After eight matches there had been six victories, but the next eight saw two wins and six losses! A run-in of four successes from six outings meant a top half final position and European competition (albeit the Shield) again in 2001-02. Doubles were achieved over Bristol, Sale and Harlequins and conceded to Wasps and Northampton.

The Tetley's Bitter Cup involved three fixtures starting with a comfortable 54-24 victory at Bedford, followed by a 42-13 thumping of ambitious Worcester at Vicarage Road, but a visit to Leicester and a 41-24 defeat in the quarter-finals ended the affair on 9th December.

A brave attempt to qualify for the latter stages of the European Cup was foiled by Cardiff, who won both Pool matches, while a trip to Franklin's Gardens in the Zurich play-offs brought an abrupt end to any hopes in that direction - a massive 45-17 success for the Saints.

Stars for the club might have included Frenchman Thomas Castaijnede, but an injury in November ended his season. So the back-play relied on McRae, Sorrell and Dan Luger for inspiration, with scrum-half Bracken as consistent as ever as he played in every match.

The forwards had excellent front-row players in Flatman (capped in North America by England), Russell and White, while any club that includes Murray, Davison, Rogues, Hill and Diprose in its back five (not to mention the superb Chesney) has few problems in that direction.

The headache now is that with Diprose already departed how many more players will be tempted by better financial offers from elsewhere by clubs, whose bank managers do not mind insolvency and spending of non-existent funds, which they hope to supplement through promised sponsorship.

The bubble must burst some day and Saracens must make sure that they do not explode with it.

Bill Mitchell

Thomas Castaignede, who scored
130 points in his 7 league games.

SARACENS

Comp.	Date	H/A	Opponents	Result & Score	Att	15	14	13	12	11
P1	20-Aug	H	Gloucester	W 50-20	7682	Castaignede/4c4p	Luger/t	Johnston/t	Sorrell/t	O'Mahony
P1	26-Aug	A	Bristol	W 34-23	4280	Sparg	Luger	Johnston	Sorrell	O'Mahony/t
P1	2-Sep	A	London Irish	L 22-27	7312	Castaignede/tc4pdg	Luger	Johnston	Sorrell	O'Mahony
P1	6-Sep	H	London Wasps	L 24-30	7312	Castaignede/2p	O'Mahony	Johnston/t	Sorrell	Luger
P1	10-Sep	H	Leicester Tigers	W 17-9	13021	Castaignede/4p	Sparg	Johnston	Sorrell	Luger
P1	16-Sep	A	Sale	W 51-6	3130	Castaignede/2t4cp	Sparg/t	Johnston(a/t)	Sorrell	Luger
P1	24-Sep	H	Rotherham	W 59-5	6092	Castaignede/2t5c3p	O'Mahony	Johnston	Sorrell	Luger/3t
P1	30-Sep	A	Bath	W 33-21	8240	Castaignede/c7p	O'Mahony/t	Johnston	Sorrell/t	Luger
P1	18-Nov	A	Gloucester	L 15-16	5909	Arasa	Shanklin	Horan	Johnston	O'Mahony
P1	26-Nov	A	Newcastle Falcons	L 27-32	5473	Arasa/2t	Haughten	Johnston	Shanklin	O'Mahony
P1	3-Dec	H	Northampton Saints	10-30	10483	Sparg	Arasa(b/t)	Johnston	Shanklin	O'Mahony
P1	17-Dec	H	Harlequins	W 26-18	7681	Sparg	Haughten	Shanklin	Sorrell/7p	Luger/t
P1	23-Dec	A	London Wasps	L 6-25	7835	Sparg	Johnston	Shanklin	Sorrell/2p	Luger
P1	27-Dec	A	Harlequins	W 30-14	5089	Sparg	Shanklin	Horan/t	Sorrell/t2c2p	Luger/t
P1	30-Dec	H	Bath	L 11-31	11193	Sparg	Shanklin	Horan	Sorrell/2p	Luger
P1	6-Jan	A	Rotherham	L 8-19	3500	Sorrell/p	Sparg	Shanklin	Johnston	Luger
P1	11-Feb	H	Sale	W 44-30	7115	Sparg	Shanklin/t	Horan/t	Sorrell/4c2p	O'Mahony/t
P1	24-Feb	A	Leicester Tigers	L 15-56	14212	Sparg	Haughten/t	Horan	Sorrell	O'Mahony/t
P1	11-Mar	H	London Irish	W 35-22	7913	Sparg	Haughten/t	Sorrell/p	Horan/t(a/t)	O'Mahony/t
P1	18-Mar	H	Bristol	W 24-13	12843	Sparg	Haughten	Horan	Sorrell/t	O'Mahony
P1	31-Mar	A	Northampton Saints	14-25	9424	Sparg	Haughten	Sorrell	Horan	Arasa
P1	15-Apr	H	Newcastle Falcons	W 34-29	10107	Sparg	O'Mahony	Arasa	Johnston(e/t)	Horan
EC	7-Oct	A	Toulouse	W 32-22	10000	Castaignede/2c4p2dg	O'Mahony/t	Johnston	Sorrell	Luger
EC	15-Oct	H	Ulster	W 55-25	11258	Castaignede/5c5p	O'Mahony	Johnston	Sorrell	Luger/3t
EC	21-Oct	H	Cardiff	L 23-32	10824	Castaignede/2cp	Sparg	Johnston	Sorrell/t	Luger
EC	27-Oct	A	Cardiff	L 14-24		Castaignede/3p	Sparg	Johnston	Sorrell/t	Luger
EC	14-Jan	H	Toulouse	W 37-30	8461	Sparg/t	O'Mahony	Shanklin	Sorrell/t	Luger
EC	19-Jan	A	Ulster		13500	Sparg	O'Mahony	Shanklin	Sorrell	Luger
TBC	4-Nov	A	Bedford	W 54-24	3012	Sparg/t	O'Mahony/2t	Horan/t	Sorrell	Arasa
TBC	12-Nov	H	Worcester	W 42-13	5183	Arasa/t	Shanklin/t	Horan/t	Johnston/t	O'Mahony/t
TBC	9-Dec	A	Leicester Tigers	L 24-41	10007	Sparg	O'Mahony	Shanklin/t	Sorrell	Luger/t
PO	28-Apr	A	Northampton Saints	L 17-45	8500	Sparg	O'Mahony/2t	Horan	Johnston	Luger

*after opponents name indicates a penalty try. Brackets after a player's name indicates he was replaced.
eg (a) means he was replaced by replacement code "a" and so on. / after a player or replacement name
is followed by any scores he made - eg /t, /c, /p, /dg or any combination of these*

LEAGUE DEBUTS

Gerald Arasa, Thomas Castaignede, Jannie De Beer, Luke Harbut, Richard Haughton, Tim Horan, Duncan McRae, James Parkes, Sean Phillips, Kieran Roche, Robbie Russell, Tom Shanklin.

EVER PRESENT

Most Appearances: 21: Kris Chesney. 20 Tony Diprose (2).

PLAYERS USED

30 plus 3 as replacement only.

MOST POINTS

Pts	Player	T	C	P	DG
133	T Castaignede	5	15	25	1
104	D McRae	4	12	17	3
83	K Sorrell	4	6	17	-
30	D Luger	6	-	-	-

MATCH FACTS

10	9	1	2	3	4	5	6	7	8
McRae	Bracken/t	Wallace	Cairns	White	Davison/t	Murray/t	Chesney	Hill	Diprose
McRae/t2c5p	Bracken	Wallace	Cairns	White	Murray	Davison	Chesney/t	Hill	Diprose
McRae	Bracken	Flatman	Cairns	White	Murray	Grewcock	Hill	Roques	Chesney
McRae/c2p	Bracken	Flatman	Cairns	White	Murray	Davison	Hill	Roques	Diprose/t
McRae/t	Bracken	Flatman	Cairns	Wallace	Murray	Grewcock	Hill	Chesney	Diprose
McRae/t	Bracken	Wallace/t	Cairns	White	Davison/t	Murray/t	Hill	Chesney	Diprose
McRae	Bracken/t	Flatman	Russell	Wallace/t	Grewcock	Davison	Hill/t	Chesney	Diprose
McRae	Bracken	Flatman	Russell	Wallace	Grewcock	Murray	Chesney	Hill	Diprose
McRae/cp	Walshe	Wallace/t	Russell/t	White	Davison	Roche	Chesney	Roques	Diprose
McRae/3c2p	Walshe	Phillips	Russell	Wallace	Davison	Murray/t	Chesney	Roques	Diprose
McRae/cp	Walshe	Harbut	Russell	Phillips	Davison	Murray	Chesney	Roques	Diprose
Horan	Bracken	Harbut	Russell	Flatman	Davison	Grewcock	Chesney	Roques	Hill
Horan	Bracken	Flatman	Russell	Wallace	Roche	Murray	Chesney	Hill	Diprose
Walshe	Bracken	Flatman	Russell	Wallace	Murray	Roche	Chesney	Hill	Diprose/t
Walshe	Bracken	Flatman	Russell	Wallace	Roche	Murray	Chesney	Hill/t	Diprose
Walshe	Bracken	Wallace	Russell	White	Murray	Davison	Chesney	Roche	Diprose/t
Walshe	Bracken	Flatman	Russell	White	Murray	Grewcock/t	Chesney	Hill/t	Diprose
McRae/cdg	Walshe	Flatman	Cairns	White	Murray	Grewcock	Chesney	Hill	Diprose
McRae/2cdg	Bracken	Flatman	Parkes	White	Davison	Grewcock	Chesney	Hill(d/t)	Diprose
McRae/c4p	Bracken	Flatman	Parkes	White/t	Davison	Grewcock	Chesney	Hill	Diprose
McRae/t2pdg	Bracken	Flatman	Parkes	White	Davison	Murray	Chesney	Hill	Diprose
De Beer/2c3p2dg	Bracken	Flatman/t	Russell	White	Davison	Murray	Hill	Chesney	Diprose/t
McRae	Bracken	Flatman	Russell	Wallace	Murray/t	Grewcock	Chesney	Hill	Diprose
McRae/t	Bracken	Flatman	Russell	Wallace	Davison	Grewcock	Chesney	Hill/2t	Diprose
McRae/2p	Bracken/t	Flatman	Russell	Wallace	Murray	Grewcock	Chesney	Hill	Diprose
McRae	Bracken	Flatman	Russell	White	Murray	Grewcock	Chesney	Hill	Diprose
McRae/4c3p	Bracken	Flatman	Russell	White	Murray/t	Davison(f/t)	Chesney	Hill	Diprose
McRae	Bracken	Flatman	Russell	Wallace	Murray	Grewcock	Chesney	Hill	Diprose
McRae/t7c	Walshe	Flatman/t	Cairns	White	Davison	Grewcock	Chesney	Roques/t	Diprose/t
McRae/6c	Bracken	Flatman	Russell	White	Davison	Grewcock	Chesney	Roques/t	Diprose
McRae/p(g/3c)	Bracken	Flatman	Russell	White	Murray	Grewcock	Diprose	Roques/t	Hill
De Beer/c	Bracken/t	Harbut	Russell	Flatman	Davison	Murray	Hill	Roques	Diprose

REPLACEMENTS　　a - G Arasa　　b - R Haighton　　c - M Cairns　　d - Roques　　e - T Shanklin　　f - K Roche　　g - N Walshe

Most replacement appearances in the league: 9 - Roques. 7 - M Cairns. 6 - K Roche.

Most times replaced: 7 - T Diprose, D Flatman, R Hill

2000-01 HIGHLIGHTS

Summer signing Thomas Castaignede started the season impressively but an injury in early November put paid to his season.

In his seven league matches he rattled up over 130 points and was well on the way to a record breaking first season in English rugby.

Saracens failed to score enough tries in the league and that was highlighted by the fact that Dan Luger finished leading try scorer with just six tries.

Their 59-5 home win against Rotherham was both the biggest score and biggest winning margin.

At the other end of the scale the 56 points they conceded at Leicester was a record for an away match.

SARACENS

LEAGUE STATISTICS
compiled by Stephen McCormack

SEASON	Division	P	W	D	L	F	A	Pts Diff	Lge Pts	Lge Pos		Most Points		Most Tries
91-92	1	12	7	1	4	176	165	11	15	5	91	Ben Rudling	4	Martin Gregory
92-93	1	12	3	0	9	137	180	-43	6	11	43	Ben Rudling	3	Daren O'Leary & Barry Crawley
93-94	2	18	11	1	6	299	238	61	23	3	149	Andy Tunningley	5	Richard Hill & Andy Tunningley
94-95	2	18	15	1	2	389	213	176	31	1	162	Andy Tunningley	7	John Green
95-96	1	18	5	0	13	284	451	-167	10	9	126	Andy Lee	4	Peter Harries
96-97	1	22	12	1	9	568	449	119	25	7	125	Michael Lynagh	9	Richard Wallace
97-98	1	22	18	1	3	584	484	100	37	2	279	Michael Lynagh	8	Richard Wallace
98-99	1	26	16	1	9	748	583	165	33	3	318	Gavin Johnson	12	Brandon Daniel
99-00	1	22	14	0	8	729	514	215	37	4	280	Thierry Lacroix	12	Ryan Constable
00-01	1	22	12	0	10	589	501	88	58	5	133	TCastaignede	6	Dan Luger

BIGGEST MARGINS

Home Win 49pts - 55-6 v Newcastle 17.10.99

Away Win 46pts - 58-12 v Sale 29.10.99

Home Defeat 43pts - 6-49 v Bath 27.4.91

Away Defeat 49pts - 3-52 v Sale 18.9.93

MOST POINTS

Scored at Home 56 v Sale 12.3.00

Scored Away 58 v Sale 29.10.99

Conceded at Home 49 v Bath 27.4.91

Conceded Away 52 v Sale 18.9.93

MOST CONSECUTIVE

Appearances 68 Brian Davies

Matches scoring Tries 6 Dave McLagen

Matches scoring points 20 Michael Lynagh/Thierry Lacroix

Victories 17

Defeats 7

MOST TRIES

Scored in a match 9 v Gosforth 22.4.89

v Bedford 16.04.00

Conceded in a match 9 v Sale 18.9.93

MOST APPEARANCES

by a forward 165(2) Tony Diprose

by a back 106 John Buckton

	MOST IN A SEASON	MOST IN A CAREER	MOST IN A MATCH	
Points	318 Gavin Johnson 98-99	462 Andy Tunningley 90-97	30 Ryan Constable	v Bedford 16.4.00 (A)
Tries	12 Brandon Daniel 98-99 Ryan Constable 99-00	30 Tony Diprose 94-00	6 Ryan Constable	v Bedford 16.4.00 (A)
Conversions	52 Gavin Johnson 98-99	53 Michael Lynagh 96-98	6 Gavin Johnson Thierry Lacroix	v Lon Scot 26.9.98 (A) v Newcastle 17.10.99 (H) v Sale 29.10.99 (A) v Bedford 16.04.00 (A)
Penalties	58 Michael Lynagh 97-98 Gavin Johnson 98-99	92 Andy Tunningley 90-97	9 Thierry Lacroix	v Wasps 27.11.99 (H)
Drop Goals	6 Andy Lee 94-95	16 Andy Lee 89-95	2 Andy Lee	v Wasps 22.2.92 (A) v Lon. Scottish 5.11.94 (H) v W. Hartlepool 14.10.95 (H)
			Ben Rudling Gareth Hughes	v Lon. Irish 11.4.92 (H) v Bath 24.4.93 (H)

PLAYING SQUAD

SARACENS

BACKS

	Ht.	Wt.	Birthdate	Birthplace	CLUB	League Apps	Tries	Pts
Gerald Asara	5.9	13.4	21.12.80		Saracens	5(4)	4	20
Duncan McRae	5.10	13.2	27.09.74		Saracens	15	4	104
Dan Luger England	6.1	14.00	11.01.75	Chiswick	Saracens Harlequins	13(1) 43	6 19	30 95
Thomas Castaignede France.	5.9	12.7	21.10.75		Saracens	7	5	133
Darragh O'Mahoney Ireland. Other club: Moseley 33/32/160	5.11	11.00	18.08.72	Cork	Saracens Bedford	35(5) 23	16 11	80 55
Ben Johnston	6.3	15.3	08.11.78		Saracens	27(2)	5	25
Nick Walshe England students. Other clubs: Rosslyn Park 23/2/10	5.10	13.00	01.11.73	Chiswick	Saracens Harlequins	21(7) 30(8)	2 7	10 39
Kyran Bracken England , U18, U16.	5.11	12.10	22.11.71	Dublin	Saracens Bristol	73(2) 47	9 7	45 35
Tom Shanklin Wales	6.1	14.2	24.11.79		Saracens	9(1)	2	10
Kevin Sorrell England A, U18.	6.0	12.08	06.03.77	Harold Wood	Saracens	54(7)	11	118
Jannie de Beer South Africa				South Africa	Saracens	1	-	19
Brett Sparg	6.0	12.10	21.03.78		Saracens	16(7)	1	5

FORWARDS

	Ht.	Wt.	Birthdate	Birthplace	CLUB	League Apps	Tries	Pts
Julian White England	6.1	19.00	14.05.73		Saracens	32(5)	3	15
Paul Wallace Ireland , British Lions 3.	6.0	16.00	30.12.71	Cork	Saracens	75(12)	13	65
Bill Davison	6.6	16.8	08.04.69		Saracens	25(3)	3	15
Scott Murray Scotland	6.6	16.07	15.01.76	Musselburgh	Saracens Bedford	25(3) 57	- 7	- 35
David Flatman	6.0	17.07	20.01.80	Maidstone	Saracens	38(11)	4	20
Matt Cairns	5.10	14.00	31.03.79	Birkenhead	Saracens	8(15)	1	5
Robert Russell Scotland.	5.10	14.06	01.05.76	Brisbane	Saracens	14(4)	1	5
Danny Grewcock England , A, Students.	6.6	17.07	07.11.72	Coventry	Saracens Coventry	60(3) 31	5 3	25 15
Richard Hill England, British Lions 2.	6.3	15.13	23.05.73	Dormansland	Saracens	120(2)	26	130
Tony Diprose England .	6.5	17.08	22.09.72	Orsett	Saracens	163(3)	34	170

SARACENS

FACT FILE

Founded: 1876
Nickname: Sarries
Web site: www.saracens.com

Colours: Black, with red shoulders/black/red
Change colours: Black, red and white

GROUND

Address: Vicarage Road Stadium, Vicarage Road, Watford. WD1 8ER
Tel: 01923 475222   Fax: 01923 475275
e-mail: general@saracens.net
Capacity: 22,000 - all covered seating

Directions: M1, junct. 6. Follow signs for Watford town centre, then signs for Watford Hospital next to ground
Nearest Railway Station: Watford Junction, 15-20 mins walk
Underground Watford Metropolitan station, 10-15 mins walk
Car Parking: No public parking available at the ground. There are several multi-storey car parks nearby.

Admission: (all covered seating)   Season   Adults £99-499   Concessions £25-£65
                                    Matchday   Adults £10-35   Concessions £5

Club Shop: Mon-Sat 9-5, Matchday 11-5. Contact 01923 229859

Clubhouse: Bramley Sports Ground, Chase Side, London N14 4AB. Snacks & restaurant available.
Functions: Contact Beeton Rumford Catering

PROGRAMME Size: B5   Pages: 64   Price: £2.50   Editor: Robin Bye
                  Advertising: Contact Commercial Department

Kyran Bracken

RECORDS SECTION

DIVISION ONE
(CURRENTLY ZURICH PREMIERSHIP ONE)

THE LAST TEN YEARS — DIVISION ONE

1991-92
Wasps — Champions
Runners-up Gloucester
Relegated Bedford
Most Penalties: 28 John Steele (Northampton)
Points: 125 John Liley (Leicester)
Conversions: 19 John Liley (Leicester)
Tries: 9 Rory Underwood (Leicester)
D.Gs: 2 Hugh Davies (Wasps)

1992-93
Bath — Champions
Runners-up Wasps
Relegated Saracens, Lon. Scottish, West Hartlepool, Rugby
Most Penalties: 31 Michael Corcoran (Lon. Irish)
Points: 122 Jon Webb (Bath)
Conversions: 19 Jon Webb (Bath)
Tries: 7 Stuart Barnes (Bath)
D.Gs: 6 Paul Burke (Lon. Irish)

1993-94
Bath — Champions
Runners-up Leicester
Relegated London Irish, Newcastle Gosforth
Most Penalties: 41 Jez Harris (Leicester)
Points: 202 Jez Harris (Leicester)
Conversions: 25 Jonathon Callard (Bath)
Tries: 11 Daren O'Leary (Harlequins)
D.Gs: 11 Jez Harris (Leicester)

1994-95
Leicester — Champions
Runners-up Bath
Relegated Northampton
Most Penalties: 56 Mark Tainton (Bristol)
Points: 196 Mark Tainton (Bristol)
Conversions: 19 Rob Andrew (Wasps)
Tries: 8 Paul Holford (Gloucester)
D.Gs: 13 Jez Harris (Leicester)

1995-96
Bath — Champions
Runners-up Leicester
Most Penalties: 64 John Liley (Leicester)
Points: 272 John Liley (Leicester)
Conversions: 43 Jonathon Callard (Bath)
Tries: 14 Daren O'Leary (Harlequins)
D.Gs: 7 David Pears (Harlequins)

1996-97
Wasps — Champions
Runners-up Bath
Relegated Orrell, West Hartlepool
Most Penalties: 62 Gareth Rees (Wasps)
Points: 291 Gareth Rees (Wasps)
Conversions: 51 Jonathon Callard (Bath)
Tries: 16 Adedayo Adebayo (Bath)
D.Gs: 6 Alex King (Wasps)

1997-98
Newcastle — Champions
Runners-up Saracens
Relegated Bristol (play-off)
Most Penalties: 58 Mark Mapletoft (Gloucester)
Points: 279 Michael Lynagh (Saracens)
Conversions: 44 Rob Andrew (Newcastle)
Tries: 17 Dominic Chapman (Richmond)
D.Gs: 4 David Humphreys (Lon. Irish)

1998-99
Leicester — Champions
Runners-up Northampton
Relegated West Hartlepool
Most Penalties: 77 John Schuster (Harlequins)
Points: 331 John Schuster (Harlequins)
Conversions: 52 Gavin Johnson (Saracens)
Tries: 16 Neil Back (Leicester)
D.Gs: 6 Jannie de Beer (Lon. Scottish)

99-2000
Leicester — Champions
Runners-up Bath
Relegated Bedford
Most Penalties: 66 Jarrod Cunningham (Lon. Irish)
Points: 324 Jarrod Cunningham (Lon. Irish)
Conversions: 52 Tim Stimpson (Leicester)
Tries: 15 Ian Balshaw (Bath)
D.Gs: 5 Alex King (Wasps)

2000-01
Leicester — Champions
Runners-up London Wasps
Relegated Rotherham
Most Penalties: 58 Paul Grayson (Northampton)
Points: 282 Kenny Logan (Lon. Wasps)
Conversions: 47 Kenny Logan (Lon. Wasps)
Tries: 11 Paul Sampson (Lon. Wasps)
D.Gs: 3 Jonny Wilkinson (Newcastle)

ALL TIME RECORDS — TEAM RECORDS — DIVISION ONE

Highest score:	106	Bedford 12 Richmond 106. 16.5.99
Highest aggregate:	118	As above
Highest score by a losing side:	41	London Irish 52 W Hartlepool 41. 28.12.96
Highest scoring draw:	38	Bath 38 v Sale 38 27.4.96
Most consecutive wins:	17	Bath 1993-94 through 1994-95
Most consecutive defeats:	18	West Hartlepool 1995-96
Most points for in a season:	863	Bath 1996-97
Least points for in a season:	70	Bedford 1989-90
Most points against in a season:	1007	West Hartlepool 1998-99
Least points against in a season:	95	Orrell 1991-92
Most tries for in a season:	116	Bath 1996-97
Most tries against in a season:	134	W Hartlepool 1998-99
Least tries for in a season:	8	Waterloo 1988-89
Least tries against in a season:	6	Bath 1988-89, Wasps 1992-93
Most conversions for in a season:	77	Bath 1996-97
Most conversions against in a season:	69	Orrell 1996-97
Least conversions for in a season:		
Least conversions against in a season:		
Most penalties for in a season:	87	Harlequins 1998-99
Most penalties against in a season:	73	Sale 1998-99
Least penalties for in a season:	7	Bedford 1989-90
Least penalties against in a season:	11	Harlequins 1987-88
Most drop goals for in a season:	13	Leicester 1994-95 & Harlequins 1995-96
Most drop goals against in a season:	8	Wasps 1993-94 & 1995-96

ALL TIME RECORDS — INDIVIDUAL RECORDS — DIVISION ONE

Most points in a season:	331	John Schuster (Harlequins) 1998-99
Most tries in a season:	17	Dominic Chapman (Richmond) 1997-98
Most conversions in a season:	52	Gavin Johnson (Saracens) 1998-99 & Tim Stimpson (Leicester) 1990-00
Most penalties in a season:	77	John Schuster (Harlequins) 1998-99
Most drop goals in a season:	13	Jez Harris (Leicester) 1994-95
Most points in a match:	32	Niall Woods, *London Irish* v Harlequins 25.4.98
Most tries in a match:	6	Ryan Constable, Bedford v *Saracens* 16.4.00
Most conversions in a match:	13	Rich Butland, Bedford v *Richmond* 16.5.99
Most penalties in a match:	9	Thierry Lacroix, *Saracens* v Wasps 7.11.99
Most drop goals in a match:	3	John Steele, *Northampton* v Wasps 23.3.91
		Jez Harris, *Leicester* v Wasps 23.11.91
		David Pears, *Harlequins* v Wasps 16.9.95
		Matthew McCarthy, *Orrell* v W Hartlepool 7.12.96

ALL TIME RECORDS — MOST POINTS IN A SEASON — DIVISION ONE

Points	Player	Club	Season	Tries	Cons.	Pens.	D.G.
331	John Schuster	Harlequins	1998-99	5	36	77	1
324	Jarrod Cunningham	London Irish	99-2000	6	46	66	
321	Tim Stimpson	Leicester	99-2000	5	52	63	1
318	Gavin Johnson	Saracens	1998-99	8	52	58	
306	Jonny Wilkinson	Newcastle	1998-99	9	51	53	
294	Mike Catt	Bath	1998-99	7	50	53	
291	Gareth Rees	Wasps	1996-97	3	45	62	
282	Simon Mannix	Gloucester	99-2000	3	36	62	3
282	Kenny Logan	London Wasps	2000-01	10	47	46	-
280	Thierry Lacroix	Saracens	99-2000	3	47	55	2
279	Michael Lynagh	Saracens	1997-98	5	37	58	2
275	Mark Mapletoft	Gloucester	1997-98	5	35	58	2
272	John Liley	Leicester	1995-96	5	26	64	1
269	Mark Mapletoft	Gloucester	1996-97	6	25	58	5
263	Kenny Logan	Wasps	1998-99	8	35	51	
260	Tim Stimpson	Leicester	2000-01	7	27	57	-
253	Joel Stransky	Leicester	1997-98	5	39	47	3
253	Gareth Rees	Wasps	1997-98	1	34	57	3
246	Shane Howarth	Sale	1998-99	9	42	37	
240	Steven Vile	W Hartlepool	1998-99	5	28	52	1
237	Niall Woods	London Irish	1997-98	8	34	43	
236	Jonathan Callard	Bath	1995-96	3	43	45	
226	Rob Andrew	Newcastle	1997-98	6	44	35	1
224	Jonathan Callard	Bath	1996-97	4	51	34	
224	Shane Howarth	Sale	1997-98	4	39	41	1
219	Paul Grayson	Northampton	2000-01	1	20	58	-
215	Niall Woods	London Irish	1998-99	12	25	35	
210	Paul Grayson	Northampton	1997-98	4	23	45	3
203	Earl Va'a	Richmond	1998-99	8	32	33	
202	Jez Harris	Leicester	1993-94	2	18	41	11
202	Joel Stransky	Leicester	1998-99	7	34	33	-
198	Mark Mapletoft	Gloucester	1998-99	6	21	41	1
198	Jonny Wilkinson	Newcastle	2000-01	2	34	37	3
196	Mark Tainton	Bristol	1994-95	-	11	56	2
195	John Liley	Leicester	1996-97	3	24	44	
189	Paul Grayson	Northampton	1994-95	1	11	52	2
189	David Humphreys	London Irish	1996-97	4	20	40	3
184	Jon Preston	Bath	99-2000	1	34	32	
183	Jon Callard	Bath	1997-98	1	32	38	
182	Barry Everitt	London Irish	2000-01	1	15	49	-
181	Jez Harris	Leicester	1994-95	-	11	40	13
178	Jonathan Callard	Bath	1993-94	4	25	36	
178	Paul Burke	Bristol	1996-97	2	27	38	
178	Henry Honiball	Bristol	99-2000	4	34	29	1
176	Thierry Lacroix	Harlequins	1996-97	2	29	33	3
172	Jon Preston	Bath	2000-01	-	23	42	-
169	Thierry Lacroix	Harlequins	1997-98	3	26	32	2
168	Jannie De Beer	London Scottish	1998-99	1	17	37	6
168	Felipe Contepomi	Bristol	2000-01	4	17	38	-
167	Rob Liley	Sale	1995-96	3	22	34	2
166	Simon Mason	Orrell	1995-96	4	16	38	
163	Jonny Wilkinson	Newcastle	99-2000	3	11	39	3
163	Nicky Little	Sale	2000-01	1	19	39	1
161	Mark Tainton	Bristol	1993-94	-	19	40	1
161	Tim Stimpson	Leicester	1998-99	2	14	41	

ALL TIME RECORDS MOST POINTS IN A MATCH DIVISION ONE

32	Niall Woods	London Irish v Harlequins	25.04.98

31	John Liley	Leicester v Rosslyn Park	21.03.92
	David Walder	Newcastle v Saracens	26.11.00
	Tim Stimpson	Leicester v Saracens	24.02.01
	Felipe Contepomi	Bristol v Northampton	16.04.01

30	Steven Vile	West Hartlepool v Richmond	17.04.99
	Ryan Constable	Saracens v Bedford	16.04.00

29	Thomas Castaignede	Saracens v Rotherham	24.09.00
	Kenny Logan	London Wasps v Sale	14.04.01
	Jonny Wilkinson	Newcastle v London Wasps	23.09.00

28	Martin Strett	Orrell v Rosslyn Park	28.04.90
	John Liley	Leicester v Bristol	28.10.95
	Gavin Johnson	Saracens v London Scottish	26.09.98
	John Schuster	Harlequins v Bath	21.11.98
	Steven Vile	West Hartlepool v Gloucester	14.03.99
	Simon Mannix	Gloucester v Northampton	16.05.99
	Kenny Logan	London Wasps v Rotherham	01.04.01

27	David Pears	Harlequins v Bedford	14.10.89
	Mark Mapletoft	Gloucester v Leicester	01.02.98
	Niall Woods	London Irish v Northampton	05.01.99
	Thierry Lacroix	Saracens v Wasps	07.11.99
	Simon Mannix	Gloucester v Harlequins	23.09.00
	Jarrod Cunningham	London Irish v Bristol	10.09.00

26	John Liley	Leicester v Bedford	23.09.89
	Stuart Barnes	Bath v West Hartlepool	27.03.93
	Paul Grayson	Northampton v Bristol	02.10.93
	Mark Tainton	Bristol v Leicester	05.12.94
	Andy Lee	Saracens v West Hartlepool	14.10.95
	Paul Challinor	Harlequins v West Hartlepool	23.03.96
	Rob Liley	Leicester v London Irish	31.10.96
	John Stabler	West Hartlepool v London Irish	28.12.96
	Simon Mannix	Sale v Northampton	09.03.97
	Mike Catt	Bath v Sale	26.04.97
	Paul Grayson	Northampton v London Irish	13.12.97
	Thierry Lacroix	Harlequins v Wasps	13.12.97
	Kenny Logan	Wasps v London Irish	19.09.98
	Mike Catt	Bath v London Scottish	15.05.99
	Rich Butland	Richmond v Bedford	16.05.99
	Jarrod Cunningham	London Irish v Newcastle	02.10.00
	Thierry Lacroix	Saracens v Leicester	05.12.99
	Kenny Logan	Wasps v Saracens	13.02.00
	Jonny Wilkinson	Newcastle v Gloucester	30.04.00
	Tim Stimpson	Leicester v Gloucester	02.12.01
	Niki Little	Sale v Bristol	06.09.00

25	John Callard	Bath v Orrell	30.09.95
	John Liley	Leicester v Leicester v Bristol	13.04.96
	Kenny Logan	Wasps v Orrell	22.03.97
	Joel Stransky	Leicester v Wasps	17.01.98
	Jonny Wilkinson	Newcastle v Northampton	14.11.98
	Jonathon Callard	Bath v Newcastle	13.11.99
	Thierry Lacroix	Saracens v Gloucester	25.01.00
	Charles Hodgson	Sale v Saracens	11.02.01

ALL TIME RECORDS   MOST TRIES IN A MATCH   DIVISION ONE

6	Ryan Constable	Saracens v Bedford	16.04.00
5	Kenny Logan	Wasps v Orrel	22.03.97
4	Gary Hartley	Nottingham v Bedford	18.11.89
	Tony Swift	Bath v Bedford	13.01.90
	Jeremy Guscott	Bath v Bedford	13.01.90
	Paul Hamer	Orrell v Rugby	13.03.93
	Tony Underwood	Leicester v Newcastle Gosforth	12.03.94
	Daren O'Leary	Harlequins v Gloucester	31.08.96
	Tom Beim	Sale v Bristol	09.11.97
	Niall Woods	London Irish v Northampton	05.01.99
	Elton Moncrieff	Gloucester v Bedford	06.05.00
	Geordan Murphy	Leicester v Saracens	24.02.01

3

Peter Shillingford	Moseley v Wasps	05.02.88
Mark Charles	Leicester v Sale	26.03.88
Andrew Harriman	Harlequins v Nottingham	01.04.88
Simon Smith	Wasps v Coventry	13.04.88
Andrew Harriman	Harlequins v Sale	23.04.88
Jeremy Guscott	Bath v Moseley	12.11.88
Mark Bailey	Wasps v Moseley	19.11.88
John Liley	Leicester v Bedford	23.09.89
Mike Wedderburn	Harlequins v Bedford	14.10.89
Mark Bailey	Wasps v Gloucester	14.10.89
Derrick Morgan	Gloucester v Rosslyn Park	11.11.89
Jonathan Callard	Bath v Bedford	13.01.90
Chris Gerard	Leicester v Moseley	13.01.90
Paul Manley	Orrell v Rosslyn Park	31.03.90
Dewi Morris	Orrell v Liverpool StH	13.10.90
Dewi Morris	Orrell v Northampton	27.10.90
Rory Underwood	Leicester v Northampton	21.01.91
Andrew Harriman	Harlequins v Bristol	30.03.91
Will Carling	Harlequins v Bristol	30.03.91
Graham Childs	Wasps v Liverpool StH	20.04.91
Rob Andrew	Wasps v Bristol	27.04.91
Rory Underwood	Leicester v Moseley	27.04.91
Steve Hackney	Leicester v Lon. Irish	04.01.92
Tony Swift	Bath v Leicester	11.01.92
Rory Underwood	Leicester v Rosslyn Park	21.03.92
Mike Lloyd	Bristol v Rugby	28.03.92
Martin Pepper	Nottingham v Rosslyn Park	04.04.92
Chris Oti	Wasps v Bristol	25.04.92
Stuart Barnes	Bath v W. Hartlepool	27.03.93
Derek Eves	Bristol v Rugby	22.03.93
Ian Wynn	Orrell v Wasps	30.04.94
Simon Morris	Gloucester v W. Hartlepool	17.09.94
Damian Hopley	Wasps v Sale	15.10.94
Jeremy Guscott	Bath v Bristol	14.10.95
Graeme Smith	Orrell v Wasps	28.10.95
Rob Kitchen	Harlequins v Bristol	06.01.96
Graeme Smith	Orrell v Saracens	13.01.96
Aadel Kardooni	Leicester v W. Hartlepool	17.02.96
Spencer Bromley	Harlequins v Sale	30.03.96
Aadel Kardooni	Leicester v Sale	17.04.96
Michael Corcoran	Harlequins v Lon. Irish	14.09.96
Adedayo Adebayo	Bath v Lon. Irish	05.10.96
Huw Harries	Harlequins v Orrell	05.10.96

Mike Lloyd	Gloucester v W. Hartlepool	18.01.97
Jonathan Sleightholme	Bath v Northampton	19.01.97
Jonathan Sleightholme	Bath v Lon. Irish	08.03.97
Domonic Chapman	Harlequins v Orrell	08.03.97
Nick Walshe	Harlequins v W. Hartlepool	22.03.97
Tom Beim	Sale v W. Hartlepool	05.04.97
Andy Nicol	Bath v Gloucester	30.04.97
Richard Wallace	Saracens v Lon. Irish	30.04.97
David Rees	Sale v Bristol	09.11.97
Gary Armstrong	Newcastle v Bristol	27.12.97
Jim Naylor	Newcastle v Lon. Irish	11.01.98
Eric Peters	Bath v Gloucester	11.02.98
Richard Wallace	Saracens v Bristol	14.02.98
Harvey Thorneycroft	Northampton v Bristol	14.03.98
Will Greenwood	Leicester v Richmond	28.03.98
Domonic Chapman	Richmond v Bristol	10.04.98
Justin Bishop	Lon. Irish v Harlequins	25.04.98
Chris Catling	Gloucester v Newcastle	17.10.98
Darragh O'Mahoney	Bedford v Richmond	31.10.98
Tony Underwood	Newcastle v Saracens	31.10.98
Pat Lam	Northampton v Sale	2.1.99
Tony Diprose	Saracens v W. Hartlepool	13.2.99
Iain Balshaw	Bath v Saracens	28.3.99
Richard Todd	London Irish v Bath	17.4.99
Gary Armstrong	Newcastle v Richmond	21.4.99
Darragh O'Mahoney	Bedford v W. Hartlepool	2.5.99
Brian Cusack	Richmond v Bedford	16.5.99
Mel Deane	Richmond v Bedford	16.5.99
Neil Back	Leicester v W. Hartlepool	16.5.99
Shaun Berne	Bath v Gloucester	9.10.99
Josh Lewsey	Wasps v Bedford	23.3.00
Darragh O'Mahoney	Saracens v Harlequins	24.4.00
Rob Henderson	Wasps v Sale	30.4.00
Neil Back	Leicester v Bath	21.5.00
Frank Schisano	Bristol v Rotherham	02.09.00
Rob Henderson	London Wasps v Gloucester	17.09.00
Dan Luger	Saracens v Rotherham	24.09.00
Steve Hanley	Sale v Harlequins	02.12.00
Kenny Logan	London Wasps v Rotherham	01.04.01
Rob Thirlby	Bath v Rotherham	14.03.01
Tom Voyce	Bath v Rotherham	14.04.01
Mike Catt	Bath v London Irish	14.03.01

TEN YEAR RECORDS — DIVISION ONE

Club	91-92	92-93	93-94	94-95	95-96	96-97	97-98	98-99	99-00	00-01
Bath	1	1	1	2	1	2	3	6	2	3
Bedford	-	-	-	-	-	-	-	13	12	-
Bristol	10	6	4	6	6	9	12	-	6	9
Gloucester	4	5	8	7	8	6	7	10	3	7
Harlequins	8	8	6	8	3	3	10	4	10	11
Leicester	6	3	2	1	2	4	4	1	1	1
London Irish	9	7	9	-	-	10	-	7	8	8
London Scottish	-	10	-	-	-	-	-	12	-	-
Moseley	-	-	-	-	-	-	-	-	-	-
Newcastle	-	-	10	-	-	-	1	8	9	6
Northampton	3	4	5	10	-	8	8	2	5	4
Nottingham	12	-	-	-	-	-	-	-	-	-
Orrell	2	9	7	5	7	12	-	-	-	-
Richmond	-	-	-	-	-	-	5	9	-	-
Rosslyn Park	13	-	-	-	-	-	-	-	-	-
Rotherham	-	-	-	-	-	-	-	-	-	12
Rugby	11	13	-	-	-	-	-	-	-	-
(Manchester) Sale	-	-	-	4	5	5	6	11	11	10
Saracens	5	11	-	-	9	7	2	3	4	5
(London) Wasps	7	2	3	3	4	1	9	5	7	2
West Hartlepool	-	12	-	9	10	11	-	14	-	-

Jason Robinson, who had a very successful tour with the Lions, seen here in action for Sale against London Wasps.

Bristol's Phil Vickery on his way to scoring a try against Bristol at Kingsholm.
Photo courtesy of Gloucestershire Picture Agency

NATIONAL DIVISION

ONE

2001-02 Season

CLUBS

Division Two Records

SEASON 2000-01

LEAGUE TABLE

	P	W	D	L	F	A	PD	Bonus Pts	Tries	Pens	PTS	Last 6 Matches W -D- L
Leeds Tykes	26	24	0	2	1032	407	625	20	140	50	116	5 -0- 1
Worcester	26	23	1	2	844	387	457	18	113	51	112	4 -1- 1
Exeter	26	14	0	12	677	563	114	15	78	56	71	4 -0- 2
Wakefield	26	15	0	11	568	503	65	10	71	42	70	5 -0- 1
Coventry	26	14	0	12	565	604	-39	10	63	58	66	4 -0- 2
London Welsh	26	13	0	13	525	616	-91	12	60	54	64	3 -0- 3
Henley Hawks	26	12	2	12	517	589	-72	10	47	71	62	3 -0- 3
Manchester	26	12	0	14	471	549	-78	5	40	68	53	2 -0- 4
Birmingham & Solihull	26	7	5	14	427	481	-54	11	42	51	49	1 -1- 4
Moseley	26	9	2	15	497	646	-149	7	50	57	47	2 -1- 4
Bedford	26	9	1	16	463	616	-153	9	55	41	47	2 -1- 3
Otley	26	9	1	16	455	630	-175	8	48	50	46	1 -1- 4
Orrell	26	8	1	17	437	661	-224	12	48	40	46	2 -0- 4
Waterloo	26	6	1	19	450	676	-216	9	51	49	35	2 -1- 3

REVIEW

Leeds Tykes finally made it to the Promised Land in a tough season when they went head-to-head with Worcester. Leeds trailed early in the season but once they found their form they rattled up the points and in the end passed the 1,000 mark for the season. They also notched up 20 bonus points, two more than second placed Worcester. However they did not end the season as they would have liked, going down to Henley Hawks on the last day of the campaign. Despite that loss they still finished four points clear of Worcester - when they met in the league campaign both sides won their home fixture.

Another 'what if' season for **Worcester** as they again failed to get their dream promotion. With the promotion and relegation issue now sorted for the next few years Worcester will again be in pursuit of that dream in the coming season. In a normal season they would have probably done enough to get promotion but for the fantastic year that Leeds Tykes had, losing just once before they came unstuck at Henley on the final day of the season. The match that really cost them was the defeat at Moseley in early December when they went down 22-15.

Exeter surprisingly finished third after spending most of the season at the wrong end of the table. This though was more to do with the fact that they were playing catch up after having a number of fixtures postponed early in the season. In the last two months of the campaign they played 10 matches winning eight and losing just twice - to Wakefield and eventual champions Leeds Tykes, both these defeats were narrow ones. They had a powerful pack that contributed 36 tries and only the Leeds Tykes forwards scored more with 38. They picked up 15 bonus points and had the third highest points total but defensively they had only the sixth best record in terms of points conceded.

Wakefield improved beyond recognition finishing fourth - their highest position in National League rugby since it went to home and away. They won more matches than Exeter who finished one place above them but only managed to pick up 10 bonus points compared to the 15 that Exeter achieved. They ran in 70 tries with the wingers, 19, and the back row, 17, making major contributions. At home they had an impressive record, after losing to Otley on the opening day of the season they went on to win 10 out of 12 with only Leeds Tykes and Worcester leaving College Grove with the points.

Coventry moved up to fifth, a one place jump on the previous season. They had their best finish since they managed third in 1996-97 behind the powerful Newcastle and Richmond sides which ran away with it. Fifth place was a remarkable achievement when you think that they made a dreadful start to the season with six defeats in their opening seven league fixtures. They then put together a run of nine wins from ten matches between November and January to move up the table rapidly. After losing their four opening home matches of the season they went on a tremendous run at Coundon Road winning their remaining nine matches of the league campaign.

London Welsh under new coach Adrian Davies dropped a place on the previous season to finish with a 50% record, 13 wins and 13 defeats, in sixth place. At home they won nine and lost four whilst away from Old Deer Park they struggled with just four wins. Apart from the top two sides the only side to do the double over the Welsh in the league were Bedford Blues. They did not score as freely as the previous season falling nearly 200 points short whilst defensively they conceded more points as well.

Henley Hawks managed a two place improvement last season as they moved up from ninth to seventh, finishing nine points clear of eighth placed Birmingham & Solihull. This was their highest ever placing in National League rugby as they improved their defensive record by over 100 points. At home they picked up nine victories including a final day win against Champions Leeds Tykes. Otley, Manchester and Worcester all did the double over Henley

Manchester finished exactly the same as the previous season in eighth place but this season managed one more win. They made a bad start to the season with just two wins coming from their opening eight matches. After losing at home to Coventry in mid November they went on a four match winning run which took them up the table, in those four matches they did the double over Otley and got a good away win at Henley Hawks. One odd fact about last season was that they picked up just five bonus points which was the lowest total in the division despite their mid table position.

Birmingham & Solihull finished a creditable ninth in their first season at this level in the National League structure. There were seven drawn matches in National One last season and Birmingham & Solihull were involved in five of them. They were the lowest scorers in the division with just 421 points and the second lowest try scorers. At the other end of the scale they were hard to score against and only the top two sides conceded less than Birmingham & Solihull. Not surprisingly then they conceded just 45 tries which was the third lowest in the division and only allowed the opposition forwards to score 10 tries against them, one less than Champions Leeds Tykes.

Moseley dropped three places from seventh to tenth last season. They conceded too many points with only the two relegated clubs, Waterloo and Orrell conceding more. They picked up nine wins but they did beat runners up Worcester, which put a huge dent in their promotion aspirations. Seven of their nine wins came at home whilst away from home they won just twice and they were their first two away matches of the season at Waterloo and Otley.

Bedford Blues were in danger of a second successive relegation but in the end did enough to survive and hopefully build for the future. Like most sides they relied heavily on their home form with seven of their nine wins coming at Goldington Road. On their travels they did pick up wins at London Welsh and Waterloo and did the double over both these sides.

Otley retained their status in the division on the final day of the season with a draw against fellow strugglers Bedford Blues. That gave them the same number of points as Orrell but they had a better points difference and survived in their first season back in the division since 1993-94 when they came straight back down. Otley suffered because of their home form picking up just four wins at Cross Green from 13 league matches, this was the worst record of any side in the division. They were though one of the few sides to actually win more away matches than home with five victories on the road. They picked up just eight bonus points which was the second lowest of all the teams in the division, only Moseley with seven collected fewer.

Orrell dropped out of the top two divisions for the first time since the introduction of league rugby back in 1987-88. It went down to the final day and it was only the draw between Otley and Bedford that sent them down. They ended up level on points with Otley and a point behind Bedford, both had a superior points difference and Orrell were down. They did pick up 12 bonus points along the way to go with their eight wins. All eight wins came at Edge Hall Road whilst on the road they picked up just one draw when they ended 15 all against the draw specialists Birmingham & Solihull.

Waterloo like Orrell drop out of the top two divisions for the first time in their league career. They managed just six wins all season and five of those came at Blundellsands whilst their one away success was at Manchester where they ran out 23-10 winners. By the end of the season they were 11 points adrift and had no cause for complaint. They finished with two wins and a draw in their last five matches but the damage had already been done and they will need to re-group quickly if they are to return to the division where they have played nearly all their league rugby.

2000-01 RECORD REVIEW (Individual Records)

The ALL-TIME RECORDS for MOST POINTS IN A MATCH, MOST POINTS IN A SEASON & MOST TRIES IN A MATCH can be found in the Records Section for this division.

MOST POINTS - IN A MATCH

This record was never seriously challenged in the season just gone. The best effort was 31 points by the prolific Worcester full back Sateki Tuipulotu against Henley Hawks in January. Tuipulotu along with the Leeds Tykes full back, Richard Le Bas, scored 20 points in a match five times. The Birmingham & Solihull outside half Steve Gough set a new record for the club with 25 points in the seasons opener at Leeds Tykes and still finished on the losing side.

EVOLUTION OF RECORD - Points in a match

26	Andy Mitchell	London Scot v North	03.10.87
28	David Johnson	New Gos v Morley	11.01.92
30	Michael Corcoran	L. Irish v Waterloo	23.09.95
42	Jez Harris	Coventry v Nott	05.10.96

Best last season:

31	Sateki Tuipulotu	Worcester v Henley Hawks	20.01.01
26	Richard Le Bas	Leeds Tykes v Orrell	17.03.01
25	Richard Le Bas	Leeds Tykes v Birmingham & Solihull	9.9.00
25	Steve Gough	Birmingham & Solihull v Leeds Tykes	9.9.00
25	Sateki Tuipulotu	Worcster v Manchester	23.09.00

MOST POINTS - IN A SEASON

Prior to this season the record stood at 324 to Simon Mason for Richmond back in 1996-97. This time round two players beat the old record. Leading the way was Worcester's Sateki Tuipulotu who ended the season with 349 points, 25 better than the previous record. Also beating the old record was the Leeds Tykes full back Richard Le Bas who finished 16 points behind Tuipulotu on 333, nine better than the previous record.

EVOLUTION OF RECORD - Points in a season

75	Andy Finnie	Bedford	1987-88
138	Andy Kennedy	Saracens	1988-89
147	David Johnson	Newcastle Gos	1991-92
172	Guy Gregory	Nottingham	1993-94
213	Mike Jackson	Wakefield	1994-95
310	Michael Corcoran	London Irish	1995-96
324	Simon Mason	Richmond	1996-97
349	Sateki Tuipulotu	Worcester	2000-01

MOST TRIES - IN A MATCH

Hat tricks were down last season to 15 and nobody challenged the divisional record of five tries in a match. Of the 15 hat tricks only one came from a forward with the Wakefield Back row forward Carl Houston being the odd man out. Six of the 15 were scored by Leeds Tykes players and three by Worcester players.
Two players, Chris Hall, Leeds Tykes, and Sateki Tuipulotu, Worcester, achieved the feat twice.

EVOLUTION OF RECORD - Tries in a match
(Only the first to reach the figure is shown)

3	Peter Shillingford	Moseley v Wasps	05.02.88
3	Jerry Macklin	Lon Scot v Northampton	03.10.87
5	Simon Verbickas	Sale v Otley	12.02.94
5	Pat Lam	Newcastle v Rotherham	04.05.97
5	Luke Nabaro	Bristol v Blackheath	13.03.99

MOST TRIES - IN A SEASON

This was dominated by players from Leeds Tykes. They had three players in the top five including the top two. The leader was centre Graham Mackay with 19, this though was four off the all time record for the division. It was though enough to put him sixth on the all time list. Just one behind Mackay was his fellow Leeds Tykes centre Shaun Woof with 18, that puts him joint seventh on the all time list.
Breaking the mould in a list dominated by players from two sides was the London Welsh full back Matt Vines who ended the season with 17 tries to his name.

EVOLUTION OF RECORD

10	Dave McLagan	Saracens	1987-88
11	Nick Grecian	Lon. Scottish	1991-92
16	Simon Verbickas	Sale	1993-94
20	Matt Allen	Northampton	1996-97
23	John Bentley	Newcastle	1996-97

ALL-TIME RECORDS

23	John Bentley	Newcastle	1996-97
21	Gary Armstrong	Newcastle	1996-97
21	Scott Quinnell	Richmond	1996-97
20	Matt Allen	Northampton	1995-96
20	Jim Fallon	Richmond	1996-97
19	Graham Mackay	Leeds Tykes	2000-01
18	Dean Lax	Rotherham	1998-99
18	Dean Lax	Rotherham	1999-00
18	Shaun Woof	Leeds Tykes	2000-01
17	Andy Smallwood	Coventry	1996-97
17	Darragh O'Mahoney	Moseley	1997-98
17	Ben Whetstone	Bedford	1997-98
17	Duncan Roke	Henley Hawks	1999-00
17	Dave Scully	Rotherham	1999-00
17	Matt Vines	London Welsh	2000-01
17	Chris Hall	Leeds Tykes	2000-01
17	Sateki Tuipulotu	Worcester	2000-01

MOST CONVERSIONS - IN A MATCH

This record seems safe for a while yet. The best last season was nine by Richard Le Bas for Leeds Tykes against Orrell. Le Bas kicked nine conversions as Leeds ran up 81 points, the highest score of the season.

EVOLUTION OF RECORD

6	Chris Howard	Rugby v Gosforth	11.11.89
9	David Johnson	New Gos v Morley	11.01.92
9	Guy Gregory	Nott v Morley	24.10.92
9	Paul Turner	Sale v Otley	12.02.94
18	Rob Andrew	Newcastle v Rugby	05.10.96

ALL-TIME RECORDS

18	Rob Andrew	Newcastle v Rugby	05.10.96
13	Jez Harris	Coventry v Nottingham	05.10.96
10	Simon Binns	Rotherham v W Hartlepool	02.10.99
10	Mike Umaga	Rotherham v Waterloo	11.03.00
10	Sam Howard	Exeter v W Hartlepool	06.05.00
9	David Johnson	New Gos v Morley	11.01.92
9	Guy Gregory	Nottingham v Morley	24.10.92
9	Paul Turner	Sale v Otley	12.02.94
9	Richard Le Bas	Leeds Tykes v Orrell	

MOST CONVERSIONS - IN A SEASON

Richard Le Bas moved into fourth place on the all time list with 72 conversions. He was though still 24 behind the all time record set by Northampton's Paul Grayson. Worcester's Sateki Tuipulotu kicked 57 conversions, to finished second behind Le Bas, and moved into 8th on the all time record for the division.

EVOLUTION OF RECORD

14	Andy Kennedy	Saracens	1988-89
24	Martin Livesey	Richmond	1989-90
31	David Johnson	Newcastle Gosforth	1991-92
76	Paul Grayson	Northampton	1995-96
95	Rob Andrew	Newcastle	1996-97

ALL-TIME RECORDS

95	Rob Andrew	Newcastle	1996-97
83	Simon Mason	Richmond	1996-97
76	Paul Grayson	Northampton	1995-96
72	Richard Le Bas	Leeds Tykes	2000-01
67	Mike Rayer	Bedford	1996-97
65	Mike Rayer	Bedford	1997-98
60	Mike Umaga	Rotherham	1999-00
57	Sateki Tuipulotu	Worcester	2000-01
55	Sam Howard	Exeter	1999-00
50	Tony Yapp	Worcester	1999-00
48	Jez Harris	Coventry	1996-97
48	Steve Gough	Coventry	1998-99

MOST PENALTIES - IN A MATCH

It was that man Richard Le Bas who figured here. The Leeds Tykes full back kicked seven penalties as Leeds Tykes beat Manchester in October. That was one short of the record of eight which has stood since the 1996-97 season when Moseley's Alastair Kerr set the record in his final season for the club. Le Bas becomes the third Leeds Tykes player to kick seven penalties in a match in this division.

EVOLUTION OF RECORD

7	Michael Corcoran	Lon Irish v Lon Scottish	13.01.96
8	Alastair Kerr	Moseley v Waterloo	17.02.96

ALL-TIME RECORDS

8	Alastair Kerr	Moseley v Water	17.02.96
7	Michael Corcoran	Lon Irish v Lon Scottish	13.01.96
7	Matt Inman	Rotherham v Richmond	14.09.96
7	Sateki Tuipulotu	Leeds v Coventry	03.01.99
7	Steve Gough	Coventry v Worcester	11.03.00
7	Jon Benson	Leeds v Manchester	08.04.00
7	Richard Le Bas	Leeds Tykes v Manchester	07.10.00

MOST PENALTIES - IN A SEASON

Coventry full back Martyn Davies ended the seaon as the top penalty kicker in the division with 51. This was enough to put him 8th on the all time list, this was though 14 of the all time record of 65. Just one behind Davies wass the Worcester full back Sateki Tuipulotu with 50 - three short of his 1998-99 total when playing for Leeds Tykes.

EVOLUTION OF RECORD

30	Andy Kennedy	Saracens	1988-89
30	David Johnson	Newcastle	1992-93
43	Guy Gregory	Nottingham	1993-94
57	Mike Jackson	Wakefield	1994-95
63	Michael Corcoran	London Irish	1995-96
65	Lyndon Griffiths	Waterloo	1997-98

ALL-TIME RECORDS

65	Lyndon Griffiths	Waterloo	1997-98
63	Michael Corcoran	London Irish	1995-96
57	Mike Jackson	Wakefield	1994-95
55	Steve Swindells	Manchester	1999-00
55	Matt Jones	Henley	1999-00
53	Steve Gough	Coventry	1998-99
53	Sateki Tuipulotu	Leeds Tykes	1998-99
51	Bryan Easson	Exeter	1998-99
51	Martyn Davies	Coventry	2000-01
50	Sateki Tuipulotu	Worcester	2000-01
48	Steve Swindells	Waterloo	1994-95
48	Richard Le Bas	Leeds Tykes	2000-01
47	John Steele	London Scottish	1996-97
46	Lyndon Griffiths	Waterloo	1998-99
45	Simon Mason	Newcastle Gosforth	1994-95

2000-01 RECORD REVIEW (Individual Records) continued

MOST DROP GOALS - IN A MATCH

Orrell outside half David Sleman kicked two drop goals in a match twice last season but could not manage a third to equal the record for the division held by two players including fromer Orrell player Matthew McCarthy.

ALL-TIME RECORDS

3	Martin Livesey	Richmond v Northampton	19.11.88
3	Murray Walker	London Scot v W Hartlepool	23.04.94

MOST DROP GOALS - IN A SEASON

David Sleman joined Guy Gregory at the top of the all time list for drop goals in a season. Sleman kicked his ninth against Exeter in March but could not manage to break the record in any of his remaining four matches of the season.

EVOLUTION OF RECORD

4	Simon Smith	Bedford	1987-88
4	David Johnson	Gosforth	1987-88
8	Jon King	Blackheath	1988-89
9	Guy Gregory	Nottingham	1992-93
9	David Sleman	Orrell	2000-01

ALL-TIME RECORDS

9	Guy Gregory	Nottingham	1992-93
9	David Sleman	Orrell	2000-01
8	Jon King	Blackheath	1988-89
6	Andy Lee	Saracens	1994-95
5	Brian Mullen	London Irish	1990-91
5	Sam Howard	Blackheath	1995-96
5	Guy Gregory	Nottingham	1993-94
5	Murray Walker	London Scot	1993-94
5	Jez Harris	Coventry	1996-97
5	Matt Jones	Moseley	1997-98
5	Sam Howard	Exeter	1999-00

Exeter scrum half Ian Sanders.　　　　　　　　Photo: Nigel Chanter

2000-01

NATIONAL LEAGUE ONE

MOST POINTS

POINTS			T	C	P	DG
349	Sateki Tuopulotu	Worcester	17	57	50	-
333	Richard Le Bas	Leeds Tykes	9	72	48	-
239	Martyn Davies	Coventry	4	33	51	-
190	Philip Belgian	Waterloo	5	21	41	-
181	Ben Harvey	Moseley	2	21	41	2
179	David Sleman	Orrell	8	17	26	9
179	Andy Lee	London Welsh	2	23	41	-
176	Steve Gough	Birmingham & Sol	2	17	42	2
171	Matt Jones	Henley Hawks	-	21	42	1
162	Steve Swindells	Manchester	1	11	45	-
134	Dan Clappison	Otley	-	19	30	2
131	Jon Hill	Exeter	2	23	25	-
126	Nick Buoy	Henley Hawks	3	12	29	-
125	Sam Howard	Exeter	5	14	21	3
111	Rob Liley	Wakefield	2	25	17	-
101	Leigh Hinton	Moseley	5	14	16	-
99	Ben Whetstone	Bedford	8	7	15	-
97	Graham Mackay	Leeds Tykes	19	1	-	-

MOST PENALTIES

51	Martyn Davies	Coventry
50	Saterki Tuopulotu	Worcester
48	Richard Le Bas	Leeds Tykes
45	Steve Swindells	Manchester
42	Matt Jones	Henley Hawks
42	Steve Gough	Birmingham & Sol
41	Andy Lee	London Welsh
41	Ben Harvey	Moseley
41	Phil Belgian	Waterloo
30	Dan Clappison	Otley
29	Nick Buoy	Henley Hawks
26	David Sleman	Orrell
25	Jon Hill	Exeter
21	Sam Howard	Exeter
20	Scott Stewart	Bedford

MOST TRIES

19	Graham Mackay	Leeds Tykes
18	Shaun Woof	Leeds Tykes
17	Matt Vines	London Welsh
17	Chris Hall	Leeds Tykes
17	Sateki Tuopulotu	Worcester
14	Kurt Johnson	Coventry
13	Alastair Murdoch	Worcester
12	Scott Benton	Leeds Tykes
10	Nick Baxter	Worcester
10	Carl Houston	Wakefield
9	Craig Emmerson	Leeds Tykes
9	Steve Bachop	Leeds Tykes
9	James Hinkins	Bedford
9	Andy Craig	Orrell

MOST CONVERSIONS

72	Richard Le Bas	Leeds Tykes
57	Sateki Tupulotu	Worcester
33	Martyn Davies	Coventry
25	Rob Liley	Wakefield
23	Andy Lee	London Welsh
23	Jon Hill	Exeter
21	Phil Belgian	Waterloo
21	Ben Harvey	Moseley
21	Matt Jones	Henley Hawks
19	Dan Clappison	Otley
17	David Sleman	Orrell
17	Phil Greenaway	Exeter
17	Steve Gough	Birmingham & Sol
16	Lyndon Griffiths	Manchester

MOST DROP GOALS

9	David Sleman	Orrell
3	Sam Howard	Exeter
3	Mark Appleson	Manchester
3	James Shanahan	Bedford
2	Ben Harvey	Moseley
2	Steve Gough	Birmingham & Sol
2	Dan Clappison	Otley
1	Matt Jones	Henley Hawks
1	Adam Bidwell	London Welsh
1	Ross Winney	Wakefield
1	James Lofthouse	Otley

NATIONAL DIVISION 1

FIXTURES 2001-02

Away Teams

HOME TEAMS	Bedford (1)	Birmingham (2)	Bracknell (3)	Coventry (4)	Exeter (5)	Henley (6)	London Welsh (7)	Manchester (8)	Moseley (9)	Otley (10)	Rotherham (11)	Rugby Lions (12)	Wakefield (13)	Worcester (14)
1 Bedford Blues		2.02	8.12	16.03	8.09	6.10	27.10	22.09	19.01	6.04	23.02	5.01	27.04	17.11
2 Birmingham Solihull	29.09		26.01	1.09	20.10	6.04	27.04	10.11	9.03	15.09	8.12	9.02	17.11	12.01
3 Bracknell	13.04	22.09		27.10	5.01	2.02	23.02	19.01	8.09	17.11	6.10	29.12	6.04	16.03
4 Coventry	10.11	5.01	9.03		1.12	8.09	22.09	29.12	13.04	20.10	19.01	30.03	2.02	9.02
5 Exeter	12.01	23.02	1.09	6.04		27.10	17.11	6.10	2.02	27.04	16.03	15.09	22.09	8.12
6 Henley	9.02	1.12	29.09	12.01	9.03		1.09	30.03	10.11	26.01	27.04	20.10	8.12	15.09
7 London Welsh	9.03	29.12	20.10	26.01	30.03	5.01		13.04	1.12	9.02	8.09	10.11	19.01	29.09
8 Manchester	26.01	16.03	15.09	27.04	9.02	17.11	8.12		20.10	12.01	6.04	29.09	27.10	5.01
9 Moseley	15.09	27.10	12.01	8.12	29.09	16.03	6.04	23.02		1.09	17.11	26.01	6.10	27.04
10 Otley	1.12	19.01	30.03	23.02	29.12	22.09	6.10	8.09	5.01		2.02	13.04	16.03	27.10
11 Rotherham	20.10	13.04	9.02	15.09	10.11	29.12	12.01	1.12	30.03	29.09		9.03	5.01	26.01
12 Rugby Lions	1.09	6.10	27.04	17.11	19.01	23.02	16.03	2.02	22.09	8.12	27.10		8.09	6.04
13 Wakefield	29.12	30.03	1.12	29.09	26.01	13.04	15.09	9.03	9.02	10.11	1.09	12.01		20.10
14 Worcester	30.03	8.09	10.11	6.10	13.04	19.01	2.02	1.09	29.12	9.03	22.09	1.12	23.02	

BEDFORD BLUES

Chairman	Geoff Irvine
Director of Rugby	Colin Jackson
Rugby Administrator	Tony Mills
Marketing Manager	c/o Tony Mills

Bedford Blues
Goldington Road
Beford MK40 3NF
Tel: 01234 347980
Fax: 01234 347511

Director of rugby Colin Jackson was aware that building a team from scratch to compete in National League One was not going to be easy. In the event he realised just how difficult it was as Bedford hung on to their current league status with a 17-17 draw at Otley in the last league match of the season.

The season did not get off to a good start with losses against Henley, Birmingham/Solihull and Worcester and a fortuitous win at London Welsh, but victories before Christmas against Orrell, Manchester, Moseley, Waterloo (twice) and Otley meant that the Blues were in a strong position at the beginning of the New Year. However, injuries to key players and an unexplained loss of form resulted in Bedford fighting to avoid relegation right up to the last game.

Captain Ben Whetstone, an ever popular figure with both players and supporters, did everything possible to keep the team afloat, even taking over goal kicking duties when injuries ruled out the more obvious candidates for this role. The signing of Andre Fox from South Africa mid way through the season ensured more stability in the forwards and it is hoped that a team with these two influential players available from match one will make more of an impression in the league this season.

John Brooks, voted the players Player of the Year, had a tremendous season and richly deserved his selection for the England Students. Daniel Browne, Philip Clarke, Cameron Thomas and Joe Ross also proved their worth in many games. In the backs Ben Hinshelwood and Riaz Fredericks, until he was injured, looked potent attacking players, and the less experienced James Hinkins, Chris Bajak and James Shanahan showed much promise for the future. Injuries and unavailability played havoc with half-back selection and, although those that took the field played whole heartedly, this was an area where stability was sorely missed.

The Blues now look forward to a more settled season and, with the introduction of a few new faces in key position, should improve on last season's position.

Back Row: Harley Crane, Nigel Clarke, Leigh Mansell, Richard Jackson, Riaz Fredericks, Chris Bajak, Ben Hinshelwood, John Rudd, John Brooks. **Middle:** Gareth Davies (team manager), Peter Smith (director), Tabo Huntley (fitness advisor), Matthew McLoughlin, Peter Hennessey, Jon Summers, David Whitehead, Richard Candlin, Thomas Suring, James Shanahan, Mark Sharp, Laurence White, Colin Jackson (director of Rugby), David Ledsom (chairman of directors). **Front:** Justin Abrahams, Phil Elphick, Martin Wallwork, Matt Skillecorn, Ben Whetstone (captain), John Saunders (president), Aaron Davies, James Hinkins, Henry Whitford.

BEDFORD

Comp.	Date	H/A	Opponents	Result & Score	Att	15	14	13	12	11
N1	9-Sep	H	Henley Hawks	L 31-34	2035	Jackson	Bejak	Whetstone	Fredericks	Wells/t
N1	16-Sep	A	London Welsh	W 20-14		Hinshelwood	Bejak/t	Whetstone/t	Fredericks	Hinkins/t
N1	23-Sep	H	Birmingham & Solihull	L 17-20	1506	Hinshelwood/t	Wells	Whetstone/t	Fredericks	Hinkins
N1	30-Sep	A	Worcester	L 25-31	2000	Hinshelwood/t	Bejak	Whetstone	Shanahan/2t	Hinkins
N1	7-Oct	H	Orrell	W 27-0	1175	Hinshelwood/t	Rudd	Whetstone/t	Shanahan	Jewell
N1	14-Oct	A	Leeds Tykes	L 6-42	1019	Hinshelwood	Rudd	Whetstone	Shanahan	Jewell
N1	28-Oct	H	Manchester	W 20-8	1431	Hinshelwood	Jewell	Whetstone	Shanahan	Hinkins/2t
N1	19-Nov	H	Moseley	W 28-14	1430	Hinshelwood	Jewell	Whetstone	Shanahan/t	Hinkins
N1	25-Nov	A	Waterloo	W 20-11	450	Hinshelwood/p	Bejak/t	Whetstone	Shanahan	Jewell
N1	2-Dec	H	Otley	W 16-15	1100	Hinshelwood	Jewell	Whetstone/t	Shanahan	Hinkins
N1	16-Dec	H	Waterloo	W 37-9	1870	Hinshelwood	Bejak/t	Whetstone/t	Shanahan/t	Hinkins/2t
N1	6-Jan	H	Coventry	L 15-20		Hinshelwood/p(a/c)	Bejak/t	Whetstone	Shanahan/t	Hinkins
N1	13-Jan	A	Moseley	L 17-24	874	Hinshelwood	Bejak/t	Whetstone	Shanahan	Hinkins/t
N1	27-Jan	A	Coventry	L 22-39	2200	Hinshelwood	Bejak	Whetstone	Rivaro	Hinkins
N1	4-Feb	A	Manchester	L 13-22	485	Stewart/p	Bejak/t	Whetstone	Hinshelwood	Hinkins
N1	10-Feb	H	Leeds Tykes	L 3-48	1255	Stewart/p	Bejak	Hinshelwood	Rivaro	Hinkins
N1	24-Feb	A	Orrell	L 14-15		Hinshelwood	Bejak	Fredericks	Rivaro	Hinkins
N1	3-Mar	A	Exeter	L 13-39	670	Hinshelwood	Bejak	Fredericks	Shanahan	Rudd
N1	10-Mar	H	Worcester	L 14-32	1880	Shanahan	Hinshelwood	Whetstone	Rivaro	Rudd/t
N1	24-Mar	A	Wakefield	L 7-56		Hinshelwood/t	Rudd	Whetstone/c	Rivaro	Hinkins
N1	31-Mar	H	London Welsh	W 23-18	1608	Hinshelwood	Bejak	Whetstone/tc2p	Fredericks	Rudd/t
N1	8-Apr	H	Wakefield	W 19-18	1320	Hinshelwood/t	Bejak	Whetstone/c4p	Fredericks	Rudd
N1	14-Apr	A	Henley Hawks	L 10-18	1005	Hinshelwood	Bejak	Whetstone/cp	Fredericks	Rudd(d/t)
N1	21-Apr	H	Exeter	L 11-33	1720	Hinshelwood	Bejak	Whetstone/t2p	Fredericks	Rudd
N1	25-Apr	A	Birmingham & Solihull	L 18-19		Hinshelwood	Rudd	Whetstone/cp	Shanahan/dg	Hinkins/t
N1	28-Apr	A	Otley	D 17-17		Hinshelwood	Rudd/t	Whetstone/tc	Shanahan/t	Hinkins
TBC	21-Oct	H	Sedgley Park	W 45-15	1019	Hinshelwood	Rudd/t	Whetstone/t	Shanahan/t	Hinkins
TBC	4-Nov	H	Saracens	L 24-54	3012	Hinshelwood	Bejak/t	Whetstone	Shanahan/2c	Hinkins/t

** after opponents name indicates a penalty try. Brackets after a player's name indicates he was replaced.
eg (a) means he was replaced by replacement code "a" and so on. / after a player or replacement name
is followed by any scores he made - eg /t, /c, /p, /dg or any combination of these*

LEAGUE DEBUTS

Paul Bernard, Chris Bejak, John Broks, Daniel Browne, Philip Clarke, Michael Count, Harley Crane, Andre Fox, Riaz Fredericks, Peter Hennessy, Ben Hinselwood, Richard Jackson, Tim Otto, Marco Rivero, James Moss, John Rudd, James Shanahan, Mark Sharp, Matt Skillecorn, John SUmmers, Thomas Surling, Thomas Cameron, R Ward, Ben Williams, Henry Whitford, Lawrence White, Dave Whitehead.

EVER PRESENT
None

Most Appearances:
26 Ben Whetstone. 25 Ben Hinshelwood.

PLAYERS USED

39 plus 2 as replacement only.

MOST POINTS

Pts	Player	T	C	P	DG
99	B Whetstone	8	7	15	-
90	S Stewart	-	15	20	-
66	J Shanahan	7	5	4	3
45	J Hinkins	9	-	-	-

MATCH FACTS

10	9	1	2	3	4	5	6	7	8
Shanahan/2c2p2dg	Crane	Hennessey	Sharp	Skillecorn	Candolin	Whitehead	Whitford/t	White	Suring
Shanahan/cp	Crane	Hennessey	Davis	Skillecorn	Summers	Whitehead	Whitford	White	Devin
Shanahan/2cp	Crane	Mansell	Thomas	Barnard	Summers	Whitehead	Elphick	White	Devin
Stewart/2c2p	Crane	Mansell	Thomas	Hennessey	Candolin	Whitehead	Summers	White	Whitford
Stewart/2cp	Crane/t	Mansell	Thomas	Hennessey	Ward	Whitehead	Summers	Elphick/t	White
Stewart/2p	Crane	Mansell	Thomas	Hennessey	Ward	Whitehead	Summers	Elphick	White
Stewart/cp	Crane	Brooks	Thomas/t	Skillecorn	Ward	Clarke	Summers	White	Browne
Stewart/2c3p	Wallwork	Brooks	Thomas/t	Skillecorn	Clarke	Ward	Browne	White	Fox/t
Stewart/c	Wallwork	Brooks	Thomas/t	Skillecorn	Clarke	Ward	Browne	White	Fox
Stewart/c3p	Wallwork	Mansell	Davis	Skillecorn	Clarke	Ward	Whitford	Browne	Fox
Stewart/3c2p	Wallwork	Brooks	Davis	Skillecorn	Summers	Ward	Whitford	White	Fox
Wallwork	Crane	Hennessey	Thomas	Skillecorn	Clarke	Ward	Whitford	White	Cook
Stewart/c	Crane/t	Brooks	Ross	Skillecorn	Candolin	Ward	Browne	Elphick	Whitford
Stewart/cp(b/t)	Wallwork/c	Mansell	Thomas/t(c/t)	Skillecorn	Clarke	Ward	Browne	White	Whitford
Shanahan	Wallwork	Mansell	Thomas	Skillecorn	Clarke	Ward	Summers	Browne	Whitford(c/t)
Whetstone	Wallwork	Brooks	Thomas	Skillecorn	Clarke	Browne	Whitford	White	Count
Whetstone/3p	Wallwork	Brooks	Thomas	Skillecorn	Summers	Browne	White	Count	Whitford
Whetstone/c2p	Wallwork	Mansell	Thomas	Skillecorn	Summers	Ward	Browne/t	White	Whitford
Stewart/3p	Williams	Mansell	Ross	Skillecorn	Clarke	Ward	Count	White	Fox
Stewart	Williams	Brooks	Ross	Skillecorn	Clarke	Ward	Count	Whitford	Fox
Shanahan	Wallwork	Brooks	Ross	Mansell	Clarke/t	Ward	Browne	White	Fox
Shanahan	Wallwork	Brooks	Ross	Otte	Clarke	Ward	Browne	White	Fox
Shanahan	Wallwork	Brooks	Sharp	Mansell	Clarke	Ward	Browne	White	Fox
Shanahan	Crane	Brooks	Sharp	Mansell	Clarke	Ward	Browne	White	Fox
Wallwork	Crane	Brooks	Thomas	Skillecorn	Clarke	Ward	Browne	White/t	Fox
Wallwork	Crane	Brooks	Thomas	Skillecorn	Clarke	Fox	Whitford	White	Count
Stewart/5c	Crane/t	Mansell	Thomas/t	Hennessey	Candolin	Ward	Summers	Elphick/t	White/t
Wallwork	Crane(e/t)	Brooks/t	Davis	Skillecorn	Clarke	Ward	Summers	Browne	White

REPLACEMENTS   a - S Stewart   b - J Shanahan   c - J Ross   d - J Hinkins   e - M Sharp

2000-01 HIGHLIGHTS

Ben Whetstone after his year away returned to the club and topped the points scorers list for the first time ever.
He fell one short of 100 points and with eight tries was the second leading try scorer.

His eight tries saw him extend his career record for Bedford passed the 50 mark, by the end of the season he was on 56.

The role of leading try scorer went to winger James Hinkins who ran in nine tries from 16 starts.

Whetstone extended his club record for league appearances to 132 and he remains the only player to top the 100 mark for the Blues.

BEDFORD

LEAGUE STATISTICS
compiled by Stephen McCormack

SEASON	Division	P	W	D	L	F	A	Pts Diff	Lge Pts	Lge Pos	Most Points		Most Tries	
91-92	2	12	4	0	8	168	204	-36	8	10	92	Andy Finnie	5	Mark Rennell
92-93	2	12	6	2	4	185	186	3	14	7r	75	Andy Finnie	3	Mark Rennell
93-94	3	18	12	0	6	332	260	72	24	3	172	Andy Finnie	8	Vince Turner
94-95	3	18	13	1	4	421	250	172	27	1p	228	Andy Finnie	6	Ben Whetstone
95-96	2	18	5	1	12	289	520	-231	11	10	85	Andy Finnie	8	Matt Oliver
96-97	2	22	15	0	7	720	482	238	30	4	238	Mike Rayer	13	Ben Whetstone
97-98	P2	22	20	0	2	791	365	426	40	1p	289	Mike Rayer	17	Ben Whetstone
98-99	P1	26	6	0	20	541	840	-299	12	13	134	Sam Howard	12	Rory Underwood
99-00	P1	22	1	0	21	396	802	-406	3	12	70	Andy Gomersall	9	Paul Sackey
00-01	N1	26	9	1	16	463	616	-153	47	11	99	Ben Whetstone	9	James Hinkins

BIGGEST MARGINS

Home Win 55pts - 64-9 v Moseley 2.11.96

Away Win 60pts - 67-7 v Fylde 27.12.97

Home Defeat 94pts - 106-12 v Richmond 16.5.99

Away Defeat 76pts - 0-76 v Bath 13.1.90

MOST CONSECUTIVE

Appearances 46 Paul Alston 19.9.92-12.4.95

Matches scoring Tries 6 Ben Whetstone & Martin Offiah

Matches scoring points 36 Andy Finnie

Victories 18

Defeats 15

MOST POINTS

Scored at Home 72 v Blackheath 22.2.97 & 25.4.98

Scored Away 67 v Fylde 27.12.97

Conceded at Home 106 v Richmond 16.5.99

Conceded Away 76 v Bath 13.1.90

MOST TRIES

Scored in a match 11 v Blackheath 22.2.97

Conceded in a match 16 v Richmond 16.5.99 (H)

MOST APPEARANCES

by a forward 97 Mark Upex

by a back 132 Ben Whetstone

	MOST IN A SEASON	MOST IN A CAREER	MOST IN A MATCH
Points	289 Mike Rayer 97-98	867 Andy Finnie 87-96	25 Andy Finnie v Coventry 27.3.93 (H)
Tries	17 Ben Whetstone 96-97	56 Ben Whetstone 92-01	4 Jason Forster v Fylde 17.1.98
Conversions	67 Mike Rayer 96-97	127 Mike rayer 96-98	8 Mike Rayer v Coventry 8.11.97 (H)
Penalties	56 Andy Finnie 94-95	203 Andy Finnie 87-96	7 Andy Finnie v Coventry 27.4.94 (H)
Drop Goals	5 Tony Yapp 98-99	22 Andy Finnie 87-96	2 Andy Finnie v Coventry 27.3.94 (H) v Clifton 14.1.95 (A)

PLAYING SQUAD

BEDFORD BLUES
1886

BEDFORD

BACKS

	Ht.	Wt.	Birthdate	Birthplace	CLUB	League Apps	Tries	Pts
James Shanahan			12.02.77		Bedford	22(4)	7	66
Ben Hinshelwood			22.03.77		Bedford	25(1)	6	36
John Rudd			26.05.81		Bedford	11(3)	4	20
Chris Bajak			01.07.74		Bedford	16(2)	6	30
Harley Crane			23.02.76		Bedford	12	2	10
Martin Wallwork			30.03.78		Bedford	15(4)	-	2
Scott Stewart Canada.	6.2	13.3	16.01.69	Vancouver	Bedford Harlequins	39(4) 14(2)	2 1	118 5
Jim Hinkins	6.1	13.7	11.05.77		Bedford Moseley	17(11) 33	9 7	45 35
Marco Rivero Italy			02.08.73		Bedford London Irish	5(1)	-	-
Ben Whetstone	5.11	14.7	29.06.70	Holbeach	Bedford London Irish	142(2) 18	56 7	342 35

FORWARDS

	Ht.	Wt.	Birthdate	Birthplace	CLUB	League Apps	Tries	Pts
Matt Skillecorn			24.02.77		Bedford	18	-	-
Michael Count			08.05.78		Bedford	5(2)	-	-
John Brooks			11.11.77		Bedford	14(8)	-	-
Aaron Davis	5.11	15.0	10.11.78	Luton	Bedford	6(17)	1	5
Andre Fox			24.08.71		Bedford	12	1	5
Phillip Clarke			19.07.77		Bedford	16(2)	1	5
Cameron Thomas			23.06.70		Bedford	15(4)	4	20
Henry Whitford			07.03.74		Bedford	14(5)	1	5
Jon Summers			18.09.76		Bedford	10(3)	-	-
Lawrence White			29.11.77		Bedford	22(2)	1	5
Richard Ward			26.11.70		Bedford	19(3)	-	-

BEDFORD

FACT FILE

Founded: 1886
Nickname: The Blues
Web Site: www.bedfordrugby.co.uk

Colours: Oxford and Cambridge blue.
Change colours: Cambridge and Oxford blue.

GROUND

Address: Goldington Road, Bedford. MK40 3NF.

Tel: 01234 347980   Fax: 01234 347511   e-mail: info@bedford.rugby.co.uk
Capacity: 6,200   Seated: 800 (covered) 400 (uncovered) Standing: 5,000

Directions: From M1 - J13 onto A421. On edge of Bedford join Southern releif road, signed Cambridge. At r'about at end of relief road, turn left to Bedford Town Centre. Ground approx. 4 miles on right.
    From A1 - Join A421 just south of St. Neots. After 8 miles this road takes you on to Goldington Road, into Bedford and ground is on the right.
    Nearest Railway Station: Bedford, Midland Road - one mile from the ground.
Car Parking: For hospitality only at ground, but plenty around the ground.

Admission: Match-day admission   £15 stand, £10 ground, concessions available

    Season Tickets   £225 stand, £150 ground, concessions available

Club Shop: Open 9-5 Tues, Wed, Friday & matchdays.

Clubhouse: Open 6.30 - 11pm Tues - Fri and 12.30-11pm on matchdays. Saturday lunches served.

Blues' captain, Ben Whetstone, chasing a kick.

PROGRAMME
Size: A5   Pages: 24
Price: £2.00
Editor: c/o Tony Mills

ADVERTISING RATES
Contact Tony Mills 01234 347980

BIRMINGHAM & SOLIHULL RFC

Chairman	Roger Murphy	Merrimans Hill Farm, Mill Lane, Danzey Green, Solihull, West Midlands B94 5BB 01564 742564 (H) 0121 328 2145 (B)
Club Secretary	Tony Moir	118 Grange Rd., Solihull, West Midlands. B91 1DA 0121 706 3928 (H) 0121 678 7304 (B)
Rugby Administrator	Keith Jervis	Earlsmere House, Warings Green Road, Earlswood, Solihull, West Midlands B94 6BS. 01564 702502 (H) 0121 359 4455 (B) 07801 453179 (M)
Commercial Manager	David Radburn	35 Yoxall Road, Shirley, Solihull, West Midlands B90 3SD 0121 694 4864 (H), 0121 705 0409 (B)

Following promotion from Jewson Division 1 at the end of the 1999/2000 season, The Bees' first game in National Division One was away to Leeds Tykes – a baptism of fire if ever there was one. Although the game was lost by 40 points to 25, the team played with power and spirit and, overall, felt satisfied with their start. Results over the next few matches were very pleasing with several wins being ground out, mainly by forward power and a miserly defence. By the end of November, the Bees were third in the league, behind Worcester and Leeds.

From that time on, however, life became very tough, with four draws and several narrow defeats. The team's league position slipped and by mid-April it was necessary to win either of the final two games to be sure of survival. In the penultimate game, at home to Bedford Blues, the Bees needed a massive performance to recover from a heart-stopping 15-nil deficit after only fifteen minutes, to record a narrow win by 19 points to 18. The curtain came down on the season with an exciting 26 points each draw, at home to Worcester.

Birmingham & Solihull finished in 9th position in the league, one place higher than local rivals, Moseley. It had been a difficult year in the league, with early optimism being replaced with survival concerns at the end of the season. Overall, the club was pleased with its performance. The Bees also experienced some success in the Tetley Bitter cup, with wins against Orrell and Darlington-Mowden Park being followed by a fifth-round defeat at Northampton. Throughout the season, the pack was immense, as was the defence generally, which conceded fewer points than any other side in the league, bar the top two clubs.

BIRMINGHAM & SOLIHULL

Comp.	Date	H/A	Opponents	Result & Score	Att.	15	14	13	12	11
N1	9-Sep	A	Leeds Tykes	L 25-40	734	Quantrill	Nicholson	Irwin	Roberts	Shepherd
N1	16-Sep	H	Manchester	W 23-19		Quantrill	Robinson	Irwin	Roberts	Shepherd
N1	23-Sep	A	Bedford	W 20-17	1506	Quantrill/t	Nicholson	Irwin	Roberts	Robinson(a/t
N1	30-Sep	H	Coventry	L 16-17	500	Quantrill	Nicholson	Irwin	Roberts	Shepherd
N1	7-Oct	A	Wakefield	L 0-11	300	Quantrill	Gough	Chapman	Irwin	Robinson
N1	14-Oct	H	Waterloo*	W 33-12	200	Quantrill	Nicholson/t	Irwin/t	Roberts	Shepherd
N1	28-Oct	A	Otley	W 8-5	400	Quantrill	Nicholson	Irwin	Roberts	Shepherd
N1	19-Nov	H	Exeter	W 27-21	250	Glackin	Nicholson/t	Irwin	Roberts	Chapman
N1	25-Nov	A	Moseley	W 14-13	638	Quantrill	Nicholson	Irwin	Roberts	Hyslop
N1	3-Dec	A	Worcester	L 16-21	1900	Quantrill	Nicholson	Irwin	Roberts	Hyslop/t
N1	16-Dec	H	Moseley	D 20-20	200	Quantrill	Nicholson	Irwin	Roberts	Hyslop
N1	6-Jan	H	Henley Hawks*	D 16-16	250	Gough/c3p	Chapman	Irwin	Roberts	Shepherd
N1	13-Jan	A	Exeter	L 6-22		Glackin	Hyslop	Irwin	Roberts	Shepherd
N1	27-Jan	A	Henley Hawks	D 18-18	520	Knight	Nicholson	Irwin	Roberts	Hyslop
N1	4-Feb	H	Otley	L 10-13	200	Knight	Nicholson	Irwin/t	Roberts	Shepherd
N1	10-Feb	A	Waterloo	L 9-12		Gough/3p	Nicholson	Hyslop	Roberts	Shepherd
N1	24-Feb	A	Wakefield	L 22-32		Knight	Nicholson/t	Irwin	Hyslop	Shepherd
N1	3-Mar	H	Orrell	D 15-15		Gough/5p	Nicholson	Irwin	Hyslop	Goodwin
N1	10-Mar	A	Coventry	L 18-23	2200	Gough/p(b/cp)	Nicholson/t	Irwin	Hyslop	Chapman
N1	24-Mar	A	London Welsh	L 7-11	600	Knight/c	Nicholson	Irwin	Hyslop	Chapman
N1	31-Mar	A	Manchester	L 13-14	385	Knight/c2p	Nicholson	Irwin	Hyslop	Chapman
N1	7-Apr	H	London Welsh*	L 13-14	400	Knight/c2p	Hyslop	Irwin	Talbot	Glackin
N1	14-Apr	H	Leeds Tykes	L 20-31		Knight/cp	Nicholson	Irwin	Hyslop	Shepherd/t
N1	21-Apr	A	Orrell*	L 13-20		Knight/c2p	Nicholson	Irwin	Hyslop	Shepherd
N1	25-Apr	H	Bedford*	W 19-18		Knight/2c	Hyslop	Irwin	Roberts	Shepherd
N1	28-Apr	H	Worcester	D 26-26		Knight/t3c	Hyslop	Irwin/t	Roberts/2t	Nicholson
TBC	21-Oct	H	Orrell	W 27-25	200	Glackin/t	Nicholson	Irwin/t	Roberts	Shepherd
TBC	11-Nov	A	Northanpton Saints**	L 14-47	3280	Quantrill	Hyslop	Irwin	Roberts	Shepherd

* after opponents name indicates a penalty try. Brackets after a player's name indicates he was replaced.
eg (a) means he was replaced by replacement code "a" and so on. / after a player or replacement name
is followed by any scores he made - eg /t, /c, /p, /dg or any combination of these

MATCH FACTS

10	9	1	2	3	4	5	6	7	8
Gough/tc6p	Lydster	Lewis	McMurray	Budgen	Hyde	Underhill	Brookes	Fakatou	Salisbury
Gough/2c3p	Lydster	Lewis	McMurray	Budgen/t	Hyde	Underhill	Brookes	Fakatou	Salisbury/t
Gough/cdg	Cattle	Lewis	Hubbleday	Budgen	Hyde	Underhill	Brookes	Fakatou/t	Salisbury
Gough/c3p	Lydster	Lewis	McMurray/t	Budgen	Hyde	Underhill	Brookes	Fakatou	Salisbury
Smart	Lydster	Linnett	McMurray	Budgen	Hyde	Underhill	Russell	Fakatou	Salisbury
Gough/t2c3p	Lydster	Lewis	McMurray	Budgen	Hyde	Underhill	Brookes	Fakatou	Salisbury
Gough/p	Lydster	Lewis	McMurray	Budgen	Hyde	Underhill	Brookes	Fakatou/t	Salisbury
Gough/3c2p	Lydster	Lewis/t	McMurray	Budgen/t	Hyde	McCrainor	Fakatou	Meadows	Brookes
Gough/3p	Lydster	Lewis	McMurray	Bullock	Hyde	Underhill	Fakatou/t	Meadows	Brookes
Gough/c2pdg	Lydster	Lewis	Hubbleday	Budgen	Hyde	McCrainor	Fakatou	Meadows	Brookes
Gough/2c2p	Lydster/t	Lewis	McMurray	Budgen/t	Hyde	McCrainor	Fakatou	Meadows	Brookes
Smart	Lydster	Lewis	Budgen	Bullock	Hyde	Underhill	Fakatou	Meadows	Salisbury
Gough/p(b/p)	Cattle	Lewis	Hubbleday	Budgen	Hyde	McCrainor	Fakatou	Brookes	Salisbury
Smart/c	Lydster	Lewis	McMurray	Bullock	Hyde	Underhill	Fakatou(c/t)	Meadows	Brookes/t
Gough/cp	Lydster	Linnett	McMurray	Budgen	Hyde	Underhill	Fakatou	Meadows	Brookes
Smart	Cattle	Lewis	McMurray	Bullock	McCrainor	Underhill	Russell	Meadows	Fakatou
Gough/2cp	Lydster	Lewis	Hubbleday	Budgen/t	Hyde	McCrainor	Fakatou/t	Meadows	Salisbury
Smart	Lydster	Lewis	Allan	Bullock	Hyde	McCrainor	Fakatou	Meadows	Brookes
Roberts/t	Lydster	Lewis	McMurray	Budgen	Hyde	Underhill	Fakatou	Meadows	Brookes
Roberts	Lydster	Lewis	McMurray	Bullock	Hyde	Underhill	Fakatou/t	Meadows	Brookes
Roberts	Cattle/t	Budgen	McMurray	Bullock	Hyde	McCrainor	Fakatou	Meadows	Brookes
Roberts	Cattle	Lewis	McMurray	Budgen	Hyde	McCrainor	Fakatou	Jordan	Brookes
Smart	Lydster	Lewis(d/t)	McMurray	Bullock	Hyde	Underhill	Salisbury	Jordan	Hensley/t
Roberts	Cattle	Lewis	Hubbleday	Bullock	Hyde	Underhill	Brookes	Fakatou	Hensley
Smart	Lydster/t	Lewis	McMurray	Bullock(c/t)	Hyde	Underhill	Salisbury	Fakatou	Brookes
Smart	Cattle	Lewis	McMurray	Budgen	Hyde	Underhill	Salisbury	Jordan	Brookes
Gough/2cp	Lydster/t	Lewis	Hubbleday	Budgen	Hyde	McCrainor	Brookes	Meadows	Fakatou/t
Smart/2c	Lydster	Lewis	McMurray	Budgen	Hyde	Underhill	Fakatou	Meadows	Brookes

REPLACEMENTS   a - B Shepherd   b - J Smart   c - C Budgen   d - M Linnett

2000-01 HIGHLIGHTS

Steve Gough, in his first season at the club, topped the scoring chart.

Gough has now finished top scorer for three clubs in a league season. He was initially with Fylde before moving on to Coventry.

In the early season match at Headingley he scored all 25 of his sides points and set a new points record for a Birmingham & Solihull player in a match.

The leading try scorer was prop Chris Budgen with just six.

Winger Ben Shepherd added a couple of tries during the season and extended his all-time career record to 31.

BIRMINGHAM & SOLIHULL

LEAGUE STATISTICS
compiled by Stephen McCormack

SEASON	Division	P	W	D	L	F	A	Pts Diff	Lge Pts	Lge Pos		Coach		Captain
91-92	Mid1	10	3	1	6	126	151	-25	7	9		R Richardson		T Ryan
92-93	Mid1	13	11	1	1	250	107	143	23	1p				
93-94	D5N	12	5	0	7	128	162	-34	10	9		M Swan		G Smith
94-95	D5N	12	5	0	7	167	226	-59	10	10		N Hurton		S Taylor
												Most Points		**Most Tries**
95-96	D5N	12	8	1	3	202	160	42	17	3	92	Jonathon Smart	3	Richard Packer
96-97	D4N	26	19	0	7	746	391	355	38	2	271	Jonathon Smart	10	David Cox
97-98	N2N	26	23	0	3	805	334	471	46	1p	296	Matt Birch	16	Ben Shepherd
98-99	JN1	26	9	0	17	422	523	101	18	11	170	Matt Birch	6	3 players
99-00	JN1	26	21	1	4	659	346	313	43	2p	166	Jon anthan Smart	14	Paul Lydster
00-01	N1	26	7	5	14	427	481	-54	48	9	176	Steve Gough	6	Chris Budgen

BIGGEST MARGINS

Home Win   46pts - 54-8 v Winnington Park 25.10.97
Away Win   62pts - 72-10 v Aspatria 30.8.97
Home Defeat   47pts - 3-50 v Wakefield 31.10.87
Away Defeat   79pts - 0-79 v Roundhay 26.11.88

MOST CONSECUTIVE

Appearances
Matches scoring Tries
Matches scoring points
Victories   9
Defeats   13

MOST POINTS

Scored at Home   55 v Stoke on Trent 21.9.96
Scored Away   72 v Aspatria 30.8.97
Conceded at Home   50 v Wakefield 31.10.87
Conceded Away   79 v Roundhay 26.11.88

MOST TRIES

Scored in a match   11 v Aspatria 30.8.97
Conceded in a match   ? v Roundhay 26.11.88

MOST APPEARANCES

by a forward   94 (15) Richard McCrainor
by a back   70 (1) Richard Chapman

	MOST IN A SEASON	MOST IN A CAREER	MOST IN A MATCH	
Points	296 Matt Birch 97-98	529 Jonathan Smart 96-00	25 Steve Gough	v Leeds 9.9.00
Tries	16 Ben Shepherd 97-98	31 Ben Shepherd 97-01	4 Steve Chapman	v Hinckley 31.1.98
Conversions	58 Matt Birch 97-98	88 Matt Birch 97-99	7 Matt Birch	v Aspatria 30.8.97
Penalties	55 Matt Birch 97-98	90 Matt Birch 97-99	6 Matt Birch	v Hinckley 8.11.97
			Steve Gough	v Leeds 9.9.00
Drop Goals	2 Steve Gough 00-01	3 Jonathon Smart 95-97	1 Jonathon Smart	(3 times)
			Steve Gough (twice)	
			Peter Glackin	

PLAYING SQUAD

BIRMINGHAM & SOLIHULL

BACKS

	Ht.	Wt.	Birthdate	Birthplace	CLUB	League Apps	Tries	Pts
Martin Roberts	6.3	15.2	26.01.68	Gloucester	Birmingham S	33	4	20
Other clubs: Gloucester					Moseley	22(1)	4	20
Jon Smart			24.01.75		Birmingham S	31(2)	3	176
					Moseley			
Adam Irwin			09.01.77		Birmingham S	50	13	65
Richard Chapman	6.0	14.04	12.02.74	Solihull	Birmingham S	72(5)	20	100
					Rugby			
Steve Chapman	6.1	13.10	27.03.70	Coventry	Birmingham S	51(7)	16	80
					Coventry			
Ben Shepherd	6.0	14.10	12.02.74	Coventry	Birmingham S	81(2)	31	155
					Coventry			
Steve Gough	5.10	13.7	22.04.66	Leigh	Birmingham S	18(1)	2	176
Other club: Fylde 118(3)/26/739					Coventry	48(1)	15	571
Mark Nicholson			05.10.65		Birmingham S	30(13)	5	25
					Coventry			
Pete Glackin			26.01.79		Birmingham S	17(12)	1	8
Paul Lydster	6.1	14.00	28.05.70	Coventry	Birmingham S	62(2)	22	110
					Coventry			
Jim Quantrill	6.2	15.00	30.05.69	Poole	Birmingham S	54	5	129
					Rugby	102(3)	13	559

FORWARDS

	Ht.	Wt.	Birthdate	Birthplace	CLUB	League Apps	Tries	Pts
Chris Budgen			21.01.73		Birmingham S	18(6)	6	30
					Nottingham	41	3	15
Warwick Bullock	6.0	17.12	09.02.70	Stourbridge	Birmingham S	56(9)	6	30
Other club: Gloucester.					Coventry			
Trent McMurray			16.06.71		Birmingham S	19(1)	1	5
					Coventry	8(10)	4	20
Adam Sturdy			03.12.76		Birmingham S	7(8)	-	-
					Nottingham	4(11)	-	-
Neil Underhill	6.10	17.00	23.06.72	Loughborough	Birmingham S	21(9)	-	-
					Rugby			
Richard McCrainor	6.4	17.07	25.01.71	Solihull	Birmingham S	93(13)	5	25
Julian Hyde	6.5	18.00	22.05.68	Coventry	Birmingham S	103	6	30
					Coventry			
Paul Meadows			27.03.75		Birmingham S	40(9)	6	30
Nick Lewis			12.07.71		Birmingham S	45(6)	1	5
Will Allen			08.01.66		Birmingham S	20(3)	4	20
Rob Salisbury	6.3	16.09	14.12.76	Birmingham	Birmingham	31(8)	7	35
					Coventry	7(8)	1	5

BIRMINGHAM & SOLIHULL

FACT FILE

Founded: 1989 (Birmingham RFC & Solihull RUFC merged)
Nickname: The Bees   **Colours**: Black shirt with yellow bands in top half, red collar
                                          Change colours: Black shirt with red bands in top half

GROUND

Address: Sharmans Cross Road, Solihull.
                Tel: 0121 705 0409   email: beesrfc@btinternet.com   Web site: www.beesrugby.com
                Capacity: 3,000   Seated: None   Standing: 3,000

Directions: From Solihull centre take Streetsbrook Road, through the traffic lights, over hump-back bridge.
                Second left into Sharmans Cross Road and the ground is 300 yards on the left.
                Nearest Railway Station: Solihull

Car Parking: Minimal spaces available at the ground.

Admission
                Season tickets Adults £100, OAPs £75
                Matchday   Adults £10, Concessions £6

Clubhouse: Open Sat. 12-11pm, Sun 10-3pm,
                Tue & Thur 7-11.30pm.
                Snacks and bar meals are available.
                Functions: Capacity 150
                contact Steve Bakewell 0121 705 7995

Club Shop: Yes, manager Dave Radburn.

Training Nights: Tuesday and Thursday.

PROGRAMME Size: A5
                Pages: 48 + cover
                Price: Included with entry
                Editor: David Radburn 0121 705 0409

Advertising Rates - Mono only (Prices + VAT)
                Full Page £475
                Half Page £250

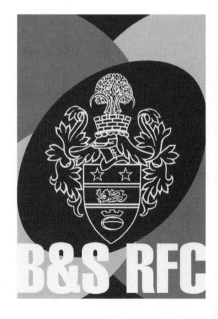

Julian Hyde, Birmingham & Solihull Captain

BRACKNELL RFC

Chairman	S J Ward	13 Arden Close, Bracknell, Berks. RG12 2SG
		Tel: 01344 420236 (H) 07774 821190 (Mobile)
Hon. Secretary	The Hon. Secretary	Bracknell RFC, Lily Hill Park, Lily Hill Drive, Bracknell, Berks. RG12 2UG
		Tel: 01344 424013 Fax: 01344 485268
		email: HonSec@Bracknellrugbyclub.com
Fixtures Secretary	S D Stevens	18 Abbey Close, Harnaswater, Bracknell, Berks RG12 9NX.
		Tel: 01344 422586 (H) 01344 789888 (B)

Bracknell Rugby Club achieved their fourth promotion in five seasons by winning National League Two in a very close competition with Rugby (also promoted) and Rosslyn Park. None of the top three sides lost a match after Christmas.

Once again Bracknell, coached by director of rugby, Paul `The Judge' Rendall, relied mainly on forward power. However, with Chris Wright (ex Harlequins & Orrell) installed as backs coach and a number of new signings Bracknell will look towards a more explosive game.

For the 2000/2001 season Top Try Scorer was Graham Sparks and Top Points Scorer was Ben Nowak.

Key matches were those at home to Harrogate and away at Wharfedale, Newbury and Kendal. Although Bracknell entered the new year two points clear in the League, they had eight away matches to play and as it turned out all eight of these plus five home matches had to be won.

Wharfedale on a wet February Saturday was a forward battle that brought Bracknell's first ever win in Yorkshire. The home win against, then championship contenders Harrogate was the performance of the season until the penultimate fixture, a re-arranged visit to Newbury, a local derby with all the usual trimmings. A 50 point victory was Paul Rendall's finest triumph in Bracknell colours.

The League was won in style at home at Lily Hill Park against an already relegated West Hartlepool who played well and entered the party atmosphere.

Bracknell are grateful to their major sponsors SkyNet Limited and Panasonic, as well as all the other sponsors, advertisers, supporters, members and friends who made the season one to be remembered.

The National Division Two championship winning Bracknell RFC squad.

BRACKNELL

Comp.	Date	H/A	Opponents	Result & Score	Att.	15	14	13	12	11
N1	2-Sep	H	Camberley	W 18-15		Kenworthy/t2p	Lutman	Boulard	Nowak	Spencer
N1	9-Sep	A	Esher	L 12-14	500	Kenworthy/4p	Lutman	Boulard	Nowak	Spencer
N1	16-Sep	H	Fylde	W 34-21		Heke	Morley/t	Boulard	Nowak	Spencer/2t
N1	23-Sep	A	Harrogate	L 27-28	350	Hoggard/2cp	Costoloe/t	Boulard	Heke/t	Lutman
N1	30-Sep	H	Wharfedale*	W 23-17		Costoloe	Morley	Boulard	Heke	Hall
N1	14-Oct	H	Newbury*	W 26-11		Costoloe	Morley	Kenworthy/3c	Heke	Boulard
N1	28-Oct	H	Preston Grasshoppers	W 28-7	300	Costoloe/t	Morley	Kenworthy	Nowak	Boulard
N1	11-Nov	A	Rosslyn Park	W 33-19		Kenworthy/3c3pdg	Nowak	Heke	Boulard	Morley
N1	18-Nov	H	Rugby Lions	W 9-6		Kenworthy/3p	Nowak	Boulard	Heke	Morley
N1	25-Nov	A	West Hartlepool	W 30-10		Kenworthy/t2c2p	Nowak	Boulard	Heke	Morley
N1	9-Dec	H	Kendal	W 31-15		Kenworthy/4cp	Costoloe/t	Heke	Nowak	Morley/t
N1	16-Dec	A	Rugby Lions	L 7-43	400	Kenworthy/c	Costoloe	Heke	Nowak	Morley
N1	23-Dec	H	Rosslyn Park	L 16-18		Costoloe	Nowak/c2pdg	Heke	Boulard	Spencer/t
N1	6-Jan	A	Preston Grasshoppers	W 40-17	450	Kenworthy/3c3p	Nowak/t	Heke	Boulard/t	Spencer/t
N1	13-Jan	H	Nottingham*	W 48-3		Kenworthy/5cp	Nowak/t	Boulard/t	Heke	Spencer/t
N1	27-Jan	H	Lydney	W 25-3		Marsh/2t	Nowak	Boulard	Heke	Spencer
N1	3-Feb	A	Lydney*	W 36-8		Marsh/t	Nowak/2t4cp	Boulard	Heke	Costoloe
N1	10-Feb	A	Wharfedale	W 22-6		Scott	Nowak/2cp	Boulard	Heke	Spencer
N1	24-Feb	H	Harrogate*	W 42-5	200	Scott	Nowak/t4c3p	Boulard/t	Heke	Spencer/t
N1	3-Mar	A	Nottingham	W 22-7		Marsh	Nowak/4p	Boulard	Heke	Spencer
N1	10-Mar	A	Fylde	W 17-6		Kenworthy/c	Nowak/t	Marsh	Heke	Spencer
N1	17-Mar	H	Esher	W 16-0		Kenworthy	Nowak/c3p	Marsh	Heke	Spencer
N1	24-Mar	A	Camberley	W 39-15		Kenworthy/tc	Nowak/2cp	Marsh	Heke	Carpente/3t
N1	31-Mar	A	Kendal	W 22-13		Kenworthy	Nowak/c	Boulard	Heke	Spencer/2t
N1	7-Apr	A	Newbury	W 53-3		Kenworthy/t3c	Nowak/2tc	Marsh	Heke/2t	Spencer/t
N1	14-Apr	H	West Hartlepool	W 76-0		Kenworthy/t4c	Nowak/4c	Marsh/2t	Heke	Spencer/3t
TBC	7-Oct	H	Dorchester	W 45-0		Costoloe	Hall	Boulard/2t	Kenworthy/t	Morley
TBC	21-Oct	H	Cheshunt	W 33-0		Costoloe	Boulard/t	Kenworthy/t	Nowak	Morley/2t
TBC	4-Nov	A	Wakefield	L 23-31	300	Costoloe	Boulard	Kenworthy/tcp	Nowak	Morley

*after opponents name indicates a penalty try. Brackets after a player's name indicates he was replaced.
eg (a) means he was replaced by replacement code "a" and so on. / after a player or replacement name
is followed by any scores he made - eg /t, /c, /p, /dg or any combination of these

EVER PRESENT   None

Most Appearances
    24   Jim Kelly.
    23   Richard Parker, Graham Sparks,
            Ben Nowak, Josh Heke.

PLAYERS USED   32 plus 1 as replacement only.

MOST POINTS

Pts	Player	T	C	P	DG
145	M Kenworthy	5	30	19	1
128	B Nowak	8	20	15	1
70	G Sparks	14	-	-	-
60	G Spencer	12	-	-	-
38	B Hoggard	2	5	6	-

MATCH FACTS

10	9	1	2	3	4	5	6	7	8
Wright/c	Morley	Kelly	Yates	Anstead	Leishman	Orugboh	Jackson	Nowak	Lamb/t
Wright	Shaw	Kelly	Yates	Anstead	Leishman	Parker	Jackson	Fee	Sparks
Wright/tc4p	Shaw	Kelly	Yates	Mosses	Leishman	Parker	Jackson	Fee	Sparks
Wright	Morley	Kelly	Turner/t	Mosses	Leishman	Orugboh/t	Parker	Nowak	Sparks
Hoggard/tc2p	Shaw	Kelly/t	Turner	Mosses	Orugboh	Parker	Jackson	Nowak	Sparks
Hoggard/t	Shaw/t	Edwards	Yates	Mosses	Leishman	Moore	Parker	Jackson/t	Sparks
Hoggard/2c3p	Shaw/t	Kelly	Yates	Mosses	Borcherds	Moore/t	Parker	Jackson	Sparks
Costoloe	Shaw	Kelly	Yates/t	Edwards	Leishman	Moore	Parker	Jackson/t	Nowak/t
Hoggard	Shaw	Kelly	Yates	Anstead	Leishman	Moore	Parker	Jackson	Nowak
Hoggard	Shaw	Edwards	Yates	Anstead	Leishman	Orugboh	Parker	Nowak/t	Sparks/2t
Hoggard	Shaw	Kelly	Yates	Mosses	Leishman	Moore/t	Parker	Jackson	Sparks/t
Hoggard	Shaw	Kelly	Yates	Mosses	Leishman	Moore	Parker/t	Jackson	Sparks
Hoggard	Shaw	Kelly	Turner	Anstead	Leishman	Moore	Parker	Jackson	Sparks
Costoloe	Shaw	Kelly	Turner	Mosses	Leishman	Moore	Parker/t	Jackson	Sparks/t
Costoloe	Wright	Kelly	Turner	Mosses	Moore(a/t)	Parker	Nowak	Jackson/t	Sparks/t
Costoloe	Shaw/t	Kelly	Turner	Mosses	Leishman	Moore	Parker	Jackson	Sparks/2t
Wright	Shaw	Kelly	Turner	Mosses	Moore	Leishman	Nowak	Jackson	Sparks/t
Costoloe/t	Wright	Kelly/t	Turner	Mosses	Leishman	Moore	Nowak	Jackson	Sparks/t
Costoloe	Wright	Kelly	Turner	Mosses	Leishman	Moore/t	Parker	Jackson	Sparks
Costoloe	Shaw	Kelly	Yates	Mosses	Leishman	Moore	Parker	Jackson	Sparks/2t
Costoloe	Wright	Kelly/t	Yates	Mosses	Leishman	Moore	Parker	Jackson	Sparks/t
Costoloe	Wright/t	Kelly	Yates	Mosses	Borcherds	Moore	Parker	Jackson	Sparks
Costoloe(b/t)	Wright	Kelly	Turner/t	Mosses	Borcherds	Moore	Parker	Nowak	Sparks
Costoloe	Wright	Kelly	Yates/t	Mosses	Leishman	Moore	Parker	Sparks/t	Lamb
Costoloe	Wright/t	Kelly	Yates/t	Mosses	Leishman	Moore/t	Parker	Nowak	Sparks
Costoloe	Shaw/2t(c/t)	Kelly	Box	Mosses	Leishman/t	Moore	Parker	Nowak/t	Sparks/t
Hoggard/5c	Shaw	Edwards/t	Yates	Mosses	Moore/t	Parker	Jackson/t	Nowak/t	Sparks
Hoggard/2c3p	Shaw	Edwards	Yates	Mosses	Leishman	Moore	Parker	Jackson	Sparks
Hoggard/c2p	Shaw	Kelly	Yates	Mosses	Leishman	Moore	Parker/t	Jackson	Sparks

REPLACEMENTS   a - J Healy   b - S Shaw   c - C Wright

2000-01 HIGHLIGHTS

Mike Kenworthy topped the scoring charts for the first time with 145 points.

Centre Ben Nowak also topped the 100 point mark to finish second.

New No 8 Graham Sparks set a new try scoring record with 14 tries during the season, he was closely followed by Winger Guy Spencer. He scored 12 times and in the process extended his club career record to 29.

The last match of the season saw then win 76-0 and set a new record for most points and biggest winning margin as they thrashed bottom of the table West Hartlepool.

They also suffered their worst ever defeat in National League rugby when losing 43-7 at Rugby Lions.

BRACKNELL

LEAGUE STATISTICS
compiled by Stephen McCormack

SEASON	Division	P	W	D	L	F	A	Pts Diff	Lge Pts	Lge Pos	Coach		Captain	
91-92	BDW1	10	9	0	1	222	50	172	19	1p				
92-93	SWSC	12	8	1	3	198	95	103	17	4				
93-94	SWSC	12	10	0	2	294	90	204	20	2				
94-95	SWSC	12	10	0	2	365	80	285	20	2				
95-96	SWSC	12	11	0	1	409	76	333	22	2				
96-97	SWSC	22	22	0	0	868	201	667	44	1p				
											Most Points		**Most Tries**	
97-98	SW1	22	18	2	2	786	271	515	38	1p	293	Carson Russell	20	Alex Poole
98-99	J2S	26	23	1	2	631	317	314	47	1p	216	Carson Russell	8	Howard Lamb & Phil Hopley
99-00	JN1	26	14	0	12	608	408	200	28	7	133	Carson Russell	10	Guy Spencer
00-01	N2	26	22	0	4	752	310	442	44	1p	145	Mike Kenworthy	14	Graham Sparks

BIGGEST MARGINS

Home Win	76pts - 76-0 v W Hartlepool 14.04.01
Away Win	54pts -64-12 v Plymouth 03.04.99
Home Defeat	15pts -13-28 v Otley 28.08.99
Away Defeat	36pts - 7-43 v Rugby Lions 16.12.00

MOST POINTS

Scored at Home	76 v W Hartlepool 14.04.01
Scored Away	64 v Plymouth 03.04.99
Conceded at Home	28 v Otley 28.08.99
Conceded Away	43 v Rugby Lions 16.12.00

MOST CONSECUTIVE

Appearances	17 Nick Robinson
Matches scoring Tries	3 John Clarke
Matches scoring points	19 Carson Russell
Victories	19
Defeats	1

MOST TRIES

Scored in a match	12 v W Hartlepool 14.04.01
Conceded in a match	7 v Rugby Lions 16.12.00

MOST APPEARANCES

by a forward	69 Alan Leishman
by a back	48 Simon Shaw

	MOST IN A SEASON	MOST IN A CAREER	MOST IN A MATCH
Points	216 Carson Russell 98-99	349 CarsonRussell 98-00	26 Carson Russell v N Walsham 27.03.99 (H)
Tries	14 Graham Sparkes 00-01	29 Guy Spencer 98-01	3 David Jackson v Bridgwater 06.02.99 (H) Jon Clarke v Plymouth 03.04.99 (A)
Conversions	39 CarsonRussell 98-99	59 Carson Russell 98-99	5 Carson Russell v Plymouth 03.04.99 (A) v Reading 07.11.99 (H)
Penalties	45 Carson Russell 98-99	76 CarsonRussell 98-99	8 Carson Russell v N Walsham 27.03.99 (H)
Drop Goals	1 Michael Kenworthy 98-99/00-01 Carson Russell 98-99 Ben Nowak 00-01	2 Michael Kenworthy 98-01	1 Michael Kenworthy v Esher 27.02.99 (H) Carson Russell v Weston s Mare 02.01.99 (A) Michael Kenworthy v Ross Park 11.11.00 (A) Ben Nowak v Ross Park 23.12.00 (H)

All records relate to National league rugby only.

PLAYING SQUAD

BRACKNELL

BACKS

	Ht.	Wt.	Birthdate	Birthplace	CLUB	League Apps	Tries	Pts
Nick Marsh					Bracknell	8	5	45
Bart Hoggard					Bracknell	9	2	38
Josh Heke					Bracknell	23	3	15
Ben Nowak	6.3	15.07	29.11.77	Hillingdon	Bracknell	51(3)	13	198
Michael Kenworthy	6.0	14.06	30.05.67	Dunedin	Bracknell	38(4)	10	281
Colin Morley	5.7	13.08	17.12.73	Slough	Bracknell	31(4)	4	20
Simon Shaw	5.9	14.00	21.08.72	High Wycombe	Bracknell High Wycombe	48(10)	15	75
Tony Scott			22.06.73		Bracknell	10	2	10
Paul Boulard			09.03.78		Bracknell Reading	19(2)	3	15
Gareth Priest	5.9	14.05	02.04.73	Hillingdon	Bracknell	11(2)	3	15
Guy Spencer Other club: Bournemouth	6.3	14.07	22.06.67	RAF Halton	Bracknell Reading	54	29	145

FORWARDS

	Ht.	Wt.	Birthdate	Birthplace	CLUB	League Apps	Tries	Pts
Jim Kelly	6.3	18.00	16.02.76	Aldershot	Bracknell London Scottish	63(7)	6	30
Richard Turner	5.11	15.00	26.04.72	Exeter	Bracknell	45(4)	4	20
Glyn Mosses	5.11	18.05	02.01.61	Birmingham	Bracknell	48(8)	4	20
Alan Leishman	6.5	16.00	19.04.75	Reading	Bracknell	69	3	15
Andy Orugboh	6.4	15.07	25.05.69	London	Bracknell	31(12)	1	5
Chris Moore					Bracknell	30(1)	7	35
Howard Lamb	6.3	18.02	13.03.69	Pinner	Bracknell	41(3)	16	80
Simon Edwards	6.0	17.07	13.06.64	Swindon	Bracknell	17(15)	-	-
David Box					Bracknelll	5	-	-
David Jackson	6.2	15.08	24.02.70	Scotland	Bracknell	66(1)	14	70
Richard Parker	6.0	15.00	03.10.71	Birmingham	Bracknell Camberley	45(6)	4	20
Andy Yates	5.9	15.06	09.01.68	Manchester	Bracknell Lymm	21(3)	3	15
Greg Anstead					Bracknell Reading	25(12)	-	-

BRACKNELL

FACT FILE

Founded: 1955
Web site: www.bracknellrugbyclub.com

Colours: Black with green & yellow hoops/black
Change colours: All black

GROUND

Address: Lily Hill Park, Lily Hill Drive, Bracknell, Berks RG12 2UG
Tel: 01344 424013   Fax: 01344 485268   email: info@Bracknellrugbyclub.com
Capacity: 1,150   1.000 uncovered standing   150 Covered seats hopefully for 2001-02

Directions: **From M4**, J10 - A329(M) Bracknell, B3408 Binfield, follow to A329 Bracknell. Through town towards Ascot, turn left at 'Running Horse' PH r'about, ground at rear.
From M3, J3 - A322 Bracknell - A332 Ascot to Heatherwood Hospital roundabout, A329 Bracknell to 'Running Horse' PH (on Right). Ground at rear.
Nearest Railway Station: Bracknell (approx 1.5 miles), frequent service London & Reading

Car Parking: 70 spaces at ground for permit holders only,
but secure off-site parking about 2 mins away. Please park as signposted.

Admission: Season ticket: £70 (standing)
Matchday: Standing - Adults: £8, Concessions £6   Seated - £11 - incl. programme

Clubhouse: Lounge bar & Players bar.
Snacks & bar meals available.
Functions: Contact Paul Adams (Bar Manager) on 01344 424013

Club Shop: Open on match days
plus Tues, Wed & Thur evenings 7.30 - 9.30

Training Nights: Tuesday & Thursday (1st & 2nd XV squads).
Lower XVs & ladies Wednesday

PROGRAMME Size: A5   Pages: 48   Editor: John Denman
Price: Included with admission
Advertising Rates Contact J Lucas 01252 621143
Per page, per season - Full page £490, Half £275, Qtr £175.

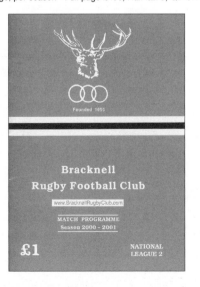

Graham Sparks -
Player of the Year 2000-01 with his trophy.

COVENTRY FC

President   J Broderick   Coventry F.C. Ltd., Barkers Butts lane, Coundon, Coventry CV6 1DU
Tel: 02476 601174   Fax: 02476 601194

Chairman   Keith Fairbrother   as above

General Manager   Ian Carvell   as above

Fixtures Secretary   Paul Ingleston   as above   Tel: 02476 502587 (H) 07801 233 921 (M)

Commercial Manager   Vivien Robinson   as above

After the opening three National Division One games played, Coventry's record read played three, lost three. Those were the bare facts and set alarm bells ringing at Coundon Road. Ahead of the fourth game at Birmingham/Solihull, head coach Harry Roberts was `stood down' by the Coundon Road board and coaching sessions were led by a group of senior players, including hooker Dave Addleton, currently out of action with a wired-up jaw after a training injury left him with a broken jaw, and captain Lee Crofts, sidelined presently with a troublesome knee injury. The players responded with a hard-fought 17-16 win at their local rivals. Relief all round on and off the pitch.

However, all the previous three losses were close enough to garner three bonus points, 12-19 at home to Exeter, 27 -33 at Henley Hawks (disappointing this as Cov had led 21-12 at the break) and a 20-25 loss at home to London Welsh. However, wins were still difficult to achieve. Worcester, at the time leaders, won 34-7 at Coundon Road, Orrell won a scrappy game in Lancashire, 11-6, while a 30-19 win at home to Preston Grasshoppers in the league was the only relief, followed by a 3-34 drubbing to Leeds at home. The corner was turned at Grove Park, Manchester, Cov winning a tense game 28-20. Then, Cov refused to be cannon fodder at Sale Sharks in the Tetley's, going down bravely 37-19.

`Old boys' and ex-England players, Peter Rossborough and Graham Robbins, by now coached Cov. A bonus point came at Wakefield in an 18-24 reverse, and the team now embarked on a run of heady success. First Waterloo fell 20-13. Followed by Wakefield, 25-9 both at home, Bedford away, 15-20, followed by Manchester at home, 18-10 made it four wins on the spin. Local rivals Moseley were then thrashed 54-7 at Coundon Road, Bedford the following week, 39-22. Orrell were vanquished next at home, 19-8, setting a new club league record of seven wins. This run was followed by a 25-20 loss at a fired-up Moseley, a strong performance at Worcester, a 16-27 loss, but, in a rearranged game injury hit Cov were taken apart by eventual champions Leeds, 68-8. Local rivalry meant a 23-18 win at home to Birmingham/Solihull, followed by third placed Cov now winning at London Welsh for the first time in twelve years, 20-14. A win at home to Henley 25-18 was followed by a heavy 48-22 loss at a resurgent Exeter. A home win in a see-saw battle with Otley and a last game defeat at Waterloo completed the campaign.

Player highlights were centre Jason Minshull making his 200th club appearance in the home London Welsh defeat whilst long serving No 8 Julian Horrobin (200th club appearance in the last game at Waterloo) and Matt Gallagher made his 100th club appearance in the same game. Leading the points tally with over 268 was composed fullback Martyn Davies, the Welshman joining from Rugby Lions close season and crowd pleasing winger Kurt Johnson who finished with sixteen tries.

Coventry forwards Lee Crofts and Mark Ellis both appeared for the Barbarians during the season and Coventry are aiming to be at the top of the heap come April 2002.

COVENTRY

Comp.	Date	H/A	Opponents	Result & Score	H-t	15	14	13	12	11
N1	9-Sep	H	Exeter	L 12-19	1000	Davies/c	Sims	Howland	Davies	Smallwood/t
N1	16-Sep	A	Henley Hawks	L 27-33	450	Davies/c5p	Sims	Minshull	Davies	Smallwood/t
N1	23-Sep	H	London Welsh	L 20-25	1500	Davies/2c2p	Johnson/2t	Minshull	Davies	Higgins
N1	30-Sep	A	Birmingham & Solihull	W 17-16	500	Davies/4p	Johnson	Minshull/t	Curtis	Smallwood
N1	7-Oct	H	Worcester	L 17-34	2200	Davies/4p	Johnson	Minshull	Curtis	Smallwood
N1	14-Oct	A	Orrell	L 6-11	600	Elphick/2p	Johnson	Frost	Curtis	Smallwood
N1	28-Oct	H	Leeds Tykes	L 3-34	1500	Davies/p	Johnson	Frost	Curtis	Smallwood
N1	19-Nov	A	Manchester	W 28-20	625	Davies/4c	Johnson	Davies	Curtis	Smallwood/t
N1	25-Nov	A	Wakefield	L 18-24	250	Davies/tc2p	Johnson	Davies	Frost/t	Smallwood
N1	2-Dec	H	Waterloo	W 20-13	1100	Davies/tcp	Johnson/t	Davies	Curtis(b/t)	Smallwood
N1	9-Dec	A	Otley	W 24-19		Davies/3p	Johnson	Minshull	Davies/t	Elphick/t
N1	16-Dec	H	Wakefield	W 25-9	1200	Davies/2c2p	Johnson	Minshull/t	Davies	Elphick/t
N1	6-Jan	A	Bedford	W 20-15		Davies/t5p	Gallagher	Davies	Minshull	Elphick
N1	13-Jan	H	Manchester	W 18-10	1256	Davies/cp	Minshull/t	Frost/t	Curtis	Gallagher/p
N1	20-Jan	H	Moseley	W 54-7	3185	Davies/5c3p	Johnson/2t	Minshull	Gallagher	Smallwood/t
N1	27-Jan	H	Bedford	W 39-22	2200	Davies/4c2p	Johnson/3t	Minshull	Davies	Smallwood
N1	10-Feb	H	Orrell*	W 19-8	1525	Gallagher/2c	Johnson/t	Minshull	Davies	Smallwood
N1	18-Feb	A	Moseley	L 20-25	880	Davies/2c2p	Johnson	Davies	Gallagher	Smallwood
N1	24-Feb	A	Worcester	L 16-27	3065	Davies/c3p	Johnson	Davies	Curtis	Minshull
N1	4-Mar	A	Leeds Tykes	L 8-68	512	Smallwood	Johnson	Read	Curtis	Maisey
N1	10-Mar	H	Birmingham & Solihull	W 23-18	2200	Davies/2c3p	Johnson/t	Davies/t	Minshull	Smallwood
N1	17-Mar	A	London Welsh	W 20-14	700	Gallagher/cp	Johnson	Davies	Minshull	Smallwood/t
N1	31-Mar	H	Henley Hawks	W 25-18	1800	Gallagher/2c2p	Johnson/t	Minshull	Davies	Smallwood
N1	14-Apr	A	Exeter	L 22-48	989	Davies/t2cp	Johnson	Minshull	Gallagher	Smallwood
N1	21-Apr	H	Otley	W 38-27	1800	Davies/3c4p	Johnson/2t	Davies	Curtis	Minshull/t
N1	28-Apr	A	Waterloo	L 26-40		Davies/c3p	Johnson/t	Davies	Minshull	Smallwood
TBC	21-Oct	H	Preston Grasshoppers	W 30-19	330	Davies/2t2c2p	Johnson/2t	Minshull	Curtis	Smallwood
TBC	5-Nov	A	Sale	L 19-37		Davies/3p	Johnson	Davies	Curtis	Smallwood/t

*after opponents name indicates a penalty try. Brackets after a player's name indicates he was replaced.
eg (a) means he was replaced by replacement code "a" and so on. / after a player or replacement name
is followed by any scores he made - eg /t, /c, /p, /dg or any combination of these*

LEAGUE DEBUTS

Perry Freshwater, Simon Frost, John Griffiths,
James Hadfield, James Hayter, Ian Higgins,
Matthew HowlandChris Maisey, John Munro,
Tim Payne, Mitch Read, Carl Southwell, Mark Tinnock,
Craig Turvey, Elisa Vunipola, Geoff Wappett.

EVER PRESENT   None

Most Appearances :
24 Trevor Revan. 22 Kurt Johnson, Anthony Dawson.

PLAYERS USED   37 plus 4 as replacement only.

MOST POINTS

Pts	Player	T	C	P	DG
239	M Davies	4	33	51	-
70	K Johnson	14	-	-	-
25	M Gallagher	-	5	5	-
25	Lee Crofts	5	-	-	-
25	Andy Smallwood	5	-	-	-

MATCH FACTS

10	9	1	2	3	4	5	6	7	8
Elphick	Dawson	Mika	Hayter	Revan	Hurrell	Griffiths	Crofts	Ellis(a/t)	Horrobin
Elphick	Dawson/t	Mika	Freshwater	Revan	Hurrell	Griffiths	Wappett	Ellis	Horrobin
Elphick	Dawson	Mika	Hayter	Revan	Hurrell	Griffiths	Wappett	Ellis	Horrobin
Elphick	Dawson	Mika	Southwell	Revan	Griffiths	Hurrell	Callaway	Munro	Horrobin
Elphick	Dawson	Payne	Southwell/t	Revan	Griffiths	Hurrell	Callaway	Munro	Ellis
Minshull	Dawson	Payne	Southwell	Revan	Griffiths	Hurrell	Callaway	Ellis	Horrobin
Vunipola	Dawson	Payne	Southwell	Revan	Griffiths	Hurrell	Crofts	Ellis	Brady
Vunipola/t	Dawson	Mika	Hayter	Revan	Griffiths	Hurrell	Ellis	Callaway/2t	Crofts
Vunipola	Dawson	Payne	Hayter	Revan	Griffiths	Hurrell	Ellis	Callaway	Crofts
Vunipola	Dawson	Mika	Addleton	Payne	Crofts	Hurrell	Ellis	Callaway	Horrobin
Vunipola	Dawson	Mika	Hayter	Revan	Griffiths	Aston	Crofts	Ellis	Horrobin/t
Vunipola/t	Dawson	Mika	Hayter	Revan	Griffiths	Aston	Crofts	Ellis	Horrobin
Vunipola	Dawson	Mika	Hayter	Revan	Griffiths	Tinnock	Crofts	Ellis	Horrobin
Vunipola	Dawson	Payne	Hayter	Revan	Griffiths	Tinnock	Crofts	Ellis	Horrobin
Vunipola	Turvey	Mika	Hayter/t(c/2t)	Revan	Hurrell	Tinnock/t	Crofts	Ellis	Horrobin
Vunipola	Dawson	Mika	Hayter/t	Revan	Hurrell	Tinnock	Crofts/t	Ellis	Horrobin
Vunipola	Turvey	Mika	Hayter	Revan	Hurrell	Tinnock/t	Crofts	Callaway	Horrobin
Vunipola	Dawson	Mika	Hayter	Revan	Hurrell	Griffiths	Crofts/t	Callaway/t	Horrobin
Vunipola	Turvey	Mika	Addleton	Revan	Hurrell	Tinnock	Crofts/t	Ellis	Horrobin
Gallagher/p	Dawson	Payne	Addleton/p	Revan	Hurrell	Butcher	Aston	Ellis	Brady/t
Vunipola	Dawson	Mika	Hayter	Revan	Hurrell	Tinnock	Griffiths	Ellis	Horrobin
Vunipola/t	Dawson	Payne	Addleton	Revan	Hurrell	Tinnock	Crofts/t	Ellis	Brady
Vunipola/t	Dawson/t	Payne	Addleton	Revan	Hurrell	Tinnock	Brady	Ellis	Horrobin
Vunipola	Dawson	Payne/t	Addleton	Hadfield(d/t)	Hurrell	Tinnock	Crofts	Ellis	Horrobin
Vunipola	Turvey	Payne	Hayter	Revan	Griffiths	Tinnock	Crofts	Callaway	Horrobin/t
Vunipola/t	Dawson	Payne	Addleton	Revan	Hurrell	Tinnock	Crofts/t	Callaway	Horrobin
Vunipola	Dawson	Mika	Southwell	Payne	Griffiths	Hurrell	Ellis	Munro	Crofts
Vunipola	Dawson	Mika	Hayter	Payne	Tinnock	Hurrell/t	Ellis	Callaway	Crofts

REPLACEMENTS　　a - R Callaway　　b - J Minshull　　c - C Southwell　　d - D Gallagher

Full back Martyn Davies, a signing from Rugby Lions, topped the scoring list in his first full season. He scored 239 points from his 21 starts and his total of 51 penalties fell just two short of the club record held by Steve Gough.

Winger Kurt Johnson finished outright leading try scorer this season after sharing the title the previous season. He has now scored an impressive 26 tries in two seasons.

The prolific Andy Smallwood added five more tries and extended his career record passed the 50 mark.

The defeat at Headingley against leeds in April set a few records. It was both their biggest defeat in terms of points scored against and as a losing margin.
It set another record as they conceded 12 tries for the first time ever in a league match.

COVENTRY

LEAGUE STATISTICS
compiled by Stephen McCormack

SEASON	Division	P	W	D	L	F	A	Pts Diff	Lge Pts	Lge Pos	Most Points		Most Tries	
91-92	2	12	7	0	5	187	196	-9	14	6	73	Steve Thomas	4	Kevin Hickey
92-93	2	12	3	0	9	192	236	-44	6	11r	53	Richard Angell	4	Barry Evans
93-94	3	18	14	0	4	406	259	197	28	1p	151	Richard Angell	9	Doug Woodman
94-95	2	18	2	0	16	213	436	-223	4	10r	90	Richard Angell	5	Mark Douglas
95-96	3	18	15	0	3	524	264	260	30	1p	84	Craig Quick	11	Julian Horrobin
96-97	2	22	16	1	5	738	394	344	33	3	236	Jez Harris	17	Andy Smallwood
97-98	P2	22	11	1	10	444	532	-88	23	7	133	Jez Harris	6	Julian Horrobin
98-99	P2	26	14	0	12	662	552	110	34	7	305	Steve Gough	15	Andy Smallwood
99-00	P2	26	15	0	11	714	589	125	30	6	266	Steve Gough	12	Andy Smallwood Kurt Johnson
00-01	N1	26	14	0	12	565	604	-39	66	5	239	Martyn Davies	14	Kurt Johnson

BIGGEST MARGINS

Home Win   80pts - 102-22 v Nottingham 5.10.96

Away Win   58pts - 61-3 v Rugby 14.9.96

Home Defeat 39pts - 6-45 v Rotherham 15.04.00

Away Defeat   60pts - 8-68 v Leeds Tykes 04.03.01

MOST CONSECUTIVE

Appearances   35 Richard Angell & Warwick Bullock

Matches scoring Tries   4 Andy Smallwood

Matches scoring points   11 Jez Harris

Victories   9

Defeats   13

MOST POINTS

Scored at Home   102 v Nottingham 5.10.96

Scored Away   61 v Rugby 14.9.96

Conceded at Home 45 v Rotherham 15.04.00

Conceded Away   68 v Leeds Tykes 03.04.01

MOST TRIES

Scored in a match   14 v Nottingham 5.10.96

Conceded in a match 12 v Leeds Tykes 03.04.01

MOST APPEARANCES

by a forward   164 (11) Dave Addleton

by a back   123 (5) Andy Smallwood

	MOST IN A SEASON	MOST IN A CAREER	MOST IN A MATCH	
Points	305 SteveGough 98-99	571 Steve Gough 98-00	42 Jez Harris	v Nottingham 5.10.96 (H)
Tries	17 Andy Smallwood 96-97	53 Andy Smallwood 96-01	4 Andy Smallwood	v Wakefield 8.5.99 (H)
Conversions	48 Jez Harris 96-97 Steve Gough 98-99	95 Steve Gough 98-00	13 Jez Harris	v Nottingham 5.10.96 (H)
Penalties	53 Steve Gough 98-99	102 Steve Gough 98-00	7 Steve Gough	v Worcester 11.02.00 (H)
Drop Goals	5 Jez Harris 96-97	10 Mark Lakey 87-95	2 Mark Lakey Jez Harris	v Moseley 3.4.93 (H) v Lon. Irish 8.10.94 (H) v Wakefield 21.9.96 (H)

PLAYING SQUAD

1874
COVENTRY

COVENTRY

BACKS

	Ht.	Wt.	Birthdate	Birthplace	CLUB	League Apps	Tries	Pts
Matt Gallagher	6.1	13.0	21.03.73	Solihull	Coventry	73(6)	12	164
					Nottingham	44	4	114
Jason Minshull	5.11	13.5	20.12.67	Leamington Spa	Coventry	103(9)	16	74
Andy Smallwood	5.10	13.11	13.06.72	Solihull	Coventry	123(5)	53	265
					Nottingham	47	12	60
Martyn Davies	1.86m	83kg	12.10.73	Glanaman	Coventry	21(1)	4	239
					Rugby Lions	54(2)	5	468
Mike Davies	6.0	15.7	07.03.77	Cwmavon	Coventry	20(15)	-	-
					Gloucester	2	1	5
Kurt Johnson	5.10	98kg	23.06.77	Slough	Coventry	46(1)	26	130
					Orrell	13(2)	10	50
Elisi Vunipola					Coventry	19(1)	5	25
Matt Sims					Coventry	6(2)	3	15
Mick Curtis	5.11	16.0	27.06.72	Coventry	Coventry	93(15)	13	65
Tigger Dawson	5.10	11.0	29.01.75	Crewe	Coventry	96(10)	14	70

FORWARDS

	Ht.	Wt.	Birthdate	Birthplace	CLUB	League Apps	Tries	Pts
Tim Payne					Coventry	12(9)	1	5
Dave Addleton	5.9	14.2	30.03.65	Coventry	Coventry	164(8)	11	55
Robbie Hurrell	6.7		13.06.77	Yeovil	Coventry	21(2)	-	-
Mark R Ellis	5.11	14.12	23.12.68	Kirby Muxloe	Coventry	36(4)	-	-
					Rugby	118(1)	12	56
Mark Tinnock	6.7	18.2	15.07.68	Christchurch	Coventry	12	2	10
					Sale	11(5)	5	25
Michael Mika	6.1	18.00	24.07.68	Lower Hutt (NZ)	Coventry	38(2)	1	5
Trevor Revan	6.0	19.00	05.12.63		Coventry	50(2)	1	5
					Rugby	148(9)	8	36
Lee Crofts	6.4	17.7	07.09.68	Coventry	Coventry	119(12)	20	100
Carl Southwell					Coventry	4(3)	3	15
					Nuneaton			
Julian Horrobin	6.3	15.4	17.04.69	Lydney	Coventry	137(3)	38	190
					Bristol	10	4	16

COVENTRY

FACT FILE

Founded: 1874
Nickname: Cov

Colours: Navy blue with white hoops
Change colours: Red & white

GROUND

Address: **Barker Butts Lane, Coundon Road, Coventry. CV6 1DU.**
Tel: 02476 601174   Fax: 02476 601194
Capacity: 9,900   Seated: 900   Standing - Covered: 4,000   Uncovered: 5,000

Directions: From ring road take the A414 to Birmingham, turn right at traffic lights and follow road across railway lights. Coming into Coventry on the A45 pick up A414 turn left at Hollyhead P.H. right at traffic lights ground on right.   Nearest Railway Station: Coventry

Car Parking: None

Admission: Standing/Seated
Season -   £90/110   OAPs £55/65   u16 £25/30   17-20 £45/55
Matchday -   To be announced

Club Shop: Open matchdays from 1 - 5.30pm.

Clubhouse: Open matchdays Noon - 11pm (except during match) & training eves, Mon & Wed.. Snacks available. Function facilities with a capacity of 200

Training Nights: Tuesday & Thursday

PROGRAMME

Size: A5   Pages: 32   Price: £1.00
Editor: Paul Ingleston

ADVERTISING RATES
Full page £1000   1/2 page £600   1/4 page £400

Lock Rob Hurrell 'on the charge' against Moseley.

EXETER CHIEFS

President	R Manley	
Chairman	K Northcott	
Hon Secretary	Steve Williams	
Director of Rugby	Ian Bremner	07710 901809
Press Officer	Neil Devons	01752 691386 (Phone/Fax)
Match Secretary	Roy Huxtable	01392 277385 (H & Fax)
Fixture Secretary	Terry Davies	01803 406566

c/o Exeter RFC,
The County Ground,
Church Road,
Exeter,
Devon EX2 9BQ
Tel: 01392 278759
Fax: 01392 427582
e-mail: exeterrugby@aol.com

A third place finish in National League Division One for Exeter Chiefs confirmed them as the highest placed semi-professional rugby club in England for the second year running and continued the progress under Director of Rugby, Ian Bremner, that has seen them finish fifth, fourth and third in successive years.

It was a remarkable season by anyone's reckoning.

Having begun strongly with an away victory at Coventry followed by a home win against a tough Wakefield side, a 50 point tally over Otley at the back end of September was to be the Chiefs last win for the rest of the year.

The next league success against Birmingham/Solihull wasn't celebrated until mid-January, but this was followed by two more defeats at the hands of Worcester at home and London Welsh away. This miserable run, the worst since the arrival of Ian Bremner as coach, culminated in the Chiefs finding themselves in the relegation zone with twelve games of the season still to go.

Mid-field frailties, injury problems (most notably a month out for influential skipper Rob Baxter with a hand infection) and a clutch of postponed matches and back-to-back away games due to the wettest winter on record combined to create a temporary drop in confidence and loss of form. However, the Chiefs recovered memorably and a storming end to the season netted ten more victories and a rise of ten league places in as many weeks.

Key signings, including Samoan international centre To'o Vaega and former Gloucester scrum-half, Ian Sanders, added experience and attacking options to Exeter's feared pack, where the back row, drawn from an outstanding quartet of Andrew Beattie, Richard Baxter, Blair Foote and player of the season Gary Willis, were in irresistible form throughout.

The Chiefs also benefited from the cover in depth provided by young and aspiring players enjoying the club's rugby Academy in association with Exeter University, many of whom played in the victorious team in the BUSA Cup Final at Twickenham.

Full back Jon Hill finished top point scorer with 131 just ahead of Sam Howard, whose 127 points included five tries and three drop goals. Winger Martin Ridley headed the try count with nine.

Despite a disastrous first half to the season, the intensity and ferocity of the Chiefs recovery both reaffirmed their undoubted character and ability as well as their serious ambition to bring Premiership rugby to the South West.

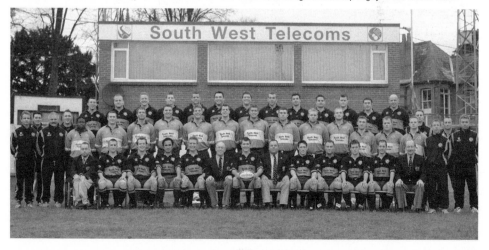

EXETER

Comp.	Date	H/A	Opponents	Result & Score	Att.	15	14	13	12	11
N1	9-Sep	A	Coventry	W 19-12	1000	Townsend	Woodman	Meinung	Salt	Holman
N1	16-Sep	H	Wakefield	W 18-16	987	Townsend	Woodman	Meinung	Eriksson	Holman
N1	23-Sep	A	Waterloo	L 14-17		Hill	Woodman	Meinung	Eriksson	Holman
N1	30-Sep	H	Otley*	W 56-17	834	Hill	Woodman/t	Meinung/t	Eriksson(a/t)	Webber
N1	7-Oct	A	Moseley	L 18-27	1102	Hill	Woodman	Meinung	Eriksson(A/T)	Webber
N1	14-Oct	A	Henley Hawks	L 24-32	750	Hill	Townsend	Meinung	Eriksson	Ridley
N1	28-Oct	H	London Welsh	L 18-24	637	Hill	Townsend	Webber	McMurray	Ridley
N1	19-Nov	A	Birmingham & Solihull	L 21-27	250	Howard/c3p	Townsend	Meinung	Greenaway	Ridley/t
N1	2-Dec	A	Manchester	L 3-21	600	Howard/p	Townsend	Meinung	McMurray	Ridley
N1	16-Dec	A	Leeds Tykes	L 13-63	657	Townsend	Woodman	Meinung	McMurray	Ridley
N1	6-Jan	A	Worcester	L 6-25	2198	Howard/p	Woodman	Meinung	Vaega	Ridley
N1	13-Jan	H	Birmingham & Solihull	W 22-6		Hill/c5p	Woodman	Vaega	Meinung	Ridley
N1	27-Jan	H	Worcester*	L 22-29		Hill/2cp	Woodman	Vaega/t	Meinung	Ridley
N1	4-Feb	A	London Welsh	L 15-24	530	Townsend	Woodman(b/t)	Vaega	Meinung	Ridley
N1	17-Feb	H	Orrell	W 48-11	538	Hill/3c3p	Woodman	Vaega	Meinung	Ridley/t
N1	24-Feb	H	Moseley	W 24-19		Hill/3p	Woodman	Vaega	Meinung	Ridley/t
N1	3-Mar	H	Bedford	W 39-13	670	Hill/t4c2p	Woodman	Vaega/t	Meinung	Ridley
N1	11-Mar	A	Otley	W 31-22		Greenaway/3c	Woodman/t	Vaega/t	Meinung	Ridley
N1	17-Mar	H	Waterloo	W 29-10	780	Hill/3cp	Woodman	Vaega	Meinung	Ridley/2t
N1	24-Mar	A	Orrell*	W 34-32		Hill/3c2p	Woodman	Vaega	Meinung(d/t)	Ridley
N1	31-Mar	A	Wakefield	L 20-21		Hill/2c2p	Woodman	Vaega/t	Meinung	Ridley
N1	14-Apr	H	Coventry	W 48-22	989	Hill/3cp(d/2c)	Wall	Vaega	Meinung/t	Ridley/t(e/t)
N1	18-Apr	H	Leeds Tykes	L 26-33	1021	Greenaway/c3p	Wall	Vaega/t	Meinung	Trethewey(f/t)
N1	21-Apr	A	Bedford	W 33-11	1720	Greenaway/3c4p	Wall(g/t)	Vaega/t	Meinung/t	Ridley
N1	25-Apr	H	Henley Hawks	W 41-8		Greenaway/5c2p	Wall	Vaega/t	Meinung	Ridley
N1	28-Apr	H	Manchester	W 35-21		Greenaway/2cp(i/p)	Wall	Vaega/t	Meinung	Ridley/t
TBC	21-Oct	H	Stourbridge	W 29-15		Hill	Townsend/t	Meinung	Salt	Ridley
TBC	4-Nov	H	London Irish	L 12-57	1850	Hill	Webber	Meinung/t	McMurray	Ridley/t

*after opponents name indicates a penalty try. Brackets after a player's name indicates he was replaced.
eg (a) means he was replaced by replacement code "a" and so on. / after a player or replacement name
is followed by any scores he made - eg /t, /c, /p, /dg or any combination of these*

LEAGUE DEBUTS

Neil Clark, Ronnie Eriksson, Chris Hanson, Jason Hobson,
Harry Holman, Carl Houston, Emori Katalua, Michael Powell,
Ben Salt, P Trethewey, To'o Vaega, Lee Webber.

EVER PRESENT
None

Most Appearances:
26 Phil Sluman. 25 Brian Meinung. 24 Rob Baxter, Sam Howard.

PLAYERS USED
35 plus 2 as replacement only.

MOST POINTS

Pts	Player	T	C	P	DG
131	J Hill	2	23	25	-
125	S Howard	5	14	21	3
64	P Greenaway	-	17	10	-
40	T Vaega	8	-	-	-
40	M Ridley	8	-	-	-

MATCH FACTS

10	9	1	2	3	4	5	6	7	8
Howard/c4p	John	Mooney	Brooking	Sluman	Baxter	Perry	Baxter	Willis/t	Beattie
Howard/4p2dg	John	Mooney	Brooking	Sluman	Brown	Baxter	Baxter	Willis	Beattie
Howard/3p	John	Mooney	Brooking	Sluman	Perry	Baxter	Baxter	Willis	Beattie/t
Howard/7c	John/2tc	Mooney	Brooking	Sluman	Perry	Baxter	Willis/t	Foote/t	Beattie
Howard/c2p	John	Mooney	Brooking	Sluman/t	Perry	Baxter	Willis	Foote	Beattie
Howard/3cp	John	Mooney	Brooking/t	Sluman	Harris	Baxter	Willis	Foote/t	Beattie/t
Howard/c2p	John/t	Mooney	Brooking	Sluman	Harris	Baxter	Baxter/t	Willis	Beattie
Hill	John	Mooney	Brooking/t	Sluman	Harris	Perry	Baxter	Foote	Beattie
Hill	John	Mooney	Brooking	Sluman	Katalau	Harris	Willis	Foote	Beattie
Hill/tc2p	John	Mooney	Brooking	Sluman	Katalau	Brown	Willis	Foote	Baxter
Hill/p	John	Mooney	Brooking	Sluman	Brown	Baxter	Baxter	Foote	Beattie
Howard	John	Mooney/t	Brooking	Sluman	Brown	Baxter	Willis	Foote	Beattie
Howard/t	John	Mooney	Brooking	Sluman	Baxter	Brown	Willis	Foote	Beattie
Hill/cp	John	Mooney	Brooking	Sluman	Brown	Baxter	Willis	Foote/t	Baxter
Howard/2tdg	Sanders	Mooney	Brooking	Sluman	Brown	Baxter	Willis/2t	Foote/t	Beattie
Howard	Sanders	Mooney	Brooking	Sluman	Brown	Baxter	Willis/t	Foote/t	Beattie
Howard	Sanders/t	Mooney/2t	Clark	Sluman	Brown	Baxter	Willis	Foote	Beattie
Howard	Sanders	Mooney	Clark	Sluman	Brown	Baxter	Willis/t	Foote/t	Beattie(c/t)
Howard	Sanders	Mooney	Clark/t	Sluman	Brown/t	Baxter	Willis	Foote	Baxter
Howard	Sanders	Mooney/2t	Clark	Sluman	Baxter	Powell	Willis	Foote	Beattie/t
Howard	Sanders	Mooney	Clark	Sluman	Brown	Baxter	Willis	Foote	Baxter/t
Howard/2t	Sanders	Porte	Clark	Sluman	Harris	Baxter	Baxter	Willis/t	Beattie/t
Howard	Sanders(j/t)	Porte	Clark	Sluman	Harris	Baxter	Baxter	Willis	Beattie
Howard	Sanders	Porte	Clark	Sluman	Harris	Baxter	Baxter	Houston	Willis
Howard	Sanders(j/t)	Porte	Clark	Sluman	Baxter	Harris	Baxter/t	Willis(h/2t)	Beattie
Howard	John	Hobson/t	Brooking	Sluman	Baxter	Harris	Hanson	Baxter/2t	Beattie
Howard/2c4p	John	Mooney/t	Brooking	Sluman	Harris	Baxter	Willis	Foote	Beattie
Howard/c	John	Mooney	Brooking	Sluman	Baxter	Harris	Willis	Foote	Baxter

REPLACEMENTS

a - B Salt	b - L Webber	c - R Baxter	d - P Greenaway	e - P Trethewey
f - M Ridley	g - C Townsend	h - C Hansen	i - J Hill	j - R John

2000-01 HIGHLIGHTS

With the kicking duties split three ways the leading scorer managed 131 points. Jon Hill ended the season with 131 - six ahead of Sam Howard.

John Hill's total of 131 was the lowest to finish top scorer since Ian Stewart was top in 1994-95 with just 35 points.

The try scoring title was split with Martin Ridley and To'o Vaega both finishing with eight tries each.

During the season they suffered their worst ever league defeat. They went down 63-13 to the Leeds Tykes and in the process conceded 10 tries for the first time ever in a match.

EXETER CHIEFS

LEAGUE STATISTICS
compiled by Stephen McCormack

SEASON	Division	P	W	D	L	F	A	Pts Diff	Lge Pts	Lge Pos	Most Points		Most Tries	
91-92	3	12	8	2	2	203	138	65	18	4	77	Andy Green	4	John Davies & Mark Chatterton
92-93	3	11	8	1	2	247	169	78	17	3	122	Andy Green	5	Andy Maunder
93-94	3	18	9	1	8	308	271	39	19	6	125	Andy Green	5	Andy Maunder
94-95	3	18	3	1	14	153	319	-166	7	10r	35	Ian Stewart	3	Mark Chatterton
95-96	4	18	14	0	4	448	230	218	28	1p	191	Andy Green	8	Andy Maunder
96-97	3	30	25	0	5	923	443	480	50	1p	300	Andy Green	15	Mark Woodman
97-98	P2	22	6	0	16	334	553	-219	12	11	174	John Fabian	6	James Alvis
98-99	P2	26	14	1	11	591	598	-7	29	5	241	Bryan Easson	9	Mark Woodman
99-00	P2	26	19	0	7	742	466	276	38	4	312	Sam Howard	10	Andrew Beattie
00-01	N1	26	14	0	12	677	563	114	71	3	131	Jon Hill	8	Martin Ridley & To'o Vaega

BIGGEST MARGINS

Home Win 81pts -81-0 v W Hartlepool 6.5.00
Away Win 57pts - 60-3 v Clifton 22.3.97
Home Defeat 34pts - 0-34 v Rotherham 22.1.00
Away Defeat 50pts - 13-63 v Leeds Tykes 16.12.00

MOST POINTS

Scored at Home 81 v W Hartlepool 6.5.00
Scored Away 60 v Clifton 22.3.97
Conceded at Home 34 v Rotherham 22.1.00
Conceded Away 63 v Leeds Tykes 16.12.00

MOST CONSECUTIVE

Appearances 88 Andy Maunder 12.9.87- 17.9.94
Matches scoring Tries 3 Andy Maunder, John Davis, Ian Dixon & Bob Armstrong.
Matches scoring points 32 Andy Green
Victories 14 **Defeats** 8

MOST TRIES

Scored in a match 11 v W Hartlepool 6.5.00 (H)
Conceded in a match 10 v Leeds Tykes 16.12.00 (A)

MOST APPEARANCES

by a forward 138 Richard Gibbins
by a back 142 (4) Andy Maunder

	MOST IN A SEASON	MOST IN A CAREER	MOST IN A MATCH	
Points	312 Sam Howard 99-00	1085 Andy Green 87-97	31 Sam Howard	v W Hartlepool 6.5.00 (H)
Tries	15 Mark Woodman 96-97	41 Andy Maunder 87-98	4 Simon Dovell / John Fabian	v Havant 21.12.96 (H) / v Waterloo 17.10.98 (H)
Conversions	58 Andy Green 96-97	140 Andy Green 87-97	10 Sam Howard	v W Hartlepool 6.5.00 (H)
Penalties	54 Sam Howard 99-00	213 Andy Green 87-97	7 Andy Green	v Fylde 5.4.97 (H)
Drop Goals	6 Andy Green 95-96	22 Andy Green 87-97	2 Andy Green	v Sheffield 23.4.88 (H)

PLAYING SQUAD

EXETER CHIEFS

BACKS

	Ht.	Wt.	Birthdate	Birthplace	CLUB	League Apps	Tries	Pts
Jon Hill					Exeter	24(6)	4	141
Sam Howard	6.0	13.07	31.07.74	Gravesend	Exeter	50	10	437
Other club: Blackheath 56(6)/6/349					Bedford	16(3)	3	134
Martin Ridley					Exeter	46(1)	15	75
Craig Townsend					Exeter	22(7)	4	20
Mark Woodman	6.0	15.0	18.09.70	Exeter	Exeter	112(1)	36	180
Devon.								
Ben Salt					Exeter	1(3)	2	10
Richard John	5.10	13.0	30.05.74	Exeter	Exeter	67(21)	7	35
South West, colts, u21.								
To'o Vaega	5.11	14.2	17.08.65		Exeter	16	8	40
					Rugby Lions	37(1)	9	45
Brian Meining					Exeter	50	10	50

FORWARDS

	Ht.	Wt.	Birthdate	Birthplace	CLUB	League Apps	Tries	Pts
Liam Mooney					Exeter	47(4)	13	65
Ian Harrison					Exeter	5(9)	1	5
Ian Brown					Exeter	13(4)	1	5
Danny Porte					Exeter	4(7)	-	-
Rob Baxter	6.5	16.7	10.03.71	Tavistock	Exeter	181	11	55
England colts, Devon.								
Blair Foote					Exeter	31(14)	10	50
Gary Willis			02.10.65	Billingham	Exeter	73(4)	13	65
Andy Beattie					Exeter	38(10)	16	80
Phil Sluman	6.0	17.0	15.03.67	Exeter	Exeter	132(10)	9	44
Devon								
Neil Clark					Exeter	9(14)	2	10

EXETER CHIEFS
FACT FILE

Founded: 1872
Nickname: The Chiefs
Web site: exeterchiefs.com

Colours: All black with Cambridge blue trim
Change colours: Cambridge blue/black

GROUND

Address: The County Ground, Church Road, St. Thomas, Exeter. EX2 9BQ.
Tel: 01392 278759   Fax: 01392 427582   e-mail: exeterrugby@aol.com
Capacity: 5,200   Seated: 700   Standing: Covered 500, Uncovered 4,000

Directions: M5 junction 31 follow A377 via A30 to city centre. Continueuntil you reach the turning for B3212 for Moreton Hampstead, turn into CowickStreet, pass under railway bridge. Turn left into Cecil Road at traffic lights, then right into Church Road and into ground
Nearest Railway Station: Exeter(St. Davids), then taxi to ground (appr 2miles)

Car Parking: None at ground.

Admission: (Children under 16 Free - accompanied by adult)
Season tickets **Standing** Adults £80, OAPs £65   **Seated** Adults £110, OAPs £90
Matchdays   **Standing** Adults £8, u16 Free   **Seated** £12

Club Shop: Open matchdays & training nights
Manager Angela Abbot 01392 278759.

Clubhouse: Open matchdays 12-11. Training nights 6-11   Snacks and bar meals available
Functions: Capacity 160/60, contact Mr J Davey or Mrs M Boxall

Training Nights: Tuesday and Thursday.

PROGRAMME Size: B6   Pages: 32
Editor: Neil Devons 01752 691386
Advertising Rates
Prices on apllication.
Contact - Eddie Trick,
MPW Limited   01392 424122

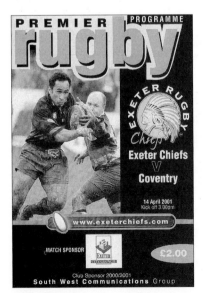

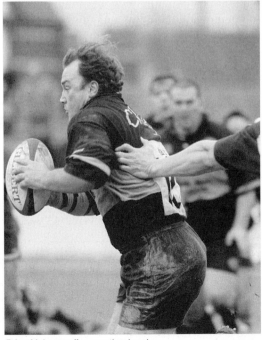

Brian Meinung off on another break.

Photo courtesy of Nigel Chanter

HENLEY HAWKS

President	Doug Ash	c/o Henley RFC, Dry Leas, Marlow Road, Henley-on-Thames RG9 2JA
		Tel: 01491 574499 Fax: 01491 412335
Chairman	Graham Horner	c/o Henley RFC, as above
Commercial Director	Martin Unsworth	c/o Henley RFC, as above
Press Officer	Noel Armstead	8 Chiswick Lodge, Liston Rd, Marlow, Bucks SL7 1AG
		01628 474398 (B & Fax). e-mail: scoop.hrfc@virgin.net
Director of Rugby & Coaching	Jim McKay	01491 574061 mobile 07968 412155
1st XV Coach	Nigel Dudding	01491 576502 Mobile 07710 110654

Although the Hawks did not achieve their target for the season, to be the best part-time professional side in the league, they did finish in a comfortable seventh place which was an improvement of two places over last season's finish of ninth and in winning two more matches and having three fewer defeats they finished in their highest position since leagues were introduced.

They had a tremendous finish to the campaign defeating Leeds Tykes who had not lost a game in 25 matches and who had already secured the championship title. The Hawks rose to the occasion at Dry Leas as they had done against Worcester in February but on that occasion they were narrowly defeated, 16-13, thanks to a referees very controversial decision to deny the Hawks a last minute try.

Showing this kind of form against the two top sides really summed up the Hawks season as 'what could have been'. They failed to be consistent finding it difficult to win away from home and as a result they only achieved three doubles and these were against the relegated teams Waterloo and Orrell plus the disappointing Bedford side who only just avoided the drop.The most disappointing performances were against Manchester and Otley who both secured the double over the Hawks and these were teams that the Hawks' coaches had targetted for maximum points. Indeed Otley were the bogey side as they also denied the Hawks a lucrative Tetley's Bitter Cup match against Leicester Tigers. All the top teams in the division were defeated at Dry Leas with the exception of Worcester.

Injuries, of course took their toll and the most severe was that suffered by new hooker Jim Hamilton-Smith who was not to play again after the first 12 games. Luckily Willie Phillips, in his testimonial year, stepped into the breach and did yeoman service. He has thoroughly deserved this the first testimonial ever awarded by the club as he has undoubtedly been the most influential player in the club's recent history and the appreciation of the members is reflected in the substantial sum raised for his benefit.

The front row was strengthened by the arrival of Lee Hall (ever present), Colm Hannon and latterly Des Brett from North Walsham.. Jerry Sampson and James Winterbottom gave stalwart service in a injury free second row. Steve Barnes was an inspiration both as a player and as captain.The return to Australia of Barbarian Trevor Walsh, in December, obviously left a hole in the centre and the biggest disappointment of the season was the injury suffered by his replacement Werner van Pitius after just four impressive games. The mercurial talents of Duncan Roke, used at full back as well as at centre, were policed effectively by well informed opponents so that last season's 17 tries were reduced to five. Matt Jones , after a quiet period in mid-season , when Nick Buoy took over kicking duties (126 pts) came back on song and was again leading points scorer with 185 points in all games. In summary coaches Nigel Dudding and Jim McKay can look back on a season of further achievement and the duo can be congratulated on producing a squad which has earned the respect of it's peers.

Henley Squad 1August 2000

HENLEY HAWKS

Comp.	Date	H/A	Opponents	Result & Score	Att.	15	14	13	12	11
N1	9-Sep	A	Bedford	W 34-31	2035	Barlow/t	Rowland/t	Walsh	Batty	Holloway/t
N1	16-Sep	H	Coventry	W 33-27	450	Barlow/t	Rowland	Roke	Walsh/2t	Holloway
N1	23-Sep	A	Wakefield	L 10-31		Barlow	Rowland	Roke	Walsh	Holloway
N1	30-Sep	H	Waterloo	W 19-18	450	Roke	Barlow	Osman	Walsh	Holloway
N1	7-Oct	A	Otley	L 10-16	400	Roke	Barlow	Van Zyl/t	Walsh	Holloway
N1	14-Oct	H	Exeter	W 32-24	750	Roke/t	Barlow	Van Zyl/t	Walsh/t	Holloway
N1	28-Oct	A	Moseley	L 12-16	678	Barlow	Rowland	Roke	Walsh	Holloway
N1	18-Nov	A	London Welsh	L 15-20	550	Barlow	Buoy/5p	Van Zyl	Walsh	Holloway
N1	25-Nov	H	Orrell	W 23-15	500	Buoy/tcp	Rowland	Roke	Van Zyl/t	Holloway
N1	2-Dec	A	Leeds Tykes	L 7-43	306	Buoy/c	Rowland	Van Zyl	Walsh	Holloway
N1	9-Dec	H	Manchester	L 13-26	550	Buoy/c2p	Rowland/t	Roke	Walsh	Holloway
N1	16-Dec	A	Orrell	W 22-17	500	Buoy/2cp	Rowland	Roke	Van Zyl/t	Holloway/t
N1	6-Jan	A	Birmingham & Solihull	D 16-16	250	Buoy/c2p	Rowland	Roke	Van Zyl	Holloway
N1	13-Jan	H	London Welsh*	W 30-12	1150	Roke	Rowland	Van Zyl	Jones(b/t3c3p)	Holloway
N1	20-Jan	A	Worcester	L 18-56	2003	Roke	Rowland	Van Zyl	Jones/c2p	Holloway/t
N1	27-Jan	A	Birmingham & Solihull	D 18-18	520	Roke	Buoy/5p	Gey van Pettius	Van Zyl	Rowland
N1	18-Feb	H	Worcester	L 13-16	705	Buoy/c2p	Rowland	Roke/t	Jones	Holloway
N1	24-Feb	H	Otley	L 20-23	535	Buoy/5p	Rowland	Roke	Jones	Holloway
N1	10-Mar	A	Waterloo	W 29-17	265	Buoy/tcp	Rowland/t	Roke/t	Gey van Pettius	Holloway
N1	17-Mar	H	Wakefield	W 24-7	310	Roke/2t	Rowland/t	Gey van Pettius/t	Van Zyl	Holloway
N1	31-Mar	A	Coventry	L 18-25	1800	Roke	Rowland	Gey van Pettius	Van Zyl	Holloway/t
N1	8-Apr	H	Moseley	W 20-12	545	Roke	Rowland/t	Batty	Van Zyl	Holloway
N1	14-Apr	H	Bedford	W 18-10	1005	Roke	Rowland	Batty	Van Zyl	Holloway
N1	21-Apr	A	Manchester	L 37-39	865	Barlow	Rowland	Batty	Roke	Holloway/t
N1	25-Apr	A	Exeter	L 8-41		Barlow	Rowland/t	Osman	Batty	Holloway
N1	28-Apr	H	Leeds Tykes	W 18-13	840	Roke	Barlow	Batty	Jones/6p	Holloway
TBC	21-Oct	A	Otley	L 24-26		Roke/t	Barlow	Van Zyl	Walsh/t	Holloway

*after opponents name indicates a penalty try. Brackets after a player's name indicates he was replaced.
eg (a) means he was replaced by replacement code "a" and so on. / after a player or replacement name
is followed by any scores he made - eg /t, /c, /p, /dg or any combination of these

LEAGUE DEBUTS

James Alvis, Dan Batty, Des Brett, Gey van Pettius
Werner, Lee Hall, J H-Smith, Colm Hannan, Tom
Holloway, Angus Moxon, Jason Niarchos, Hugo Selby,
James Street.

MOST APPEARANCES

26 Lee Hall, James Winterbottom.
25 Matt Jones, Tom Holloway.

PLAYERS USED

35 plus 8 as replacements only

MOST POINTS

Pts	Player	T	C	P	DG
171	M Jones	-	21	42	1
126	N Buoy	3	12	29	-
30	B Rowland	6	-	-	-
25	D Roke	5	-	-	-
25	Tom Holloway	5	-	-	-

MATCH FACTS

10	9	1	2	3	4	5	6	7	8
Jones/2c5p	Ayers	Penney	Hamilton-Smith	Hall	Sampson	Winterbottom	Barnes	Venner	Phillips
Jones/3c4p	Ayers	Penney	Hamilton-Smith	Hall	Sampson	Winterbottom	Barnes	Street	Phillips
Jones/cp	Ayers	Penney	Hamilton-Smith	Hall	Sampson/t	Winterbottom	Barnes	Venner	Phillips
Jones/2c	Smaje/2t	Penney	Hamilton-Smith	Hall	Sampson	Winterbottom	Barnes	Phillips	Metcalfe/t
Jones/cp	Smaje	Selby	Hamilton-Smith	Hall	Sampson	Winterbottom	Phillips	Street	Metcalfe
Jones/3c2p	Ayers/t	Fuller	Hamilton-Smith	Hall	Glossop	Winterbottom	Barnes	Venner	Metcalfe
Jones/4p	Ayers	Penney	Hamilton-Smith	Hall	Glossop	Winterbottom	Barnes	Venner	Phillips
Roke	Ayers	Hannan	Hamilton-Smith	Hall	Sampson	Winterbottom	Barnes	Venner	Metcalfe
Jones/p	Smaje	Hannan	Hamilton-Smith/t	Hall	Sampson	Winterbottom	Barnes	Venner	Metcalfe
Jones	Smaje	Hannan	Hamilton-Smith	Hall	Sampson	Winterbottom	Barnes	Venner	Metcalfe
Jones	Smaje	Hannan	Hamilton-Smith	Hall	Sampson	Winterbottom	Barnes	Venner	Metcalfe
Jones	Ayers/t	Hannan	Phillips	Hall	Sampson	Winterbottom	Barnes	Venner	Metcalfe
Jones/p	Ayers	Heginbotham/t	Phillips	Hall	Sampson	Winterbottom	Barnes	Venner	Metcalfe
Niarchos	Ayers/t	Hall	Phillips	Alvis	Sampson	Winterbottom	Barnes	Street	Metcalfe
Niarchos	Ayers	Hallc/t)	Harris	Alvis	Moxon	Winterbottom	Barnes	Street	Metcalfe
Jones/p	Ayers	Hall	Phillips	Alvis	Sampson	Winterbottom	Barnes	Hendriksz	Metcalfe
Osman	Ayers	Hall	Phillips	Hannan	Sampson	Winterbottom	Barnes	Venner	Metcalfe
Osman	Ayers	Hannan	Phillips	Hall	Sampson	Winterbottom	Street	Venner/t	Metcalfe
Jones/2c	Smaje	Hannan	Phillips	Hall	Sampson/t	Winterbottom	Barnes	Venner	Metcalfe
Jones/2c	Smaje	Hannan	Phillips	Hall	Sampson	Winterbottom	Barnes	Hendriksz	Metcalfe
Jones/p(b/cp)	Smaje/t	Hannan	Hall	Brett	Sampson	Winterbottom	Barnes	Phillips	Metcalfe
Jones/2cpdg	Smaje	Hannan	Phillips	Hall/t	Sampson	Winterbottom	Hendriksz	Metcalfe	Venner
Jones/5p(b/p)	Smaje	Hannan	Phillips	Hall	Sampson	Winterbottom	Barnes	Venner	Hendriksz
Jones/2c6p	Ayers(d/t)	Hannan	Phillips	Hall	Sampson	Winterbottom	Barnes	Venner/t	Metcalfe
Jones/p	Smaje	Hannan	Hall	Alvis	Sampson	Winterbottom	Street	Venner	Metcalfe
Osman	Smaje	Hannan	Phillips	Hall	Sampson	Winterbottom	Barnes	Venner	Metcalfe
Jones/c4p	Ayers	Fuller	Hamilton-Smith	Hall	Glossop	Winterbottom	Barnes	Venner	Metcalfe

REPLACEMENTS   a -B Ayers   c -N Buoy   c - R Hegginbotham   d - D Smaje

2000-01 HIGHLIGHTS

Matt Jones tops the scoring chart for the second season and has moved to the top of the Henley all time points scorers in league rugby. Jones now has 407 points and moved passed Matt Maudsley.

Winger Bruce Rowland in his second season at the club, since joining from Reading, topped the try scorers list with just six tries.

In the away defeat at Worcester at the turn of the year they conceded 56 points - their most ever in a league match. In this match they conceded eight tries for just the second time in a league match.

Willie Phillips extended his appearance record to 134 during the last season - but we have to see if he finally does call it a day.

HENLEY HAWKS

LEAGUE STATISTICS
compiled by Stephen McCormack

SEASON	Division	P	W	D	L	F	A	Pts Diff	Lge Pts	Lge Pos	Coach	Captain
91-92	SW2	10	8	1	1	283	103	180	17	1p	C Woodward	M Duffelen
92-93	SW1	12	9	0	3	312	143	169	18	2	C Woodward	
93-94	SW1	12	12	0	0	328	125	203	24	1p	C Woodward	
94-95	D5S	12	5	0	7	190	299	-109	10	9	C Woodward	R Heginbotham

SEASON	Division	P	W	D	L	F	A	Pts Diff	Lge Pts	Lge Pos	Most Points	Most Tries
95-96	D5S	12	8	0	4	349	192	157	16	3	176 Richard Perkins	10 Richard Perkins
96-97	D4S	26	20	2	4	768	456	312	42	2	140 Matt Maudsley	12 Gavin Sharp / Matt Maudsley
97-98	N2S	26	22	0	4	772	384	388	44	2p	204 Nick Buoy	15 Mark Venner
98-99	JN1	26	22	1	3	644	299	345	45	1P	118 Duncan Roke	14 Peter Davies
99-00	P2	26	10	1	15	599	696	-97	21	9	236 Matt Jones	17 Duncan Roke
00-01	N1	26	12	2	12	517	589	-72	62	7	171 Matt Jones	6 Bruce Rowland

BIGGEST MARGINS

Home Win 85pts - 93-8 v Met. Police 28.3.98
Away Win 35pts - 47-12 v Camberley 30.3.96
Home Defeat 36pts - 15-41 v Leeds Tykes 11.3.00
Away Defeat 46pts - 3-49 v High Wycombe 25.4.94
7-53 v Rotherham 18.12.99

MOST CONSECUTIVE

Appearances	-
Matches scoring Tries	
Matches scoring points	
Victories	11
Defeats	3

MOST POINTS

Scored at Home 93 v Met. Police 28.3.98
Scored Away 47 v Camberley 30.3.96
Conceded at Home 51 v Leeds Tykes 11.3.00
Conceded Away 56 v Worcester 20.01.01

MOST TRIES

Scored in a match 15 v Met. Police 28.3.98 (H)
Conceded in a match 8 v Rotherham 25.4.94 (A)
v Worcester 20.01.01

MOST APPEARANCES

by a forward 134 (12) Willie Phillips
by a back 75 (15) Matt Maudsley

	MOST IN A SEASON	MOST IN A CAREER	MOST IN A MATCH
Points	236 Matt Jones 99-00	407 Matt Jones 99-01	34 Chris Spencer v Charlton Park 12.4.97(H)
Tries	17 Duncan Roke 99-00	37 Matt Maudsley 94-99	4 Chris Spencer v Charlton Park 12.4.97 (H)
Conversions	30 Matt Jones 99-00	58 Matt Maudsley 96-00	8 Phil Osman v Met. Police 28.03.98 (H)
Penalties	55 Matt Jones 99-00	97 Matt Jones 99-00	8 Matt Jones v Rugby Lions 15.01.00 (A)
Drop Goals	5 Phil Osman 98-99	8 Phil Osman 97-99	2 Phil Osman v Reading (A)

PLAYING SQUAD

HENLEY HAWKS

BACKS

Name	Ht.	Wt.	Birthdate	Birthplace	CLUB	League Apps	Tries	Pts
Russell Osman	6.2	13.8	17.6.72	Southampton	Henley	30(13)	11	55
					Newbury	29(3)	11	55
Tim Barlow	6.0	14.0			Henley	31(4)	7	35
England schools, U21. Other club: Bristol					Leicester			
Matt Jones	5.9	12.0			Henley	48	1	407
England U21, students, colts, U18, U16. Other club: Leicester					London Irish			
Matt Maudsley	6.0	14.0	16.10.70	Morecambe	Henley	75(15)	37	391
England Students, Oxfordshire								
Duncan Roke	6.2	13.0	5.07.74	Malta	Henley	60(2)	28	247
Barbarians					Leicester			
Phil Osman	6.0	13.7	18.12.68	Exeter	Henley	42(3)	8	131
Hampshire								
Gavin Sharp	5.9	13.7	04.01.75	Scarboriugh	Henley	51(10)	34	170
Combined Services, RAF, Oxfordshire					Bristol	20	25	5
Peter Davies	5.8	12.0	1.12.75	Newport	Henley	43(3)	23	115
Welsh u21, Univ, Schools.								
Ben Ayers			7.05.74	Crickhowell	Henley	49(12)	12	60
Oxfordshire								
Liam Smye	5.10	11.8	18.01.78	Oxford	Henley	23(19)	2	10
South West U21								
Trevor Walsh	6.0	14.0	18.01.72	Tombsvlle(Aust)	Henley	70(1)	15	75
Queensland Univ, Australian Univ								
John Stebbings	5.11	13.6	28.10.76	Wokingham	Henley	11(10)	3	70
England students, Irish exiles.								
Tom Holloway	5.9	12.7	16.10.73		Henley	25	5	25
Other club: Wakefield 1(1)/2/10					Newbury	87(1)	44	220

FORWARDS

Name	Ht.	Wt.	Birthdate	Birthplace	CLUB	League Apps	Tries	Pts
James Alvis					Henley	4(5)	-	-
James Winterbottom	6.6	17.07			Henley	46(6)	-	-
England U21, students, U18, U16. Other club: Wasps					Camberley			
Lee Hall					Henley	26	1	5
Other club: Rotherham					London Welsh			
JJ Harris					Henley	5(8)	-	-
					Reading			
Dave Penney	6.0	17.10	04.06.70	Newfoundland	Henley	50(3)	1	5
Willie Phillips	5.10	15.11	16.04.58	New Zealand	Henley	134(12)	20	100
NZ Moaris, N Auckland								
Rowan Fuller	5.10	16.07	1.11.72		Henley	31(15)	1	5
Oxfordshire								
Jerry Sampson	6.0	16.08	04.06.68	Weston S Mare	Henley	120(3)	10	50
Kent, Somerset, Oxon.								
Mark Venner	6.2	15.00	14.04.69	Weston S Mare	Henley	101(2)	31	155
Somerset								
Ali Matcalfe					Henley	30(3)	1	5
Other clubs: Saracens, Reading					Tabard			
James Street					Henley	6(9)	-	-
Janik Hendriksz	6.4	18.02	29.01.70	Cape Town	Henley	27(2)	4	20
Western Province B					Clifton	21	9	45
Steve Barnes			29.10.71	Henley on T	Henley	60(3)	-	-
					Northampton			

HENLEY HAWKS

FACT FILE

Founded: 1930
Nickname: Hawks

Colours: Gold with navy & dark green hoops
Change colours: Dark green with navy & gold hoops

GROUND

Address: Dry Leas, Marlow Rd, Henley-on-Thames, Oxon RG9 2JA

Tel. 01491 574499   Fax: 01491 412335
Website: www.henleyrugbyclub.org.uk   email: admin@henleyrugbyclub.org.uk
Capacity: 3,000   Seated: Covered 120   Standing: Uncovered 2,880

Directions: Centre of Henley follow signs to Marlow, ground on left 100 yards past roundabout
Nearest Railway Station: Henley, follow signs from Town Centre to Marlow - ground 100yds left at start of Marlow Rd. **Car Parking:** 600 at ground

Admission: Season   Standing Adult Members £65, Non-Members £85
(Children/OAPs half price)   Matchday   Standing Adults £8, Seated Adults £11

Clubhouse: Tues, Wed, Thurs eves. Matchdays incl Sundays.   Snacks & bar meals available.
            Functions: Capacity 200
Club Shop: Yes

PROGRAMME

Size: A5   Pages: 48   Price: £1
Editor: Noel Armstead 01628 474398

Training Nights: Tuesday/Thursday; Women Wednesday

ADVERTISING RATES
Inside covers £1000 (colour)
Full page £450 (Mono)
Half page £250 (Mono)

"Willie not come back again!?"

Willie Phillips extended his appearance record to 134 last season - but we will have to wait and see whether the 43 year-old finally calls it a day.

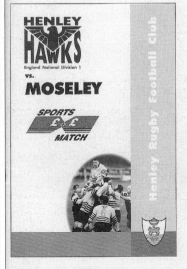

LONDON WELSH RFC

President	S J Dawes OBE
Chairman	David Hammond
Club Secretary	Tudor Roberts
General Manager	Ron Holley
Coach	Adrian Davies
Press Officer	Allan Price
Academy Director	Martin Jones

c/o London Welsh RFC,
Old Deer Park,
Kew Road,
Richmond,
Surrey TW9 2AZ
Tel: 0208 940 2368
Fax: 0208 940 1106

It was a frustrating season for London Welsh, and new coach Adrian Davies. Despite having a talented and experienced squad, the Welsh had to endure their worst injury list in living memory and dropped one place to sixth. Not once were the Welsh able to field the same side on successive Saturdays, while many top players were absent for long periods.

Not that the Welsh were without their moments. A fine double was achieved over Exeter, Coventry were beaten at Coundon Road, and another good cup run took the side to the Fifth Round, with London Irish winning the Exile derby in front of a rain swept, but bumper Old Deer Park crowd.

Among the newcomers, there were fine contributions from former England centre, Steve Ravenscroft, Ireland flanker Ken O'Connell, scrum-half Richard Elliott, Kiwi lock Chad Eagle, England A hooker Simon Mitchell, French Sevens cap Florent Rossigneux, prop Joel Brannigan and centre Adam Bidwell. Ravenscroft, O'Connell and prop Steve Pope were all selected for the National League side, which beat the South African tourists at Worcester, Richard Elliott played for the Barbarians, and Matt Vince, who came close to breaking a club record with 25 tries, often played for Wales at Sevens.

For the coming season, Matt Fitzgerald will take over from Luke Jones as club captain, and the Welsh are now developing a strong Academy side to secure its long term future.

Former England centre, Steve Ravenscroft. makes a telling break in the 24-15 defeat of Exeter at Old Deer Park.

LONDON WELSH

Comp.	Date	H/A	Opponents	Result & Score	Att.	15	14	13	12	11
N1	9-Sep	A	Manchester	L 18-26	785	Vines	Jones/t	Bidwell	Prins	Philip/t
N1	16-Sep	H	Bedford	L 14-20		Vines/t	Bidwell	Rayner	Prins	Giraud
N1	23-Sep	A	Coventry	W 25-20	1500	Vines	Philip	Lewsey	Bidwell	Giraud
N1	30-Sep	H	Wakefield	W 34-19	1100	Vines/2tcp	Philip	Rayner	Bidwell	Giraud
N1	7-Oct	A	Waterloo	L 18-25	350	Vines/p	Jones	Rayner(c/t)	Ravenscroft	Giraud
N1	14-Oct	H	Otley	W 38-26	1050	Vines/2t	Jones	Lewsey(d/t)	Ravenscroft	Giraud
N1	28-Oct	A	Exeter	W 24-18	637	Vines	Jones/t	Roskell/t	Ravenscroft	Bidwell
N1	18-Nov	H	Henley Hawks	W 20-15	550	Vines/t	Jones	Roskell/t	Bidwell	Philip
N1	25-Nov	H	Worcester	L 12-29	700	Vines	Jones	Roskell	Ravenscroft	Bidwell
N1	2-Dec	H	Orrell*	W 33-32	550	Vines/3t	Shaw	Roskell/t	Ravenscroft	Giraud
N1	9-Dec	H	Leeds Tykes	L 12-35	800	Vines/t	Shaw	Bidwell	Ravenscroft	Philip/t
N1	16-Dec	A	Worcester	L 3-51	2002	Vines	Shaw	Roskell	Ravenscroft	Bidwell
N1	6-Jan	H	Moseley	W 34-6	1150	Vines/t	Jones/t	Bidwell	Ravenscroft/t	Giraud
N1	13-Jan	A	Henley Hawks	L 12-30	1150	Mardon	Shaw	Bidwell	Ravenscroft	Jones
N1	27-Jan	A	Moseley	W 32-17	776	Vines/2t	Jones/2t	Bidwell	Ravenscroft	Shaw
N1	4-Feb	H	Exeter	W 24-15	530	Mardon	Jones	Bidwell	Ravenscroft	Shaw/t
N1	10-Feb	A	Otley	L 0-7		Mardon	Jones	Roskell	Ravenscroft	Shaw
N1	24-Feb	H	Waterloo	W 31-16	700	Vines/2t	Shaw/t	Frost	Ravenscroft/t	Jones
N1	10-Mar	A	Wakefield	L 15-38		Vines	Shaw	Frost	Ravenscroft	Jones(f/t)
N1	17-Mar	H	Coventry	L 14-20	700	Vines	Frost	Bidwell	Ravenscroft/t	Shaw
N1	24-Mar	H	Birmingham & Solihull	W 11-7	600	Vines	Shaw	Frost	Ravenscroft	Prins/t
N1	31-Mar	A	Bedford	L 18-23	1608	Prins/t	Shaw/t	Bidwell	Ravenscroft	Mardon
N1	7-Apr	A	Birmingham & Solihull	W 14-13	400	Prins	Shaw	Bidwell	Ravenscroft	Jones/t
N1	14-Apr	H	Manchester	W 31-30	900	Vines/2t	Shaw	Bidwell	Ravenscroft	Prins
N1	21-Apr	A	Leeds Tykes	L 16-55	1254	Vines	Shaw	Bidwell/tdg	Ravenscroft	Prins
N1	28-Apr	A	Orrell	L 22-23	700	Vines	Shaw	Mardon	Ravenscroft/t	Prins/t
TBC	21-Oct	H	Blackheath	W 44-3	500	Vines/3t	Jones/2t	Roskell/t	Ravenscroft	Philip/t
TBC	5-Nov	A	New Brighton	W 32-17		Vines	Jones	Roskell	Bidwell	Giraud/2t
TBC	11-Nov	H	London Irish	L 10-33	2800	Vines	Jones	Roskell	Bidwell	Philip

*after opponents name indicates a penalty try. Brackets after a player's name indicates he was replaced.
eg (a) means he was replaced by replacement code "a" and so on. / after a player or replacement name
is followed by any scores he made - eg /t, /c, /p, /dg or any combination of these*

Adam Bidwell, Trevor Boynton, Joel Brannighan, Chad Eagle, Richard Elliott, Richard Griffith, Andrew Johnson, Adam Kelly, Richard Liddington, Richard Mahony, Ken O'Connell, Jurianus Prins, Steve Ravenscroft, Ed Rayner, Florent Rossingneux.

24 Richard Elliott.
22 Joel Brannighan

35 plus 6 as replacement only.

Pts	Player	T	C	P	DG
179	A Lee	2	23	41	-
93	M Vines	17	1	2	-
45	R Mahony	-	6	11	-
30	A Jones	6	-	-	-

MATCH FACTS

10	9	1	2	3	4	5	6	7	8
Stanley	Taylor	Owen	Bennett	Cormack	Morahan	Mole	Bird	Kronfeld	Wilkins
Stanley/dg	Taylor	Owen	Bennett	Cormack	Mole	Morahan	Wilkins	Kronfeld	Butterworth
Stanley	Mulraine	Smith	Seymour	Cormack(a/t)	Mole	Morahan	Wilkins	Kronfeld	Butterworth
Bonney	Mulraine	Davies	Seymour	Cormack	Mole	Johnson	Wilkins	Davison/t	Butterworth
Bonney/dg	Taylor	Davies	Seymour	Cormack	Morahan	Johnson	Wilkins	Davison	Butterworth
Bonney/t	Mulraine	Cormack	Bennett	Smith	Johnson/t	Mole	Wilkins	Davison/t	Butterworth
Bonney	Mulraine	Cormack	Seymour	Smith	Mole	Johnson	Butterworth	Davison	Wilkins/t
Bonney	Taylor	Cormack	Seymour	Smith	Mole	Johnson	Butterworth	Davison	Wilkins
Bonney	Taylor	Cormack	Bennett	Smith	Owen	Dixon	Butterworth	Kronfeld	Wilkins/t
Bonney/dg	Taylor	Cormack	Bennett	Smith	Dixon	Morahan	Butterworth	Bird	Wilkins
Stanley	Mulraine	Cormack	Bennett	Davies	Dixon	Morahan/t	Butterworth	Kronfeld	Wilkins
Stanley	Mulraine	Seymour	Waddington	Smith	Dixon	Owen/t	Butterworth	Kronfeld	Wilkins
Stanley	Mulraine	Cormack	Seymour	Smith	Dixon	Johnson	Butterworth	Kronfeld/t	Wilkins
Stanley	Mulraine	Cormack/t	Seymour	Smith	Dixon/t	Owen	Butterworth	Kronfeld	Wilkins
Stanley	Mulraine	Cormack	Bennett	Seymour	Hart	Morahan	Butterworth	Bird	Wilkins
Stanley	Barr	Cormack	Bennett	Seymour	Hart	Morahan/2t	Bird	Kronfeld/t	Wilkins
Stanley	Mulraine	Cormack	Bennett	Smith	Hart	Morahan	Butterworth	Bird	Wilkins/t
Stanley	Mulraine	Cormack	Seymour	Smith	Mole	Morahan/t	Butterworth	Bird	Wilkins
Stanley/2p	Barr	Cormack	Bennett	Smith	Morahan	Mole	Butterworth	Bird	Wilkins
Stanley	Mulraine	Cormack	Seymour	Smith	Mole	Morahan	Owen	Bird(b/t)	Wilkins
Stanley	Mulraine	Cormack	Bennett	Seymour	Mole	Morahan	Butterworth(c/t)	Kronfeld	Wilkins
Stanley	Mulraine	Cormack	Bennett	Smith	Mole	Morahan	Butterworth	Bird	Wilkins
Stanley	Mulraine	Cormack	Bennett	Smith	Mole	Morahan	Owen	Kronfeld	Wilkins/t
Stanley/t	Mulraine	Cormack	Seymour/t	Smith	Mole	Morahan	Owen	Kronfeld	Wilkins
Stanley/t	Bird/2t	Cormack/t	Bennett	Seymour	Mole(b/t)	Johnson	Bird/t	Davison/2t	Wilkins/2t
Stanley	Bird	Cormack	Bennett	Seymour	Mole	Johnson	Bird	Davison	Wilkins
Bonney/dg	Mulraine	Cormack	Seymour	Smith	Mole	Johnson	Butterworth	Davison	Wilkins
Bonney/t	Barr	Cormack/2t	Seymour	Smith	Mole	Johnson	Butterworth	Davison	Wilkins
Bonney	Mulraine	Cormack	Seymour	Smith	Dixon/t	Johnson	Butterworth	Kronfeld	Wilkins

REPLACEMENTS   a - M Bennett   b - C Kronfeld   c - Simon Owen   d - C Mulraine

2000-01 HIGHLIGHTS

John Gregory topped the scoring list for a third consecutive season and should pass the 1,000 league points total for the club next season.

He equalled his own record of eight conversions in a match in the game against W Hartlepool late in the season.

He also finished as joint leading try scorer along with centre Paul Flood.

Esher suffered their worst ever run of defeats in league rugby when losing four consecutive matches in March.

They also suffered their biggest ever league defeats, both at home and away, during the season.

In the match against Newbury at home they lost 39-17, this was also the highest number of points scored against them - either at home or away, and their worst ever away defeat was the 31-10 loss at Harrogate in September.

ESHER

SEASON	Division	P	W	D	L	F	A	Pts Diff	Lge Pts	Lge Pos	Most Points	Most Tries
91-92	L2S	10	5	0	5	153	146	7	9	6		
92-93	L2S	12	7	0	5	201	189	12	14	3		
93-94	L2S	12	10	2	0	382	95	287	22	1p		
94-95	L1	12	10	0	2	344	132	212	20	2		
95-96	L1	12	9	0	3	280	159	121	18	3		
96-97	L1	13	12	0	1	458	171	287	24	1p		
97-98	N2S	26	18	1	7	651	448	203	37	4	92 Ray Dudman	12 Mark Butterworth
98-99	N2S	26	23	0	3	864	308	566	46	2	303 Jon Gregory	16 Nana Dontah
99-00	N2S	26	23	0	3	1018	356	662	46	1	351 Jon Gregory	15 Michael Corcoran
00-01	N2	26	11	1	14	577	484	93	23	8	260 John Gregory	7 John Gregory

BIGGEST MARGINS

Home Win	97pts - 104-7 v Met Police
Away Win	43pts - 56-13 v Norwich
Home Defeat	22pts - 17-39 v Rugby 31.3.01
Away Defeat	21pts -10-31 v Harrogate 16.9.00

MOST CONSECUTIVE

Appearances	
Matches scoring Tries	
Matches scoring points	
Victories	15
Defeats	4

MOST POINTS

Scored at Home	104 v Met Police
Scored Away	57 v Met Police 14.2.98
Conceded at Home	39 v Rugby 31.3.01
Conceded Away	36 v Plymouth 25.10.97

MOST TRIES

Scored in a match	17 v Met Police
Conceded in a match	5 v Plymouth 25.10.97

MOST APPEARANCES

by a forward	
by a back	

	MOST IN A SEASON	MOST IN A CAREER	MOST IN A MATCH
Points	351 Jon Gregory 1999-00	914 Jon Gregory 1998-01	34 Michael Corcoran v Cheltenham 13.2.99
Tries	16 Nana Dontah 1998-99	30 Michael Corcoran 1998-00	4 Nana Dontah v Plymouth 10.10.98 (H) / Michael Corcoran v Cheltenham 13.2.99(H)
Conversions	78 Jon Gregory 1999-00	Jon Gregory 1998-01	8 Jon Gregory v Clifton 2.10.99 (H) / v W Hartelpool 8.4.01 (H)
Penalties	52 Jon Gregory 1998-99	Jon Gregory 1998-01	7 Jon Gregory v Tabard (A)
Drop Goals	3 Richard Bailey 1998-99	3 Richard Bailey 1998-00	1 By seven players

PLAYING SQUAD

ESHER

BACKS

	Ht.	Wt.	Birthdate	Birthplace	CLUB	League Apps	Tries	Pts
Jonathan Gregory	6.1	14.0	02.06.73	Chertsey	Esher Richmond	72	23	914
Billy Stanley Other club: Barking			27.03.78		Esher Harlequins	20	2	19
Simon Dixon	6.1	13.05	03.04.70		Esher	58	15	75
Paul Flood Other club: Bridgend	6.0	13.10	25.11.70	Birmingham	Esher London Welsh	31	14	70
Jim Bird			13.05.71	Somerset	Esher Hornets	35(27)	12	60
Jan Bonney Other clubs: Chingford, Moseley	6.1	15.05	27.01.71	Chingford	Esher London Scottish	47	11	64
Roland White			17.04.77		Esher	20	12	60
Dan Taylor			27.02.72	Somerset	Esher Hornets	21(1)	4	20
Alastair Sandilands Other clubs: Sheffield, London Welsh	5.10	14.08	21.01.68		Esher Rosslyn Park	14(2)	7	35
Charlie Mulraine			24.12.73		Esher Blackheath	16(2)	2	10
Campbell Aitken					Esher	2	5	25
Sean Burns			10.06.71		Esher Camberley	18(1) 34	3 5	15 25
Jeff Alexander	6.2	15.05	28.11.70	Kensington	Esher Harlequins	69(1)	11	55

FORWARDS

	Ht.	Wt.	Birthdate	Birthplace	CLUB	League Apps	Tries	Pts
Andy White			05.09.64	Surrey	Esher Richmond	52(11)	13	68
Mark Bennett	5.9	14.00	27.08.73	Kingston	Esher	46(14)	4	20
Duncan Cormack	6.0	15.04	03.04.75	London	Esher London Irish	45(8)	6	30
Chris Wilkins Other club: Blackheath			03.01.71		Esher	26	6	30
Peter Mole			21.02.66		Esher	70(13)	6	30
Paddy Seymour			18.07.78		Esher	16(7)	1	5
Ciaran Bird	6.2	16.00	29.11.71	Chingford	Esher	46(8)	21	105
Mark Butterworth	6.0	15.00	21.02.73	Croyden	Esher	89(4)	25	125
Caleb Kronfeld	1.78m	90kg	06.01.76	Hastings(NZ)	Esher	27(10)	10	50
Ollie Hankey	6.3	16.00	05.01.75		Esher Harlequins	5(13)	1	5
Jeff Smith Other club: Alnwick	6.1	18.07	25.03.76	Ashington	Esher Newcastle Falcons	27(14)	3	15
Matthew Morahan	1.95m	105kg	09.07.74	Australia	Esher	36(1)	12	60

ESHER

Founded: 1923-24

Colours: Black with amber collar

Change Colours: Amber with black collar

Nickname: The EE's

GROUND

Address: The Rugby Ground, 369 Molesey Road, Hersham, Surrey KT12 3PF
Tel: 01932 220295 (Office), 01932 254627 (Fax), 01932 224834 (Clubhouse)
Web site: http://www.esherrfc.org   email: webmaster@esherrfc.org
Capacity: 3,000   Seated: 1,200   Standing: Uncovered 1,800

Directions: M25 Junc 10, A3 to London. After 1 mile left to Walton-on-Thames (A245), after 1/4 mile right at lights into Seven Hills Road (B365).Turn right at r/about into Burwood Road & follow into Hersham Village, bear right into Molesey Road. After the railway bridge (Hersham BR) the ground is 300yds on the left . NB Low bridge at Hersham BR station.
Nearest Railway Station: Hersham (Waterloo-Woking line)

Car Parking: 1,000 on ground

Admission: Season - £50.   Matchdays £5   Under 16: Free

Clubhouse: Open matchdays & training nights.
Snacks & bar meals available.

Functions: Up to 200, contact Phil Beebe 01932 220295.
Sponsors' lounges available

Club Shop: Open matchdays & training days.
Contact Tim Bale 01932 220295

Training Nights: Monday & Wednesday 7pm

PROGRAMME

Size: A5
Price: £1
Pages: 40
Editor: David Page 07973 488142
Advertising Rates
Contact David Alexander 0777 332 9047
Colour - Full page £500, Half £300, Qtr £200

ENGLISH CLUBS CHAMPIONSHIP 2000-2001 NATIONAL DIVISION 2

Sunday 8th April 2001
National Division 2
West Hartlepool RFC
Kick-off 2pm

TODAY'S
MATCH
SPONSOR

scrum.com

FYLDE RUFC

President	Graham Sharman	6 Hedge Row, Wrea Green, Preston PR4 2PP
		01772 684118 (T) 01772 672963 (Fax)
Chairman	Arnie Halford	6 St Hildas Road, St. Annes, Lancs. FY8 2PT
		01253 713765 (H) 01253 739137 (Fax)
Club Secretary	David Walsh	33 Kingsway, Lytham
		01253 738452 (H) 01253 739137 (B) 01253 739137 (Fax)
Chairman of Rugby	Tony Todd	c/o Fylde Rugby Club Tel/Fax: 01253 739137
Press Officer	Stewart Brown	179 Hardhorn Road, Poulton-le-Fylde, Lancs. FY6 8ES
		01253 883100 (H) 01253 739137 (Fax)
1st Team Manager	Steve Rigby	01257 450580 (H) 01257 450991 (B) 07831 403400 (M)
Coach	Dean Kenny	c/o Fylde Rugby Club 01253 739137 (club)
		01942 498480 (B) 07909 981791 (M)
Forwards Coach	Dave Baldwin	c/o Fylde Rugby Club 0161 718 6080 (H) 07909 981791 (M)
Fitness Coach	Brendan Hanavan	c/o Fylde Rugby Club 01253 739137 (club)

This is my final report for the club. After three years I have stepped down as coach, in what I hope will prove to be the best interest of the club.

Over the period of my tenure the club has fought many battles on and off the field and where many others have succumbed to the pressures, Fylde has withstood the onslaught and are still hanging in there.

It is important to realise that National Division Two next season will consist of the following: Orrell, Waterloo, Harrogate, Kendal, Wharfedale, Preston, Nottingham, Plymouth, Newbury, Rosslyn Park, Sedgley Park/Launceston, Fylde and Esher. This is not too dissimilar to the Third Division of ten or fifteen years ago.

Whilst we may not have set the world alight over the past three seasons, we have maintained status on limited resources, which is an achievement in itself. Consider Gosforth, West Hartlepool, Liverpool St. Helens, Richmond, London Scottish, Blackheath and Lydney as examples of what can happen to once proud and prosperous clubs.

What have been the highlights? It is difficult to pinpoint events, more the attitude and commitment of the people involved at Fylde. On the playing side, the `old guard' have come through when it mattered and a crop of young players have come through their baptism of fire with credit. There have been three captains in my term, Ian Barclay, Martin Scott and Matt Filipo. I would like to thank them all sincerely.

In summing up, I wish everyone concerned with Fylde the very best future. Next season will be hard, but there is a strength within the club, which will hold together, of that I am sure.

MARK NELSON

Greg Anderton, shown on the cover of the matchday programme, was Fylde's top try scorer last season.

FYLDE

Comp.	Date	H/A	Opponents	Result & Score	Att.	15	14	13	12	11
N2	2-Sep	A	West Hartlepool	W 16-3	285	Evans	Armitage	Connell	Irving	Anderton/tcp
N2	9-Sep	H	Camberley	L 16-24	400	Evans	Armitage	Kenyon/2p	Irving	Anderton/t
N2	16-Sep	A	Bracknell	L 21-34		Evans/t	Armitage	Kenyon/cp	Jones	Lavin
N2	23-Sep	A	Wharfedale	L 10-72		Evans	Lavin	Kenyon	Jones	Anderton/t
N2	30-Sep	H	Newbury	W 12-6	450	Godfrey	Lavin	Kenyon	Carson	Evans
N2	14-Oct	H	Rugby Lions	W 14-13		Godfrey	Lavin	Kenyon	Anderton	Evans
N2	28-Oct	H	Esher	L 14-20		Godfrey	Lavin	Kenyon/t	Jones/t	Anderton
N2	11-Nov	A	Harrogate	L 17-31	450	Godfrey	Lavin	Kenyon/t	Anderton	Evans
N2	18-Nov	H	Lydney	L 13-18	450	Godfrey	Lavin	Kenyon	Evans	Anderton/t
N2	25-Nov	A	Nottingham	W 17-15		Godfrey	Lavin	Kenyon	Connell	Anderton
N2	2-Dec	A	Preston Grasshoppers	L 9-17	550	Godfrey	Lavin	Kenyon/3p	Connell	Anderton
N2	9-Dec	H	Rosslyn Park	W 21-16		Godfrey/3p	Lavin	Evans	Connell	Anderton
N2	16-Dec	A	Lydney*	W 13-9		Godfrey/c2p	Wilkinson	Evans	Connell	Lavin
N2	23-Dec	H	Harrogate	L 12-18		Godfrey/4p	Lavin	Evans	Connell	Anderton
N2	6-Jan	N	Esher	L 10-29	400	Godfrey/cp	Lavin	Jones	Connell	Carson
N2	13-Jan	H	Kendal	W 17-13		Godfrey/c	Evans	Carson	Connell	Anderton
N2	27-Jan	H	Preston Grasshoppers	W 20-12		Godfrey/2c2p	Evans	Connell	Jones	Anderton/t
N2	10-Feb	A	Newbury	D 10-10		Godfrey/cp	Lavin	Evans	Jones	Wyles
N2	24-Feb	H	Wharfedale	W 29-8	500	Godfrey/3cp	Lavin(a/t)	Evans	Connell	Anderton/2t
N2	10-Mar	H	Bracknell	L 6-17		Godfrey/2p	Long	Connell	Jones	Evans
N2	17-Mar	A	Camberley	W 28-24		Godfrey/t2c3p	Long	Kenyon	Connell	Wyles
N2	24-Mar	H	West Hartlepool	W 27-0		Moffatt/c	Long	Evans	Connell	Wyles/t
N2	31-Mar	A	Rosslyn Park	L 0-59		Wyles	Evans	Kenyon	Connell	Longman
N2	6-Apr	A	Rugby Lions	L 7-72		Moffatt	Long	Evans	Connell	Wyles
N2	14-Apr	H	Nottingham	L 3-23		Wyles/p	Long	Kenyon	Connell	Lavin
N2	28-Apr	A	Kendal	L 15-31		Godfrey	Evans	Long	Connell	Wyles
TBC	7-Oct	H	Whitchurch	W 16-11	300	Evans	Lavin	Kenyon	Carson	Anderton/t

*after opponents name indicates a penalty try. Brackets after a player's name indicates he was replaced.
eg (a) means he was replaced by replacement code "a" and so on. / after a player or replacement name
is followed by any scores he made - eg /t, /c, /p, /dg or any combination of these*

EVER PRESENT
Dylan O'Grady.

Most Appearances:
26	Dylan O'Grady.
25	Matt Filipo.
24	Mike Dreyer.
22	David Wiseman.

PLAYERS USED
41 plus 2 as replacements only

MOST POINTS

Pts	Player	T	C	P	DG
84	B Godfrey	1	11	19	-
61	D Wiseman	1	7	14	-
40	G Anderton	7	1	1	-
32	R Kenyon	2	2	6	-
30	D O'Grady	6	-	-	-

MATCH FACTS

10	9	1	2	3	4	5	6	7	8
Wiseman/2p	Condon	Webster	Scott	Filipo	Dreyer	Holmes	Kay	Lavin	O'Grady
Wiseman	Condon	Clarke	Scott/t	Filipo	Holmes	Dreyer	Kay	Lavin	O'Grady
Wiseman/2p	Condon/t	Filipo	Scott	Bradwell	Crompton	Dreyer	Kay	Lavin	O'Grady
Wiseman/cp	Rudd	Webster	Clarke	Gaulton	Crompton	Filipo	Kay	O'Grady	Dreyer
Wiseman/4p	Rudd	Filipo	McIntyre	Webster	Holmes	Dreyer	Kay	Lavin	O'Grady
Wiseman/3p	Knight	Webster	McIntyre	Filipo	Holmes	Collins	O'Grady	Lavin	Dreyer/t
Wiseman/2c	Condon	Webster	McIntyre	Filipo	Holmes	Collins	O'Grady	Lavin	Dreyer
Wiseman/2cp	Condon	Clarke/t	McIntyre	Filipo	Wilson	Collins	O'Grady	Bradwell	Dreyer
Wiseman/p	Condon	Clarke	McIntyre	Filipo	Collins	Wilson	O'Grady/t	Lavin	Dreyer
Wiseman/c	Rudd	Filipo	McIntyre/2t	Webster	Taylor	Wilson	O'Grady/t	Lavin	Dreyer
Wiseman	Rudd	Filipo	McIntyre	Webster	Taylor	Wilson	O'Grady	Lavin	Dreyer
Kenyon/c	Condon	Filipo	Scott	Webster	Wilson	Taylor/t	O'Grady/t	Bradwell	Dreyer
Kenyon	Condon	Filipo	Scott	Webster	Wilson	Taylor	O'Grady	Bradwell	Dreyer
Kenyon	Condon	Rigby	Scott	Webster	Wilson	Taylor	O'Grady	Bradwell	Dreyer
Wiseman	Condon	Filipo	McIntyre	Rigby	Collins/t	Wilson	O'Grady	Bradwell	Dreyer
Wiseman	Condon	Filipo/2t	Scott	Webster	Taylor	Wilson/t	O'Grady	Lavin	Dreyer
Wiseman	Condon	Filipo	Scott	Webster	Taylor	Wilson	O'Grady	Lavin/t	Dreyer
Wiseman/t	Hatley	Filipo	Scott	Webster	Wilson	Taylor	O'Grady	Lavin	Dreyer
Wiseman	Condon	Filipo	Clarke	Webster	Wilson	Taylor	Wilson	Lavin	O'Grady/t
Wiseman	Condon	Filipo	Scott	Webster	Taylor	Collins	O'Grady	Lavin	Dreyer
Wiseman	Condon	Filipo	Scott	Webster	Collins	Taylor	O'Grady	Lavin/t	Dreyer/t
Wiseman	Condon/t	Filipo	McIntyre/t	Webster	Taylor	Collins	O'Grady/t	Lavin	Dreyer/t
Wiseman	Condon	Filipo	McIntyre	Clarke	Collins	Taylor	O'Grady	Lavin	Dreyer
Wiseman/c	Castle	Filipo(b/t)	Scott	Collard	Dreyer	Collins	Bradwell	Lavin	O'Grady
Wiseman	Condon	Filipo	Scott	Rigby	O'Neill	Collins	Bradwell	O'Grady	Dreyer
Kenyon	Condon	Filipo	Scott	Rigby	O'Neill/t	Taylor	Wilson	Lavin/t	O'Grady/t
Wiseman/pdg	Rudd	Webster	McIntyre/t	Filipo	Collins	Holmes	Kay	O'Grady	Dreyer

REPLACEMENTS   a - K Long   b - C McIntyre

2000-01 HIGHLIGHTS

Ben Godfrey in his debut season topped the points scoring list. He scored 84 points, 23 ahead of David Wiseman.

Winger Greg Anderton topped the try scorers list with seven. It was the fourth time he had topped the try scorers list but only the second time on his own.

They suffered two heavy defeats in the season which set new records. They twice had 72 points put passed them in the away matches at Wharfedale and Rugby Lions.

In the match against Rugby Lions they lost by 65 points which was their largest ever loss in a league match.

FYLDE

LEAGUE STATISTICS
compiled by Stephen McCormack

SEASON	Division	P	W	D	L	F	A	Pts Diff	Lge Pts	Lge Pos	Most Points		Most Tries	
91-92	3	12	9	1	2	198	109	89	19	2p	106	Mike Jackson	4	Anthony Ireland
92-93	2	12	0	3	9	108	290	-182	0	12r	40	Mike Jackson	2	Steve Gough & John Nicholson
93-94	3	18	13	0	5	339	219	120	26	2p	109	Andy Parker	12	Brendan Hanavan
94-95	2	18	8	0	10	250	329	-79	16	9r	91	Andy Parker	5	Brendan Hanavan, Steve Gough & Greg Anderton
95-96	3	18	3	1	14	283	448	-165	7	10	138	Steve Gough	5	Greg Anderton
96-97	3	30	24	1	5	813	439	374	49	2p	404	Steve Gough	20	Mark Preston
97-98	P2	22	2	0	20	258	710	-452	4	12	98	Steve Gough	6	Mark Preston
98-99	P2	26	4	1	21	375	805	-430	9	14r	72	Alun Peacock	6	Mark Evans Carl Lavin
99-00	JN1	26	10	1	15	387	485	-98	21	9	194	Nick Booth	6	Richard Kenyon Greg Anderton
00-01	N2	26	11	1	14	377	594	-217	21(-2)	10	84	Ben Godfrey	7	Greg Anderton

BIGGEST MARGINS

Home Win   61pts - 68-7 v Birmingham 7.11.87

Away Win   47pts - 60-13 v Havant 15.2.97

Home Defeat   60pts - 7-67 v Bedford 27.12.97

Away Defeat   65pts - 7-72 v Rugby 6.4.01

MOST CONSECUTIVE

Appearances   41 Andy Parker 12.3.94 to date

Matches scoring Tries   4 Greg Anderton

Matches scoring points 20 Steve Burnage

Victories   9

Defeats   7

MOST POINTS

Scored at Home   68 v Birmingham 7.11.87

Scored Away   60 v Havant 15.2.97

Conceded at Home   67 v Bedford 27.12.97

Conceded Away   72 v Wharfedale 23.9.00 & Rugby

MOST TRIES

Scored in a match   10 v Birmingham 7.11.87 (H)
                           v Redruth 9.4.94 (H)

Conceded in a match   10 v West Hartlepool 14.2.98

MOST APPEARANCES

by a forward   168 (9) John Taylor

by a back   148(2) Ian Barclay

	MOST IN A SEASON	MOST IN A CAREER	MOST IN A MATCH	
Points	404 Steve Gough 96-97	739 Steve Gough 92-98	28 Steve Burnage	v Birmingham 7.11.87 (H)
Tries	20 Mark Preston 96-97	41 Brendan Hanavan 87-96	4 Brendan Hanavan	v Exeter 3.10.87 (H) v Birmingham 7.11.87 (H) v Redruth 9.4.94 (H)
Conversions	57 Steve Gough 96-97	85 Steve Gough 92-98	9 Steve Burnage	v Birmingham 7.11.87 (H)
Penalties	82 Steve Gough 96-97	143 Steve Gough 92-98	6 Steve Gough	v Walsall 21.9.96 (H) v Morley 25.1.97 (A)
Drop Goals	5 Ian Barclay 94-95	7 Ian Barclay 87-95	2 Ian Barclay	v Waterloo 25.3.95 (A)

PLAYING SQUAD

FYLDE

BACKS

	Ht.	Wt.	Birthdate	Birthplace	CLUB	League Apps	Tries	Pts
Ben Godfrey					Fylde	18(1)	1	84
Richard Kenyon England u21, B.					Fylde	36(13)	8	62
Chris Jones					Fylde	7(1)	1	5
Laurence Condon					Fylde London Irish	41(1)	5	25
Stuart Connell Cumbria	5.11	14.0	17.04.67	Bolton	Fylde	79(6)	2	8
Julian Irving	6.0	14.3	13.02.71	Oldham	Fylde	31(6)	3	15
Mark Evans	5.11	13.0	21.02.75	Leeds	Fylde	89(5)	13	65
David Wiseman					Fylde	30(1)	3	80
Greg Anderton Lancashire, North.	5.11	16.05	26.02.75		Fylde			
Tim Wyles					Fylde	7	1	8

FORWARDS

	Ht.	Wt.	Birthdate	Birthplace	CLUB	League Apps	Tries	Pts
Mike Dreyer					Fylde	45(1)	7	35
Martin Scott Scotland 1, A, u21.	6.0	15.10	05.07.67	Falkirk	Fylde Orrell	71(7) 28	7 1	35 5
Matt Filipo					Fylde	25	2	10
Sam Clark England U-21, students.	5.11	15.11	05.06.77		Fylde	16(11)	1	5
Mike Bradwell					Fylde	8(6)	-	-
Richard Wilson					Fylde	12	1	5
John Taylor Lancashire	6.5	16.8	05.10.66	S Point (Aden)	Fylde	169(5)	9	45
Dylan O' Grady					Fylde Sale	41(3)	8	40
Steve Rigby	5.10	17.6	05.06.59	Lytham	Fylde	51(10)	-	-

FYLDE

FACT FILE

Founded: 1919

Colours: Claret, gold and white/white/claret
Change colours: Maroon

GROUND
Address: Woodlands Memorial Ground, Blackpool Road, Ansdell, Lytham St. Annes. FY8 4EL
Tel: 01253 734733   Fax:
Capacity: 5,440   Seated: 440   Standing: 5,000

Directions: From the end of the M55 follow signs for Lytham St. Annes -B5230 then B5261 onto
Queensway - ground is three miles on the left opposite Blossoms P.H. and R.C. Church.
Nearest Railway Station: Ansdell & Fairhaven. Left outside station, down the hill away from the sea, along
Woodlands Rd to T junction (R.C. Church & Blossoms PH) - ground is opposite to the right.

Car Parking: 150 spaces available F.O.C. at the ground.

Admission: (Standing only)
Matchdays   Non members £8, OAPs £4;
                   Members £6, OAPs £5.
Season tickets   Members only £60 OAPs £35.

Club Shop: Open matchdays 1-6pm & Sundays 10-Noon.
Contact D Walsh 01253729253.

Clubhouse: Open matchdays Noon-11, Sun Noon-3, Tue,Thur, Fri 7.30-11pm. 3 bars.
Snacks and bar meals available.
Functions: Approx 400   Contact D Walsh 01253 729253.

Training Nights: Tuesday and Thursday.

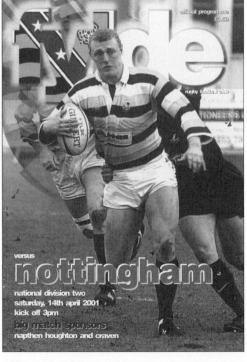

HARROGATE RUFC

President	Roy Guy	4 Southway, Harrogate HG2 0CA 01423 503054
Chairman	Frank Carter	6 Blackthorn Lane, Burn Bridge, Harrogate HG3 1NW 01423 870654
Club Secretary	Ian Gair	Glenshee, Spofforth Lane, Follifoot, Harrogate HG3 7EG 01423 871743
Treasurer	Nic Davies	3 Hereford Road, Harrogate HG1 2NP 01423 522066
Fixtures Secretary	Bill Barrack	15 Eastgate Close, Bramhope, Leeds LS16 9AR 0113 284 2540

FACT FILE

Founded: 1871
Nickname: Gate
Web site: harrogaterufc.or.uk

Colours: Red, amber & black
Change colours: Red

GROUND

Address: The County Ground, Claro Road, Harrogate. HG1 4AG.
Tel : 01423 566966   Fax: 01423 509073   E-mail: hrufc@lineone.net
Capacity: 2,999   Seated: 4990 Standing: 2,500

Directions: Claro Road is on the north side of the A59 (York Skipton road), just off the Stray (open grassed area adjacent to the town centre).
Nearest Railway Station: Harrogate, exit to East Parade turn left, right onto Parkview continues into Kingsway & Walkers passage, cross Stray to Claro Rd (10mins).

Car Parking: 400 at the ground, unlimited nearby

Admission   Matchday: £6

Club Shop: Matchdays only.   Contact Pam Oswin 01423 871905.

Clubhouse: Mon - Fri 7-11, Sat 11-11, Sun 10-2, bar meals available.
Functions: Up to 120, contact Mick Lancaster at club

Training Nights: Tuesday and Thursday

PROGRAMME Size: A5   Pages: 32   Price: £1   Editor: Stuart Young 01423 500263

Advertising Rates Mono (Contact Club)   Full page £300   1/2 page £160   1/4 page £90

HARROGATE

Comp.	Date	H/A	Opponents	Result & Score	Att.	15	14	13	12	11
N2	2-Sep	H	Rugby Lions*	L 12-19	450	Smithies	Clayton/t	Duncombe	Douglas	Tapster
N2	9-Sep	A	Kendal	W 33-10	400	Smithies/t	Clayton	Duncombe	Sarjaent	Tapster/t
N2	16-Sep	H	Esher	W 31-10	400	Smithies/t	Clayton	Duncombe	Sarjaent	Tapster/3t
N2	23-Sep	H	Bracknell	W 28-27	350	Smithies	Clayton/t	Duncombe	Sarjaent	Tapster/t
N2	30-Sep	A	Lydney	W 24-3	200	Smithies/t	Clayton	Duncombe	Sarjaent	Tapster
N2	14-Oct	A	Rosslyn Park	L 17-19	200	Smithies	Clayton	Duncombe	Sarjaent/t	Tapster
N2	28-Oct	A	Camberley	L 15-16	150	Smithies/t	Clayton	Duncombe	Sarjaent/t	Tapster
N2	4-Nov	H	West Hartlepool	W 60-0	250	Smithies/3t	Clayton	Duncombe/4c	Sarjaent	Tapster/2t
N2	11-Nov	H	Fylde*	W 31-17	450	Smithies/3t	Clayton	Duncombe	Sarjaent	Tapster/t
N2	18-Nov	A	Wharfedale	L 0-25	700	Smithies	Clayton	Duncombe	Sarjaent	Tapster
N2	25-Nov	H	Newbury	W 17-9	300	Smithies	Clayton	Duncombe	Sarjaent	Tapster/t
N2	2-Dec	H	Nottingham	W 38-16	300	Smithies/t	Clayton/2t	Duncombe	Sarjaent	Tapster/t
N2	9-Dec	A	Preston Grasshoppers	D 22-22	450	Smithies	Clayton	Duncombe	Reed	Tapster/t
N2	16-Dec	H	Wharfedale	L 18-20	600	Smithies	Clayton	Duncombe	Sarjaent	Tapster/t
N2	23-Dec	A	Fylde	W 18-12		Smithies/t	Reed	Duncombe	Sarjaent	Tapster
N2	6-Jan	H	Camberley	W 49-5	400	Smithies/2t	Reed/t	Duncombe/t	Sarjaent	Tapster/2t
N2	13-Jan	A	West Hartlepool	W 70-14	150	Smithies/t	Reed	Duncombe/3t	Sarjaent/t	Tapster
N2	27-Jan	A	Nottingham*	W 10-3		Smithies	Farrar	Duncombe	Sarjaent	Tapster
N2	3-Feb	H	Rosslyn Park	L 10-13	550	Smithies	Farrar/t	Reed	Sarjaent	Tapster
N2	10-Feb	H	Lydney	W 29-16	350	Smithies	Windle/2c	Reed/t	Sarjaent	Tapster/t
N2	24-Feb	A	Bracknell	L 5-42	200	Smithies	Clayton	Reed	Sarjaent	Tapster
N2	10-Mar	A	Esher*	W 25-23		Smithies	Clayton	Reed	Sarjaent	Tapster
N2	17-Mar	H	Kendal	L 17-41	350	Smithies/t	Clayton	Reed	Duncombe	Tapster
N2	24-Mar	A	Rugby Lions	L 13-25	350	Smithies/t	Farrar/t	Reed	Duncombe	Tapster
N2	31-Mar	H	Preston Grasshoppers	D 13-13		Smithies	Clayton	Duncombe/dg	Sarjaent	Tapster
N2	14-Apr	A	Newbury	L 12-22		Smithies	Clayton	Duncombe	Sarjaent	Tapster/t
TBC	7-Oct	A	Rugby Lions	L 15-16		Smithies/t	Clayton	Woodcock	Sarjaent	Tapster/t

after opponents name indicates a penalty try. Brackets after a player's name indicates he was replaced. eg (a) means he was replaced by replacement code "a" and so on. / after a player or replacement name is followed by any scores he made - eg /t, /c, /p, /dg or any combination of these

EVER PRESENT				

James Tapster, Ed Smithies.

Most Appearances
26 James Tapster, Ed Smithies.
25 Iain Salkeld, Lee Cholewa, Mark Pinder

PLAYERS USED

29 plus 6 as replacement only

MOST POINTS				
Pts	Player	T	C	P	DG
---	---	---	---	---	---
161	L Cholewa	3	31	28	-
85	E Smithies	17	-	-	-
80	J Tapster	16	-	-	-
35	R Morgan	7	-	-	-
30	R Wade	6	-	-	-

MATCH FACTS

10	9	1	2	3	4	5	6	7	8
Cholewa/c	Morgan	Pinder	McNeish	Wilson	Clark	Taylor	Worden	Hobson	Wade
Cholewa/2c3p	Morgan/2t	Pinder	Salkeld	Wilson	Clark	Taylor	Worden	Hobson	Wade
Cholewa/3c	Morgan	Pinder	Salkeld	Wilson	Clark	Taylor	Worden	Hobson/t	Wade
Cholewa/2c3p	Morgan/t	Pinder	Salkeld	Wilson	Clark	Taylor	Boyle	Hobson	Wade
Cholewa/3cp	Morgan/2t	Pinder	Salkeld	Wilson	Clark	Taylor	Houghton	Hobson	Wade
Cholewa/2cp	Morgan	Pinder	Salkeld	Bevan	Clark	Taylor/t	Worden	Hobson	Wade
Cholewa/cp	Drane	Pinder	Salkeld	Wilson	Clark	Houghton	Taylor	Worden	Wade
Cholewa/c	Drane	Pinder	Salkeld	Wilson	Clark	Houghton	Taylor	Worden/2t	Wade/3t
Cholewa/3c	Drane	Pinder	Salkeld	Wilson	Clark	Taylor	Worden	Hobson	Wade
Cholewa	Drane	Pinder	Salkeld	Wilson	Clark	Taylor	Worden	Hobson	Dudley
Cholewa/4p	Morgan	Pinder	Salkeld	Wilson	Clark	Taylor	Worden	Hobson	Dudley
Cholewa/2c3p	Morgan	Pinder	Salkeld	Wilson	Dudley/t	Clark	Worden	Hobson	Wade
Cholewa/4p	Morgan/t	Pinder	Salkeld	Wilson	Taylor	Clark	Worden	Hobson	Dudley
Cholewa/c2p	Morgan/t	Pinder	Salkeld	Wilson	Dudley	Clark	Worden	Hobson	Wade
Windle/2p(a/c)	Morgan	Pinder	Salkeld	Wilson	Taylor	Clark	Worden	Hobson	Dudley/t
Cholewa/t3cp	Morgan	Pinder	Salkeld	Wilson	Taylor	Clark	Dudley/t	Worden	Wade
Cholewa(b/4c)	Morgan	Pinder	Salkeld/t	Wilson	Taylor/3t	Clark/t	Dudley	Hobson/2cp	Wade/t
Cholewa	Morgan	Pinder	Salkeld	Wilson	Taylor	Clark	Worden	Hobson/cp	Dudley
Cholewa	Morgan	Pinder	Salkeld	Wilson	Taylor/t	Clark	Worden	Hobson	Dudley
Cholewa	Morgan	Pinder	Salkeld	Wilson	Taylor	Dudley/t	Worden/2t	Hobson	Wade
Cholewa/t	Morgan	Pinder	Salkeld	Wilson	Dudley	Boyle	Worden	Hobson	Wade
Cholewa/2c2p	Morgan	Pinder	Salkeld	Wilson	Fforde	Taylor	Dudley/2t	Hobson	Wade
Cholewa/t2cp	Morgan	Halligan	Salkeld	Wilson	Taylor	Fforde	Dudley	Hobson	Wade
Cholewa/p	Morgan	Pinder	Salkeld	Wilson	Dudley	Clark	Boyle	Worden	Wade
Cholewa/cp	Morgan	Pinder	Salkeld	Wilson	Dudley	Clark	Boyle	Worden	Wade/t
Cholewa/c	Morgan	Pinder	Salkeld	Wilson	Dudley	Clark	Worden	Hobson	Wade/t
Cholewa/cp	Morgan	Pinder	Salkeld	Bevan	Clark	Houghton	Taylor	Hobson	Wade

REPLACEMENTS   a - L Cholewa   b - R Windle

2000-01 HIGHLIGHTS

Lee Cholewa topped the points scoring list with 161 points. This was a total only beaten by Ralph Zoing and Matt Duncombe previously for the club.

It was in the try scoring where the records were broken. Ed Smithies topped the list for a second successive season, this time though he set a new league record for the club.

He beat the old record by four whilst fellow team mate James Tapster also broke the old record 16 tries to his credit in the season just finished.

In the away match at West Hartlepool they secured their biggest ever away win with a 70-14 result. They ran in 70 points which eclipsed the old record and they won by a record 56 point margin. Both previous records dated from the 41-13 win at Clifton back in November 1996.

HARROGATE

LEAGUE STATISTICS
compiled by Stephen McCormack

SEASON	Division	P	W	D	L	F	A	Pts Diff	Lge Pts	Lge Pos	Most Points		Most Tries	
91-92	D4N	12	6	0	6	170	175	-5	12	7	45	Ralph Zoing	3	Steve Baker
92-93	D4N	12	10	1	1	363	115	248	21	1	131	Ralph Zoing	9	Steve Baker Guy Easterby
93-94	4	18	14	2	2	479	219	260	30	2	105	Ralph Zoing	13	Jeremy Hopkinson
94-95	3	18	7	2	9	275	404	-129	16	7	110	Dan Clappison	7	Rob Bell
95-96	3	18	6	3	9	333	387	-54	15	6	215	Ralph Zoing	5	Richard Marcroft
96-97	3	30	18	0	12	832	595	237	36	5	305	Ralph Zoing	13	Rob Bell, Mike Farrar & Kerry Morley
97-98	JN1	26	4	1	21	463	707	-244	9	14	79	Neil James	10	Lee Feurer
98-99	JN1	26	8	2	16	309	461	-152	18	12	61	Ralph Zoing	5	Mark Farrar
99-00	JN1	26	14	1	11	508	449	59	29	6	190	Matt Duncombe	11	Ed Smithies
00-01	N1	26	14	2	10	617	422	195	30	5	161	L Cholewa	17	Ed Smithies

BIGGEST MARGINS

Home Win 72pts - 79-7 v Clifton 5.4.97

Away Win 56pts - 70-14 v W Hartlepool 13.01.01

Home Defeat 54pts - 12-66 v Leeds 21.3.98

Away Defeat 47pts - 3-50 v Worcester 31.1.98

MOST CONSECUTIVE

Appearances 49 Rob Bell 9.92 -9.9.95

Matches scoring Tries 6 Clive Ware

Matches scoring points 24 Ralph Zoing

Victories 5

Defeats 10

MOST POINTS

Scored at Home 79 v Clifton 5.4.97

Scored Away 70 v W Hartlepool 13.1.01

Conceded at Home 66 v Leeds 21.3.98

Conceded Away 50 v Worcester 31.1.98

MOST TRIES

Scored in a match 14 v Aspatria 30.4.94

Conceded in a match 10 v Leeds 21.3.98 (H)

MOST APPEARANCES

by a forward 166(2) Peter Taylor

by a back 149 (9) Craig Reed

	MOST IN A SEASON	MOST IN A CAREER	MOST IN A MATCH
Points	305 Ralph Zoing 96-97	1086 Ralph Zoing 87-99	27 Ralph Zoing v Fylde 14.10.95 (H)
Tries	17 Ed Smithies 00-01	42 Jeremy Hopkinson 90-98	5 Steve Baker v Lichfield 14.11.92 (H)
Conversions	63 Ralph Zoing 96-97	175 Ralph Zoing 87-99	9 Ralph Zoing v Towcestrians 13.3.93 (H)
Penalties	51 Ralph Zoing 95-96	209 Ralph Zoing 87-99	7 Ralph Zoing v Halifax 18.11.90 (H)
Drop Goals	5 Ralph Zoing 96-97	16 Ralph Zoing 87-99	2 Ralph Zoing v Askeans 20.11.93 (H)

PLAYING SQUAD

HARROGATE

BACKS

	Ht.	Wt.	Birthdate	Birthplace	CLUB	League Apps	Tries	Pts
Graeme Sarjaent	5.10	13.0	25.09.75	Carlisle	Harrogate	22(2)	3	15
					Kendal	12(9)	2	14
Ed Smithies					Harrogate	52	27	135
Craig Reed					Harrogate	149(9)	27	149
Rhys Morgan					Harrogate	63(1)	16	80
					Leeds	35(9)	8	40
Mark Farrar					Harrogate	100(7)	39	195
Lee Cholewa					Harrogate	25(1)	3	161
Gareth Drane					Harogate	10(12)	-	-
Richard Windle					Harrogate	3(4)	1	38
James Tapster					Harrogate	36(1)	20	100
Matt Duncombe					Harrogate	47(2)	11	221
Andy Caldwell					Harrogate	103	16	76
					Leeds	2(1)	-	-
Lee Douglas					Harrogate	7(3)	1	5

FORWARDS

	Ht.	Wt.	Birthdate	Birthplace	CLUB	League Apps	Tries	Pts
Scott Wilson					Harrogate	134(6)	1	5
Matt Pinder	6.0	16.7	18.12.70	Rotherham	Harrogate	137	5	25
					Rotherham	27(26)	-	-
Paul Clark					Harrogate	42	2	10
Steve Hobson					Harrogate	21	1	17
Ian Salkeld					Harrogate	53	3	15
Richard Wade					Harrogate	20(5)	6	30
Peter Taylor					Harrogate	169(2)	20	115
Simon Brown					Harrogate	84(7)	2	9
Rob Wilson					Harrogate	16(8)	-	-
Mike Worden					Harrogate	55(8)	7	35

KENDAL RFC

President	J D Healey	55 Calder Drive, Kendal LA9 6LR. 01539 723913 (H)
Chairman	Ian W Hutton	168 Vicarage Drive, Kendal, Cumbria, LA9 5BX 01539 733152 (H), 01539 733333 (B)
Hon/Match Secretary	Roger Wilson	31 Hills Wood Avenue, Kendal, Cumbria. 01539740449 (H)
Fixture Secretary	Andrew Quarry	Watchgate Farm, Selside, Kendal, Cumbria LA8 9JX 07733 111868 (M)
Rugby Manager	Chris Hayton	106 Burneside Road, Kendal, Cumbria LA9 4RT. 01539 724600 (H)
Press Secretary	John Hutton	168 Vicarage Drive, Kendal LA9 5BX 01539 733152(H)

Kendal newly promoted to National League Two, had a very successful first season finishing in fourth place.

In what was a challenging campaign, Kendal managed to produce some excellent rugby from the opening game of the season when they convincingly won at newly promoted Esher.

However, the following week Harrogate gave them a lesson in how rugby was played in the higher league, a lesson Kendal learnt from quickly, and after a defeat away at Lydney they beat Nottingham at home, and then produced the fight back of the season to turn a 17-3 deficit away at Rosslyn Park into a 25-29 victory. That victory kick started their season and wins against Wharfedale, over whom they did the double, and Newbury (18-0) followed, as well as a credible draw against Rugby to get them close to the top of the league. Newbury avenged their defeat the Saturday before Christmas and that day was made worse for Kendal when centre Ian Voortman broke his leg in two places and brought an early end to his season

Late January brought Kendal a club record victory of 92-0 against West Hartlepool, and fullback Mike Scott a personal league record of 42 points. Five consecutive league wins followed, to place Kendal in promotion contention going into the last month of the season. Unfortunately they could not match the mighty power of champions Bracknell and were on the receiving end of a brilliant display of running rugby by Rugby, who finished second. So Kendal had to settle for fourth behind Rosslyn Park

Kendal enjoyed life in the higher league and will look to build on the success of last season and hope to go all the way this season.

Action from last season's match against Esher.

KENDAL

Comp.	Date	H/A	Opponents	Result & Score	Att.	15	14	13	12	11	10
N2	2-Sep	A	Esher	W 21-6	450	Scott/c3p	Balmer	Healey	Voortman	Stephens(a/t)	Mee
N2	9-Sep	H	Harrogate	L 10-33	400	Scott/cp	Balmer	Healey	Voortman	Dodds	Mee
N2	16-Sep	A	Lydney	L 16-20		Scott/c3p	Balmer	Healey	Voortman/t	Dodds	Mee
N2	23-Sep	H	Nottingham*	W 25-12		Scott/tcp	Balmer	Healey	Voortman/t	Dodds	Mee/t
N2	30-Sep	A	Rosslyn Park	W 29-25		Scott/2c4pdg	Balmer	Healey	Voortman	Dodds	Mee
N2	14-Oct	A	Camberley	W 15-13	250	Scott	Balmer	Healey	Voortman	Dodds/t	Mee
N2	28-Oct	A	Wharfedale	W 21-14		Scott/2p	Balmer	Healey	Voortman	Dodds/t	Mee
N2	11-Nov	H	Newbury	W 18-0	400	Scott/c2p	Balmer	Healey	Voortman	Dodds	Mee
N2	18-Nov	A	Preston Grasshoppers	L 18-25	630	Scott/c2p	Balmer	Healey	Voortman/t	Dodds	Mee
N2	25-Nov	H	Rugby Lions	D 17-17	400	Scott/2cp	Balmer	Healey	Voortman	Dodds	Mee
N2	9-Dec	A	Bracknell	L 15-31		Scott/cp	Balmer	Healey	Voortman/t	Dodds	Mee/t
N2	16-Dec	H	Preston Grasshoppers*	W 20-14		Dodds	Pearson	Healey	Voortman	Airey	Mee/tcp
N2	23-Dec	A	Newbury	L 12-35		Dodds	Balmer	Healey	Voortman(d/t)	Pearson	Mee/c
N2	6-Jan	H	Wharfedale	W 6-0		Scott/2p	Balmer	Healey	Stephens	Dodds	Mee
N2	13-Jan	A	Fylde	L 13-17		Scott/p	Balmer	Healey	Stephens	Dodds/t	Mee
N2	27-Jan	H	West Hartlepool	W 92-0		Scott/4t11c	Balmer/3t	Healey/t	Stephens/t	Dodds/t	Mee/2t
N2	17-Feb	A	West Hartlepool	W 42-11		Scott/3c2p	Balmer	Stephens	Healey/t	Dodds	Mee
N2	24-Feb	A	Nottingham	W 27-25		Scott/3cpdg	Myers	Healey	Stephens	Dodds	Mee
N2	10-Mar	H	Lydney	W 33-9		Scott/2c3p	Balmer	Healey	Stephens	Dodds/t	Mee
N2	17-Mar	A	Harrogate	W 41-17	350	Scott/4cp	Balmer/3t	Healey/t	Stephens	Dodds	Mee
N2	24-Mar	H	Esher	W 32-17		Scott/2cp	Balmer/t	Healey	Stephens/t	Dodds	Mee
N2	31-Mar	H	Bracknell	L 13-22		Scott/c2p	Balmer	Healey	Stephens	Dodds	Mee(g/t)
N2	7-Apr	H	Camberley	W 24-5		Dodds	Spiby	Healey/t	Stephens	Airey/2t	Scott/2c
N2	14-Apr	A	Rugby Lions	L 21-62		Stephens	Airey(h/t)	Healey	Mee	Dodds	Scott/c3p
N2	21-Apr	H	Rosslyn Park	L 10-22		Dodds	Airey	Stephens	Thompson	Myers	Scott
N2	28-Apr	H	Fylde	W 31-15		Dodds/t	Balmer	Stephens	Healey	Airey	Scott/t4cp
TBC	7-Oct	A	Sedgley Park	L 9-17		Scott/3p	Balmer	Healey	Voortman	Dodds	Mee

*after opponents name indicates a penalty try. Brackets after a player's name indicates he was replaced.
eg (a) means he was replaced by replacement code "a" and so on. / after a player or replacement name
is followed by any scores he made - eg /t, /c, /p, /dg or any combination of these*

EVER PRESENT None

Most Appearances:
26   Billy Coxon, Jimmy Thompson.
25   Adian Bateson, Paul Dodds, Stephen Healey

PLAYERS USED 25 plus four as a replacement

MOST POINTS

Pts	Player	T	C	P	DG
235	M Scott	6	44	37	2
37	C Mee	6	2	1	-
35	J Balmer	7	-	-	-
35	P Dodds	7	-	-	-
35	C Wolstenholme	7	-	-	-

MATCH FACTS

9	1	2	3	4	5	6	7	8
Thompson	Coxon/t	Gowing	Thompson	Harryman	Robinson	Wolstenholme	Bland	Bateson
Thompson	Coxon	Gowing	Thompson	Harryman	Capstick	Robinson(b/t)	Bland	Bateson
Thompson	Coxon	Gowing	Thompson	Harryman	Capstick	Wolstenholme	Bland	Bateson
Thompson	Coxon	Gowing	Thompson	Harryman	Capstick	Robinson	Bland	Bateson
Thompson	Coxon	Gowing/t	Thompson	Harryman/t	Capstick	Bland	Robinson	Bateson
Thompson	Coxon	Gowing	Thompson	Robinson/2t	Capstick	Wolstenholme	Bland	Bateson
Thompson	Coxon	Gowing/t	Thompson	Robinson	Capstick	Wolstenholme/t	Bland	Bateson
Thompson	Coxon	Gowing	Harryman	Robinson/t(c/t)	Capstick	Wolstenholme	Bland	Bateson
Thompson	Coxon	Gowing/t	Thompson	Robinson	Capstick	Wolstenholme	Bland	Bateson
Thompson	Coxon	Thompson/t	Pearson	Harryman/t	Capstick	Robinson	Bland	Bateson
Thompson	Coxon	Gowing	Thompson	Robinson	Capstick	Wolstenholme	Bland	Bateson
Thompson	Coxon	Gowing	Thompson	Harryman	Capstick/t	Wolstenholme	Bland	Bateson
Thompson	Coxon	Gowing	Thompson	Harryman/t	Capstick	Wolstenholme	Robinson	Bateson
Thompson	Coxon	Gowing	Thompson	Robinson	Capstick	Wolstenholme	Bland	Bateson
Thompson	Coxon	Gowing	Thompson	Robinson(e/t)	Capstick	Wolstenholme	Bland	Bateson
Thompson	Coxon	Gowing	Thompson	Harryman	Capstick	Wolstenholme/t	Bland	Bateson/t
Thompson/t	Coxon	Gowing/t	Harryman	Robinson(e/t)	Capstick	Wolstenholme/t	Bowman/2t	Bateson
Thompson/t	Coxon	Gowing	Thompson	Robinson	Capstick	Wolstenholme	Bland	Bateson/t
Thompson/t	Coxon	Gowing	Thompson	Harryman	Capstick	Wolstenholme/2t	Bland/t	Bateson
Thompson/t	Coxon	Gowing/t	Thompson	Harryman	Capstick	Wolstenholme	Bland	Bateson
Thompson	Coxon	Gowing/t	Harryman	Robinson	Capstick	Wolstenholme/t(f/t)	Bland	Bateson
Thompson	Coxon	Gowing	Harryman	Robinson	Capstick	Wolstenholme	Bland	Bateson
Thompson/t	Coxon	Gowing	Pearson	Robinson	Capstick	Wolstenholme	Bowman	Bateson
Thompson	Coxon	Gowing	Harryman	Robinson	Capstick	Wolstenholme	Bland/t	Bowman
Mee/t	Coxon	Gowing	Harryman/t	Robinson	Quarry	Bowman	Bland	Bateson
Thompson	Coxon	Holmes/2t	Pearson	Robinson	Capstick	Bowman	Bland	Bateson
Thompson	Pearson	Gowing	Harryman	Robinson	Capstick	Wolstenholme	Bland	Bateson

REPLACEMENTS
a - P Dodds b - C Wolstenholme c - C Wilson d - M Healey e - R Harryman
f - Mark Bowman g - M Airey h - A Myers

2000-01 HIGHLIGHTS

Mike Scott in his first season for the club topped the points scoring list with 235.

He becomes the second man after Casey Mee to score 200 points in a league season.

Mee became the first Kendal player to reach 500 National League points.

Scott also finished 4th in the try scoring list with six, four of those coming in just one match, against West Hartlepool in January. In that match he also kicked 22 points for a new division record of 42 point in a match.

The 22 points consisted of 11 conversions which also a new record for the club in league rugby.

Suffered their worst ever defeat when losing 21-62

KENDAL

LEAGUE STATISTICS
compiled by Stephen McCormack

SEASON	Division	P	W	D	L	F	A	Pts Diff	Lge Pts	Lge Pos		Coach	Captain
91-92	D4N	12	8	1	3	157	123	34	17	3		R Lee	S Hulme
92-93	D4N	12	6	0	6	182	189	-7	12	6			
93-94	D5N	12	4	1	7	142	171	-29	9	10			
94-95	D5N	12	9	1	2	226	162	64	19	2		P Kremer	J Nicholson
												Most Points	**Most Tries**
95-96	D5N	12	5	0	7	215	227	-12	10	9	36	Paul Dodds	6 Paul Dodds
96-97	D4N	26	11	1	14	541	451	90	23	9	163	Jason Hudson	7 Paul Dodds
97-98	N2N	26	18	2	6	614	357	257	38	3	135	Jon Nicholson	15 Jason Balmer
98-99	N2N	26	18	0	8	635	347	288	36	4	200	Casey Mee	12 Jason Balmer
99-00	N2N	26	24	0	2	817	305	512	48	1	273	Casey Mee	15 Jason Balmer
00-01	N2	26	16	1	9	622	467	155	33	4	235	Mike Scott	7 by Three players

BIGGEST MARGINS

Home Win	92pts - 92-0 v W Hartlepool27.1.01
Away Win	51pts - 56-5 v Liverpool StH
Home Defeat	28pts - 6-34 v Harrogate 3.10.92
Away Defeat	41pts - 21-62 v Rugby 14.4.01

MOST CONSECUTIVE

Appearances	
Matches scoring Tries	
Matches scoring points	
Victories	19
Defeats	5

MOST POINTS

Scored at Home	92 v W Hartlepool 27.01.01
Scored Away	56 v Liverpool StH
Conceded at Home	39 v Wharfedale 13.1.96
Conceded Away	62 v Rugby 14.4.01

MOST TRIES

Scored in a match	14 v Hereford 12.4.97
Conceded in a match	6 v Preston 21.2.98

MOST APPEARANCES

by a forward

by a back

	MOST IN A SEASON	MOST IN A CAREER	MOST IN A MATCH
Points	273 Casey Mee 1999-20	510 Casey Mee 1998-01	42 Mike Scott v W Hartlepool 27.1.01
Tries	15 Jason Balmer 1997-98 & 1999-00	49 Jason Balmer 1997-01	6 Jason Slater v Barker's Butts 14.1.95
Conversions	53 Casey Mee 1999-00	92 Casey Mee 1998-01	11 Mike Scott v W Hartlepool 27.1.01 (H)
Penalties	44 Casey Mee 1999-00	76 Casey Mee 1998-01	7 Jon Nicholson v Sandal 27.12.97 (A)
Drop Goals	3 David Bell 1996-97	3 David Bell 1996-97	1 By numerous players

PLAYING SQUAD

KENDAL

BACKS

	Ht.	Wt.	Birthdate	Birthplace	CLUB	League Apps	Tries	Pts
Stephen Healey	5.11	13.7	21.07.71	Kendal	Kendal	130(1)+	29+	145+
Dan Stephens	6.2	14.0	20.09.77	Kendal	Kendal	72(3)	15	80
Jason Balmer	5.11	13.7	16.04.71	Burnley	Kendal	87(1)	49	245
Ian Voortman	6.3	15.6	13.04.74	Cape Town	Kendal	79	28	142
Mike Scott					Kendal Aspatria, Orrell	24	6	235
Paul Dodds	5.10	12.7	29.01.71	Kendal	Kendal	129(3)	28	160
Casey Mee	5.8	12.8	11.06.73	Dunedin	Kendal	74	19	508
Jimmy Thompson			01.07.71		Kendal	72(2)	22	110
Aaron Myers					Kendal	2(6)	-	-
Scott Pearson					Kendal	2(4)	-	-
Mark Airey					Kendal	31(10)	11	55

FORWARDS

	Ht.	Wt.	Birthdate	Birthplace	CLUB	League Apps	Tries	Pts
Adrian Bateson	6.4	15.7	14.02.76	Whitehaven	Kendal	77	10	50
Keith Robinson	6.4	15.7	09.03.70	Penrith	Kendal	88(9)+	15+	75+
Colin Wolstenholme	5.11	14.7	18.03.67	Kendal	Kendal	90(15)	33	165
Nathan Bland	6.0	14.10	25.05.77	Kendal	Kendal	43(4)	4	20
Richard Harryman	6.2	19.7	16.11.76	Kendal	Kendal	94(15)	34	170
Mike Capstick	6.5	18.0	29.04.74	Kendal	Kendal			
Nigel Pearson	5.11	17.7	17.06.67	Kendal	Kendal	73(37)+	4+	20+
Billy Coxon	6.0	16.0	27.07.75	Peterlee	Kendal	135(1)+	9+	45+
Ian Gowing	5.11	17.7	13.07.75	Natick (USA)	Kendal	56(10)	9	45
Ian Thompson	5.11	15.7	31.10.69	Penrith	Kendal	74(12)+	1	5
Alan Homes					Kendal	1(1)	2	10
Craig Wilson					Kendal	(5)	-	-

KENDAL

FACT FILE

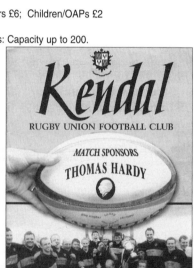

Founded : 1905
Nickname : The Black & Ambers
Colours: Black and amber.
Change colours: Amber jerseys with black trim

GROUND

Address: Mint Bridge, Shap Road, Kendal. LA9 6DL.
Tel: 01539 734039
Capacity: 1900   Seated: 400   Standing: 1500

Directions: From the M6 junction 36 take A591. Then A6 (Kendal to Penrith). Keep left at the `Duke of Cumberland' and the ground is 400 metres onthe left.
Nearest Railway Station: Kendal (via Oxenholme)

Car Parking: Space for 120 cars on ground.

Admission: Matchdays - Adults members £4.00 non-members £6; Children/OAPs £2
Season Ticket: £35 (members only)
Clubhouse: Has two bars and has food available.   Functions: Capacity up to 200.

Club Shop: Shop manager - David Robinson 01539 720355

Training Nights: Tuesday and Thursday

PROGRAMME Size: A5   Price: £1   Pages: 24 + cover
Editor: John Kremer 01539 734039
Advertising Rates   Prices on application
Contact MTP Publications Ltd. 01539 740937

Action from last season's match against Lydney.

NEWBURY RFC

Newbury RFC, Monks Lane, Newbury. RG14 7RW
Tel: 01635 40103   Fax: 01635 40533 email: info@newburyrfc.co.uk

President	David G H Smith	c/o Newbury RFC	01264 342342 (B), 07801 666116 (M)
Club Secretary	Rosie Golby	c/o Newbury RFC	07775 915785 (M)
Rugby Co-ordinator	Ally Pankhurst	c/o Newbury RFC	07771 550494 (M)
Chairman of Rugby	Pete Simmons	c/o Newbury RFC	01635 863242
Commercial Manager	Morgan Davis	c/o Newbury RFC	01635 40103 (B) 07785 525816 (M)
Ist XV Manager	Simon Little	c/o Newbury RFC	07768 710577 (M)
Fixture Co-ordinator	John Mills	c/o Newbury RFC	01635 200743

After the promise of a best ever fifth placing the previous year, Newbury's 2000-01 season turned out to be a massive disappointment.

The new coaching team of Richard Greed and Julian Brammer snapped up several experienced close season signings and they appeared to herald a promotion drive, while an opening day win at Nottingham suggested that Newbury had found the steel to grind out results on their travels.

Despite a home defeat at the hands of Rosslyn Park, Newbury led the league briefly until they went to then bottom of the table Fylde and a 12-6 defeat at the end of September set off a run that produced eleven straight away league defeats and eventually saw Blues plummet into the relegation battle.

Home wins over Rugby and Kendal provided highlights and signs of what the side could do at its best. But, when home form also began to suffer with defeats at the hands of Wharfedale and Preston and a disappointing draw in the return with Fylde, then Newbury were well and truly involved in the survival battle.

It was a 31-5 defeat at Esher in February that prompted Newbury to turn again to coach Keith Richardson for help, as he had helped to steer them through the National Leagues before setting off back to Gloucester and then Coventry. Back at Monks Lane, he helped to focus the task and despite disappointing defeats at Camberley and at home to champions Bracknell by a record 53-3 scoreline, Blues did enough to secure their safety with home wins over West Hartlepool (53-3), Nottingham (23-11) and finally Harrogate (22-12).

Injuries over the season hardly helped as Blues fielded more than 40 players in league games, but there were plus marks in the performances of winger Jo Czerpak, Matt Cornish and Chris Simmons and, with Richardson now back on board as director of rugby, Blues will be hoping to find the consistency to ward off any fears of a repeat this term.

Back Row: Lee Woodhouse, Ben Shand, Richard Parker, Nigel Hill, Andy Binnie, Phil Clarke. **Middle:** Sid Little, Jeremy Griffiths, Dave Griffiths, Chris Hart, Ben Butler, Nick Hunt, Gareth Evans, Bill Nicholas, Craig Davies, Julian Brammer. **Front:** Mal Roberts, Andy Evans, Simon Stoker, Morgan Davis, John Kingdon, Simon Gully, Brett Wakfer, Bernie Williams.

NEWBURY

Comp.	Date	H/A	Opponents	Result & Score	Att.	15	14	13	12	11
N2	2-Sep	A	Nottingham	W 26-14		Griffiths/c3p	Lucas	Griffiths/t	Hill	Simmons
N2	9-Sep	H	Rosslyn Park	L 17-26		Griffiths/2cp	Starter-Smith	Evans	Hill	Simmons
N2	16-Sep	A	West Hartlepool	W 34-3		Griffiths/4c2p	Lucas	Griffiths/2t	Hill	Simmons
N2	23-Sep	H	Camberley*	W 34-13	300	Griffiths/2c	Hart	Evans	Hill	Simmons/3t
N2	30-Sep	A	Fylde	L 6-12	450	Griffiths/2p	Hart	Griffiths	Hill	Simmons
N2	14-Oct	A	Bracknell	L 11-26		Griffiths/2p	Roberts	Griffiths	Evans	Clarke
N2	28-Oct	H	Rugby Lions	W 22-19		Griffiths/2cp	Roberts	Evans/t	Hill	Griffiths/t
N2	11-Nov	A	Kendal	L 0-18	400	Griffiths	Roberts	Evans	Hill	Griffiths
N2	18-Nov	H	Esher	W 19-18		Roberts/t3p	Hart	Evans	Hill	Griffiths
N2	25-Nov	A	Harrogate	L 9-17	300	Griffiths/3p	Hart	Roberts	Hill	Griffiths
N2	2-Dec	H	Wharfedale	L 10-25		Griffiths/cp	Clarke	Evans	Hill	Griffiths
N2	9-Dec	H	Lydney	W 24-12		Roberts/2c	Stoker	Griffiths/t	Evans	McClennan
N2	23-Dec	H	Kendal	W 35-12		Roberts/3c3p	Stoker/t	Griffiths	Evans	Simmons/2t
N2	6-Jan	A	Rugby Lions	L 3-24		Roberts/p	Stoker	Griffiths	Evans	Simmons
N2	13-Jan	H	Preston Grasshoppers	L 10-25		Roberts/c	Stoker	Griffiths/t	Evans	Czerpak
N2	27-Jan	A	Wharfedale	L 7-37		Roberts/c	Flett	Evans/t	Hill	Czerpak
N2	10-Feb	H	Fylde	D 10-10		Roberts	Griffiths/t	Evans	Hill	Czerpak
N2	17-Feb	A	Esher	L 5-31	250	Roberts	Smith	Griffiths	Evans	Czerpak/t
N2	24-Feb	A	Camberley	L 16-23	200	Roberts/2p	Hart/t	Griffiths	Evans	Flett
N2	3-Mar	A	Preston Grasshoppers	L 17-27		Roberts/tc	Griffiths	Jennings	Evans	Czerpak/t
N2	10-Mar	H	West Hartlepool	W 53-3		Roberts/5cp	Griffiths	Jennings/t	Evans	Czerpak/2t
N2	17-Mar	A	Rosslyn Park*	L 16-31		Roberts/c3p	Hart	Griffiths	Evans	Czerpak
N2	24-Mar	H	Nottingham	W 23-11		Czerpak	Jennings	Griffiths	Hill	Roberts/c2p
N2	7-Apr	H	Bracknell	L 3-53		Morgan/p	Simmons	Evans	Hill	Griffiths
N2	14-Apr	H	Harrogate	W 22-12		Morgan/c4pdg	Simmons	Griffiths/t	Hill	Czerpak
TBC	7-Oct	H	Haywards Heath	W 45-0		Griffiths/t4c4p	Hart	Roberts	Evans	Griffiths/t
TBC	21-Oct	A	New Brighton	L 11-15		Griffiths	Haslam	Griffiths/2p	Hill	Evans

*after opponents name indicates a penalty try. Brackets after a player's name indicates he was replaced.
eg (a) means he was replaced by replacement code "a" and so on. / after a player or replacement name
is followed by any scores he made - eg /t, /c, /p, /dg or any combination of these*

EVER PRESENT None

Most Appearances:
24   Ben Butler.
22   Jeremy Griffiths.
20   Matt Baker, Rob Faulkner.

PLAYERS USED

41 plus four as replacement only

MOST POINTS

Pts	Player	T	C	P	DG
85	M Roberts	2	15	15	-
69	D Griffiths	-	12	15	-
40	J Griffiths	8	-	-	-
30	S Stoker	6	-	-	-

MATCH FACTS

10	9	1	2	3	4	5	6	7	8
Davis	Stoker	Faulkner	Baker	Williams	Hunt	Butler	Hart/t	Kingdon	Davies/t
Davis	Stoker/t	Faulkner	Baker	Williams	Hunt	Butler	Evans	Kingdon	Davies/t
Long	Stoker	Faulkner/t	Baker	Williams	Hunt	Butler	Nicholas/t	Kingdon	Davies
Davis	Stoker/t	Faulkner	Baker	Williams	Hunt	Butler	Nicholas	Kingdon	Davies/t
Davis	Stoker	Faulkner	Baker	Williams	Hunt	Butler	Nicholas	Kingdon	Davies
Davis	Shand/t	Faulkner	Baker	Williams	Hunt	Butler	Nicholas	Gully	Davies
Davis	Stoker	Faulkner	Baker/t	Binnie	Harrison	Butler	Nicholas	Gully	Davies
Davis	Stoker	Faulkner	Baker	Williams	Harrison	Butler	Nicholas	Gully	Davies
Davis	Stoker	Faulkner/t	Baker	Binnie	Harrison	Butler	Nicholas	Gully	Davies
Davis	Stoker	Faulkner	Bentley	Baker	Harrison	Butler	Nicholas	Gully	Davies
Roberts	Stoker/t	Faulkner	Baker	Williams	Harrison	Butler	Nicholas	Gully	Davies
Westall	Wakfer	Faulkner	Bentley	Binnie	Harrison/t	Butler	Nicholas	Kingdon	McCormick/2t
Davis	Wakfer	Faulkner	Bentley	Binnie/t	Harrison	Butler	Woodhouse	Nicholas	McCormick
Davis	Wakfer	Binnie	Bentley	Williams	Harrison	Butler	Davies	Nicholas	McCormick
Westall/p	Wakfer	Crowther	Bentley	Williams	Hunt	Butler	Davies	Nicholas	McCormick
Morgan	Wakfer	Binnie	Bentley	Williams	Hunt	Butler	Hart	Cornish	McCormick
Morgan/cp	Wakfer	Binnie	Baker	Williams	Hunt	Butler	Nicholas	Cornish	McCormick
Morgan	Wakfer	Faulkner	Baker	Binnie	Hart	Butler	Nicholas	Cornish	McCormick
Czerpak	Wakfer	Faulkner	Baker/t	Binnie	Hunt	Butler	Davis	Cornish	Nicholas
Davis	Stoker	Faulkner	Baker	Binnie/t	Hunt	Butler	Woodhouse	Cornish	Nicholas
Davis/t	Stoker/2t	Faulkner	Baker/t	Binnie	Hunt	Miall	Nicholas	Cornish	Davies/t
Davis	Stoker	Faulkner	Baker	Binnie	Hunt	Butler	Miall	Cornish	Davies
Davis	Ryan/t	Faulkner/t	Baker/t	Binnie	Hunt	Butler	Gully	Cornish	Davies
Davis	Stoker	Faulkner	Baker	Binnie	Hunt	Butler	Miall	Cornish	Hart
Davis	Stoker	Binnie	Baker	Williams	Harrison	Butler	Hart	Cornish	Davies
Davis	Wakfer/t	Binnie	Baker/t	Williams	Hunt	Butler	Nicholas	Gully	Davies/t
Roberts	Wakfer	Binnie	Baker(a/t)	Williams	Harrison	Butler	Gully	Woodhouse	Davies

REPLACEMENTS	a - C Bentley

2000-01 HIGHLIGHTS

Mal Roberts topped the scoring chart with a lowly 85 points, he scored a couple of tris and and kicked 15 penalties and conversions each.

Jeremy Griffiths topped the try scoring for the second successive season with eight which was two fewer than last season.

Craig Davies extended his club appearance record in league rugby to 99 and also took his club record for tries to 55.

Suffered their worst ever league defeat in National League rugby going down 53-3 to Bracknell on the 7th April. They also suffered their biggest ever away defeat when going down by 30 points at Wharfedale, 7-37.

NEWBURY

LEAGUE STATISTICS
compiled by Stephen McCormack

SEASON	Division	P	W	D	L	F	A	Pts Diff	Lge Pts	Lge Pos	Coach	Captain
91-92	SW1	10	5	0	5	142	145	-3	10	6	T Burwell	W Phillips
92-93	SW1	12	8	1	3	251	158	93	17	3	T Burwell	W Phillips
93-94	SW1	12	8	1	3	173	165	8	17	3	T Burwell	J Booth
94-95	SW1	12	9	1	2	376	113	263	19	2	S Czerpak	J Brammer
95-96	SW1	12	11	0	1	364	169	195	22	1p	S Czerpak	J Brammer

SEASON	Division	P	W	D	L	F	A	Pts Diff	Lge Pts	Lge Pos		Most Points		Most Tries
96-97	D4S	25	25	0	0	1170	295	875	50	1p	398	Nick Grecian	27	Brian Johnson
97-98	JN1	26	12	2	12	639	545	94	26	6	172	Nick Grecian	16	Criag Davies
98-99	JN1	26	14	1	11	552	476	76	29	6	72	Justin Poihippi	10	Tyrone Howe
99-00	JN1	26	15	1	10	550	483	67	31	5	123	Dave Griffiths	10	Jeremy Griffiths
00-01	N2	*25	10	1	14	437	502	-65	21	9	85	Mal Roberts	8	Jeremy Griffiths

BIGGEST MARGINS

Home Win 87pts - 87-0 v Met. Police 22.2.97
Away Win 69pts - 74-5 v Askeans 19.4.87
Home Defeat 50pts - 3-53 v Bracknell 7.4.01
Away Defeat 30pts - 7-37 v Wharfedale 27.1.01

MOST POINTS

Scored at Home 91 v Tabard 28.3.97
Scored Away 74 v Askeans 19.4.97
Conceded at Home 53 v Bracknell 7.4.01
Conceded Away 41 v Worcester 7.3.98

MOST CONSECUTIVE

Appearances 30 Colin Hall
Matches scoring Tries 5 Brian Johnson
Matches scoring points 24 Nick Grecian
Victories 26
Defeats 4

MOST TRIES

Scored in a match 15 v Tabard 28.3.97
Conceded in a match 6 v Worcester 7.3.98

MOST APPEARANCES

by a forward 99 (4) Craig Davies
by a back 87(1) Tom Holloway

	MOST IN A SEASON	MOST IN A CAREER	MOST IN A MATCH
Points	391 Nick Grecian 96-97	563 Nick Grecian 96-98	32 Nick Grecian v Charlton Park 25.1.97 (H) v Met. Police 22.2.97 (H)
Tries	27 Brian Johnson 96-97	55 Craig Davies 96-99	4 Brian Johnson v Askeans 19.4.97 (A) v Plymouth 26.4.97 (H)
Conversions	100 Nick Grecian 96-97	135 Nick Grecian 96-98	11 Nick Grecian v Charlton Park 25.1.97 (H)
Penalties	42 Nick Grecian 96-97	71 Nick Grecian 96-98	5 Nick Grecian v Liverpool St. Helens 21.2.98 (H)
Drop Goals	2 Morgan Davis 99-00	3 Morgan Davis 97-00	1 Morgan Davis (x3), Howard Graham (x1) Simon Morgan (x1)

PLAYING SQUAD

NEWBURY

BACKS

	Ht.	Wt.	Birthdate	Birthplace	CLUB	League Apps	Tries	Pts
Ian Morgan			05.05.75		Newbury	5	-	25
Chris Simmons			07.11.80		Newbury	9(1)	5	25
Nigel Hill			04.12.67		Newbury Preston	15(3)	-	-
Simon Stoker			27.12.77		Newbury	19(1)	6	30
David Griffiths			29.04.74		Newbury	28	4	192
Jeremy Griffiths Welsh Youth	6.0	13.00	10.05.74	Camarthen	Newbury Llandovery	61	27	135
Mal Roberts			04.08.77		Newbury	29	4	140
Andrew Evans			22.03.76		Newbury	28	4	20
Brett Wakfer RAF, Combined Services.	5.9	12.07	15.04.73	St Ives	Newbury Clifton	28(15)	2	10
Morgan Davis England Students	6.0	14.00	03.02.75	Ascot	Newbury Wasps	60(2)	11	66

FORWARDS

	Ht.	Wt.	Birthdate	Birthplace	CLUB	League Apps	Tries	Pts
Julian Brammer Army, Combined Services, Oxfordshire, Eastern Counties.	5.8	17.00	22.11.63	Whitehaven	Newbury	46(3)	4	20
Bernie Williams RAF.	6.0	15.07	01.06.68	Cardiff	Newbury Coventry	26(7)	-	-
Chris Hart Dorset & Wiltshire.	6.4	17.00	20.12.74	Swindon	Newbury Swindon	48(7)	13	65
Simon Gully England colts, South West colts. Other clubs: Torquay, Bristol	5.10	16.00	12.08.75	Torquay	Newbury Weston s Mare	45(7)	8	40
Craig Davies Wales u21, Students.	6.3	17.06	25.11.69	Swansea	Newbury	99(4)	55	275
John Kingdon Devon	6.1	14.07	24.06.67	Barnstaple	Newbury	78(12)	4	20
Harry Harrison			27.04.71		Newbury	20(7)	7	35
Liam McCormick			14.08.72		Newbury	7(1)	2	10
Matt Cornish Berkshire			14.04.77	Eastbourne	Newbury	10	-	-
Gareth Evans			30.08.78		Newbury	5(7)	-	-
Simon Miall England Students	6.5	16.00	13.03.76	Winchester	Newbury	47(4)	1	5

NEWBURY

FACT FILE

Founded: 1928
Nickname: The Blues
Web site: www.newburyrfc.co.uk

Colours: Navy, sky & white irregular hoops
Change colours: Red

GROUND

Address: Monks Lane, Newbury, Berkshire RG14 7RW

Tel : 01635 40103   Fax: 01635 40533   e-mail: info@newburyrfc.co.uk
Capacity: 7,850   Seated: 350   Standing: 7,500

Directions: From M4 take A34 to Newbury, at 4th r'about on Newbury ring road(A34) turn right. Keep left at mini-r'about, ground is half mile on left. From south turn left at1st r'about on A34 ring road.
Nearest Railway Station: Newbury (10 minutes walk from ground)

Car Parking: 300 on ground, 1000 nearby @ £1.

Admission:
Season   Adults Standing £90, Seated £150.
             No concessions
Matchday   Standing: Adults £7, Children £4, OAPs £3
             Seated: Adults £8,Children £5, OAPs £4.

Club Shop: Open weekends & training evenings

Clubhouse: Normal licensing hours - 3 bars.
             Snacks & bar food available.
Functions: 4 rooms avail. Corporate hospitality available.
             Contact Andy McKelvie 01635 40103

Training Nights: Tuesday & Thursday

PROGRAMME

Size: A5   Pages: 40
Price: £1   Editor: Morgan Davis
ADVERTISING RATES
Colour   Page £600   Half £400   Qtr. £250

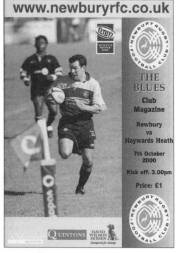

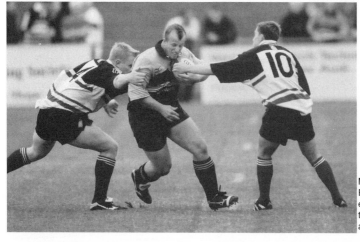

Matt Baker, Newbury's Player of the Year 2000-01, easing past Ian Balshaw in the pre-season match against Bath last August.

NOTTINGHAM RFC

Chairman	Bryan Ford,	c/o Nottingham RFC
Secretary	Keith Mitchell	Ireland Avenue
Director of Coaching	Mike Pennistone	Beeston
		Nottingham
Treasurer	John Hughes	NG9 1JD.
Administrator	Janet Allen	Tel: 0115 925 4238
		Fax: 0115 925 4255
Advertising	Nigel Eatch	

Notoriously poor starters Nottingham again lost their opening game last season, but then won four of their next six giving them their best start to a league campaign for many years. But any hopes of finishing in the top half of the table evaporated as an appaling run of form saw them lose seventeen out of nineteen games. Indeed, relegation looked a strong possibility until one last desperate effort up at Fylde gave them a life line with a 23-3 victory in their final outing of the season.

Financial constraints left Nottingham with little option but to blood their own home-grown talent, and several youngsters rose to the challenge admirably. The exciting counter-attacking runs from full-back Ben Murphy, for example, earned him the supporters `player of the year' award. Tenacious hooker Stuart Bailey made a big impression, whilst second row forwards Ben Blackwall and James Quick progressed well. Nottingham also boasted one of the Division's leading try-scorers, as Jamie Morley broke the club record by crossing the line seventeen times.

The club's second XV, the Corsairs, had a far more productive season, finishing top of the NCA (Central) Second Team Competition. They won eleven of their sixteen games, with the points awarded from another three that were cancelled by the opposition. Again it was the younger players who led the way with outside-half Dave Jackson particularly impressive, and forcing his way onto the first team replacement bench by the end of the season.

The trend continued down through the Junior sides, whilst the club's Minis again proved themselves among the best in the Midlands. All of which underlines that Nottingham have a good production line of talent in place. But they will hope to see more of that youthful exuberance rise to first team level and reverse a worrying trend of relegation battles in recent years.

NOTTINGHAM

Comp.	Date	H/A	Opponents	Result & Score	Att.	15	14	13	12	11
N2	2-Sep	H	Newbury	L 14-26		Murphy/t	Booth/3p	Morley	Clark	Spencer
N2	9-Sep	A	Preston Grasshoppers	W 32-17	350	Murphy	Reynolds	Morley/3t	Clark	Spencer
N2	16-Sep	H	Rugby Lions	W 15-12		Murphy	Carroll(a/c)	Morley	Clark/t	Spencer
N2	23-Sep	A	Kendal	L 12-25		Murphy	Carroll	Morley	Clark	Spencer
N2	30-Sep	H	Esher	W 20-18		Murphy	Carroll	Morley/t	Clark	Spencer
N2	14-Oct	H	Lydney	W 44-22		Murphy/2t	Clark	Rolt	Morley	Spencer/t
N2	28-Oct	A	Rosslyn Park	L 24-35		Murphy	Swetman	Morley/t	Rolt/t	Spencer
N2	25-Nov	H	Fylde	L 15-17		Murphy	Reynolds	Morley	Rolt	Spencer
N2	2-Dec	A	Harrogate	L 16-38	300	Murphy/t	Reynolds	Carroll	Rolt	Spencer
N2	9-Dec	A	Wharfedale	W 21-12		Murphy	Morley	Carroll	Rolt	Clark/t
N2	16-Dec	H	Camberley	W 33-12	300	Murphy/t	Morley/t	Carroll/t	Rolt	Clark/t
N2	23-Dec	A	West Hartlepool	W 45-5		Murphy/t	Morley/3t	Carroll/t	Rolt	Clark
N2	6-Jan	H	Rosslyn Park	L 31-40		Murphy/t	Morley/t	Carroll	Rolt	Clark
N2	13-Jan	A	Bracknell	L 3-48		Murphy	Morley	Carroll	Rolt	Clark
N2	20-Jan	A	Lydney	W 28-21	400	Murphy	Morley	Carroll	Rolt(b/t)	Spencer/t
N2	27-Jan	H	Harrogate	L 3-10		Murphy	Morley	Swetman	Carroll	Spencer
N2	3-Feb	H	West Hartlepool	W 48-15		Murphy/2t	Morley/3t	Carroll	Swetman/t	Spencer
N2	10-Feb	A	Esher	L 5-20	250	Murphy/t	Morley	Robinson	Swetman	Spencer
N2	17-Feb	A	Camberley	L 15-24		Murphy	Morley/t	Robinson	Carroll	Spencer/t
N2	24-Feb	H	Kendal	L 25-27		Murphy	Morley/t	Robinson	Swetman	Clark
N2	3-Mar	H	Bracknell	L 7-22		Murphy	Morley	Robinson	Swetman	Clark
N2	10-Mar	A	Rugby Lions	L 17-29		Murphy	Morley/t	Robinson/t	Swetman	Clark
N2	17-Mar	H	Preston Grasshoppers	L 15-37		Murphy/t	Morley	Robinson	Swetman/tcp	Clark
N2	24-Mar	A	Newbury	L 11-23		Murphy/t	Morley	Robinson	Swetman/2p	Clark
N2	31-Mar	H	Wharfedale	L 22-26		Murphy	Morley	Carroll	Swetman/t4p	Clark
N2	14-Apr	A	Fylde	W 23-3		Murphy	Morley	Southam/tc	Swetman/tcp	Clark
TBC	7-Oct	H	Morley	L 19-23		Murphy	Clark/t	Morley	Rolt/2p	Spencer

* after opponents name indicates a penalty try. Brackets after a player's name indicates he was replaced. eg (a) means he was replaced by replacement code "a" and so on. / after a player or replacement name is followed by any scores he made - eg /t, /c, /p, /dg or any combination of these

EVER PRESENT
Stuart Bailey, Ben Murphy.

Most Appearances:
26 Stuart Bailey, Ben Murphy.
25 Mark Bradley, Richard Lloyd, Jamie Morley.

PLAYERS USED
31 plus two as replacements only

MOST POINTS

Pts	Player	T	C	P	DG
219	R Southam	9	36	33	1
80	J Morley	16	-	-	-
60	B Murphy	12	-	-	-
53	M Swetman	5	2	8	-
18	T Rolt	2	1	-	2

MATCH FACTS

10	9	1	2	3	4	5	6	7	8
Southam	Taylor	Adams	Bailey	Fowkes	Quick	Blackwell	Chubb	Lloyd	Bradley
Southam/3cpdg	Carroll	Holland	Bailey	Adams/t	Quick	Johnston	Chubb	Lloyd	Bradley
Southam/cp	Taylor(a/t)	Ireland	Bailey	Adams	Quick	Johnston	Chubb	Lloyd	Bradley
Southam	Taylor	Ireland	Bailey	Adams	Quick	Johnston/t	Chubb	Lloyd/t	Bradley
Southam/t2c2p	Taylor	Freer	Bailey	Adams	Blackwell	Quick	Johnston	Lloyd	Bradley
Southam/t4c2p	Taylor/t	Freer	Bailey	Adams	Blackwell	Johnston	Chubb	Lloyd/t	Bradley
Southam/c4p	Taylor	Ireland	Bailey	Holland	Quick	Johnston	Charteris	Lloyd	Bradley
Southam/tcp	Taylor	Freer	Bailey	Holland	Quick	Johnston/t	Charteris	Lloyd	Bradley
Southam/c3p	Taylor	Freer	Bailey	Holland	Blackwell	Johnston	Charteris	Lloyd	Bradley
Southam/tc3p	Taylor	Freer	Bailey	Holland	Blackwell	Quick	Monaghan	Lloyd	Bradley
Southam/4c	Taylor	Freer	Bailey/t	Holland	Blackwell	Quick	Monaghan	Lloyd	Bradley
Southam/t5c	Taylor	Freer/t	Bailey	Holland	Blackwell	Quick	Monaghan	Lloyd	Bradley
Southam/2c4p	Taylor/t	Freer	Bailey	Holland	Blackwell	Quick	Monaghan	Lloyd	Bradley
Southam/p	Taylor	Freer	Bailey	Holland	Blackwell	Quick	Monaghan	Lloyd	Roberts
Southam/t2c3p	Taylor	Fowkes	Bailey	Holland	Quick	Chubb	Roberts	Lloyd	Bradley
Southam/p	Taylor	Fowkes	Bailey	Holland	Quick	Chubb	Monaghan	Lloyd	Bradley
Southam/2c3p	Taylor	Fowkes	Bailey	Holland	Quick	Chubb	Monaghan(c/t)	Lloyd	Bradley
Southam	Taylor	Fowkes	Bailey	Holland	Quick	Chubb	Corcoran	Lloyd	Bradley
Southam/cp	Taylor	Freer	Bailey	Holland	Williams	Chubb	Corcoran	Lloyd	Bradley
Southam/t2c2p	Taylor/t	Freer	Bailey	Holland	Quick	Chubb	Bradley	Lloyd	Schrafft
Southam/tc	Taylor	Freer	Bailey	Holland	Williams	Chubb	Bradley	Lloyd	Schrafft
Southam/2cp	Taylor	Freer	Bailey	Fowkes	Quick	Chubb	Bradley	Lloyd	Schrafft
Southam	Taylor	Freer	Bailey	Fowkes	Quick	Chubb	Bradley	Lloyd	Schrafft
Rolt	Royer	Freer	Bailey	Holland	Johnston	Chubb	Bradley	Lloyd	Schrafft
Rolt	Royer	Freer	Bailey	Fowkes	Monaghan	Chubb	Bradley/t	Lloyd	Schrafft
Rolt/2dg	Royer	Freer	Bailey	Fowkes	Monaghan	Chubb	Corcoran	Schrafft	Bradley
Southam/c2p	Taylor	Freer	Bailey	Adams	Blackwell	Johnston	Roberts	Lloyd	Bradley

REPLACEMENTS   a - T Rolt   b - M Swetman   c - A Corcoran

2000-01 HIGHLIGHTS

Russell Southam in his first season at Nottingham tops the points scoring with 219.

He is only the second man, after Chris Atkinson, to score 200 points in a season for the club.

He also scored nine tries which in nearly every season at Nottingham would have been enough to top the try scorers, but not this season.

Southam set a new record for conversions in a season with 36 one more than the old record held by Chris Atkinson.

Jamie Morley set a new record with 16 tries from his 25 matches, in that total were three hat tricks as well.

Full back Ben Murphy was second in the try scorers with 12 which was the third highest ever for the club.

NOTTINGHAM

LEAGUE STATISTICS
compiled by Stephen McCormack

SEASON	Division	P	W	D	L	F	A	Pts Diff	Lge Pts	Lge Pos	Most Points		Most Tries	
91-92	1	12	2	1	9	133	204	-71	5	12r	48	Guy Gregory	4	Martin Pepper
92-93	2	12	8	0	4	249	145	104	16	4	106	Guy Gregory	3	Richard Byrom
93-94	2	18	8	1	9	254	326	-62	17	6	171	Guy Gregory	5	Andy Smallwood
94-95	2	18	8	1	9	299	322	-23	17	7	97	Ian Stent	4	Andy Smallwood
95-96	2	18	5	1	12	333	433	-100	11	9	158	Simon Hodgkinson	7	Alan Royer
96-97	2	22	2	0	20	344	827	-483	4	12r	55	David Evans	5	Richard Bygrave
97-98	JN1	26	13	0	13	527	602	-75	26	7	262	Chris Atkinson	7	Alan Royer
98-99	JN1	26	16	0	10	590	467	123	32	4	272	Chris Atkinson	13	Alan Royer
99-00	JN1	26	8	1	17	460	574	-114	17	11	155	Tom Rolt	7	Tom Rolt
00-01	N2	26	10	0	16	544	584	-40	20	11	219	Russell Southam	16	Jamie Morley

BIGGEST MARGINS

Home Win	78pts - 78-0 v Morley 24.10.92
Away Win	55pts - 55-0 v Liverpool StH 28.11.98
Home Defeat	65pts - 5-70 v Richmond 16.11.96
Away Defeat	80pts - 22-102 v Coventry 5.10.96

MOST CONSECUTIVE

Appearances	41 Guy Gregory 23.11.91 - 30.4.94
Matches scoring Tries	4 Andy Smallwood
Matches scoring points	38 Chris Atkinson
Victories	5
Defeats	12

MOST POINTS

Scored at Home	78 v Morley 24.10.92
Scored Away	55 v Liverpool StH 28.11.98
Conceded at Home	74 v Newcastle 14.9.96
Conceded Away	102 v Coventry 5.10.96

MOST TRIES

Scored in a match	12 v Morley 24.10.92 (H)
Conceded in a match	14 v Coventry 5.10.96 (A)

MOST APPEARANCES

by a forward	197(6) Martin Freer
by a back	167 (3) Richard Byrom

	MOST IN A SEASON	MOST IN A CAREER	MOST IN A MATCH
Points	272 Chris Atkinson 98-99	597 Simon Hodgkinson 87-93 & 95-97	25 Guy Gregory v Otley 11.9.93 (H)
Tries	16 Jamie Morley 00-01	37 Alan Royer 94-00	4 Gary Hartley v Morley 24.10.92 (H) Alan Royer v Liverpool St H 28.11.98 (A)
Conversions	36 Russell Southam 00-01	65 Chris Atkinson 97-99	9 Guy Gregory v Morley 24.10.92 (H)
Penalties	64 Chris Atkinson 97-98 & 98-99	142 Simon Hodgkinson 87-93 & 95-97	6 Guy Gregory v Saracens 12.3.94 Chris Atkinson v Camberley 19.09.98 (A)
Drop Goals	9 Guy Gregory 92-93	19 Guy Gregory 91-94	2 Andy Sutton v Harlequins 31.3.90 (A) Guy Gregory v Rosslyn Park 4.4.92 (H) v Rosslyn Park 21.1.92 (A) v Fylde 9.1.93 (H) & v Bedford 13.2.93 (A) Simon Hodgkinson v L Irish 17.2.96 (A)

PLAYING SQUAD

RUGBY LIONS

BACKS

	Ht.	Wt.	Birthdate	Birthplace	CLUB	League Apps	Tries	Pts
Matt Tassell					Rugby	24	6	30
Mark Jasnkowski	6.0	14.04	16.01.73	Kingston	Rugby	46(3)	4	38
					Leicester	1	-	-
Barry Muir					Rugby	6(1)	3	56
Gary Becconsall					Rugby	16(2)	6	30
					Fylde			
Jaques Steyn					Rugby	14	15	120
Dan Bailey			28.03.75	Kettering	Rugby	22(19)	5	25
Eddie Saunders	6.0	12.07	02.11.60	Birmingham	Rugby	207	97	455
					Coventry			

FORWARDS

	Ht.	Wt.	Birthdate	Birthplace	CLUB	League Apps	Tries	Pts
Kevin Dunn					Rugby	33(2)	5	25
Paul Shadbolt					Rugby	23(6)	3	15
Angus Innes					Rugby	13	1	5
Tim Collier					Rugby	26	11	55
					Leicester			
Oscar Wingham					Rugby	40	11	55
Jim Withers				Stratford	Rugby	16(21)	7	35
Paul Thompson	6.4	15.07	24.09.74	Warwick	Rugby	62(15)	6	30
Rob Field	6.7	18.00	22.06.71	Coventry	Rugby	74(12)	6	30

RUGBY LIONS

FACT FILE

Founded: 1873

Nickname: The Lions

Web sites: www.the rugbylions.com
www.the rugbyfootballclub.com

Club Colours: Black shirt with red trim/black/black with red trim

Change colours: Red shirt with black trim/black/black with red trim

GROUND

Address: Webb Ellis Road, Rugby. CV22 7AU.

Tel: 01788 334466   Fax: 01788 334888   email: mal@therugbyfootballclub.com

Capacity: 3,396   Seated: 240   Standing: Covered 600; Uncovered 2,556

Directions: Second turn right, half mile south west of town centre on A4071,Bilton Road.
From NW: M6 Jnc 1 A426 Rugby A4071   From NE: M1 Jnc 20 A426 Rugby A4071:
From SE: M1 Jnc 17/M45/A4071 towards Rugby.
Nearest Railway Station: Rugby - recommend taxi 2 miles to ground

Car Parking: Available at ground

Admission: Season: V.P. £80   OAPs £45   u16 Free £60
Matchday: Adults £8   OAPs £5

Club Shop: Matchday 12-5, Mon-Fri 9-5 or by appointment.

Clubhouse: Matchdays 12-late & training nights
Functions: Capacity 120-200

Training Nights: Monday, Tuesday & Thursday evenings 6pm

PROGRAMME Size: B4   Pages: 30   Price: £1.50   Editor: Dennis Keen
Advertising Rates: Contact Linda Dainty 01788 34882

L-R - Back: 'Mal' Malik (chief exec.), Richard Kinsey (coach), Rob Field, Darren Schraaft, Neal Underhill, Jim Wingham, Eddie Saunders (club captain), Oscar Wingham, Jim Withers, Paul Thompson, Sean Brady, Paul Jackson (physio), Alan Collins (asst. physio), David Owen (club chairman).
Front: Mark Jasnikowski, Tom Woolrich, Trevor Powell, Martyn Davies, Paul Bale, Andy Gallagher, Steve Evans, Ged Galloway, Rob Harding, Duncan Blowers, Kelvin Todd. Mascot: Thomas Orland

WAKEFIELD RFC

President   J A Birkinshaw   c/o Wakefield RFC,
College Grove, Eastmoor Rd., Wakefield WF1 3RR
Tel: 01924 374801   Fax: 01924 290069

Chairman   D Beaumont   c/o Wakefield RFC, as above

Club Secretary   J B Coulson   39 Melbourne Road, St. Johns, Wakefield. WF1 2RL
01924 373586 (H)

Director of Rugby   S Townend   59 Gowthorpe, Selby, YO8 4HE

Wakefield's best season since the inception of professionalism began inauspiciously with an opening day defeat by newly promoted Otley. A further ten games up until Christmas produced five wins and five defeats and a steady mid-table position.

However, after Christmas Wakefield produced some magnificent rugby with ten victories and only five defeats out of the fifteen league games played. Thus we finished in a fine fourth position only one point behind Exeter, having won one more game, but significantly five fewer bonus points. Therefore, we finished one bonus point away from being the
country's best full-time team. We also held the third best defence in the division and recorded doubles over Birmingham/Solihull, Manchester, Moseley and Waterloo with other victories over Bedford (over 50 points), Coventry, Exeter, Henley, Orrell, Otley and London Welsh. Also we were the only club in the division that didn't concede 40 points or more in all our games against Leeds/Worcester.

Other highlights included club captain Mark Sowerby leading England in the J.R.B. World Sevens series in Dubai and South Africa's Reuben Bijl capped by the Netherlands. Nick Lloyd and Carl Houston playing for the Scottish Exiles, Ross Winney for England U21, Danny Scarborough playing and scoring for the National Division 1 side that memorably defeated South Africa at Worcester and six players helping Yorkshire defeat Cornwall at Twickenham in May in the County Challenge.

Off the field the new season will herald Wakefield RFC Centenary season and it promises to be a wonderful year. The Centenary Year and Centenary book were launched to unanimous acclaim at a splendid ball in June and, with many other events in the pipeline and high hopes for our on field performances, the year promises to be both memorable and exciting.

Here's to the next one hundred!

Back Row: Stephen Townend (Dir. of Rugby), Neil Summers, Nick Lloyd, Glen Wilson, Richard Hughes, Gareth Manuel, Paul Stewart, Paul Rees, Mark Sowerby, Reuben Bijl, Richard Wigham, Tom Rhodes, Carl Houston, Roger Burman (coach), Andy Gomersal (Team Manager). **Middle:** Diccon Edwards, Sam Blythe, Mike Cawthorne, Robert Liley, Alex Birkby, Aaron Callaghan, Danny Scarborough, John Feeley, Ross Winney, Andy Metcalfe, Peter Hall. **Front:** Richard Wareham, Dale Harrison, Darren Fletcher, Adie Marshall, Matt Lowe, N Stewart.

WAKEFIELD

Comp.	Date	H/A	Opponents	Result & Score	Att.	15	14	13	12	11
N1	9-Sep	H	Otley	L 22-33	600	Cawthorne	Scarborough	Edwards	Callaghan(b/2t)	Metcalfe/t
N1	16-Sep	A	Exeter*	L 16-18	987	Cawthorne	Scarborough	Edwards	Summers	Metcalfe
N1	23-Sep	H	Henley Hawks	W 31-10		Summers/t	Scarborough	Edwards	Callaghan	Feeley
N1	30-Sep	A	London Welsh	L 19-34	1100	Cawthorne	Scarborough/t	Summers	Callaghan	Metcalfe
N1	7-Oct	H	Birmingham & Solihull	W 11-0	300	Scarborough	Stewart	Callaghan	Summers	Metcalfe/t
N1	14-Oct	A	Worcester	L 3-22		Cawthorne	Stewart	Callaghan	Summers	Metcalfe
N1	28-Oct	H	Orrell	W 20-13	400	Scarborough/2t	Stewart	Summers	Winney/cp	Metcalfe/t
N1	19-Nov	A	Leeds Tykes	L 21-32	1578	Scarborough	Stewart	Summers	Winney/c3p	Metcalfe
N1	25-Nov	H	Coventry	W 24-18	250	Scarborough	Feeley/t	Cawthorne	Winney/t	Metcalfe
N1	2-Dec	H	Moseley	W 22-19	300	Scarborough	Feeley	Winney	Summers/t	Stewart
N1	16-Dec	A	Coventry	L 9-25	1200	Scarborough	Stewart	Winney/2p	Summers	Metcalfe
N1	6-Jan	A	Manchester	W 29-28	520	Scarborough	Stewart/2t	Summers	Callaghan	Metcalfe
N1	13-Jan	H	Leeds Tykes	L 25-38	600	Scarborough/t	Stewart	Summers	Callaghan	Feeley/2t
N1	27-Jan	H	Manchester	W 21-18	300	Scarborough	Feeley	Summers	Callaghan	Metcalfe/2t
N1	3-Feb	A	Orrell	L 10-16		Scarborough	Stewart/t	Summers	Winney/cp	Metcalfe
N1	10-Feb	H	Worcester	L 5-23	300	Summers	Stewart	Callaghan	Winney	Scarborough
N1	17-Feb	A	Waterloo	W 17-16		Cawthorne/2t	Feeley	Summers	Callaghan	Metcalfe
N1	24-Feb	A	Birmingham & Solihull	W 32-22		Cawthorne	Scarborough	Summers	Callaghan	Metcalfe
N1	10-Mar	H	London Welsh	W 38-15		Cawthorne/t	Scarborough	Summers	Callaghan	Metcalfe/t
N1	17-Mar	A	Henley Hawks	L 7-24	310	Cawthorne	Scarborough	Summers	Callaghan	Metcalfe/t
N1	24-Mar	H	Bedford	W 56-7		Scarborough/3t	Edwards/2t	Summers	Callaghan	Metcalfe
N1	31-Mar	H	Exeter	W 21-20		Scarborough	Edwards	Winney/dg	Callaghan	Metcalfe/t
N1	8-Apr	A	Bedford	L 18-19	1320	Scarborough	Edwards/t	Summers	Callaghan	Stewart
N1	14-Apr	A	Otley	W 20-3		Scarborough	Edwards	Summers	Winney	Metcalfe
N1	21-Apr	H	Waterloo	W 35-13	250	Scarborough/t	Edwards	Summers/t	Callaghan	Stewart
N1	28-Apr	A	Moseley	W 36-17	729	Scarborough	Edwards/t	Summers	Winney	Metcalfe
TBC	21-Oct	A	Penzance & Newlyn	W 26-22	1800	Cawthorne	Stewart/t	Summers	Callaghan	Metcalfe
TBC	4-Nov	H	Bracknell	W 31-23	300	Scarborough	Stewart/2t	Summers	Winney/c2pdg	Metcalfe/2t
TBC	11-Nov	H	Waterloo	L 23-35	250	Scarborough	Stewart/t	Summers/2t	Winney/c2p	Metcalfe

*after opponents name indicates a penalty try. Brackets after a player's name indicates he was replaced.
eg (a) means he was replaced by replacement code "a" and so on. / after a player or replacement name
is followed by any scores he made - eg /t, /c, /p, /dg or any combination of these

LEAGUE DEBUTS

Jon Feeley, Lance Hamilton, Dan Harper, Richard Horton, Nick Lloyd, Gareth Manuel, Paul Rees, Norpera Stewart, Mick Watson.

MOST APPEARANCES

25   Nick Lloyd.
24   Glen Wilson, Danny Scarborough.

PLAYERS USED

27 plus 2 as replacement only.

MOST POINTS

Pts	Player	T	C	P	DG
111	R Liley	2	25	17	-
66	R Winney	1	5	16	1
50	C Houston	10	-	-	-
41	T Rhodes	2	8	5	-
40	D Scarborough	8	-	-	-

MATCH FACTS

10	9	1	2	3	4	5	6	7	8
Winney(a/tc)	Birkby	Lloyd	Horton	Harper	Rees	Stewart	Watson	Houston	Wilson
Winney/2p(a/cp)	Birkby	Lloyd	Horton	Harper	Manuel	Stewart	Watson	Sowerby	Wilson
Winney/2c4p	Birkby	Lloyd/t	Horton	Harper	Manuel	Stewart	Sowerby	Houston/t	Watson
Winney/3p	Birkby	Lloyd	Horton	Harper	Manuel	Stewart	Wilson/t	Houston	Watson
Liley/2p	Birkby	Lloyd	Horton	Harper	Hughes	Rees	Wilson	Houston	Watson
Liley/p	Birkby	Lloyd	Blythe	Harper	Hughes	Rees	Wilson	Sowerby	Watson
Liley	Birkby	Lloyd	Blythe	Harper	Hughes	Rees	Wilson	Sowerby	Watson
Rhodes	Birkby/t	Lloyd	Blythe	Harper	Hughes	Rees	Wilson	Wigham	Watson/t
Rhodes/t3cp	Birkby	Lloyd	Horton	Harper	Manuel	Rees	Hughes	Wilson	Watson
Rhodes/2cp	Cawthorne	Lloyd	Horton	Harper/t	Manuel	Rees	Hughes	Wilson	Watson/t
Rhodes/p	Cawthorne	Lloyd	Horton	Harper	Manuel	Rees	Wilson	Hamilton	Watson
Rhodes/cp	Birkby/2c	Lloyd/t	Horton	Bijl	Watson/t	Rees	Hughes	Houston	Wilson
Liley	Birkby/c2p(c/c)	Lloyd	Horton	Bijl	Watson	Rees	Hughes	Houston	Wilson
Liley	Birkby/2p	Lloyd	Horton	Bijl	Watson	Rees/t	Sowerby	Houston	Wilson
Liley	Cawthorne	Lloyd	Horton	Harper	Watson	Rees	Hughes	Hamilton	Wilson
Liley	Birkby	Lloyd	Horton	Harper	Manuel	Rees	Hughes	Houston	Wilson
Liley/2cp	Birkby	Lloyd	Horton	Harper	Watson	Manuel	Sowerby	Houston	Wilson
Liley/t3c2p	Birkby/t	Lloyd	Blythe	Harper	Hughes	Manuel	Sowerby	Houston/t	Wilson/t
Liley/4c	Birkby	Lloyd	Blythe	Harper	Hughes	Manuel	Sowerby	Houston/3t	Wilson/t
Liley/c	Birkby	Lloyd	Blythe	Harper	Watson	Manuel	Sowerby	Houston	Wilson
Liley/4cp	Birkby/t	Bijl	Horton	Harper/t	Hughes	Watson/t	Sowerby	Houston/t	Wilson
Liley/c2p	Birkby	Lloyd	Horton	Harper	Hughes	Watson	Sowerby	Houston/t	Wilson
Liley/c2p	Birkby/t	Lloyd	Blythe	Harper	Hughes	Manuel	Sowerby	Houston	Wilson
Liley/2c2p	Birkby	Lloyd	Horton	Bijl	Hughes	Manuel	Sowerby	Houston/2t	Wilson
Liley/t3c3p	Birkby	Lloyd	Horton	Bijl	Rees	Manuel	Sowerby/t	Houston	Wilson
Liley/4cp	Birkby	Lloyd/t	Horton	Harper	Watson/t	Manuel	Hughes	Houston/t	Sowerby
Winney/2c3p(a/t)	Birkby	Lloyd/t	Blythe	Harper	Hughes	Rees	Wilson	Sowerby	Watson
Rhodes	Birkby	Lloyd	Horton	Harper	Hughes	Stewart	Wilson	Sowerby	Watson
Rhodes	Birkby	Lloyd	Horton	Harper	Hughes	Rees	Wilson	Sowerby	Watson

REPLACEMENTS a - T Rhodes b - N Summers c - M Cawthorne

2000-01 HIGHLIGHTS

Rob Liley returned to the top of the Wakefield points scorers list for the first time since 1992-93.
He ended the season with 111 which was 10 more than his last season at the club.

Back row forward Carl Houston made a big impact and topped the try scoring list in his first season at the club, he ended the season on 10 tries, just two off the Wakefield record for tries in a league season.

Wakefield finished a highly creditable fourth, their best showing in the league since the 1995-96 season. Their best ever was second back in 1994-95, the season before.

WAKEFIELD

LEAGUE STATISTICS
compiled by Stephen McCormack

SEASON	Division	P	W	D	L	F	A	Pts Diff	Lge Pts	Lge Pos	Most Points	Most Tries
91-92	2	12	7	0	5	187	194	-7	14		32 Rob Liley / John Sleightholme	8 Jon Sleightholme
92-93	2	12	8	1	3	186	123	63	17		101 Rob Liley	7 Jon Sleightholme
93-94	2	18	8	3	7	347	240	107	19		90 Mike Jackson	12 Jon Sleightholme
94-95	2	18	12	1	5	354	261	93	25		213 Mike Jackson	7 Richard Thompson
95-96	2	18	8	0	10	328	331	-3	16		177 Mike Jackson	7 Dave Scully
96-97	2	22	11	0	11	504	557	-53	22		199 Mike jackson	9 Dave Scully
97-98	P2	22	6	0	16	382	556	-174	12		141 Greg Miller	6 Dave Scully
98-99	P2	26	6	0	20	469	812	-343	12		76 Phil Ure	10 Ian Breheny
99-00	P2	26	10	0	16	547	638	-91	20	10	93 Tom Rhodes	9 Danny Scarborough
00-01	N1	26	15	0	11	568	503	65	70	4	111 Rob Liley	10 Carl Houston

BIGGEST MARGINS

Home Win 70pts - 70-0 v MetropolitanPolice 24.9.88

Away Win 47pts - 50-3 v Birmingham 31.10.87

Home Defeat 69pts - 15-84 v Worcester 16.10.99

Away Defeat 48pts - 19-67 v Worcester 17.4.99

MOST POINTS

Scored at Home 70 v Metropolitan Police 24.9.88

Scored Away 50 v Birmingham 31.01.87

Conceded at Home 84 v Worcester 16.10.99

Conceded Away 67 v Worcester 17.4.99

MOST CONSECUTIVE

Appearances 49 Dave Scully

Matches scoring Tries 4 Leroy McKenzie

Matches scoring points 21 Mike Jackson

Victories 10

Defeats 7

MOST TRIES

Scored in a match 14 v Metropolitan Police 24.9.88

Conceded in a match 13 v Worcester 16.10.99

MOST APPEARANCES

by a forward 139(9) Rod Latham

by a back 160 (1) Dave Scully

	MOST IN A SEASON	MOST IN A CAREER	MOST IN A MATCH	
Points	213 Mike Jackson 94-95	707 Mike Jackson 93-98	23 Rob Liley	v Rugby 11.9.93 (H)
Tries	12 Jon Sleightholme 93-94	52 Dave Scully 87-98	4 Ian Breheny	v Moseley 24.4.99 (H)
Conversions	33 Mike Jackson 96-97	82 Mike jackson 93-98	7 Ray Adamson	v Birmingham31.10.87 (A)
Penalties	57 Mike Jackson 94-95	165 Mike Jackson 93-98	6 Ray Adamson / Mike Jackson / Greg Miller	v Vale of Lune 27.2.88 (H) / v Nottingham 1.10.94 (A) / v Lon. Irish 22.10.94 (H) / v Blackheath 18.4.98 (H)
Drop Goals	3 Greg Miller 97-98	3 Greg Miller 97-98	1 by 8 players	on 14 occasions incl Greg Miller(x3) Rob Liley(x3) Steve Townend(x2)

PLAYING SQUAD

WAKEFIELD

BACKS

	Ht.	Wt.	Birthdate	Birthplace	CLUB	League Apps	Tries	Pts
Tom Rhodes	6.2	14.00	29.11.78		Wakefield	17(10)	3	132
					Leeds	16	2	12
Aaron Callaghan			13.02.72		Wakefield	35(3)	2	10
Ross Winney			25.05.81		Wakefield	14(6)	2	86
Andrew Metcalfe			16.07.69		Wakefield Sandal	20(7)	9	45
Neil Summers			10.10.68	Leeds	Wakefield	86(2)	19	95
Danny Scarborough			16.02.78		Wakefield	43(2)	17	85
Ian Breheny			02.01.78		Wakefield	41(2)	15	75
Alex Birkby	5.9	12.05	21.07.77	Sheffield	Wakefield	64(7)	10	80

FORWARDS

	Ht.	Wt.	Birthdate	Birthplace	CLUB	League Apps	Tries	Pts
Nick Lloyd			12.10.76		Wakefield	56(7)	6	30
Richard Wareham Other club: Rotherham			24.01.68		Wakefield Moseley	9(17)	-	-
Richard Hughes			12.06.76	Dewsbury	Wakefield	42(11)	2	10
Glen Wilson	6.1	15.02	31.07.76	Wakefield	Wakefield	94(5)	13	65
Mark Sowerby	6.4	16.5	03.09.69		Wakefield	106(32)	2	10
Dan Harper North, Yorkshire.			09.03.75		Wakefield	21(3)	2	10
Paul Rees			10.04.73		Wakefield	14(10)	1	5
Carl Houston			28.04.75		Wakefield	41(2)	18	90
Ritchie Horton			22.06.76		Wakefield Newcastle	19(6)	-	-
Mick Watson			02.08.65		Wakefield	20(4)	5	25

WAKEFIELD
FACT FILE

Founded: 1901
Nickname: Field

Colours: Black with 2 gold bands on rt sleeve/black/black
Change colours: Gold with irregular black hoops/black/black

GROUND

Address: College Grove, Eastmoor Road, Wakefield. WF1 3RR
Tel: 01924 374801   Fax: 01924 290069
Capacity: 2,450   Seated: 450   Standing: 2,000

Directions: From M1 Jnc 41, A650 into Wakefield City Centre, turn left at Queen Elizabeth Grammar School onto Westfield Road, ground in front 250 yards
From M62 Jnc 30, A642 into Wakefield, turn right at traffic lights immediately after Hospital onto Eastmoor Road, ground 300 yards on left
Nearest Railway Station: Wakefield Westgate

Car Parking: No parking in ground, 200 spaces nearby £1

Admission: Season   Standing Adult £85
                             OAP £50, Children (12-17) £15
                             Family (2 adults & children) £150
                  Matchday Seated Adults £9, OAP/Children £4.50
                             Standing Adult £8, OAP/Children £4

Club Shop: Yes; Manager George Stephens via club
Clubhouse: Open during normal Licensing Hours.
Three bars with snacks & bar meals available
Functions: Contact John Scones via club.
Also Hospitality lounge seating 72

Training Nights: Tuesday & Thursday

PROGRAMME Size: B5   Pages: 30   Price: £1
ADVERTISING RATES
Colour: Page £350   1/2 page £200
Mono: Page £300   1/2 page £175   1/4 page £100

NATIONAL LEAGUE
DIVISION ONE
Official Match Programme £1.00

Wakefield
versus
Bedford Blues

Saturday
24th March 2001
Kick-off 3.00pm

DELIVERING
THE WINNING
COMBINATION

WAKEFIELD RUGBY FOOTBALL CLUB

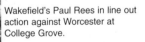

Wakefield's Paul Rees in line out action against Worcester at College Grove.

Photo courtesy of Richard Lowther

WORCESTER RFC

Honorary Secretary	Adrian Harling	
Commercial Manager	Kathy Leather	01905 459326
Operations Director	Mike Robins	01905 459324
Press Officer	Nicola Goodwin	01905 459335
WRFC Trading Ltd. **Chairman**	Cecil Duckworth	01905 459301
Chief Executive	Geoff Cooke OBE	01905 459301

c/o Worcester RFC
Pershore Lane, Hindlip,
Worcester WR3 8ZE

Tel: 01905 454183 (Switchboard)
Fax: 01905 459333
email: rugby@wrfc.co.uk

Worcester Rugby enjoyed their most successful season to date in 2000/2001; but the club was overwhelmed by disappointment after failing to gain promotion to the Premiership yet again.

Chief Exeutive and Director of Rugby Geoff Cooke together with new coach Adrian Skeggs assembled a solid squad including former Australian international Alistair Murdoch; former Welsh internationals Mathew Back and Andrew Lamerton and Great Britain rugby league centre Scott Barrow; but sadly a wrist injury kept promising England Under 21 centre Andrew Higgins sidelined for the season.

The year started well, with ten straight league victories including a 40-13 victory over Leeds. Defeat away at Moseley in December cost the club dearly, and they counted the costs for that sloppy performance at the end of the year. A credible cup run ended with a 42-13 away defeat at the hands of Saracens, but gave the club confidence for the future.

The New Year saw Worcester again back to winning ways, with a further eleven wins on the trot. The crucial match of the season against Leeds at Headingley was the promotion spot battle; but despite a following of more than 3,000 supporters Worcester couldnt manage the victory and went down 30-13. They battled courageously for the last three matches, gaining two wins and a draw but Leeds took the illusive promotion spot as once again Worcester were pipped to the post.

The club as a whole continues to grow and strengthen; the amateur team Worcester Wanderers lost just one match in their inaugural league season, the Ladies 2nd team were promoted for the third year in succession and the Ladies U16 squad won the National Sevens. The Mini and Junior section enjoyed much success and sent three age groups to their respective finals at Twickenham. Players gained international and representative honours throughout the squads and the Conference Centre continues to grow in reputation and stature.The 2001/2002 season will see Worcester once again push for Promotion to the Premiership; and a mouth-watering list of new signings including Ben Clarke and Kingsley Jones will boost their promotion bid.

Centre Scott Barrow on the attack against Waterloo.

WORCESTER

Comp.	Date	H/A	Opponents	Result & Score	Att.	15	14	13	12	11
N1	9-Sep	A	Orrell	W 47-8	800	Back/2t	Tuipulotu/2cp	Higgins	Murdoch/2t	Bromley
N1	16-Sep	H	Leeds Tykes	W 40-13	3002	Back/t	Tuipulotu/t3c4p	Langkilde	Higgins/t	Murdoch
N1	23-Sep	A	Manchester	W 40-12	895	Back	McLean	Tuipulotu/t4c4p	Murdoch/2t	Baxter
N1	30-Sep	H	Bedford	W 31-25	2000	Back	Tuipulotu/2c4p	Murdoch	Langkilde/2t	Baxter
N1	7-Oct	A	Coventry*	W 34-17	2200	Back/t	Tuipulotu/3cp	Langkilde	Murdoch/t	Bromley/t
N1	14-Oct	H	Wakefield	W 22-3		Calder/t	Tuipulotu/2cp	Murdoch	Langkilde	Bromley
N1	28-Oct	A	Waterloo	W 32-19	450	Back	Baxter	Murdoch/t	Kiel	Bromley/t
N1	19-Nov	H	Otley	W 37-12	1600	Back	Tuipulotu/t4c3p	Murdoch/t	Kiel	McLean
N1	25-Nov	A	London Welsh	W 29-12	700	Back/t	Tuipulotu/2c	Murdoch/t	Kiel	McLean/3t
N1	3-Dec	H	Birmingham & Solihull	W 21-16	1900	Back	Tuipulotu/2t2p	Murdoch	Kiel	McLean/t
N1	9-Dec	A	Moseley	L 15-22	1024	Back	Tuipulotu/5p	Murdoch	Kiel	McLean
N1	16-Dec	H	London Welsh*	W 51-3	2002	Calder/t	Tuipulotu/t5c2p	Murdoch	Kiel/t	Bromley
N1	6-Jan	H	Exeter*	W 25-6	2198	Calder	Tuipulotu/t2c2p	Murdoch	Kiel	Bromley
N1	13-Jan	A	Otley	W 31-19		Calder	Tuipulotu/4cp	Murdoch/t	Kiel	Baxter/2t
N1	20-Jan	H	Henley Hawks	W 56-18	2003	Calder	Tuipulotu/3t5c2p	Barrow	Murdoch/2t	Baxter
N1	27-Jan	A	Exeter	W 29-22		Calder	Tuipulotu/t3cp	Barrow/t	Kiel/t	Murdoch
N1	4-Feb	H	Waterloo	W 30-18	1988	Calder	Tuipulotu/3c3p	Barrow	Kiel	Bromley/t
N1	10-Feb	A	Wakefield	W 23-5	300	Back/t	Tuipulotu/p	Barrow	Murdoch	Baxter/2t
N1	18-Feb	A	Henley Hawks	W 16-13	705	Back	Tuipulotu/c3p	Barrow	Murdoch	Baxter
N1	24-Feb	H	Coventry	W 27-16	3065	Back	Tuipulotu/2cp	Barrow	Kiel/t	Murdoch/2t
N1	10-Mar	A	Bedford	W 32-14	1880	Back/t	Tuipulotu/t2cp	Murdoch	Kiel	Bromley/3t
N1	17-Mar	H	Manchester	W 27-8	2108	Tuipulotu/3tc	Baxter/t	Murdoch	Kiel	Bromley/t
N1	1-Apr	A	Leeds Tykes	L 13-30	5509	Tuipulotu/c2p	Baxter	Murdoch	Kiel	Bromley
N1	14-Apr	H	Orrell	W 67-13		Tuipulotu/2t4c	Murdoch	Barrow	Kiel/t	Bromley/t
N1	21-Apr	H	Moseley	W 43-17		Tuipulotu/2c3p	Murdoch	Barrow/t	Kiel	Baxter/t
N1	28-Apr	A	Birmingham & Solihull	D 26-26		Tuipulotu/3p	Murdoch	Barrow	Va'a	Baxter/2t
TBC	21-Oct	A	Moseley	W 34-6	2502	Back/t	Tuipulotu/c4p	Murdoch/t	Langkilde	Bromley/t
TBC	4-Nov	A	Tynedale	W 76-12	600	Back	Tuipulotu/4t8c	Murdoch/2t	Kiel	Bromley/3t
TBC	12-Nov	A	Saracens	L 13-42	5183	Back	Tuipulotu/c2p	Murdoch/t	Kiel	Bromley

after opponents name indicates a penalty try. Brackets after a player's name indicates he was replaced. eg (a) means he was replaced by replacement code "a" and so on. / after a player or replacement name is followed by any scores he made - eg /t, /c, /p, /dg or any combination of these

LEAGUE DEBUTS

Matthew Back, Scott Barrow, M Benbouhout, Spencer Bromley, Nick Broughton, Ian Calder, Chris Evans, Andrew Collins, Fryday, Chris Hall, Virgil Hartland, Richard Jarman, Rudi Keil, Andrew Lamerton, Laulala Langkilde, Cameron Mather, Ally McLean, Andrew Moretti, Alastair Murdoch, R Pellow, Dave Sims, Sateki Tuipulotu, Earl Va'a, Tom Warren, Danny Zaltman.

MOST APPEARANCES

25 S Tuipulotu, Fryday, Alastair Murdoch.

PLAYERS USED

34 plus 1 as replacement only.

MOST POINTS

Pts	Player	T	C	P	DG
349	S Tuipulotu	17	57	50	-
65	A Murdoch	13	-	-	-
50	N Baxter	10	-	-	-
40	S Bromley	8	-	-	-
40	Earl Va'a	8	-	-	-

MATCH FACTS

10	9	1	2	3	4	5	6	7	8
Va'a/t	Simpson-Daniel	Lyman	Moretti/t	Benbouhout	Zaltman	Sims/t	Fryday	Carter	Merlin
Va'a	Simpson-Daniel	Windo	Moretti	Lyman/t	Sims	Zaltman	Evans	Carter	Fryday
Va'a	Pellow	Windo/t	Lamerton	Lyman	Zaltman	Sims	Evans	Carter	Fryday
Va'a	Pellow	Lyman	Lamerton/t	Collins	Zaltman	Sims	Evans	Carter	Fryday
Va'a	Simpson-Daniel/t	Collins	Lamerton	Lyman	Zaltman	Denhardt	Mather	Carter	Fryday
Va'a/t	Simpson-Daniel/t	Windo	Moretti	Collins	Denhardt	Sims	Mather	Carter	Fryday
Yapp/2cp	Jarman/2t	Lyman	Lamerton/t	Collins	Zaltman	Sims	Fryday	Carter	Merlin
Va'a/t	Jarman	Windo	Lamerton/t	Lyman	Sims	Denhardt	Evans	Carter	Fryday
Va'a	Jarman	Windo	Lamerton	Lyman	Sims	Zaltman	Evans	Carter	Fryday
Va'a	Jarman	Windo	Lamerton	Lyman	Zaltman	Sims	Evans	Carter	Fryday
Va'a	Jarman	Windo	Lamerton	Hartland	Sims	Zaltman	Evans	Carter	Fryday
Va'a	Jarman	Windo	Lamerton/t	Hartland	Sims	Zaltman	Evans	Broughton/t	Fryday
Va'a	Jarman	Windo	Lamerton	Hartland	Denhardt	Zaltman	Evans	Broughton/t	Fryday
Va'a	Simpson-Daniel/t	Windo	Hall	Hartland	Sims	Zaltman	Evans	Broughton	Mather
Va'a	Simpson-Daniel/t	Windo	Lamerton	Collins	Sims	Zaltman	Evans/t	Mather	Fryday
Va'a/t	Simpson-Daniel	Windo	Lamerton	Collins	Sims	Zaltman	Evans	Mather	Fryday
Va'a	Pellow/t	Windo	Lamerton	Lyman	Zaltman	Sims/t	Evans	Mather	Fryday
Va'a/t	Pellow	Windo	Lamerton	Lyman	Zaltman	Sims	Evans	Mather	Fryday
Va'a	Jarman	Windo	Lamerton	Lyman	Zaltman/t	Sims	Evans	Mather	Fryday
Yapp	Simpson-Daniel	Windo/t	Lamerton	Lyman	Sims	Zaltman	Evans	Carter	Fryday
Yapp	Simpson-Daniel	Windo	Hall	Lyman	Sims	Zaltman	Evans	Carter	Fryday
Yapp	Simpson-Daniel	Lyman	Moretti	Windo	Zaltman	Sims	Evans	Carter	Fryday
Va'a/t	Pellow	Windo	Lamerton	Lyman	Sims	Zaltman	Evans	Carter	Fryday
Yapp/2c	Jarman	Windo	Moretti	Lyman/t	Zaltman/t	Sims	Evans	Carter	Fryday
Yapp	Jarman	Windo	Hall/t	Lyman	Sims	Zaltman	Evans	Carter	Fryday
Yapp/tc	Jarman	Windo	Moretti	Lyman	Sims	Zaltman	Evans	Warren	Fryday
Va'a	Simpson-Daniel	Lyman	Lamerton	Collins	Zaltman	Sims	Mather	Carter	Fryday
Calder/t	Jarman/t	Windo	Lamerton/t	Lyman	Sims	Denhardt	Broughton	Carter	Fryday
Calder	Jarman	Lyman	Lamerton	Collins	Sims	Denhardt	Evans	Carter	Fryday

REPLACEMENTS

a - L Langkilde	b - I Calder	c - R Denhardt	d - C Hall	e - N Baxter
f - R Pellow	g - E Va'a	h - A Collins	i - T Warren	j - R Jarman
k - C Mather				

2000-01 HIGHLIGHTS

New signing Sateki Tuipulotu set new standards as he re-wrote the Worcester scoring records finishing as leading scorer in the division.

He added 107 points to the previous record for points in a season and in the process set a new record for penalties in a season and a career with 50.

He now needs just 30 points to pass Richard Le Bas as the clubs' all time leading scorer in league rugby.

Apart from his exceptional kicking he also finished as top try scorer for the club and third overall in the league.

The prolific try scorer Nick Baxter continued his amazing run - he scored 10 tries during the season from just 11 starts taking his career total to 88 from just 94 appearances plus seven as a replacement.

WORCESTER

SEASON	Division	P	W	D	L	F	A	Pts Diff	Lge Pts	Lge Pos		Coach	Captain
91-92	Mid 2W	10	7	0	3	175	131	44	14	3			R Everton
92-93	Mid. 2	11	9	0	2	188	89	99	18	2p			
93-94	Mid. 1	12	8	0	4	234	104	130	16	2			
94-95	Mid. 1	12	11	1	0	278	82	196	23	1p		P Maynard	N Stoodley
												Most Points	**Most Tries**
95-96	D5N	12	9	0	3	317	187	130	18	2	50	Spencer Bradley	10 Spencer Bradley
96-97	D4N	26	23	3	0	830	375	455	49	1p	242	Tim Smith	18 Nick Baxter
97-98	JN1	26	24	0	2	1001	331	670	48	1p	221	Richard Le Bas	29 Nick Baxter
98-99	P2	26	18	0	8	716	409	307	34*	3	162	Richard Le Bas	13 Nick Baxter
99-00	P2	26	19	0	7	865	450	415	38	3	229	Tony Yapp	13 Nick Baxter
00-01	N1	26	23	1	2	844	387	457	112	2	349	Sateki Tuipulotu	17 Sateki Tuipulotu

BIGGEST MARGINS

Home Win   68pts - 78-10 v Waterloo 20.11.99

Away Win   69pts - 84-15 v Wakefield 16.10.99

Home Defeat   15pts - 13-28 v Lon. Welsh 25.10.97

Away Defeat   42pts - 0-42 v Rotherham 8.4.00

MOST CONSECUTIVE

Appearances	24 Duncan Hughes
Matches scoring Tries	9 Nick Baxter
Matches scoring points	17 Tim Smith
Victories	18
Defeats	1

MOST POINTS

Scored at Home	78 v Liverpool St Helens 21.3.98
	v Waterloo 20.11.99
Scored Away	68 v Otley 21.12.98
Conceded at Home	32 v Orrell 4.12.99
	v Wakefield 26.2.00
Conceded Away	42 v Rotherham 8.4.00

MOST TRIES

Scored in a match	13 v Wakefield 16.10.99 (A)
Conceded in a match	6 v Rotherham 8.4.00 (A)

MOST APPEARANCES

by a forward	88(4) Craig Raymond
by a back	94(7) Nick Baxter

	MOST IN A SEASON	MOST IN A CAREER	MOST IN A MATCH
Points	349 Sateki Tuipulotu 00-01	378 Richard Le Bas 97-98	31 Sateki Tuipulotu v Henley 20.1.01
Tries	29 Nick Baxter 97-98	88 Nick Baxter 95-01	6 Nick Baxter v Otley 21.2.98 (A)
Conversions	61 Tim Smith 96-97	86 Richard Le Bas 97-99	9 Richard Le Bas v Liverpool St H 21.3.98 (H)
			Tony Yapp v Waterloo 20.11.99 (H)
Penalties	50 Sateki Tuipulotu 00-01	50 Sateki Tuipulotu 00-01	5 Tim Smith v Leeds 27.12.97 (A)
Drop Goals	2 Rich Wylde 95-96	2 Rich Wylde 95-98	1 Ulan Richards v Birmingham 14.10.95 (A)
	Gareth Hughes 96-97	Gareth Hughes 96-97	Rich Wylde v Kendal 23.9.95 (A)
		Greg Harwood 95-98	v Broughton Park 13.1.95 (A)
			Greg Harwood v Sandal 10.2.96 (A)
			v Kendal 28.9.96 (H)
			Gareth Hughes v Lichfield 1.3.97 (A)
			v Preston G. 8.3.97 (H)
			Richard Le Bas v Rugby 25.4.98 (A)

PLAYING SQUAD

WORCESTER

BACKS

	Ht.	Wt.	Birthdate	Birthplace	CLUB	League Apps	Tries	Pts
Andrew Higgins					Worcester	22	8	40
Tony Yapp	5.10	12.6	26.07.77	Ludlow	Worcester	27(7)	7	247
Nick Baxter	6.0	14.07	13.04.73	Birmingham	Worcester Kings Norton	94(7)	86	430
Sateki Tuipulotu Tonga.	6.00	13.04	03.07.71	Tonga	Worcester Leeds	41 76	25 26	396 772
Earl Va'a					Worcester Richmond	2(3)	2	10
Matthew Back			05.05.71		Worcester Bristol	14(1) 11(4)	7 4	35 47
Alastair Murdoch	6.1	14.7	09.05.67	Sydney	Worcester Bedford	25 49(1)	13 12	65 60
Chris Simpson-Daniel	5.9	13.7	15.07.78	York	Worcester Wakefield Newcastle	13(5) 12(6) 1	4 4 -	20 20 -

FORWARDS

	Ht.	Wt.	Birthdate	Birthplace	CLUB	League Apps	Tries	Pts
Tony Windo England A.	6.0	16.00	30.04.69	Gloucester	Worcester Gloucester	47(2) 86	6 11	30 55
Dave Sims					Worcester	30	4	20
Neil Lyman	6.1	18.00	06.05.70	Bedford	Worcester Moseley	87(14) 13	12 -	60 -
Danny Zaltman Other clubs: Saracens, Leicester	6.6	17.6	26.12.76	Hendon	Worcester Bedford Coventry	24(1) 28(3) 12	2 4 -	10 20 -
Richard Denhardt New Zealand colts, Auckland	6.5	18.00	13.09.67	Birmingham	Worcester Moseley	32(22) 59	6 2	30 10
Andrew Moretti					Worcester	6(9)	1	5
Christian Evans Welsh Students	6.4	16.9	27.12.69	Bridgend	Worcester Bristol	22(1) 17(4)	1 3	5 15
Andy Collins					Worcester	12(9)	2	10
Nathan Carter	6.0	15.0	22.06.72	Gloucester	Worcester Gloucester	41(7) 59(3)	2 5	10 25
D Fryday					Worcester	25	-	-

WORCESTER

FACT FILE

Founded: 1871
Nickname: Gold `n` Blues

Colours: Old gold and navy
Change colours: White, old gold and navy

GROUND

Address: Sixways, Pershore Lane, Hindlip, Worcester. WR3 8ZE
Tel: 01905 454183   Fax: 01905 459333
email: rugby@wrfc.co.uk   Website: www.wrfc.co.uk
Capacity: 5,300   Seated: 4,000(covered) 1,000 (uncovered) Standing: 300

Directions: M5 junction 6 (Worcester North) and follow the signs for Worcester Rugby Centre. Take B4538 to Droitwich and the ground is 300 yards on the left.
For Parking: M5 junction 6 and follow AA signs for Park And Walk at Shire Business Park.
Car Parking: 1,000 on site
Nearest Railway Station: Worcester (Shrub Hill).
For bus links Worcester Foregate Street and walk to Bus Station.

Admission: Season   From £88 (Adults)
Matchday   Adults £8, £10, £12 - Child discounts available.

Club Shop: Open Tue., Thur. & Fri. 9.30-3.30; Sat. 12-3 or 12-6 (1st XV matchdays) & Sun. 9.30-1.30
Contact Shop Manager Jane Fudger 01905 459308.

Clubhouse: Available for hire throughout the week. The Sixways Conference Centre offers exclusive hospitality and catering facilities. Contact Commercial Dept. 01905 459326

Training Nights: u19, u21 & Ladies - Tues & Thur., Amateur Men - Wed., Mini/Junior - Sunday am

PROGRAMME Size: A5   Pages: 68   Price: £2
Editor: Nicola Goodwin

Advertising Rates
Contact Commercial Manager - Kathy Leather

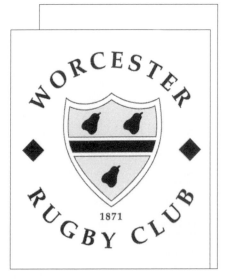

Dave Sims
Player of the Year 2000-01

RECORDS SECTION

DIVISION TWO
(CURRENTLY NATIONAL LEAGUE ONE)

THE LAST TEN YEARS — DIVISION TWO

1991-92

	Champions	Runners-up	Relegated
	London Scottish	West Hartlepool	Plymouth Albion, Liverpool St Helens

Most
Penalties: 31 David Johnson (Newc. Gos.)

Points: 147 David Johnson (Newc. Gos.)
Conversions: 26 David Johnson (Newc. Gos.)
John Stabler (West Hartlepool)

Tries: 11 Nick Grecian (Lon. Scottish)
D.Gs: 3 Andy Finnie (Bedford)

1992-93

	Champions	Runners-up	Relegated
	Newcastle Gosforth	Waterloo	Bedford, Rosslyn Park, Richmond Blackheath, Coventry, Fylde & Morley.

Most
Penalties: 16 David Johnson (Newc. Gos.)

Points: 136 David Johnson (Newc. Gos.)
Conversions: 30 David Johnson (Newc. Gos.)

Tries: 7 Jon Sleightholme (Wakefield)
D.Gs: 9 Guy Gregory (Nottingham)

1993-94

	Champions	Runners-up	Relegated
	Sale	West Hartlepool	Rugby, Otley.

Most
Penalties: 29 Paul Turner (Sale)

Points: 172 Guy Gregory (Nottingham)
Conversions: 43 Guy Gregory (Nottingham)

Tries: 16 Simon Verbickas (Sale)
D.Gs: 5 Guy Gregory (Nottingham)
Murray Walker (Lon. Scottish)

1994-95

	Champions	Runners-up	Relegated
	Saracens	Wakefield	Fylde, Coventry.

Most
Penalties: 21 Simon Mason (Newc. Gos.)
Andy Tunningley (Saracens)

Points: 213 Mike Jackson (Wakefield)
Conversions: 57 Mike Jackson (Wakefield)

Tries: 8 Tony Penn (Newcastle Gosforth)
D.Gs: 6 Andy Lee (Saracens)

1995-96

	Champions	Runners-up	Relegated
	Northampton	London Irish	-

Most
Penalties: 76 Paul Grayson (Northampton)

Points: 301 Michael Corcoran (Lon. Irish)
Conversions: 63 Michael Corcoran (Lon. Irish)

Tries: 20 Matt Allen (Northampton)
D.Gs: 5 Sam Howard (Blackheath)

1996-97

	Champions	Runners-up	Relegated
	Richmond	Newcastle	Rugby, Nottingham.

Most
Penalties: 47 John Steele (Lon. Scottish)

Points: 334 Simon Mason (Richmond)
Conversions: 95 Rob Andrew (Newcastle)

Tries: 23 John Bentley (Newcastle)
D.Gs: 5 Jez Harris (Coventry)

1997-98

	Champions	Runners-up	Relegated
	Bedford	West Hartlepool	Bristol (play-off)

Most

Points: 289 Mike Rayer (Bedford)

Tries: 17 Darragh O'Mahoney (Moseley)
Ben Whetstone (Bedford)

Penalties: 66 Lyndon Griffiths (Waterloo)
Conversions: 65 Mike Rayer (Bedford)
D.Gs: 5 Matt Jones (Moseley)

1998-99

	Champions	Runners-up	Relegated
	Bristol	Rotherham	Blackheath, Fylde

Most
Penalties: 53 Steve Gough (Coventry)

Points: 305 Steve Gough (Coventry)
Conversions: 48 Steve Gough (Coventry)

Tries: 18 Dean Lax (Rotherham)
D.Gs: 3 by four players

99-2000

	Champions	Runners-up	Relegated
	Rotherham	Leeds Tykes	Rugby Lions, West Hartlepool

Most
Penalties: 55 Matt Jones (Henley)
Steve Swindells (Manchester)

Points: 312 Sam Howard (Exeter)
Conversions: 60 Mike Umaga (Rotherham)

Tries: 18 Dean Lax (Rotherham)
D.Gs: 5 Sam Howard (Exeter)

2000-01

	Champions	Runners-up	Relegated
	Leeds Tykes	Worcester	Orrell, Waterloo

Most
Penalties: 51 Martyn Davies (Coventry)

Points: 349 Sateki Tuipulotu (Worcester)
Conversions: 72 Richard Le Bas (Leeds)

Tries: 19 Graham Mackay (Leeds Tykes)
D.Gs: 9 David Sleman (Orrell)

ALL TIME RECORDS TEAM RECORDS DIVISION TWO

Highest score:	156	Newcastle 156 Rugby 5. 5.10.96
Highest aggregate:	161	As above
Highest score by a losing side:	36	Moseley 36 Blackheath 51. 27.4.96
Highest scoring draw:	24	London Scottish v London Welsh 13.4.88
		Nottingham v Newcastle Gosforth 13.1.96
Most consecutive wins:	22	Rotherham 1999-00
Most consecutive defeats:	14	West Hartlepool 1999-00
Most points for in a season:	1255	Newcastle 1996-97
Least points for in a season:	81	Northampton 1987-88
Most points against in a season:	1114	West Hartlepool 1999-00
Least points against in a season:	80	Saracens 1989-90
Most tries for in a season:	189	Newcastle 1996-97
Most tries against in a season:	151	West Hartlepool 1999-00
Least tries for in a season:	7	Morley 1992-93
Least tries against in a season:	5	Sale 1992-93
Most conversions for in a season:	119	Newcastle 1996-97
Most conversions against in a season:	101	Orrell 1996-97
Most penalties for in a season:	66	Waterloo 1997-98
Most penalties against in a season:	54	London Scottish 1996-97
Least penalties for in a season:	6	Gosforth 1987-88
Least penalties against in a season:	8	Saracens 1987-88, Sale 1990-91
Most drop goals for in a season:	11	London Scottish 1994-95
Most drop goals against in a season:	12	London Irish 1994-95

ALL TIME RECORDS INDIVIDUAL RECORDS DIVISION TWO

Most points in a season:	334	Simon Mason (Richmond) 1996-97
Most tries in a season:	23	John Bentley (Newcastle) 1996-97
Most conversions in a season:	95	Rob Andrew (Newcastle) 1996-97
Most penalties in a season:	66	Lyndon Griffiths (Waterloo) 1997-98
Most drop goals in a season:	8	Guy Gregory (Nottingham) 1992-93
Most points in a match:	42	Jez Harris, *Coventry* v Nottingham 5.10.96
Most tries in a match:	5	Simon Verbickas, *Sale* v Otley 12.2.94
		Pat Lam, *Newcastle* v Rotherham 4.5.97
		Luke Nabaro, *Bristol* v Blackheath 13.3.99
Most conversions in a match:	18	Rob Andrew, *Newcastle* v Rugby 5.10.96
Most penalties in a match:	8	Alastair Kerr, *Moseley* v Waterloo 17.2.96
Most drop goals in a match:	3	Martin Livesey, Richmond v Northampton 19.11.88
		Murray Walker, Lon. Scottish v W. Hartlepool 23.4.94

MOST POINTS IN A SEASON

ALL TIME RECORDS   DIVISION TWO

Points	Player	Club	Season	Tries	Cons.	Pens.	D.G.
349	Sateki Tuopulotu	Worcester	2000-01	17	57	50	-
333	Richard Le Bas	Leeds Tykes	2000-01	9	72	48	-
324	Simon Mason	Richmond	1996-97	10	83	36	
312	Sam Howard	Exeter	99-2000	5	55	54	5
310	Michael Corcoran	London Irish	1995-96	8	36	63	
305	Steve Gough	Coventry	1998-99	10	48	53	0
297	Rob Andrew	Newcastle	1996-97	7	95	23	1
289	Mike Rayer	Bedford	1997-98	6	65	43	
266	Steve Gough	Coventry	99-2000	5	47	49	-
261	Lyndon Griffiths	Waterloo	1997-98	1	29	66	
256	John Steele	Northampton	1996-97	5	39	47	4
251	Mike Umaga	Rotherham	99-2000	5	60	33	-
250	Sateki Tuipulotu	Leeds Tykes	1998-99	3	38	53	-
244	Simon Binns	Rotherham	1997-98	8	39	41	1
241	Steven Vile	West Hartlepool	1997-98	8	33	43	2
241	Bryan Easson	Exeter	1998-99	2	39	51	-
239	Martyn Davies	Coventry	2000-01	4	33	51	-
238	Mike Rayer	Bedford	1996-97	7	67	23	
237	Steve Swindells	Manchester	99-2000	2	31	55	-
236	Jez Harris	Coventry	1996-97	4	48	35	5
236	Matt Jones	Henley Hawks	99-2000	1	30	55	1
229	Tony Yapp	Worcester	99-2000	6	50	33	-
224	Simon Verbickas	Orrell	1998-99	13	30	33	-
218	Paul Grayson	Northampton	1995-96	3	76	14	3
213	Mike Jackson	Wakefield	1994-95	2	16	57	
201	Lyndon Griffiths	Waterloo	99-2000	-	33	45	-
199	Mike Jackson	Wakefield	1996-97	5	33	35	1
198	Lyndon Griffiths	Waterloo	1998-99	2	25	46	-
198	Andy Lee	London Welsh	99-2000	2	46	32	-
193	Simon Mason	Newcastle	1994-95	1	21	45	2
190	Jon Benson	Leeds Tykes	99-2000	4	40	40	-
190	Philip Belgian	Waterloo	2000-01	5	21	41	-
189	Martyn Davies	Rugby Lions	1998-99	4	23	41	-
181	Ben Harvey	Moseley	2000-01	2	21	41	2
179	Martyn Davies	Rugby Lions	99-2000	1	21	42	2
179	David Sleman	Orrell	2000-01	8	17	26	9
179	Andy Lee	London Welsh	2000-01	2	23	41	-
178	Matt Jones	Moseley	1997-98	3	26	32	5
177	Mike Jackson	Wakefield	1995-96	2	19	43	
177	Richard Le Bas	Moseley	1996-97	3	27	36	
176	Steve Gough	Birmingham & Sol	2000-01	2	17	42	2
174	Jon Fabian	Exeter	1997-98	2	16	44	
172	Alastair Kerr	Moseley	1995-96	7	13	36	2
171	Guy Gregory	Nottingham	1993-94	1	11	43	5
171	Matt Jones	Henley Hawks	2000-01	-	21	42	1
165	Simon Verbickas	Orrell	1997-98	12	24	19	
164	Michael Corcoran	London Irish	1994-95	3	16	38	1
164	Paul Hull	Bristol	1998-99	5	35	23	-
162	Andy Tunningley	Saracens	1994-95	3	21	35	
162	Richard LeBas	Worcester	1998-99	4	26	30	-
162	Steve Swindells	Manchester	2000-01	1	11	45	-
160	Steve Swindells	Waterloo	1994-95		8	48	
159	Simon Binns	Rotherham	99-2000	10	26	16	3
158	Simon Hodgkinson	Nottingham	1995-96	1	18	35	4
156	Simon Hodgkinson	Moseley	1994-95		12	41	3
153	Sam Howard	Blackheath	1995-96	2	19	30	5

ALL TIME RECORDS   MOST POINTS IN A MATCH   DIVISION TWO

42	Jez Harris	Coventry v Nottingham	05.10.96
41	Simon Binns	Rotherham v West Hartlepool	02.10.99
36	Rob Andrew	Newcastle v Rugby	05.10.96
34	Steve Gough	Coventry v London Welsh	10.10.98
33	Mike Umaga	Rotherham v Waterloo	11.03.00
31	Sam Howard	Exeter v West Hartlepool	06.05.00
	Sateki Tuipulotu	Worcester v Henley Hawks	20.01.01
30	Michael Corcoran	London Irish v Waterloo	23.09.95
	John Steele	London Scottish v Rugby	29.03.97
	Andy Lee	London Welsh v Rugby	08.12.99
29	Simon Mason	Richmond v Rotherham	14.09.96
	Simon Verbickas	Orrell v Wakefield	25.04.98
	Tony Yapp	Worcester v Wakefield	16.10.99
28	David Johnson	Newcastle Gosforth v Morley	11.01.92
	David Johnson	Newcastle Gosforth v Liverpool StH	29.02.93
27	Simon Hodgkinson	Moseley v London Irish	08.04.95
	Simon Verbickas	Orrell v Waterloo	08.05.99
26	Andy Mitchell	London Scottish v Northampton	03.10.87
	Michael Corcoran	London Irish v Bedford	21.10.95
	Michael Corcoran	London Irish v Blackheath	28.10.95
	Steven Vile	West Hartlepool v Fylde	14.02.98
	Jon Benson	Leeds Tykes v Manchester	05.04.00
	Richard Le Bas	Leeds v Orrell	17.03.01
25	Chris Howard	Rugby v Newcastle Gosforth	11.11.89
	Andy Finnie	Bedford v Coventry	27.03.93
	Guy Gregory	Nottingham v Otley	11.09.93
	Simon Verbickas	Sale v Otley	12.02.94
	John Steele	London Scottish v Bedford	14.10.95
	Simon Mason	Richmond v Nottingham	16.11.96
	Pat Lam	Newcastle v Rotherham	04.05.97
	Richard Le Bas	Worcester v Exeter	10.10.98
	Steve Swindells	Manchester v Exeter	09.10.99
	Steve Gough	Coventry v Worcester	11.03.00
	Richard Le Bas	Leeds v Birmingham & Solihull	09.09.00
	Steve Gough	Birmingham & Solihull v Leeds Tykes	09.09.00
	Sateki Tuipulotu	Worcester v Manchester	23.09.00
24	Simon Irving	Headingley v London Scottish	12.11.88
	Andy Kennedy	Saracens v Nottingham	12.11.88
	Nick Grecian	London Scottish v Blackheath	16.11.91
	Alastair Kerr	Moseley v Waterloo	17.02.96
	Simon Mason	Richmond v London Scottish	12.10.96
	Jez Harris	Coventry v London Scottish	19.10.96
	Simon Mason	Richmond v Rugby	22.03.97
	Steve Gough	Coventry v Fylde	26.09.98
	Steve Gough	Coventry v Rugby	29.04.00
	Matt Jones	Henley v Rugby	15.01.00
	Steve Swindells	Manchester v Moseley	14.10.00

ALL TIME RECORDS — MOST TRIES IN A MATCH — DIVISION TWO

5

Simon Verbickas	Sale v Otley	12.02.94
Pat Lam	Newcastle v Rotherham	04.05.97
Luke Nabaro	Bristol v Blackheath	13.03.99

4

Craig Moir	Northampton v Waterloo	13.04.96
Gary Armstrong	Newcastle v Nottingham	14.09.96
Scott Quinnell	Richmond v Waterloo	02.11.96
John Bentley	Newcastle v Wakefield	08.03.97
John Clarke	Blackheath v Fylde	20.09.97
Jason Foster	Bedford v Fylde	17.01.98
Ben Wade	Rotherham v Exeter	25.04.98
John Fabian	Exeter v Waterloo	17.10.98
Lennie Woodward	Lon. Welsh v Fylde	12.12.98
Jonathon Scales	Leeds Tykes v Exeter	07.02.99
Dean Lax	Rotherham v Orrell	13.02.99
Ian Breheny	Wakefield v Moseley	24.04.99
Andy Smallwood	Coventry v Wakefield	08.05.99
Andy Currier	London Welsh v Waterloo	06.10.99

3

Jerry Macklin	Lon. Scottish v Northampton	03.10.87
Orsen Blewitt	Northampton v Bedford	21.11.87
John Roberts	Headingley v Northampton	16.04.88
Pete Rowland	Coventry v Lon. Irish	10.09.88
Dave Kennell	Headingley v Gosforth	14.01.89
Laurie Smith	Saracens v Gosforth	22.04.89
Nigel Saunders	Plymouth v Blackheath	14.10.89
Graham Robbins	Coventry v Waterloo	13.01.90
Rob Saunders	Lon. Irish v Rugby	13.10.90
Jonathan Wrigley	W Hartlepool v Moseley	14.12.91
Peter Walton	Newcastle G. v Blackheath	14.12.91
Jon Sleightholme	Wakefield v Blackheath	04.01.92
Gary Clark	Newcastle G. v Liverpool StH	29.02.92
Richard Arnold	Newcastle G. v Liverpool StH	29.02.92
Dave Spiller	Moseley v Sale	04.04.92
Richard Gee	Coventry v Moseley	19.09.92
Malcolm Walker	Nottingham v Moseley	24.10.92
Mark Warr	Sale v Otley	12.02.94
Matt Allen	Northampton v Lon. Irish	09.09.95
Conor O'Shea	Lon. Irish v Moseley	30.09.95
Gregor Townsend	Northampton v Blackheath	14.10.95
Grant Seeley	Northampton v Blackheath	14.10.95
Matt Allen	Northampton v Newcastle G.	21.10.95
Matt Allen	Northampton v Waterloo	28.10.95
Gregor Townsend	Northampton v Lon. Scottish	04.11.95
Gregor Townsend	Northampton v Lon. Irish	11.11.95
Gary Armstrong	Newcastle G. v Waterloo	30.03.96
Alan Royer	Nottingham v Moseley	30.03.96
Matt Allen	Northampton v Lon. Scottish	27.04.96
Mitch Hoare	Blackheath v Rotherham	07.09.96
Scott Quinnell	Richmond v Rotherham	14.09.96
Andy McAdam	Coventry v Nottingham	05.10.96
Derek Eves	Coventry v Nottingham	05.10.96
Jim Fallon	Richmond v Moseley	05.10.96
Scott Quinnell	Richmond v Moseley	05.10.96
Gary Armstrong	Newcastle v Rugby	05.10.96
Ross Nesdale	Newcastle v Rugby	05.10.96
George Graham	Newcastle v Rugby	05.10.96
Dean Ryan	Newcastle v Rugby	05.10.96
Eddie Saunders	Rugby v Moseley	12.10.96
Jim Fallon	Richmond v Rugby	19.10.96
John Bentley	Newcastle v Moseley	19.10.96
Andy McAdam	Coventry v Lon. Irish	19.10.96
Steve Wichary	Lon. Scottish v Moseley	26.10.96
Craig Quinnell	Richmond v Waterloo	02.11.96
Tim Stimpson	Newcastle v Lon. Scottish	16.11.96
Darragh O'Mahoney	Moseley v Nottingham	02.02.97

John Bentley	Newcastle v Rugby	08.02.97
Julian Horrobin	Coventry v Blackheath	08.03.97
Steve Bates	Newcastle v Nottingham	16.03.97
John Bentley	Newcastle v Moseley	22.03.97
Va'aiga Tuigamala	Newcastle v Moseley	22.03.97
Scott Quinnell	Richmond v Rugby	22.03.97
Matt Griffiths	Blackheath v Waterloo	19.04.97
Jason Hall	Nottingham v Rugby	19.04.97
Jim Fallon	Richmond v Wakefield	19.04.97
Ronnie Eriksson	Lon. Scottish v Fylde	30.08.97
Cunan Sharman	Lon. Scottish v Bedford	20.09.97
Nigel Heslop	Orrell v Fylde	04.10.97
Ben Whetstone	Bedford v Coventry	08.11.97
Jason Forster	Bedford v Fylde	27.12.97
Simon Verbickas	Orrell v Coventry	24.01.98
Darragh O'Mahoney	Moseley v Waterloo	14.02.98
Jason Minshull	Coventry v Waterloo	07.03.98
Julian Horrobin	Coventry v West Hartlepool	28.03.98
Darragh O'Mahoney	Moseley v Fylde	25.04.98
Richard Stone	Bedford v Blackheath	25.04.98
Simon Verbickas	Orrell v Wakefield	25.04.98
Rob Myler	Worcester v Wakefield	12.09.98
Wayne Kilford	Coventry v Fylde	26.09.98
Adam Larkin	Bristol v Blackheath	03.10.98
Steve Gough	Coventry v L. Welsh	10.10.98
Mike White	Lon. Welsh v Wakefield	17.10.98
Andy Currier	Lon. Welsh v Exeter	21.11.98
Wendal Sailor	Leeds Tykes v Fylde	17.01.99
Ben Wade	Rotherham v Leeds Tykes	23.01.99
Richard baxter	Exeter v Fylde	23.01.99
Andy Currier	Lon. Welsh v Coventry	27.02.99
Karl Johnson	Orrell v Bristol	27.02.99
Luke Nabaro	Bristol v Rugby Lions	03.04.99
Neil Marden	Lon. Welsh v Blackheath	17.04.99
Lennie Woodward	Lon. Welsh v Blackheath	17.04.99
Nick Baxter	Worcester v Wakefield	17.04.99
Dean Lax	Rotherham v Waterloo	24.04.99
Matt Walker	Rotherham v Worcester	01.05.99
Wayne Reed	Exeter v Orrell	01.05.99
Simon Verbickas	Orrell v Waterloo	08.05.99
Simon Binns	Rotherham v W. Hartlepool	02.10.99
Howard Parr	Rotherham v W. Hartlepool	02.10.99
Nigel Cane	Coventry v W. Hartlepool	16.10.99
Martin Dawson	Rotherham v Orrell	23.10.99
Duncan Roke	Henley v Moseley	20.11.99
Jim Jenner	Worcester v Watreloo	20.11.99
Dave Scully	Rotherham v Exeter	22.01.00
Carl Houston	Wakefield v Manchester	12.02.00
Matt Sims	Coventry v W. Hartlepool	19.02.00
Simon Frost	London Welsh v Waterloo	19.02.00
Doug Trivela	Rotherham v Waterloo	11.03.00
Peter Buckton	Moseley v Coventry	18.03.00
Nick Drake	London Welsh v Manchester	19.03.00
Simon Frost	London Welsh v Wakefield	15.04.00
Kurt Johnson	Coventry v Henley	22.04.00
Andy Beattie	Exeter v W. Hartlepool	06.05.00
Richard Le Bas	Leeds v Wakefield	19.11.00
Alastair McLean	Worcester v London Welsh	25.11.00
Matt Vines	London Welsh v Orrell	02.12.00
Scott Benton	Leeds v Waterloo	06.01.01
Sateki Tuipulotu	Worcester v Henley Hawks	20.01.01
Kurt Johnson	Coventry v Bedford	27.01.01
Shaun Woof	Leeds v Bedford	10.02.01
Danny Scarbrough	Wakefield v Bedford	24.02.01
Chris Hall	Leeds v Manchester	24.02.01
Spencer Bromley	Worcester v Bedford	10.03.01
Chris Hall	Leeds v Moseley	10.03.01
Carl Houston	Wakefield v London Welsh	10.03.01
Steve Bachop	Leeds v Orrell	17.03.01
Sateki Tuipulotu	Worcester v Manchester	17.03.01
Graham Mackay	Leeds London Welsh	21.04.01

TEN YEAR RECORDS — DIVISION TWO

Club	SEASONS									
	91-92	92-93	93-94	94-95	95-96	96-97	97-98	98-99	99-00	00-01
Bedford	10	7	-	-	10	4	1	-	-	11
Birmingham Solihull	-	-	-	-	-	-	-	-	-	1
Blackheath	11	10	-	-	7	10	9	13	-	-
Bristol	-	-	-	-	-	-	-	1	-	-
Coventry	6	11	-	10	-	3	7	7	6	5
Exeter	-	-	-	-	-	-	11	5	4	3
Fylde	-	12	-	9	-	-	12	14	-	-
Gosforth/Newcastle	4	1	-	3	8	2	-	-	-	-
Henley Hawks	-	-	-	-	-	-	-	-	9	7
Leeds (Tykes)	-	-	-	-	-	-	-	6	2	1
Liverpool St. Helens	13	-	-	-	-	-	-	-	-	-
London Irish	-	-	-	5	2	-	-	-	-	-
London Scottish	1	-	8	4	3	5	3	-	-	-
London Welsh	-	-	-	-	-	-	-	4	5	6
Manchester	-	-	-	-	-	-	-	-	8	8
Morley	9	13	-	-	-	-	-	-	-	-
Moseley	7	6	5	6	6	8	6	10	7	10
Northampton	-	-	-	-	1	-	-	-	-	-
Nottingham	-	4	6	7	9	12	-	-	-	-
Orrell	-	-	-	-	-	-	5	8	11	13
Otley	-	-	10	-	-	-	-	-	-	12
Plymouth Albion	12	-	-	-	-	-	-	-	-	-
Richmond	-	9	-	-	-	1	-	-	-	-
Rosslyn Park	-	8	-	-	-	-	-	-	-	-
Rotherham	-	-	-	-	-	7	4	2	1	-
Rugby (Lions)	-	-	9	-	-	11	-	11	13	-
Sale	8	5	1	-	-	-	-	-	-	-
Saracens	-	-	3	1	-	-	-	-	-	-
Wakefield	5	3	4	2	4	6	10	12	10	4
Waterloo	3	2	7	8	5	9	8	9	12	14
West Hartlepool	2	-	2	-	-	-	2	-	14	-
Worcester	-	-	-	-	-	-	-	3	3	2

Last season's action - at Coventry (above) and at Bedford (below).

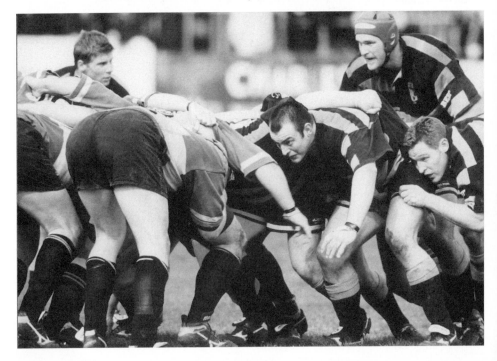

NATIONAL DIVISION

TWO

LEAGUE TABLE SEASON 2000-01

	P	W	D	L	F	A	PD	Tries	Pens	PTS	Last 6 Matches W -D- L
Bracknell	26	22	0	4	752	310	442	100	44	**44**	6 -0- 0
Rugby Lions	25	19	2	4	889	320	669	124	33	**40**	6 -0- 0
Rosslyn Park	25	19	2	4	752	436	316	98	48	**40**	6 -0- 0
Kendal	26	16	1	9	622	467	155	82	38	**33**	3 -0- 3
Harrogate	26	14	2	10	617	442	175	86	32	**30**	1 -1- 4
Wharfedale	25	14	0	11	591	475	116	66	59	**28**	3 -0- 3
Preston	26	12	2	12	566	517	49	72	39	**26**	5 -1- 0
Esher	26	11	1	14	577	481	96	66	50	**23**	1 -0- 5
Fylde	26	11	1	14	377	594	-217	42	41	**23**	2 -0- 4
Newbury	25	10	1	14	432	502	-70	52	37	**21**	3 -0- 3
Nottingham	26	10	0	16	544	584	-40	65	44	**20**	1 -0- 5
Camberley	26	8	0	18	426	733	-307	50	35	**16**	1 -0- 5
Lydney	22	6	0	16	308	566	-258	30	40	**12**	1 -0- 5
West Hartlepool	26	0	0	26	240	1266	-1026	28	24	**0**	0 -0- 6

REVIEW OF THE SEASON

Bracknell continue their meteoric rise up the league structure with a third successive Championship. South West One, National Three South and now National Two titles have come their way. They had the meanest defence, conceding just 310 points in their 26 league matches. The kicking duties were shared between Ben Nowak and Mike Kenworthy and both topped the 100 point mark. The honour of leading try scorer went to No 8 Graham Sparks, who joined from Reading.

Rugby Lions moved back into the National One division after a season away. They were the top points and try scorers in the league running in 124 tries and over 900 points. In the try scoring stakes it was that man Eddie Saunders who was their leading try scorer with his best ever haul, 16 tries. They end the season with a 569 points difference which was the best in the division. Paul Turner came on in a number of matches, weaved his magic and changed the course of the game; between him and Saunders they must have a joint age of over 80 years yet still managed to produce the goods when required.

Rosslyn Park staged a late run but ended up losing out to Rugby Lions on points difference, ending the season with a winning run of six matches and overall they were unbeaten in their last 13 games. The damage was done earlier in the season when they drew away at Esher and lost at Fylde. Paul Roblin came back into first team rugby for the first time in a number of years and make a big impression. He topped the scoring list and his overall game was excellent. Hooker Chris Ritchie had a great season and scored 14 tries which normally would be enough to top the Park try scoring, but winger James Justice took that honour with 16 tries.

Kendal were the surprise package in the division and in their first season at this level fourth place was a brilliant performance. Just after Christmas they turned in a six match winning run, which helped them maintain all their good work before taking on the top three in a four week spell. They lost to them all but still finished three points clear of fifth placed Harrogate. Full back Mike Scott in his first season at the club led the scoring with 235 points.

Harrogate were fifth and equalled their best ever performance in this league which they previously achieved back in the 1996-97 season. They ran an impressive 86 tries and leading the way were Ed Smithies with 17 and James Tapster with 16. Lee Cholewa in his first season at the club topped the points scoring list. They will be disappointed with their run in at the end of the season when they managed just one win in their last six matches.

Wharfedale dropped three places to sixth, but it was still their second best ever finish in National League rugby. Whilst not in the top six try scoring sides, they did lead the way in penalties putting over 59 in total, the highest figure in the division.

Preston Grasshoppers improved one place on last season as they moved up to seventh place. They managed this as they ended the season in good form and in their last six matches they won five and drew one in an unbeaten run. Chris Glynn led the way with 219 points, whilst the honour of leading try scorer went to second row forward Josh Williams.

Esher in their first ever season at this level finished a highly respectable eighth, three points behind Preston Grasshoppers. The Esher cause was helped by the superb kicking of Jonathan Gregory whose strike rate was exceptional. The full back was the leading scorer in the division with 260 points and he is now nearing the 1000 mark for the club after just three seasons. They could have improved on the final finishing position but one win in their last five matches was a poor return.

Fylde managed ninth place in a mixed season. They had excellent home wins against both Rosslyn Park and Rugby Lions and against the three nearest to them geographically they were also triumphant, beating Preston, Kendal and Wharfedale after the New Year. Still they need to find a good goal kicker to win those close matches.

Newbury will be disappointed with tenth place, which is a five place drop on the previous campaign and their worst ever finish in the division in four years. Their season fell apart at the turn of the year with a run of seven matches without a win which included six defeats. In the new year they managed just three wins in 12 matches and will need to address the situation if they are to have a good campaign in the coming season.

Despite running in an impressive 65 tries Nottingham struggled all season and equalled their worst ever finish in National League rugby of 11th which they managed the previous season. They found a good goal kicker in Russell Southam and both Jamie Morley and Ben Murphy found the try line on a regular basis, but they still ended up at the wrong end of the table. Nottingham finished the season badly and managed just one win in their last six matches.

Camberley were relegated after finishing in 12th place as they did the season before. With the play-offs in place it means a third side is relegated now and they finished four points adrift of Nottingham. They end their three year stay in the division, but despite going down they are positive that the new coaching regime will come good and Ian Pickup is highly thought of.

Lydney end their five year stay in the division after finishing 13th. They managed just six wins and were unable to complete four of their matches due to the foot and mouth crisis. Four of their five wins were by narrow margins of less than five points. They had trouble finding a successful goal kicker with a number of players having a go during the season.

West Hartlepool failed to register a win from their 26 matches and were again relegated and now go into National Three North for the first time ever. They ended the season with a points difference of minus 1026 and will hope to re-group for the new campaign ahead.

NATIONAL LEAGUE TWO

2000-01 RECORD REVIEW (Individual Records)

The ALL-TIME RECORDS for MOST POINTS IN A MATCH, MOST POINTS IN A SEASON & MOST TRIES IN A MATCH can be found in the Records Section for this division.

MOST POINTS - IN A MATCH

Paul Brett's four year old record was finally broken last season. It was beaten by the Kendal full back Mike Scott. Scott, a summer signing from Aspatria, scored four tries and kicked 11 conversions as Kendal thrashed West Hartlepool 92-0 to record their biggest ever win. The next best was 28 points by Rugby Lion's South African Jaques Steyn in the win against Camberley in December.

EVOLUTION OF RECORD - Points in a match

28	Steve Burnage	Fylde v Birmingham	07.11.87
29	Paul Morris	Lydney v Otley	14.09.96
29	Rob Ashworth	Havant v Clifton	21.09.96
30	Paul Brett	Liverpool v Redruth	01.02.97
39	Paul Brett	Liverepool v Clifton	15.02.97
42	Mike Scott	Kendal v W Hartlepool	27/01/01

MOST POINTS - IN A SEASON

Esher Full back Jonathan Gregory top scored with 260 points which was way off the all time record set by Fylde's Steve Gough back in 1996-97.

EVOLUTION OF RECORD - Points in a season

121	Steve Burnage	Fylde	1987-88
123	Chris Howard	Rugby	1988-89
172	Andy Finnie	Bedford	1993-94
228	Andy Finnie	Bedford	1994-95
404	Steve Gough	Fylde	1996-97

MOST TRIES - IN A MATCH

The only player to score four tries in a match during last season was the Kendal full back Mike Scott, he did so as his club beat West Hartlepool 92-0 in late January. In all we had 25 hat tricks and two players scored three hat tricks each, veteran Rugby Lions winger Eddie Saunders and Nottingham right wing/centre Jamie Morley.

EVOLUTION OF RECORD - Tries in a match
(Only the first to reach the figure is shown)

3	Kevin Norris	Plymouth v Sheffield	12.09.87
4	Brendan Hanavan	Fylde v Exeter	03.10.87
5	Mark Kirkby	Otley v Redruth	08.02.97
6	Nick Baxter	Worcester v Otley	21.02.98

MOST TRIES - IN A SEASON

Harrogate's Ed Smithies just tops the try scorers list with five players seperated by just one try.
He also sets a new club record in the process. One of the players just behind him was his team mate James Tapster. In the group on 16 were James Justice, Jamie Morley and Eddie Saunders, all three set new club records for a season for Rosslyn Park, Nottingham and Rugby Lions respectively.

EVOLUTION OF RECORD

10	Brendan Hanavan	Fylde	1987-88
12	Brendan Hanavan	Fylde	1993-94
12	Colin Phillips	Reading	1994-95
22	Mark Kirkby	Otley	1996-97
29	Nick Baxter	Worcester	1997-98

ALL-TIME RECORDS

29	Nick Baxter	Worcester	1997-98
22	Mark Kirkby	Otley	1996-97
22	Mark Kirkby	Otley	1999-00
21	Andrew Hodgson	Wharfedale	1996-97
20	Mark Preston	Fylde	1996-97
19	Andrew Hodgson	Wharfedale	1999-00
17	Ben Wade	Morley	1996-97
17	Simon Middleton	Leeds	1997-98
17	Scott Roskell	London Welsh	1997-98
17	Ed Smithies	Harrogate	2000-01
16	Mark Appleson	Leeds	1996-97
16	Jim Jenner	Worcester	1997-98
16	Craig Davies	Newbury	1997-98
16	James Tapster	Harrogate	2000-01
16	Jamie Morley	Nottingham	2000-01
16	James Justice	Rosslyn Park	2000-01
16	Eddie Saunders	Rugby Lions	2000-01

MOST PENALTIES - IN A MATCH

The record of nine was never seriously challenged with nobody managing to kick more than six penalties in a match all season.
The feat of kicking seven penalties in a match in this division has only been achieved twice in the last three seasons.

EVOLUTION OF RECORD

6	John Stabler	W Hart v Met Police	06.01.88
7	Andy Finnie	Bedford v Coventry	23.04.94
9	Paul Morris	Lydney v Otley	14.09.96

ALL-TIME RECORDS

9	Paul Morris	Lydney v Otley	14.09.96
9	Rob Ashworth	Havant v Clifton	21.09.96
8	Richard Mills	Walsall v Leeds	12.10.96
7	Andy Finnie	Bedford v Coventry	23.04.94
7	Denzil Evans	Rugby v Richmond	15.10.94
7	Phil Belshaw	Reading v Morley	14.10.95
7	Jamie Grayshon	Morley v Rugby	21.10.95
7	Andy Green	Exeter v Fylde	05.04.97
7	Richard Mills	Walsall v Redruth	19.04.97
7	Nat Saumi	Redruth v Clifton	03.05.97
7	Guy Gregory	Camberley v Birm &Solihull	19.12.98
7	Ben Stafford	Camberley v Nottingham	10.10.99

MOST PENALTIES - IN A SEASON

Leading the way in season 2000-01 was the Esher Full Back Jonathan Gregory with 47. This was not enough to get him into the all time top 10.

EVOLUTION OF RECORD

21	Ray Adamson	Wakefield	1987-88
22	Andy Higgin	Vale of Lune	1989-90
26	Mike Jackson	Fylde	1991-92
31	Andy Green	Exeter	1992-93
45	Andy Finnie	Bedford	1993-94
56	Andy Finnie	Bedford	1994-95
82	Steve Gough	Fylde	1996-97

ALL-TIME RECORDS

82	Steve Gough	Fylde	1996-97
81	Richard Mills	Walsall	1996-97
70	Steve Swindells	Manchester	1998-99
66	Paul Morris	Lydney	1996-97
64	Chris Atkinson	Nottingham	1997-98
64	Chris Atkinson	Nottingham	1998-99
57	Craig Raymond	London Welsh	1996-97
56	Andy Finnie	Bedford	1994-95
55	Adam Mounsey	Wharfedale	1999-00

MOST CONVERSIONS - IN A MATCH

Mike Scott moved into second place on the list after kicking 11 conversions in Kendal's 92-0 win over West Hartlepool at the end of January. He kicked 11 out of 14 attempts.
Rosslyn Park's Paul Roblin kicked nine conversions for his side as they beat West Hartlepool 78-7, he converted nine of the 12 tries that Park scored and moved into fifth on the all time list for the division.

EVOLUTION OF RECORD

9	Steve Burnage	Fylde v Birmingham	07.11.87
9	Gerry Ainscough	Leeds v Clifton	07.12.96
12	Paul Brett	Liverpool v Clifton	15.02.96

ALL-TIME RECORDS

12	Paul Brett	Liverpool v Clifton	15.02.96
11	Mike Scott	Kendal v W Hartlepool	27.01.01
10	Dan Clappison	Otley v Blackheath	04.12.99
10	Chris Glynn	Preston v Camberley	25.03.00

9	Steve Burnage	Fylde v Birmingham	07.11.87
9	Gerry Ainscough	Leeds v Clifton	07.12.96
9	Jason Dance	Reading v Redruth	15.02.97
9	Jamie Grayshon	Morley v Walsall	17.05.97
9	Paul Roblin	Rosslyn Pv W Hartlepool	16.12.20

MOST CONVERSIONS - IN A SEASON

The most for the season was 44 by Mike Scott, Kendal, but that was not enough to put him into the all time top 10 list.

ALL-TIME RECORDS

64	Craig Raymond	London Welsh	1997-98
63	Ralph Zoing	Harrogate	1996-97
61	Jason Dance	Reading	1996-97
61	Dan Clappison	Otley	1999-00
60	Sateki Tuipulotu	Leeds Tykes	1997-98
60	Richard LeBas	Worcester	1997-98
60	Steve Swindells	Manchester	1998-99
58	Andy Green	Exeter	1996-97

MOST DROP GOALS - IN A MATCH

There were three players who managed three drop goals all season and nobody managed more than on in a match.

ALL-TIME RECORD

4	Andy Rimmer	Broughton P v Sheffield	17.11.90

Wharfedale's line-out specialist Anthony Capstick flying high.

Photo: Craven Herald.

2000-01

NATIONAL LEAGUE TWO

MOST POINTS

POINTS			T	C	P	DG
260	Jonathan Gregory	Esher	7	42	47	-
235	Mike Scott	Kendal	6	44	37	2
219	Chris Glynn	Preston	8	40	33	-
219	Russell Southam	Nottingham	9	36	33	1
171	Adam Mounsey	Wharfedale	7	11	38	-
161	Lee Cholewa	Harrogate	3	31	28	-
157	Paul Roblin	Rosslyn Park	2	39	21	2
145	Mike Kenworthy	Bracknell	5	30	19	1
128	Ben Nowak	Bracknell	8	20	15	1
120	Jaques Steyn	Rugby Lions	15	18	3	-
100	Paul Turner	Rugby Lions	2	36	6	-
96	David Pears	Wharfedale	2	36	6	-
96	Brad Mooar	Rosslyn Park	1	14	21	-
85	Ed Smithies	Harrogate	17	-	-	-
85	Mal Roberts	Newbury	2	15	15	-
84	Ben Godfrey	Fylde	1	11	19	-

MOST PENALTIES

47	Jonathan Gregory	Richmond
38	Adam Mounsey	Wharfedale
37	Mike Scott	Kendal
33	Chris Glynn	Preston
33	Russell Southam	Nottingham
28	Lee Cholewa	Harrogate
21	Paul Roblin	Rosslyn Park
21	Brad Mooar	Rosslyn Park
19	Ben Godfrey	Fylde
19	Mike Kenworthy	Bracknell
16	David Pears	Wharfedale
15	Mal ROberts	Newbury
15	Ben Nowak	Bracknell
15	Stephen Ward	Lydney
15	David Griffiths	Newbury

MOST TRIES

17	Ed Smithies	Harrogate
16	James Tapster	Harrogate
16	Jamie Morley	Nottingham
16	James Justice	Rosslyn Park
16	Eddie Saunders	Rugby Lions
15	Jaques Steyn	Rugby Lions
14	Graham Sparks	Bracknell
14	Chris Ritchie	Rosslyn Park
12	Guy Spencer	Bracknell
12	Ben Murphy	Nottingham
10	Josh Williams	Preston
9	Tim Lough	Preston
9	Tim Collier	Rugny Lions
9	Russell Southam	Nottingham

MOST CONVERSIONS

44	Mike Scott	Kendal
42	Jonathan Gregory	Esher
40	Chris Glynn	Preston
39	Paul Roblin	Rosslyn Park
36	Russell Southam	Nottingham
36	Paul Turner	Rugby Lions
31	Lee Cholewa	Harrogate
30	Mike Kenworthy	Bracknell
20	Ben Nowak	Bracknell
19	David Pears	Wharfedale
18	Jaques Steyn	Rugby Lions
15	Mal Roberts	Newbury
14	Brad Mooar	Rosslyn Park
12	David Griffiths	Newbury
12	Jonathan Davies	Wharfedale

MOST DROP GOALS

3	Howard Graham	Camberley
2	Mike Scott	Kendal
2	Tom Rolt	Nottingham
2	Jan Bonney	Esher
2	Paul Roblin	Rosslyn Park
1	Russell Southam	Nottingham
1	Mike Kenworthy	Bracknell
1	Ben Nowak	Bracknell
1	Barry Muir	Rugby Lions
1	Matt Duncombe	Harrogate
1	Denzil Evans	Rugby Lions
1	Billy Stanley	Esher
1	Martin Emmett	Preston
1	Ian Morgan	Newbury

NATIONAL DIVISION TWO

FIXTURES 2001-2002

Away Teams

HOME TEAMS	Esher (1)	Fylde (2)	Harrogate (3)	Kendal (4)	Newbury (5)	Nottingham (6)	Orrell (7)	Plymouth Albion (8)	Preston G. (9)	Rosslyn Park (10)	Sedgley Park (11)	Stourbridge (12)	Waterloo (13)	Wharfedale (14)
1 Esher		22.09	24.11	10.11	8.09	12.01	13.04	22.12	1.12	26.01	20.10	15.12	9.03	9.02
2 Fylde	23.02		15.09	1.09	19.01	16.03	6.10	24.11	27.10	6.04	8.12	2.02	17.11	22.12
3 Harrogate	5.01	9.03		26.01	1.12	10.11	30.03	12.01	15.12	20.10	9.02	13.04	8.09	22.09
4 Kendal	19.01	1.12	27.10		13.04	2.02	17.11	9.02	30.03	22.09	9.03	5.01	15.12	8.09
5 Newbury	16.03	10.11	1.09	8.12		6.04	15.09	20.10	6.10	22.12	24.11	23.02	26.01	12.01
6 Nottingham	17.11	8.09	19.01	20.10	15.12		5.01	26.01	13.04	9.02	22.09	30.03	1.12	9.03
7 Orrell	8.12	9.02	22.12	12.01	9.03	24.11		6.04	8.09	10.11	26.01	1.12	22.09	20.10
8 Plymouth Albion	30.03	5.01	17.11	6.10	2.02	27.10	15.12		23.02	15.09	1.09	16.03	19.01	13.04
9 Preston Grasshoppers	1.09	26.01	6.04	22.12	9.02	8.12	16.03	22.09		24.11	12.01	15.09	20.10	10.11
10 Rosslyn Park	27.10	15.12	2.02	23.02	30.03	6.10	19.01	9.03	5.01		8.09	17.11	13.04	1.12
11 Sedgley Park	2.02	13.04	6.10	15.09	5.01	23.02	27.10	1.12	17.11	16.03		19.01	30.03	15.12
12 Stourbridge	6.04	20.10	8.12	24.11	22.09	22.12	1.09	8.09	9.03	12.01	10.11		9.02	26.01
13 Waterloo	15.09	12.01	16.03	6.04	27.10	1.09	23.02	10.11	2.02	8.12	22.12	9.02		24.11
14 Wharfedale	6.10	30.03	23.02	16.03	17.11	15.09	2.02	8.12	19.01	1.09	6.04	27.10	5.01	

ESHER RFC

President	R C Howard	
Chairman	Tim Bale	
Club Secretary	Wally Grey	
Director of Rugby	Hugh McHardy	
Rugby Managers	John Inverdale, Bob Stratton & David Page	
Fixtures Secretary	Simon Gardner	01962 869846 (H).

Correspondence to:
c/o Esher RFC,
The Rugby Ground,
369 Molesey Road,
Hersham,
Surrey KT12 3PF
01932 220295 (B)

1st XV Manager/	David Page	35 Misty's Field, Walton on Thames,Surrey KT12 2BG
Press Officer		07973 488142 (M) 0870 131 5073 (Fax)
		email: pageyd14@aol.com

To say that Esher's first season in National Division Two was a disaster would be one of rugby's bigger understatements of the past twelve months. As if playing half of the season without a clubhouse wasn't bad enough (and our apologies to all our opponents who had to endure the rather woeful showering arrangements that were there as a stop gap), the normally excellent pitch was flooded for months on end forcing many home fixtures to be transferred to Metropolitan Police's ground, with a consequent substantial loss of revenue. Things, as they say, can only get better. Or so one likes to think.

Under the leadership of Ciaran Bird once again, Esher played some excellent fifteen-man rugby in spells, but lost far too many matches in the last ten minutes. Three games on the trot were surrendered to the last kick of the 80 minutes. Oscar Wilde would have said that was more than just carelessness. In the forthcoming year, more attention will need to be paid to fitness levels, as that was one aspect of the step up in grade that surprised certain elements of the club.

Esher's player of the season was undoubtedly Chris Wilkins. The No 8, who joined the club from Blackheath, was a tower of strength in a pack that was small in comparison to many in the league, and together with various combinations of Bird, Caleb Kronfeld and Mark Butterworth, Esher's back row was a match for most. In the backs, Billy Stanley, a recruit from Saracens, grew in stature as the season progressed, and much will be expected of him in the future. With the retirement after many years outstanding service of Jeff Alexander, the club has lost one of its key players, so the onus is on Jan Bonney, the new club captain, to act as the driving force in the back division.

The new clubhouse will be up and running come the start of the season. Esher will hope that their play on the field mirrors the standard of the new facilities off it.

John Inverdale

John Gregory - National Division Two Top Points Scorer 2000-2001

ESHER

Comp.	Date	H/A	Opponents	Result & Score	Att.	15	14	13	12	11
N2	2-Sep	H	Kendal	L 6-21	450	Gregory/2p	Cook	Burns	Bonney	Alexander
N2	9-Sep	H	Bracknell	W 14-12	500	Gregory/2p	Cook	Burns	Bonney	White/t
N2	16-Sep	A	Harrogate	L 10-31	400	Cook	Cowell	Burns	Bonney	White/t
N2	23-Sep	H	Lydney	W 30-17	450	Gregory/3c3p	Cook	Burns	Flood/t	White/t
N2	30-Sep	A	Nottingham	L 18-20		Gregory/5p	Sandilands	Cook	Burns	White
N2	14-Oct	A	West Hartlepool	W 47-5		Gregory/6c	Aitken/3t	Stanley	Burns	White/t
N2	28-Oct	A	Fylde	W 20-14		Gregory/cp	Aitken/2t	Alexander	Burns	White
N2	11-Nov	H	Wharfedale	L 20-22	150	Gregory/t2c2p	Flood/t	Alexander	Burns	White
N2	18-Nov	A	Newbury	L 18-19		Gregory/c2p	Flood	Alexander	Burns/t	White
N2	2-Dec	N	Rosslyn Park	D 10-10	200	Gregory/c	Flood	Alexander/t	Burns	White
N2	9-Dec	A	Rugby Lions	L 14-34		Gregory/3p	Clouston	Flood	Bonney	Swift
N2	23-Dec	A	Wharfedale	L 22-33		Gregory/2cp	Clouston	Alexander	Bonney/t	Flood/t
N2	6-Jan	N	Fylde	W 29-10	400	Gregory/tc4p	Flood	Burns/t	Bonney	Alexander
N2	13-Jan	A	Camberley	W 33-22	150	Gregory/2c3p	Flood/t	Burns	Bonney	Alexander/t
N2	27-Jan	A	Rosslyn Park	L 19-22		Gregory/c4p	Flood/t	Alexander	Bonney	White
N2	3-Feb	N	Preston Grasshoppers	W 30-21	200	Gregory/3c3p	Flood	Alexander	Bonney	Agyarko
N2	10-Feb	H	Nottingham	W 20-5	250	Gregory/2c2p	Chadwick	Flood/t	Bonney	Cook
N2	17-Feb	H	Newbury	W 31-5	250	Gregory/3t4cp	Cook	Cook	Bonney	Swift
N2	24-Feb	A	Lydney	L 6-9		Cook	Cook	Bonney	Flood	Swift
N2	3-Mar	H	Camberley	W 27-10	250	Gregory/4p	Cook	Alexander	Bonney/t	Burns/t
N2	10-Mar	H	Harrogate	L 23-25		Gregory/t2c3p	Flood	Alexander	Bonney	Burns
N2	17-Mar	A	Bracknell	L 0-16		Gregory	Flood	Alexander	Bonney	Burns
N2	24-Mar	A	Kendal	L 17-32		Cook	Flood/t	Cowell/2cp	Bonney	Burns
N2	31-Mar	H	Rugby Lions	L 17-39		Gregory/2cp	Flood	Bonney	Burns	Cook
N2	8-Apr	H	West Hartlepool	W 86-5	400	Gregory/t8c	Flood	Burns(d/t)	Bonney/t	Cook
N2	14-Apr	A	Preston Grasshoppers	L 10-22		Gregory/cp	Flood	Alexander/t	Bonney	Cook
TBC	7-Oct	A	Redruth	W 14-10	700	Gregory/t2p	Aitken	Cook	Burns	White
TBC	21-Oct	H	Camberley	W 38-24	350	Gregory/2c3p	Aitken	Alexander	Burns	White/2t
TBC	4-Nov	H	Waterloo	L 26-27	400	Gregory/3c	Aitken	Alexander	Burns/t	White/2t

** after opponents name indicates a penalty try. Brackets after a player's name indicates he was replaced.
eg (a) means he was replaced by replacement code "a" and so on. / after a player or replacement name
is followed by any scores he made - eg /t, /c, /p, /dg or any combination of these*

MATCH FACTS

10	9	1	2	3	4	5	6	7	8
Stanley	Taylor	Owen	Bennett	Cormack	Morahan	Mole	Bird	Kronfeld	Wilkins
Stanley/dg	Taylor	Owen	Bennett	Cormack	Mole	Morahan	Wilkins	Kronfeld	Butterworth
Stanley	Mulraine	Smith	Seymour	Cormack(a/t)	Mole	Morahan	Wilkins	Kronfeld	Butterworth
Bonney	Mulraine	Davies	Seymour	Cormack	Mole	Johnson	Wilkins	Davison/t	Butterworth
Bonney/dg	Taylor	Davies	Seymour	Cormack	Morahan	Johnson	Wilkins	Davison	Butterworth
Bonney/t	Mulraine	Cormack	Bennett	Smith	Johnson/t	Mole	Wilkins	Davison/t	Butterworth
Bonney	Mulraine	Cormack	Seymour	Smith	Mole	Johnson	Butterworth	Davison	Wilkins/t
Bonney	Taylor	Cormack	Seymour	Smith	Mole	Johnson	Butterworth	Davison	Wilkins
Bonney	Taylor	Cormack	Bennett	Smith	Owen	Dixon	Butterworth	Kronfeld	Wilkins/t
Bonney/dg	Taylor	Cormack	Bennett	Smith	Dixon	Morahan	Butterworth	Bird	Wilkins
Stanley	Mulraine	Cormack	Bennett	Davies	Dixon	Morahan/t	Butterworth	Kronfeld	Wilkins
Stanley	Mulraine	Seymour	Waddington	Smith	Dixon	Owen/t	Butterworth	Kronfeld	Wilkins
Stanley	Mulraine	Cormack	Seymour	Smith	Dixon	Johnson	Butterworth	Kronfeld/t	Wilkins
Stanley	Mulraine	Cormack/t	Seymour	Smith	Dixon/t	Owen	Butterworth	Kronfeld	Wilkins
Stanley	Mulraine	Cormack	Bennett	Seymour	Hart	Morahan	Butterworth	Bird	Wilkins
Stanley	Barr	Cormack	Bennett	Seymour	Hart	Morahan/2t	Bird	Kronfeld/t	Wilkins
Stanley	Mulraine	Cormack	Bennett	Smith	Hart	Morahan	Butterworth	Bird	Wilkins/t
Stanley	Mulraine	Cormack	Seymour	Smith	Mole	Morahan/t	Butterworth	Bird	Wilkins
Stanley/2p	Barr	Cormack	Bennett	Smith	Morahan	Mole	Butterworth	Bird	Wilkins
Stanley	Mulraine	Cormack	Seymour	Smith	Mole	Morahan	Owen	Bird(b/t)	Wilkins
Stanley	Mulraine	Cormack	Bennett	Seymour	Mole	Morahan	Butterworth(c/t)	Kronfeld	Wilkins
Stanley	Mulraine	Cormack	Bennett	Smith	Mole	Morahan	Butterworth	Bird	Wilkins
Stanley	Mulraine	Cormack	Bennett	Smith	Mole	Morahan	Owen	Kronfeld	Wilkins/t
Stanley/t	Mulraine	Cormack	Seymour/t	Smith	Mole	Morahan	Owen	Kronfeld	Wilkins
Stanley/t	Bird/2t	Cormack/t	Bennett	Seymour	Mole(b/t)	Johnson	Bird/t	Davison/2t	Wilkins/2t
Stanley	Bird	Cormack	Bennett	Seymour	Mole	Johnson	Bird	Davison	Wilkins
Bonney/dg	Mulraine	Cormack	Seymour	Smith	Mole	Johnson	Butterworth	Davison	Wilkins
Bonney/t	Barr	Cormack/2t	Seymour	Smith	Mole	Johnson	Butterworth	Davison	Wilkins
Bonney	Mulraine	Cormack	Seymour	Smith	Dixon/t	Johnson	Butterworth	Kronfeld	Wilkins

REPLACEMENTS a - M Bennett b - C Kronfeld c - Simon Owen d - C Mulraine

2000-01 HIGHLIGHTS

John Gregory topped the scoring list for a third consecutive season and should pass the 1,000 league points total for the club next season.

He equalled his own record of eight conversions in a match in the game against W Hartlepool late in the season.

He also finished as joint leading try scorer along with centre Paul Flood.

Esher suffered their worst ever run of defeats in league rugby when losing four consecutive matches in March.

They also suffered their biggest ever league defeats, both at home and away, during the season.

In the match against Newbury at home they lost 39-17, this was also the highest number of points scored against them - either at home or away, and their worst ever away defeat was the 31-10 loss at Harrogate in September.

ESHER

LEAGUE STATISTICS
compiled by Stephen McCormack

SEASON	Division	P	W	D	L	F	A	Pts Diff	Lge Pts	Lge Pos	Most Points	Most Tries
91-92	L2S	10	5	0	5	153	146	7	9	6		
92-93	L2S	12	7	0	5	201	189	12	14	3		
93-94	L2S	12	10	2	0	382	95	287	22	1p		
94-95	L1	12	10	0	2	344	132	212	20	2		
95-96	L1	12	9	0	3	280	159	121	18	3		
96-97	L1	13	12	0	1	458	171	287	24	1p		
97-98	N2S	26	18	1	7	651	448	203	37	4	92 Ray Dudman	12 Mark Butterworth
98-99	N2S	26	23	0	3	864	308	566	46	2	303 Jon Gregory	16 Nana Dontah
99-00	N2S	26	23	0	3	1018	356	662	46	1	351 Jon Gregory	15 Michael Corcoran
00-01	N2	26	11	1	14	577	484	93	23	8	260 John Gregory	7 John Gregory

BIGGEST MARGINS

Home Win	97pts - 104-7 v Met Police
Away Win	43pts - 56-13 v Norwich
Home Defeat	22pts - 17-39 v Rugby 31.3.01
Away Defeat	21pts -10-31 v Harrogate 16.9.00

MOST CONSECUTIVE

Appearances	
Matches scoring Tries	
Matches scoring points	
Victories	15
Defeats	4

MOST POINTS

Scored at Home	104 v Met Police
Scored Away	57 v Met Police 14.2.98
Conceded at Home	39 v Rugby 31.3.01
Conceded Away	36 v Plymouth 25.10.97

MOST TRIES

Scored in a match	17 v Met Police
Conceded in a match	5 v Plymouth 25.10.97

MOST APPEARANCES

by a forward	
by a back	

	MOST IN A SEASON	MOST IN A CAREER	MOST IN A MATCH
Points	351 Jon Gregory 1999-00	914 Jon Gregory 1998-01	34 Michael Corcoran v Cheltenham 13.2.99
Tries	16 Nana Dontah 1998-99	30 Michael Corcoran 1998-00	4 Nana Dontah v Plymouth 10.10.98 (H) / Michael Corcoran v Cheltenham 13.2.99(H)
Conversions	78 Jon Gregory 1999-00	Jon Gregory 1998-01	8 Jon Gregory v Clifton 2.10.99 (H) / v W Hartelpool 8.4.01 (H)
Penalties	52 Jon Gregory 1998-99	Jon Gregory 1998-01	7 Jon Gregory v Tabard (A)
Drop Goals	3 Richard Bailey 1998-99	3 Richard Bailey 1998-00	1 By seven players

PLAYING SQUAD

ESHER

BACKS

	Ht.	Wt.	Birthdate	Birthplace	CLUB	League Apps	Tries	Pts
Jonathan Gregory	6.1	14.0	02.06.73	Chertsey	Esher Richmond	72	23	914
Billy Stanley Other club: Barking			27.03.78		Esher Harlequins	20	2	19
Simon Dixon	6.1	13.05	03.04.70		Esher	58	15	75
Paul Flood Other club: Bridgend	6.0	13.10	25.11.70	Birmingham	Esher London Welsh	31	14	70
Jim Bird			13.05.71	Somerset	Esher Hornets	35(27)	12	60
Jan Bonney Other clubs: Chingford, Moseley	6.1	15.05	27.01.71	Chingford	Esher London Scottish	47	11	64
Roland White			17.04.77		Esher	20	12	60
Dan Taylor			27.02.72	Somerset	Esher Hornets	21(1)	4	20
Alastair Sandilands Other clubs: Sheffield, London Welsh	5.10	14.08	21.01.68		Esher Rosslyn Park	14(2)	7	35
Charlie Mulraine			24.12.73		Esher Blackheath	16(2)	2	10
Campbell Aitken					Esher	2	5	25
Sean Burns			10.06.71		Esher Camberley	18(1) 34	3 5	15 25
Jeff Alexander	6.2	15.05	28.11.70	Kensington	Esher Harlequins	69(1)	11	55

FORWARDS

	Ht.	Wt.	Birthdate	Birthplace	CLUB	League Apps	Tries	Pts
Andy White			05.09.64	Surrey	Esher Richmond	52(11)	13	68
Mark Bennett	5.9	14.00	27.08.73	Kingston	Esher	46(14)	4	20
Duncan Cormack	6.0	15.04	03.04.75	London	Esher London Irish	45(8)	6	30
Chris Wilkins Other club: Blackheath			03.01.71		Esher	26	6	30
Peter Mole			21.02.66		Esher	70(13)	6	30
Paddy Seymour			18.07.78		Esher	16(7)	1	5
Ciaran Bird	6.2	16.00	29.11.71	Chingford	Esher	46(8)	21	105
Mark Butterworth	6.0	15.00	21.02.73	Croyden	Esher	89(4)	25	125
Caleb Kronfeld	1.78m	90kg	06.01.76	Hastings(NZ)	Esher	27(10)	10	50
Ollie Hankey	6.3	16.00	05.01.75		Esher Harlequins	5(13)	1	5
Jeff Smith Other club: Alnwick	6.1	18.07	25.03.76	Ashington	Esher Newcastle Falcons	27(14)	3	15
Matthew Morahan	1.95m	105kg	09.07.74	Australia	Esher	36(1)	12	60

ESHER

Founded: 1923-24

Colours: Black with amber collar

Change Colours: Amber with black collar

Nickname: The EE's

GROUND

Address: The Rugby Ground, 369 Molesey Road, Hersham, Surrey KT12 3PF

Tel: 01932 220295 (Office), 01932 254627 (Fax), 01932 224834 (Clubhouse)

Web site: http://www.esherrfc.org   email: webmaster@esherrfc.org

Capacity: 3,000   Seated: 1,200   Standing: Uncovered 1,800

Directions: M25 Junc 10, A3 to London. After 1 mile left to Walton-on-Thames (A245), after 1/4 mile right at lights into Seven Hills Road (B365).Turn right at r/about into Burwood Road & follow into Hersham Village, bear right into Molesey Road. After the railway bridge (Hersham BR) the ground is 300yds on the left . NB Low bridge at Hersham BR station.

Nearest Railway Station: Hersham (Waterloo-Woking line)

Car Parking: 1,000 on ground

Admission: Season - £50.   Matchdays £5   Under 16: Free

Clubhouse: Open matchdays & training nights.
Snacks & bar meals available.

Functions: Up to 200, contact Phil Beebe 01932 220295.
Sponsors' lounges available

Club Shop: Open matchdays & training days.
Contact Tim Bale 01932 220295

Training Nights: Monday & Wednesday 7pm

PROGRAMME

Size: A5
Price: £1
Pages: 40
Editor: David Page 07973 488142
Advertising Rates
Contact David Alexander 0777 332 9047
Colour - Full page £500, Half £300, Qtr £200

Sunday 8th April 2001
National Division 2
West Hartlepool RFC
Kick-off 2pm

FYLDE RUFC

President	Graham Sharman	6 Hedge Row, Wrea Green, Preston PR4 2PP
		01772 684118 (T) 01772 672963 (Fax)
Chairman	Arnie Halford	6 St Hildas Road, St. Annes, Lancs. FY8 2PT
		01253 713765 (H) 01253 739137 (Fax)
Club Secretary	David Walsh	33 Kingsway, Lytham
		01253 738452 (H) 01253 739137 (B) 01253 739137 (Fax)
Chairman of Rugby	Tony Todd	c/o Fylde Rugby Club Tel/Fax: 01253 739137
Press Officer	Stewart Brown	179 Hardhorn Road, Poulton-le-Fylde, Lancs. FY6 8ES
		01253 883100 (H) 01253 739137 (Fax)
1st Team Manager	Steve Rigby	01257 450580 (H) 01257 450991 (B) 07831 403400 (M)
Coach	Dean Kenny	c/o Fylde Rugby Club 01253 739137 (club)
		01942 498480 (B) 07909 981791 (M)
Forwards Coach	Dave Baldwin	c/o Fylde Rugby Club 0161 718 6080 (H) 07909 981791 (M)
Fitness Coach	Brendan Hanavan	c/o Fylde Rugby Club 01253 739137 (club)

This is my final report for the club. After three years I have stepped down as coach, in what I hope will prove to be the best interest of the club.

Over the period of my tenure the club has fought many battles on and off the field and where many others have succumbed to the pressures, Fylde has withstood the onslaught and are still hanging in there.

It is important to realise that National Division Two next season will consist of the following: Orrell, Waterloo, Harrogate, Kendal, Wharfedale, Preston, Nottingham, Plymouth, Newbury, Rosslyn Park, Sedgley Park/Launceston, Fylde and Esher. This is not too dissimilar to the Third Division of ten or fifteen years ago.

Whilst we may not have set the world alight over the past three seasons, we have maintained status on limited resources, which is an achievement in itself. Consider Gosforth, West Hartlepool, Liverpool St. Helens, Richmond, London Scottish, Blackheath and Lydney as examples of what can happen to once proud and prosperous clubs.

What have been the highlights? It is difficult to pinpoint events, more the attitude and commitment of the people involved at Fylde. On the playing side, the `old guard' have come through when it mattered and a crop of young players have come through their baptism of fire with credit. There have been three captains in my term, Ian Barclay, Martin Scott and Matt Filipo. I would like to thank them all sincerely.

In summing up, I wish everyone concerned with Fylde the very best future. Next season will be hard, but there is a strength within the club, which will hold together, of that I am sure.

MARK NELSON

Greg Anderton, shown on the cover of the matchday programme, was Fylde's top try scorer last season.

FYLDE

Comp.	Date	H/A	Opponents	Result & Score	Att.	15	14	13	12	11
N2	2-Sep	A	West Hartlepool	W 16-3	285	Evans	Armitage	Connell	Irving	Anderton/tcp
N2	9-Sep	H	Camberley	L 16-24	400	Evans	Armitage	Kenyon/2p	Irving	Anderton/t
N2	16-Sep	A	Bracknell	L 21-34		Evans/t	Armitage	Kenyon/cp	Jones	Lavin
N2	23-Sep	A	Wharfedale	L 10-72		Evans	Lavin	Kenyon	Jones	Anderton/t
N2	30-Sep	H	Newbury	W 12-6	450	Godfrey	Lavin	Kenyon	Carson	Evans
N2	14-Oct	H	Rugby Lions	W 14-13		Godfrey	Lavin	Kenyon	Anderton	Evans
N2	28-Oct	H	Esher	L 14-20		Godfrey	Lavin	Kenyon/t	Jones/t	Anderton
N2	11-Nov	A	Harrogate	L 17-31	450	Godfrey	Lavin	Kenyon/t	Anderton	Evans
N2	18-Nov	H	Lydney	L 13-18	450	Godfrey	Lavin	Kenyon	Evans	Anderton/t
N2	25-Nov	A	Nottingham	W 17-15		Godfrey	Lavin	Kenyon	Connell	Anderton
N2	2-Dec	A	Preston Grasshoppers	L 9-17	550	Godfrey	Lavin	Kenyon/3p	Connell	Anderton
N2	9-Dec	H	Rosslyn Park	W 21-16		Godfrey/3p	Lavin	Evans	Connell	Anderton
N2	16-Dec	A	Lydney*	W 13-9		Godfrey/c2p	Wilkinson	Evans	Connell	Lavin
N2	23-Dec	H	Harrogate	L 12-18		Godfrey/4p	Lavin	Evans	Connell	Anderton
N2	6-Jan	N	Esher	L 10-29	400	Godfrey/cp	Lavin	Jones	Connell	Carson
N2	13-Jan	H	Kendal	W 17-13		Godfrey/c	Evans	Carson	Connell	Anderton
N2	27-Jan	H	Preston Grasshoppers	W 20-12		Godfrey/2c2p	Evans	Connell	Jones	Anderton/t
N2	10-Feb	A	Newbury	D 10-10		Godfrey/cp	Lavin	Evans	Jones	Wyles
N2	24-Feb	H	Wharfedale	W 29-8	500	Godfrey/3cp	Lavin(a/t)	Evans	Connell	Anderton/2t
N2	10-Mar	H	Bracknell	L 6-17		Godfrey/2p	Long	Connell	Jones	Evans
N2	17-Mar	A	Camberley	W 28-24		Godfrey/t2c3p	Long	Kenyon	Connell	Wyles
N2	24-Mar	H	West Hartlepool	W 27-0		Moffatt/c	Long	Evans	Connell	Wyles/t
N2	31-Mar	A	Rosslyn Park	L 0-59		Wyles	Evans	Kenyon	Connell	Longman
N2	6-Apr	A	Rugby Lions	L 7-72		Moffatt	Long	Evans	Connell	Wyles
N2	14-Apr	H	Nottingham	L 3-23		Wyles/p	Long	Kenyon	Connell	Lavin
N2	28-Apr	A	Kendal	L 15-31		Godfrey	Evans	Long	Connell	Wyles
TBC	7-Oct	H	Whitchurch	W 16-11	300	Evans	Lavin	Kenyon	Carson	Anderton/t

* after opponents name indicates a penalty try. Brackets after a player's name indicates he was replaced.
eg (a) means he was replaced by replacement code "a" and so on. / after a player or replacement name
is followed by any scores he made - eg /t, /c, /p, /dg or any combination of these

EVER PRESENT Dylan O'Grady.

Most Appearances:

26	Dylan O'Grady.
25	Matt Filipo.
24	Mike Dreyer.
22	David Wiseman.

PLAYERS USED 41 plus 2 as replacements only

MOST POINTS

Pts	Player	T	C	P	DG
84	B Godfrey	1	11	19	-
61	D Wiseman	1	7	14	-
40	G Anderton	7	1	1	-
32	R Kenyon	2	2	6	-
30	D O'Grady	6	-	-	-

MATCH FACTS

10	9	1	2	3	4	5	6	7	8
Wiseman/2p	Condon	Webster	Scott	Filipo	Dreyer	Holmes	Kay	Lavin	O'Grady
Wiseman	Condon	Clarke	Scott/t	Filipo	Holmes	Dreyer	Kay	Lavin	O'Grady
Wiseman/2p	Condon/t	Filipo	Scott	Bradwell	Crompton	Dreyer	Kay	Lavin	O'Grady
Wiseman/cp	Rudd	Webster	Clarke	Gaulton	Crompton	Filipo	Kay	O'Grady	Dreyer
Wiseman/4p	Rudd	Filipo	McIntyre	Webster	Holmes	Dreyer	Kay	Lavin	O'Grady
Wiseman/3p	Knight	Webster	McIntyre	Filipo	Holmes	Collins	O'Grady	Lavin	Dreyer/t
Wiseman/2c	Condon	Webster	McIntyre	Filipo	Holmes	Collins	O'Grady	Lavin	Dreyer
Wiseman/2cp	Condon	Clarke/t	McIntyre	Filipo	Wilson	Collins	O'Grady	Bradwell	Dreyer
Wiseman/p	Condon	Clarke	McIntyre	Filipo	Collins	Wilson	O'Grady/t	Lavin	Dreyer
Wiseman/c	Rudd	Filipo	McIntyre/2t	Webster	Taylor	Wilson	O'Grady/t	Lavin	Dreyer
Wiseman	Rudd	Filipo	McIntyre	Webster	Taylor	Wilson	O'Grady	Lavin	Dreyer
Kenyon/c	Condon	Filipo	Scott	Webster	Wilson	Taylor/t	O'Grady/t	Bradwell	Dreyer
Kenyon	Condon	Filipo	Scott	Webster	Wilson	Taylor	O'Grady	Bradwell	Dreyer
Kenyon	Condon	Rigby	Scott	Webster	Wilson	Taylor	O'Grady	Bradwell	Dreyer
Wiseman	Condon	Filipo	McIntyre	Rigby	Collins/t	Wilson	O'Grady	Bradwell	Dreyer
Wiseman	Condon	Filipo/2t	Scott	Webster	Taylor	Wilson/t	O'Grady	Lavin	Dreyer
Wiseman	Condon	Filipo	Scott	Webster	Taylor	Wilson	O'Grady	Lavin/t	Dreyer
Wiseman/t	Hatley	Filipo	Scott	Webster	Wilson	Taylor	O'Grady	Lavin	Dreyer
Wiseman	Condon	Filipo	Clarke	Webster	Wilson	Taylor	Wilson	Lavin	O'Grady/t
Wiseman	Condon	Filipo	Scott	Webster	Taylor	Collins	O'Grady	Lavin	Dreyer
Wiseman	Condon	Filipo	Scott	Webster	Collins	Taylor	O'Grady	Lavin/t	Dreyer/t
Wiseman	Condon/t	Filipo	McIntyre/t	Webster	Taylor	Collins	O'Grady/t	Lavin	Dreyer/t
Wiseman	Condon	Filipo	McIntyre	Clarke	Collins	Taylor	O'Grady	Lavin	Dreyer
Wiseman/c	Castle	Filipo(b/t)	Scott	Collard	Dreyer	Collins	Bradwell	Lavin	O'Grady
Wiseman	Condon	Filipo	Scott	Rigby	O'Neill	Collins	Bradwell	O'Grady	Dreyer
Kenyon	Condon	Filipo	Scott	Rigby	O'Neill/t	Taylor	Wilson	Lavin/t	O'Grady/t
Wiseman/pdg	Rudd	Webster	McIntyre/t	Filipo	Collins	Holmes	Kay	O'Grady	Dreyer

REPLACEMENTS   a - K Long   b - C McIntyre

2000-01 HIGHLIGHTS

Ben Godfrey in his debut season topped the points scoring list. He scored 84 points, 23 ahead of David Wiseman.

Winger Greg Anderton topped the try scorers list with seven. It was the fourth time he had topped the try scorers list but only the second time on his own.

They suffered two heavy defeats in the season which set new records. They twice had 72 points put passed them in the away matches at Wharfedale and Rugby Lions.

In the match against Rugby Lions they lost by 65 points which was their largest ever loss in a league match.

FYLDE

LEAGUE STATISTICS
compiled by Stephen McCormack

SEASON	Division	P	W	D	L	F	A	Pts Diff	Lge Pts	Lge Pos	Most Points		Most Tries	
91-92	3	12	9	1	2	198	109	89	19	2p	106	Mike Jackson	4	Anthony Ireland
92-93	2	12	0	3	9	108	290	-182	0	12r	40	Mike Jackson	2	Steve Gough & John Nicholson
93-94	3	18	13	0	5	339	219	120	26	2p	109	Andy Parker	12	Brendan Hanavan
94-95	2	18	8	0	10	250	329	-79	16	9r	91	Andy Parker	5	Brendan Hanavan, Steve Gough & Greg Anderton
95-96	3	18	3	1	14	283	448	-165	7	10	138	Steve Gough	5	Greg Anderton
96-97	3	30	24	1	5	813	439	374	49	2p	404	Steve Gough	20	Mark Preston
97-98	P2	22	2	0	20	258	710	-452	4	12	98	Steve Gough	6	Mark Preston
98-99	P2	26	4	1	21	375	805	-430	9	14r	72	Alun Peacock	6	Mark Evans Carl Lavin
99-00	JN1	26	10	1	15	387	485	-98	21	9	194	Nick Booth	6	Richard Kenyon Greg Anderton
00-01	N2	26	11	1	14	377	594	-217	21(-2)	10	84	Ben Godfrey	7	Greg Anderton

BIGGEST MARGINS

Home Win 61pts - 68-7 v Birmingham 7.11.87

Away Win 47pts - 60-13 v Havant 15.2.97

Home Defeat 60pts - 7-67 v Bedford 27.12.97

Away Defeat 65pts - 7-72 v Rugby 6.4.01

MOST CONSECUTIVE

Appearances 41 Andy Parker 12.3.94 to date

Matches scoring Tries 4 Greg Anderton

Matches scoring points 20 Steve Burnage

Victories 9

Defeats 7

MOST POINTS

Scored at Home 68 v Birmingham 7.11.87

Scored Away 60 v Havant 15.2.97

Conceded at Home 67 v Bedford 27.12.97

Conceded Away 72 v Wharfedale 23.9.00 & Rugby

MOST TRIES

Scored in a match 10 v Birmingham 7.11.87 (H) v Redruth 9.4.94 (H)

Conceded in a match 10 v West Hartlepool 14.2.98

MOST APPEARANCES

by a forward 168 (9) John Taylor

by a back 148(2) Ian Barclay

	MOST IN A SEASON	MOST IN A CAREER	MOST IN A MATCH	
Points	404 Steve Gough 96-97	739 Steve Gough 92-98	28 Steve Burnage	v Birmingham 7.11.87 (H)
Tries	20 Mark Preston 96-97	41 Brendan Hanavan 87-96	4 Brendan Hanavan	v Exeter 3.10.87 (H) v Birmingham 7.11.87 (H) v Redruth 9.4.94 (H)
Conversions	57 Steve Gough 96-97	85 Steve Gough 92-98	9 Steve Burnage	v Birmingham 7.11.87 (H)
Penalties	82 Steve Gough 96-97	143 Steve Gough 92-98	6 Steve Gough	v Walsall 21.9.96 (H) v Morley 25.1.97 (A)
Drop Goals	5 Ian Barclay 94-95	7 Ian Barclay 87-95	2 Ian Barclay	v Waterloo 25.3.95 (A)

PLAYING SQUAD

FYLDE

BACKS

	Ht.	Wt.	Birthdate	Birthplace	CLUB	League Apps	Tries	Pts
Ben Godfrey					Fylde	18(1)	1	84
Richard Kenyon England u21, B.					Fylde	36(13)	8	62
Chris Jones					Fylde	7(1)	1	5
Laurence Condon					Fylde London Irish	41(1)	5	25
Stuart Connell Cumbria	5.11	14.0	17.04.67	Bolton	Fylde	79(6)	2	8
Julian Irving	6.0	14.3	13.02.71	Oldham	Fylde	31(6)	3	15
Mark Evans	5.11	13.0	21.02.75	Leeds	Fylde	89(5)	13	65
David Wiseman					Fylde	30(1)	3	80
Greg Anderton Lancashire, North.	5.11	16.05	26.02.75		Fylde			
Tim Wyles					Fylde	7	1	8

FORWARDS

	Ht.	Wt.	Birthdate	Birthplace	CLUB	League Apps	Tries	Pts
Mike Dreyer					Fylde	45(1)	7	35
Martin Scott Scotland 1, A, u21.	6.0	15.10	05.07.67	Falkirk	Fylde Orrell	71(7) 28	7 1	35 5
Matt Filipo					Fylde	25	2	10
Sam Clark England U-21, students.	5.11	15.11	05.06.77		Fylde	16(11)	1	5
Mike Bradwell					Fylde	8(6)	-	-
Richard Wilson					Fylde	12	1	5
John Taylor Lancashire	6.5	16.8	05.10.66	S Point (Aden)	Fylde	169(5)	9	45
Dylan O' Grady					Fylde Sale	41(3)	8	40
Steve Rigby	5.10	17.6	05.06.59	Lytham	Fylde	51(10)	-	-

FYLDE

FACT FILE

Founded: 1919

Colours: Claret, gold and white/white/claret
Change colours: Maroon

GROUND

Address: Woodlands Memorial Ground, Blackpool Road, Ansdell, Lytham St. Annes. FY8 4EL
Tel: 01253 734733   Fax:
Capacity: 5,440   Seated: 440   Standing: 5,000

Directions: From the end of the M55 follow signs for Lytham St. Annes -B5230 then B5261 onto Queensway - ground is three miles on the left opposite Blossoms P.H. and R.C. Church.
Nearest Railway Station: Ansdell & Fairhaven. Left outside station, down the hill away from the sea, along Woodlands Rd to T junction (R.C. Church & Blossoms PH) - ground is opposite to the right.

Car Parking: 150 spaces available F.O.C. at the ground.

Admission: (Standing only)
Matchdays   Non members £8, OAPs £4;
                   Members £6, OAPs £5.
Season tickets   Members only £60 OAPs £35.

Club Shop: Open matchdays 1-6pm & Sundays 10-Noon.
Contact D Walsh 01253729253.

Clubhouse: Open matchdays Noon-11, Sun Noon-3, Tue,Thur, Fri 7.30-11pm. 3 bars.
Snacks and bar meals available.
Functions: Approx 400   Contact D Walsh 01253 729253.

Training Nights: Tuesday and Thursday.

PROGRAMME

Size: A5   Pages: 40

Price: Free with admission

Editor: Malcolm Jones,
Commercial Manager 01253 739731

ADVERTISING RATES

Full page: Colour £650 Two Tone £450
1/2 page Colour £350 Two Tone £250
1/4 page: Colour £200 Two Tone £150
Back page (teams): Colour £650

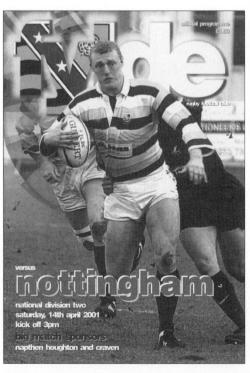

versus **nottingham**
national division two
saturday, 14th april 2001
kick off 3pm
big match sponsors
napthen houghton and craven

HARROGATE RUFC

President	Roy Guy	4 Southway, Harrogate HG2 0CA 01423 503054
Chairman	Frank Carter	6 Blackthorn Lane, Burn Bridge, Harrogate HG3 1NW 01423 870654
Club Secretary	Ian Gair	Glenshee, Spofforth Lane, Follifoot, Harrogate HG3 7EG 01423 871743
Treasurer	Nic Davies	3 Hereford Road, Harrogate HG1 2NP 01423 522066
Fixtures Secretary	Bill Barrack	15 Eastgate Close, Bramhope, Leeds LS16 9AR 0113 284 2540

FACT FILE

Founded: 1871
Nickname: Gate
Web site: harrogaterufc.or.uk

Colours: Red, amber & black
Change colours: Red

GROUND
Address: The County Ground, Claro Road, Harrogate. HG1 4AG.
Tel : 01423 566966   Fax: 01423 509073   E-mail: hrufc@lineone.net
Capacity: 2,999   Seated: 4990 Standing: 2,500

Directions: Claro Road is on the north side of the A59 (York Skipton road), just off the Stray (open grassed area adjacent to the town centre).
Nearest Railway Station: Harrogate, exit to East Parade turn left, right onto Parkview continues into Kingsway & Walkers passage, cross Stray to Claro Rd (10mins).

Car Parking: 400 at the ground, unlimited nearby

Admission   **Matchday:** £6

Club Shop: Matchdays only.   Contact Pam Oswin 01423 871905.

Clubhouse: Mon - Fri 7-11, Sat 11-11, Sun 10-2, bar meals available.
Functions: Up to 120, contact Mick Lancaster at club

Training Nights: Tuesday and Thursday

PROGRAMME Size: A5   Pages: 32   Price: £1   Editor: Stuart Young 01423 500263

Advertising Rates Mono (Contact Club)   Full page £300   1/2 page £160   1/4 page £90

HARROGATE

Comp.	Date	H/A	Opponents	Result & Score	Att.	15	14	13	12	11
N2	2-Sep	H	Rugby Lions*	L 12-19	450	Smithies	Clayton/t	Duncombe	Douglas	Tapster
N2	9-Sep	A	Kendal	W 33-10	400	Smithies/t	Clayton	Duncombe	Sarjaent	Tapster/t
N2	16-Sep	H	Esher	W 31-10	400	Smithies/t	Clayton	Duncombe	Sarjaent	Tapster/3t
N2	23-Sep	H	Bracknell	W 28-27	350	Smithies	Clayton/t	Duncombe	Sarjaent	Tapster/t
N2	30-Sep	A	Lydney	W 24-3	200	Smithies/t	Clayton	Duncombe	Sarjaent	Tapster
N2	14-Oct	A	Rosslyn Park	L 17-19	200	Smithies	Clayton	Duncombe	Sarjaent/t	Tapster
N2	28-Oct	A	Camberley	L 15-16	150	Smithies/t	Clayton	Duncombe	Sarjaent/t	Tapster
N2	4-Nov	H	West Hartlepool	W 60-0	250	Smithies/3t	Clayton	Duncombe/4c	Sarjaent	Tapster/2t
N2	11-Nov	H	Fylde*	W 31-17	450	Smithies/3t	Clayton	Duncombe	Sarjaent	Tapster/t
N2	18-Nov	A	Wharfedale	L 0-25	700	Smithies	Clayton	Duncombe	Sarjaent	Tapster
N2	25-Nov	H	Newbury	W 17-9	300	Smithies	Clayton	Duncombe	Sarjaent	Tapster/t
N2	2-Dec	H	Nottingham	W 38-16	300	Smithies/t	Clayton/2t	Duncombe	Sarjaent	Tapster/t
N2	9-Dec	A	Preston Grasshoppers	D 22-22	450	Smithies	Clayton	Duncombe	Reed	Tapster/t
N2	16-Dec	H	Wharfedale	L 18-20	600	Smithies	Clayton	Duncombe	Sarjaent	Tapster/t
N2	23-Dec	A	Fylde	W 18-12		Smithies/t	Reed	Duncombe	Sarjaent	Tapster
N2	6-Jan	H	Camberley	W 49-5	400	Smithies/2t	Reed/t	Duncombe/t	Sarjaent	Tapster/2t
N2	13-Jan	A	West Hartlepool	W 70-14	150	Smithies/t	Reed	Duncombe/3t	Sarjaent/t	Tapster
N2	27-Jan	A	Nottingham*	W 10-3		Smithies	Farrar	Duncombe	Sarjaent	Tapster
N2	3-Feb	H	Rosslyn Park	L 10-13	550	Smithies	Farrar/t	Reed	Sarjaent	Tapster
N2	10-Feb	H	Lydney	W 29-16	350	Smithies	Windle/2c	Reed/t	Sarjaent	Tapster/t
N2	24-Feb	A	Bracknell	L 5-42	200	Smithies	Clayton	Reed	Sarjaent	Tapster
N2	10-Mar	A	Esher*	W 25-23		Smithies	Clayton	Reed	Sarjaent	Tapster
N2	17-Mar	H	Kendal	L 17-41	350	Smithies/t	Clayton	Reed	Duncombe	Tapster
N2	24-Mar	A	Rugby Lions	L 13-25	350	Smithies/t	Farrar/t	Reed	Duncombe	Tapster
N2	31-Mar	H	Preston Grasshoppers	D 13-13		Smithies	Clayton	Duncombe/dg	Sarjaent	Tapster
N2	14-Apr	A	Newbury	L 12-22		Smithies	Clayton	Duncombe	Sarjaent	Tapster/t
TBC	7-Oct	A	Rugby Lions	L 15-16		Smithies/t	Clayton	Woodcock	Sarjaent	Tapster/t

*after opponents name indicates a penalty try. Brackets after a player's name indicates he was replaced.
eg (a) means he was replaced by replacement code "a" and so on. / after a player or replacement name
is followed by any scores he made - eg /t, /c, /p, /dg or any combination of these

EVER PRESENT

James Tapster, Ed Smithies.

Most Appearances
26 James Tapster, Ed Smithies.
25 Iain Salkeld, Lee Cholewa, Mark Pinder

PLAYERS USED
29 plus 6 as replacement only

MOST POINTS

Pts	Player	T	C	P	DG
161	L Cholewa	3	31	28	-
85	E Smithies	17	-	-	-
80	J Tapster	16	-	-	-
35	R Morgan	7	-	-	-
30	R Wade	6	-	-	-

MATCH FACTS

10	9	1	2	3	4	5	6	7	8
Cholewa/c	Morgan	Pinder	McNeish	Wilson	Clark	Taylor	Worden	Hobson	Wade
Cholewa/2c3p	Morgan/2t	Pinder	Salkeld	Wilson	Clark	Taylor	Worden	Hobson	Wade
Cholewa/3c	Morgan	Pinder	Salkeld	Wilson	Clark	Taylor	Worden	Hobson/t	Wade
Cholewa/2c3p	Morgan/t	Pinder	Salkeld	Wilson	Clark	Taylor	Boyle	Hobson	Wade
Cholewa/3cp	Morgan/2t	Pinder	Salkeld	Wilson	Clark	Taylor	Houghton	Hobson	Wade
Cholewa/2cp	Morgan	Pinder	Salkeld	Bevan	Clark	Taylor/t	Worden	Hobson	Wade
Cholewa/cp	Drane	Pinder	Salkeld	Wilson	Clark	Houghton	Taylor	Worden	Wade
Cholewa/c	Drane	Pinder	Salkeld	Wilson	Clark	Houghton	Taylor	Worden/2t	Wade/3t
Cholewa/3c	Drane	Pinder	Salkeld	Wilson	Clark	Taylor	Worden	Hobson	Wade
Cholewa	Drane	Pinder	Salkeld	Wilson	Clark	Taylor	Worden	Hobson	Dudley
Cholewa/4p	Morgan	Pinder	Salkeld	Wilson	Clark	Taylor	Worden	Hobson	Dudley
Cholewa/2c3p	Morgan	Pinder	Salkeld	Wilson	Dudley/t	Clark	Worden	Hobson	Wade
Cholewa/4p	Morgan/t	Pinder	Salkeld	Wilson	Taylor	Clark	Worden	Hobson	Dudley
Cholewa/c2p	Morgan/t	Pinder	Salkeld	Wilson	Dudley	Clark	Worden	Hobson	Wade
Windle/2p(a/c)	Morgan	Pinder	Salkeld	Wilson	Taylor	Clark	Worden	Hobson	Dudley/t
Cholewa/t3cp	Morgan	Pinder	Salkeld	Wilson	Taylor	Clark	Dudley/t	Worden	Wade
Cholewa(b/4c)	Morgan	Pinder	Salkeld/t	Wilson	Taylor/3t	Clark/t	Dudley	Hobson/2cp	Wade/t
Cholewa	Morgan	Pinder	Salkeld	Wilson	Taylor	Clark	Worden	Hobson/cp	Dudley
Cholewa	Morgan	Pinder	Salkeld	Wilson	Taylor/t	Clark	Worden	Hobson	Dudley
Cholewa	Morgan	Pinder	Salkeld	Wilson	Taylor	Dudley/t	Worden/2t	Hobson	Wade
Cholewa/t	Morgan	Pinder	Salkeld	Wilson	Dudley	Boyle	Worden	Hobson	Wade
Cholewa/2c2p	Morgan	Pinder	Salkeld	Wilson	Fforde	Taylor	Dudley/2t	Hobson	Wade
Cholewa/t2cp	Morgan	Halligan	Salkeld	Wilson	Taylor	Fforde	Dudley	Hobson	Wade
Cholewa/p	Morgan	Pinder	Salkeld	Wilson	Dudley	Clark	Boyle	Worden	Wade
Cholewa/cp	Morgan	Pinder	Salkeld	Wilson	Dudley	Clark	Boyle	Worden	Wade/t
Cholewa/c	Morgan	Pinder	Salkeld	Wilson	Dudley	Clark	Worden	Hobson	Wade/t
Cholewa/cp	Morgan	Pinder	Salkeld	Bevan	Clark	Houghton	Taylor	Hobson	Wade

REPLACEMENTS   a - L Cholewa   b - R Windle

2000-01 HIGHLIGHTS

Lee Cholewa topped the points scoring list with 161 points. This was a total only beaten by Ralph Zoing and Matt Duncombe previously for the club.

It was in the try scoring where the records were broken. Ed Smithies topped the list for a second successive season, this time though he set a new league record for the club.

He beat the old record by four whilst fellow team mate James Tapster also broke the old record 16 tries to his credit in the season just finished.

In the away match at West Hartlepool they secured their biggest ever away win with a 70-14 result. They ran in 70 points which eclipsed the old record and they won by a record 56 point margin. Both previous records dated from the 41-13 win at Clifton back in November 1996.

HARROGATE

LEAGUE STATISTICS
compiled by Stephen McCormack

SEASON	Division	P	W	D	L	F	A	Pts Diff	Lge Pts	Lge Pos	Most Points		Most Tries
91-92	D4N	12	6	0	6	170	175	-5	12	7	45	Ralph Zoing	3 Steve Baker
92-93	D4N	12	10	1	1	363	115	248	21	1	131	Ralph Zoing	9 Steve Baker Guy Easterby
93-94	4	18	14	2	2	479	219	260	30	2	105	Ralph Zoing	13 Jeremy Hopkinson
94-95	3	18	7	2	9	275	404	-129	16	7	110	Dan Clappison	7 Rob Bell
95-96	3	18	6	3	9	333	387	-54	15	6	215	Ralph Zoing	5 Richard Marcroft
96-97	3	30	18	0	12	832	595	237	36	5	305	Ralph Zoing	13 Rob Bell, Mike Farrar & Kerry Morley
97-98	JN1	26	4	1	21	463	707	-244	9	14	79	Neil James	10 Lee Feurer
98-99	JN1	26	8	2	16	309	461	-152	18	12	61	Ralph Zoing	5 Mark Farrar
99-00	JN1	26	14	1	11	508	449	59	29	6	190	Matt Duncombe	11 Ed Smithies
00-01	N1	26	14	2	10	617	422	195	30	5	161	L Cholewa	17 Ed Smithies

BIGGEST MARGINS

Home Win 72pts - 79-7 v Clifton 5.4.97
Away Win 56pts - 70-14 v W Hartlepool 13.01.01
Home Defeat 54pts - 12-66 v Leeds 21.3.98
Away Defeat 47pts - 3-50 v Worcester 31.1.98

MOST CONSECUTIVE

Appearances 49 Rob Bell 9.92 -9.9.95
Matches scoring Tries 6 Clive Ware
Matches scoring points 24 Ralph Zoing
Victories 5
Defeats 10

MOST POINTS

Scored at Home 79 v Clifton 5.4.97
Scored Away 70 v W Hartlepool 13.1.01
Conceded at Home 66 v Leeds 21.3.98
Conceded Away 50 v Worcester 31.1.98

MOST TRIES

Scored in a match 14 v Aspatria 30.4.94
Conceded in a match 10 v Leeds 21.3.98 (H)

MOST APPEARANCES

by a forward 166(2) Peter Taylor
by a back 149 (9) Craig Reed

	MOST IN A SEASON	MOST IN A CAREER	MOST IN A MATCH
Points	305 Ralph Zoing 96-97	1086 Ralph Zoing 87-99	27 Ralph Zoing v Fylde 14.10.95 (H)
Tries	17 Ed Smithies 00-01	42 Jeremy Hopkinson 90-98	5 Steve Baker v Lichfield 14.11.92 (H)
Conversions	63 Ralph Zoing 96-97	175 Ralph Zoing 87-99	9 Ralph Zoing v Towcestrians 13.3.93 (H)
Penalties	51 Ralph Zoing 95-96	209 Ralph Zoing 87-99	7 Ralph Zoing v Halifax 18.11.90 (H)
Drop Goals	5 Ralph Zoing 96-97	16 Ralph Zoing 87-99	2 Ralph Zoing v Askeans 20.11.93 (H)

PLAYING SQUAD

HARROGATE

BACKS

	Ht.	Wt.	Birthdate	Birthplace	CLUB	League Apps	Tries	Pts
Graeme Sarjaent	5.10	13.0	25.09.75	Carlisle	Harrogate	22(2)	3	15
					Kendal	12(9)	2	14
Ed Smithies					Harrogate	52	27	135
Craig Reed					Harrogate	149(9)	27	149
Rhys Morgan					Harrogate	63(1)	16	80
					Leeds	35(9)	8	40
Mark Farrar					Harrogate	100(7)	39	195
Lee Cholewa					Harrogate	25(1)	3	161
Gareth Drane					Harogate	10(12)	-	-
Richard Windle					Harrogate	3(4)	1	38
James Tapster					Harrogate	36(1)	20	100
Matt Duncombe					Harrogate	47(2)	11	221
Andy Caldwell					Harrogate	103	16	76
					Leeds	2(1)	-	-
Lee Douglas					Harrogate	7(3)	1	5

FORWARDS

	Ht.	Wt.	Birthdate	Birthplace	CLUB	League Apps	Tries	Pts
Scott Wilson					Harrogate	134(6)	1	5
Matt Pinder	6.0	16.7	18.12.70	Rotherham	Harrogate	137	5	25
					Rotherham	27(26)	-	-
Paul Clark					Harrogate	42	2	10
Steve Hobson					Harrogate	21	1	17
Ian Salkeld					Harrogate	53	3	15
Richard Wade					Harrogate	20(5)	6	30
Peter Taylor					Harrogate	169(2)	20	115
Simon Brown					Harrogate	84(7)	2	9
Rob Wilson					Harrogate	16(8)	-	-
Mike Worden					Harrogate	55(8)	7	35

KENDAL RFC

President	J D Healey	55 Calder Drive, Kendal LA9 6LR. 01539 723913 (H)
Chairman	Ian W Hutton	168 Vicarage Drive, Kendal, Cumbria, LA9 5BX 01539 733152 (H), 01539 733333 (B)
Hon/Match Secretary	Roger Wilson	31 Hills Wood Avenue, Kendal, Cumbria. 01539740449 (H)
Fixture Secretary	Andrew Quarry	Watchgate Farm, Selside, Kendal, Cumbria LA8 9JX 07733 111868 (M)
Rugby Manager	Chris Hayton	106 Burneside Road, Kendal, Cumbria LA9 4RT. 01539 724600 (H)
Press Secretary	John Hutton	168 Vicarage Drive, Kendal LA9 5BX 01539 733152(H)

Kendal newly promoted to National League Two, had a very successful first season finishing in fourth place.

In what was a challenging campaign, Kendal managed to produce some excellent rugby from the opening game of the season when they convincingly won at newly promoted Esher.

However, the following week Harrogate gave them a lesson in how rugby was played in the higher league, a lesson Kendal learnt from quickly, and after a defeat away at Lydney they beat Nottingham at home, and then produced the fight back of the season to turn a 17-3 deficit away at Rosslyn Park into a 25-29 victory. That victory kick started their season and wins against Wharfedale, over whom they did the double, and Newbury (18-0) followed, as well as a credible draw against Rugby to get them close to the top of the league. Newbury avenged their defeat the Saturday before Christmas and that day was made worse for Kendal when centre Ian Voortman broke his leg in two places and brought an early end to his season

Late January brought Kendal a club record victory of 92-0 against West Hartlepool, and fullback Mike Scott a personal league record of 42 points. Five consecutive league wins followed, to place Kendal in promotion contention going into the last month of the season. Unfortunately they could not match the mighty power of champions Bracknell and were on the receiving end of a brilliant display of running rugby by Rugby, who finished second. So Kendal had to settle for fourth behind Rosslyn Park

Kendal enjoyed life in the higher league and will look to build on the success of last season and hope to go all the way this season.

Action from last season's match against Esher.

KENDAL

Comp.	Date	H/A	Opponents	Result & Score	Att.	15	14	13	12	11	10
N2	2-Sep	A	Esher	W 21-6	450	Scott/c3p	Balmer	Healey	Voortman	Stephens(a/t)	Mee
N2	9-Sep	H	Harrogate	L 10-33	400	Scott/cp	Balmer	Healey	Voortman	Dodds	Mee
N2	16-Sep	A	Lydney	L 16-20		Scott/c3p	Balmer	Healey	Voortman/t	Dodds	Mee
N2	23-Sep	H	Nottingham*	W 25-12		Scott/tcp	Balmer	Healey	Voortman/t	Dodds	Mee/t
N2	30-Sep	A	Rosslyn Park	W 29-25		Scott/2c4pdg	Balmer	Healey	Voortman	Dodds	Mee
N2	14-Oct	A	Camberley	W 15-13	250	Scott	Balmer	Healey	Voortman	Dodds/t	Mee
N2	28-Oct	A	Wharfedale	W 21-14		Scott/2p	Balmer	Healey	Voortman	Dodds/t	Mee
N2	11-Nov	H	Newbury	W 18-0	400	Scott/c2p	Balmer	Healey	Voortman	Dodds	Mee
N2	18-Nov	A	Preston Grasshoppers	L 18-25	630	Scott/c2p	Balmer	Healey	Voortman/t	Dodds	Mee
N2	25-Nov	H	Rugby Lions	D 17-17	400	Scott/2cp	Balmer	Healey	Voortman	Dodds	Mee
N2	9-Dec	A	Bracknell	L 15-31		Scott/cp	Balmer	Healey	Voortman/t	Dodds	Mee/t
N2	16-Dec	H	Preston Grasshoppers*	W 20-14		Dodds	Pearson	Healey	Voortman	Airey	Mee/tcp
N2	23-Dec	A	Newbury	L 12-35		Dodds	Balmer	Healey	Voortman(d/t)	Pearson	Mee/c
N2	6-Jan	H	Wharfedale	W 6-0		Scott/2p	Balmer	Healey	Stephens	Dodds	Mee
N2	13-Jan	A	Fylde	L 13-17		Scott/p	Balmer	Healey	Stephens	Dodds/t	Mee
N2	27-Jan	H	West Hartlepool	W 92-0		Scott/4t11c	Balmer/3t	Healey/t	Stephens/t	Dodds/t	Mee/2t
N2	17-Feb	A	West Hartlepool	W 42-11		Scott/3c2p	Balmer	Stephens	Healey/t	Dodds	Mee
N2	24-Feb	A	Nottingham	W 27-25		Scott/3cpdg	Myers	Healey	Stephens	Dodds	Mee
N2	10-Mar	H	Lydney	W 33-9		Scott/2c3p	Balmer	Healey	Stephens	Dodds/t	Mee
N2	17-Mar	A	Harrogate	W 41-17	350	Scott/4cp	Balmer/3t	Healey/t	Stephens	Dodds	Mee
N2	24-Mar	H	Esher	W 32-17		Scott/2cp	Balmer/t	Healey	Stephens/t	Dodds	Mee
N2	31-Mar	H	Bracknell	L 13-22		Scott/c2p	Balmer	Healey	Stephens	Dodds	Mee(g/t)
N2	7-Apr	H	Camberley	W 24-5		Dodds	Spiby	Healey/t	Stephens	Airey/2t	Scott/2c
N2	14-Apr	A	Rugby Lions	L 21-62		Stephens	Airey(h/t)	Healey	Mee	Dodds	Scott/c3p
N2	21-Apr	H	Rosslyn Park	L 10-22		Dodds	Airey	Stephens	Thompson	Myers	Scott
N2	28-Apr	H	Fylde	W 31-15		Dodds/t	Balmer	Stephens	Healey	Airey	Scott/t4cp
TBC	7-Oct	A	Sedgley Park	L 9-17		Scott/3p	Balmer	Healey	Voortman	Dodds	Mee

*after opponents name indicates a penalty try. Brackets after a player's name indicates he was replaced.
eg (a) means he was replaced by replacement code "a" and so on. / after a player or replacement name
is followed by any scores he made - eg /t, /c, /p, /dg or any combination of these

EVER PRESENT None

Most Appearances:
26   Billy Coxon, Jimmy Thompson.
25   Adian Bateson, Paul Dodds, Stephen Healey

PLAYERS USED   25 plus four as a replacement

MOST POINTS

Pts	Player	T	C	P	DG
235	M Scott	6	44	37	2
37	C Mee	6	2	1	-
35	J Balmer	7	-	-	-
35	P Dodds	7	-	-	-
35	C Wolstenholme	7	-	-	-

MATCH FACTS

9	1	2	3	4	5	6	7	8
Thompson	Coxon/t	Gowing	Thompson	Harryman	Robinson	Wolstenholme	Bland	Bateson
Thompson	Coxon	Gowing	Thompson	Harryman	Capstick	Robinson(b/t)	Bland	Bateson
Thompson	Coxon	Gowing	Thompson	Harryman	Capstick	Wolstenholme	Bland	Bateson
Thompson	Coxon	Gowing	Thompson	Harryman	Capstick	Robinson	Bland	Bateson
Thompson	Coxon	Gowing/t	Thompson	Harryman/t	Capstick	Bland	Robinson	Bateson
Thompson	Coxon	Gowing	Thompson	Robinson/2t	Capstick	Wolstenholme	Bland	Bateson
Thompson	Coxon	Gowing/t	Thompson	Robinson	Capstick	Wolstenholme/t	Bland	Bateson
Thompson	Coxon	Gowing	Harryman	Robinson/t(c/t)	Capstick	Wolstenholme	Bland	Bateson
Thompson	Coxon	Gowing/t	Thompson	Robinson	Capstick	Wolstenholme	Bland	Bateson
Thompson	Coxon	Thompson/t	Pearson	Harryman/t	Capstick	Robinson	Bland	Bateson
Thompson	Coxon	Gowing	Thompson	Robinson	Capstick	Wolstenholme	Bland	Bateson
Thompson	Coxon	Gowing	Thompson	Harryman	Capstick/t	Wolstenholme	Bland	Bateson
Thompson	Coxon	Gowing	Thompson	Harryman/t	Capstick	Wolstenholme	Robinson	Bateson
Thompson	Coxon	Gowing	Thompson	Robinson	Capstick	Wolstenholme	Bland	Bateson
Thompson	Coxon	Gowing	Thompson	Robinson(e/t)	Capstick	Wolstenholme	Bland	Bateson
Thompson	Coxon	Gowing	Thompson	Harryman	Capstick	Wolstenholme/t	Bland	Bateson/t
Thompson/t	Coxon	Gowing/t	Harryman	Robinson(e/t)	Capstick	Wolstenholme/t	Bowman/2t	Bateson
Thompson/t	Coxon	Gowing	Thompson	Robinson	Capstick	Wolstenholme	Bland	Bateson/t
Thompson	Coxon	Gowing	Thompson	Harryman	Capstick	Wolstenholme/2t	Bland/t	Bateson
Thompson/t	Coxon	Gowing/t	Thompson	Harryman	Capstick	Wolstenholme	Bland	Bateson
Thompson	Coxon	Gowing/t	Harryman	Robinson	Capstick	Wolstenholme/t(f/t)	Bland	Bateson
Thompson	Coxon	Gowing	Harryman	Robinson	Capstick	Wolstenholme	Bland	Bateson
Thompson/t	Coxon	Gowing	Pearson	Robinson	Capstick	Wolstenholme	Bowman	Bateson
Thompson	Coxon	Gowing	Harryman	Robinson	Capstick	Wolstenholme	Bland/t	Bowman
Mee/t	Coxon	Gowing	Harryman/t	Robinson	Quarry	Bowman	Bland	Bateson
Thompson	Coxon	Holmes/2t	Pearson	Robinson	Capstick	Bowman	Bland	Bateson
Thompson	Pearson	Gowing	Harryman	Robinson	Capstick	Wolstenholme	Bland	Bateson

REPLACEMENTS

a - P Dodds	b - C Wolstenholme	c - C Wilson	d - M Healey	e - R Harryman
f - Mark Bowman	g - M Airey	h - A Myers		

2000-01 HIGHLIGHTS

Mike Scott in his first season for the club topped the points scoring list with 235.

He becomes the second man after Casey Mee to score 200 points in a league season.

Mee became the first Kendal player to reach 500 National League points.

Scott also finished 4th in the try scoring list with six, four of those coming in just one match, against West Hartlepool in January. In that match he also kicked 22 points for a new division record of 42 point in a match.

The 22 points consisted of 11 conversions which also a new record for the club in league rugby.

Suffered their worst ever defeat when losing 21-62

KENDAL

LEAGUE STATISTICS
compiled by Stephen McCormack

SEASON	Division	P	W	D	L	F	A	Pts Diff	Lge Pts	Lge Pos		Coach	Captain
91-92	D4N	12	8	1	3	157	123	34	17	3		R Lee	S Hulme
92-93	D4N	12	6	0	6	182	189	-7	12	6			
93-94	D5N	12	4	1	7	142	171	-29	9	10			
94-95	D5N	12	9	1	2	226	162	64	19	2		P Kremer	J Nicholson
												Most Points	Most Tries
95-96	D5N	12	5	0	7	215	227	-12	10	9	36	Paul Dodds	6 Paul Dodds
96-97	D4N	26	11	1	14	541	451	90	23	9	163	Jason Hudson	7 Paul Dodds
97-98	N2N	26	18	2	6	614	357	257	38	3	135	Jon Nicholson	15 Jason Balmer
98-99	N2N	26	18	0	8	635	347	288	36	4	200	Casey Mee	12 Jason Balmer
99-00	N2N	26	24	0	2	817	305	512	48	1	273	Casey Mee	15 Jason Balmer
00-01	N2	26	16	1	9	622	467	155	33	4	235	Mike Scott	7 by Three players

BIGGEST MARGINS

Home Win	92pts - 92-0 v W Hartlepool 27.1.01
Away Win	51pts - 56-5 v Liverpool StH
Home Defeat	28pts - 6-34 v Harrogate 3.10.92
Away Defeat	41pts - 21-62 v Rugby 14.4.01

MOST CONSECUTIVE

Appearances	
Matches scoring Tries	
Matches scoring points	
Victories	19
Defeats	5

MOST POINTS

Scored at Home	92 v W Hartlepool 27.01.01
Scored Away	56 v Liverpool StH
Conceded at Home	39 v Wharfedale 13.1.96
Conceded Away	62 v Rugby 14.4.01

MOST TRIES

Scored in a match	14 v Hereford 12.4.97
Conceded in a match	6 v Preston 21.2.98

MOST APPEARANCES

by a forward	
by a back	

	MOST IN A SEASON	MOST IN A CAREER	MOST IN A MATCH
Points	273 Casey Mee 1999-20	510 Casey Mee 1998-01	42 Mike Scott v W Hartlepool 27.1.01
Tries	15 Jason Balmer 1997-98 & 1999-00	49 Jason Balmer 1997-01	6 Jason Slater v Barker's Butts 14.1.95
Conversions	53 Casey Mee 1999-00	92 Casey Mee 1998-01	11 Mike Scott v W Hartlepool 27.1.01 (H)
Penalties	44 Casey Mee 1999-00	76 Casey Mee 1998-01	7 Jon Nicholson v Sandal 27.12.97 (A)
Drop Goals	3 David Bell 1996-97	3 David Bell 1996-97	1 By numerous players

PLAYING SQUAD

KENDAL

BACKS

	Ht.	Wt.	Birthdate	Birthplace	CLUB	League Apps	Tries	Pts
Stephen Healey	5.11	13.7	21.07.71	Kendal	Kendal	130(1)+	29+	145+
Dan Stephens	6.2	14.0	20.09.77	Kendal	Kendal	72(3)	15	80
Jason Balmer	5.11	13.7	16.04.71	Burnley	Kendal	87(1)	49	245
Ian Voortman	6.3	15.6	13.04.74	Cape Town	Kendal	79	28	142
Mike Scott					Kendal Aspatria, Orrell	24	6	235
Paul Dodds	5.10	12.7	29.01.71	Kendal	Kendal	129(3)	28	160
Casey Mee	5.8	12.8	11.06.73	Dunedin	Kendal	74	19	508
Jimmy Thompson			01.07.71		Kendal	72(2)	22	110
Aaron Myers					Kendal	2(6)	-	-
Scott Pearson					Kendal	2(4)	-	-
Mark Airey					Kendal	31(10)	11	55

FORWARDS

	Ht.	Wt.	Birthdate	Birthplace	CLUB	League Apps	Tries	Pts
Adrian Bateson	6.4	15.7	14.02.76	Whitehaven	Kendal	77	10	50
Keith Robinson	6.4	15.7	09.03.70	Penrith	Kendal	88(9)+	15+	75+
Colin Wolstenholme	5.11	14.7	18.03.67	Kendal	Kendal	90(15)	33	165
Nathan Bland	6.0	14.10	25.05.77	Kendal	Kendal	43(4)	4	20
Richard Harryman	6.2	19.7	16.11.76	Kendal	Kendal	94(15)	34	170
Mike Capstick	6.5	18.0	29.04.74	Kendal	Kendal			
Nigel Pearson	5.11	17.7	17.06.67	Kendal	Kendal	73(37)+	4+	20+
Billy Coxon	6.0	16.0	27.07.75	Peterlee	Kendal	135(1)+	9+	45+
Ian Gowing	5.11	17.7	13.07.75	Natick (USA)	Kendal	56(10)	9	45
Ian Thompson	5.11	15.7	31.10.69	Penrith	Kendal	74(12)+	1	5
Alan Homes					Kendal	1(1)	2	10
Craig Wilson					Kendal	(5)	-	-

KENDAL

FACT FILE

Founded : 1905
Nickname : The Black & Ambers
Colours: Black and amber.
Change colours: Amber jerseys with black trim

GROUND
Address: Mint Bridge, Shap Road, Kendal. LA9 6DL.
Tel: 01539 734039
Capacity: 1900   Seated: 400   Standing: 1500

Directions: From the M6 junction 36 take A591. Then A6 (Kendal to Penrith). Keep left at the `Duke of Cumberland' and the ground is 400 metres onthe left.
Nearest Railway Station: Kendal (via Oxenholme)

Car Parking: Space for 120 cars on ground.

Admission: Matchdays - Adults members £4.00 non-members £6; Children/OAPs £2
Season Ticket: £35 (members only)
Clubhouse: Has two bars and has food available.   Functions: Capacity up to 200.

Club Shop: Shop manager - David Robinson 01539 720355

Training Nights: Tuesday and Thursday

PROGRAMME Size: A5   Price: £1   Pages: 24 + cover
Editor: John Kremer 01539 734039
Advertising Rates   Prices on application
Contact MTP Publications Ltd. 01539 740937

Action from last season's match against Lydney.

NEWBURY RFC

Newbury RFC, Monks Lane, Newbury. RG14 7RW
Tel: 01635 40103   Fax: 01635 40533   email: info@newburyrfc.co.uk

President	David G H Smith	c/o Newbury RFC	01264 342342 (B), 07801 666116 (M)
Club Secretary	Rosie Golby	c/o Newbury RFC	07775 915785 (M)
Rugby Co-ordinator	Ally Pankhurst	c/o Newbury RFC	07771 550494 (M)
Chairman of Rugby	Pete Simmons	c/o Newbury RFC	01635 863242
Commercial Manager	Morgan Davis	c/o Newbury RFC	01635 40103 (B) 07785 525816 (M)
Ist XV Manager	Simon Little	c/o Newbury RFC	07768 710577 (M)
Fixture Co-ordinator	John Mills	c/o Newbury RFC	01635 200743

After the promise of a best ever fifth placing the previous year, Newbury's 2000-01 season turned out to be a massive disappointment.

The new coaching team of Richard Greed and Julian Brammer snapped up several experienced close season signings and they appeared to herald a promotion drive, while an opening day win at Nottingham suggested that Newbury had found the steel to grind out results on their travels.

Despite a home defeat at the hands of Rosslyn Park, Newbury led the league briefly until they went to then bottom of the table Fylde and a 12-6 defeat at the end of September set off a run that produced eleven straight away league defeats and eventually saw Blues plummet into the relegation battle.

Home wins over Rugby and Kendal provided highlights and signs of what the side could do at its best. But, when home form also began to suffer with defeats at the hands of Wharfedale and Preston and a disappointing draw in the return with Fylde, then Newbury were well and truly involved in the survival battle.

It was a 31-5 defeat at Esher in February that prompted Newbury to turn again to coach Keith Richardson for help, as he had helped to steer them through the National Leagues before setting off back to Gloucester and then Coventry. Back at Monks Lane, he helped to focus the task and despite disappointing defeats at Camberley and at home to champions Bracknell by a record 53-3 scoreline, Blues did enough to secure their safety with home wins over West Hartlepool (53-3), Nottingham (23-11) and finally Harrogate (22-12).

Injuries over the season hardly helped as Blues fielded more than 40 players in league games, but there were plus marks in the performances of winger Jo Czerpak, Matt Cornish and Chris Simmons and, with Richardson now back on board as director of rugby, Blues will be hoping to find the consistency to ward off any fears of a repeat this term.

Back Row: Lee Woodhouse, Ben Shand, Richard Parker, Nigel Hill, Andy Binnie, Phil Clarke. **Middle:** Sid Little, Jeremy Griffiths, Dave Griffiths, Chris Hart, Ben Butler, Nick Hunt, Gareth Evans, Bill Nicholas, Craig Davies, Julian Brammer.
Front: Mal Roberts, Andy Evans, Simon Stoker, Morgan Davis, John Kingdon, Simon Gully, Brett Wakfer, Bernie Williams.

NEWBURY

Comp.	Date	H/A	Opponents	Result & Score	Att.	15	14	13	12	11
N2	2-Sep	A	Nottingham	W 26-14		Griffiths/c3p	Lucas	Griffiths/t	Hill	Simmons
N2	9-Sep	H	Rosslyn Park	L 17-26		Griffiths/2cp	Starter-Smith	Evans	Hill	Simmons
N2	16-Sep	A	West Hartlepool	W 34-3		Griffiths/4c2p	Lucas	Griffiths/2t	Hill	Simmons
N2	23-Sep	H	Camberley*	W 34-13	300	Griffiths/2c	Hart	Evans	Hill	Simmons/3t
N2	30-Sep	A	Fylde	L 6-12	450	Griffiths/2p	Hart	Griffiths	Hill	Simmons
N2	14-Oct	A	Bracknell	L 11-26		Griffiths/2p	Roberts	Griffiths	Evans	Clarke
N2	28-Oct	H	Rugby Lions	W 22-19		Griffiths/2cp	Roberts	Evans/t	Hill	Griffiths/t
N2	11-Nov	A	Kendal	L 0-18	400	Griffiths	Roberts	Evans	Hill	Griffiths
N2	18-Nov	H	Esher	W 19-18		Roberts/t3p	Hart	Evans	Hill	Griffiths
N2	25-Nov	A	Harrogate	L 9-17	300	Griffiths/3p	Hart	Roberts	Hill	Griffiths
N2	2-Dec	H	Wharfedale	L 10-25		Griffiths/cp	Clarke	Evans	Hill	Griffiths
N2	9-Dec	H	Lydney	W 24-12		Roberts/2c	Stoker	Griffiths/t	Evans	McClennan
N2	23-Dec	H	Kendal	W 35-12		Roberts/3c3p	Stoker/t	Griffiths	Evans	Simmons/2t
N2	6-Jan	A	Rugby Lions	L 3-24		Roberts/p	Stoker	Griffiths	Evans	Simmons
N2	13-Jan	H	Preston Grasshoppers	L 10-25		Roberts/c	Stoker	Griffiths/t	Evans	Czerpak
N2	27-Jan	A	Wharfedale	L 7-37		Roberts/c	Flett	Evans/t	Hill	Czerpak
N2	10-Feb	H	Fylde	D 10-10		Roberts	Griffiths/t	Evans	Hill	Czerpak
N2	17-Feb	A	Esher	L 5-31	250	Roberts	Smith	Griffiths	Evans	Czerpak/t
N2	24-Feb	A	Camberley	L 16-23	200	Roberts/2p	Hart/t	Griffiths	Evans	Flett
N2	3-Mar	A	Preston Grasshoppers	L 17-27		Roberts/tc	Griffiths	Jennings	Evans	Czerpak/t
N2	10-Mar	H	West Hartlepool	W 53-3		Roberts/5cp	Griffiths	Jennings/t	Evans	Czerpak/2t
N2	17-Mar	A	Rosslyn Park*	L 16-31		Roberts/c3p	Hart	Griffiths	Evans	Czerpak
N2	24-Mar	H	Nottingham	W 23-11		Czerpak	Jennings	Griffiths	Hill	Roberts/c2p
N2	7-Apr	H	Bracknell	L 3-53		Morgan/p	Simmons	Evans	Hill	Griffiths
N2	14-Apr	H	Harrogate	W 22-12		Morgan/c4pdg	Simmons	Griffiths/t	Hill	Czerpak
TBC	7-Oct	H	Haywards Heath	W 45-0		Griffiths/t4c4p	Hart	Roberts	Evans	Griffiths/t
TBC	21-Oct	A	New Brighton	L 11-15		Griffiths	Haslam	Griffiths/2p	Hill	Evans

*after opponents name indicates a penalty try. Brackets after a player's name indicates he was replaced.
eg (a) means he was replaced by replacement code "a" and so on. / after a player or replacement name
is followed by any scores he made - eg /t, /c, /p, /dg or any combination of these*

EVER PRESENT		MOST POINTS					
None							

Most Appearances:
24 Ben Butler.
22 Jeremy Griffiths.
20 Matt Baker, Rob Faulkner.

Pts	Player	T	C	P	DG
85	M Roberts	2	15	15	-
69	D Griffiths	-	12	15	-
40	J Griffiths	8	-	-	-
30	S Stoker	6	-	-	-

PLAYERS USED

41 plus four as replacement only

MATCH FACTS

10	9	1	2	3	4	5	6	7	8
Davis	Stoker	Faulkner	Baker	Williams	Hunt	Butler	Hart/t	Kingdon	Davies/t
Davis	Stoker/t	Faulkner	Baker	Williams	Hunt	Butler	Evans	Kingdon	Davies/t
Long	Stoker	Faulkner/t	Baker	Williams	Hunt	Butler	Nicholas/t	Kingdon	Davies
Davis	Stoker/t	Faulkner	Baker	Williams	Hunt	Butler	Nicholas	Kingdon	Davies/t
Davis	Stoker	Faulkner	Baker	Williams	Hunt	Butler	Nicholas	Kingdon	Davies
Davis	Shand/t	Faulkner	Baker	Williams	Hunt	Butler	Nicholas	Gully	Davies
Davis	Stoker	Faulkner	Baker/t	Binnie	Harrison	Butler	Nicholas	Gully	Davies
Davis	Stoker	Faulkner	Baker	Williams	Harrison	Butler	Nicholas	Gully	Davies
Davis	Stoker	Faulkner/t	Baker	Binnie	Harrison	Butler	Nicholas	Gully	Davies
Davis	Stoker	Faulkner	Bentley	Baker	Harrison	Butler	Nicholas	Gully	Davies
Roberts	Stoker/t	Faulkner	Baker	Williams	Harrison	Butler	Nicholas	Gully	Davies
Westall	Wakfer	Faulkner	Bentley	Binnie	Harrison/t	Butler	Nicholas	Kingdon	McCormick/2t
Davis	Wakfer	Faulkner	Bentley	Binnie/t	Harrison	Butler	Woodhouse	Nicholas	McCormick
Davis	Wakfer	Binnie	Bentley	Williams	Harrison	Butler	Davies	Nicholas	McCormick
Westall/p	Wakfer	Crowther	Bentley	Williams	Hunt	Butler	Davies	Nicholas	McCormick
Morgan	Wakfer	Binnie	Bentley	Williams	Hunt	Butler	Hart	Cornish	McCormick
Morgan/cp	Wakfer	Binnie	Baker	Williams	Hunt	Butler	Nicholas	Cornish	McCormick
Morgan	Wakfer	Faulkner	Baker	Binnie	Hart	Butler	Nicholas	Cornish	McCormick
Czerpak	Wakfer	Faulkner	Baker/t	Binnie	Hunt	Butler	Davis	Cornish	Nicholas
Davis	Stoker	Faulkner	Baker	Binnie/t	Hunt	Butler	Woodhouse	Cornish	Nicholas
Davis/t	Stoker/2t	Faulkner	Baker/t	Binnie	Hunt	Miall	Nicholas	Cornish	Davies/t
Davis	Stoker	Faulkner	Baker	Binnie	Hunt	Butler	Miall	Cornish	Davies
Davis	Ryan/t	Faulkner/t	Baker/t	Binnie	Hunt	Butler	Gully	Cornish	Davies
Davis	Stoker	Faulkner	Baker	Binnie	Hunt	Butler	Miall	Cornish	Hart
Davis	Stoker	Binnie	Baker	Williams	Harrison	Butler	Hart	Cornish	Davies
Davis	Wakfer/t	Binnie	Baker/t	Williams	Hunt	Butler	Nicholas	Gully	Davies/t
Roberts	Wakfer	Binnie	Baker(a/t)	Williams	Harrison	Butler	Gully	Woodhouse	Davies

REPLACEMENTS	a - C Bentley

2000-01 HIGHLIGHTS

Mal Roberts topped the scoring chart with a lowly 85 points, he scored a couple of tris and and kicked 15 penalties and conversions each.

Jeremy Griffiths topped the try scoring for the second successive season with eight which was two fewer than last season.

Craig Davies extended his club appearance record in league rugby to 99 and also took his club record for tries to 55.

Suffered their worst ever league defeat in National League rugby going down 53-3 to Bracknell on the 7th April. They also suffered their biggest ever away defeat when going down by 30 points at Wharfedale, 7-37.

NEWBURY

LEAGUE STATISTICS
compiled by Stephen McCormack

SEASON	Division	P	W	D	L	F	A	Pts Diff	Lge Pts	Lge Pos		Coach		Captain
91-92	SW1	10	5	0	5	142	145	-3	10	6		T Burwell		W Phillips
92-93	SW1	12	8	1	3	251	158	93	17	3		T Burwell		W Phillips
93-94	SW1	12	8	1	3	173	165	8	17	3		T Burwell		J Booth
94-95	SW1	12	9	1	2	376	113	263	19	2		S Czerpak		J Brammer
95-96	SW1	12	11	0	1	364	169	195	22	1p		S Czerpak		J Brammer
												Most Points		**Most Tries**
96-97	D4S	25	25	0	0	1170	295	875	50	1p	398	Nick Grecian	27	Brian Johnson
97-98	JN1	26	12	2	12	639	545	94	26	6	172	Nick Grecian	16	Criag Davies
98-99	JN1	26	14	1	11	552	476	76	29	6	72	Justin Poihippi	10	Tyrone Howe
99-00	JN1	26	15	1	10	550	483	67	31	5	123	Dave Griffiths	10	Jeremy Griffiths
00-01	N2	*25	10	1	14	437	502	-65	21	9	85	Mal Roberts	8	Jeremy Griffiths

BIGGEST MARGINS

Home Win	87pts - 87-0 v Met. Police 22.2.97
Away Win	69pts - 74-5 v Askeans 19.4.87
Home Defeat	50pts - 3-53 v Bracknell 7.4.01
Away Defeat	30pts - 7-37 v Wharfedale 27.1.01

MOST CONSECUTIVE

Appearances	30 Colin Hall
Matches scoring Tries	5 Brian Johnson
Matches scoring points	24 Nick Grecian
Victories	26
Defeats	4

MOST POINTS

Scored at Home	91 v Tabard 28.3.97
Scored Away	74 v Askeans 19.4.97
Conceded at Home	53 v Bracknell 7.4.01
Conceded Away	41 v Worcester 7.3.98

MOST TRIES

Scored in a match	15 v Tabard 28.3.97
Conceded in a match	6 v Worcester 7.3.98

MOST APPEARANCES

by a forward	99 (4) Craig Davies
by a back	87(1) Tom Holloway

	MOST IN A SEASON	MOST IN A CAREER	MOST IN A MATCH
Points	391 Nick Grecian 96-97	563 Nick Grecian 96-98	32 Nick Grecian v Charlton Park 25.1.97 (H) / v Met. Police 22.2.97 (H)
Tries	27 Brian Johnson 96-97	55 Craig Davies 96-99	4 Brian Johnson v Askeans 19.4.97 (A) / v Plymouth 26.4.97 (H)
Conversions	100 Nick Grecian 96-97	135 Nick Grecian 96-98	11 Nick Grecian v Charlton Park 25.1.97 (H)
Penalties	42 Nick Grecian 96-97	71 Nick Grecian 96-98	5 Nick Grecian v Liverpool St. Helens 21.2.98 (H)
Drop Goals	2 Morgan Davis 99-00	3 Morgan Davis 97-00	1 Morgan Davis (x3), Howard Graham (x1) / Simon Morgan (x1)

PLAYING SQUAD

NEWBURY

BACKS

	Ht.	Wt.	Birthdate	Birthplace	CLUB	League Apps	Tries	Pts
Ian Morgan			05.05.75		Newbury	5	-	25
Chris Simmons			07.11.80		Newbury	9(1)	5	25
Nigel Hill			04.12.67		Newbury Preston	15(3)	-	-
Simon Stoker			27.12.77		Newbury	19(1)	6	30
David Griffiths			29.04.74		Newbury	28	4	192
Jeremy Griffiths Welsh Youth	6.0	13.00	10.05.74	Camarthen	Newbury Llandovery	61	27	135
Mal Roberts			04.08.77		Newbury	29	4	140
Andrew Evans			22.03.76		Newbury	28	4	20
Brett Wakfer RAF, Combined Services.	5.9	12.07	15.04.73	St Ives	Newbury Clifton	28(15)	2	10
Morgan Davis England Students	6.0	14.00	03.02.75	Ascot	Newbury Wasps	60(2)	11	66

FORWARDS

	Ht.	Wt.	Birthdate	Birthplace	CLUB	League Apps	Tries	Pts
Julian Brammer Army, Combined Services, Oxfordshire, Eastern Counties.	5.8	17.00	22.11.63	Whitehaven	Newbury	46(3)	4	20
Bernie Williams RAF.	6.0	15.07	01.06.68	Cardiff	Newbury Coventry	26(7)	-	-
Chris Hart Dorset & Wiltshire.	6.4	17.00	20.12.74	Swindon	Newbury Swindon	48(7)	13	65
Simon Gully England colts, South West colts. Other clubs: Torquay, Bristol	5.10	16.00	12.08.75	Torquay	Newbury Weston s Mare	45(7)	8	40
Craig Davies Wales u21, Students.	6.3	17.06	25.11.69	Swansea	Newbury	99(4)	55	275
John Kingdon Devon	6.1	14.07	24.06.67	Barnstaple	Newbury	78(12)	4	20
Harry Harrison			27.04.71		Newbury	20(7)	7	35
Liam McCormick			14.08.72		Newbury	7(1)	2	10
Matt Cornish Berkshire			14.04.77	Eastbourne	Newbury	10	-	-
Gareth Evans			30.08.78		Newbury	5(7)	-	-
Simon Miall England Students	6.5	16.00	13.03.76	Winchester	Newbury	47(4)	1	5

NEWBURY

FACT FILE

Founded: 1928
Nickname: The Blues
Web site: www.newburyrfc.co.uk

Colours: Navy, sky & white irregular hoops
Change colours: Red

GROUND

Address: Monks Lane, Newbury, Berkshire RG14 7RW

Tel : 01635 40103   Fax: 01635 40533   e-mail: info@newburyrfc.co.uk
Capacity: 7,850   Seated: 350   Standing: 7,500

Directions: From M4 take A34 to Newbury, at 4th r'about on Newbury ring road(A34) turn right. Keep left at mini-r'about, ground is half mile on left. From south turn left at1st r'about on A34 ring road. Nearest Railway Station: Newbury (10 minutes walk from ground)

Car Parking: 300 on ground, 1000 nearby @ £1.

Admission: Season   Adults Standing £90, Seated £150.
                              No concessions
                 Matchday   Standing: Adults £7, Children £4, OAPs £3
                              Seated: Adults £8,Children £5, OAPs £4.

Club Shop: Open weekends & training evenings

Clubhouse: Normal licensing hours - 3 bars.
                 Snacks & bar food available.
Functions: 4 rooms avail. Corporate hospitality available.
                 Contact Andy McKelvie 01635 40103

Training Nights: Tuesday & Thursday

PROGRAMME

Size: A5   Pages: 40
Price: £1   Editor: Morgan Davis
ADVERTISING RATES
Colour   Page £600   Half £400   Qtr. £250

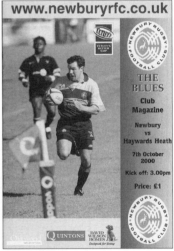

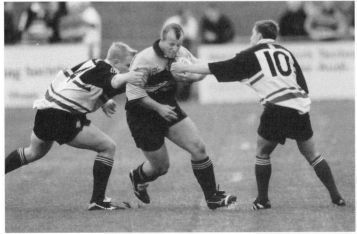

Matt Baker, Newbury's Player of the Year 2000-01, easing past Ian Balshaw in the pre-season match against Bath last August.

NOTTINGHAM RFC

Chairman Bryan Ford,

Secretary Keith Mitchell

Director of Coaching Mike Pennistone

Treasurer John Hughes

Administrator Janet Allen

Advertising Nigel Eatch

c/o Nottingham RFC
Ireland Avenue
Beeston
Nottingham
NG9 1JD.
Tel: 0115 925 4238
Fax: 0115 925 4255

Notoriously poor starters Nottingham again lost their opening game last season, but then won four of their next six giving them their best start to a league campaign for many years. But any hopes of finishing in the top half of the table evaporated as an appaling run of form saw them lose seventeen out of nineteen games. Indeed, relegation looked a strong possibility until one last desperate effort up at Fylde gave them a life line with a 23-3 victory in their final outing of the season.

Financial constraints left Nottingham with little option but to blood their own home-grown talent, and several youngsters rose to the challenge admirably. The exciting counter-attacking runs from full-back Ben Murphy, for example, earned him the supporters `player of the year' award. Tenacious hooker Stuart Bailey made a big impression, whilst second row forwards Ben Blackwall and James Quick progressed well. Nottingham also boasted one of the Division's leading try-scorers, as Jamie Morley broke the club record by crossing the line seventeen times.

The club's second XV, the Corsairs, had a far more productive season, finishing top of the NCA (Central) Second Team Competition. They won eleven of their sixteen games, with the points awarded from another three that were cancelled by the opposition. Again it was the younger players who led the way with outside-half Dave Jackson particularly impressive, and forcing his way onto the first team replacement bench by the end of the season.

The trend continued down through the Junior sides, whilst the club's Minis again proved themselves among the best in the Midlands. All of which underlines that Nottingham have a good production line of talent in place. But they will hope to see more of that youthful exuberance rise to first team level and reverse a worrying trend of relegation battles in recent years.

NOTTINGHAM

Comp.	Date	H/A	Opponents	Result & Score	Att.	15	14	13	12	11
N2	2-Sep	H	Newbury	L 14-26		Murphy/t	Booth/3p	Morley	Clark	Spencer
N2	9-Sep	A	Preston Grasshoppers	W 32-17	350	Murphy	Reynolds	Morley/3t	Clark	Spencer
N2	16-Sep	H	Rugby Lions	W 15-12		Murphy	Carroll(a/c)	Morley	Clark/t	Spencer
N2	23-Sep	A	Kendal	L 12-25		Murphy	Carroll	Morley	Clark	Spencer
N2	30-Sep	H	Esher	W 20-18		Murphy	Carroll	Morley/t	Clark	Spencer
N2	14-Oct	H	Lydney	W 44-22		Murphy/2t	Clark	Rolt	Morley	Spencer/t
N2	28-Oct	A	Rosslyn Park	L 24-35		Murphy	Swetman	Morley/t	Rolt/t	Spencer
N2	25-Nov	H	Fylde	L 15-17		Murphy	Reynolds	Morley	Rolt	Spencer
N2	2-Dec	A	Harrogate	L 16-38	300	Murphy/t	Reynolds	Carroll	Rolt	Spencer
N2	9-Dec	A	Wharfedale	W 21-12		Murphy	Morley	Carroll	Rolt	Clark/t
N2	16-Dec	H	Camberley	W 33-12	300	Murphy/t	Morley/t	Carroll/t	Rolt	Clark/t
N2	23-Dec	A	West Hartlepool	W 45-5		Murphy/t	Morley/3t	Carroll/t	Rolt	Clark
N2	6-Jan	H	Rosslyn Park	L 31-40		Murphy/t	Morley/t	Carroll	Rolt	Clark
N2	13-Jan	A	Bracknell	L 3-48		Murphy	Morley	Carroll	Rolt	Clark
N2	20-Jan	A	Lydney	W 28-21	400	Murphy	Morley	Carroll	Rolt(b/t)	Spencer/t
N2	27-Jan	H	Harrogate	L 3-10		Murphy	Morley	Swetman	Carroll	Spencer
N2	3-Feb	H	West Hartlepool	W 48-15		Murphy/2t	Morley/3t	Carroll	Swetman/t	Spencer
N2	10-Feb	A	Esher	L 5-20	250	Murphy/t	Morley	Robinson	Swetman	Spencer
N2	17-Feb	A	Camberley	L 15-24		Murphy	Morley/t	Robinson	Carroll	Spencer/t
N2	24-Feb	H	Kendal	L 25-27		Murphy	Morley/t	Robinson	Swetman	Clark
N2	3-Mar	H	Bracknell	L 7-22		Murphy	Morley	Robinson	Swetman	Clark
N2	10-Mar	A	Rugby Lions	L 17-29		Murphy	Morley/t	Robinson/t	Swetman	Clark
N2	17-Mar	H	Preston Grasshoppers	L 15-37		Murphy/t	Morley	Robinson	Swetman/tcp	Clark
N2	24-Mar	A	Newbury	L 11-23		Murphy/t	Morley	Robinson	Swetman/2p	Clark
N2	31-Mar	H	Wharfedale	L 22-26		Murphy	Morley	Carroll	Swetman/t4p	Clark
N2	14-Apr	A	Fylde	W 23-3		Murphy	Morley	Southam/tc	Swetman/tcp	Clark
TBC	7-Oct	H	Morley	L 19-23		Murphy	Clark/t	Morley	Rolt/2p	Spencer

** after opponents name indicates a penalty try. Brackets after a player's name indicates he was replaced.
eg (a) means he was replaced by replacement code "a" and so on. / after a player or replacement name
is followed by any scores he made - eg /t, /c, /p, /dg or any combination of these*

EVER PRESENT
Stuart Bailey, Ben Murphy.

Most Appearances:
26 Stuart Bailey, Ben Murphy.
25 Mark Bradley, Richard Lloyd, Jamie Morley.

PLAYERS USED
31 plus two as replacements only

MOST POINTS

Pts	Player	T	C	P	DG
219	R Southam	9	36	33	1
80	J Morley	16	-	-	-
60	B Murphy	12	-	-	-
53	M Swetman	5	2	8	-
18	T Rolt	2	1	-	2

MATCH FACTS

10	9	1	2	3	4	5	6	7	8
Southam	Taylor	Adams	Bailey	Fowkes	Quick	Blackwell	Chubb	Lloyd	Bradley
Southam/3cpdg	Carroll	Holland	Bailey	Adams/t	Quick	Johnston	Chubb	Lloyd	Bradley
Southam/cp	Taylor(a/t)	Ireland	Bailey	Adams	Quick	Johnston	Chubb	Lloyd	Bradley
Southam	Taylor	Ireland	Bailey	Adams	Quick	Johnston/t	Chubb	Lloyd/t	Bradley
Southam/t2c2p	Taylor	Freer	Bailey	Adams	Blackwell	Quick	Johnston	Lloyd	Bradley
Southam/t4c2p	Taylor/t	Freer	Bailey	Adams	Blackwell	Johnston	Chubb	Lloyd/t	Bradley
Southam/c4p	Taylor	Ireland	Bailey	Holland	Quick	Johnston	Charteris	Lloyd	Bradley
Southam/tcp	Taylor	Freer	Bailey	Holland	Quick	Johnston/t	Charteris	Lloyd	Bradley
Southam/c3p	Taylor	Freer	Bailey	Holland	Blackwell	Johnston	Charteris	Lloyd	Bradley
Southam/tc3p	Taylor	Freer	Bailey	Holland	Blackwell	Quick	Monaghan	Lloyd	Bradley
Southam/4c	Taylor	Freer	Bailey/t	Holland	Blackwell	Quick	Monaghan	Lloyd	Bradley
Southam/t5c	Taylor	Freer/t	Bailey	Holland	Blackwell	Quick	Monaghan	Lloyd	Bradley
Southam/2c4p	Taylor/t	Freer	Bailey	Holland	Blackwell	Quick	Monaghan	Lloyd	Bradley
Southam/p	Taylor	Freer	Bailey	Holland	Blackwell	Quick	Monaghan	Lloyd	Roberts
Southam/t2c3p	Taylor	Fowkes	Bailey	Holland	Quick	Chubb	Roberts	Lloyd	Bradley
Southam/p	Taylor	Fowkes	Bailey	Holland	Quick	Chubb	Monaghan	Lloyd	Bradley
Southam/2c3p	Taylor	Fowkes	Bailey	Holland	Quick	Chubb	Monaghan(c/t)	Lloyd	Bradley
Southam	Taylor	Fowkes	Bailey	Holland	Quick	Chubb	Corcoran	Lloyd	Bradley
Southam/cp	Taylor	Freer	Bailey	Holland	Williams	Chubb	Corcoran	Lloyd	Bradley
Southam/t2c2p	Taylor/t	Freer	Bailey	Holland	Quick	Chubb	Bradley	Lloyd	Schrafft
Southam/tc	Taylor	Freer	Bailey	Holland	Williams	Chubb	Bradley	Lloyd	Schrafft
Southam/2cp	Taylor	Freer	Bailey	Fowkes	Quick	Chubb	Bradley	Lloyd	Schrafft
Southam	Taylor	Freer	Bailey	Fowkes	Quick	Chubb	Bradley	Lloyd	Schrafft
Rolt	Royer	Freer	Bailey	Holland	Johnston	Chubb	Bradley	Lloyd	Schrafft
Rolt	Royer	Freer	Bailey	Fowkes	Monaghan	Chubb	Bradley/t	Lloyd	Schrafft
Rolt/2dg	Royer	Freer	Bailey	Fowkes	Monaghan	Chubb	Corcoran	Schrafft	Bradley
Southam/c2p	Taylor	Freer	Bailey	Adams	Blackwell	Johnston	Roberts	Lloyd	Bradley

REPLACEMENTS   a - T Rolt   b - M Swetman   c - A Corcoran

2000-01 HIGHLIGHTS

Russell Southam in his first season at Nottingham tops the points scoring with 219.

He is only the second man, after Chris Atkinson, to score 200 points in a season for the club.

He also scored nine tries which in nearly every season at Nottingham would have been enough to top the try scorers, but not this season.

Southam set a new record for conversions in a season with 36 one more than the old record held by Chris Atkinson.

Jamie Morley set a new record with 16 tries from his 25 matches, in that total were three hat tricks as well.

Full back Ben Murphy was second in the try scorers with 12 which was the third highest ever for the club.

NOTTINGHAM

LEAGUE STATISTICS
compiled by Stephen McCormack

SEASON	Division	P	W	D	L	F	A	Pts Diff	Lge Pts	Lge Pos	Most Points		Most Tries	
91-92	1	12	2	1	9	133	204	-71	5	12r	48	Guy Gregory	4	Martin Pepper
92-93	2	12	8	0	4	249	145	104	16	4	106	Guy Gregory	3	Richard Byrom
93-94	2	18	8	1	9	254	326	-62	17	6	171	Guy Gregory	5	Andy Smallwood
94-95	2	18	8	1	9	299	322	-23	17	7	97	Ian Stent	4	Andy Smallwood
95-96	2	18	5	1	12	333	433	-100	11	9	158	Simon Hodgkinson	7	Alan Royer
96-97	2	22	2	0	20	344	827	-483	4	12r	55	David Evans	5	Richard Bygrave
97-98	JN1	26	13	0	13	527	602	-75	26	7	262	Chris Atkinson	7	Alan Royer
98-99	JN1	26	16	0	10	590	467	123	32	4	272	Chris Atkinson	13	Alan Royer
99-00	JN1	26	8	1	17	460	574	-114	17	11	155	Tom Rolt	7	Tom Rolt
00-01	N2	26	10	0	16	544	584	-40	20	11	219	Russell Southam	16	Jamie Morley

BIGGEST MARGINS

Home Win 78pts - 78-0 v Morley 24.10.92

Away Win 55pts - 55-0 v Liverpool StH 28.11.98

Home Defeat 65pts - 5-70 v Richmond 16.11.96

Away Defeat 80pts - 22-102 v Coventry 5.10.96

MOST CONSECUTIVE

Appearances 41 Guy Gregory 23.11.91 - 30.4.94

Matches scoring Tries 4 Andy Smallwood

Matches scoring points 38 Chris Atkinson

Victories 5

Defeats 12

MOST POINTS

Scored at Home 78 v Morley 24.10.92

Scored Away 55 v Liverpool StH 28.11.98

Conceded at Home 74 v Newcastle 14.9.96

Conceded Away 102 v Coventry 5.10.96

MOST TRIES

Scored in a match 12 v Morley 24.10.92 (H)

Conceded in a match 14 v Coventry 5.10.96 (A)

MOST APPEARANCES

by a forward 197(6) Martin Freer

by a back 167 (3) Richard Byrom

	MOST IN A SEASON	MOST IN A CAREER	MOST IN A MATCH
Points	272 Chris Atkinson 98-99	597 Simon Hodgkinson 87-93 & 95-97	25 Guy Gregory v Otley 11.9.93 (H)
Tries	16 Jamie Morley 00-01	37 Alan Royer 94-00	4 Gary Hartley v Morley 24.10.92 (H) Alan Royer v Liverpool St H 28.11.98 (A)
Conversions	36 Russell Southam 00-01	65 Chris Atkinson 97-99	9 Guy Gregory v Morley 24.10.92 (H)
Penalties	64 Chris Atkinson 97-98 & 98-99	142 Simon Hodgkinson 87-93 & 95-97	6 Guy Gregory v Saracens 12.3.94 Chris Atkinson v Camberley 19.09.98 (A)
Drop Goals	9 Guy Gregory 92-93	19 Guy Gregory 91-94	2 Andy Sutton v Harlequins 31.3.90 (A) Guy Gregory v Rosslyn Park 4.4.92 (H) v Rosslyn Park 21.1.92 (A) v Fylde 9.1.93 (H) & v Bedford 13.2.93 (A) Simon Hodgkinson v L Irish 17.2.96 (A)

PLAYING SQUAD

NOTTINGHAM

BACKS

	Ht.	Wt.	Birthdate	Birthplace	CLUB	League Apps	Tries	Pts
Jamie Morley			17.05.71		Nottingham Sheffield	51	21	105
Russell Southam			28.04.74		Nottingham	24	9	219
Alan Royer	6.0	12.07	01.12.70	Leicester	Nottingham Leicester	124(1)	38	190
Nick Carroll	5.11	12.07	09.01.70	Liverpool	Nottingham Moderns	34(4)	4	64
Ben Murphy			03.09.80		Nottingham	50(2)	18	90
Gareth Taylor			19.11.79		Nottingham	29	4	20
Nick Booth			28.10.76		Nottingham Fylde	1	-	9
Mike Swetman			26.11.80		Nottingham Linwood	11(3)	5	53
Elliott Spencer	0	13.00	05.02.71	Oakham	Nottingham Leicester	30(3)	13	65
Tom Rolt			05.08.79		Nottingham	35(14)	9	173

FORWARDS

	Ht.	Wt.	Birthdate	Birthplace	CLUB	League Apps	Tries	Pts
Martin Freer	5.11	15.07	15.10.63	Chatham	Nottingham	197(5)	10	49
Harry Roberts					Nottingham	2(6)	-	-
Mark Bradley	6.3	15.07	21.12.69	Derby	Nottingham	160(4)	16	80
Ben Blackwell			07.06.80		Nottingham	9(2)	-	-
Dan Charteris			24.06.73		Nottingham	11(1)	3	15
Tom Chubb			30.11.77		Nottingham	17(1)	-	-
Duncan Holland			15.05.74		Nottingham	19(9)	-	-
Richard Lloyd			02.12.77		Nottingham Coventry	69 4(1)	9 1	45 5
Stuart Bailey			23.03.79		Nottingham	27(2)	1	5
Neil Fowkes			05.11.80		Nottingham	12(10)	-	-
James Quick			23.11.78		Nottingham	19(1)	-	-
Aaron Johnston			05.11.73		Nottingham	9(1)	2	10
Matt Monaghan			19.04.78		Nottingham	9(6)	-	-

NOTTINGHAM

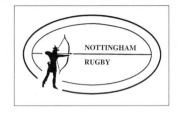

FACT FILE

Founded: 1877

Colours: Green & white hoops
Change colours: Yellow

Nickname: 'Green & Whites'
Web Site: nottinghamrugby.co.uk

GROUND
Address: Ireland Avenue, Dovecote Lane, Beeston, Nottingham. NG9 1JD.
Tel: 0115 925 4238 Fax: 0115 925 4255 email: enquiries@nottinghamrugby.co.uk
Capacity: 4,950   Seated: 450 Standing: 4,500

Directions: Off Queens Road, Beeston. Main Nottingham to Long Eaton Road
Nearest Railway Station: Beeston (200 yards from the ground)

Car Parking: 175 on ground

Admission: Matchday
Adults £7
OAPs/Children £3

Club Shop: Open matchdays.
Club Marketing 0115 925 4238

Clubhouse: Open matchday & training nights,
snacks available.
Functions: Yes

Training Nights: Tuesdays & Thursdays (Sen.)

PROGRAMME
Size: A5
Pages: 36 + cover
Price: £1
Editor: George Holohan
0115 925 4238

Advertising Rates

Colour   Full page £500
Half page £250

Mono   Full page £300
Half page £150

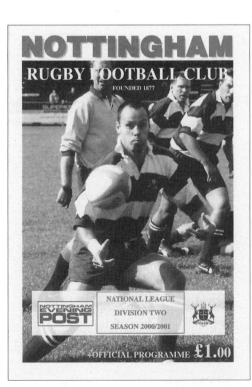

ORRELL RUFC

President	Jim Lloyd	e-mail:	Jim.Lloyd@orrellrugby.co.uk
Chairman	Ron Pimblett	e-mail:	Ron.Pimblett@orrellrugby.co.uk
Chairman of Finance	Alan Houghton	e-mail:	Alan.Houghton@orrellrugby.co.uk
Chairman of Rugby	D V Southern	e-mail:	Sammy.Southern@orrellrugby.co.uk
Chairman of Colts & Juniors	Paul Liptrot	e-mail:	Paul.Liptrot@orrellrugby.co.uk
Office Manager	Mrs Wendy Hamer	e-mail:	Wendy.Hamer@orrellrugby.co.uk

c/o Orrell RUFC, Edge Hall Road, Orrell, Nr Wigan WN58TL
Tel: 01695 623193 Fax: 01695 632116

Media Liaison   Geoff Lightfoot Media   01744 603199 (Tel & Fax)   0378 006567 (Mobile)
e-mail: gcl@rapid.co.uk

Not the best of seasons either on or off the field with the side suffering relegation for the second time in five seasons and will now play their rugby in National Division Two this coming season.

The campaign began full of high optimism with the club managing to hang onto most of its first team squad for the first time for a number of seasons. Wins over Moseley, Manchester and Coventry and a fighting performance against champions Leeds, where they took the losing bonus point, in the opening weeks indicated that their pre-season optimism was well justified.

They were knocked out of the cup with a try in the final minute at Birmingham Solihull but came back with a tremendous performance against already league strugglers Waterloo at Edge Hall Road taking the four try bonus point as well.

Unfortunately from there on in things went drastically wrong. A narrow defeat away at Henley was followed by a one point reversal away at London Welsh. Then they lost to Henley at home in very controversial circumstances. They were a score away from taking the game with a push over try on the cards, when the referee ordered uncontested scrums as the visitors had a prop injured and the replacement sent to the sin bin for taking it down. Why a penalty try was not awarded is still a sore point in the Edge Hall Road clubhouse with the defeat contributing to their relegation on points difference at the end of the season.

That result proved to be the real turning point. With five targetted and winnable matches in the new year they proceeded to lose them all as confidence ebbed away. Wins against Wakefield and Bedford at home in February and a draw at Birmingham provided only tempory relief as further losses pushed them deep into the relegation zone. Yet with at least four other sides in similar danger all was still not lost.

In the end it came down to the wire but even wins at home to Birmingham and London Welsh in the final two games of the season were not enough and Orrell were relegated by the smallest of margins.
the club intend to bounce back at the first go. It will not be easy but as Southern says.

"Through all the problems the spirit amongst the players in the dressing room has always been first class. We have a group of young men here who genuinely want to play for Orrell and win enough matches to see us bounce straight back.

"They know that money is going to be tight but I have told them that if we all stick together we can get back to where we belong"

Geoff Lightfoot

Hooker Alex Moffatt proving it's not just backs who can get past the opposition.

ORRELL

Comp.	Date	H/A	Opponents	Result & Score	Att	15	14	13	12	11
N1	9-Sep	H	Worcester	L 8-47	800	Hitchmough/tp	Roach	Welding	Wynn	Verbickas
N1	16-Sep	H	Moseley	W 19-9	600	Hitchmough	Roach	Welding	Wynn	Verbickas
N1	23-Sep	H	Leeds Tykes	L 17-24	500	Hitchmough/t	Roach	Welding	Wynn/t	Verbickas
N1	30-Sep	H	Manchester	W 21-6	650	Hitchmough	Roach	Welding/t	Wynn	Verbickas/3c
N1	7-Oct	A	Bedford	L 0-27	1175	Hitchmough	Roach	Welding	Wynn	Verbickas
N1	14-Oct	H	Coventry	W 11-6	600	Hitchmough	Roach/t	Wynn	Welding	Verbickas/2p
N1	28-Oct	A	Wakefield	L 13-20	400	Hitchmough	Roach	Hitchen	Kerfoot	Verbickas/c2p
N1	18-Nov	H	Waterloo*	W 35-11	400	Beauchamp	Roach	Craig/2t	Hitchen	Verbickas/3cp
N1	25-Nov	A	Henley Hawks	L 15-23	500	Hitchmough/t	Roach/t	Hitchen	Craig	Verbickas/p
N1	2-Dec	A	London Welsh	L 32-33	550	Welding	Roach/t	Craig	Hitchen	Verbickas/c3p
N1	16-Dec	H	Henley Hawks	L 17-22	500	Welding	Roach	Craig	Hitchen	Verbickas/4p
N1	6-Jan	H	Otley	L 20-23		Beauchamp	Roach	Craig	Welding	Wakelam/t
N1	13-Jan	A	Waterloo	L 16-35		Sleman/2p	Kerfoot	Craig/t	Welding	Wakelam
N1	27-Jan	A	Otley	L 22-24	450	Beauchamp	Kerfoot	Craig/2t	Wynn	Welding
N1	3-Feb	H	Wakefield	W 16-10		Beauchamp	Kerfoot	Craig	Wynn	Welding
N1	10-Feb	A	Coventry	L 8-19	1525	Welding/t	Roach	Craig	Hitchen	Kerfoot
N1	17-Feb	A	Exeter	L 11-48	538	Welding/t	Kerfoot	Craig	Wynn	Roach
N1	24-Feb	H	Bedford	W 15-14		Welding	Kerfoot/t	Craig	Wynn	Verbickas
N1	3-Mar	A	Birmingham & Solihull	D 15-15		Welding	Roach/t	Craig/t	Hitchen	Verbickas
N1	10-Mar	A	Manchester	L 3-8	942	Welding	Kerfoot	Craig	Hitchen	Roach
N1	17-Mar	A	Leeds Tykes	L 20-81	480	Welding	Kerfoot	Craig	Wynn	Verbickas
N1	24-Mar	H	Exeter	L 32-34		Welding/t	Roach	Craig/2t	Wynn	Verbickas
N1	31-Mar	A	Moseley	L 15-20	571	Wynn	Roach	Craig	Hitchen	Kerfoot/t
N1	14-Apr	A	Worcester	L 13-67		Verbickas	Roach	Craig	Wynn	Kerfoot
N1	21-Apr	H	Birmingham & Solihull	W 20-13		Welding	Roach/t	Craig	Wynn	Kerfoot
N1	28-Apr	H	London Welsh	W 23-22	700	Welding	Roach	Craig/t	Wynn	Kerfoot
TBC	21-Oct	A	Birmingham & Solihull	L 25-27	200	Beauchamp	Roach	Craig/2t	Hitchen	Verbickas/2cpdg

*after opponents name indicates a penalty try. Brackets after a player's name indicates he was replaced.
eg (a) means he was replaced by replacement code "a" and so on. / after a player or replacement name
is followed by any scores he made - eg /t, /c, /p, /dg or any combination of these*

EVER PRESENT Chris Bentley.

Most Appearances

26	Chris Bentley.
25	David Sleman.
24	A Cramont.

PLAYERS USED

30 plus two as replacement only.

MOST POINTS

Pts	Player	T	C	P	DG
179	D Sleman	8	17	26	9
55	S Verbickas	-	8	13	-
45	A Craig	9	-	-	-
25	J Roach	5	-	-	-
20	R Welding	4	-	-	-
20	A Cramont	4	-	-	-

MATCH FACTS

10	9	1	2	3	4	5	6	7	8
Broxson	Newton	Kelly	Hitchen	Cundick	Bentley	Atkinson	Grainey	Millachip	Cramant
Sleman/c4p	Newton	Kelly	Moffatt	Cundick	Cusani	Bentley	Grainey	Millachip	Cramant
Sleman/c	Newton	Kelly	Moffatt	Cundick	Cusani	Bentley	Riley	Grainey	Cramant/t
Sleman/t	Wood	Kelly	Hitchen	Cundick	Bentley	Atkinson/t	Riley	Grainey	Cramant
Sleman	Wood	Kelly	Hitchen	Cundick	Bentley	Atkinson	Riley	Grainey	Cramant
Sleman	Newton	Kelly	Hitchen	Livesey	Bentley	Atkinson	Riley	Grainey	Cramant
Sleman/t	Newton	Livesey	Hitchen	Cundick	Bentley	Atkinson	Atkinson	Lloyd	Cramant
Sleman/2dg	Newton	Kelly	Hitchen	Cundick	Bentley/t	Atkinson	Lloyd	Grainey	Cramant
Sleman/c	Newton	Kelly	Hitchen	Cundick	Bentley	Atkinson	Lloyd	Grainey	Cramant
Sleman/2dg	Broxson/t	Livesey	Hitchen	Kelly	Bentley	Cusani	Atkinson	Grainey	Cramant/t
Sleman/t	Newton	Livesey	Hitchen	Cundick	Bentley	Cusani	Atkinson	Grainey	Cramant
Sleman/4pdg	Broxson	Livesey	Moffatt	Cundick	Bentley	Cusani	Cramant	Lloyd	Duncan
Beauchamp	Newton(a/t)	Livesey	Moffatt	Cundick	Bentley	Cusani	Grainey	Lloyd	Duncan
Sleman/2tc	Newton	Livesey	Moffatt	Cundick	Bentley	Cusani	Atkinson	Lloyd	Cramant
Sleman/tcp2dg	Newton	Livesey	Moffatt	Cundick	Bentley	Cusani	Atkinson	Lloyd	Cramant
Sleman/p	Broxson	Livesey	Moffatt	Cundick	Bentley	Cusani	Grainey	Lloyd	Cramant
Sleman/2p	Broxson	Livesey	Moffatt	Kelly	Bentley	Atkinson	Grainey	Lloyd	Cramant
Sleman/cp	Newton	Livesey	Moffatt	Kelly	Bentley	Atkinson	Riley	Lloyd	Cramant/t
Sleman/cp	Newton	Livesey	Moffatt	Kelly	Bentley	Atkinson	Grainey	Lloyd	Duncan
Sleman/p	Newton	Kelly	Hitchen	Cundick	Bentley	Atkinson	Grainey	Lloyd	Cramant
Sleman/2cpdg	Broxson	Livesey/t	Hitchen	Cundick	Bentley	Atkinson	Riley/t	Lloyd	Cramant
Sleman/3cpdg	Newton/t	Livesey	Moffatt	Kelly	Bentley	Atkinson	Riley	Lloyd	Cramant
Sleman/cp	Broxson	Livesey	Coombs	Cundick	Bentley	Atkinson	Riley	Lloyd	Cramant/t
Sleman/c2p	Broxson	Livesey	Coombs	Cundick	Bentley/t	Atkinson	Riley	Lloyd	Cramant
Sleman/t2c2p	Broxson	Livesey	Hitchen	Cundick	Bentley	Cusani	Riley	Lloyd	Cramant
Sleman/tc2p	Broxson	Livesey	Hitchen/t	Cundick	Cusani	Bentley	Riley	Lloyd	Cramant
Sleman	Newton	Kelly	Coombs	Cundick	Atkinson/t	Bentley	Riley	Lloyd	Cramant

REPLACEMENTS   a - John Broxson

2000-01 HIGHLIGHTS

David Sleman topped the scoring list for the second consecutive season. His 179 was he best seaon total to date.

Included in that total was a record nine drop goals.
He also scored an impressive eight tries but could not stop his side going down to National Two for the first time ever.

Centre Andy Craig scored nine tries in his debut season to top the try scoring list, one ahead of Sleman.

Charles Cusani continued to expand the appearance record and his 11 starts took his all time career total to 128 (2).

ORRELL

LEAGUE STATISTICS
compiled by Stephen McCormack

SEASON	Division	P	W	D	L	F	A	Pts Diff	Lge Pts	Lge Pos	Most Points		Most Tries	
91-92	1	12	10	0	2	204	95	109	20		104	Martin Strett	7	Dewi Morris
92-93	1	12	5	0	7	175	183	-8	10		63	Gerry Ainscough	6	Dewi Morris
93-94	1	18	8	0	10	327	302	25	16		84	Simon Langford	8	James Naylor
94-95	1	18	6	3	9	256	326	-70	15		81	Simon Langford	7	Ian Wynn
95-96	1	18	7	0	11	323	477	-154	14		166	Simon Mason	10	Graeme Smith
96-97	1	22	3	0	19	352	886	-534	6		116	Matthew McCarthy	5	Jim Naylor
97-98	P2	22	12	0	10	533	400	133	24		165	Simon Verbickas	12	Simon Verbickas
98-99	P2	26	12	0	14	566	483	83	24	8	224	SimonVerbickas	13	Simon Verbickas
99-00	P2	26	7	0	19	388	682	-294	14	11	146	David Sleman	7	Rob Hitchmough & Alex Bennett
00-01	N1	26	8	1	17	437	661	-224	46	13	179	David Sleman	9	Andy Craig

MOST POINTS

Scored at Home	66 v Rugby 13.3.93
Scored Away	36 v Bristol 17.11.90
Conceded at Home	56 v Bath 31.8.96
	v Harlequins 8.3.97
Conceded Away	89 v Harlequins 5.10.96

MOST CONSECUTIVE

Appearances	39 David Southern 26.9.87 - 17.11.90
Matches scoring Tries	3 Gerry Ainscough, Martin Strett & Phil Hassall
Matches scoring points	**17 Martin Strett**
Victories	5
Defeats	11

BIGGEST MARGINS

Home Win	66pts - 66-0 v Rugby 13.3.93
Away Win	33pts - 36-3 v Bristol 17.11.90
Home Defeat	43pts - 13-56 v Bath 31.8.96
Away Defeat	71pts - 18-89 v Harlequins 5.10.96

MOST TRIES

Scored in a match	11 v Rugby 13.3.93 (H)
	v Northampton 27.10.90 (H)
	v Rosslyn P. 28.4.90 (H)
Conceded in a match	14 v Harlequins 5.10.96 (A)

MOST APPEARANCES

by a forward	128 (2) Charles Cusani
by a back	96 (5) SteveTabener

	MOST IN A SEASON	MOST IN A CAREER	MOST IN A MATCH	
Points	224 Simon Verbickas 98-99	389 Simon Verbickas 97-99	29 Simon Verbickas	v Wakefield 25.4.98 (H)
Tries	13 Simon Verbickas 98-99	26 Nigel Heslop 89-98	4 Paul Hamer	v Rugby 13.3.94 (H)
Conversions	30 Simon Verbickas 98-99	54 Simon Verbickas 97-99	8 Martin Strett	v Rosslyn P. 28.4.90 (H)
Penalties	38 Simon Mason 95-96	71 Gerry Ainscough 87-95	6 Martin Strett / Matthew McCarthy	v Gloucester 28.3.92 (H) / v Lon. Irish 22.2.97 (H)
Drop Goals	9 David Sleman 96-97	13 David Sleman 99-01	3 Matthew McCarthy	v W. Hartlepool 7.12.97(H)

PLAYING SQUAD

ORRELL

BACKS

	Ht.	Wt.	Birthdate	Birthplace	CLUB	League Apps	Tries	Pts
John Broxson			05.10.80		Orrell	10(5)	2	10
Michael Hitchen			04.05.72		Orrell Liverpool StH	25(10)	-	-
Richard Welding			28.01.81		Orrell	31(1)	4	25
Andy Craig			16.03.76		Orrell	19(1)	9	45
Clint Beauchamp					Orrell	5(2)		
Jason Roach			02.05.73		Orrell	21(2)	5	25
David Sleman	6.2	13.09	12.09.78		Orrell	59	16	358
Lee Wakelam			18.09.79		Orrell	15(2)	4	20
Paul Newton Ireland A			29.04.78	Penrith	Orrell	44(16)	3	15
Rob Hitchmough England U21. Other club Harlequins	5.10	12.07	17.12.75	St Helens	Orrell Wakefield	50(8) 13	15 2	88 10

FORWARDS

	Ht.	Wt.	Birthdate	Birthplace	CLUB	League Apps	Tries	Pts
Jason Cundick	6.0	17.0	09.09.73	Manchester	Orrell	102(8)	1	5
John Hitchen			05.07.70		Orrell Liverpool StH	29(15)	1	5
Alex Moffatt	5.4	13.00	29.06.68	Workington	Orrell	62(20)	1	5
Chris Bentley			24.05.79		Orrell New Brighton	50(1)	2	10
Steve Kelly			11.05.72	Manchester	Orrell	54(19)	5	25
Chas Cusani	6.6	17.0	22.10.65	Wigan	Orrell	150(4)	4	17
Jon Duncan			30.11.73		Orrell Sedgley Park	3(5)	-	-
Anton Cramont			02.01.77		Orrell Sedgley Park	42(6)	6	30
Peter Millerchip			01.09.69	Bowden	Orrell	36(4)	1	5
Jeff Huxley	6.3	16.7	28.06.63	Billinge	Orrell	52(5)	2	10
Alastair Livesey			07.10.80		Orrell Fylde	23(11)	1	5
Ian Grainey			21.04.78		Orrell	26(8)	-	-

ORRELL

FACT FILE

Founded: 1927
Colours: Amber & black
Change colours: Red

GROUND
Address: Edgehall Road, Orrell, Wigan, Lancs. WN5 8TL.
Tel: 01695 623193   Fax: 01695 632116
Capacity: 6,000   Seated: Covered 1,000   Standing: Covered 2,000, Uncovered 3,000

Directions: Ground is about 2 miles from M6 junct. 26. Left at traffic lights at end of slip road, then left at lights at the Stag Inn. After about 400 yds. left again at lights & after another 400 yds. left again at lights which take you into Edgehall Road.
Nearest Railway Station: Orrell

Car Parking: 250 spaces at the ground, 250 nearby

Admission: Matchday   Standing Adults £6   Children/OAPs £3.
Admission to stand by programme.

Club Shop: Yes, contact Office Manager 01695 623193

Clubhouse: Open normal licensing hours. Snacks, bar meals & restaurant available
Functions: Capacity 250/300, contact Mr C Cusani House Manager

Training Nights: Tuesday and Thursday.

PROGRAMME (full colour)   Size: A5   Pages: 40   Price: £1.60
Editorial: Geoff Lightfoot Media   01744 603199 (Tel & Fax) e-mail: gcl@rapid.co.uk

ADVERTISING RATES -   Contact - Club Office

Skipper Geoff Wynn checking his options.

PLYMOUTH ALBION RFC

Director of Rugby	Graham Dawe	c/o Plymouth Albion RFC, Beacon Park, Plymouth PL2 3JP 01752 777454 (Club), 01752 777454 (Fax)
Press Officer	Paddy Marsh	Hardwick Farmhouse, Drunken Bridge Hill, Plymouth PL7 1UG 01752 343631 (H), 01752 773187 (B)
Club Secretary	Geoff Morris	c/o Plymouth Albion RFC, Beacon Park, Plymouth PL2 3JP 01752 777454 (Club) 01752 661640 (H) 01752 305639 (B)
Fixtures Secretary	Terry Brown	c/o Plymouth Albion RFC, as above 01752 837742 (H), 01752 777454 (B), 01752 777454 (Fax)

Plymouth Albion had a league season that couldn't have been bettered and will be remembered for years to come. Under the guidance of Director of Rugby, Graham Dawe and his assistant Dave Rule they finished with a 100 per cent league record, their 26 victories eclipsing Newbury's 25 wins four years ago.

Four victories at the end of the previous season saw Albion establish a National League record of 30 victories a figure they will hope to extend even further in Division 2. In a league that had seven clubs from the South West a mixture of attractive running rugby and a number of local derbies saw the crowds flocking back to Beacon Park.

As well as a successful league season Albion reached the Fourth Round of the Tetley's Bitter Cup before going down 36-8 to Harlequins in front of 3,500 at Beacon Park.

In their 26 league games Albion scored 133 tries and conceded only 22 to finish with the tightest defence in National League rugby. Albion strengthened their side with a number of new players.

Winger Andy Matchett, who finished with fourteen tries made the move from Sidmouth and quickly established himself as a regular in the team. Jason Hart, normally a flanker, moved from Brixham and did an excellent job in the second row while Danny Thomas who joined from Barnstaple and became a permanent fixture in the side taking over the captaincy in the second half of the season. Nigel Cane who originally played for Albion as a Junior rejoined from Coventry and started every league game in the No 9 jersey.

Richard Thompson who started the season at full back and moved to the wing had the satisfaction of being the only player to start every match Albion played. Thompson, who passed 150 league appearances, had played through all the lean seasons before being part of the Albion Renaissance which they will be hoping to continue.

Paddy Marsh

Plymouth Albion RFC 2000-01   Photo courtesy of Mike Cox

PLYMOUTH

Comp.	Date	H/A	Opponents	Result & Score		15	14	13	12	11
N3 S	2-Sep	H	Penzance & Newlyn	W 19-0	1500	Thompson	Walklin	Henwood	Thompson	Matchett
N3 S	23-Sep	H	Tabard	W 58-17	1000	Thompson	Walklin/t	Thompson/t	Henwood	Williams
N3 S	30-Sep	A	Weston super Mare	W 43-7	250	Thompson	Walklin	Thompson/2t	Henwood	Williams
N3 S	14-Oct	H	Blackheath	W 41-0	700	Thompson/t	Williams	Henwood	Thompson	Matchett/2t
N3 S	28-Oct	H	North Walsham	W 20-14	900	Thompson	Williams	Henwood	Thompson	Matchett
N3 S	11-Nov	H	Barking	W 26-10	1000	Thompson	Williams	Henwood	Thompson	Matchett
N3 S	18-Nov	A	Redruth	W 30-19	1000	Thompson	Williams(a/p)	Henwood	Thompson	Matchett/t
N3 S	25-Nov	H	Westcombe Park	W 51-10	850	Atkinson/cdg	Thompson	Henwood/t	Thompson	Matchett
N3 S	2-Dec	A	Basingstoke	W 32-0		Atkinson/3c2p	Thompson	Henwood	Thompson	Matchett/t
N3 S	9-Dec	H	Cheltenham	W 50-10	1000	Atkinson	Thompson/t	Thompson	Henwood	Matchett/2t
N3 S	16-Dec	A	Launceston	W 13-6	2000	Atkinson/c2p	Thompson	Henwood	Thompson/t	Matchett
N3 S	23-Dec	H	Basingstoke	W 72-6	1200	Atkinson/7c	Thompson/t	Henwood(c/t)	Thompson	Matchett/2t
N3 S	6-Jan	H	Redruth	W 30-10	2000	Atkinson/cp	Thompson/2t	Henwood	Thompson	Matchett
N3 S	13-Jan	A	Barking	W 37-36		Atkinson/3c2p	Thompson/t	Thompson/t	Henwood	Matchett/2t
N3 S	27-Jan	H	Clifton	W 49-0	1200	Atkinson/t	Thompson/t	Bell	Thompson	Matchett
N3 S	3-Feb	A	Reading	W 38-0	270	Atkinson/4c	Thompson	Thompson/t	Bell/t	Matchett/t
N3 S	10-Feb	A	Blackheath	W 19-13		Atkinson/c4p	Thompson	Bell	Thompson	Matchett
N3 S	17-Feb	A	Clifton	W 37-12		Atkinson/2c2p	Thompson/t	Bell	MacDonald	Matchett/t
N3 S	24-Feb	H	Weston super Mare	W 52-0	1100	Proctor	Thompson/2t	Henwood	MacDonald/2t	Matchett
N3 S	3-Mar	A	Westcombe Park	W 32-11	300	Proctor	Thompson/t	Bell	Thompson	Matchett
N3 S	10-Mar	A	Tabard	W 43-8		Proctor/2t	Thompson/t	Bell	Thompson/t	Matchett
N3 S	17-Mar	H	Reading	W 29-0	1200	Proctor/t	Thompson	MacDonald	Thompson/t	Matchett
N3 S	24-Mar	A	Penzance & Newlyn	W 36-13	2000	Proctor	Thompson/2t	Henwood	Thompson	Matchett/t
N3 S	31-Mar	H	Launceston	W 13-6	3000	Proctor/t	Thompson	Henwood	Thompson	Matchett
N3 S	7-Apr	A	North Walsham	W 20-17		Atkinson	Thompson	Henwood	Thompson	Matchett
N3 S	14-Apr	A	Cheltenham	W 20-15		Williams	Thompson	MacDonald	Henwood	Matchett
TBC	7-Oct	H	Westcombe Park	W 56-6	800	Thompson	Walklin(d/t)	Henwood/t	Thompson	Williams
TBC	21-Oct	H	Wharfedale	W 21-11	800	Thompson	Walklin	Henwood	Thompson	Matchett
TBC	4-Nov	H	Harlequins	L 8-36	3500	Thompson	Walklin	Henwood	Thompson	Matchett

** after opponents name indicates a penalty try. Brackets after a player's name indicates he was replaced.
eg (a) means he was replaced by replacement code "a" and so on. / after a player or replacement name
is followed by any scores he made - eg /t, /c, /p, /dg or any combination of these*

EVER PRESENT

None

Most Appearances: 26
Nigel Cane, Wayne Reed,
Richard Thompson, Dan Ward-Smith.

PLAYERS USED

25 plus two as replacement only.

MOST POINTS

Pts	Player	T	C	P	DG
255	T Barlow	12	42	32	5
110	C Atkinson	1	30	14	1
100	D Ward-Smith	1	30	14	1
70	Rich Thompson	14	-	-	-
65	A Matchett	13	-	-	-

MATCH FACTS

10	9	1	2	3	4	5	6	7	8
Barlow/tc4p	Cane	Paver	Dawe	Reed	Goldsmith	Lockley	Durbin	Thomas	Ward-Smith
Barlow/6c2p	Cane/t	Paver/t	Dawe	Reed	Goldsmith/t	Lockley/t	Durbin	Thomas/t	Ward-Smith/t
Barlow/4c	Cane	Paver/t	Dawe	Reed	Lockley	Goldsmith	Hart/t	Thomas	Ward-Smith/2t
Atkinson/3c	Cane	Bartlett	Dawe	Reed	Lockley	Hart/t	Durbin	Thomas	Ward-Smith/3t
Barlow/3p2dg	Cane	Bartlett	Dawe	Reed	Goldsmith	Hart/t	Thompson	Thomas	Ward-Smith
Barlow/t2p	Cane	Bartlett	Dawe	Reed/t	Goldsmith	Hart/t	Thompson/t	Thomas	Ward-Smith
Barlow/3cpdg	Cane	Paver	Dawe/t	Reed	Goldsmith	Hart	Durbin	Thompson/t	Ward-Smith
Barlow/t4cp	Cane/2t	Paver	Dawe/t	Reed	Willis	Lockley(b/t)	Hart	Thompson	Ward-Smith/t
Barlow	Cane	Paver	Dawe/t	Reed/t	Willis	Lockley	Hart	Thompson	Ward-Smith/t
Barlow/5c	Cane	Paver	Dawe/t	Reed	Lockley	Willis	Hart/t	Thompson/t	Ward-Smith/2t
Barlow	Cane	Paver	Dawe	Reed	Hart	Lockley	Thompson	Thomas	Ward-Smith
Barlow/tdg	Cane	Bartlett	Dawe	Reed/t	Hart	Lockley	Thomas	Thompson/2t	Ward-Smith/3t
Barlow/t	Cane	Bartlett	Dawe	Reed/t	Hart	Lockley	Thomas	Thompson	Ward-Smith/t
Barlow	Cane	Bartlett	Dawe	Reed	Lockley	Willis	Thompson	Thomas/t	Ward-Smith
Barlow/t2c	Cane	Bartlett	Dawe	Reed/t	Hart	Lockley	Thompson/3t	Thomas	Ward-Smith/2t
Barlow/t	Cane/t	Bartlett	Dawe	Reed	Hart	Willis	Thompson/t	Thomas	Ward-Smith
Barlow	Cane/t	Bartlett	Grigg	Reed	Hart	Willis	Thomas	Thompson	Ward-Smith
Barlow/c	Cane/t	Bartlett	Dawe	Reed/t	Willis	Lockley	Thomas	Thompson	Ward-Smith/t
Barlow/c3p	Cane/t	Bartlett	Dawe	Reed	Willis	Lockley	Thomas	Thompson(f/t)	Ward-Smith/t
Barlow/tc5p	Cane	Paver	Dawe	Reed	Lockley	Hart	Thompson	Thomas	Ward-Smith/t
Barlow/2t4cp(a/c)	Cane	Paver	Dawe	Reed	Hart	Willis	Thompson	Thomas	Ward-Smith
Barlow/2c5p	Cane	Paver	Dawe	Reed	Lockley	Willis	Hart	Thomas	Ward-Smith
Barlow/t4cp	Cane	Paver	Dawe	Reed	Lockley	Hart	Thompson	Thomas/t	Ward-Smith
Barlow/p	Cane/t	Paver	Dawe	Reed	Hart	Lockley	Thompson	Thomas	Ward-Smith
Barlow/2c2p	Cane	Paver	Grigg	Reed	Hart	Lockley	Thompson	Thomas	Ward-Smith/t
Barlow/t2cpdg	Cane	Bartlett	Dawe	Reed	Hart	Lockley	Thompson/t	Thomas	Ward-Smith
Barlow/2c2p(a/2c)	Cane/c	Paver	Trivett	Reed	Goldsmith	Hart/2t	Thompson	Thomas/t	Ward-Smith/3t
Atkinson/c3p	Williams	Bartlett	Trivett	Reed	Hart	Goldsmith	Durbin(e/t)	Thomas	Ward-Smith/t
Barlow/p	Cane	Paver	Dawe	Reed	Goldsmith	Hart	Thompson/t	Thomas	Ward-Smith

REPLACEMENTS   a - Chris Atkinson   b - I Goldsmith   c - Dean Willis   d - A Matchett   e - Roger Thompson   f - R Durbin

2000-01 HIGHLIGHTS

Tom Barlow in his first season at the club fell just five points short of Chris Atkinson's record of 260 points.

Included in that total was a club record of 42 coversions in a season.

Dan Ward-Smith, another new boy, topped the try scoring list with 20 which was a new club record.

It beat the 15 that Steve Walklin scored in 1997-98.

They won all 26 of their league matches and set a new record for consecutive wins in league rugby.

PLYMOUTH ALBION

LEAGUE STATISTICS
compiled by Stephen McCormack

SEASON	Division	P	W	D	L	F	A	Pts Diff	Lge Pts	Lge Pos		Most Points		Most Tries
91-92	D2	12	3	0	9	153	209	-56	6	12r	62	Mark Slade	2	by five players
92-93	D3	11	0	0	11	130	305	-175	0	12r	26	Martin Thompson	3	Mark Haimes
93-94	D4	18	9	0	9	286	416	-130	18	4	90	Martin Thompson	5	Roger Bailey
94-95	D4	18	4	2	12	324	381	-57	10	8	129	Martin Thompson	6	Steve Walklin
95-96	D4	18	4	0	14	268	545	-277	8	10	61	Mark Slade	6	Steve Walklin
96-97	D4S	26	13	3	10	709	591	118	29	6	131	Martin Thompson	12	Steve Walklin
97-98	N2S	26	6	0	20	472	756	-284	12	13	131	Martin Thompson	15	Steve Walklin
98-99	N2S	26	7	1	18	457	666	-209	15	12	89	Richard Thompson	6	Richard Thompson, Martin Ridley & Roger Thompson
99-00	N2S	26	17	2	7	664	382	282	36	4	260	Chris Atkinson	15	Steve Walklin
00-01	N3S	26	26	0	0	910	240	670	52	1p	255	Tom Barlow	20	Dan Ward-Smith

MOST POINTS

Scored at Home	73	v Charlton Park 29.03.97
Scored Away	46	v Birmingham 17.10.87
Conceded at Home	64	v Bracknell 03.04.99
Conceded Away	70	v Esher 07.02.98

MOST CONSECUTIVE

Appearances	43	Kevin Turton 12.09.87 - 23.03.91
Matches scoring Tries		
Matches scoring points	19	Chris Atkinson
Victories	26	
Defeats	8	

BIGGEST MARGINS

Home Win	66pts	72-6 v Basingstoke 23.12.00
Away Win	43pts	46-3 v Birmingham 17.10.87
Home Defeat	52pts	12-64 v Bracknell 03.04.99
Away Defeat	70pts	0-70 v Esher 07.02.98

MOST TRIES

Scored in a match	11	v Charlton Park 29.03.97
	11	v Basingstoke 23.12.00
Conceded in a match	10	v Esher 07.02.98

MOST APPEARANCES

by a forward

by a back

	MOST IN A SEASON		MOST IN A CAREER		MOST IN A MATCH	
Points	260	Chris Atkinson 1999-00	566	Martin Thompson 1989-99	25	Domonic Cundy v Met Police 26.11.88 (H) Nick Burt v Charlton Park 29.03.97 (H)
Tries	20	Dan Ward-Smith 200-01	77	Steve Walklin 1987-00	4	Steve Walklin v Birmingham 17.10.87 (A) Ian Russell v Fylde 31.10.87 (A)
Conversions	42	Tom Barlow 2000-01	76	Martin Thompson 89-99	8	Dominic Cundy v Met Police 26.11.88 (H)
Penalties	59	Chris Atkinson 1999-00	93	Martin Thompson 89-99	6	Mark Slade v Bedford 14.12.91 (H)
Drop Goals	5	Tom Barlow 2000-01	16	Martin Thompson 89-99	3	Mark Slade v Liverpool St H 09.02.96 (H)

PLAYING SQUAD

PLYMOUTH ALBION

BACKS

	Ht.	Wt.	Birthdate	Birthplace	CLUB	League Apps	Tries	Pts
Andrew Matchett			24.08.73		Plymouth	24	13	65
Chris Atkinson			19.05.74		Plymouth	37(7)	2	370
Tom Barlow			28.09.77		Plymouth	44(1)	18	301
Nigel Cane			19.98.77		Plymouth	26	8	40
Nick Proctor					Plymouth	6(2)	4	20
Chris Bell					Plymouth	6	1	5
Tamaka MacDonald					Plymouth	4	2	10
Russell Henwood			14.06.77		Plymouth	55(1)	3	15
Russell Thompson			21.08.76		Plymouth	46	15	75
Phil Williams			29.11.78		Plymouth	14(8)	3	15
Richard Thompson			24.08.73		Plymouth	150(2)	41	332

FORWARDS

	Ht.	Wt.	Birthdate	Birthplace	CLUB	League Apps	Tries	Pts
Alan Paver			28.11.77		Plymouth	40(12)	5	25
Wayne Reed			27.10.71		Plymouth Exeter	47(2)	12	60
Nick Bartlett			10.04.69		Plymouth	12(4)	-	-
Graham Dawe Other club: Bath			04.09.59		Plymouth Sale	48	7	35
Jason Hart			23.07.72		Plymouth	21(1)	5	25
Jason Lockley			21.04.68		Plymouth	32	1	5
Dean Willis			17.04.72		Plymouth	10(5)	1	5
Roger Thompson			27.04.76		Plymouth	63(5)	22	110
Dan Ward-Smith			02.01.78		Plymouth	35	21	105
Danny Thomas			12.05.76		Plymouth	22	3	15
Ian Goldsmith			21.04.73		Plymouth	93(5)	12	60

PLYMOUTH ALBION

FACT FILE

Founded: 1876
Nickname: Albion

Colours: White with broad cherry band edged with green.
Change colours: Red.

GROUND

Address: Beacon Park, Beacon Park Road, Plymouth, PL2 3JP
Tel: 01752 777454   Fax 01752 777454
Capacity: 3,000   Seated: 500   Standing: 2,500

Directions: On approaching Plymouth follow signs for Plymouth Argyle FC. 200 yards past Safeway
Superstore at 3rd traffic lights turn right, turn left at Cherry Tree Pub into Langstone Rd, ground
500yards on right.
Nearest Railway Station: Plymouth North Road

Car Parking: 50 within ground

Admission: Matchday - Seated Adults £8 Children/OAPs £4.
Ground Adults £6, Children/OAPs £3 -members £1 reduction into ground.

Clubhouse: Normal licensing hours. Snacks & bar meals available
Functions: Capacity 120, contact Squash Club 01752 777454

Club Shop: Open matchdays only. Other times from bar staff Manager Maggie Fuge 01752 777454

Training Nights: Tuesday & Thursday

PROGRAMME
Size: A5   Price: £1.50
Pages: 36 + cover
Editor: John Crow 01752 219836

ADVERTISING RATES
Colour
Full page £300, Half £175, Qtr £100
Mono
Full page £175, Half £90, Qtr £50

Prop Alan Paver on the charge against Tabard at Beacon Park.
Photo courtesy of Mike Cox

PRESTON GRASSHOPPERS RFC

President	Lawrie Holland		c/o Preston Grasshoppers RFC,
Chairman	John Heritage		Lightfoot Green,Fulwood,
Club Secretary	Peter Ashcroft	01772744066 (H).	Preston, Lancs PR4 0AP
			Tel: 01772 863546
Admin Officer/	Ken Moore	01772 720878 (H) .	Fax: 01772 861605
Commercial			
Fixtures Secretary	John Powell	121 Bare Lane, Bare, Morecambe, Lancs. LA4 4RD.	
		01524 424514 (H), 01772 861605 (Fax)	
Press Officer	John Hetherington	01772 712162 (H), 01772 863546 (B)	

In many ways, Hoppers second season at this level was the reverse of the first. In 1999/2000 Hoppers set off at a fair pace but a slump in the second half of the season saw the team slip from promotion contenders to a mid table position.

This time, the promise of a first day victory at Lydney soon evaporated and, by the end of February, with only 13 points from 18 games the side had become involved in the relegation battle.

The final two months of the season produced promotion rather than relegation form, however. 13 points from a possible 16 produced a steady climb up the table and a final position of seventh.

As in the promotion run two seasons earlier, the fact that Hoppers were able to field the same second row in all games provided the side with a solid foundation. Indeed, Josh Williams' determined charges and occasional side step saw him end up as leading try scorer and winner of the club's player of the year award. His partner Martin Boyd frustrated opponents throughout the season with his ability to steal line out ball. Also in the pack, the continued development of flanker Rob Parkinson and prop Paul Shepherd was pleasing.

In the backs, scrum half Charlie Du Pre seized his chance when injury ended John Bleasdale's season early.Chris Glynn continued to kick goals and pose a threat with his runs from full back. The arrival of centre Paul Barrow from rugby league and winger Tim Lough from Australia intensified the competition for places.

The coming season sees Neil Ashton step down as captain after three succesful season. Michael Lough takes over and will lead a side which is expected to show one or two changes and which will aim to carry on the good work of March and April. The club remains committed to National League rugby but is nevertheless delighted that seven of its opponents in 2001/2002 can be reached in an hour or less.

Back Row: C Dew (Asst. Coach), J Brittin, R Flynn, P Shepherd, A Jebb, M Boyd, M Bailey, S Fee, K Fenton, G Dewhurst, C Glynn, B Wellens (Head Coach). **Front:** D Chadwick, I Bruce, N Hill, J Chesworth, G Thompson (President), N Ashton (Captain), M Lough, G Monaghan, J Bleasdale, Mrs H Thompson (Physio).

Photo courtesy of Lancashire Evening Post.

PRESTON

Comp.	Date	H/A	Opponents	Result & Score	Att.	15	14	13	12	11
N2	2-Sep	A	Lydney*	W 22-9	500	Glynn/2cp	Bruce/t	Nunn	Chesworth	Flynn
N2	9-Sep	H	Nottingham	L 17-32	350	Glynn/tc	Bruce	Bailey/t	Chesworth	Flynn
N2	16-Sep	A	Rosslyn Park	L 19-47		Bailey/2c	Bruce	Nunn	Chesworth	Flynn
N2	23-Sep	H	West Hartlepool	W 25-22	320	Bailey/5p	Bruce/t	Lough	Nunn	Flynn
N2	30-Sep	A	Camberley*	W 33-8	200	Glynn/3c4p	Bruce(a/t)	Lough/t	Nunn	Flynn
N2	14-Oct	A	Wharfedale	L 14-17		Glynn/3p	Bruce	Lough	Nunn	Flynn
N2	28-Oct	A	Bracknell	L 7-28	300	Glynn/c	Bruce	Lough/t	Nunn	Bailey
N2	11-Nov	A	Rugby Lions	L 8-20		Glynn	Bruce	Lough	Barrow	Bailey/p
N2	18-Nov	H	Kendal	W 25-18	630	Glynn/tcp	Bruce	Lough	Barrow	Bailey/t
N2	2-Dec	H	Fylde	W 17-9	550	Glynn/2cp	Bruce	Lough	Barrow	Bailey/t
N2	9-Dec	H	Harrogate	D 22-22	450	Glynn/t2cp	Bruce	Lough	Barrow	Bailey/t
N2	16-Dec	A	Kendal	L 14-20		Glynn/t3p	Lough	Lough	Barrow	Bailey
N2	23-Dec	H	Rugby Lions	L 10-27		Glynn/c	Lough	Lough	Barrow	Bailey
N2	6-Jan	H	Bracknell	L 17-40	450	Glynn/2cp	Lough/2t	Lough	Chesworth	Flynn
N2	13-Jan	A	Newbury	W 25-10		Glynn/t2c2p	Lough	Lough	Chesworth	Bailey
N2	27-Jan	A	Fylde*	L 12-20		Bailey	Lough	Lough	Chesworth	Flynn
N2	3-Feb	N	Esher	L 21-30	200	Glynn/c3p	Lough/t	Lough	Chesworth	Flynn
N2	10-Feb	H	Camberley	L 15-21	220	Glynn/cp	Lough/t	Barrow	Chesworth	Flynn
N2	3-Mar	H	Newbury	W 27-17		Glynn/3c2p	Lough	Barrow	Chesworth	Bailey
N2	10-Mar	H	Rosslyn Park	L 20-24		Glynn/tcp	Lough/2t	Barrow	Chesworth	Bailey
N2	17-Mar	A	Nottingham	W 37-15		Glynn/t3c2p	Lough	Barrow	Chesworth	Bailey
N2	24-Mar	H	Lydney	W 50-18		Glynn/5c	Lough/t	Barrow/2t	Chesworth	Bailey/t
N2	31-Mar	A	Harrogate	D 13-13		Glynn/c2p	Lough	Barrow	Chesworth	Bailey/t
N2	7-Apr	H	Wharfedale	W 20-3		Glynn/2c2p	Lough	Barrow	Chesworth/t	Bailey/t
N2	14-Apr	H	Esher	W 22-10		Glynn/tc	McKenna/t	Barrow/t	Chesworth	Bailey
N2	21-Apr	A	West Hartlepool	W 54-17		Glynn/5c3p	McKenna	Barrow	Chesworth	Bailey
TBC	7-Oct	H	Bedford Athletic*	W 49-19	250	Glynn/5c3p	Bruce/t	Lough	Nunn	Flynn/t
TBC	21-Oct	A	Coventry	L 19-30	330	Glynn/2c	Bruce	Lough/t	Nunn/t	Flynn

*after opponents name indicates a penalty try. Brackets after a player's name indicates he was replaced. eg (a) means he was replaced by replacement code "a" and so on. / after a player or replacement name is followed by any scores he made - eg /t, /c, /p, /dg or any combination of these

EVER PRESENT Martin Boyd, Josh Williams

Most Appearances :
26   Martin Boyd, Josh Williams.
25   Jason Brittin, Michael Lough.
24   Karl Fenton.

PLAYERS USED
30 plus three as replacements only.

MOST POINTS

Pts	Player	T	C	P	DG
219	C Glynn	8	40	33	-
62	P Bailey	8	2	6	-
50	J Williams	10	-	-	-
45	T Lough	9	-	-	-

MATCH FACTS

10	9	1	2	3	4	5	6	7	8
Lough	Bleasdale	Fenton/t	Brittin	Chadwick	Williams	Boyd	Parkinson	Dewhurst	Ashton
Lough	Bleasdale/t	Chadwick	Brittin	Fenton	Williams	Boyd	Parkinson	Dewhurst	Ashton
Lough/t	Bleasdale	Chadwick	Brittin/t	Fenton	Williams/t	Boyd	Parkinson	Ashton	Bailey
Lough/t	Bleasdale	Chadwick	Brittin	Fenton	Williams	Boyd	Bailey	Welsh	Ashton
Lough	Bleasdale	Fenton	Brittin	Hanson	Williams	Boyd	Ashton	Welsh	Manley
Lough	Bleasdale	Fenton	Carter	Hanson	Williams	Boyd/t	Dewhurst	Manley	Ashton
Lough	Bleasdale	Chadwick	Brittin	Fenton	Williams	Boyd	Dewhurst	Bailey	Ashton
Lough	Bleasdale	Fenton	Brittin	Chadwick	Williams	Boyd	Parkinson	Dewhurst/t	Ashton
Lough	Bleasdale	Fenton	Brittin/t	Chadwick	Williams/t	Boyd	Parkinson	Dewhurst	Ashton
Lough	Bleasdale	Shepherd	Brittin	Fenton	Williams	Boyd	Parkinson	Dewhurst/t	Ashton
Lough/t	Bleasdale	Chadwick	Brittin	Fenton	Williams	Boyd	Parkinson	Dewhurst	Ashton
Emmett	Bleasdale	Shepherd	Brittin	Fenton	Williams	Boyd	Parkinson	Evans	Ashton
Emmett/dg	Dupre	Shepherd	Brittin/t	Fenton	Boyd	Williams	Parkinson	Roberts	Evans
Emmett	Dupre	Chadwick	Brittin	Shepherd	Williams	Boyd	Parkinson	Dewhurst	Evans
Emmett	Dupre	Brittin/t	Fenton/t	Shepherd	Williams	Boyd	Parkinson	Dewhurst	Sword
Emmett/c	Dupre	Fenton	Brittin	Shepherd	Williams	Boyd	Parkinson/t	Dewhurst	Ashton
Emmett	Dupre	Fenton	Brittin	Shepherd	Williams/t	Boyd	Parkinson	Dewhurst	Evans
Emmett	Dupre	Chadwick	Brittin	Shepherd	Williams/t	Boyd	Parkinson	Welsh	Ashton
Lough	Dupre	Fenton	Brittin	Shepherd	Williams/t	Boyd/t	Parkinson	Welsh	Ashton/t
Lough	Dupre	Fenton	Brittin	Shepherd	Williams	Boyd	Parkinson	Ashton	Evans
Lough	Dupre	Fenton/t	Brittin	Shepherd	Williams/t	Boyd	Parkinson	Ashton/t	Evans/t
Lough	Dupre/t	Fenton	Brittin	Shepherd	Williams/2t	Boyd	Parkinson	Ashton/t	Evans
Lough	Dupre	Fenton	Brittin	Shepherd	Williams	Boyd	Parkinson	Dewhurst	Ashton
Lough	Dupre	Fenton	Brittin	Shepherd	Williams	Boyd	Parkinson	Dewhurst	Ashton
Lough	Dupre	Fenton	Brittin	Shepherd	Williams	Boyd	Parkinson	Dewhurst	Ashton/t
Lough/t	Dupre	Fenton	Brittin/t	Shepherd	Williams/2t	Boyd	Parkinson/2t	Dewhurst/t	Ashton
Lough	Bleasdale	Fenton/t	Chadwick	Hanson	Williams/t	Boyd	Ashton	Welsh(b/t)	Manley
Lough	Bleasdale	Fenton	Carter	Hanson	Williams	Boyd/t	Dewhurst	Manley	Ashton

REPLACEMENTS   a - P Bailey   b - G Dewhurst

2000-01 HIGHLIGHTS

Full back Chris Glynn tops the scoring for a second consecutive season and scores the second highest for Preston in League rugby.

Lock forward Josh Williams topped the try scorers with 10 - the best ever return for a forward in a league season at Preston Grasshoppers.

Three times during the season they equlled their worst ever run of defeats - three.

Winger Iain Bruce in his final season at the club added two more tries to his all time record and finished with 57.

PRESTON GRASSHOPPERS

LEAGUE STATISTICS
compiled by Stephen McCormack

SEASON	Division	P	W	D	L	F	A	Pts Diff	Lge Pts	Lge Pos		Coach		Captain
91-92	D4N	12	8	0	4	195	123	72	16	4	127	Paul Grayson	4	D Percy, P Grayson
92-93	D4N	12	8	0	4	144	140	4	16	3	27	Andy Taylorson	3	John Bleasdale
93-94	D5N	12	10	0	2	191	128	63	20	2	62	Mark Kirby	3	Joe Hindle
94-95	D5N	12	8	1	3	187	137	50	17	3	94	Willie Mould	2	Three players
95-96	D5N	12	5	1	6	167	209	-42	11	8	45	Nick Bell	3	Three players
96-97	D4N	26	17	2	7	568	394	174	36	3	317	Steve Kerry	7	Glyn Dewhurst
97-98	J2N	26	14	2	10	549	469	80	30	4	91	Rob Smith	15	Iain Bruce
98-99	J2N	26	23	0	3	822	341	481	46	1p	216	Martin Emmett	27	Michael Lough
99-00	JN1	26	12	0	14	608	580	28	24	8	110	Chris Glynn	15	Iain Bruce
00-01	N2	26	12	2	12	569	517	52	26	7	219	Chris Glynn	10	Josh Williams

BIGGEST MARGINS

Home Win 71pts - 83-12 v Camberley 25.03.00
Away Win 49pts -52-3 v Hereford 25.01.97
Home Defeat 23pts -17-40 v Bracknell 6.1.01
Away Defeat 33pts -3-36 v Harrogate 09.01.93

MOST CONSECUTIVE

Appearances
Matches scoring Tries 5 Michael Lough & Iain Bruce
Matches scoring points 26 Steve Kerry
Victories 10
Defeats 3

MOST POINTS

Scored at Home 83 v Camberley 25.03.00
Scored Away 65 v Walsall 07.11.98
Conceded at Home 40 v Bracknell 6.1.01
Conceded Away 60 v Rosslyn Park 18.03.00

MOST TRIES

Scored in a match 12 v Camberley 25.03.00
Conceded in a match 8 v Rosslyn Park 18.03.00

MOST APPEARANCES

by a forward 151 (5) Mike Bailey
by a back 155 (4) John Chesworth

	MOST IN A SEASON	MOST IN A CAREER	MOST IN A MATCH
Points	317 Steve Kerry 96-97	489 Steve Kerry 87-89,96-97	25 Iain Bruce v Winnington Park .03.99 (H)
Tries	27 Michael Lough 98-99	57 Iain Bruce 97-00	5 Iain Bruce v Winnington Park
Conversions	53 Martin Emmett 98-99	55 Steve Kerry 87-89,96-97	10 Chris Glynn v Camberley 25.03.00
Penalties	64 Steve Kerry 96-97	99 Steve Kerry 87-89,96-97	6 Paul Grayson v Northern 28.03.92 (A) Steve Kerry v Hereford 31.08.96 Steve Kerry v Sandal 03.05.97
Drop Goals	9 Steve Kerry 96-97	14 Steve Kerry 87-89,96-97	4 Steve Kerry v Aspatria 07.09.96 (A)

PLAYING SQUAD

PRESTON GRASSHOPPERS

BACKS

	Ht.	Wt.	Birthdate	Birthplace	CLUB	League Apps	Tries	Pts
Michael Lough	6.1	15.00	20.10.75	Port Lincoln	Preston	93	47	235
Australia 7s, South Australia, Lancashire. Other club: Burnside (S Aust.)								
Iain Bruce	5.9	14.07	14.09.72	Preston	Preston	84(11)	57	285
Scotland U-21, Exiles, Lancashire. Other club: Oreell					Waterloo	21	6	30
Tim Lough			15.08.77		Preston	21	9	45
Paul Bailey			04.11.79		Preston	20(3)	8	62
					Waterloo			
John Chesworth	6.1	15.04	05.05.71	Preston	Preston	159	17	95
Lancashire								
John Bleasdale	5.8	12.00	19.12.69	Lancaster	Preston	149	19	104
Lancashire								
Martin Emmett	5.9	13.05	04.05.71	St Helens	Preston	52(3)	5	382
Lancashire, England students					Waterloo	18	1	152
Chris Glynn			24.09.78		Preston	48(1)	10	329
					Liverpool StH			
Chris Dupre			30.06.79		Preston	15(1)	-	-
Russell Flynn			10.08.81		Preston	15(1)	3	15

FORWARDS

	Ht.	Wt.	Birthdate	Birthplace	CLUB	League Apps	Tries	Pts
Neil Ashton	6.3	16.00	08.02.70	Preston	Preston	138	24	120
Lancashire, British Police								
Michael Baiey	6.5	16.00	20.12.68	Preston	Preston	153(1)	19	93
Lancashire								
David Chadwick	5.8	15.07	19.02.71	Burnley	Preston	85(8)	1	5
					Calder Vale			
Kieron Chadwick	5.8	14.00	02.01.76	Burnley	Preston	24(1)	4	20
Lancashire								
Glyn Dewhurst	6.0	15.07	20.04.74	Preston	Preston	81(2)	18	90
Lancashire, South Australia								
Martin Boyd			05.12.74		Preston	51	3	15
James Porteous	5.10	14.00	07.07.77	Preston	Preston	9(2)	-	-
Lancashire U-21								
Karl Fenton	6.0	17.00	29.01.69	Londonderry	Preston	88	11	55
Lancashire, British students. Other clubs: Orrell 2					Waterloo	7	-	-
Josh Williams	6.4	19.00	28.08.70	Ormskirk	Preston	80	18	140
Lancashire, Army U-21, Combined Services U-21								
Mike Sword	6.4	17.00	28.11.68	Bury	Preston	85	5	23
Notts, Lincs & Derby U-21.								
Rob Parkinson			07.11.79		Preston	22	3	15
Paul Shepherd	6.0	19.00	26.04.78	Preston	Preston	19(1)	-	-
Andy Roberts	6.2	14.00	18.08.71	Burnley	Preston	42	4	20
					Calder Vale			

PRESTON GRASSHOPPERS

FACT FILE

Founded: 1869
Nickname: Hoppers

Colours: White with navy blue hoops/navy blue/navy blue & white
Change colours: Emerald green, red collar & cuffs.

GROUND

Address: Lightfoot Green, Fulwood, Preston, Lancs. PR4 0AP.
Web site: www.pgrfc.co.uk   e-mail: info@pgrfc.co.uk
Tel: 01772 863546   Fax: 01772 861605   Press Line: 01772 861605
Capacity: 3,700   Seated: 250   Standing: 3,450

Directions: Leave the M6 at Junct. 32 and head towards A6 Garstang. Turnleft at the end of the slip road towards Preston. Take first left and followsigns for Ingol. The ground is 1/2 mile on the right. Nearest Railway Station: Preston (BR)

Car Parking: 400 spaces available adjacent to the ground.

Admission: Match days - Adults - Members £4, Others £6
OAPs £3 Under 14s Free

Clubhouse: Open Mon-Thurs 4.30-11.00,
Fri 12-12, Sat 12-11, Sun 12-10.30,
snacks, bar meals & restaurant available
Functions: Capacity 250,
Contact K Moore 01772 863546

Club Shop: Open daily
Contact K Moore 01772 863546

PROGRAMME

Size: A5   Pages: 32 + cover
Price: With admission
Editor: John Hetherington 01772 863546

Advertising Rates
Colour
Full page £300, half £175
Mono
Full page £250,
half £140, qtr £85

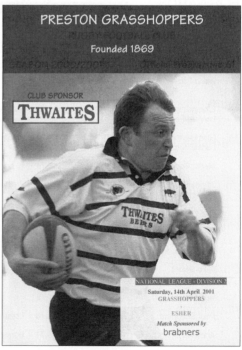

PRESTON GRASSHOPPERS

Founded 1869

CLUB SPONSOR

THWAITES

NATIONAL LEAGUE - DIVISION 2
Saturday, 14th April 2001
GRASSHOPPERS
v
ESHER
Match Sponsored by
brabners

ROSSLYN PARK FC

President	David E Whittam FRCS	37 Queens Road, Kingston-on-Thames, Surrey KT2 7SL
		0208 549 4209 (H), 0208 944 6594 (B), 0208 944 8059 (Fax)
Chairman	Peter Warrener	c/o Warrener Stewart & Co., Harwood House, Harwood Rd.,
		London SW6 4QP 0207 731 6163 (B)
Club Secretary	Bernard Wiggins	01403 711299 (H), 01273 323434 (B), 01273 202627(Fax)
Press Officer	Bernard Wiggins	01403 711299 (H), 01273 323434 (B), 01273 202627(Fax)
Fixtures Secretary	David Booth	7 Catherine Road, Surbiton, Surre. KT6 4HA
		0208 399 0955 (H) 0208 339 9300 (Fax)

So close and yet so far. What a great season it was for the Club, yet we were beaten into third place by two teams whose wages bill in National League Two will be as equally unsustainable in National League 1. It is a moot point for discussion whether promotion can ever be achieved without paying players, yet we will have another go next season!

Injuries abounded, too many to mention individually but it was a measure of the quality in depth that the side kept on winning when the team put out was rarely if ever the same one as the previous week.

Three straight wins at the start Wharfedale 33-12 Newbury 26-17 and Preston Grasshoppers 47-19 were followed by a heavy defeat 10-31 at Rugby and then a dreadful defeat at home to Kendal 25-29 inexcusable when Park had led 17-0.

October saw 4 straight wins, Lydney 30-3 in the cup Harrogate 19-17(dead lucky when you consider Lee Cholewa missed a penalty close to the sticks with the last kick of the match.), Barking 29-17(losing both James Wyatt and Tom Colburn for the season with dislocated shoulders) and Nottingham 35-24.

Everyone was vying for selection against Newcastle in the Cup, the team reached a peak not seen before and despite the defeat 13-25, Newcastle knew they had been in a match. Who can forget Lysander Strong's tackle on Marius Hurter the 18/19 stone prop?

In league fixtures in November a defeat at home to Bracknell the eventual champions19-31, but winning against two relegated sides West Hartlepool 43-31 and Camberley 23-10 kept Park in the hunt.

Two crucial matches in December 10-10 away at Esher, a sending off and a penalty missed in the first minute, and defeat at Fylde 16-21 when Park just couldn't get enough possession (Fylde giving us a lesson in ball retention), made life difficult, though not impossible.

The rest of the season came down to the forthcoming fixture against Rugby at Park in February as Park then won five on the trot West Hartlepool 78-7, Bracknell away 18-16 (a last minute drop goal from Paul Roblin 40 metres out) Nottingham 40-31 Lydney 60-7 and Esher 22-19. Esher was a remarkable game again, Jon Gregory went over the dead ball line in trying to get round under the sticks Esher spurned two kickable penalties in the last 10 minutes and then Gregory missed a difficult one with the last kick of the match).

A real team performance at Harrogate 13-10, (3rd v 4th), when the pack dogged it out and denied possession for long periods and then Rugby at home.

Despite leading 16-3 Rugby, probably the biggest side ever seen in the division clawed their way back to lead 19-16; but Park equalised late on.

With Bracknell looking like champions destiny was no longer in our hands and though Park won all their remaining fixtures Preston Grasshoppers 24-20 Newbury 31-16 Wharfedale AWAY 37-20(another ghost exorcised) Fylde 59-0 Camberley 23-10 and Kendal 22-10, the top two won everything too and that was that.

Before I wind up, I must mention James Justice's 16 tries and Chris Ritchie' 14, an outstanding effort from both players.

On a personal note, It was a privilege to be involved in Playing Admin once again and I would like to take this opportunity to thank the players coaches and the playing admin team for all their hard work in a great season for the Club.

Lastly Congratulations to Lysander Strong (Player of the season) and Jim Hayes (most improved player of the season).

MOMENT TO SAVOUR

There are so many great moments to consider but my enduring memory will be look on the Wharfedale centre's face when Paul Roblin left him for dead, to score in the corner and Kent Bray's dry summing up of the game "Paul Roblin, Man of the Match for both sides".!!!!!

Bernard Wiggins

ROSSLYN PARK

Comp.	Date	H/A	Opponents	Result & Score	Att.	15	14	13	12	11
N2	2-Sep	H	Wharfedale	W 33-12		Maddock	Henderson	Wyatt	Marval/t	Fanning
N2	9-Sep	A	Newbury	W 26-17		Maddock/t	Henderson	Wyatt	Marval	Justice/t
N2	16-Sep	H	Preston Grasshoppers*	W 47-19		Justice	Henderson	Wyatt	Marval	Adams(a/t)
N2	23-Sep	A	Rugby Lions	L 10-31		Maddock	Adams	Wyatt	Marval/2t	Justice
N2	30-Sep	H	Kendal	L 25-29		Maddock	Thompson/t	Wyatt/t	Marval/t	Justice
N2	14-Oct	H	Harrogate	W 19-17	200	Maddock	Thompson	Wyatt	Marval/t	Justice
N2	28-Oct	H	Nottingham	W 35-24		Maddock	Adams	Thompson	Marval	Justice/3t
N2	11-Nov	H	Bracknell	L 19-33		Maddock	Henderson	Thompson	Marval	Justice
N2	18-Nov	A	West Hartlepool*	W 43-31		Maddock/t	Thompson	Hendy	Marval/t	Justice
N2	25-Nov	H	Camberley*	W 23-10	200	Maddock	Casado	Brady	Thompson	Hartigan
N2	2-Dec	N	Esher*	D 10-10	200	Maddock	Thompson	Brady	Marval	Justice
N2	9-Dec	A	Fylde*	L 16-21		Maddock	Casado	Thompson	Brady	Justice
N2	16-Dec	H	West Hartlepool	W 78-7		Justice/t	Casado/2t	Maddock/t	Brady	Hartigan/t
N2	23-Dec	A	Bracknell	W 18-16		Justice/t	Henderson	Thompson	Maddock/t	Hartigan
N2	6-Jan	A	Nottingham	W 40-31		Justice	Casado/t	Dowse	Thompson	Hartigan
N2	13-Jan	H	Lydney	W 60-7		Justice/2t	Casado/2t	Dowse/t	Thompson	Hartigan
N2	27-Jan	H	Esher	W 22-19		Justice	Casado	Marval	Thompson/t	Hartigan
N2	3-Feb	A	Harrogate	W 13-10	550	Justice	Casado	Thompson	Marval/t	Hartigan
N2	24-Feb	H	Rugby Lions	D 19-19		Justice/t	Casado	Thompson	Marval	Hartigan
N2	10-Mar	A	Preston Grasshoppers	W 24-20		Justice/t	Casado	Thompson/t	Marval	Hartigan
N2	17-Mar	H	Newbury	W 31-16		Justice/t	Casado	Brady	Marval	Thompson/t
N2	24-Mar	A	Wharfedale	W 37-17		Justice/2t	Casado	Brady	Marval/t	Thompson
N2	31-Mar	H	Fylde	W 59-0		Justice/2t	Casado/t	Brady	Fanning	Thompson
N2	14-Apr	A	Camberley	W 23-10		Justice	Casado/t	Thompson	Maddock	Hartigan
N2	21-Apr	A	Kendal	W 22-10		Justice/t	Casado/t	Thompson	Dowse	Hartigan
N2										
TBC	21-Oct	A	Barking	W 29-17		Maddock	Thompson/t	Marval/t	Wyatt	Justice
TBC	4-Nov	H	Newcastle Falcons	L 13-25	1500	Maddock	Henderson	Thompson	Marval	Justice

*after opponents name indicates a penalty try. Brackets after a player's name indicates he was replaced.
eg (a) means he was replaced by replacement code "a" and so on. / after a player or replacement name
is followed by any scores he made - eg /t, /c, /p, /dg or any combination of these*

None

Most Appearances:
- 24   Lee Gibson.
- 23   James Justice.
- 20   Gavin Thompson, Ben Fennell, James Hayes.

41 plus two as replacement only.

Pts	Player	T	C	P	DG
157	P Roblin	2	39	21	2
96	B Mooar	1	14	21	-
80	J Justice	16	-	-	-
70	C Ritchie	14	-	-	-

MATCH FACTS

10	9	1	2	3	4	5	6	7	8
Mooar/2c3p	Hendy/t	Fennell	Ritchie/2t	Cano	Craig	Gibson	Strong	Boardman	Rakison
Mooar/c3p	Hendy/t	Fennell	Harding	Cano	Craig	Gibson	Strong	Cable	Hayes
Mooar/5c4p	Hendy/2t	Fennell	Harding	Allen	Hayes	Gibson	Strong	Cable	Rakison/t
Mooar	Hendy	Fennell	Ritchie	Cano	Gibson	Craig	Strong	Cable	Hayes
Mooar/2c2p	Hendy	Cano	Ritchie	Allen	Hayes	Gibson	Boardman	Cable	McDonald
Mooar/t3p	Hendy	Fennell	Ritchie	Cano	Gibson	Hayes	Strong	Rakison	Rollitt
Hallett/2c2p	Campbell/t	Cooke	Kearns	Cano	Hayes	Gibson	Strong	Rollitt	Rakison/t
Hallett/c4p	Campbell	Fennell	Ritchie/t	Cano	Craig	Gibson	Strong	Rollitt	Rakison
Mooar/3c4p	Campbell	Fennell	Kearns/t	Cooke	Gibson	Goodbody	Kirkham	Blankley	Walker/t
Mooar/c2p	Campbell	Fennell	Codo(b/t)	Cano	Hayes/t	Gibson	Strong	Boardman	McDonald
Roblin/cp	Campbell	Cano	Ritchie	Cooke	Hayes	Gibson	Strong	Boardman	Rollitt
Roblin/c3p	Campbell	Fennell	Ritchie	Cooke	Hayes	Gibson	McDonald	Boardman	Rollitt
Roblin/9c	Young/t	Fennell	Kearns/3t	Cano	Joint	Hayes	Strong	Boardman/t	Walker/2t
Roblin/cpdg	Young	Fennell	Ritchie	Cooke	Hayes	Gibson	Strong	Boardman	Walker
Roblin/3c3p	Young	Fennell/t	Ritchie/2t	Cano	Joint/t	Gibson	Strong	Boardman	Walker
Roblin/5c	Young	Fennell	Ritchie/3t	Cooke/t	Hayes	Gibson	Rollitt	Boardman	Walker/t
Roblin/t2cp	Young	Fennell	Ritchie/t	Cano	Hayes	Gibson	Strong	Boardman	Walker
Roblin/p	Young	Fennell	Ritchie/t	Cano	Hayes	Gibson	Rollitt	Boardman	Walker
Roblin/c3pdg	Young	Fennell	Ritchie	Cooke	Hayes	Gibson	Rollitt	Boardman	Walker
Roblin/3cp	Young	Fennell	Kearns	Cooke	Hayes	Gibson	McBride/t	Boardman	Walker
Roblin/c3p	Young	Fennell	Ritchie/t	Cano	Joint	Gibson	Strong	McBride	Walker/t
Roblin/t2cp	Young	Cano	Ritchie/t	Cooke	Hayes	Gibson	Strong	Boardman	Walker/t
Roblin/7c	Young/t	Cooke(c/t)	Kearns/t	Cano	Hayes/2t	Gibson	Strong	Boardman	Walker/t
Roblin/2c3p	Young	Fennell	Ritchie/t	Cooke	Hayes	Gibson	Strong	Walker	Rollitt
Roblin/c	Young	Fennell	Ritchie	Cano	Hayes	Gibson	Strong	McBride/t	Walker/t
Mooar/t2cp(e/c)	Hendy(d/t)	Cano	Kearns	Cooke	Hayes	Gibson	Strong	McBride	McDonald
Hallett/cp(f/p)	Campbell	Fennell	Ritchie	Cano	Hayes	Gibson	Strong/t	Rollitt	Rakison

REPLACEMENTS   a - G Thompson   b - C Ritchie   c - B Fennell   d - T Colburn   e - N Hallett   f - B Mooar

2000-01 HIGHLIGHTS

Park finished the season superbly with 12 wins and a draw from their last 13 matches.

Paul Roblin who topped the points scoring back in 1993-94 did so again last season with an impressive 157 points from his 15 matches - he averaged over 10 points per match.

He set a new record for conversions in a season with 39, which was 11 better than the previous record.

Brad Mooar equalled the record for points in a match with 22 against Preston early in the season.

Roblin broke the record for conversions in a match with nine against West Hartlepool in December.

ROSSLYN PARK

LEAGUE STATISTICS
compiled by Stephen McCormack

SEASON	Division	P	W	D	L	F	A	Pts Diff	Lge Pts	Lge Pos	Most Points	Most Tries
91-92	1	12	0	1	11	111	258	-147	1	13r	53 John Graves	2 Mark Thomas & Kelvin Wyles
92-93	2	12	5	0	7	209	199	10	10	8r	61 John Graves & Gary Abraham	3 Paul Essenhigh
93-94	3	18	10	1	7	372	240	132	21	5	59 Paul Robin	9 Shane Roiser
94-95	3	18	10	0	8	313	280	33	20	4	54 Mike Griffin	5 Tim Smither & Adam Vander
95-96	3	18	3	2	13	290	426	-136	8	9	45 John Rowlands	5 Mike Griffin
96-97	3	30	17	0	13	630	620	10	34	8	121 Andy Holder	9 Toby Rakison
97-98	JN1	26	13	1	12	486	537	-51	27	5	178 Andy Maddock	11 Liam McCormick
98-99	JN1	26	17	1	8	588	371	217	35	3	93 Andy Maddock	7 Nick Marval
99-00	JN1	26	17	2	7	694	371	323	36	4	145 Stuart Hibbert	12 Crawford Henderson
00-01	N2	*25	19	2	4	752	439	313	40	3	157 Paul Roblin	18 James Justice

BIGGEST MARGINS

Home Win 71pts - 78-7 v W Hartlepool 16.12.00

Away Win 43pts - 55-12 v Camberley 11.3.00

Home Defeat 31pts - 8-39 v Rugby 21.2.98

Away Defeat 50pts - 14-64 v Orrell 28.4.90

MOST CONSECUTIVE

Appearances 45 John Graves 19.9.87 - 27.4.91

Matches scoring Tries 5 James Justice

Matches scoring points 25 John Graves

Victories 7

Defeats 8

MOST POINTS

Scored at Home 78 v W Hartlepool 16.12.00

Scored Away 55 v Camberely 11.3.00

Conceded at Home 46 v Coventry 2.3.96

Conceded Away 64 v Orrell 28.4.90

MOST TRIES

Scored in a match 12 v W Hartlepool 16.12.00 (H)

Conceded in a match 11 v Orrell 28.4.90 (A)

MOST APPEARANCES

by a forward 116 (3) Lee Gibson

by a back 100(1) Andy Maddock

	MOST IN A SEASON	MOST IN A CAREER	MOST IN A MATCH
Points	178 Andy Maddock 97-98	454 John Graves 87-93 & 96	22 John Graves 13.2.93 (H)
Tries	16 James Justice 00-01	27 James Justice 98-01	4 Toby Rakison v Otley 29.3.97 (H)
Conversions	39 Paul Roblin 00-01	44 John Graves 87-93 & 96	5 Alex King v Harrogate 29.4.95 (A) Stuart Hibbert v Blackheath 27.11.99 (A) Andy Maddock v Nottingham 15.01.00 (H)
Penalties	32 Staurt Hibbert 99-00	117 John Graves 87-93 & 96	7 Sean Burns v Leeds 10.1.98 (A)
Drop Goals	3 Andy Maddock 94-95 & 95-96 John Rowland 95-96	7 Andy Maddock 94-98	2 Paul Robin v Gloucester 4.1.92 (A) Andy Maddock v Rotherham 6.4.96 (A)

PLAYING SQUAD

ROSSLYN PARK

BACKS

	Ht.	Wt.	Birthdate	Birthplace	CLUB	League Apps	Tries	Pts
Brad Mooar			28.08.74		Rosslyn Park	8	1	96
Dan Campbell			11.01.75		Rosslyn Park	10	1	5
Crawford Henderson	6.1	14.00	11.02.69		Rosslyn Park	38(1)	19	95
Scotland u21, Anglo Scots u21, Middlesex.					Harlequins	6	1	5
James Wyatt			03.01.75		Rosslyn Park	24	2	20
Lee Fanning	5.10	13.00	08.07.72	Romford	Rosslyn Park	26	5	25
Yorkshire					Reading	86	20	100
James Hendy			09.03.76		Rosslyn Park	13(5)	5	40
Neil Hallett			18.02.80		Rosslyn Park	6	-	40
Simon Young			05.12.74		Rosslyn Park	23(3)	2	10
Gavin Thompson			30.08.69		Rosslyn Park	30(1)	7	35
London u21, Surrey u21.					Camberley			
Paul Futter			16.04.71		Rosslyn Park	71(2)	21	105
London, Surrey.					Clifton	20	2	14
Andy Maddock			01.10.72		Rosslyn Park	132	21	435
England u21, Students, u18, London					Wasps	8	1	16
James Justice			12.11.75		Rosslyn Park	39(6)	27	135
Nick Marval			23.09.72		Rosslyn Park	66(1)	27	141

FORWARDS

	Ht.	Wt.	Birthdate	Birthplace	CLUB	League Apps	Tries	Pts
Ben Fennell			16.08.71		Rosslyn Park	102(10)	14	70
Chris Ritchie			03.11.70		Rosslyn Park	108(13)	25	125
London, Surrey, Welsh Univ.								
Jason Ford			11.08.71		Rosslyn Park	62(9)	3	15
England u21 squad, Hampshire.					Havant			
James Hayes			19.07.74		Rosslyn Park	20(2)	3	15
Eden Rollitt					Rosslyn Park	9(4)	-	-
Toby Rakison			29.09.74		Rosslyn Park	62(2)	21	105
Steve Kearns			12.02.74		Rosslyn Park	5(2)	5	25
Chris Cano			25.01.77		Rosslyn Park	30(5)	2	10
Graham Boardman			04.04.71		Rosslyn Park	104(1)	7	35
Surrey, Scottish Univ.					Watsonians			
Lysander Strong			13.08.74		Rosslyn Park	36(16)	4	20
East Midlands Colts.					Rugby			
Lee Gibson			12.08.72		Rosslyn Park	116(3)	4	20
Richard Cable			02.06.72		Rosslyn Park	11(4)	-	-

ROSSLYN PARK

FACT FILE

Founded: 1879
Nickname: The Park

Colours: Red and white hoops.
Change colours: Dark blue

GROUND

Address: Priory Lane, Roehampton, London SW15 5JH

Tel: 0208 876 1879 (Clubhouse) 0208 876 6044 (Admin)   Fax: 0208 878 7527
e-mail: rugby@rosslynparkfc.freeserve.co.uk
Capacity: 4,630   Seated: 630   Standing: 4,000

Directions: Ground situated at the junction of Upper Richmond Rd (Sth Circular) and Roehampton Lane
Nearest Railway Station: Barnes BR Southern from Waterloo.
Leave station on downside, cross strip of common to Upper Richmond Rd traffic lights.
Turn right entrance on Upper Richmond Rd.

Car Parking: 200 in the ground @ £1

Admission   Season: Adult £85   Matchday: Adults £8, Concessions forChildren/OAPs

Club Shop: Yes, open Tues/Thurs/Sat/Sun Contact Sarah Hughes 0208 876 6044

Clubhouse: Open every day, except Wednesday. Snacks, barmeals & restaurant available.
Functions: Capacity 300, contact Sarah Hughes 020 8876 6044

Training Nights: Tuesday & Thursday

PROGRAMME

Size: A5   Price: £1
Pages: 32 + cover
Editor: Sarah Hughes 0208 876 6044

Advertising Rates
Colour   Page £600   Half £400
Mono   Page £400   Half £250

Rosslyn Park FC

SEDGLEY PARK RUFC

President	Geoff Roberts	Salesis Farm, Salesis Lane, Walmersley, Bury BL9 6TH
		0161 764 6914 (H), 0161 834 1626 (B), 0161 833 2872 (Fax)
Chairman	David Smith	95 Bury Old Road, Whitefield, Manchester.
		0161 280 2921 (H), 0161 280 3509 (B).
Club Secretary	Mark Mold	32 Vicarage Avenue, Cheadle Hulme, Cheadle, Ches. SK8 7JW
		0161 486 0496 (H)
Treasurer	Peter Ratcliffe	22 Hilltop Avenue, Wilmslow, Cheshire SK9 2JE
		01625 535542 (H)
Commercial Manager	Ray Austin	12 Glebelands Road, Prestwich, Manchester M25 1NE
		07720 555323 (M)0161 773 8796 (H) 0161 834 9437 (B)
Press Officer	Colin Stephens	c/o club 0161 796 2626
Fixture Secretary	Ray Fallon	c/o club 0161 724 7282 (H) 07831 460709 (M)

The 2000/01 season was the most successful season to date for Sedgley Park, who not only reached the final of the Lancashire Cup, the first time in the club's history, but also managing to gain promotion to National League Two on a fabulously sunny day at the end of May.

There was a terrible start for the club in the league campaign, with three of the first five games lost, but from this position they improved steadily. Playing open attractive rugby Sedgley put together a run of only one loss in twenty league games to finish in second place behind Stourbridge.

Promotion was gained in a `Play-off' fixture against the second placed team in the Division Three South, Launceston RFC - the Cornish All Blacks. The sun shone brightly suitably reflecting the quality of rugby produced by both teams with Sedgley winning 40-23, a special day for the club. Players such as Jon Scales, Mike Wilcock, Richard Senior and `Player of the Year' Dave McCormack were not only influential in the win, but throughout the season.

Top try scorer Mike Willcock, playing on the wing, reached twenty tries for the season and the other wing Paul Morris together with fullback Rob Moon both collected fourteen tries each which clearly reflects the expansive rugby being played at Park Lane.

This is a tribute to the coaching principles brought in by the player coach, South African Tim Fourie, whose appointment in July 2000 must rank as the most inspired signing in the last few years. His appointment of Colin Stephens, the former Welsh international, as his assistant was the second most astute move and together they produced some of the best rugby ever seen at Sedgley Park.

Sedgeley Park celebrate gaining promotion to National Division Two. Photo: Peter Barton

SEDGLEY PARK

Comp.	Date	H/A	Opponents	Result & Score	Att.	15	14	13	12	11
N3 N	2-Sep	A	New Brighton	L 9-12	200	Wilcock	Morris	Peacock	O'Hare	Kinsey
N3 N	23-Sep	A	Stourbridge	L 12-49	400	Peacock	Wilcock	O'Hare	Scales	Kinsey/t
N3 N	30-Sep	H	Walsall	W 25-7	300	Moon	Wilcock	O'Hare	Scales/2t	Sobanjo
N3 N	14-Oct	A	Bedford Athletic	L 18-23	300	Moon/t	Kinsey	O'Hare	Scales	Sobanjo
N3 N	28-Oct	A	Morley	W 23-15	250	Peacock/t	Morris	Moon	Scales	O'Hare
N3 N	4-Nov	H	Dudley Kingwinsford	W 37-5	200	Moon/t	Wilcock/2t	O'Hare	Scales	Morris
N3 N	11-Nov	H	Nuneaton	W 57-3	250	Moon/t	Wilcock/2t	O'Hare	Scales/2t	Morris/t
N3 N	18-Nov	A	Aspatria	W 21-10	100	Moon	Wilcock/t	O'Hare	Scales/t	Morris/t
N3 N	25-Nov	N	Tynedale	W 18-8	200	Moon	Wilcock	O'Hare/2t	Scales	Morris
N3 N	2-Dec	H	Whitchurch	W 59-3	200	Moon	Wilcock/4t	O'Hare/t	Scales/t	Morris
N3 N	9-Dec	A	Doncaster	L 13-18	800	Moon/t	Wilcock	O'Hare	Scales	Morris
N3 N	16-Dec	H	Liverpool St Helens	W 43-13	350	Moon/2t5cp	Wilcock	O'Hare/t	Peacock/t	Morris
N3 N	23-Dec	A	Whitchurch	W 39-14	415	Moon/t	Wilcock/t	O'Hare	Peacock	Morris
N3 N	6-Jan	H	Aspatria	W 57-3		Moon	Wilcock/t	Scales/2t	O'Hare/t	Morris
N3 N	13-Jan	A	Nuneaton	W 56-17	250	Moon	Wilcock/t	O'Hare	Scales	Morris/2t
N3 N	27-Jan	A	Dudley Kingwinsford	W 23-11	350	Moon	Wilcock	Bullough/t	O'Hare	Morris
N3 N	3-Feb	H	Sandal	W 47-16	250	Moon/3c2p	Wilcock	Bullough/2t	O'Hare	Morris/t
N3 N	10-Feb	H	Bedford Athletic	W 69-0		Moon/3t8cp	Wilcock	O'Hare/t	Bullough	Morris/t
N3 N	17-Feb	H	Morley	W 63-7	270	Moon/5cp	Wilcock/2t	Bullough/2t	O'Hare	Morris/3t
N3 N	24-Feb	A	Walsall	W 34-29	250	Moon/3c2p	Wilcock	O'Hare/t	Bullough/t	Morris
N3 N	10-Mar	H	Stourbridge	W 39-20	800	Moon/t	Wilcock/t	Scales	O'Hare	Morris/t
N3 N	17-Mar	A	Sandal	W 66-19	300	Moon/2t	Wilcock/2t	O'Hare	Scales/t	Morris/t
N3 N	24-Mar	A	New Brighton	W 26-10	1200	Moon/t	Wilcock	O'Hare/t	Scales	Morris
N3 N	31-Mar	A	Liverpool St Helens	W 20-5	150	Moon	Wilcock	O'Hare	Scales	Morris/2t
N3 N	14-Apr	H	Doncaster	D 10-10	1000	Moon	Wilcock/t	O'Hare	Scales/t	Morris
TBC	7-Oct	H	Kendal	W 17-9		Moon	Kinsey	O'Hare	Scales	Sobanjo
TBC	21-Oct	A	Bedford	L 15-45	1019	Moon	Sobanjo/t	O'Hare	Peacock	Kinsey
NL Po	26-May	H	Launceston	W 40-23	1500	Wilcock/2t	Bullough/t	O'Hare	Scales	Morris/t

* after opponents name indicates a penalty try. Brackets after a player's name indicates he was replaced. eg (a) means he was replaced by replacement code "a" and so on. / after a player or replacement name is followed by any scores he made - eg /t, /c, /p, /dg or any combination of these

Dave McCormack, Tim Fourie, Sion O'Hare.

Most Appearances:
25   Dave McCormack, Tim Fourie, Sion O'Hare.
23   Krn Yates, Mike Wilcock,
        Rob Moon, Christian Raducanu.

PLAYERS USED

26 plus three as replacement only

MOST POINTS

Pts	Player	T	C	P	DG
235	C Stephens	6	50	31	4
139	R Moon	14	24	7	-
90	M Wilcock	18	-	-	-
65	P Morris	13	-	-	-
50	J Scales	10	-	-	-

MATCH FACTS

10	9	1	2	3	4	5	6	7
Stephens/2pdg	McCormack	Young	Tresco	Ridehalgh	Arnold	Raducanu	Senior	Yates	Fourie
Stephens/c	McCormack	Young	Losty	Ridehalgh	Arnold	Raducanu	Senior/t	Yates	Fourie
Stephens/2c2p	McCormack/t	Young	Byford	Roberts	Arnold	Raducanu	Senior	Yates	Fourie
Stephens/c2p	McCormack	Young	Byford	Roberts	Arnold/t	Raducanu	Senior	Yates	Fourie
Stephens/c2p	McCormack	Alcock	Byford	Roberts	Kimmins	Raducanu/t	Senior	Yates	Fourie/t
Stephens/t3c2p	McCormack	Alcock	Byford	Roberts	Kimmins	Raducanu/t	Senior	Yates	Fourie
Stephens/4c3p	McCormack	Alcock	Byford	Roberts/t	Kimmins	Raducanu	Senior/t	Yates	Fourie
Stephens/pdg	McCormack	Alcock	Byford	Roberts	Kimmins	Raducanu	Senior	Yates	Fourie
Stephens/c2p	McCormack	Alcock	Byford	Roberts	Kimmins	Raducanu	Senior	Yates	Fourie
Stephens/7c	McCormack	Alcock	Byford/t	Roberts	Kimmins	Arnold	Senior/2t	Hogg	Fourie
Stephens/cpdg	McCormack	Alcock	Byford	Ridehalgh	Kimmins	Raducanu	Senior	Hogg	Fourie
Seymour	McCormack	Alcock	Tresco	Ridehalgh	Kimmins	Raducanu/t	Senior	Yates(a/t)	Fourie
Stephens/4c2p	McCormack/t	Alcock	Tresco	Ridehalgh	Kimmins	Raducanu	Senior	Yates/2t	Fourie
Stephens/t7cp	McCormack	Alcock	Tresco	Ridehalgh	Kimmins	Raducanu/3t	Senior	Yates	Fourie
Stephens/2t6c2pdg	McCormack	Alcock	Tresco	Ridehalgh	Kimmins	Raducanu	Senior/t	Yates	Fourie/t
Stephens/2c3p	McCormack	Alcock	Tresco	Roberts	Kimmins	Raducanu	Senior/t	Yates	Fourie
Seymour	McCormack	Alcock	Tresco/t	Roberts/t	Kimmins/t	Raducanu	Senior	Yates	Fourie/t
Seymour/t	McCormack	Alcock	Tresco	Ridehalgh	Kimmins	Raducanu/t	Senior/t	Yates/t	Fourie/t
Seymour	McCormack	Alcock/t	Tresco	Ridehalgh	Kimmins/t	Raducanu	Senior/t	Yates	Fourie
Seymour(b/tc)	McCormack	Alcock	Tresco/t	Ridehalgh	Kimmins	Raducanu	Senior	Yates	Fourie
Stephens/t3cp	McCormack/t	Alcock	Tresco	Ridehalgh	Kimmins/t	Raducanu	Senior	Yates	Fourie
Stephens/4cp	McCormack/2t	Alcock	Tresco	Ridehalgh/t	Kimmins	Arnold	Senior	Yates/t	Fourie/t
Stephens/c3p	McCormack	Alcock	Byford	Ridehalgh	Kimmins	Raducanu/t	Senior	Yates	Fourie
Stephens/cp	McCormack	Alcock	Byford	Ridehalgh	Kimmins	Raducanu/t	Senior	Yates	Fourie
Stephens	McCormack	Alcock	Byford	Ridehalgh	Kimmins	Raducanu	Senior	Yates	Fourie
Stephens/4p	McCormack	Young/t	Byford	Roberts	Arnold	Raducanu	Senior	Yates	Fourie
Stephens/cp	McCormack/t	Young	Byford	Roberts	Arnold	Raducanu	Senior	Yates	Fourie
Stephens/3c2pdg	McCormack/t	Alcock	Tresco	Ridehalgh	Arnold	Raducanu	Senior	Yates	Fourie

REPLACEMENTS   a - D Hartley   b - C Stephens

2000-01 HIGHLIGHTS

Park lost three of their four matches at the start of the season and then lost just one of their next 21 as they finished as runners up in National Three North.

Rob Moon topped 100 points for the third consecutive season but the title of leading scorer went to Colin Stephens.

He set a new record for the club in League rugby with 235 points.

Full back/ winger Mike Wilcock set a new record for tries in a season with 18, second in the division. Not far behind him was Rob Moon with 14.

Tim Fourie and Dave McCormack were both ever presents in their first season at the club.

SEDGLEY PARK

LEAGUE STATISTICS
compiled by Stephen McCormack

SEASON	Division	P	W	D	L	F	A	Pts Diff	Lge Pts	Lge Pos		Coach		Captain
91-92	NW 1	10	5	1	4	119	145	-26	11	6		V Baker		R Hall
92-93	NW 1	12	4	0	8	149	188	-36	6*	11		V Baker		P Renwick
93-94	NW 1	12	5	2	5	201	134	67	12	5		C Hebbut		R Hall
94-95	NW 1	12	12	0	0	421	60	361	24	1p		K Fletcher		P Egan
95-96	North 2	12	10	0	2	257	141	116	20	2p		K Fletcher		R KImmins
96-97	North 1	22	17	1	4	650	398	252	35	1p		K Fletcher		R Kimmins
												Most Points		**Most Tries**
97-98	N2N	26	14	2	10	655	595	109	30	5	97	Darren Weatherall	10	Jon Duncan / Mike Wilcox
98-99	N2N	26	12	1	13	710	553	157	25	8	150	Rob Moon	13	Jon Duncan
99-00	N2N	26	14	2	10	686	484	202	30	5	141	Rob Moon	12	Elijah Sobanjo
00-01	N3N	*25	21	0	4	887	327	560	42	2	235	Colin Stephens	18	Mike Wilcock

MOST POINTS

Scored at Home	70 v Winnington Park 05.12.98
Scored Away	66 v Sandal 17.03.01
Conceded at Home	43 v Stourbridge 27.03.99
Conceded Away	49 v Stourbridge 23.09.00

MOST CONSECUTIVE

Appearances	29	Mike Wilcock
Matches scoring Tries	6	Christian Raducanu 1999-00
Matches scoring points	19	Colin Stephens 2000-01
Victories	13	2000-01
Defeats	3	

BIGGEST MARGINS

Home Win	69pts	69-0 v Bedford Ath 10.02.01
Away Win	51pts	51-0 v Whitchurch 10.10.98
Home Defeat	10pts	24-43 v Stourbridge 27.03.99
Away Defeat	37pts	12-49 v Stourbridge 23.09.00

MOST TRIES

Scored in a match	11 v Sandal 17.03.01
Conceded in a match 8	v Stourbridge 23.09.00

MOST APPEARANCES

by a forward	93	Andy Kimmins
by a back	90	Mike Wilcock

	MOST IN A SEASON	MOST IN A CAREER	MOST IN A MATCH
Points	235 Colin Stephens 2000-01	430 Rob Moon 1998-01	34 Rob Moon v Bedford Ath 10.02.01 (H)
Tries	18 Mike Wilcock 2000-01	47 Mike Wilcock 1997-01	4 Ben Cohen v Winnington Park 27.12.98 (H) / Mike Wilcock v Whitchurch 02.12.00 (H)
Conversions	50 Colin Stephens 2000-01	81 Rob Moon 1998-01	8 Rob Moon v Bedford Ath 10.02.01 (H)
Penalties	31 Colin Stephens 2000-01	36 Rob Moon 1998-01	8 Neil Lomax v Stourbridge 27.03.99 (H)
Drop Goals	4 Colin Stephens 2000-01	4 Colin Stephens 2000-01	1 Five times - most-IColin Stephens (4)

PLAYING SQUAD

SEDGLEY PARK

BACKS

	Ht.	Wt.	Birthdate	Birthplace	CLUB	League Apps	Tries	Pts
Colin Stephens			29.11.69		Sedgley Park	20(1)	6	235
Daivd McCormack			20.05.79		Sedgley Park	25	5	25
Ross Bullough			19.02.76		Sedgley Park	5(2)	6	30
Taui Seymour			31.03.69		Sedgley Park	5	1	5
Jon Scales			28.07.74		Sedgley Park	17	10	50
Sion O'Hare			24.01.78		Sedgley Park	44	10	50
Rob Moon			27.03.76		Sedgley Park	60	32	430
Paul Morris			10.12.74		Sedgley Park	89	40	200
Mike Wilcock			05.05.72		Sedgley Park	90	47	235
Alun Peacock			16.01.74		Sedgley Park	5	2	10
Chris Kinsey					Sedgley Park	16(10)	7	35

FORWARDS

	Ht.	Wt.	Birthdate	Birthplace	CLUB	League Apps	Tries	Pts
Leon Treco			27.09.78		Sedgley Park	12(1)	2	10
Andy Ridehalgh			25.05.70		Sedgley Park	15(1)	1	5
Gareth Roberts			30.04.81		Sedgley Park	10(2)	2	10
Richard Senior			17.11.71		Sedgley Park Doncaster	25	8	40
Kern Yates			12.02.74		Sedgley Park	43	12	60
Tim Fourie			12.03.68		Sedgley Park Leeds Tykes	25	5	25
Paul Arnold			30.07.80		Sedgley Park	6	1	5
John Young			26.01.75		Sedgley Park	24	1	5
Steven Byford			25.04.77		Sedgley Park	31(4)	2	10
Andy Kimmins			04.02.70		Sedgley Park	93	14	70
Christian Radacanu			02.10.67		Sedgley Park	53	24	120

SEDGLEY PARK

FACT FILE

Founded: 1932
Nickname: Tigers
Website: www.sprufc.com

Colours: Black shirts with fine gold, white & claret hoops, black shorts & socks
Change: Gold shirts with fine black, claret & white hoops, black shorts & socks

GROUND

Address: Park Lane, Whitefield, Manchester M45 7DZ
Tel: 0161 766 5050 / 0161 796 2626   e-mail: admin@sprufc.com
Capacity: 2,500   Seated: 300   Standing: 2,200

Directions: From M60, junction 17 onto A56 for Bury. take the left filter at the 2nd set of traffic lights, left at the next lights (Park Lane),ground 1/2 mile on left
Nearest Railway Station: Whitefield (Manchester Metro), take taxi about £2

Car Parking: 150 on ground, 150 nearby free.

Admission: Season tickets - Adult standing £45
Matchdays - Adult £5   Children Free

Clubhouse: Normal licensing hours, snacks & bar meals available
Functions: Capacity 150 - 2 function rooms & lounge   Contact John Grundy 07774 637064, 0161 280 5752

Club Shop: Yes, in club

Training Nights: Tuesday & Thursday (seniors)
Juniors -Wed.

PROGRAMME
Size: A5   Price: £1   Pages: 40
Editor: Simon Tushingham
Tel/Fax: 0161 796 7755 or 0161 796 2626
e-mail: admin@sprufc.com
Advertising Rates
Mono - Full page £170, half £90, Qtr £50

'Park' captain Christian Raducanu.   Photo: Peter Barton

STOURBRIDGE
RUGBY FOOTBALL CLUB

STOURBRIDGE RFC

President	Paul Davies	Tel: 01384 873477 01384 442612 (Fax)
Chairman	Norman Robertson	16A Middlefield Lane, West Hagley, Stourbridge DY90PX
	Tel: 01562 886011 (H), 01384 455555 (B), 01384 455264 (Fax)	
	email: njr90@hotmail.com	
Secretary	Robert Browne	01562 882020 (H), 01905 761458 (B)
	email - rharvey.browne@virgin.net (H) robert.browne@gpupower.com (B)	
1st XV Manager	Nick Perry	6 Woodchester, Hagley, Stouirbridge DY9 0NF
	01562 882129 email: nick-perry@lineone.net (H) nick@perrywell.co.uk (B)	
Director of Coaching	Philip Maynard	166 Green Acres Road, Kings Norton, NBirmingham B38 8NL
	0121 603 8169 (H)	
Press Officer	Vernon Davies	36 Beckman Road, Pedmore, Stourbridge.
	Tel: 01562 883640 (H) 01562 720534 (Fax) email: davies-email@breathemail.net	

At last, Stourbridge have rid themselves of the rather boring tag of being the only club, below the Premiership, never to change its status since the Leagues began in 1987. Fortunately the movement was in the right direction. After the trauma of two seasons as runners up there was a danger that the drive for promotion had run out of steam, but the essential new impetus was provided by the appointment of a new director of coaching, Phil Maynard.

He brought with him some good players from Worcester who strengthened a squad that was tested to its limits by a spate of mid season injuries that threatened to frustrate the clubs' ambitions yet again. He was aided by coaches Gary Meacham and player-coach Bruce Fenley. Halfbacks, Fenley and Duncan Hughes were the crucial decision makers, but the quality of play was high throughout and it is generally accepted that this was Stourbridge's best ever side.

Basically, it was the invincibility of Stourbridge at Stourton that clinched promotion. For the first time in its 124 years history, they were unbeaten at home. They have only lost twice at `fortress Stourton' out of the last 49 League and Cup fixtures. With three games lost away to nearest rivals, New Brighton, Doncaster and Sedgley Park it was essential to win the corresponding return fixtures. With the only other hiccup a draw against Nuneaton the title was secured by a single point margin.

Amongst a host of club records, pride of place must go to captain Simon Baylie, who scored his 50th try in his 102nd league game. This would be a proud achievement for a predatory wing, but for a prop! Duncan Hughes smashed Chris Mann's scoring record by amassing 224 points in his 25 games, despite handing over the kicking role to Baylie and Tim Smith after a mid term injury and his fifteen tries equalled Kevin Hickey's achievement in 1996-7. Three players reached the landmark of a century of league appearances during the season. Jacob John (100) the only back, Jon Russell (111), Simon Baylie (104), but the record breaker was hooker, Bob Merritt who advanced his total to 149 including an unbroken record 48 consecutive appearances.

The run in the Cup was short and sweet, a hard earned victory against Doncaster followed by a brave narrow defeat at Exeter. For the first time ever, the demands of Cup and League were so intensive that there were no friendly games.

As for the foot and mouth epidemic. It added extra tension and doubt to the latter part of the season once it was realised that the away game against Aspatria would never be played. The club was well supported home and away. Indeed, on the two occasions that the away game against the Cumbrian side was cancelled in late December because of snow and later because of the foot and mouth crisis, large numbers of Stourbridge alickadoos refused to cancel their planned weekend in the Lake district and enjoyed the hospitality of their Bowness Hotel without ever seeing a ball kicked in anger.

Stourbridge RFC First XV Squad - 2000-01

STOURBRIDGE

Comp.	Date	H/A	Opponents	Result & Score	Att.	15	14	13	12	11
N3 N	2-Sep	H	Morley	W 72-17	400	Wylde/2t	Myler	McLaughlin/2t	John/2t	Hall/t
N3 N	16-Sep	A	Nuneaton	W 46-5		Wylde	Myler	McLaughlin/t	John/2t	Hall
N3 N	23-Sep	H	Sedgley Park	W 49-12	400	Wylde	Anderson/t	McLaughlin	John/t	Hall/t
N3 N	30-Sep	N	Tynedale*	W 35-16		Wylde	Anderson/t	McLaughlin/t	John	Richardson
N3 N	14-Oct	H	Whitchurch	W 65-7	450	Wylde	Anderson	Myler	McLaughlin/t	Hall/t
N3 N	28-Oct	H	Liverpool St Helens*	W 26-19	400	Wylde	Trigg	Beauchamp	McLaughlin	Hall
N3 N	4-Nov	A	Doncaster	L 16-17	900	Wylde	Myler	James/t	McLaughlin	Hall
N3 N	11-Nov	A	New Brighton*	L 15-27	400	Beauchamp	Wylde	Myler/t	McLaughlin	Hall
N3 N	18-Nov	H	Sandal	W 65-10	300	Beauchamp	Myler/t	James(a/t)	McLaughlin	Hall/2t
N3 N	25-Nov	H	Aspatria	W 33-10	350	Edwards	Myler/t	John	McLaughlin	Hall/2t
N3 N	16-Dec	A	Dudley Kingwinsford	W 29-14	1500	Beauchamp	Myler/t	Edwards	McLaughlin	Hall
N3 N	23-Dec	H	Walsall	W 46-6	450	Beauchamp/t	Myler/2t	Edwards/c	McLaughlin	Hall/t
N3 N	6-Jan	A	Sandal	W 47-27		Beauchamp	Myler/2t	John/t	McLaughlin	Hall(c/c)
N3 N	13-Jan	H	New Brighton	W 31-10	800	Beauchamp(c/c)Myler		John	McLaughlin	Hall/t
N3 N	27-Jan	H	Doncaster	W 13-10	900	Beauchamp	Myler	Edwards/p	McLaughlin/t	Hall/t
N3 N	3-Feb	A	Walsall	W 25-22	500	Beauchamp	Myler/t	McLaughlin	Edwards/p	Hall
N3 N	10-Feb	A	Whitchurch	W 17-10	540	Beauchamp	Myler	John/c	McLaughlin	Hall/2t
N3 N	17-Feb	H	Bedford Athletic	W 37-20	200	Beauchamp	Myler/t	John/t	McLaughlin	Hall
N3 N	24-Feb	H	Tynedale	W 18-0	400	Beauchamp	Myler	John	McLaughlin	Anderson
N3 N	10-Mar	A	Sedgley Park	L 20-39	800	Beauchamp	Sleight	John/t	McLaughlin	Anderson
N3 N	17-Mar	H	Nuneaton	D 13-13	400	Wylde	Sleight	Hughes	McLaughlin	Beauchamp
N3 N	24-Mar	A	Morley	W 38-16	300	Beauchamp	Sleight	Edwards/c	McLaughlin	James
N3 N	31-Mar	H	Dudley Kingwinsford	W 24-12	1500	Smith/t2c	James	McLaughlin	Edwards	Beauchamp
N3 N	14-Apr	A	Bedford Athletic	W 27-13		Smith/3c2p	James	McLaughlin	Edwards	Beauchamp/t
N3 N	21-Apr	A	Liverpool St Helens	W 48-16		Smith/t3c4p	Beauchamp	McLaughlin	James	Myler
TBC	7-Oct	H	Doncaster	W 13-9	400	Wylde	Anderson	Parsons	John/t	Hall
TBC	21-Oct	A	Exeter	L 15-29		Wylde	Trigg/t	McLaughlin	Myler/t	Hall

*after opponents name indicates a penalty try. Brackets after a player's name indicates he was replaced.
eg (a) means he was replaced by replacement code "a" and so on. / after a player or replacement name
is followed by any scores he made - eg /t, /c, /p, /dg or any combination of these

EVER PRESENT

Duncan Hughes, Ali McLaughlin

Most Appearances:
25 Duncan Hughes, Ali McLaughlin.
24 Nathan Webber, Ben Fenley.
23 Rob Merritt.
22 Simon Baylie

PLAYERS USED
33 plus 1 as replacement only.

MOST POINTS

Pts	Player	T	C	P	DG
224	D Hughes	15	37	25	-
91	S Baylie	10	7	9	-
60	J Hall	12	-	-	-
57	J John	11	1	-	-
50	R Myler	10	-	-	-
50	S Bradley	10	-	-	-
50	B Fenley	10	-	-	-

MATCH FACTS

10	9	1	2	3	4	5	6	7	8
Hughes/t6c	Fenley	Baylie/t	Merritt	Webber/t	Tisdale	Jones	Russell/t	Hall/t	Maurino
Hughes/2tc4p	Fenley	Baylie/c	Merritt	Webber	Tisdale	Jones/t	Russell	Bradley	Maurino
Hughes/t3cp	Fenley/t	Baylie/t	Merritt	Webber	Taylor	Russell	Friend/t	Bradley/t	Maurino
Hughes/2c2p	Fenley	Baylie/t	Merritt	Webber	Taylor/t	Tisdale	Russell	Bradley	Maurino
Hughes/t7c2p	Fenley/2t	Baylie/t	Merritt	Webber	Taylor/t	Tisdale	Jones	Bradley/2t	Russell
Hughes/c3p	Fenley/t	Ferguson	Merritt	Webber	Taylor/t	Tisdale	Friend	Maurino	Russell
Hughes/2p	Fenley	Baylie	Merritt	Webber	Taylor	Tisdale	Russell	Maurino	Bradley/t
Hughes/cp	Fenley	Baylie	Merritt	Webber	Taylor	Tisdale	Russell	Maurino	Bradley
Hughes/t6cp	Fenley/t	Baylie/t	Ball	Webber	Jones	Tisdale	Friend/t	Maurino/t	Bradley/t
Hughes/2c3p	Fenley/t	Baylie	Ball	Webber	Jones	Hynes	Friend	Bradley	Merlin
Hughes/t3p	Fenley/t	Baylie/t	Merritt	Webber	Thurston	Taylor	Russell	Bradley	Merlin
Hughes/t3cp	Fenley/t	Baylie	Merritt	Webber	Thurston	Taylor	Russell	Bradley	Merlin
Hughes/2c2p	Fenley	Baylie	Merritt/t	Webber	Thurston	Tisdale(b/t)	Russell	Bradley/t	Maurino/t
Hughes/2c	Fenley	Baylie/2t	Merritt/t	Webber	Taylor	Tisdale/t	Jones	Bradley	Scriven
Hughes	Fenley	Baylie	Merritt	Webber	Taylor	Tisdale	Jones	Bradley	Scriven
Hughes/t	Fenley	Baylie/2cp	Merritt	Webber	Tisdale	Taylor	Hynes	Bradley	Scriven
Hughes	Fenley	Ferguson	Merritt	Webber	Taylor	Tisdale	Hynes	Jones	Scriven/t
Hughes/t	Fenley/t	Baylie/2cp	Merritt/t	Ferguson	Thurston	Tisdale	Hynes	Rawle	Scriven/t
Hughes	Fenley(d/t)	Baylie/c2p	Merritt	Webber	Taylor	Tisdale	Scriven/t	Bradley	Merlin
Edwards	Hughes/t	Baylie/tcp	Merritt	Webber	Taylor	Tisdale	Scriven	Maurino	Merlin
Edwards	Fenley	Baylie/p	Merritt	Webber	Taylor	Tisdale	Hynes(e/cp)	Bradley/t	Merlin
Hughes/2tc	Fenley	Baylie/t3p	Merritt	Webber	Taylor	Tisdale	Hynes/t	Bradley	Merlin(f/t)
Hughes/t	Fenley	Richardson	Merritt	Webber	Taylor/t	Tisdale	Russell	Bradley/t	Scriven
Hughes/t	Fenley	Baylie	Merritt	Webber	Taylor/t	Tisdale	Russell	Bradley	Scriven
Hughes	Fenley/t	Baylie	Merritt	Webber	Taylor/t	Tisdale	Russell	Bradley/2t	Scriven/t
Hughes/c2p	Fenley	Ferguson	Merritt	Webber	Taylor	Tisdale	Friend	Bradley	Jones
Hughes/cp	Fenley	Ferguson	Merritt	Webber	Taylor	Tisdale	Jones	Maurino	Russell

REPLACEMENTS   a - J John   b - G Taylor   c - T Edwards   d - J Hynes   e - T Smith   f - J Russell

2000-01 HIGHLIGHTS

Third time lucky for Stourbridge - after successive seasons as runners up they finally make promotion.

New boy Duncan Hughes led the way as he topped both the points and try scoring lists with 224 and 15 respectively.

He set a new record for points in a season and equalled the record for tries in a season.

Nearly managed a 100% record at home, but a 13 all draw against Nuneaton late in the season put paid to that.

Prop Simon Baylie was again amongst the leading try scorers and finished the season with 10, a number beaten by just three players at the club.

STOURBRIDGE

LEAGUE STATISTICS
compiled by Stephen McCormack

SEASON	Division	P	W	D	L	F	A	Pts Diff	Lge Pts	Lge Pos		Most Points		Most Tries
91-92	D4N	12	6	0	6	163	137	26	12	6	34	Adrian Taft	5	Richard Trigg
92-93	D4N	12	5	1	6	161	144	17	11	9	108	Simon Pennington	2	Mark Wilson/Richard Trigg/Dale Smallman
93-94	D5N	12	6	0	6	162	188	-26	12	5	90	Chris Mann	5	Richard Trigg
94-95	D5N	12	6	0	6	166	174	-8	12	6	98	Chris Mann	4	Adrian James
95-96	D5N	12	6	0	6	200	177	23	12	7	100	Chris Mann	4	Richard Trigg
96-97	D4N	26	14	1	11	704	579	125	29	6	206	Chris Mann	15	Kevin Hickey
97-98	N2N	26	14	0	12	685	605	80	28	6	107	Chris Mann	14	Alan Dickens
98-99	N2N	26	22	0	4	895	413	482	44	2	105	Simon Baylie	13	Richard Trigg & Simon Baylie
99-00	N2N	26	21	1	4	730	411	319	43	2	116	Hamish Pearson	10	Jacob John & Spencer Bradley
00-01	N3N	*25	21	1	3	861	368	493	43	1p	224	Duncan Hughes	15	Duncan Hughes

MOST POINTS

Scored at Home	72	v Morley 02.09.90
Scored Away	74	v Lichfield 17.04.99
Conceded at Home	45	v Aspatria 19.10.96
Conceded Away	62	v Manchester 31.01.98

BIGGEST MARGINS

Home Win	58pts	65-7 v Whitchurch 14.10.00
Away Win	74pts	74-0 v Lichfield 17.04.99
Home Defeat	25pts	7-32 v Otley 02.03.91
Away Defeat	45pts	17-62 v Manchester 31.01.98

MOST CONSECUTIVE

Appearances	48	Bob Merritt
Matches scoring Tries	6	Rob Myler 2000-01
Matches scoring points	24	Chris Mann 1993-96
Victories	12	1998-99
Defeats	6	1993

MOST TRIES

Scored in a match 12 v Morley 02.09.00 / v Lichfield 17.04.99

Conceded in a match 8 v Manchester 31.01.98

MOST APPEARANCES

by a forward	149	Bob Merritt
by a back	100	Jacob John

	MOST IN A SEASON	MOST IN A CAREER	MOST IN A MATCH
Points	224 Duncan Hughes 2000-01	635 Chris Mann 1993-99	25 Chris Mann v Herefrod 28.09.96
Tries	15 Kevin Hickey 1996-97 / Duncan Hughes 2000-01	43 Richard Trigg 1987-00	3 by eight players - twice each by Simon Baylie and Richard Trigg
Conversions	47 Chris Mann 1996-97	105 Chris Mann 1993-99	7 Duncan Hughes v Whitchurch 14.10.00
Penalties	32 Chris Mann 1996-97	116 Chris Mann 1993-99	8 Steve Baker v Hereford 26.01.91
Drop Goals	2 Andy Dickens 1987-88 / Chris Mann 1995-96	4 Chris Mann 1993-99	2 Chris Mann v Birmingham & Sol 30.09.95

PLAYING SQUAD

STOURBRIDGE RUGBY FOOTBALL CLUB

STOURBRIDGE

BACKS

	Ht.	Wt.	Birthdate	Birthplace	CLUB	League Apps	Tries	Pts
Eral Anderson	5.6	12.07	29.10.73	Leeds	Stourbridge Moseley	28(2)	11	55
Mark Beauchamp	6.0	14.01	09.12.72	Hong Kong	Stourbridge Moseley	18(2)	2	10
Tumai Edwatds	6.0	13.05	20.02.80	Auckland	Stourbridge	10(5)	-	14
Bruce Fenley	5.8	13.00	07.09.68	Cheltenham	Stourbridge Worcester	24	10	50
Jon Hall	6.0	12.07	20.04.78	Cannock	Stourbridge	46(11)	20	100
Duncan Hughes	5.11	14.06	14.07.72	Derby	Stourbridge Worcester	25	15	224
Ed James			06.06.70		Stourbridge	9(3)	1	5
Jacob John	5.10	13.04	02.12.75	Kidderminster	Stourbridge	89(11)	40	233
Ally McLaughlin	5.10	14.08	31.05.76	Darlington	Stourbridge Worcester	33	10	50
Rob Myler	6.0	15.00	04.03.70	Widnes	Stourbridge Worcester	17(1)	10	50
Tim Smith	5.11	13.02	10.05.62	Gloucester	Stourbridge Worcester	3(1)	2	52
Richard Wylde	5.11	12.11	09.11.73	Birkenhead	Stourbridge	28(5)	6	30

FORWARDS

	Ht.	Wt.	Birthdate	Birthplace	CLUB	League Apps	Tries	Pts
Simon Baylie	6.1	19.02	26.03.69	Wordsley	Stourbridge	101(3)	50	370
Spencer Bradley	5.11	15.00	26.06.69	Worcester	Stourbridge Worcester	59(3)	27	135
Matt Ferguson	5.10	20.00	12.06.78	Ludlow	Stourbridge	33(10)	2	10
Jon Friend	6.2	16.04	07.03.75	London	Stourbridge	5(4)	4	20
Darron Hall	6.0	14.07	01.06.76	Sutton Coldfield	Stourbridge	10(23)	1	5
James Hynes	6.4	18.00	01.05.79	Solihull	Stourbridge	12(4)	3	15
Mabon Jones	6.3	17.00	24.03.78	West Bromwich	Stourbridge	8(11)	1	5
Dave Merlin	6.5	18.11	22.05.72	Leeds	Stourbridge	7(1)	-	-
Rob Merritt	5.11	16.11	05.02.72	Bromsgrove	Stourbridge	147)2)	25	125
Rob Maurino	6.0	15.04	14.09.70	Leamington Spa	Stourbridge	40(10)	10	50
Matt Richardson	6.0	16.07	24.01.75	Worcester	Stourbridge	6(4)	2	10
Jon Russell	6.3	16.00	29.06.72	County Down	Stourbridge	106(5)	10	50
Gareth Taylor	6.3	16.08	01.03.76	Shrewsbury	Stourbridge	53(10)	10	50
Nick Tisdale	6.5	17.00	26.08.70	C'bury Mortimer	Stourbridge	71(1)	6	30
Nathan Webber	6.1	19.08	20.07.74	Cardiff	Stourbridge	37(3)	4	20

STOURBRIDGE

FACT FILE

Founded: 1876

Colours: Navy blue with narrow white bands
Change colours: Red & white hoops, trimmed navy blue

GROUND

Address: Bridgnorth Road, Stourton, Stourbridge, W. Midlands. DY7 6QZ
Tel: 01384 393889.
Capacity: 3500   Seated: 499   Standing: 3001

Directions: The ground is situated on the A458 (Bridgnorth road), two miles west of Stourbridge town centre. The ground is on the left hand side 1/2mile past the `Foresters Arms' public house. Nearest Railway Station: Stourbridge Junction.

Car Parking: 200 spaces are available at the ground.

Admission: Matchday - Adults £7, including prog.,
          U16 No charge

Clubhouse: Three bars and food is available.
Functions: Three rooms able to hold functions.
Contact Steward

Club Shop: Open match days only

Training Nights: Tuesday and Thursday.

PROGRAMME

Size: A5   Price: With admission
Pages: 40 plus cover
Editor: Vernon Davies 01562 883640

Advertising Rates: Full page £100.

Duncan Hughes broke Chris Mann's record in his first season with 224 league points.

STOURBRIDGE
RUGBY FOOTBALL CLUB

Front row - Nathan Webber, Bob Merritt and Matt Richardson. Merritt holds the club record with 124 league appearances and 48 consecutive appearances.

Photos: Mark Denison

WATERLOO FC

President	J R H Greenwood	Maitland House, Maitland Stt., Preston PR1 5YP 01772 796600
Chairman	C Brennand	6 St Antonys Road, Blundellsands, Liverpool L23 0151 924 1599
Club Secretary	Keith Alderson	66 St Michaels Road, Blundellsands, Liverpool.L23 7UW 0151 924 1168 (H)
Marketing	Paul Coyne	c/o Waterloo FC, St Anthonys Road, Blundellsands, Liverpool, L23 8TW 0151 924 4552 (H) 0151 924 1111 (B)
Director of Rugby	Paul Coyne	as above
Coach/Manager	Steve Oliver	c/o Waterloo FC, as above (T) 0151 925 4552
Fixtures Secretary	John Rimmer	01772 814277 (H) 01772 885000 (B)

The Waterloo season was one of ups and downs and finally down. Some of the early results were excellent, as defeats for Exeter and London Welsh at Blundellsands promised great things for the season, but one point defeats by Otley and Henley, along with several other near-misses, ended all hopes of staying in Division One.

A good run in the Tetley's Bitter Cup brought some joy and an entertaining home tie against Dudley Kingswinford gave the home crowd plenty of tries to applaud. A long away trip to a very muddy Esher did nothing for the home crowd when Waterloo snatched victory with the last kick of the game. The reward for that exercise was another away trip this time to Wakefield who were a confident home side, leaving us fully expecting the next tie against one of the big boys in the Premiership.

Yet again the home supporters were disappointed as Waterloo marched on to meet the likes of Jason Robinson, Apollo Perlini, Bryan Redpath and the other internationally known names that comprised the Sale squad. It was a bridge too far for the Blundellsands side, but they gave a creditable performance for the full 80 minutes, and managed the latest of later tackles when the Sale mascot, Sammy the Shark, was tackled after the game, and left sitting in a puddle to the amusement of both teams and both sets of supporters.

The resignation of coach Steve Olivier was announced early in the New Year, and it could have destroyed any team spirit. However, the side still maintained a positive attitude towards their games, and morale remained at a high level.

This season has seen a good pre-season atmosphere developing under the new coach, Australian Tony Cross. A majority of players have opted to stay with the club, and, with that experienced and popular player Tony Handley taking on the captain's role, there is a lot to look forward to in the coming months.

WATERLOO

Comp.	Date	H/A	Opponents	Result & Score	H-t	15	14	13	12	11
N1	9-Sep	H	Moseley	L 25-46	375	Worsfold	Harrison	Payne/t	Hartary	Brennand
N1	16-Sep	A	Otley	L 15-16		Worsfold	Harrison	Ball	Davies	Payne
N1	23-Sep	H	Exeter*	W 17-14		Belgian/2cp	Harrison	Payne	Davies/t	Ball
N1	30-Sep	A	Henley Hawks	L 18-19	450	Belgian/c2p	Harrison	Payne/t	Davies	Ball
N1	7-Oct	H	London Welsh	W 25-18	350	Belgian/t2c2p	Worsfold	Payne	Davies	Harrison
N1	14-Oct	A	Birmingham & Solihull	L 12-33	200	Belgian/4p	Brennand	Payne	Davies	Worsfold
N1	28-Oct	H	Worcester	L 19-32	450	Belgian/2c	Brennand	Payne	Davies	Ball
N1	18-Nov	A	Orrell	L 11-35	400	Belgian/2p	Brennand/t	Payne	Davies	Ball
N1	25-Nov	H	Bedford	L 11-20	450	Belgian	Brennand	Payne	Davies	Ball
N1	2-Dec	A	Coventry	L 13-20	1100	Worsfold	Brennand	Payne	Davies	Ball
N1	16-Dec	A	Bedford	L 9-37	1870	Belgian/3p	Brennand	Ball	Telford	Payne
N1	6-Jan	A	Leeds Tykes	L 0-45		Belgian	Cook	Payne	Davies	Ball
N1	13-Jan	H	Orrell	W 35-16		Belgian/3c3p	Brennand/t	Payne/2t	Davies/t	Ball
N1	27-Jan	H	Leeds Tykes	L 17-45	320	Belgian/c(a/t)	Brennand/t	Payne	Davies	Ball
N1	4-Feb	A	Worcester	L 18-30	1988	Belgian/2p	Brennand/t	Payne	Davies	Hitchmough
N1	10-Feb	H	Birmingham & Solihull	W 12-9		Hitchmough	Brennand(d/3p)	Payne	Davies	Ball
N1	17-Feb	H	Wakefield	L 16-17		Hitchmough	Brennand(d/p)	Payne/t	Davies/t	Ball
N1	24-Feb	A	London Welsh	L 16-31	700	Belgian/t2p	Brennand(e/t)	Payne	Davies	Hitchmough
N1	3-Mar	H	Manchester	L 14-16		Belgian/p	Worsfold	Ball	Davies	Hitchmough
N1	10-Mar	H	Henley Hawks	L 17-29	265	Hitchmough	Worsfold	Payne	Davies	Ball/t
N1	17-Mar	A	Exeter	L 10-29	780	Belgian/cp	Worsfold	Payne	Davies	Billington
N1	24-Mar	A	Manchester	W 23-10	325	Belgian/c2p	Worsfold/2t	Payne	Davies	Hitchmough
N1	31-Mar	H	Otley	L 15-19		Belgian/tcp	Worsfold	Payne	Davies	Hitchmough
N1	14-Apr	A	Moseley	D 29-29	475	Belgian/2t3p	Worsfold/t	Telford	Davies	Hitchmough
N1	21-Apr	A	Wakefield	L 13-35	250	Belgian/c2p	Worsfold	Telford/t	Davies	Hitchmough
N1	28-Apr	H	Coventry	W 40-26		Belgian/3c3p	Worsfold	Telford/2t	Davies	Hitchmough/t
TBC	21-Oct	H	Dudley Kingswinsford	W 57-29		Belgian/6c	Brennand/t	Payne	Davies/2t	Worsfold/t
TBC	4-Nov	A	Esher	W 27-26	400	Belgian/t3c2p	Brennand	Payne	Davies	Ball/t
TBC	11-Nov	A	Wakefield	W 35-23	250	Belgian/3c3p	Brennand	Payne	Davies	Harrison
TBC	10-Dec	A	Sale	L 12-59	2028	Brennand	Harrison	Payne	Telford/c	Edwards

*after opponents name indicates a penalty try. Brackets after a player's name indicates he was replaced.
eg (a) means he was replaced by replacement code "a" and so on. / after a player or replacement name
is followed by any scores he made - eg /t, /c, /p, /dg or any combination of these

---

EVER PRESENT David Blyth.

Most Appearances
26 David Blyth.
25 Paul White.
24 Gareth Davies, Steve Dennehy.
23 Matt Holt

PLAYERS USED

32 plus four as replacement only.

MOST POINTS

Pts	Player	T	C	P	DG
190	P Belgian	5	21	41	-
53	D Telford	5	2	8	-
30	M Holt	6	-	-	-
25	F Payne	5	-	-	-
20	J Brennand	4	-	-	-
20	R Worsfold	4	-	-	-

MATCH FACTS

10	9	1	2	3	4	5	6	7	8
Belgian/2c2p	Morris	O'Keefe	Holt/t	Dennehy	White	McGowan/t	Wolfenden	Pilkington	Blyth
Belgian/cp	Morris/t	Reay	Holt/t	Dennehy	Newsham	Allica	Wolfenden	Smith	Blyth
Handley	Morris	Reay	Holt	Dennehy	White	Allica	Wolfenden	Mercer	Blyth
Handley	Morris	O'Keefe	Holt	Dennehy	White	Allica	Wolfenden	Mercer	Blyth/t
Telford	Morris/t	O'Keefe	Holt	Dennehy	White/t	McGowan	Wolfenden	Pilkington	Blyth
Telford	Morris	O'Keefe	Holt	Dennehy	White	Allica	Wolfenden	Wands	Blyth
Telford/t	Morris	O'Keefe	Holt/t	Dennehy	White	Allica	Wolfenden/t	Wands	Blyth
Telford	Morris	O'Keefe	Holt	Dennehy	White	McGowan	Wolfenden	Smith	Blyth
Telford/2p	Aikman	O'Keefe	Holt	Dennehy	White	McGowan	Wolfenden	Wands/t	Blyth
Telford/c2p	Morris	O'Keefe/t	Holt	Dennehy	White	Allica	Wolfenden	Wands	Blyth
Handley	Morris	O'Keefe	Holt	Dennehy	White	Allica	Wolfenden	Pilkington	Blyth
Telford	Morris	O'Keefe	Holt	Dennehy	White	Allica	Wolfenden	Pilkington	Blyth
Telford	Aikman	Reay	Tyms	Dennehy	White	Allica	Mercer	Pilkington	Blyth
Telford	Aikman	Reay	Rusk	Dennehy	White	Allica	Mercer/t	Smith	Blyth
Handley(b/c)	Morris(c/t)	O'Keefe	Rusk	Dennehy	White	Allica	Mercer	Smith	Blyth
Telford/p	Aikman	O'Keefe	Holt	Dennehy	White	Allica	Mercer	Wands	Blyth
Telford/p	Morris	O'Keefe	Holt	Dennehy	White	McGowan	Mercer	Pilkington	Blyth
Telford	Morris	O'Keefe	Holt	Dennehy	White	Allica	Wolfenden	Pilkington	Blyth
Telford/2p	Aikman	O'Keefe/t	Holt	Dennehy	White	Allica	Wolfenden	Pilkington	Blyth
Handley/c(b/t)	Morris	O'Keefe	Holt/t	Reay	White	McGowan	Wolfenden	Pilkington	Blyth
Handley	Worsley	O'Keefe	Holt/t	Dennehy	White	McGowan	Wolfenden	Wands	Blyth
Handley	Morris	O'Keefe	Holt	Dennehy	White	Allica	Mercer	Pilkington/t	Blyth
Telford	Morris	O'Keefe	Holt	Dennehy	White	Allica	Mercer	Pilkington	Blyth/t
Handley	Aikman	O'Keefe	Holt/t	Reay	White	McGowan	Mercer	Pilkington	Blyth
Handley	Aikman	O'Keefe	Holt	Dennehy	White	McGowan	Mercer	Pilkington	Blyth
Handley/t	Morris	O'Keefe	Holt	Dennehy	White	McGowan	Mercer	Pilkington	Blyth/t
Telford	Aikman	O'Keefe	Nicholas(f/t)	Dennehy	White	McGowan/t	Wolfenden/t(g/t)	Wands	Blyth/t
Telford	Aikman(h/t)	O'Keefe	Holt	Dennehy	White	Allica	Wolfenden	Wands	Blyth
Telford	Morris	O'Keefe/t	Holt/t	Dennehy	White	McGowan/t	Wolfenden	Smith	Blyth/t
Handley	Morris(c/2t)	O'Keefe	Holt	Dennehy	White	Allica	Wolfenden	Pilkington	Blyth

REPLACEMENTS   a - R Hitchmough   b - D Telford   c - C Aitman   d - P Belgian   e - R Worsfold
f - M Holt   g - D Smith   h - W Morris

2000-01 HIGHLIGHTS

Waterloo were relegated to National Two for the first time ever in the history of the club.

Philip Belgian topped the scoring list in his first season with with the club scoring 190 points.

David Blyth was the only ever present and played in every minute of every match to take his appearance record to 142.

Leading try scorer was hooker Matthew Holt with six which was better than the two previous seasons when five tries was enough to top the list.

WATERLOO

LEAGUE STATISTICS
compiled by Stephen McCormack

SEASON	Division	P	W	D	L	F	A	Pts Diff	Lge Pts	Lge Pos	Most Points		Most Tries	
91-92	2	12	8	0	4	206	184	22	16		92	Ian Aitchison	4	Gary Meredith
92-93	2	12	10	0	2	228	138	90	20		126	Paul Grayson	3	Austin Healey
93-94	2	18	6	2	10	231	346	-115	14		137	Steve Swindells	2	Gary Meredith, Steve Swindells & John Ashcroft
94-95	2	18	8	0	10	287	331	-44	16		160	Steve Swindells	4	Neil Ryan & Steve Wright
95-96	2	18	7	2	9	309	482	-173	16		134	Martin Emmett	4	Peter McCaugheran
96-97	2	22	7	0	15	506	661	-155	14		99	Lyndon Griffiths	7	David Blyth
97-98	P2	22	11	0	11	510	525	-15	22		261	Lyndon Griffiths	7	Marcus Coates & Shaun Woof
98-99	P2	26	12	0	14	419	634	-215	24		198	Lyndon Griffiths	5	Shaun Woof
99-00	P2	26	6	2	18	441	830	-389	14	12	201	Lyndon Griffiths	5	Gareth Davies & Karelle Dixon
00-01	N1	26	6	1	19	450	676	-226	35	14r	190	Phil Belgian	6	Matt Holt

BIGGEST MARGINS

Home Win	35pts - 51-16 v Blackheath 27.9.97
Away Win	41pts - 56-15 v Rugby 16.11.96
Home Defeat	66pts - 3-69 v Northampton 28.10.96
Away Defeat	68pts - 10-78 v Worcester 20.11.99
	10-78 v Rotherham 11.3.00

MOST CONSECUTIVE

Appearances	39 Shaun Gallagher
Matches scoring Tries	4 Steve Bracegirdle
Matches scoring points	44 Lyndon Griffiths
Victories	7
Defeats	11

MOST POINTS

Scored at Home	51 v Blackheath 27.9.97
Scored Away	56 v Rugby 16.11.96
Conceded at Home	69 v Northampton 28.10.96
Conceded Away	78 v Worcester 20.11.99
	78 v Rotherham 11.3.00

MOST TRIES

Scored in a match	7 v Rugby 26.4.97
Conceded in a match	12 v Worcester 20.11.99

MOST APPEARANCES

by a forward	142 (3) David Blyth
by a back	121 (19) Tony Handley

	MOST IN A SEASON	MOST IN A CAREER	MOST IN A MATCH	
Points	261 Lyndon Griffiths 97-98	759 Lyndon Griffiths 96-00	23 Martin Emmett	v Bedford 13.1.96 (H)
Tries	8 Steve Bracegirdle 90-91	16 Shaun Woof 96-99	2 by 15 players incl Steve Bracegirdle twice	
Conversions	33 Lyndon Griffiths 99-00	107 Lyndon Griffiths 96-00	6 Lyndon Griffiths	v Blackheath 19.4.97 (A) v Blackheath 27.9.97 (H)
Penalties	66 Lyndon Griffiths 97-98	175 Lyndon Griffiths 96-00	6 Ian Aitchison Steve Swindells	v Blackheath 25.4.92 (A) v Otley 12.3.94 (A) v Newcastle G. 10.9.94 (H) v Rugby Lions 25.9.99 (H)
Drop Goals	6 Paul Grayson 92-93	9 Ian Aitchison 87-95	2 Ian Aitchison	v Gloucester 31.10.87 (H) v Sale 2.1.88 (H)
			Ian Croper Paul Grayson Neil Ryan	v Sale 9.3.91 (H) v Sale 13.3.93 (H) v Lon. Irish 24.9.94 (H) v Newcastle G. 14.10.95 (A)

PLAYING SQUAD

WATERLOO

BACKS

	Ht.	Wt.	Birthdate	Birthplace	CLUB	League Apps	Tries	Pts
Anthony Handley	5.11	13.7	12.11.73	Salford	Waterloo	122(16)	6	113
Craig Griffies					Waterloo	7(12)	-	-
David Telford					Waterloo	18(3)	5	53
James Edwards					Waterloo	14(7)	2	10
Rob Worsfold					Waterloo	13(4)	4	20
Phil Belgian					Waterloo	22(2)	5	190
Wayne Morris	6.0	12.8	06.12.72	Swansea	Waterloo	77(14)	16	80
Gareth Davies			02.08.73		Waterloo	67(1)	9	47
Craig Aikman					Waterloo	7(12)	1	5
Cambell Ball					Waterloo New Brighton	35	4	20
Freeman Payne					Waterloo	22(4)	5	25

FORWARDS

	Ht.	Wt.	Birthdate	Birthplace	CLUB	League Apps	Tries	Pts
Nick Allica					Waterloo	16(8)	-	-
Will Pilkington					Waterloo Liverpool St Helens	29(7)	4	20
Matt Holt	6.0	16.0	30.10.71	Brisbane	Waterloo	85(11)	17	85
Louis McGowan	6.5	16.4	17.10.77	Liverpool	Waterloo	32(21)	2	10
Paul White	6.4	17.2	08.05.70	Worthing	Waterloo	123(3)	8	40
Steve Nicholas					Waterloo	11(4)	-	-
Stephen Dennehy					Waterloo	38(3)	-	-
David Blyth	6.3	17.0	14.03.71	Glasgow	Waterloo W Hartlepool	142(3) 9	18 -	90 -
Steve Wands					Waterloo	41(12)	3	15
Carl Wolfenden	6.2	15.11	05.02.69	Waterloo	Waterloo	47(42)	10	50
Alex Reay					Waterloo	6(15)	-	-

WATERLOO
FACT FILE

Founded: 1882
Colours: Myrtle, scarlet & white hoops/ myrtle shorts
Change colours: White with myrtle,scarlet & white thin striped `V'

GROUND
Address: The Pavillion, St Anthony's Rd., Blundellsands, Liverpool. L23 8TW
Tel: 0151 924 4552
Capacity: 6,000   Standing:6,000

Directions: From the end of the M57/58 follow signs for Crosby.
Waterloo FC is then sign-posted to the ground.
Nearest Railway Station: Crosby & Blundellsands, 1/2 mile down St Anthony's Road.

Car Parking: 100 spaces, Saturday only.

Admission   Matchdays   Adults £8, OAPs & Children u16 Free

Club Shop: Open only on matchdays. Contact the club on other days.
Clubhouse: Open during normal licensing hours on matchdays. Three bars, with snacks and meals available.
Functions: Capacity 150, contact Paul Coyne 0151 924 4552.

Training Nights: Monday, Tuesday and Thursday.

PROGRAMME Size: A5   Pages: 34
Price: £1.50
Editor: Geoff Lightfoot
Advertising Rates   Colour: Page £500   Half £275

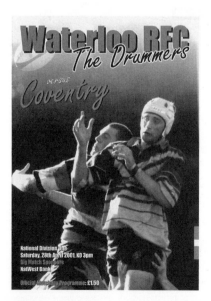

WHARFEDALE RUFC

President	John Spencer	High Pasture, Threshfield, Nr Skipton, N Yorks BD23 5NS 01756 752456 (H), 01756 753015 (B), 01756 753020 (Fax)
Club Secretary	Antony Davies	21 Raikeswood Drive, Skipton, N. Yorks. BD23 1NA 01756 798435 (H), 01756 797696 (B), 01756 797565 (Fax)
Director of Rugby/ **Fixture Secretary**	Michael Harrison	Old Hall Farm,Threshfield, Skipton, N. Yorks. BD23 5PL 01756 752777 (H & B & Fax)
Administration Officer	Graham Currier	Fell View Cottage, Hartlington Raikes, Burnsall, N. Yorks. BD23 6BX 01756 720257 (Tel & Fax)
Press Officer	Chris Ellwood	28 Carleton Avenue, Skipton, N. Yorks. BD23 2TE 01756 798077 (Tel & Fax), email: ellwood@netcomuk.co.uk
Chairman	Frank House	Stocks House, Main St., Threshfield, Skipton, N Yorks BD23 5HD. 01756 753546 (H)

Wharfedale's pre-season 'favourites for promotion' tag was questioned at the very outset of the league programme. A 33-12 defeat at Rosslyn Park brought them firmly back to earth. As things turned out, that patchy performance (the Greens looked likely winners for most of the match, but conceded an avalanche of late points) had set the tone for an erratic season. There were games to savour, the 'double' over neighbours Harrogate (particularly the breathtaking encounter at Claro Road) being dearest to the hearts of Wharfedale fans; and a record 72-10 victory over Fylde. However, the over-riding memory of 2000-01 is one of frustration and unfulfilled promise.

At the beginning of December Wharfedale were well in contention, following a run of 4 wins, including 3 away from home. Then, defeat against Nottingham – one of a previously unheard-of 5 home league reverses – heralded a wildly inconsistent second half to the campaign. Ultimately doubled by the top four in the final table, and having to contend with disruption by weather and the foot & mouth crisis, Wharfedale settled for 6th place. It is the second highest placing ever achieved by the club, but after being so close to promotion the previous season, a distinct disappointment.

One man does not make a team, but the retirement of Charlie Vyvyan left a gap that the forwards always struggled to compensate for. They were never bested for mobility, but suffered when up against the heavyweight packs of the division. Influential stand-off David Pears had an unfortunate season with injury, and while the backs produced some occasionally scintillating stuff, consistency – as for the team as a whole – was missing.

A traditional strength of the club is player loyalty. No fewer than 11 of the first-team squad began their Wharfedale careers at junior level. One such is flanker Hedley Verity. His remarkable run of 86 successive league appearances, ended by injury in January, is a record for the National Leagues during the 'professional' era.

Scrum half Graham Smith launches a massed Wharfedale attack at Camberley. Photo: Lee Crabb

WHARFEDALE

Comp.	Date	H/A	Opponents	Result & Score	Att.	15	14	13	12	11
N2	2-Sep	A	Rosslyn Park	L 12-33		Davies	Mounsey	Heseltine	Whitfield	Whitefield
N2	9-Sep	H	West Hartlepool	W 51-14		Davies/2t	Mounsey	Heseltine/2t	Whitfield	Whitefield/2t
N2	23-Sep	H	Fylde	W 72-10		Davies	Mounsey/2t	Heseltine/t	Whitfield	Whitefield/t
N2	30-Sep	A	Bracknell	L 17-23		Davies	Mounsey	Heseltine	Whitfield	Whitefield/t
N2	14-Oct	H	Preston Grasshoppers	W 17-14		Davies	Mounsey/p	Heseltine	Whitfield	Armitage/t
N2	28-Oct	H	Kendal	L 14-21		Davies	Mounsey/3p	Johnson	Whitfield	Armitage/t
N2	11-Nov	A	Esher	W 22-20	150	Davies/t	Mounsey/4p	Hodgson	Whitfield	Armitage/t
N2	18-Nov	H	Harrogate	W 25-0	700	Davies	Mounsey/2c2p	Hodgson/t	Whitfield	Armitage/t
N2	25-Nov	A	Lydney	W 9-0	400	Davies	Mounsey/3p	Hodgson	Whitfield	Armitage
N2	2-Dec	A	Newbury	W 25-10		Davies	Mounsey/2c2p	Hodgson/t	Johnson	Armitage
N2	9-Dec	H	Nottingham	L 12-21		Davies	Mounsey/2tc	Hodgson	Whitfield	Armitage
N2	16-Dec	A	Harrogate	W 20-18	600	Davies	Mounsey/5p	Hodgson	Whitfield	Armitage
N2	23-Dec	H	Esher	W 33-22		Davies	Mounsey/2t2c3p	Hodgson/t	Whitfield	Armitage/t
N2	6-Jan	A	Kendal	L 0-6		Davies	Mounsey	Hodgson	Whitfield	Armitage
N2	13-Jan	H	Rugby Lions	L 24-31		Davies	Mounsey/t4p	Heseltine	Hodgson	Armitage
N2	27-Jan	H	Newbury	W 37-7		Davies	Mounsey/c5p	Heseltine	Hodgson(a/t)	Armitage/t
N2	3-Feb	A	Camberley	W 30-24		Davies	Mounsey/3c3p	Hodgson/t	Whitfield	Armitage/t
N2	10-Feb	H	Bracknell	L 6-22		Davies	Mounsey/2p	Heseltine	Hodgson	Armitage
N2	17-Feb	A	Rugby Lions	L 18-37		Davies/c2p	Eccleston	Hodgson	Johnson	Armitage
N2	24-Feb	A	Fylde	L 8-29	500	Davies	Mounsey/p	Hodgson	Johnson	Armitage
N2	17-Mar	A	West Hartlepool	W 44-18		Davies/3cp	Heseltine/t	Hodgson	Johnson	Armitage
N2	24-Mar	H	Rosslyn Park	L 17-37		Davies	Heseltine	Hodgson	Johnson/2t	Armitage
N2	31-Mar	A	Nottingham	W 26-22		Davies/cp	Heseltine	Hodgson	Johnson	Armitage
N2	7-Apr	A	Preston Grasshoppers	L 3-20		Davies/p	Eccleston	Hodgson	Johnson	Armitage
N2	28-Apr	H	Camberley	W 49-16		Davies/2t7c	Eccleston/t	Hodgson/2t	Johnson/t	Armitage
TBC	7-Oct	H	Darlington	W 28-0		Davies	Armitage	Heseltine/2t	Whitfield	Whitefield
TBC	21-Oct	A	Plymouth Albion	L 11-21	800	Davies	Mounsey/2p	Heseltine	Whitfield	Armitage/t

* after opponents name indicates a penalty try. Brackets after a player's name indicates he was replaced. eg (a) means he was replaced by replacement code "a" and so on. / after a player or replacement name is followed by any scores he made - eg /t, /c, /p, /dg or any combination of these

MOST POINTS

Pts	Player	T	C	P	DG
171	A Mounsey	7	11	38	-
96	D Pears	2	19	16	-
64	J Davies	5	12	5	-
35	C Armitage	7	-	-	-
30	A Hodgson	6	-	-	-

MATCH FACTS

10	9	1	2	3	4	5	6	7	8
Pears/4p	Smith	Ingram	Lawn	Dickinson	Lister	Evans	Verity	Allen	Jackson
Pears/5c2p	Smith	Ingram	Lawn	Dickinson	Lister	Evans	Allen	Verity/t	Jackson
Pears/t8c2p	Smith	Ingram	Lawn/2t	Dickinson	Lister	Evans/t	Allen	Verity/t	Jackson/t
Pears/t2cp	Smith	Ingram	Lawn	Dickinson	Lister	Evans	Allen	Verity	Jackson
Pears/3p	Smith	Lancaster	Lawn	Ingram	Lister	Evans	Allen	Verity	Jackson
Heseltine	Smith	Lancaster	Lawn	Ingram	Lister	Evans	Allen	Verity	Jackson
Heseltine	Smith	Lancaster	Lawn	Dickinson	Lister	Capstick	Allen	Verity	Jackson
Heseltine	Smith	Lancaster	Lawn	Dickinson	Lister	Capstick	Evans/t	Verity	Buckroyd
Heseltine	Smith	Lancaster	Lawn	Ingram	Lister	Capstick	Evans	Verity	Buckroyd
Heseltine	Smith	Lancaster	Lawn	Dickinson	Lister	Capstick/t	Jackson/t	Verity	Buckroyd
Heseltine	Smith	Peel	Ogden	Dickinson	Lister	Capstick	Evans	Verity	Jackson
Heseltine	Smith	Lancaster	Hindle	Dickinson	Lister	Capstick	Evans	Verity	Buckroyd/t
Heseltine	Smith	Lancaster	Lawn	Dickinson	Lister	Capstick	Evans	Verity	Jackson
Heseltine	Smith	Lancaster	Lawn	Dickinson	Lister	Capstick	Evans	Verity	Jackson
Pears/c	Smith/t	Lancaster	Lawn	Dickinson	Lister	Capstick	Evans	Verity	Buckroyd
Pears	Smith	Ingram(b/t)	Lawn/t	Dickinson	Lister	Capstick	Evans	Verity	Buckroyd
Heseltine	Smith	Ingram	Lawn	Dickinson	Lister	Capstick	Evans	Allen	Buckroyd/t
Pears	Smith	Lancaster	Lawn	Ingram	Lister	Capstick	Evans	Verity	Buckroyd
Heseltine	Smith	Lancaster	Lawn	Ingram	Lister	Capstick	Allen	Verity/t	Buckroyd/t
Heseltine	Smith	Lancaster	Lawn	Dickinson	Lister	Capstick	Allen	Verity	Buckroyd/t
Pears(c/t)	Smith	Lancaster/t	Lawn	Ingram	Lister/t	Capstick	Evans/2t	Verity	Buckroyd/t
Pears/2cp	Smith	Lancaster	Lawn	Dickinson	Lister	Capstick	Evans	Verity	Buckroyd
Pears/c3p	Smith	Lancaster	Lawn/t	Dickinson	Lister	Capstick	Evans/t	Verity	Buckroyd
Heseltine	Smith	Ingram	Lawn	Dickinson	Lister	Capstick	Hargreaves	Verity	Buckroyd
Heseltine	Smith	Peel	Lawn	Ingram	Lister	Capstick	Evans	Verity/t	Buckroyd
Pears/2c3p	Smith	Lancaster	Lawn	Ingram	Lister	Capstick	Allen	Verity	Buckroyd/t
Pears	Smith	Lancaster	Lawn	Ingram	Lister	Evans	Allen	Verity	Jackson

REPLACEMENTS   a - D Whitfield   b - R Lancaster   c - C Eccleston

2000-01 HIGHLIGHTS

Adam Mounsey topped the scoring for Wharfedale for the fourth time in five seasons.

His total of 171 was his lowest but both David Pears and Jonathan Davies kicked as well with Mounsey starting 19 matches.

David Pears did manage to break a couple of records - he set a new record for points in a match with 27 against Fylde and in the same match kicked a record eight conversions.

Their 72-10 home win against Fylde was a record for most points and biggest win eclipsing the 59-0 win against Liverpool St Helens two seasons previously.

Winger Chris Armitage scored on his debut and then went to score in his next three matches.

Adam Mounsey extended his record for conversions and penalties to 123 and 175 respectively.

WHARFEDALE

LEAGUE STATISTICS
compiled by Stephen McCormack

SEASON	Division	P	W	D	L	F	A	Pts Diff	Lge Pts	Lge Pos	Most Points		Most Tries	
91-92	North 2	10	10	0	0	254	55	199	20	1p	111	Russ Buckroyd	11	Les Ingham
92-93	North 1	12	7	0	5	216	207	9	14	3	45	Mark Toseland	5	Glen Harrison
93-94	North 1	12	12	0	0	327	77	250	24	1p	127	Alex Howarth	8	Alex Howarth & Simon Slater
94-95	5N	12	6	1	5	209	198	11	13	4	94	Alex Howarth	5	Daniel Harrison
95-96	5N	12	12	0	0	331	146	185	24	1p	143	Alex Howarth	10	Neil Heseltine
96-97	3	30	17	0	13	710	635	75	34	7	182	Adam Mounsey	21	Andrew Hodgson
97-98	JN1	26	8	3	15	476	684	-208	19	10	247	Adam Mounsey	8	Jonathon Davies
98-99	JN1	26	13	1	12	477	421	51	27	7	235	David Pears	8	Adam Mounsey
99-00	JN1	26	19	1	6	646	317	329	39	3	274	Adam Mounsey	19	Andrew Hodgson
00-01	N2	*25	14	0	11	594	475	119	28	6	171	Adam Mounsey	7	Adam Mounsey & Chris Armitage

BIGGEST MARGINS
Home Win 62pts - 72-10 v Fylde 23.9.00
Away Win 34pts - 68-34 v Lichfield 30.3.96
Home Defeat 42pts - 8-50 v Walsall 25.3.95
Away Defeat 47pts - 24-71 v London Welsh 21.3.98

MOST CONSECUTIVE
Appearances 61 Denis Wood 13.4.91 - 14.9.96
Matches scoring Tries 6 Andrew Hodgson
Matches scoring points 50 Adam Mounsey
Victories 14 x 2
Defeats 8 (18.4.98 - 10.10.98)

MOST POINTS
Scored at Home 72 v Fylde 23.9.00
Scored Away 68 v Lichfield 30.3.96
Conceded at Home 53 v Worcester
Conceded Away 71 v London Welsh 21.3.98

MOST TRIES
Scored in a match 12 v Sandbach 29.2.92
Conceded in a match 11 v London Welsh 21.3.98 (A)

MOST APPEARANCES
by a forward 189 Hedley Verity
by a back 162 Neil Heseltine

	MOST IN A SEASON	MOST IN A CAREER	MOST IN A MATCH
Points	274 Adam Mounsey 99-00	951 AdamMounsey 96-01	29 Adam Mounsey v Reading 15.01.00
Tries	21 Andrew Hodgson 96-97	52 Andrew Hodgson 96-01	6 Les Ingham v Sandbach 29.2.92
Conversions	39 Adam Mounsey 96-97	123 Adam Mounsey 96-00	8 David Pears v Fylde 23.9.00
Penalties	55 Adam Mounsey 97-98 & 99-00	175 Adam Mounsey 96-00	6 Mark Toseland v Lymm 14.1.89 David Pears v Liverpool St H 7.11.98
Drop Goals	4 David Pears 98-99	9 Russ Buckroyd 87-97	1 on 20 occasions including 9 times by Russ Buckroyd

PLAYING SQUAD

WHARFEDALE

BACKS

	Ht.	Wt.	Birthdate	Birthplace	CLUB	League Apps	Tries	Pts
Jonathan Davies Wales Youth.	6.0	14.00	28.03.72	Bangor	Wharfedale Bangor(Wales)	104(2)	22	187
Craig Eccleston North Colts	5.11	12.05	19.04.78	Keighley	Wharfedale N Ribblesdale	13(4)	6	30
Sean Gilbert England Students(RL), Yorkshire Colts.	5.11	13.05	14.06.69	Norwich Leeds	Wharfedale	11(4)	1	5
Dan Harrison Yorkshire	5.11	13.00	26.10.71	Skipton	Wharfedale	92(3)	22	110
David Pears Other clubs: Aspatria, Sale, Harlequins 41/7/434, Worcester 1/-/-.	5.10	12.7	06.12.67	Workington	Wharfedale	32	7	331
Neil Heseltine Yorkshire	5.9	13.00	16.07.68	Skipton	Wharfedale Kelso	162	31	158
Andy Hodgson North u21.	5.11	13.00	09.02.76	Skipton	Wharfedale	95(1)	52	260
Chris Armitage					Wharfedale Fylde	21	7	35
David McCabe North Colts.	6.00	12.05	07.09.79	Manchester	Wharfedale Broughton Park	4	-	3
Steve McManus Yorkshire colts.	5.11	13.00	19.05.72	Keighley	Wharfedale W Hartlepool	65	13	65
Adam Mounsey Yorkshire u18.	5.10	13.05	18.09.72	Bradford	Wharfedale Morley	103	36	951
Ben Whitfield	5.11	13.00	20.10.75	Skipton	Wharfedale	35(4)	9	45
Craig Walker North Colts.	5.11	14.00	03.08.67	Keighley	Wharfedale Keighley	66	12	60
David Whitfield	6.0	13.03	08.08.72	Leeds	Wharfedale Selly Oak	56(11)	6	30

FORWARDS

	Ht.	Wt.	Birthdate	Birthplace	CLUB	League Apps	Tries	Pts
Sam Allen North u21.	6.2	14.00	23.07.78	Skipton	Wharfedale	23(25)	1	5
Russ Buckroyd Yorkshire	6.0	14.05	31.01.67	Liverpool	Wharfedale	129(11)	27	256
Neil Dickinson	6.0	15.05	30.07.69	Otley	Wharfedale	98(9)	1	5
Paul Evans North, Yorkshire.	6.3	17.00	03.01.67	Bridlington	Wharfedale W Hartlepool	88(7) 55(3)	13 6	65 28
John Hartley Yorkshire u21.	6.1	14.07	17.08.75	Skipton	Wharfedale	5(1)	1	5
John Lancaster	6.00	16.00	11.06.68	Skipton	Wharfedale	48(2)	-	-
John Lawn Yorkshire	5.7	14.00	07.08.70	Bradford	Wharfedale	168(1)	20	100
David Lister Yorkshire	6.5	16.00	19.10.73	Keighley	Keighley	128	12	60
Anthony Capstick Yorkshire	6.4	15.0	26.12.74	Steeton	Wharfedale	20(5)	1	5
Tony Jackson Yorkshire u21.					Wharfedale	13(6)	2	10
Hedley Verity Yorkshire	6.0	14.00	20.04.70	Harrogate	Wharfedale	189	33	158
Rob Sugden	5.10	13.00	19.12.74	Harrogate	Wharfedale Bradford & Bing	3(2)	-	-
Charlie Vyvyan England Univ, North, Yorkshire. Other clubs: Richmond, Sale	6.6	17.00	01.09.65	Wimbledon	Wharfedale	85	15	75
Craig Ingrams England Univ.	5.11	16.00	04.07.74	Shrewsbury	Wharfedale Newport(Salop)	24(18)	1	5
Richard Lancaster Cumbria	6.1	17.00	12.03.73	Lancaster	Wharfedale Kirkby Lonsdale	54(9)	5	25

WHARFEDALE

FACT FILE

Founded: 1923

Colours: Emerald green

Nickname: Green Machine

Change colours: Scarlet & white hoops

GROUND

Address: Wharfeside Avenue, Threshfield, Skipton, N Yorks BD23 5ND

Tel : 01756 752547   Fax: 01756 720257   e-mail: elephant@netcomuk.co.uk
web site: http://www.wharfedalerugby.co.uk

Capacity: 3,000   Seated: 120   Standing: Covered 180, Uncovered 2,700

Directions: Take B6256 from Skipton bypass, signed Grassington after 8 miles turn right after Old Hall Inn in Threshfield, left after 400 metres down 'The Avenue'
Nearest Station: Skipton, no bus service. Group transport can be arranged through club secretary

Car Parking: 120 adjacent, no charge

Admission: Season Adults £100   Matchday   Adults (incl. prog.) £5, u16 No Charge

Club Shop: Open 1 hour before & after 1st XV matches. Manager Mary Watkinson 01756 790282

Clubhouse: Normal licensing hours matchdays. Snacks etc available.
Functions   Capacity 120 Contact Chairman Frank House 01756 753546

Training Nights: Monday & Wednesday

PROGRAMME   Size: A5   Pages: 44 + cover   Price: Included with entry
Editor: Gordon Brown 01756 752410
Advertising Rates   Colour: Negotiable   Mono: Full page £300   Half page £150

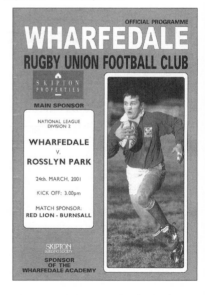

LEFT: Hedley Verity set a record for consecutive league appearances. Photo: Craven Herald

RECORDS SECTION

DIVISION THREE
(CURRENTLY NATIONAL LEAGUE TWO)

THE LAST TEN YEARS — DIVISION THREE

1991-92	Champions	Runners-up	Relegated
	Richmond	Fylde	Lydney, Nuneaton

Most
Penalties: 16 Simon Hogg (Clifton)

Points: Mike Jackson (Fylde)
Conversions: 26 Mike Jackson (Fylde)

Tries: 8 Matt Brain (Clifton)
D.Gs: 2 by 5 players

1992-93	Champions	Runners-up	Relegated
	Otley	Havant	Sheffield, Leeds, Clifton, Askeans, Liverpool St. H, Aspatria, Plymouth Albion, Broughton Park

Most

Penalties: 14 Peter Rutledge (Otley)

Points: 122 Andy Green (Exeter)

Conversions: 31 Andy Green (Exeter)

Tries: 8 Martin Kelly (Broughton Park)
Mark Sephton (Liverpool St. Helens)
D.Gs: 3 Andy Green (Exeter)
Simon Hogg (Clifton)

1993-94	Champions	Runners-up	Relegated
	Coventry	Fylde	Havant, Redruth

Most
Penalties: 45 Andy Finnie (Bedford)

Points: 172 Andy Finnie (Bedford)
Conversions: 23 Richard Angell (Coventry)

Tries: 12 Bendan Hanavan (Fylde)
D.Gs: 3 Jamie Grayshon (Morley)

1994-95	Champions	Runners-up	Relegated
	Bedford	Blackheath	Clifton, Exeter

Most
Penalties: 56 Andy Finnie (Bedford)

Points: 228 Andy Finnie (Bedford)
Conversions: 24 Andy Finnie (Bedford)

Tries: 8 David Bishop (Rugby)
D.Gs: 5 Jamie Grayshon (Morley)

1995-96	Champions	Runners-up	Relegated
	Coventry	Richmond	-

Most
Penalties: 53 Ralph Zoing (Harrogate)

Points: 215 Ralph Zoing (Harrogate))
Conversions: 28 John Gregory (Richmond)

Tries: 12 Colin Phillips (Reading)
D.Gs: 8 Jamie Grayshon (Morley)

1996-97	Champions	Runners-up	Relegated
	Exeter	Fylde	Walsall, Havant, Redruth, Clifton

Most
Penalties: 82 Steve Gough (Fylde)

Points: 404 Steve Gough (Fylde)
Conversions: 63 Ralph Zoing (Harrogate)

Tries: 22 Mark Kirkby (Otley)
D.Gs: 7 Craig Raymond (Lon. Welsh)

1997-98	Champions	Runners-up	Relegated
	Worcester	Leeds	-

Most
Penalties: 64 Chris Atkinson (Nottingham)

Points: 322 Sateki Tuipolotu (Leeds)
Conversions: 64 Craig Raymond (Lon. Welsh)

Tries: 29 Nick Baxter (Worcester)
D.Gs: 4 Colin Stephens (Leeds)

1998-99	Champions	Runners-up	Relegated
	Henley	Manchester	Morley, Liverpool St. Helens

Most

Penalties: 70 Steve Swindells (Manchester)

Points: 365 Steve Swindells (Manchester)
Conversions: 60 Steve Swindells (Manchester)

Tries: 15 Lafaele Filipo (Otley)
Adam Standeven (Morley)
D.Gs: 5 Phil Osman(Henley) & Sam Jack(Nottm)

99-2000	Champions	Runners-up	Relegated
	Otley	Birmingham & Solihull	Reading & Blackheath

Most
Penalties: 61 Lee Osborne (Lydney)

Points: 274 Adam Mounsey (Wharfedale)
Conversions: 61 Dan Clappison (Otley)

Tries: 22 Mark Kirby (Otley)
D.Gs: 3 by three players

2000-01	Champions	Runners-up	Relegated
	Bracknell	Rugby Lions	Camberley, Lydney & West Hartlepool

Most
Penalties: 47 Jonathan Gregory (Esher)

Points: 260 Jonathan Gregory (Esher)
Conversions: 44 Mike Scott (Kendal)

Tries: 17 Ed Smithies (Harrogate)
D.Gs: 2 by three players

ALL TIME RECORDS — TEAM RECORDS — DIVISION THREE

Highest score:	103	Otley 103 Blackheath 3. 04.12.99
Highest aggregate:	106	As above
Highest score by a losing side:	42	Walsall 42 Reading 44. 12.4.97
Highest scoring draw:	34	Reading v Rosslyn Park. 17.2.96
Most consecutive wins:	14	Exeter 1996-97
Most consecutive defeats:	26	26 West Hartlepool 2000-01
Most points for in a season:	1209	Leeds 1996-97
Least points for in a season:	46	Birmingham Solihull 1987-88
Most points against in a season:	1347	Clifton 1996-97
Least points against in a season:	89	Plymouth 1988-89
Most tries for in a season:	158	Leeds 1996-97
Most tries against in a season:	184	Clifton 1996-97
Least tries for in a season:	3	Birmingham Solihull 1987-88
Least tries against in a season:	5	Plymouth 1988-89
Most conversions for in a season:	94	Leeds 1996-97
Most conversions against in a season:	125	Clifton 1996-97
Most penalties for in a season:	85	Fylde 1996-97
Most penalties against in a season:	74	Otley 1996-97
Least penalties for in a season:	8	Morley 1987-88
Least penalties against in a season:	10	West Hartlepool 1990-91
Most drop goals for in a season:	8	Morley 1994-95, London Welsh 1996-97
Most drop goals against in a season:	8	Rotherham 1995-96, Havant 1996-97

ALL TIME RECORDS — INDIVIDUAL RECORDS — DIVISION THREE

Most points in a season:	404	Steve Gough (Fylde) 1996-97
Most tries in a season:	29	Nick Baxter (Worcester) 1997-98
Most conversions in a season:	64	Craig Raymond (London Welsh) 1997-98
Most penalties in a season:	82	Steve Gough (Fylde) 1996-97
Most drop goals in a season:	8	Jamie Grayson (Morley) 1995-96
Most points in a match:	42	Mike Scott *Kendal* v W Hartlepool 27.1.01
Most tries in a match:	6	Nick Baxter, *Worcester* v Otley 21.2.98
Most conversions in a match:	12	Paul Brett, *Liverpool St. Helens* v Clifton 15.2.97
Most penalties in a match:	9	Paul Morris, *Lydney* v Otley 14.9.96
		Rob Ashworth, *Havant* v Clifton 21.9.96
Most drop goals in a match:	4	Andy Rimmer, *Broughton Park* v Sheffield 17.11.90

ALL TIME RECORDS — MOST POINTS IN A SEASON — DIVISION THREE

Points	Player	Club	Season	Tries	Cons.	Pens.	D.G.
404	Steve Gough	Fylde	1996-97	7	57	82	3
365	Steve Swindells	Manchester	1998-99	7	60	70	0
338	Richard Mills	Walsall	1996-97	1	42	81	2
322	Sateki Tuipulotu	Leeds	1997-98	11	60	49	
307	Gerry Ainscough	Leeds	1996-97	14	45	49	
305	Ralph Zoing	Harrogate	1996-97	4	63	48	5
300	Andy Green	Exeter	1996-97	5	58	50	3
300	Craig Raymond	London Welsh	1996-97	6	39	57	7
287	Peter Rutledge	Otley	1996-97	8	56	45	
281	Jason Dance	Reading	1996-97	6	61	43	
275	Paul Morris	Lydney	1996-97	3	31	66	
274	Adam Mounsey	Wharfedale	99-2000	7	37	55	
272	Chris Atkinson	Nottingham	1998-99	2	35	64	
264	Craig Raymond	London Welsh	1997-98	8	64	29	3
262	Chris Atkinson	Nottingham	1997-98	6	30	64	
262	Dan Clappison	Otley	99-2000	1	61	42	3
260	Jonathan Gregory	Esher	2000-01	7	42	47	-
248	Lee Osborne	Lydney	99-2000	3	25	61	
247	Adam Mounsey	Wharfedale	1997-98	4	31	55	
246	Jason Dance	Reading	1997-98	4	35	52	
235	David Pears	Wharfedale	1998-99	5	24	50	4
235	Mike Scott	Kendal	2000-01	6	44	37	2
228	Andy Finnie	Bedford	1994-95		24	56	4
221	Guy Gregory	Camberley	1998-99	2	29	50	1
219	Chris Glynn	Preston	2000-01	8	40	33	-
219	Russell Southam	Nottingham	2000-01	9	36	33	1
216	Richard Lebas	Worcester	1997-98	9	60	16	1
215	Ralph Zoing	Harrogate	1995-96	3	19	51	3
210	Paul Brett	Liverpool St Helens	1996-97	14	40	20	
206	Jamie Grayshon	Morley	1995-96	2	20	44	8
197	Sateki Tuipulotu	Leeds	1996-97	15	37	16	
196	John Gregory	Richmond	1995-96	4	28	40	
195	Jamie Grayshon	Morley	1996-97	2	40	31	4
194	Nick Booth	Fylde	99-2000	4	24	42	
193	Jason Dance	Reading	1998-99	1	28	49	
190	Matt Duncombe	Harrogate	99-2000	7	31	28	3
183	Jim Quantrill	Rugby	1995-96	3	21	42	
182	Adam Mounsey	Wharfedale	1996-97	10	39	18	
178	Andy Maddock	Rosslyn Park	1997-98	4	28	32	2
172	Andy Finnie	Bedford	1993-94		14	45	3
172	Nick Grecian	Newbury	1997-98	3	35	29	
171	Jim Quantrill	Rugby	1997-98	6	33	25	
171	Adam Mounsey	Wharfedale	2000-01	7	11	38	-
170	Matt Birch	Birmingham & S	1998-99	1	30	35	
167	Peter Rutledge	Otley	1994-95	6	13	37	
166	Jamie Grayshon	Morley	1994-95	2	12	39	5
166	Jonathan Smart	Birm & Solihull	99-2000	3	23	34	1
161	Lee Cholewa	Harrogate	2000-01	3	31	28	-
157	Paul Roblin	Rosslyn Park	2000-01	2	39	21	2
155	Kevin Plant	Rotherham	1995-96		18	35	5
155	Tom Rolt	Nottingham	99-2000	7	24	24	
150	Peter Rutledge	Otley	1997-98	3	21	31	

ALL TIME RECORDS — MOST POINTS IN A MATCH — DIVISION THREE

42	Mike Scott	Kendal v W Hartlepool	27.01.01
39	Paul Brett	Liverpool St Helens v Clifton	15.02.97
30	Paul Brett	Liverpool St Helens v Redruth	01.02.97
	Nick Baxter	Worcester v Otley	21.02.98
29	Paul Morris	Lydney v Otley	14.09.96
	Rob Ashworth	Havant v Clifton	21.09.96
	Adam Mounsey	Wharfedale v Reading	15.01.00
28	Steve Burnage	Fylde v Birmingham	07.11.87
	Craig Raymond	London Welsh v Clifton	28.12.96
	Jaques Steyn	Rugby v Camberley	02.12.00

27

Ralph Zoing	Harrogate v Fylde	14.10.95
Gerry Ainscough	Leeds v Rosslyn Park	14.09.96
Craig Raymond	London Welsh v Lydney	09.11.96
Gerry Ainscough	Leeds v Walsall	01.03.97
Nat Saumi	Redruth v Clifton	03.05.97
Adam Standeven	Morley v Newbury	25.04.98
David Pears	Wharfedale v Fylde	23.09.00

26

Greg Way	Reading v Harrogate	16.09.95
Andy Green	Exeter v Wharfedale	07.09.96
Richard Mills	Walsall v Clifton	07.09.96
Sateki Tuipulotu	Leeds v Nottingham	18.10.97
Craig Raymond	London Welsh v Wharfedale	21.03.98
Jason Dance	Reading v Liverpool St H	25.04.98
Duncan Roke	Henley Hawks v Camberley	06.02.99
John Gregory	Esher v Newbury	17.02.01

25

Domonic Cundy	Plymouth v Met Police	26.11.89
Mark Rodgers	Sheffield v Askeans	13.03.93
Richard Angell	Coventry v Redruth	30.04.94
Steve Gough	Fylde v Rosslyn Park	26.10.96
Mark Kirkby	Otley v Redruth	08.02.97
Jason Dance	Reading v Clifton	01.03.97
Richard Mills	Walsall v Redruth	19.04.97
Simon Middleton	Leeds v Morley	14.02.98
Matt Hoskin	Manchester v Camberley	12.09.98
Steve Swindells	Manchester v Liverpool St H	28.12.98
Steve Swindells	Manchester v Wharfedale	17.04.99
Matt Duncombe	Harrogate v Blackheath	18.03.00
Jim Quantrill	Birmingham Solihull v Preston G	23.10.99

24

Chris Howard	Rugby v Maidstone	26.11.88
Richard Mills	Walsall v Leeds	12.10.96
Jason Dance	Reading v Walsall	29.03.97
Ralph Zoing	Harrogate v Clifton	05.04.97
Steve Gough	Fylde v London Welsh	26.04.97
Ralph Zoing	Harrogate v Liverpool St H	17.05.97
Nick Booth	Fylde v Blackheath	15.01.00

23

John Stabler	West Hartlepool v Broughton Park	09.03.91
Ralph Zoing	Harrogate v Reading	16.09.95
John Gregory	Richmond v Rotherham	30.09.95
Phil Belshaw	Reading v Morley	14.10.95
Peter Rutledge	Otley v Walsall	09.11.96
Craig Raymond	London Welsh v Rosslyn Park	18.02.97
Jamie Grayshon	Morley v London Welsh	12.04.97
Murray Withington	Morley v Lydney	22.11.97
Richard Le Bas	Worcester v Otley	07.02.98
Nick Grecian	Newbury v Liverpool St H	21.02.98
Morgan Davies	Newbury v Nottingham	11.04.98
Nick Paisley	Lydney v Reading	05.12.98
Guy Gregory	Camberley v Birmingham & S	19.12.98
Ben Stafford	Camberley v Nottingham	10.10.99
Dan Clappison	Otley v Blackheath	04.12.99
Chris Glynn	Preston v Camberley	25.03.00
Adam Mounsey	Wharfedale v Esher	23.12.00

22

Andy Atkinson	Wakefield v Met Police	24.09.88
Simon Hogg	Clifton v Lydney	28.03.92
Kevin O'Brien	Broughton Park v Askeans	11.04.92
Martin Livesey	Richmond v Blackheath	13.11.93
Peter Rutledge	Otley v Harrogate	29.10.94
Gerry Ainscough	Leeds v Harrogate	05.10.96
Sateki Tuipulotu	Leeds v Lydney	15.03.97
Richard Mills	Walsall v Reading	12.04.97
Gerry Ainscough	Leeds v Havant	26.04.97
James Reid	Lydney v Harrogate	17.01.98
Steve Swindells	Manchester v Camberley	12.09.98
David Pears	Wharfedale v Liverpool St. H	07.11.98
Lee Osborne	Lydney v Liverpool St. H	13.03.99
Ben Stafford	Camberley v Manchester	13.03.99
Stuart Hibbert	Rosslyn Park v Harrogate	30.10.99
Ben Nowak	Bracknell v Harrogate	24.02.01
Brad Mooar	Rosslyn Park v Preston	16.09.00
Barry Muir	Rugby v W Hartlepool	30.09.00
Paul Turner	Rugby v Kendal	14.04.01
Ross Winney	W Hartlepool v Preston	23.09.00

ALL TIME RECORDS — MOST TRIES IN A MATCH — DIVISION THREE

6

Nick Baxter	Worcester v Otley	21.02.98

5

Mark Kirkby	Otley v Redruth	08.02.97
Simon Middleton	Leeds v Morley	14.02.98
Matt Hoskin	Manchester v Camberley	12.09.98

4

Brendan Hanavan	Fylde v Exeter	03.10.87
Steve Walklin	Plymouth v Birmingham	17.10.87
Ian Russell	Plymouth v Fylde	31.10.87
Brendan Hanavan	Fylde v Birmingham	07.11.87
Dan Cottrell	Clifton v Askeans	04.01.92
Mark Sephton	Liverpool St H v Aspatria	13.03.93
Dean Crompton	Liverpool St H v Aspatria	13.03.93
Mark Farrar	Otley v Askeans	27.03.93
Brendan Hanavan	Fylde v Redruth	09.04.94
Richard Matthias	Leeds v Clifton	07.12.96
Simon Dovell	Exeter v Havant	21.12.96
Ben Wade	Morley v Clifton	18.01.97
Mark Sephton	Liverpool StH v Clifton	15.02.97
Colin Stephens	Leeds v Lydney	15.03.97
Toby Rakison	Rosslyn Park v Otley	29.03.97
Steve Bartliffe	Leeds v Havant	26.04.97
Nick Baxter	Worcester v L St Helens	21.03.98
Alan Royer	Nottingham v L St. Helens	28.11.98
Jeremy Griffiths	Newbury v Harrogate	02.01.99
Lafaele Filipo	Otley v Reading	03.04.99
Mark Kirby	Otley v Blackheath	04.12.99
Iain Bruce	Preston G. v Camberley	25.03.00
Mike Scott	Kendal v W Hartlepool	27.01.01

3

Kevin Norris	Plymouth v Sheffield	12.09.87
Mark Preston	Fylde v Morley	17.10.87
Simon Cowling	Wakefield v Birmingham	31.10.87
Simon Cowling	Wakefield v Nuneaton	05.12.87
Andy Holloway	Wakefield v Morley	12.03.88
Mike Cathery	Exeter v Birmingham	26.03.88
Owen Evans	W Hartlepool v Nuneaton	23.04.88
Chris Howard	Rugby v Vale of Lune	10.09.88
Mike Harrison	Wakefield v Met Police	24.09.88
Andy Atkinson	Wakefield v Met Police	24.09.88
Simon Hughes	Plymouth v Fylde	19.11.88
Paul Galvin	Met Police v Maidstone	14.01.89
Mike Murtagh	Wakefield v Askeans	11.11.89
Gareth Hughes	Lon. Welsh v Fylde	13.01.90
Mike Harrison	Wakefield v Lon. Welsh	28.04.90
Dan Cottrell	Clifton v Broughton Park	13.10.90
Andy Green	Exeter v Met Police	10.11.90
Mark Spearman	Clifton v Exeter	17.11.90
Peter Robinson	W Hartlepool v Vale of Lune	02.03.91
Gary Walker	Roundhay v Askeans	06.04.91
Mark Chatterton	Exeter v Headingley	23.11.91
Andy Ireland	Fylde v Askeans	14.12.91
Phil Della-Savina	Richmond v Nuneaton	28.03.92
Glyn Mellville	Otley v Aspatria	24.10.92
Chris Thornton	Leeds v Exeter	13.03.93
Harry Langley	Exeter v Broughton Park	24.04.93
Martin Kelly	Broughton Park v Exeter	24.04.93
Mike Friday	Blackheath v Morley	06.11.93
Tony Brooks	Rosslyn Park v Havant	12.03.94
Tony Clark	Morley v Bedford	25.02.92
Eddie Saunders	Rugby v Bedford	12.04.92
Eddie Saunders	Rugby v Rotherham	23.09.92
Julian Horrobin	Coventry v Otley	30.03.96
Andy Clarke	Richmond v Rosslyn Park	13.04.96
Mark Preston	Fylde v Clifton	14.09.96

Simon Dovell	Exeter v Harrogate	21.09.96
Mark Kirkby	Otley v Clifton	05.10.96
Brian Gabrial	Morley v Wharfedale	19.10.96
Bob Armstrong	Exeter v Redruth	19.10.96
Richard Matthias	Leeds v Redruth	09.11.96
Andrew Hodgson	Wharfedale v Walsall	18.01.97
Paul Brett	Liverpool StH v Redruth	01.02.97
Guy Spencer	Reading v Lydney	08.02.97
Andrew Hodgson	Wharfedale v Lon. Welsh	15.02.97
Paul Brett	Liverpool StH v Clifton	15.02.97
Julian Hill	Lydney v Lon. Welsh	22.02.97
Brit Pearce	Havant v Walsall	22.02.97
Mark Farrar	Harrogate v Lon. Welsh	01.03.97
Gerry Ainscough	Leeds v Walsall	01.03.97
Mark Scharrenberg	Reading v Liverpool St H	22.03.97
Danny Jones	Liverpool St H v Exeter	29.03.97
Mark Kirkby	Otley v Rosslyn Park	12.04.97
Nick Green	Leeds v Clifton	12.04.97
Mark Appleson	Leeds v Clifton	12.04.97
Iain Dixon	Exeter v Otley	26.04.97
Andrew Hodgson	Wharfedale v Rosslyn Park	03.05.97
Kevin Hickey	Worcester v Wharfedale	11.10.97
Jim Jenner	Worcester v Morley	08.11.97
Brian Johnson	Newbury v Wharfedale	08.11.97
Craig Davies	Newbury v Harrogate	15.11.97
Chris Scott	Worcester v Reading	13.12.97
Tom Holloway	Newbury v Harrogate	10.01.98
Scott Roskell	London Welsh v Lydney	10.01.98
Nick Baxter	Worcester v Harrogate	31.01.98
Simon Middleton	Leeds v Nottingham	31.01.98
Nick Baxter	Worcester v Wharfedale	07.02.98
Craig Davies	Newbury v Liverpool St H.	21.02.98
Mark Farrar	Harrogate v Nottingham	21.02.98
Liam McCormick	Rosslyn Park v Nottingham	14.03.98
Rob Myler	Worcester v Liverpool St. H.	21.03.98
Liam McCormick	Rosslyn Park v Wharfedale	18.04.98
Simon Middleton	Leeds v Nottingham	25.04.98
David Casado	Rosslyn Park v Birmingham & S	26.09.98
Dwayne Edwards	Lydney v Morley	07.11.98
Gavin Sharp	Henley Hawks v Liverpool St. H.	12.12.98
Tom Holloway	Newbury v Harrogate	02.01.99
Tyrone Howe	Newbury v Morley	16.01.99
Adam Mounsey	Wharfedale v Morley	27.02.99
Hugh Owen	Camberley v Nottingham	27.02.99
Elliott Spencer	Nottingham v Camberley	27.02.99
Sam Gardner	Otley v Birmingham Solihull	13.03.99
Peter Davies	Henley Hawks v Harrogate	27.03.99
Paul Price	Lydney v Camberley	02.10.99
Gary Monaghan	Preston G v Blackheath	06.11.99
Lafaele Filipo	Otley v Blackheath	04.12.99
Michael Lough	Preston G v Blackheath	18.12.99
Crawford Henderson	Rosslyn Park v Nottingham	15.01.00
Jamie Morley	Nottingham v Preston	12.02.00
Andrew Hodgson	Wharfedale v Blackheath	26.02.00
Mark Kirby	Otley v Reading	18.03.00
Mark Farrar	Harrogate v Blackheath	18.03.00
Mark Bradley	Nottingham v Blackheath	25.03.00
Mark Kirby	Otley v Blackheath	15.04.00
Crawford Henderson	Rosslyn Park v Blackheath	22.04.00
Jamie Morley	Nottingham v Preston	09.09.00
James Tapster	Harrogate v Esher	16.09.00
Chris Simmons	Newbury v Camberley	23.09.00
Campbell Aitken	Esher v W Hartlepool	14.10.00
James Justice	Rosslyn Park v Nottingham	28.10.00
Richard Wade	Harrogate v W Hartlepool	04.11.00
Ed Smithies	Harrogate v W Hartlepool	04.11.00
Ed Smithies	Harrogate v Fylde	11.11.00
Eddie Saunders	Rugby v Camberley	02.12.00
Steve Kearns	Rosslyn Park v W Hartlepool	16.12.00
Jaques Steyn	Rugby v Bracknell	16.12.00
Tim Collier	Rugby v Preston	23.12.00
Jamie Morley	Nottingham v W Hartlepool	23.12.00
Chris Ritchie	Rosslyn Park v Lydney	13.01.01
Matt Duncombe	Harroagte v W Hartlepool	13.01.01
Peter Taylor	Harrogate v W Hartlepool	13.01.01
Jason Balmer	Kendal v W Hartlepool	27.01.01
Jamie Morley	Nottingham v W Hartlepool	03.02.01
Jonathan Gregory	Esher v Newbury	17.02.01
Jason Balmer	Kendal v Harrogate	17.03.01
Guy Spencer	Bracknell v W Hartlepool	14.04.01
Guy Carpente	Bracknell v Camberley	24.03.01
Eddie Saunders	Rugby v Fylde	06.04.01
Eddie Saunders	Rugby v Camberley	21.04.01

TEN YEAR RECORDS   DIVISION THREE

SEASONS

Club	91-92	92-93	93-94	94-95	95-96	96-97	97-98	98-99	99-00	00-01
Askeans	7	10	-	-	-	-	-	-	-	-
Aspatria	-	9	-	-	-	-	-	-	-	-
Birmingham & Solihull	-	-	-	-	-	-	-	11	2	-
Broughton Park	6	11	-	-	-	-	-	-	-	-
Bedford	-	-	3	1	-	-	-	-	-	-
Blackheath	-	-	4	2	-	-	-	-	14	-
Bracknell	-	-	-	-	-	-	-	-	7	1
Camberley	-	-	-	-	-	-	-	9	12	-
Clifton	3	8	-	9	-	16	-	-	-	12
Coventry	-	-	1	-	1	-	-	-	-	-
Esher	-	-	-	-	-	-	-	-	-	8
Exeter	4	3	6	10	-	1	-	-	-	-
Fylde	2	-	2	-	10	2	-	-	9	9
Harrogate	-	-	-	7	6	5	14	12	6	5
Havant	-	2	9	-	-	14	-	-	-	-
Headingley	11	-	-	-	-	-	-	-	-	-
Henley	-	-	-	-	-	-	-	1	-	-
Kendal	-	-	-	-	-	-	-	-	-	4
Leeds	-	6	-	-	-	3	2	-	-	-
Liverpool St Helens	-	7	-	-	-	12	11	14	-	-
London Welsh	-	-	-	-	-	11	3	-	-	-
Lydney	13	-	-	-	-	10	12	8	10	13
Manchester	-	-	-	-	-	-	-	2	-	-
Morley	-	-	8	5	5	4	13	13	-	-
Newbury	-	-	-	-	-	-	6	6	5	10
Nottingham	-	-	-	-	-	-	7	4	11	11
Nuneaton	12	-	-	-	-	-	-	-	-	-
Otley	9	1	-	6	7	9	9	5	1	-
Plymouth Albion	-	12	-	-	-	-	-	-	-	-
Preston Grasshoppers	-	-	-	-	-	-	-	-	8	7
Reading	-	-	-	-	8	6	8	10	13	-
Redruth	5	4	10	-	-	15	-	-	-	-
Richmond	1	-	7	8	2	-	-	-	-	-
Rosslyn Park	-	-	5	4	9	8	5	3	4	3
Rotherham	-	-	-	-	4	-	-	-	-	-
Roundhay	10	-	-	-	-	-	-	-	-	-
Rugby	-	-	-	3	3	-	4	-	-	2
Sheffield	8	5	-	-	-	-	-	-	-	-
Walsall	-	-	-	-	-	13	-	-	-	-
Wharfedale	-	-	-	-	-	7	10	7	3	6
West Hartlepool	-	-	-	-	-	-	-	-	-	14
Worcester	-	-	-	-	-	-	1	-	-	-

NATIONAL DIVISION

THREE NORTH

LEAGUE TABLE SEASON 2000-01

	P	W	D	L	F	A	PD	Tries	Pens	PTS	Last 6 Matches W-D-L
Stourbridge	25	21	1	3	855	368	487	122	43	43	4-1-1
Sedgley Park	25	20	1	4	884	327	557	122	38	41	5-1-0
New Brighton	24	19	0	5	668	330	338	91	43	38	3-0-3
Doncaster	23	16	1	6	579	349	230	71	44	33	2-1-3
Nuneaton	26	15	1	10	594	605	-11	80	32	31	3-1-2
Dudley Kingswinford	24	11	1	12	485	516	-31	60	39	23	3-0-3
Liverpool St. Helens	25	10	0	15	511	666	-155	55	51	20	2-0-4
Bedford Athletic	24	8	0	16	368	611	-243	49	27	16	3-0-3
Morley	25	8	0	17	468	720	-252	61	31	16	1-0-5
Whitchurch	21	8	0	13	360	641	-281	44	24	16	0-0-6
Walsall	24	7	0	17	538	601	-63	71	38	14	2-0-4
Sandal	24	7	0	17	540	868	-328	73	27	14	3-0-3
Tynedale	18	6	1	11	279	311	-32	25	43	13	1-0-5
Aspatria	18	4	0	15	307	541	-234	35	30	8	1-0-5

REVIEW OF THE SEASON

Stourbridge finally got out of the division after spending their entire league career there. They have had a couple of near misses recently, finishing second in the two previous seasons, but this time they finally made it. Their new half back partnership of Bruce Fenley and Duncan Hughes had a major effect on the season and Hughes broke the record for points in a season and equaled the record for tries for the club in league rugby.

Sedgley Park after four years in the Division finally got some consistency away from home and pushed Stourbridge all the way. This season second place got you into a Play-off against the second placed side in National Three South with the winners getting promoted to National Two. New player coach Tim Fourie gave the side a new tougher mental edge and it paid dividends. Another new boy Colin Stephens, who controlled the backs and took on the kicking duties with great success, ably aided him.

New Brighton finished third for the third consecutive season in National Three North. They started the season well and put together an impressive run of 17 wins from their first 19 matches, the two losses were at Doncaster and Stourbridge. Their home record was impressive with excellent wins against both Stourbridge and Sedgley Park. Paul Brett had another outstanding season and led the division with 258 points whilst No 8 Steve Bellis ran in 16 tries in his first full season.

Doncaster finished fourth which was a two-place improvement on their first season in the division. They made the most impressive start to the season of all the sides and ran up nine successive wins before losing in a shock result at Dudley Kingswinford. At home they lost just once but away from home defeats at Nuneaton and Morley were costly.

Nuneaton had their best season in a while and will look to build on it in the coming season. Fifth placed equaled their best ever finish in this league which they achieved in the 1998-99 season. They only lost two successive matches once all season and did manage to put a dent in Stourbridges impressive home record coming away with a 13 all draw. Winger Gary Marshall had a brilliant season and notched up 20 tries easily the best ever by a Nuneaton player in league rugby.

Dudley Kingswinford acquitted themselves well in their first season off National League and finished a creditable sixth with 11 wins from their 24 matches. They started the season well and in their first six matches with four wins and a draw after losing at Walsall on the opening day of the season. They slipped up in December and January with five defeats from six matches. Full back Steve Smart made a major contribution with 230 points, which included an impressive 11 tries.

Tynedale had their season badly disrupted by the foot and mouth out break and only completed 18 of their 26 league fixtures. In their first season at National League level they had a mixed season but will be glad to stay up and have a full campaign in the coming season to do themselves justice. Outside half Alan Moses got quickly in the groove and his kicking proved vital in a number of matches. They did the double over Aspatria but overall they did not score enough points through tries, something they will need to work on for the coming season.

Liverpool St Helens managed 10 wins last season as they finished a credible seventh in the division, which was their best performance since 1995-96 when they won 11 matches in National Four. They found a reliable goal kicker, which helped their cause tremendously. Simon Worsley topped the 200-point mark as he set a new record for the club in a league season.

Bedford Athletic had an inconsistent season finishing eighth level on points with Morley and Whithurch, a one place improvement on the previous season. They did not score enough points with no player managing to pass the 100- point mark.

Morley had a disjointed season winning eight matches along the way. They only once managed to win more than one match in a row but did manage a four and five match losing run. They scored plenty of points but let in far to many

Whitchurch continue to defy the odds and thanks to some excellent home form again maintained their place in National League rugby. They had a run in November/December when they won five straight league matches, this run proved vital for their survival in the division. Outside half John Canney again topped the points scoring but could not do anything as they slumped to six straight defeats at the end of the season.

Sandal managed to maintain their National League status after the RFU awarded points for the matches not played because of the foot and mouth outbreak. They ended the season with two two-point wins in high scoring matches, which proved vital in their survival. Overall they managed four wins from their last seven matches having won just three of their first 17 league matches. They did find two try scorers in Jamie Barker and David Howarth and in Mark Sales they have one of the best goal kickers in the division so this coming season they will hope to be in the top half of the table.

Walsall found themselves relegated after the league table was adjusted after the fixtures not played because of the Foot and Mouth disease were decided by the RFU. After winning their opening match of the season they went on a run that was to be their downfall by the end of the season, they managed just one win out of the next 12 matches. A dreadful away record did not help their cause; they managed just one win on the road all season, that was a win at Nuneaton late in the season. Walsall go out of the National Leagues for the first time since 1991-92.

Aspatria played just 18 matches and had eight fixtures left when the official season ended. Aspatria had been a mainstay of the division and did remarkably well year in and year out despite having such a small catchment area and losing their better players to Rugby League. This season after struggling for four successive seasons this one proved too much and they fell out of the National Leagues for the first time since 1990-91. Over the last few years their home form has kept them out of the relegation area but their home form failed them and that proved vital.

2000-2001
RECORD REVIEW
(Individual Records)

MOST POINTS - IN A SEASON

Paul Brett topped the points scorers list for the second season in a row and becomes the first player to score 250 points in a season twice in the division. John Liley just fails to score 250 for a second successvie season finishing on 244.

EVOLUTION OF RECORD

118	Steve Kerry	Preston G'hoppers	1987-88
127	Paul Grayson	Preston G'hoppers	1991-92
131	Ralph Zoing	Harrogate	1992-93
164	Richard Mills	Walsall	1994-95
317	Steve Kerry	Preston G'hoppers	1996-97
398	Steve Swindells	Manchester	1997-98

ALL-TIME LIST

398	Steve Swindells	Manchester	1997-98
317	Steve Kerry	Preston G.	1996-97
302	Paul Brett	New Brighton	1999-00
296	Matt Birch	Birmingham & Sol.	1997-98
273	John Liley	Doncaster	1999-00
273	Casey Mee	Kendal	1999-00
271	Jonathon Smart	Birmingham & Sol.	1996-97
268	Ian Shuttleworth	Sandal	1997-98
258	Paul Brett	New Brighton	2000-01
251	Mike Scott	Aspatria	1996-97
251	Steve Swindells	Manchester	1996-97
248	Mark Hardcastle	Sandal	1996-97
244	John Liley	Doncaster	2000-01
243	Rob Pound	Sheffield	1997-98
242	Tim Smith	Worcester	1996-97

MOST TRIES - IN A SEASON

Nuneaton winger Gary Marshall topped the try scoring list with 20 tries - two clear of Mike Wilcock - both were club records for National League rugby. Next on the list was New Brighton No 8 Steve Bellis who scored 16 which was one short of the record for a forward held by his team mate Geoff Jones.

EVOLUTION OF RECORD

7	Eddie Saunders	Rugby	1987-88
10	Jim Mallinder	Roundhay	1988-89
16	Jon Walker	Otley	1990-91
18	Nick Baxter	Worcester	1996-97
21	Matt Hoskin	Manchester	1997-98
27	Michael Lough	Preston	1998-99

ALL-TIME LIST

27	Michael Lough	Preston	1998-99
25	Iain Bruce	Preston	1998-99
22	Chris Hall	Morley	1999-00
21	Matt Hoskin	Manchester	1997-98
20	Gary Marshall	Nuneaton	2000-01
19	Chris Conway	Doncaster	1999-00
19	Stephen Hanley	Aspatria	1997-98
18	Nick Baxter	Worcester	1996-97
18	Mike Wilcock	Sedgley Park	2000-01
17	Craig Marriott	Aspatria	1996-97
17	Richard Marsh	Walsall	1997-98
17	Ian Kennedy	New Brighton	1998-99
17	Gary Monaghan	Preston	1998-99
17	Geoff Jones	New Brighton	1999-00
16	Jon Walker	Otley	1990-91
16	Ben Shepherd	Birmingham & Sol.	1997-98
16	Steve Bellis	New Brighton	2000-01

MOST PENALTIES - IN A SEASON

Liverpool St Helens Simon Worsley was the leader in penalties last season with 50. That was enough to put him joint seventh on the All time list but some 14 off the record of 64.

EVOLUTION OF RECORD

21	Steve Kerry	Preston G'hoppers	1987-88
23	Jamie Grayshon	Morley	1988-89
28	Paul Grayson	Preston G'Hoppers	1990-91
31	Simon Pennington	Stourbridge	1992-93
31	Richard Mills	Walsall	1994-95
64	Steve Kerry	Preston G'hoppers	1996-97

ALL-TIME LIST

64	Steve Kerry	Preston G.	1996-97
62	Steve Swindells	Manchester	1997-98
55	Matt Birch	Birmingham & Sol.	1997-98
55	Ian Shuttleworth	Sandal	1997-98
53	Mark Hardcastle	Sandal	1996-97
48	Mike Scott	Aspatria	1996-97
48	Simon Worsley	Liverpool St H	2000-01
43	Jonathan Smart	Birmingham & Sol	1996-97
43	Rob Pound	Sheffield	1997-98
43	Alan Moses	Tynedale	2000-01
43	Paul Brett	New Brighton	2000-01

MOST CONVERSIONS - IN A SEASON

Not a season for conversions with Cloin Stephens the only man to reach 50. He did so in his debut season for the club as they finished second in the table and went on to win the Play-off against Launceston for the right to go into National Two.

EVOLUTION OF RECORD

12	Steve Kerry	Preston G'hoppers	1987-88
	Chris Howard	Rugby	1987-88
13	Gary Walker	Roundhay	1988-89
17	Jon Howarth	Otley	1990-91
28	Ralph Zoing	Harrogate	1992-93
29	Richard Mills	Walsall	1994-95
61	Tim Smith	Worcester	1996-97
91	Steve Swindells	Manchester	1997-98

ALL-TIME LIST

91	Steve Swindells	Manchester	1997-98
61	Tim Smith	Worcester	1996-97
58	Matt Birch	Birmingham & Solihull	1997-98
53	Martin Emmett	Preston	1998-99
53	Casey Mee	Kendal	1999-00
51	Paul Brett	New Brighton	1999-00
50	Colin Stephens	Sedgley Park	2000-01
50	Chris Mann	Stourbridge	1996-97
50	Colin Stephens	Sedgley Park	2000-01
49	Steve Swindells	Manchester	1996-97
47	Jonathan Smart	Birmingham & Solihull	1996-97

MOST DROP GOALS - IN A SEASON

Liverpool St Helens' outside half Simon Worsley finished leading drop goal scorer as well as penalty kicker with five. That was enough to put him into joint third on the all time list.

EVOLUTION OF RECORD

5	Steve Kerry	Preston G'hoppers	1987-88
6	Paul Grayson	Preston G'hoppers	1991-92
9	Steve Kerry	Preston G'hoppers	1996-97

ALL-TIME LIST

9	Steve Kerry	Preston G'hoppers	1996-97
6	Paul Grayson	Preston G'hoppers	1991-92
5	Steve Kerry	Preston G'hoppers	1987-88
5	Simon Worsley	Liverpool St Helens	2000-01
4	Richard Mills	Walsall	1990-91
4	Ian Shuttleworth	Sandal	1997-98
4	Rob Pound	Sheffield	1997-98
4	Colin Stephens	Sedgley Park	2000-01

2000-01

NATIONAL DIVISION THREE NORTH

MOST POINTS

POINTS			T	C	P	DG
258	Paul Brett	New Brighton	9	42	43	-
244	John Liley	Doncaster	9	41	39	-
235	Colin Stephens	Sedgley Park	6	50	31	4
230	Steve Smart	Dudley King'ford	11	32	37	-
228	Simon Worsley	Liverpool St Helens	1	32	48	5
224	Duncan Hughes	Stourbridge	15	37	25	-
167	Mike Crisp	Walsall	3	25	33	1
163	David Evans	Morley	4	28	29	-
159	Alan Moses	Tynedale	1	11	43	1
145	John Canney	Whitchurch	1	34	24	-
139	Rob Moon	Sedgley Park	14	24	7	-
139	Warwick Masser	Nuneaton	1	37	20	-
135	Mark Sales	Sandal	1	38	18	-
100	Garry Marshall	Nuneaton	20	-	-	-
94	Ashley Tapper	Bedford Athletic	3	14	17	-
91	Simon Baylie	Stourbridge	10	7	9	-
90	Mike Wilcock	Sedgley Park	18	-	-	-
80	Steve Bellis	New Brighton	16	-	-	-

MOST PENALTIES

48	Simon Worsley	Liverpool St H
43	Paul Brett	New Brighton
43	Alan Moses	Tynedale
39	John Liley	Doncaster
37	Steve Smart	Dudley Kings'ford
33	Mike Crisp	Walsall
31	Colin Stephens	Sedgley Park
29	Dave Evans	Morley
25	Duncan Hughes	Stourbridge
24	John Canney	Whitchurch
20	Warwick Masser	Nuneaton
18	Mark Sales	Sandal
17	Ashley Tapper	Bedford Ath
14	Steven Stoddart	Aspatria

MOST TRIES

20	Garry Marshall	Nuneaton
18	Mike Wilcock	Sedgley Park
16	Steve Bellis	New Brighton
15	Duncan Hughes	Stourbridge
15	Jamie Barker	Sandal
14	Rob Moon	Sedgley Park
13	Paul Morris	Sedgley Park
13	Emrys Evans	New Brighton
13	Geoff Jones	New Brighton
13	Derek Eves	Doncaster
12	Shaun Perry	Dudley Kings'ford
12	Jon Hall	Stourbridge
12	David Howarth	Sandal
11	Steve Smart	Dudley Kings'ford
11	Jacob John	Stourbridge
11	Tom Beechy	Walsall
10	Simon Baylie	Stourbridge
10	Rob Myler	Stourbridge
10	Ben Fenley	Stourbridge
10	Spencer Bradley	Stourbridge
10	Jon Scales	Sedgley Park

MOST CONVERSIONS

50	Colin Stephens	Sedgley Park
42	Paul Brett	New Brighton
41	John Liley	Doncaster
38	Mark Sales	Sandal
37	Duncan Hughes	Stourbridge
37	Warwick Masser	Nuneaton
34	John Canney	Whitchurch
32	Simon Worsley	Liverpool StH
32	Steve Smart	Dudley K
28	David Evans	Morley
25	Mike Crisp	Walsall
14	Ashley Tapper	Bedford Ath
12	Steven Stoddart	Aspatria
11	Alan Moses	Tynedale

MOST DROP GOALS

5	Simon Worsley	Liverpool St. H
4	Colin Stephens	Sedgley Park
2	Gareth Williams	Bedford Ath
1	Mike Crisp	Walsall
1	Alan Moses	Tynedale
1	Jamie Grayshon	Morley
1	Scott Evans	Morley

NATIONAL DIVISION 3 NORTH

FIXTURES 2001-02

NATIONAL DIVISION THREE NORTH

Away Teams

HOME TEAMS	1 Bedford Athletic	2 Blaydon	3 Darlington M.P.	4 Doncaster	5 Dudley K.	6 Liverpool-St H.	7 Morley	8 New Brighton	9 Nuneaton	10 Sandal	11 Scunthorpe	12 Tynedale	13 West Hartlepool	14 Whitchurch
1 Bedford Athletic		22.09	2.02	20.10	1.09	30.03	5.01	6.04	17.11	19.01	8.12	3.11	23.02	16.03
2 Blaydon	9.03		5.01	17.11	9.02	8.09	1.12	6.10	15.12	13.04	26.01	30.03	19.01	27.10
3 Darlington Mowden Park	27.10	24.11		8.12	10.11	9.02	6.10	26.01	9.03	8.09	6.04	1.12	22.12	12.01
4 Doncaster	9.02	12.01	13.04		26.01	6.10	9.03	27.10	8.09	1.12	22.12	15.12	24.11	10.11
5 Dudley Kingswinford	1.12	20.10	19.01	3.11		15.12	13.04	8.09	30.03	5.01	9.03	17.11	2.02	23.02
6 Liverpool-St Helens	22.12	16.03	20.10	23.02	6.04		17.11	8.12	19.01	3.11	24.11	2.02	22.09	1.09
7 Morley	24.11	1.09	23.02	22.09	8.12	12.01		22.12	3.11	2.02	10.11	20.10	16.03	6.04
8 New Brighton	15.12	23.02	3.11	2.02	16.03	13.04	30.03		5.01	17.11	1.12	19.01	20.10	22.09
9 Nuneaton	12.01	6.04	22.09	16.03	22.12	10.11	26.01	24.11		20.10	27.10	23.02	1.09	8.12
10 Sandal	10.11	8.12	16.03	1.09	24.11	26.01	27.10	12.01	9.02		6.10	22.09	6.04	22.12
11 Scunthorpe	13.04	3.11	15.12	30.03	22.09	5.01	19.01	1.09	2.02	23.02		16.03	17.11	20.10
12 Tynedale	26.01	22.12	1.09	6.04	12.01	27.10	9.02	10.11	6.10	9.03	8.09		8.12	24.11
13 West Hartlepool	6.10	10.11	30.03	5.01	27.10	9.03	8.09	9.02	1.12	15.12	12.01	13.04		26.01
14 Whitchurch	8.09	2.02	17.11	19.01	6.10	1.12	15.12	9.03	13.04	30.03	9.02	5.01	3.11	

BEDFORD ATHLETIC RUFC

Chairman	Paul McGuckian	c/o Bedford Athletic RUFC, Putnoe Wood, Wentworth Drive, Bedford MK41 8QA 01234 350874
Secretary	Paul Bowker	Flat 5, 74 Chaucer Road, Bedford MK40 2AP 01234 342442 (H) 07720 769310 (M)
Fixture Secretary	John Ross	63 Avon Drive, Bedford MK41 7UR 01234 305814 (H) 01234 225116 (B)
Programme Advertising	Jenny Cullen	14 Wilden Road, Renhold, Beds. MK41 0JP 01234 772007 (H) 0410 044400 (B)

An eventful, unsettling season that saw the 'Ath' not only having to deal with the havoc to fixtures caused by the Foot and Mouth outbreak but also the resignations of the Club Coach and 1st Team Manager due to the poor performances of the team. However, help was at hand in the shape of Neil Beytell and Steve Spring, the successful team that guided the 'Ath' to their unbeaten season in 1999-2000. Neil and Steve, ably assisted by new forwards coach, Chris Godfrey, achieved their immediate goal of keeping the club in National Three.

Although, the club has lost Giles Witheat to Bedford Blues, they have been fortunate enough to recruit players such as Phil and Jamie Elphick and Tim Otte from senior clubs with more players in the pipeline. Most of last season's squad have remained with the club and players such as Ashley Tapper, Simon Lincoln, Andy Gallagher, Mike Hudson, Ian Skingsley, Paul Simmonds and Jon Wells cannot wait to carry on where they left off last season.

The club has also been successful on the Colts front with Dean Taylor and Simon Williams coming through to play for the 1st XV, justifying that players within the club can make it to the required level.

Under the coaching of Neil and Chris the standard of personal fitness is high and training on Tuesdays and Thursdays, is for the whole club and not just the 1st XV squad. Moral is also very high and with James Thorpe being appointed as 1st Team Captain, the club are looking to a very exciting season and hope to provide some of the best rugby in the Bedfordshire area.

FACT FILE

Founded: 1908
Nickname: 'The Ath'

Colours: Black and white hoops/black/black
Change colours: Black shirts, blue shorts

GROUND
Address: Putnoe Woods, Wentworth Drive, Bedford MK41 8QA
Tel: 01234 350874   Website: www.bedfordathrugby.com

Capacity: 400 all uncovered standing

Nearest Railway station: Bedford Midland Road

Car Parking: Spaces for approx. 50 cars at clubhouse.

Admission: £5 incl. programme   Senior citizens £2.50   u16s Free

Clubhouse: Open matchdays and training evenings.

Club Shop: Selling general rugby kit & 'Ath' polo shirts & sweaters etc.

Training Nights   Tuesday & Thursday

PROGRAMME   Size: A5   Price: with admission   Pages: 24 + cover
Advertising: Contact Jenny Cullen

BEDFORD ATHLETIC

Comp.	Date	H/A	Opponents	Result & Score	Att	15	14	13	12	11
N3 N	2-Sep	A	Aspatria	L 20-30	200	Guguen	Williams	Lincoln	Philips	Witheat
N3 N	16-Sep	A	Dudley Kingswinford	L 7-21	500	Guguen	Witheat	Smith	Philips	Morrison
N3 N	23-Sep	H	Morley	W 25-17	250	Guguen	Witheat	Lincoln/t	Philips	Jackson
N3 N	30-Sep	A	Nuneaton	L 13-22		Guguen	Philips	Lincoln	Smith	Jackson/t
N3 N	14-Oct	H	Sedgley Park	W 23-18	300	Guguen	Morrison	Lincoln/2c	Witheat/t	Jackson
N3 N	28-Oct	H	Whitchurch	L 10-26		Tapper	Gallagher	Lincoln	Witheat	Morrison/t
N3 N	11-Nov	A	Doncaster	L 17-32	450	Guguen	Wells/t	Philips	Witheat	Lincoln
N3 N	18-Nov	H	Liverpool St Helens	L 19-20	400	Guguen	Wells	Lincoln	Witheat	Morrison/t
N3 N	25-Nov	A	New Brighton	L 7-31	250	Guguen	Lincoln	Philips	Witheat	Morrison
N3 N	2-Dec	H	Sandal	W 24-19		Guguen	Wells	Philips	Witheat	Lincoln/2t
N3 N	16-Dec	H	Walsall	W 24-16	200	Guguen/t	Wells	Philips	Witheat/t	Lincoln
N3 N	23-Dec	A	Sandal	L 18-24		Guguen	Wells/t	Philips/t	Tapper	Jackson
N3 N	6-Jan	A	Liverpool St Helens	L 20-26		Tapper/t2c2p	Wells	Lincoln	Philips	Houghton
N3 N	13-Jan	H	Doncaster	L 0-18		Tapper	Guguen	Lincoln	Witheat	Wells
N3 N	27-Jan	H	Tynedale	W 29-22	150	Guguen	Vucucevic	Lincoln/t	Witheat/t	Wells
N3 N	3-Feb	A	Tynedale*	L 10-24	200	Guguen	Wells	Lincoln	Witheat	Vuvucevic
N3 N	10-Feb	A	Sedgley Park	L 0-69		Williams	Guguen	Vuvucevic	Witheat	Lincoln
N3 N	17-Feb	A	Stourbridge	L 20-37	200	Guguen	Lincoln	Philips	Witheat	Williams/t
N3 N	24-Feb	H	Nuneaton	L 8-25		Guguen	Lincoln	Philips	Witheat	Williams
N3 N	10-Mar	A	Morley	L 14-35		Williams	Wells	Lincoln	Witheat	Philips
N3 N	31-Mar	A	Walsall	W 15-10		Williams	Wells	Lincoln	Witheat/t	Philips
N3 N	14-Apr	H	Stourbridge	L 13-27		Guguen	Wells	Witheat	Lincoln	Philips
N3 N	28-Apr	H	Dudley Kingswinford	W 27-22	150	Wells/t	Taylor	Lincoln	Witheat/t	Philips
N3 N	5-May	H	New Brighton	W 23-20		Wells/t	Taylor/t	Lincoln	Witheat	Philips
TBC	7-Oct	A	Preston G'hoppers	L 19-49	250	Guguen	Smith/t	Lincoln	Philips	Jackson

*after opponents name indicates a penalty try. Brackets after a player's name indicates he was replaced.
eg (a) means he was replaced by replacement code "a" and so on. / after a player or replacement name
is followed by any scores he made - eg /t, /c, /p, /dg or any combination of these*

EVER PRESENT	None

MOST APPEARANCES

22	Simon Lincoln.
21	Giles Witheat.
20	Ross Thompson.
19	Andy Gallagher, Gareth Williams.

MOST POINTS

Pts	Player	T	C	P	DG
97	A Tapper	3	14	18	-
61	G Williams	2	9	9	2
25	A Gallagher	5	-	-	-
25	G Witheat	5	-	-	-
24	S Lincoln	4	2	-	-

MATCH FACTS

10	9	1	2	3	4	5	6	7	8
Tapper/2c2p	Gallagher/t	Steele	Simmonds/t	Buckle	Mihajlovic	Wells	Brown	Reynolds	Thompson
Tapper/c	Gallagher	Blower/t	Stapleton	Dorling	Mihajlovic	Wells	Thompson	Thorp	Alston
Tapper/t2c2p	Gallagher	Blower	Stapleton	Dorling	Mihajlovic	Wells	Thompson	Thorp/t	Alston
Tapper/c2p	Gallagher	Blower	Stapleton	Dorling	Mihajlovic	Wells	Thompson	Thorp	Alston
Williams/dg(a/2p)	Gallagher	Blower	Simmonds/t	Dorling	Mihajlovic	Thompson	Mann	Thorp	Alston
Williams	Jackson	Blower/t	Simmonds	Buckle	Mihajlovic	Thompson	Mann	Thorp	Alston
Williams/2cp	Gallagher	Blower	Stapleton	Rainbow	Mihajlovic	Hudson	Mann	Reynolds/t	Thorp
Williams/3p	Gallagher	Blower	Stapleton	Rainbow	Mihajlovic	Hudson	Thorp	Reynolds	Alston
Williams/tc	Gallagher	Blower	Stapleton	Rainbow	Thompson	Hudson	Mann	Reynolds	Thorp
Williams/c	Gallagher/t	Haines	Stapleton/c	Dorling	Mihajlovic	Hudson	Periera	Thorp	Alston/t
Williams/3cdg	Gallagher/t	Haines	Simmonds	Dorling	Mihajlovic	Hudson	Thompson	Reynolds	Alston
Williams/c2p	Gallagher	Dorling	Simmonds	Blower	Wells	Hudson	Reynolds	Rainbow	Alston
Williams	Jackson	Haines	Simmonds	Dorling	Thompson	Hudson	Periera/t	Reynolds	Alston
Williams	Jackson	Haines	Simmonds	Dorling	Thompson	Hudson	Periera	Reynolds	Alston
Williams/p(a/3c)	Gallagher	Haines	Simmonds/t	Dorling/t	Mihajlovic	Hudson	Periera	Reynolds	Thompson
Williams/cp	Gallagher	Dorling	Simmonds	Haines	Mihajlovic	Hudson	Periera	Reynolds	Thompson
Tapper	Gallagher	Porter	Stapleton	Haines	Curry	Hudson	Periera	Reynolds	Thompson
Tapper/2c2p	Gallagher	Dorling	Reynolds/t	Haines	Curry	Hudson	Periera	Egan	Thompson
Tapper	Gallagher	Dorling	Reynolds	Haines	Curry	Hudson	Periera	Egan	Thompson
Tapper/3p	Jackson	Haines	Stapleton	Buckle	Mihajlovic	Hudson	Thorp	Reynolds	Thompson/t
Tapper	Gallagher	Dorling/t	Reynolds	Haines	Hudson/t	Thompson	Thorp	Egan	Skingsley
Tapper/tc2p	Jackson	Dorling	Reynolds	Buckle	Hudson	Mihajlovic	Thorp	Thompson	Skingsley
Tapper	Jackson	Dorling	Stapleton/tc	Buckle/t	Hudson	Thompson	Thorp	Reynolds	Skingsley/t
Williams/p	Gallagher/t	Dorling	Stapleton	Buckle	Hudson	Thompson	Thorp/t	Reynolds	Skingsley
Williams/c	Gallagher/t	Blower	Simmonds	Dorling	Mihajlovic/t	Thompson	Brown/c	Thorp	Alston

REPLACEMENTS   A Tapper

2000-01 HIGHLIGHTS

Outside half Ashley Tapper again topped the scoring charts for Bedford Athletic.

Tapper finished ahead of Gareth Williams, but it was the latter who scored using all four methods.

They were one of only four sides that managed to beat second placed Sedgley Park and they ended the season well with three wins from their last four league matches.

The only side they managed to do the double over were Walsall.

BEDFORD ATHLETIC

SEASON	Division	P	W	D	L	F	A	Pts Diff	Lge Pts	Lge Pos		Most Points		Most Tries
95-96	Mid 2	12	3	2	7	150	163	-13	8	10				
96-97	Mid 2	17	11	1	5	362	206	156	23	7				
97-98	Mid 2	16	16	0	0	718	151	567	32	1				
98-99	Mid 1	16	15	0	1	569	163	406	30	1		Ashley Tapper		Mike Curry & Adam Lowles
99-00	N2N	26	11	0	15	563	729	-162	22	9	164	Ashley Tapper	10	Paul Alston
00-01	N2N	*24	8	0	16	386	613	-227	16	10	94	Ashley Tapper	7	Simon Lincoln

BLAYDON RFC

President	James Buchanan FRCS	c/o Blaydon RFC	0191 285 3232 (H)
Chairman	Jim Huxley	The Mount, 59 Sunniside Rd., Sunniside, Newcastle upon Tyne NE16 5NF	
		0191 488 7280 P/F	0788 4358060
Director of Rugby	Andy Howells	c/o Blaydon RFC	07950 927745 (M)
Secretary	George March	c/o Blaydon RFC	01207 545397 (H)
Fixture Secretary	Hedley Redpath	13 Bridgewater Close, West Denton, Newcastle upon Tyne NE15 8UT.	
		0191 267 3805 (H)	

Blaydon RFC, Crow Trees, Hexham Rd., Swalwell, Newcastle upon Tyne NE16 3BM 0191 420 0505

After three seasons in North One, second place and a play-off success against Leicester Lions was well earned and satisfying for both the coaching and playing staff with supporters able to watch, undoubtedly, some of the best rugby ever seen at Crow Trees, a far cry from second bottom place in North East 1 in the inaugural season of league rugby.

Much of the credit must go to Director of Rugby Andy Howells who assembled a youthful and enthusiastic squad, ably led by David Guthrie in his seventh season as captain and under the auspices of New Zealander Graham Clarkson in his first season as player/coach.

It would be unfair to single out any player in particular, but the increasing presence of centre Dean Michniewicz, as the season progressed, along with the foraging runs of full back Gareth King gave the side both flair and continuity. This, backed up by a strong mobile pack, was always too strong for all the opposition sides excluding the league winner, who defeated us twice in well-contested games.

The club was also delighted to make an appearance at Twickenham in the Intermediate Cup Final, only to be beaten 25-24; given another five minutes the game would have been ours, having recovered from a 25-3 deficit and the opposition wilting. However, it was not to be, but three weeks later the club achieved us our main aim - promotion.

Blaydon are looking forward to the challenge in Three North, meeting new opposition and renewing old rivalries with Tynedale, New Brighton, Doncaster and West Hartlepool. We surely have the infrastructure to compete at this level with floodlights (two sets, match standard), a tremendous playing surface and what must be one of the best clubhouses in the region with its well appointed bars and supporting gymnasium, (Sportique).

The season opens at Morley and the week after Liverpool St. Helens are the first visitors, so Blaydon looks for-

Blaydon players and support staff celebrate winning the play-off for promotion to League 3 North.

BLAYDON

Comp.	Date	H/A	Opponents	Result & Score	15	14	13	12	11
North 1	02.09	H	Wigton	W 20-17	Knight/t	Gandy	Marriott/t	Hirst	I Dixon
North 1	16.09	A	Northern	W 43-15	King/t	Gandy/2t	Marriott/t	Michniewicz	Savory(c/t)
North 1	23.09	A	Chester	W 19-08	King	Hirst	Marriott	Michniewicz/t	Savory
North 1	30.09	A	Driffield	W 33-26	King	Spearman	Michniewicz/2t	Hirst	Savory
North 1	14.10	H	Middlesbrough	W 20-14	Michniewicz	Savory/t(f)	Marriott	Beattie	King
North 1	21.10	H	Sheffield	W 25-21	Michniewicz/2t	Hirst	Marriott	Beattie	King/2t
North 1	28.10	A	Stockton	W 35-17	Michniewicz/t	King/t	Marriott/t	Beattie(f)	Savory
North 1	11.11	H	Darlington M.P.	L 10-22	King/t	Savory	Marriott/t	Michniewicz(f)	Spearman
North 1	18.11	A	Hull Ionians	W 20-10	King/3t	Savory	Marriott	Hirst	Spearman
North 1	25.11	H	Bradford & Bingley	W 18-08	King/t	Savory	Marriott	Michniewicz	Spearman
North 1	09.12	A	Macclesfield	W 17-07	King	Savory	Marriott	Michniewicz/t	Spearman
North 1	23.12	H	Hull Ionians	W 31-08	King	Savory	Marriott	I Dixon/2t	Spearman
North 1	13.01	H	Stockton	W 55-05	King	Savory(c)	Marriott	Hirst/t	Spearman/t
North 1	10.02	H	Driffield	W 22-00	King/t	Savory	Michniewicz/t	I Dixon/cp	Spearman/t
North 1	17.02	A	Middlesbrough	W 16-12	King	Savory	Michniewicz	I Dixon/2p	Spearman
North 1	10.03	H	Northern	W 64-07	King/2t	I Dixon/2t2p4c	Michniewicz/t	Kilburn(f)	Savory/3t
North 1	31.03	H	Macclesfield	W 23-14	King	Savory	Michniewicz/t	I Dixon(p)	Spearman
North 1	14.04	A	Bradford & Bingley	W 40-31	King/2t	Wilson	I Dixon	Hirst/t	Spearman
North 1	28.04	A	Chester	W 39-25	King	Savory	Hirst	Michniewicz/t	Alexander/t
North 1	05.05	A	Sheffield	W 25-05	King/2t	Wilson(q)	Michniewicz	Hirst	Spearman/t
North 1	12.05	A	Darlington M.P.	L 15-34	King	Savory/t	Michniewicz	Hirst	Spearman/t
Play-Off	19.05	H	Leicester Lions	W 34-12	King	Savory/t	Kilburn/t(f)	Michniewicz/t	Spearman
IC 2	07.10	H	Westoe	W 30-13	Michniewicz/t	Spearman	Marriott/t	Beattie	Barlow/t(t)
IC 3	04.11	H	Ryton	W 49-20	I Dixon(v)	Savory/t	Marriott/t	Hirst/tdg	Spearman
IC 4	02.12	H	Old Aldwinians	W 41-08	King	I Dixon	Marriott/t	Michniewicz	Spearman(w/t)
IC 5	06.01	H	Old Laurentians	W 39-20	King/2t	Savory	Marriott/t(y)	I Dixon	Spearman/t
IC 6	27.01	A	Lymm	W 21-20	King	Savory	Michniewicz/t	Hirst	Spearman/t
IC QF	24.02	H	Kettering *	W 32-13	King	Savory	Michniewicz	I Dixon/t2p3c	Spearman(z)
IC SF	17.03	H	Richmond	W 22-10	King	Spearman	I Dixon(f)	Michniewicz	Savory
IC Final	21.04	N	Old Patesians	L 24-25	King	Savory	Michniewicz/t	Hirst	Spearman(p)

* after opponents name indicates a penalty try. Brackets after a player's name indicates he was replaced. eg (a) means he was replaced by replacement code "a" and so on. / after a player or replacement name is followed by any scores he made - eg /t, /c, /p, /dg or any combination of these

EVER PRESENT	None

Most Appearances:

29	David Guthrie
28	Oakes
27	Gareth King
23	Dean Michniewicz (+1)

MOST POINTS

Pts	Player	T	C	P	DG
189	Ryan Roberts	8	34	26	1
115	Gareth King	23			
101	Ian Dixon	7	18	10	
85	Dean Michniewicz	17			
50	Andrew Savory				

PLAYERS USED 47

MATCH FACTS

10	9	1	2	3	4	5	6	7	8
Roberts	Foreman/2t	Marshall	Ritson	Donoghue(a)	Davidson(b)	Oakes	O'Neill	Clarkson	Guthrie
Roberts/2t4c	Foreman	Marshall(d)	Ritson	Boyd	Davidson(b)	Oakes	Rudd	Clarkson	Guthrie
Hogarth/4pc	Foreman	Marshall	Ritson	Donoghue	Oakes	Guthrie(e)	O'Neill(d)	Russell	Otuvaka
Roberts/t2c3p	Mason	Marshall(d/t)	Ritson	Donoghue	Guthrie	Oakes(e)	O'Neill	Russell	Otuvaka
Roberts/dgp2c	Mason	Harrison	Marshall	Donoghue	Guthrie	Oakes	O'Neill	Clarkson	Otuvaka(e)
Roberts/pc	Mason	Marshall	Phillips	Boyd9g)	Guthrie	Oakes	O'Neill(h)	Russell	Otuvaka
Roberts/t3c3p	Foreman	Marshall	Phillips	Boyd(g)	Oakes	Guthrie	Urwin	Russell	Dye(C)
Roberts	Stevenson	Marshall	R Clarke	Boyd(g)	Guthrie	Oakes	O'Neill	Russell	Otuvaka
Roberts/pc	Stevenson	Harrison	R Clarke	Donoghue(j)	Oakes	Guthrie	Russell	O'Neill(i)	Dye
Roberts/c2p	Stevenson/t	Harrison	R Clarke	Donoghue	Oakes	Bird	Dye(i)	Russell	Guthrie(k)
Roberts/p2c	Stevenson	Harrison(j)	R Clarke	Donoghue	Oakes(l)	Bird	Dye	Russell	Guthrie/t
Roberts/2c4p	Stevenson/t(m)	Harrison	R Clarke	Marshall(g)	Oakes(l)	Bird	Dye	Russell	Guthrie
Roberts/t4c4p	Stevenson	Donoghue(n)	R Clarke	Harrison/t	Houghton(i)	Oakes	Dye	Russell/2t	Guthrie/t
Clarkson	Stevenson	Donoghue(j)	R Clarke	Harrison	Houghton	Oakes	Dye(o)	Russell	Guthrie
Clarkson/t	Stevenson	Harrison	R Clarke	Donoghue	Oakes	Houghton/t	Guthrie	Dye	Goose
Dalrymple	Stevenson/t	Marshall(d)	Ritson/t	D Dixon	Houghton	Oakes	Guthrie(h)	Russell	Goose
Dalrymple/t2pc	Foreman/t	Harrison	Ritson	Donoghue(j)	Bird	Oakes	Guthrie	Russell	Goose(h)
Dalrymple/t2p3c	Foreman	Harrison	Ritson	J Clarke	Oakes	Guthrie	Dye	Russell/t	Clarkson
I Dixon/tp3c	Foreman	Harrison	Ritson	Donoghue(k)	Oakes/t	Houghton	Guthrie/t	Russell(h)	Goose/t
I Dixon/2p2c	Foreman	Harrison	Ritson	J Clarke(r)	Houghton	Oakes	Guthrie	Dye(i)	Goose
I Dixon/pc	Foreman(s)	Harrison	Ritson	Donoghue	Houghton	Oakes	Dye(i)	Russell	Goose
Dalrymple/p3c	Foreman	J Clarke/t	Ritson	Donoghue(n)	Oakes	Houghton	Guthrie	Russell(h/t)	Goose
Roberts/tpc	Mason	Harrison	R Clarke(j)	Donoghue	Guthrie	Davidson/t	O'Neill(u)	Rudd	Clarkson
Roberts/3c	Foreman(s)	Marshall	Phillips	Boyd(d)	Guthrie	Oakes	Urwin/t	Dye	Otuvaka/4t
Roberts/2t4cp	Stevenson/t	Harrison(k)	R Clarke	Donoghue/t(x)	Bird	Oakes	Dye(l)	Russell	Guthrie
Roberts/3cp	Stevenson	Donoghue(j)	R Clarke	Harrison	Guthrie	Bird	Dye	Russell/2t	Clarkson(k)
Roberts/3pc	Stevenson	Harrison	R Clarke	Donoghue	Oakes	Bird	Dye	Russell	Guthrie
Clarkson(B)	Stevenson	Donoghue(j)	R Clarke(A)	Harrison	Bird	Oakes	Rudd	Russell	Guthrie/t
Dalrymple/c	Stevenson	Harrison(j)	Ritson/t	Donoghue	Bird/t	Oakes	Dye(i/t)	G Stainsby	Guthrie
Dalrymple/p(c/3p)	Foreman(s)	Harrison(k)	Ritson	Donoghue	Oakes	Guthrie	Dye/t	Russell/t	Clarkson

REPLACEMENTS

a - J Boyd	b - T Russell	c - I Dixon	d - C Harrison	e - S Davidson	f - J Hirst
g - G Donoghue	h - J Dye	i - G Clarkson	j - R Marshall	k - J Clarke	l - J Rudd
m - A Foreman	n - D Dixon	o - J Goose	p - M Wilson	q - P Kilburn	r - B Rowland
s - B Stevenson	t - N Gandy	u - D Morley	v - D Michriewicz	w - A Savory	x - N Powell
y - M Beattie	z - P Alexander	A - P Ritson	B - D Dalrymple	C S Otuvaka	

HIGHLIGHTS

Winning promotion to National League 3 North - the third promotion in 6 seasons.

Appearing at Twickenham in the Intermediate Cup Final.

Winger Graeme Spearman in his 20th season of senior rugby.

Gareth King scoring 23 tries in all competitions including his hat-trick against Hull Ionians.

BLAYDON

David Guthrie, Blaydon captain, proudly leading the club out at Twickenham for the Intermediate Cup Final against Old Patesians. David will retain his position next season - his eighth as captain.

LEAGUE STATISTICS
compiled by Stephen McCormack

SEASON	Division	P	W	D	L	F	A	Pts Diff	Lge Pts	Lge Pos
91-92	NE1	10	7	0	3	189	106	83	14	3
92-93	NE1	12	8	2	2	307	92	215	18	2
93-94	NE1	12	6	1	5	171	106	65	13	4
94-95	NE1	12	11	0	1	212	116	96	22	1c
95-96	N2	12	9	1	2	247	80	167	19	3
96-97	N2	22	14	0	8	479	382	97	28	3
97-98	N2	22	19	1	2	568	251	317	37	2p
98-99	N1	22	13	2	7	483	308	145	28	5
99-00	N1	22	10	1	11	402	457	-55	21	6
00-01	N1	21	19	0	2	588	306	282	40	2

Most Pts   Most Tries
189 Ryan Roberts   23 Gareth King

FACT FILE

Founded: 1888
Colours: Red and white

GROUND
Address: Crow Trees Ground, Hexham Road, Swalwell, Newcastle upon Tyne NE16 3BM
Tel: 0191 420 0505 (Reception)
Tel/Fax: 0191 420 0506 (Office)
Capacity: unlimited   Covered seating: 400

Directions   Take A1 north past Gateshead Metro Centre, then take the next exit for Swalwell. Over mini roundabout, through the village to the lights and the ground is straight ahead.

Car Parking: 500 spaces approx. at the ground
Nearest Railway station: Newcastle Central

Admission   £4 incl. programme   Season Tickets £35

Clubhouse   Open daily 7am - 11.30pm.

Bar meals available. Public gymnasium.

Private functions & corporate hospitality.

Club Shop   Yes open with clubhouse.

Programme
Size: A5   Pages: 32   Price: with admission
Editor: Jim Huxley

BLAYDON RUGBY FOOTBALL CLUB
Crow Trees, Swalwell

Founded 1888 - 112 years of Rugby

OFFICIAL PROGRAMME
Season 2000/2001

Rugby Football Union Championship
League North One

SPORTS MATCH

Fore Logistics

KooGa
MADE FOR RUGBY

P&O Forwarding

unitech

DARLINGTON MOWDEN PARK RFC

President	Tony Hammond	49 Neville Road, Darlington, Co. Durham Tel: 01325 381390
Chairman	John Parkinson	c/o Darlington Mowden Park RFC Tel: 07764 177545 (M)
Treasurer	John Heslop	5 Netherby Drive, Darlington DL3 8SE Tel: 01325 488568 (H)
Secretary / **Fixture Sec.**	George Nevill	7 Millbank Crescent, Darlington, Co. Durham DL3 8LY Tel: 01325 469001(H/Fax) 07790 569289 (M)
Director of Rugby	John Parkinson	as Chairman

The clubs' successes continued in season 2000/2001 with promotion to National League Three being achieved at the first attempt and with the added distinction of being crowned champions of Thwaites North One. Everyone at Yiewsley Drive is looking forward immensely to the challenge of competing on the national stage and we are enormously proud of contributing towards putting Darlington very firmly on the rugby map.

Whilst the league was always the priority, another fascinating run in the Tetley's Bitter Cup was enjoyed by all and whilst our involvement ended in a narrow defeat at Birmingham/Solihull 16-10 in an exciting Fourth Round tie there was a sense of relief that we had avoided a head on collision with Northampton in the last sixteen matches to be played the following week.

The nucleus of the side has now been together for a number of seasons and represents an appropriate blend of experience and youth. Players with the pedigree of Dave Mitchell, Kevan Oliphant, Antony Elwine dovetail extremely well with the precocious talents of Mark Bedworth, Danny Brown and Ian James. With the junior and colts sides at the club flourishing, it is hoped that the progression of talented players through to the senior sides will continue in the years ahead.

As well as steady progress on the playing side, the club is close to making a final decision on whether to leave its existing home and relocate to a new site on the western outskirts of the town where it will be able to boast outstanding facilities for players, members and spectators alike.

So, an interesting year in store and the club hopes it will be able to acquit itself capably with the additional demands it will face in National League Three. Come what may, we shall certainly enjoy ourselves and look forward to the renewal of some old friendships and the cementing of new ones along the way.

DARLINGTON MOWDEN PARK

Comp.	Date	H/A	Opponents	Result & Score	15	14	13	12	11
North 1	02.09	H	Bradford & Bingley	W 43-9	McCallum	Jo Malcolm	Bedworth	Stewart(a)	Kent/t
North 1	30.09	A	Northern	W 57-0	McCallum	Mattison	Bedworth/2t	Thompson	Kent(f)
North 1	14.10	H	Chester	W 36-3	Bedworth/t2c	Mattison	Stewart	Thompson	Kent/t(h)
North 1	28.10	H	Middlesbrough	W 33-3	McCallum/t	Jo Malcolm	Bedworth/2t	Howland/t	Thompson(i)
North 1	11.11	A	Blaydon	W 22-10	McCallum	Mattison	Bedworth	Howland	Thompson(h/t)
North 1	18.11	H	Stockton	W 60-3	McCallum	Mattison(h)	Bedworth/2tc	Howland/2t	Thomspon/t
North 1	25.11	H	Sheffield	W 22-12	McCallum(l)	Mattison/t	Bedworth	Howland	Thompson
North 1	09.12	A	Hull Ionians	W 46-9	McCallum/t	Mattison	Bedworth/t	Howland(n/t)	Kent/t
North 1	23.12	A	Driffield	W 29-21	McCallum	Mattison/t	Bedworth	Kent/t	Jones/t(p)
North 1	06.01	A	Stockton	W 57-6	Gologhtly	McCallum/3t(h)	Bedworth/2tc	Stewart	Kent/2t
North 1	13.01	A	Middlesbrough	W 23-18	McCallum/t	Jones	Bedworth/22pc	Stewart	Kent
North 1	20.01	H	Driffield	W 37-0	Bedworth(i)	Jones/t	Golightly/t	Elwine	Kent
North 1	27.01	A	Chester	W 27-6	McCallum	Jones/t	Bedworth/2tc	Elwine	Kent
North 1	10.02	H	Northern	W 62-0	McCallum(q)	Jones/t	Bedworth/t6c	Elwine/t	Kent/2t
North 1	10.03	H	Macclesfield	W 24-7	McCallum/t	Jones	Bedworth/t	Stewart	Kent
North 1	17.03	A	Bradford & Bingley	W 22-10	McCallum	Jones	Bedworth/t	Stewart/t	Kent
North 1	07.04	A	Macclesfield	W 28-18	McCallum/t	Jones	Bedworth/t	Stewart	Kent
North 1	14.04	A	Sheffield	W 6-3	McCallum	Jones	Golightly/t	Stewart(p)	Kent
North 1	21.04	H	Hull Ionians *	W 51-10	McCallum	Mattison	Bedworth/p	Elwine/t	Jones
North 1	12.05	H	Blaydon	W 34-15	McCallum/t	Jones/3t	Bedworth/2t	Elwine	Kent
TBC P	09.09	H	Workington *	W 38-25	McCallum	J Brown/t(y)	Bedworth/c	Outhwaite(x)	Kent/t(w)
TBC 1	23.09	H	Broughton Park	W 38-14	McCallum(f)	J Brown(w)	Bedworth/t	Thompson(i)	Kent
TBC 2	07.10	H	West park St. Helens	W 21-3	McCallum/t(i)	Mattison	Bedworth	Thompson	Kent
TBC 3	21.10	H	North Walsham	W 27-10	McCallum	Jo Malcolm	Bedworth	Thomspon	Kent/2t
TBC 4	04.11	A	Birmingham & Solihull	L 10-16	McCallum	Thompson	Bedworth	Howland	Mattison/t

* after opponents name indicates a penalty try. Brackets after a player's name indicates he was replaced.
eg (a) means he was replaced by replacement code "a" and so on. / after a player or replacement name
is followed by any scores he made - eg /t, /c, /p, /dg or any combination of these

EVER PRESENT

Tasi Tuhana, Darren McKinnon

Most Appearances:

25	Tasi Tuhana, Darren McKinnon
24	Mark Bedworth
23	Ian Keeligan (+2), Kevin Oliphant (+2), Kevin McCallum
22	Dave Sinclair,

PLAYERS USED

32 + 4 as replacement only

MOST POINTS

Pts	Player	T	C	P	DG
218	Kevin Oliphant	5	65	21	
135	Mark Bedworth	20	13	3	
70	Topny Irwin	14			
65	Tasi Tuhana	13			
60	Mick Kent	12			
50	Kevin McCallum	10			

MATCH FACTS

10	9	1	2	3	4	5	6	7	8
Oliphant/p5c	Harvey	D Brown/t(b)	Tuhana/2t	Sinclair	Sanderson(c)	Ja Malcolm	McKinnon	Irwin/2t	Radaelli
Oliphant/t6c	Harvey	Keeligan	Tuhana/2t	Sinclair(d)	Sanderson(e)	Ja Malcolm	McKinnon	Irwin/3t	Radaelli/t
Oliphant/2tc	Harvey	Keeligan(g)	Tuhana	Sinclair/t	Sanderson(c)	James	McKinnon	Irwin	Radaelli/t
Oliphant/4c	Harvey	Keeligan(g)	Tuhana	Sinclair	Sanderson(e)	Ja Malcom	Russell	Irwin/t	McKinnon
Oliphant/p2c	Harvey	Keeligan/t	Tuhana	Sinclair(j)	Sanderson	Ja Malcom	Russell	Irwin/t	McKinnon
Oliphant/tp5c	Green/t	Keeligan	Tuhana/t	Sinclair(g)	James	Ja Malcom	Russell(k/t)	Irwin	McKinnon
Oliphant/c	Harvey/t	Keeligan(g)	Tuhana/t	Sinclair	Sanderson	James(m)	Russell	Irwin	McKinnon/t
Oliphant/p4c	Harvey	Keeligan(j)	Tuhana	Sinclair	Sanderson	Ja Malcom	Mitchell(o)	Irwin/2t	McKinnon/t
Oliphant/p3c	Green	Keeligan	Tuhana	D Brown(j)	Sanderson	Ja Malcom	Russell	Irwin	McKinnon/t
Oliphant/5c	Green/t	Keeligan	Tuhana(g/t)	Sinclair	Sanderson(o)	Ja Malcom	James	Irwin	McKinnon
Golightly(q)	Green	Keeligan(g)	Tuhana/t	Sinclair	Sanderson	Ja Malcom	Russell(o)	Irwin/t	McKinnon
Oliphant/5p3c	Green	Keeligan	Tuhana/t(g)	Sinclair	Sanderson	James	McKinnon	Irwin/t	Radaelli/t(o)
Oliphant/pc	Green	Keeligan	Tuhana	Sinclair	Sanderson	James	McKinnon/t	Irwin	Radaelli
Golightly	Green	Keeligan	Tuhana/t	Sinclair	Sanderson/t	James	McKinnon/2t	Irwin/t(g)	Radaelli(o)
Oliphant/p3c	Green/t	Keeligan(j)	Tuhana	Sinclair	Sanderson	James	McKinnon	Irwin	Radaelli(o)
Oliphant/p2c	Green	Keeligan(g)	Tuhana	Sinclair	Russell	James	McKinnon	Irwin/t	Radaelli9r)
Oliphant/3p2c	Golightly	Keeligan(j)	Tuhana/t	Sinclair	Sanderson	James	Cassidy	Mawby	McKinnon
Oliphant/2p	Green	Keeligan	Tuhana	Hodgeon	Sanderson	James	Cassidy	Mawby(s)	McKinnon
Oliphant/3c(l/t)	Green/2t	Keeligan(t)	Tuhana	Hodgeon	Sanderson	James	McKinnon	Irwin	Radaelli(o)
Oliphant/tp4c	Green/t	Keeligan(g)	Tuhana/t	Sinclair	Sanderson	James	McKinnon(o)	Irwin	Radaelli
Oliphant/4c	Harvey	Keeligan	Tuhana/t(d)	Sinclair	Sanderson	James(m)	Russell	McKinnon	Radaelli(u)
Oliphant/t2c	Harvey(y)	Beeken(b)	Tuhana/t	Sinclair/t	Sanderson/t(e)	Ja Malcolm	Russell/t	McKinnon	Radaelli/t
Oliphant/3c	Harvey	Keeligan(g)	Tuhana	Sinclair(j)	Sanderson	Ja Malcolm	McKinnon(c)	Irwin/t	Radaelli
Oliphant/t2p3c	Harvey	Keeligan	Tuhana	Sinclair	Sanderson	James(m)pc	McKinnon	Irwin	Radaelli
Oliphant/	Harvey	Keeligan(g)	Tuhana	Sinclair	Sanderson	Ja Malcolm(e)	Russell(r)	Irwin	McKinnon

REPLACEMENTS

a - Outhwaite b - Keeligan c - Russell d - Throw e - James f - Jo Malcolm
g - D Brown h - J Brown i - Stewart j - Hodgeon k - Sanderson l - Kent
m - Ja Malcolm n - Jones o - Cassidy p - Golightly q - Oliphant r - Mawby
s - Radaelli t - Brooks u - Kerr v - Lavidelli w - Mattison x - Thompson y - Green

DARLINGTON MOWDEN PARK

LEAGUE STATISTICS compiled by Stephen McCormack

SEASON	Division	P	W	D	L	F	A	Pts Diff	Lge Pts	Lge Pos		Most Pts		Most Tries
91-92	D&N 1	10	7	0	3	140	72	68	14	4				
92-93	D&N 1	12	7	0	5	185	130	55	14	5				
93-94	D&N 1	12	12	0	0	256	76	180	24	1p				
94-95	NE2	12	7	1	4	168	106	62	15	4				
95-96	NE2	12	9	0	3	272	139	133	18	3				
96-97	NE2	18	9	1	8	417	330	87	19	6		Most Pts		Most Tries
97-98	NE2	18	17	0	1	617	147	470	36	1p		164 Kevin Oliphant	15	Mick Kent
98-99	NE1	18	18	0	0	729	223	506	36	1p		231 Kevin Oliphant	25	Mick Kent
99-00	N2	22	21	0	1	893	277	616	42	1p		224 Kevin Oliphant	21	Mick Kent
00-01	N1	20	20	0	0	719	163	556	40	1p		171 Kevin Oliphant	17	Mark Bedworth

FACT FILE

Founded: 1946
Nickname:

Colours: Royal blue with white & red piping
Change colours: White, with royal blue top & red piping

GROUND

Address 22 Yiewslew Drive, Darlington, Co. Durham DL3 9XS
Tel: 01325 465932   Web site: dmprfc.co.uk
Capacity: 1,200   Seated: 300

Directions Travelling **South**
From A1(M) follow A68 into Darlington. Follow signs to Staindrop and turn left at Mowden pub into Barnes Rd. At 'T' junction turn right into Fulthorpe Ave. and first right into Yiewsley Dr.
Travelling **North**
From A1(M) follow A66(M). At the 2nd r'about take 1st exit and turn left at next r'about onto A67 Barnard Castle Rd. At the 40mph sign turn right into Edinburgh Dr. which merges with Fulthorpe Ave.. Yiewsley Dr. is 1st left after shopping precinct car park.
Nearest Railway Station: Darlington (BR)

Car Parking Limited, but 100 close by.

Admission Matchday - £5 incl. programme
Children £2
Season Ticket £50

Clubhouse Open Mon-Wed 7.30-11pm, Thur. 6.30-11pm,
Fri. 4-11pm & Sat & Sun 12-11pm

Club Shop Yes, contact Colin Pearson or Martin Sayers

Training Nights Monday & Thursday 6.45

PROGRAMME

Size: A5   Pages: 16   Price: with admission
Editor: Glen Wilson 01325 288364

DONCASTER RFC

President	A De Mulder	c/o Doncaster RFC Ltd., Armthorpe Rd., Doncaster DN2 5QB
		01302 832388 (Club)
Secretary	J Lowe	57 Wroot Road, Finningley, Doncaster DN9 3DR
		01302 770275 (H)
Fixtures Secretary	H Potts	29 Nutwell Lane, Armthorpe, Doncaster DN3 3JH
		01302 300319 (H) 01430 422471 (B)
Director of Playing	J Blount	7 Scaftworth Close, Bessacarr, Doncaster DN4 7RH
		01302 537972 (H) 01302 320626 (B)
Coaching Co-ordinator	Paul Morris	25 Ravenswood Drive, Auckley, Doncaster DN9 3PA
		01302 770890 (H)

Doncaster's second season in the National Leagues was marked by the appointment of Derek Eves as Director of Rugby. His impact was immediately evident and the team led the league into January, despite surprise away defeats at Dudley and Nuneaton. Home wins over leading clubs Stourbridge, Sedgley Park and New Brighton had supported early hopes of promotion but narrow away defeats to all three clubs made the surprise losses to Liverpool and Morley critical in the end. Nevertheless a final fourth place was an improvement on the sixth place the previous year and has left the squad determined to do better next season.

The new clubhouse was opened in November. Its 12 changing rooms, 4 social rooms, 4 full size, 2 junior and many mini pitches make it arguably the best rugby facility in the North. Castle Park is also a major event centre in the region midweek. The club is grateful for the £1.79m lottery grant that made it all possible. The floodlights were also improved this past season.

Our Ladies side has now become a regular feature within the Club, and we hope we can find more opposition for them this season.

The club emphasis on Youth has remained strong. It has the largest mini/junior section in Yorkshire. The junior season was marked by the Colts reaching the semi final of the National Colts Cup (losing narrowly at Bath); and winning the Yorkshire Colts Cup Final. Some 75% of the 1st XV squad have come through the Youth section, and several of the current cohort will graduate to our senior side this season.

Doncaster 1st XV Squad 2000-01

DONCASTER

Comp.	Date	H/A	Opponents	Result & Score	Att	15	14	13	12	11
N3N	2-Sep	H	Whitchurch	W 64-21	265	Ellis/t	Whale	Mortimore/t	Brain/t	Conway/t
N3N	9-Sep	A	Liverpool St Helens	W 33-14	200	Ellis	Whale	Mortimore	Brain/t	Conway
N3N	23-Sep	H	Sandal	W 55-33		Ellis	Whale/t	Mortimore	Brain/t	Conway/t
N3N	30-Sep	H	New Brighton	W 11-3		Ellis	Whale	Mortimore	Brain	Conway
N3N	14-Oct	A	Sandal	W 53-11	250	Ellis	Whale/2t	Mortimore	Brain	Conway
N3N	21-Oct	H	Aspatria	W 43-20	650	Ellis/t	Mortimore/2t	Brain	Sini/t	Whale
N3N	28-Oct	A	Walsall	W 17-5	250	Ellis	Mortimore	Sini	Brain	Conway
N3N	4-Nov	H	Stourbridge	W 17-16	900	Ellis/t	Mortimore	Brain	Cochrane	Conway
N3N	11-Nov	H	Bedford Athletic	W 32-17	450	Liley/2c6p	Ellis	Brain	Mortimore	Conway
N3N	18-Nov	A	Dudley Kingswinsford	L 3-33	350	Liley/p	Ellis	Brain	Mortimore	Conway
N3N	25-Nov	H	Morley	W 25-15	850	Ellis	Mortimore	Brain	Cochrane	Conway
N3N	2-Dec	A	Nuneaton	L 12-22	200	Liley/c	Mortimore	Brain/t	Cochrane	Conway/t
N3N	9-Dec	H	Sedgley Park	W 18-13	800	Poskitt	Mortimore	Brain	Cochrane	Conway/t
N3N	23-Dec	H	Nuneaton	W 38-11	800	Poskitt/t	Mortimore/t	Brain/t	Cochrane/t	Whale
N3N	6-Jan	H	Dudley Kingswinsford	W 46-7	700	Poskitt	Whale/t	Brain(c/t)	Cochrane/t	Conway/t
N3N	13-Jan	A	Bedford Athletic	W 18-0		Poskitt	Whale	Brain	Cochrane	Conway/t
N3N	27-Jan	A	Stourbridge	L 10-13	900	Poskitt	Whale	Brain	Cochrane	Conway/t
N3N	3-Feb	A	Morley	L 5-22		Poskitt	Whale	Brain	Cochrane	Conway
N3N	17-Feb	A	Tynedale	W 6-0		Poskitt	Whale	Brain	Cochrane	Conway
N3N	24-Feb	A	New Brighton	L 16-18		Ellis	Storey/c3p	Brain	Cochrane	Conway
N3N	10-Mar	H	Liverpool St Helens	L 8-23	800	Poskitt	Mortimore	Brain/t	Cochrane	Conway
N3N	7-Apr	H	Walsall	W 39-22		Ellis	Manson	Donkin	Mortimore/2t	Conway/2t
N3N	14-Apr	A	Sedgley Park	D 10-10	1000	Ellis	Donkin	Brain/t	Mortimore	Conway
TBC	7-Oct	A	Stourbridge	L 9-13	400	Liley/3p	Whale	Mortimore	Brain	Conway

** after opponents name indicates a penalty try. Brackets after a player's name indicates he was replaced.
eg (a) means he was replaced by replacement code "a" and so on. / after a player or replacement name
is followed by any scores he made - eg /t, /c, /p, /dg or any combination of these*

EVER PRESENT
Derek Eves

Most Appearances:
- 23 Derek Eves.
- 22 Matt Brain, Simon Greenslade.
- 21 Scott Plevey, Chris Conway, Gavin Baldwin.

PLAYERS USED
29 plus five as replacement only.

MOST POINTS

Pts	Player	T	C	P	DG
244	J Liley	9	41	39	-
65	D Eves	13	-	-	-
45	C Conway	9	-	-	-
35	M Brain	7	-	-	-
30	J Mortimore	6	-	-	-
25	S Greenslade	5	-	-	-

MATCH FACTS

10	9	1	2	3	4	5	6	7	8
Liley/2t8cp	Pascoe	Baldwin	Plevey	Fish	Hill	Norris	Ward/t	Eves/2t	Harfoot
Liley/t2c3p	Greenslade/t	Baldwin	Plevey	Fish	Hill	Norris	Ward	Eves/t	Harfoot
Liley/2t6cp	Greenslade	Baldwin	Plevey/t	Fish	Hill	Norris	Ward	Eves/2t	Harfoot
Liley/2p	Greenslade	Baldwin	Plevey	Fish	Hill	Norris	Ward/t	Eves	Longworth
Liley/t3c4p	Greenslade/2t	Baldwin	Plevey	Waddington	Norris	Bailey	Ward	Senior/t	Eves/t
Liley/t5cp	Greenslade	Baldwin	Plevey	Waddington(a/t)	Bailey	Norris	Ward	Senior	Eves
Liley/c	Greenslade	Baldwin	Ward/t	Fish	Hill	Norris	Senior	Eves/2t	Longworth
Liley/4p	Greenslade	Baldwin	Plevey	Fish	Bailey	Norris	Ward	Eves	Longworth
Poskitt/t	Greenslade	Waddington	Plevey	Fish	Hill	Norris	Ward	Eves/t	Heath
Poskitt	Greenslade	Waddington	Plevey	Fish	Hill	Norris	Ward	Eves	Longworth
Liley/t2c2p	Greenslade/t	Baldwin	Plevey	Waddington(b/t)	Bailey	Hill	Ward	Eves	Longworth
Ure	Greenslade	Baldwin	Plevey	Waddington	Hill	Norris	Fish	Eves	Longworth
Liley/c2p	Greenslade	Baldwin	Plevey	Fish	Bailey	Norris	Ward	Senior	Eves/t
Liley/3c4p	Greenslade	Baldwin	Plevey	Fish	Bailey	Norris	Ward	Senior	Eves
Liley/t5c2p	Greenslade/t	Baldwin	Plevey	Fish	Bailey	Harfoot	Ward	Senior	Eves
Liley/p	Greenslade	Baldwin	Plevey	Fish/t	Bailey	Norris	Ward	Eves/t	Harfoot
Liley/cp	Greenslade	Baldwin	Plevey	Fish	Bailey	Stewart	Ward	Eves	Longworth
Liley	Greenslade	Baldwin	Plevey	Fish	Norris	Sini	Ward	Eves/t	Longworth
Liley/2p	Greenslade	Baldwin	Plevey	Fish	Rutherford	Stewart	Ward	Eves	Longworth
Poskitt	Greenslade	Baldwin	Plevey	Fish	Rutherford	Stewart	Ward	Senior	Eves/t
Liley/p	Greenslade	Baldwin	Ward	Fish	Rutherford	Stewart	Eves	Senior	Longworth
Ure/4c2p	Greenslade	Baldwin	Plevey	Fish	Norris	Stewart	Heath(d/t)	Senior	Eves
Liley/cp	Greenslade	Baldwin	Plevey	Fish	Norris	Stewart	Heath	Senior	Eves
Poskitt	Greenslade	Baldwin	Plevey	Fish	Hill	Bailey	Ward	Eves	Longworth

REPLACEMENTS   a - A Fish   b - Poskitt   c - A Ellis   d - R Ward

John Liley topped the scoring list for the second successive season at Doncaster.

Included in his total of 244 were nine tries.

Player coach Derek Eves topped the try scoring with 13 whilst last season's leading try scorer, Chris Conway, finished joint second with John Liley on nine.

Eves was also the only ever present starting all 23 matches.

Liley scored 29 points as Doncaster thrashed Whitchurch 64-21 on the opening day of the season. He scored two tries, converted eight of the nine tries and kicked a penalty.

DONCASTER

LEAGUE STATISTICS *compiled by Stephen McCormack*

SEASON	Division	P	W	D	L	F	A	Pts Diff	Lge Pts	Lge Pos
91-92	Yorks 1	10	8	0	2	163	100	63	16	2p
92-93	North E 2	12	11	0	1	294	39	255	22	1p
93-94	North E1	12	11	0	1	232	70	162	22	1p
94-95	North 2	12	7	0	5	136	155	-19	14	6
95-96	North 2	12	4	2	6	183	168	15	10	9
96-97	North 2	22	22	0	0	690	259	431	44	1p
97-98	North 1	22	17	2	3	489	285	204	36	2
98-99	North 1	22	18	1	3	550	214	336	37	1p
99-00	JN2N	26	12	2	12	656	539	117	26	6
00-01	N3N	*23	16	0	7	579	352	227	32	4

	Most Points	Most Tries
98-99		
99-00	273 John Liley	19 Chris Conway
00-01	244 John Liley	13 Derek Eves

FACT FILE

Founded: 1875   **Colours**: Navy blue with 2 thin red & white bands
Change colours:

GROUND
Address: Armthorpe Road, Doncaster DN2 5QB   Web Site: www.drfc.co.uk
Tel: 01302 831388   Fax: 01302 831496   e-mail: admin@drfc.co.uk
Capacity: 4.252   Seated: 252   Standing: 4,200 (200 covered)

Directions: Leave M18 at junction 4 and follow signs to Doncaster. At 2nd roundabout turn left towards Armthorpe. At next roundabout turn right and the ground is 1.25 miles on the left.
Nearest Railway station: Doncaster

Car Parking: Spaces for 400 cars at the ground

Admission:
Season   £45
Matchday   Adults £4; Members £2; Children/OAPs £1

Clubhouse: Open every evening except Sunday
Functions: Yes - Contact club to book

Club Shop: Yes - contact Paul Turton at club.

Training Nights: Monday & Thursday, 7.15pm

PROGRAMME
Size: A5   Price: With admission
Pages: 36 + cover   Editor: John Lowe
ADVERTISING RATES
Colour: Full Page £200
Mono: Full Page £160   Half £85

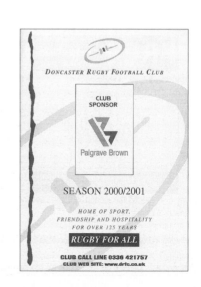

DONCASTER RUGBY FOOTBALL CLUB

CLUB SPONSOR

Palgrave Brown

SEASON 2000/2001

HOME OF SPORT,
FRIENDSHIP AND HOSPITALITY
FOR OVER 125 YEARS

RUGBY FOR ALL

CLUB CALL LINE 0336 421757
CLUB WEB SITE: www.drfc.co.uk

DUDLEY KINGSWINFORD RFC

President	David Evans	156 Common Road, Wombourne, West Midlands WV5 0LT
		Tel: 01902 894463 (H)
Chairman	Roger Port	Church House, High St., Claverley, Shropshire WV5 7DU
		01746 710793 (H)
Secretary	Ken Crane	Two Oaks, Penstone Lane, Lower Penn, Wolverhampton WV4 4XE
		01902 332952 (H) 07970 855729 (M)
Fixture Secretary	Bill Jones	54 Dingle View, Sedgley, West Midlands DY3 3LE
		Tel: 01902 674685 (H) 0121 557 3949 (B)
Match Confirmer &	Bill McLachlan	32 Lynwood Ave., Wallheath, Kingswinford, W. Mids. DY6 9AJ
Referees Contact		
Director of Rugby	Gordon Bannatyne	47 Windermere Drive, Kingswinford, W. Mids DY6 8AN
		01384 271863 (H) 07850 395544 (M)
Director of Coaching	Mark Wilson	50 Gladston Drive, Solihull B91 3YE
		0121 709 2183 (H) 07967 047157 (M)

Following their steady rise through the ranks of Midlands league rugby, the Dudley Kingswinford club prepared thoroughly through July and August for the new challenges of National League Rugby. A training weekend, trial matches and the introduction of new players and especially a group of three young players from an exchange scheme with the Teachers Eastern club in Auckland saw a stronger and fitter squad embark on its first ever league match against local rivals Walsall.

A harsh introduction resulted with the club losing 16-9, but gaining a clear idea of what was required at this new level against a club tipping themselves for promotion. As the season developed it became clear that a few clubs had made the investments necessary to challenge for promotion and that a sensible target for a newcomer would be in the top half of the table.

The coaching team of Mark Wilson as Director of Coaching, Dale Smallman as Forwards coach and Fitness Adviser ably assisted by Neil Shillingford, all under the guidance of Gordon Bannatyne as Director of Rugby, forged a cohesive and enthusiastic group of young players imbued with the DK ethos of the game. Learning quickly from the set back at Walsall the team bounced back with five straight league victories until a Cup defeat at Waterloo brought this purple patch to an end.

Other notable victories saw them end high flying Doncaster's nine game unbeaten run, and Liverpool St Helen's home and away. The elite sub group in the league proved too strong but taught the club the levels expected to be serious challengers for the future.

Off the field the Management group led by Chairman Roger Port and President David Evans oversaw the completion of a new 250 seater stand, financed by club members and generous donations from Past president Errol Mason. The stand is dedicated to the memory of Paul Keeton, a former 1st xv captain who died after a long illness just before the start of the season.

The second XV entered the Midlands 2nd XV Merit Table, managed by Andy Gallis and coached by Tony Lanaway, the club's coaching consultant, managed a very creditable fourth place in the league, especially when you consider they used 70 plus players during the season!

The colts XV, ably managed & coached by Graham Robbins and Brian Westwood triumphed in the North Midlands Colts Final beating old rivals Luctonians in a very tense game. This victory gives the club great hope for the future as its dependence on developing its own players is a strength of the club.

A successful first season for this homely and welcoming club, one that they hope to build on as the remaining North Midlands Club in National League 3 North.

DUDLEY KINGSWINFORD

Comp.	Date	H/A	Opponents	Result & Score	Att	15	14	13	12	11
N3N	2-Sep	A	Walsall	L 9-16	470	Smart/3p	Gowland	Halstead	G Davies	Lindsay
N3N	9-Sep	A	Aspatria	W 20-13	175	Smart/cp	Gowland/t	Halstead	G Davies	Lindsay
N3N	16-Sep	H	Bedford Athletic	W 21-7	500	Smart/c2p	Gowland/t	Halstead	G Davies	Lindsay
N3N	30-Sep	H	Morley	W 17-16	450	Smart/t2cp	Gowland	W Port/t	G Davies	Lindsay
N3N	14-Oct	H	Nuneaton	W 48-13	500	Wagstaffe/t	Gowland	W Port	G Davies/t	Smart/t3c4p
N3N	28-Oct	H	Tynedale	D 13-13	250	Wagstaffe	Smart/c2p	W Port	G Davies/t	Lindsay
N3N	4-Nov	A	Sedgley Park	L 5-37	200	Wagstaffe	Smart/t	W Port	G Davies	Lindsay
N3N	11-Nov	A	Whitchurch	L 11-13	300	Wagstaffe	Smart/2p	W Port	G Davies/t	Lindsay
N3N	18-Nov	H	Doncaster	W 33-3	350	Halstead/t	Smart/2c3p	W Port/t	G Davies	Lindsay/t
N3N	25-Nov	A	Liverpool St Helens	W 36-14	150	Halstead	Smart/3t2cp	W Port	G Davies	Lindsay
N3N	2-Dec	H	New Brighton	L 11-24	450	Halstead	Smart/2p	W Port	G Davies	Lindsay
N3N	16-Dec	H	Stourbridge	L 14-29	1500	Halstead	Smart/3p	W Port	G Davies	Lindsay
N3N	23-Dec	A	New Brighton	L 13-32	350	Halstead	Midler-Price	W Port	G Davies	Lindsay
N3N	6-Jan	A	Doncaster	L 7-46	700	Wagstaffe	Midler-Price	W Port	G Davies	Smart/tc
N3N	13-Jan	H	Whitchurch*	W 29-19		Smart/2c	Midler-Price/t	W Port/2t	G Davies	Lindsay/t
N3N	27-Jan	H	Sedgley Park	L 11-23	350	Smart/2p	Midler-Price	Baker	G Davies	Lindsay
N3N	3-Feb	H	Liverpool St Helens*	W 44-31	350	Smart/2t4c2p	Midler-Price	W Port	Baker/t	Lindsay
N3N	10-Feb	A	Nuneaton	L 0-29	200	Smart	Midler-Price	W Port	Baker	Lindsay
N3N	17-Feb	A	Sandal	L 21-39		Smart/3c	Midler-Price	W Port	Wagstaffe/2t	Lindsay
N3N	24-Feb	H	Morley	W 20-10		Smart/2c2p	Midler-Price	W Port	G Davies	Gowland
N3N	10-Mar	H	Sandal*	W 47-20	450	Smart/t4c3p	Midler-Price	W Port/t	G Davies/t	Gowland
N3N	24-Mar	H	Walsall*	W 21-18	800	Smart/c3p	Midler-Price	Halstead	G Davies	Gowland
N3N	31-Mar	A	Stourbridge	L 12-24	1500	Smart/tc	Midler-Price/t	Halstead	Wagstaffe	Gowland
N3N	28-Apr	A	Bedford Athletic	L 22-27	150	Smart/2cp	Benedict/t	Wagstaffe	Smith/t	Baker
TBC	23-Sept	A	Dunstabilians	W 34-26						
TBC	7-Oct	A	Walsall	W 21-17						
TBC	21-Oct	A	Waterloo	L 29-57		Wagstaffe	Lindsay/t	Port	Davies/2t	Smart/3cp

> * after opponents name indicates a penalty try.
> Brackets after a player's name indicates he was replaced. eg (a) means he was replaced by replacement code "a" and so on.
> / after a player or replacement name is followed by any scores he made - eg /t, /c, /p, /dg or any combination of these

EVER PRESENT Ian Langford

MOST POINTS

Most Appearances:
- 24 Ian Langford.
- 23 Steve Smart.
- 22 Shaun Perry, John Davies, Gareth Davies.

PLAYERS USED 33

Pts	Player	T	C	P	DG
230	S Smart	11	32	37	-
63	S Perry	12	-	1	-
30	W Port	6	-	-	-
20	Penalty Try	4	-	-	-
20	G Davies	4	-	-	-

MATCH FACTS

10	9	1	2	3	4	5	6	7	8
Smith	Perry	Homer	M Davies	Lockley	J Davies	Lowe	Langford	Loutogo	O'Neil
Smith/t	Perry	Fallon	M Davies	Lockley	Lowe	J Davies	Langford	Loutogo	Connett/t
Smith/p	Perry	Homer	M Davies(a/t)	Lockley	Lowe	J Davies	Langford	Loutogo	Connett
Smith	Perry	Millard	M Davies	Lockley	J Davies	McCrae	R Port	Loutogo	Langford
Smith	Perry/t	Homer	M Davies	Fallon	J Davies/t	Page	Langford/t	R Port	Shillingford
Barker	Perry	Millard	MDavies	Lockley	Lowe	J Davies	Langford	RPort	Connett
Barker	Perry	Homer	M Davies	Fallon	Lowe	J Davies	Langford	R Port	Shillingford
Smith	Perry	Millard	M Davies	Fallon	Page	J Davies	O'Neil	Langford	Shillingford
Smith	Perry/t	Millard	M Davies	Fallon	J Davies	McCrae	O'Neil	Langford	Shillingford
Smith	Perry/2t	Homer	M Davies	Fallon	J Davies	McCrae	Langford	R Port/2c	Shillingford
Smith	Perry	Millard	M Davies	Fallon	McCrae	J Davies	Langford	RPort/t	Shillingford
Barker	Perry	Millard/t	M Davies	Fallon	Lowe	J Davies	Langford	R Port	Shillingford
Barker	Perry/2tp	Homer	Timoloa	Fallon	Page	Lowe	Langford	Loutogo	O'Neil
Smith	Perry	Millard	M Davies	Fallon	J Davies	Lowe	Langford	R Port	O'Neil
Smith	Perry	Millard	M Davies	Fallon	J Davies	Lowe	Langford	R Port	Shillingford
Smith(b/t)	Perry	Millard	M Davies	Lockley	J Davies	Lowe	Langford	R Port	Shillingford
Smith	Perry/2t	Millard	M Davies	Fallon	J Davies	Lowe	Langford	R Port	Shillingford
Smith	Perry	Millard	Timoloa	Fallon	J Davies	Lowe	Langford	R Port	Shillingford
Smith	Perry/t	Homer	M Davies	Fallon	J Davies	Lowe	Jones	Langford	Wilkinson
Smith	Perry/2t	Homer	M Davies	Fallon	J Davies	Lowe	Jones	R Port	Langford
Smith/t	Perry	Homer	M Davies	Fallon	J Davies	Lowe	Langford/t	R Port	Wilkinson
Smith	Perry/t	Homer	M Davies	Fallon	J Davies	Lowe	Shillingford	Langford	Wilkinson
Smith	G Davies	Homer	M Davies	Fallon	J Davies	Lowe	Shillingford	Langford	Wilkinson
Halstead	G Davies	Homer	Craig	Fallon/t	Lowe	Tipper	Langford	Connett	Shillingford
Smith	Perry	Millard	M Davies	Lockley	Page	J Davies	Langford/t	Connett	Shillingford

REPLACEMENTS   a - J Timoloa   b - W Port

Steve Smart just missed out on doing the double again as he finished top of the points scorers and second in the try scoring, one behind Shaun Perry.

He actually scored more tries than the previous season but Perry managed 12.

Smart topped the 200 point mark for the season scoring 34 more points than when Dudley won Midlands One.

The only only ever present was the back row forward Ian Langford who played in all three back row positions.

DUDLEY KINGSWINFORD

LEAGUE STATISTICS compiled by Stephen McCormack

Ian Langford
Captain for 2nd season

SEASON	Division	P	W	D	L	F	A	Pts Diff	Lge Pts	Lge Pos
91-92										
92-93	M W1	12	5	1	6	152	119	33	11	7
93-94	M W1	12	7	1	4	167	160	7	15	4
94-95	M W1	12	8	0	4	157	107	50	*14	5
95-96	M W1	12	9	0	3	202	181	21	18	2p
96-97	M 2	17	13	0	4	434	212	222	*24	6
97-98	M 2	16	14	1	1	528	145	383	29	2p
98-99	M 1	15	13	0	2	391	205	186	26	3
99-00	M 1	16	14	1	1	412	194	218	29	1p
00-01	N3N	*24	11	1	12	485	519	-34	23	6

	Most Points	Most Tries
99-00	196 Steve Smart	10 Steve Smart
00-01	230 Steve Smark	12 Shaun Perry

FACT FILE

Founded: 1927 **Colours**: Cambridge blue and navy hoops, navy shorts
Nickname: "D.K" **Change colours:** White/red/navy
Web site: www.dkrfc.co.uk (under contruction)

GROUND

Address Heathbrook, Swindon Road, Wallheath, Kingswinford, W. Mids. DY6 0AW
Tel/Fax: 01384 287006 e-mail: gordon@lastdrop.fsnet.co.uk
Capacity: 2,700 Covered Seating: 250 Uncovered Standing: 2,500

Directions: Just off the A449 at Wallheath, midway between Kidderminster and Wolverhampton.
Nearest Railway Station: Stourbridge or Wolverhampton

Car Parking: Spaces for 300+ at the ground

Admission: Matchday: £5 non-members, £4 members.
Season tickets are available.

Clubhouse: Open 7 days per week, from 7pm ,
also lunch-times at weekend.

Club Shop: Open matchdays and Sunday lunch 12-2

Training Nights: Tuesday & Thursday 7.30pm

Programme: Size: A5 Pages: 20
Price: incl with admission
Editor: David Coyle 01384 830508

Advertising Contact Martin Chard 01384 274560 (H)

Steve Smart -
DK's leading points scorer 2000-01

LIVERPOOL St. HELENS RFC

President	Ray French	
Chairman	Alan Walker	
Club Secretary	Terry Ryan	Trenance, Ben Lane, Bickerstaffe L39 0HL
		01695 722986 (H)
Fixtures Secretary	Ron Hall	21 Childwall Abbey Road, Liverpool. L16 0JL.
		0151 722 3588 (H & Fax)
Director of Rugby	Eric Hughes	
Press Officer	John Williams	18 Old Lane, Rainford, St. Helens
		01744 886270 (H) 0161 796 7222 (B)
Treasurer		

Liverpool St Helens began the 2000/01 campaign full of renewed hope, The new partnership with Sporting Club St Helens promised a new era for Rugby Union and delivered a new coaching team in Eric Hughes, Mike Rush and Kevin Greaves.

Early defeats against Tynedale, Doncaster and New Brighton and a position of second bottom after six games, however, indicated another disappointing season. This was not the case. Success in the Tetley's Cup against Driffield and Nuneaton brought Rugby Lions to Moss Lions for a Third Round encounter. Although losing heavily the game signalled the beginning of an upturn in fortune, which was to carry the side throughout the rest of the campaign. Observers at Moss Lane could see a renewed fighting spirit throughout the side, which brought a further nine league victories. The cup-tie against Rugby marked the LSH debut of former Swinton skipper Sean Casey, who together with skipper Steve Cook, stand off Simon Worsley and the fans' favourite Njike Tchakoute had a major impact on LSH's progress this season.

The second half of the campaign saw continued improvement and a climb up the league table; the return of stalwart Dave Lupton; progress in the Lancashire Cup; and on the debit side a tendency to surrender half time leads as at Walsall, Dudley and Aspatria. The defeat by neighbours New Brighton was particularly hard to take with a try conceded in the fourth minute of injury time. The win at title chasing Doncaster in March was the undoubted highlight of the season. A league finishing position of seventh is a marked improvement and signals well for the future.

Eric Hughes reflecting on the season after the last match against Stourbridge proclaimed himself well satisfied with the overall performance of the side and looked forward to further progress next year.

JOHN WILLIAMS

LIVERPOOL St HELENS

Comp.	Date	H/A	Opponents	Result & Score	Att	15	14	13	12	11
N3N	2-Sep	H	Tynedale	L 6-31	200	M Jones	Pilgrim	Walker	Simms	Sephton
N3N	9-Sep	H	Doncaster	L 14-33	200	M Jones/t	Pilgrim	Walker	Makin	Sephton/t
N3N	16-Sep	A	Whitchurch	L 17-30	450	M Jones	Harris	Simms(a/t)	Pilgrim	Sephton
N3N	30-Sep	H	Aspatria	W 19-10		M Jones	D Jones/t	Walker	Stabler	Sephton
N3N	14-Oct	A	New Brighton	L 9-24	600	M Jones	D Jones	Walker	Casey	Stabler
N3N	28-Oct	A	Stourbridge*	L 19-26	400	M Jones	Harris/t	Casey/t	Walker	Stabler
N3N	4-Nov	H	Sandal	W 21-13	250	Carter	Harris/t	Casey	Walker	Stabler
N3N	11-Nov	H	Walsall	W 33-20	250	McCormack	Harris/2t	Walker	Stabler	M Jones
N3N	18-Nov	A	Bedford Athletic	W 20-19	400	M Jones	Harris	Walker	Casey	Stabler
N3N	25-Nov	H	Dudley Kingswinford	L 14-36	150	M Jones	Harris/t	Walker	Casey	Stabler
N3N	2-Dec	A	Morley	L 24-31	400	Hull	D Jones/t	Walker	Casey	M Jones
N3N	9-Dec	H	Nuneaton	W 25-15	250	Hull/t	D Jones	Walker	Hazlett	M Jones/t
N3N	16-Dec	A	Sedgley Park	L 13-43	350	Hull	D Jones	Carter	Stabler	M Jones
N3N	23-Dec	H	Morley	W 34-18	200	M Jones	Walker/t	Casey/2t	Hazlett	D Jones
N3N	6-Jan	H	Bedford Athletic	W 26-20		M Jones/t	Walker	Casey/t	Hazlett	D Jones
N3N	13-Jan	A	Walsall	L 15-48		M Jones/t	Harris	Hazlett	Casey	D Jones
N3N	27-Jan	A	Sandal	W 34-22		M Jones	Harris	Casey/t	Walker/t	D Jones/t
N3N	3-Feb	A	Dudley Kingswinford	L 31-44	350	M Jones	Harris	Casey/2t	Walker	D Jones/tc
N3N	10-Feb	H	New Brighton	L 17-21	250	M Jones	Harris	Walker/t	Casey/t	D Jones
N3N	24-Feb	A	Aspatria	W 19-0		Hull	D Jones/t	Walker	Hazlett	M Jones
N3N	10-Mar	A	Doncaster	W 23-8	800	M Jones	D Jones/t	Casey	Walker	Walker/t
N3N	17-Mar	H	Whitchurch	W 35-10		M Jones	D Jones/t	Walker/t	Casey/t	Walker
N3N	31-Mar	A	Sedgley Park	L 5-20	150	M Jones	Hull	Casey	Walker	Walker/t
N3N	14-Apr	A	Nuneaton	L 22-46		M Jones/t	D Jones	Walker	Casey	Walker
N3N	21-Apr	H	Stourbridge	L 16-48		M Jones/3p	D Jones/c	Walker	Hazlett	Harris/t
TBC	23-Sep	H	Driffield	W 33-0	300	M Jones	D Jones/t	Walker	Makin/t	Sephton
TBC	7-Oct	H	Nuneaton	W 23-7		M Jones	D Jones	Walker	Stabler	Sephton/t
TBC	21-Oct	H	Rugby Lions	L 17-48		M Jones	D Jones	Walker	Casey	Stabler

after opponents name indicates a penalty try. Brackets after a player's name indicates he was replaced. eg (a) means he was replaced by replacement code "a" and so on. / after a player or replacement name is followed by any scores he made - eg /t, /c, /p, /dg or any combination of these

MOST POINTS

Pts	Player	T	C	P	DG
228	S Worlsey	1	32	48	5
45	S Casey	9	-	-	-
44	D Jones	8	2	-	-
35	S Cook	7	-	-	-
34	M Jones	5	-	3	-
30	F Harris	6	-	-	-

MATCH FACTS

10	9	1	2	3	4	5	6	7	8
Worsley/2p	McCormack	Jackson	Grigg	Lever	Tchakoute	Nugent	Gaskell	N Jones	D Bailey
Simms	Worsley/2c	Jackson	Grigg	O'Keefe	Tchakoute	Marsh	Gaskell	N Jones	D Bailey
Worsley/4p	Cook	Jackson	Grigg	O'Keefe	Nugent	Tchakoute	Gaskell	N Jones	D Bailey
Worsley/c3pdg	Cook	Botha	Grigg	Jackson	Nugent	R Bailey	Gaskell	Crilly	D Bailey
Worsley/2pdg	Cook	O'Keefe	Grigg	Botha	Nugent	R Bailey	Gaskell	Crilly	D Bailey
Worsley/2c	Cook	Botha	Grigg	Jackson	Nugent	R Bailey	Gaskell	Crilly	D Bailey
Worsley/c3p	Cook	Botha	Grigg	Jackson	Marsh	Tchakoute	Gaskell	Crilly/t	D Bailey
Worsley/2c3p	Cook/t	Botha	Grigg	O'Keefe	Nugent/t	Tchakoute	Gaskell	Crilly	D Bailey
Worsley/3p2dg	Cook/t	Botha	Jackson	O'Keefe	Nugent	R Bailey	D Bailey	Crilly	Tchakoute
Worsley/3p	Cook	Botha	Jackson	O'Keefe	Nugent	R Bailey	Gaskell	Crilly	D Bailey
Worsley/c4p	Cook/t	Botha	Thomson	O'Keefe	Nugent	R Bailey	D Bailey	Crilly	Tchakoute
Worsley/cp	Cook	Botha	Jackson	Lever	R Bailey(b/t)	Tchakoute	Gaskell	Crilly/t	D Bailey
Worsley/c2p	Cook/t	Botha	Jackson	O'Keefe	Nugent	R Bailey	D Bailey	Crilly	Tchakoute
Worsley/4c2p	Cook	Botha	Jackson	O'Keefe	Nugent	Marsh	Tchakoute	Crilly/t	D Bailey
Worsley/2c4p	Cook	O'Keefe	Jackson	Botha	Nugent	Marsh	R Bailey	Crilly	D Bailey
Worsley/cp	Cook/t	Botha	Jackson	O'Keefe	Marsh	Nugent	R Bailey	Crilly	D Bailey
Worsley/4cpdg	Cook	O'Keefe	Keenaghan/t	Jackson	Marsh	R Bailey	D Bailey	Crilly	Tchakoute
Worsley/3cp	Cook/t	Jackson	Madle	Hewitt	Marsh	R Bailey	D Bailey	Crilly	Tchakoute
Worsley/2cp	Cook	Jackson	Keenaghan	O'Keefe	Marsh	R Bailey	D Bailey	Crilly	Tchakoute
Worsley/c4p	N Jones	Hewitt	Keenaghan	Jackson	Marsh	R Bailey	Gaskell	Crilly	Tchakoute
Worsley/c2p	Cook	Jackson	Keenaghan	Hewitt	R Bailey	Tchakoute/t	Gaskell	Crilly	Lupton
Worsley/2c2p	Cook	Jackson	Keenaghan/t	Hewitt	Tchakoute	R Bailey	Gaskell	Crilly/t	Lupton
Worsley	Cook	Jackson	Keenaghan	Hewitt	R Bailey	Tchakoute	Gaskell	Crilly	Lupton
Worsley/tc	Cook/t	Hewitt	Madle	Jackson/t	R Bailey	Tchakoute	Gaskell	Crilly	Lupton
Casey	Cook	Hewitt	Keenaghan	Howell	Marsh	Nugent	Gaskell	Nugent	DBailey
Worsley/3c3pdg	Cook/t	Jackson	Grigg	O'Keefe	Nugent	R Bailey	Lever	Gaskell	D Bailey
Worsley/2tc2p	Cook	Botha	Grigg	Jackson	Nugent	R Bailey	Gaskell	Crilly	D Bailey
Worsley/2cp	Cook/2t	O'Keefe	Grigg	Botha	Nugent	R Bailey	Gaskell	Crilly	D Bailey

REPLACEMENTS   a - D Jones   b - M Nugent

2000-01 HIGHLIGHTS

Simon Worlsey sets a new record for points scored in a league season.

Worlsey, who managed just 38 the season before, became the second man after Paul Brett to pass 200 points and then went on to finish on the new record total of 228.

Included in that total was a new record for penalties - his 48 smashed the previous record of 30 whilst he also set a new record for drop goals in a season with five. The previous record for drop goals was four and was set by Andy Higgin back in 1992-93.

Centre Sean Casey topped the try scoring with nine tries which was two clear of Steve Cook who managed seven.

LIVERPOOL St. HELENS

LEAGUE STATISTICS compiled by Stephen McCormack

SEASON	Division	P	W	D	L	F	A	Pts Diff	Lge Pts	Lge Pos	Most Points		Most Tries	
91-92	2	12	0	0	12	87	418	-331	0		26	Paul Ramsden	4	Mark Elliott
92-93	3	11	5	0	6	203	130	73	10		98	Andy Higgin	8	Mark Sephton
93-94	4	18	11	1	6	396	275	121	23		140	Simon Mason	9	Mark Sephton
94-95	4	18	10	3	5	374	243	134	23		155	Andy Higgin	7	Mark Sephton
95-96	4	18	11	1	6	471	343	128	23		120	Mark Wellens	14	Simon Humphreys
96-97	3	30	8	0	22	665	827	162	16		210	Paul Brett	14	Paul Brett
97-98	JN1	26	8	1	17	430	767	-337	17		85	Paul Brett	8	Mark Sephton
98-99	JN1	26	4	0	22	335	859	-524	8	14r	55	Chris Glynn	9	Mark Sephton
99-00	N2N	26	5	0	21	335	848	-513	10	13	88	Paul Cumming	7	Mark Sephton
00-01	N3N	*25	10	0	15	511	666	-155	20	9	228	Simon Worsley	9	Sean Casey

FACT FILE

Founded: 1857 (Merged 1986)
Nickname: LSH

Colours: Red with blue sleeves & white banding
Change colours: Blue with red sleeves & white banding

GROUND

Address: Moss Lane (off Rainford Rd.) Windle, St. Helens. WA11 7PL.
Tel : 01744 25708
Capacity: 2300   Seated: 300   Standing: 2000

Directions: M6, leave at A580 (Haydock) towards Liverpool. After approx 4 miles, take A570 (right), immediate left, left again and follow lane straight ahead - the clubhouse will come into view on the left after 1/2 mile.
Nearest Railway Station: St Helens, 5mins by taxi

Car Parking: 200

Admission: Season tickets   £60
Matchdays   Adults £4 (incl prog)
Children/OAPs £1.

Club Shop: Yes.

Clubhouse: 3 bars & has food available.
Functions: Up to 100 seated can be catered.
Contact Alan Brown c/o Club

Training Nights: Monday & Wednesday.

PROGRAMME
Size: A5   Pages: 20 + cover   Price: £1
Editor: Correspondence c/o Club.

Advertising Rates
Full page £300

MORLEY RFC

President	Bob Lloyd	c/o Morley RFC
		Tel:01924 494612 (H) 07885 741396 (M)
Club Secretary	Dennis R Elam	26 The Roundway, Morley, W. Yorks. LS27 0JS
		Tel: 0113 252 4348 (H) 07751 443059 (M)
		e-mail: dennis.elam@ukgateway.net
Chairman of Rugby	Ken Higgins	c/o Morley RFC
		Tel: 01924 823135 (B) 01977 658582 (H)
Fixtures Secretary	Peter Kneale	c/o Morley RFC
		e-mail: peter@kneale7.freeserve.co.uk
		Tel: 0113 282 4373 (H) 0795 7784571 (M)
Hon. Treasurer	Ian Juniper	c/o Morley RFC 077 111 37034 (M)
		Tel: 0113 249 7511 (B) 01924 422206 (H)

Morley RFC, Scatcherd Lane, Morley, WestYorkshire LS27 0JJ

Morley's youngsters suffered some horrendous defeats in 2000-2001 due to a lack of experience in key positions. However, the spirit within this young side ensured that heads were held high.

Early season victories were limited to Aspatria and Walsall and a hard season was in prospect. It was only a run of 6 consecutive home wins kept Morley just above the relegation zone. Even during this purple patch, Morley could not find the answer of how to win away from home. In the Tetley Bitter Cup, a tremendous defensive display at Nottingham allowed Morley the opportunity to suffer their worst ever defeat at the hands of Leeds – who suffered a similar fate in their match against Northampton. Morley's dreadful away form also put paid to a run in the Yorkshire Cup when Selby played a limited but correct game plan to gain a surprising but deserved victory over a lack lustre Maroon side.

Following the retirement of captain Mark Burrow, the addition of lock Richard White showed that a team needs a blend of youth and experience to successfully compete in today's rugby. The move of top League try scorer, Chris Hall to Leeds Tykes was a crucial loss. Ken Higgins moves to Chairman of Rugby, and along with coach Kevin Plant and captain Nick Sykes, will be trying to improve Morley's performance on the pitch. Only Dave (top points scorer) and Jon Kite appeared in all 25 League matches and 37 players were used as the coaches had to cope with serious injuries. Wing Ed Hutchinson was top try scorer with 7 tries to his credit, closely followed by David Hopton and Chris Johnson on 6 each. The players' player of the year (open only to red-haired flankers) was won deservedly by Tim Wilks, who put in a consistently good peformance, week after week.

We wish Stourbridge and Sedgley Park good fortune in their new league and welcome Blaydon, Mowden Park and Scunthorpe for the first league visits to Scatcherd Lane. West Hartlepool will return as old friends.

Dennis Elam

Standing: Peter Seabourne, Ed Hutchinson, David Wilks, Jon Kite, Simon Chippendale, Peter Fletcher, Hayley Smith, Richard White, Scott Evans,Buzza, Richard Binks. **Seated:** Alan Benn, Stewart Kneale, Neil Murray, Kevin Plant, Nick Sykes, Ken Higgins, Dean Drane, Paul Gabriel, Matthew Smith. **Front:** Chris Johnson and Dave Evans

MORLEY

Comp.	Date	H/A	Opponents	Result & Score	Att	15	14	13	12	11
N3N	2-Sep	A	Stourbridge	L 17-72	400	S Evans	Johnson/t	Murray	Drane	Clarke
N3N	16-Sep	H	Walsall	W 12-10	400	S Evans	Johnson	Murray	Drane	Hutchinson
N3N	23-Sep	A	Bedford Athletic	L 17-25	250	S Evans	Johnson	Murray	Drane	Hutchinson
N3N	30-Sep	H	Dudley Kingswinford	L 16-17	450	S Evans	Johnson/t	Murray	Drane	Hutchinson/t
N3N	14-Oct	H	Aspatria*	W 40-26	150	S Evans	Johnson/t	Murray/t	Driver(b/t)	Hutchinson/2t
N3N	28-Oct	H	Sedgley Park	L 15-23	250	Johnson	Luxton	O'Callaghan	Drane/t	Hutchinson/t
N3N	4-Nov	A	Nuneaton	L 27-50	250	Dobson	Luxton/t	O'Callaghan/t	Murray	Hutchinson
N3N	11-Nov	A	Tynedale	L 5-9		Johnson	Leathley	D Evans	Sales	Hutchinson
N3N	18-Nov	H	Whitchurch	L 13-23	400	Johnson	Wilson	D Evans/p	Sales	Hutchinson
N3N	25-Nov	A	Doncaster	L 15-25	850	Johnson	Wilson	D Evans/c	Sales/t	Hutchinson
N3N	2-Dec	H	Liverpool St Helens	W 31-24	400	Johnson	Wilson	D Evans/tc3p	Dobson	Hutchinson/t
N3N	9-Dec	A	New Brighton	L 0-79	350	Johnson	Wilson	O'Callaghan	Dobson	Hutchinson
N3N	16-Dec	H	Sandal*	W 29-15	400	Johnson	Murray/t	D Evans/3cp	Dobson	Hutchinson
N3N	23-Dec	A	Liverpool St Helens	L 18-34	200	Johnson	Murray	D Evans/c2p	Dobson	Hutchinson
N3N	6-Jan	A	Whitchurch	L 16-34		Johnson	D Evans/2p	Murray	Dobson	Hutchinson
N3N	13-Jan	H	Tynedale	W 23-11		S Evans	Johnson	Murray	Dobson	Hutchinson/t
N3N	27-Jan	H	Nuneaton	W 26-16	400	S Evans/dg	Johnson	Murray/t	Drane	Hutchinson/t
N3N	3-Feb	H	Doncaster	W 22-5		S Evans	Johnson	Murray/t	Drane/t	Hutchinson
N3N	17-Feb	A	Sedgley Park	L 7-63	270	S Evans	Johnson	Murray	Drane	Hutchinson
N3N	24-Feb	N	Dudley Kingswinford	L 10-20		S Evans	Johnson/t	Murray	Drane	Hutchinson
N3N	10-Mar	H	Bedford Athletic	W 35-14		S Evans	Johnson/t	Murray	Drane	Hutchinson
N3N	24-Mar	H	Stourbridge	L 16-38	300	S Evans	Johnson	Murray	Drane	Hutchinson
N3N	31-Mar	A	Sandal	L 27-29		S Evans	Hutchinson	Murray/t	Drane/t	Johnson
N3N	14-Apr	H	New Brighton	L 18-31		S Evans/t	Johnson	D Evans/c2p	Drane	Hutchinson
N3N	21-Apr	A	Walsall	L 13-27		S Evans	Johnson/t	D Evans	Maynard	Luxton
N3N										
TBC	7-Oct	A	Nottingham	W 23-19		S Evans	Johnson	Murray/t	Sales	Hutchinson/t
TBC	21-Oct	A	Leeds Tykes	L 0-100	501	S Evans	Johnson	Murray	Driver	Hutchinson

** after opponents name indicates a penalty try. Brackets after a player's name indicates he was replaced.
eg (a) means he was replaced by replacement code "a" and so on. / after a player or replacement name
is followed by any scores he made - eg /t, /c, /p, /dg or any combination of these*

EVER PRESENT   David Evans

Most Appearances:

25	David Evans.
24	Nick Sykes, Chris Johnson.
23	Jon Kite, Ed Hutchinson.
21	S Kneale, M Smith.

PLAYERS USED

33 plus two as replacement only.

MOST POINTS

Pts	Player	T	C	P	DG
163	D Evans	4	28	29	-
35	E Hutchinson	7	-	-	-
30	D Hopton	6	-	-	-
30	C Johnson	6	-	-	-
25	N Murray	5	-	-	-
25	S Kneale	5	-	-	-

MATCH FACTS

10	9	1	2	3	4	5	6	7	8
D Evans/cp(a/c)	Smith	Gabriel	Kneale/t	Sykes	Fletcher	Chippendale	Kite	Hopton	Ball
Grayshon/c	D Evans	Gabriel	Kneale	Sykes	Burrows	Fletcher	Kite/t	Ball/t	Chippendale
Grayshon	D Evans/2tc	Gabriel	Kneale	Sykes/t	Burrows	Fletcher	Kite	Ball	Chippendale
D Evans/2p	Smith	Gabriel	Kneale	Sykes	Burrows	Fletcher	Kite	Hopton	Ball
Sales	D Evans/5c	Gabriel	Kneale	Sykes	Fletcher	Crosby	Kite	Wheelwright	Ball
D Evans/cp	Dadland	Gabriel	Kneale	Sykes	Fletcher	Chippendale	Kite	Wheelwright	Ball
D Evans/3c2p	Smith	Benn	Kneale	Sykes	Fletcher	Chippendale	Kite	Wheelwright(c/t)	Ball
Grayshon	Smith	Gabriel/t	Kneale	Sykes	Fletcher	Chippendale	Kite	Field	Ball
Grayshon/t	Smith	Gabriel/t	Kneale	Sykes	Fletcher	Chippendale	Kite	Hopton	Ball
Grayshon/dg	Smith/t	Gabriel	Kneale	Sykes	Fletcher	Chippendale	Kite	Wilks	Ball
Grayshon	Smith	Gabriel	Wheelwright	Sykes	Fletcher	Burrows/2t	Kite	Wilks	Ball
D Evans	Smith	Benn	Gabriel	Sykes	Chippendale	Burrows	Kite	Wilks	Ball
Grayshon	Smith	Gabriel/t	Kneale	Sykes	Chippendale	Fletcher	Kite	Wilks	Ball(d/t)
Grayshon	Smith/t	Gabriel	Kneale	Sykes	Chippendale	Fletcher	Kite	Wilks	Hopton/t
Sales	Smith	Gabriel	Kneale	Sykes/t	Fletcher	Chippendale	Kite	Wilks	Hopton/t
D Evans/2c3p	Smith	Gabriel	Kneale	Sykes	White	Chippendale	Ball	Wilks	Hopton/t
D Evans/c2p	Smith	Benn	Kneale/t	Sykes	White	Chippendale	Kite	Ball	Hopton
D Evans/t2cp	Smith	Benn	Kneale	Sykes	White	Chippendale	Kite	Wilks	Hopton
D Evans(a/c)	Smith	Benn	Kneale	Sykes/t	White	Chippendale	Kite	Ball	Hopton
D Evans/cp	Smith	Benn	Gabriel	Sykes	White	Chippendale	Kite	Wilks	Ball
D Evans/2c2p	Smith/t	Benn	Kneale	Sykes	Fletcher/t	White/t	Kite	Wilks/t	Ball
D Evans/c3p	Smith	Gabriel	Wilks	Benn	Fletcher	White	Kite	Hopton/t	Ball
D Evans/c	Smith	Gabriel	Kneale/3t	Sykes	Fletcher	Chippendale	Wilks	Hopton	Ball
Grayshon	Smith	Benn	Kneale	Sykes	Fletcher	White	Kite	Wilks	Hopton/t
Grayshon/c2p	Smith	Benn	Kneale	Sykes	Fletcher	White	Kite	Wilks	Hopton
D Evans/2c3p	Smith	Gabriel	Kneale	Sykes	Kite	Crosby	Field	Wheelwright	Ball
Drane	D Evans	Gabriel	Kneale	Sykes	Fletcher	Crosby	Kite	Wheelwright	Ball

REPLACEMENTS   a - J Grayshon   b - D Drane   c - C Field   d - D Hopton

MORLEY

LEAGUE STATISTICS *compiled by Stephen McCormack*

SEASON	Division	P	W	D	L	F	A	Pts Diff	Lge Pts	Lge Pos	Most Points	Most Tries
91-92	2	12	4	0	8	171	202	-31	8		57 Jamie Grayshon	4 Tony Clark
92-93	2	12	0	1	11	107	374	-267	1		66 Jamie Grayshon	2 Tony Clark
93-94	3	18	6	0	12	245	334	-89	12		17 Jamie Grayshon	8 Tony Clark
94-95	3	18	9	2	7	277	326	-49	20		166 Jamie Grayshon	7 Tony Clark
95-96	3	18	9	2	7	336	328	8	20		206 Jamie Grayshon	5 Ben Wade
96-97	3	30	22	0	8	928	572	356	44		195 Jamie Grayshon	17 Ben wade
97-98	JN1	26	5	0	21	372	844	-472	10	13	78 Adam Standeven	5 Ian Tulloch Adam Standeven
98-99	JN1	26	7	1	18	468	643	-175	15	13	119 Tom Bamber	15 Adam Standeven
99-00	JN2N	26	12	1	13	611	547	64	25	7	217 Jamie Grayshon	22 Chris Hall
	N3N	*25	8	0	17	468	720	-252	16	11	163 David Evans	7 Ed Hitchinson

FACT FILE

Founded: 1878
Nickname: Maroons

Colours: Maroon & white quarters/maroon/maroon & white
Change colours: All Blue.

GROUND

Address: Scatcherd Lane, Morley, West Yorkshire, LS27 0JJ
Tel. 0113 253 3487   Fax: 0113 253 4144   Website: www.morleyrfc.co.uk
Capacity: 2,899   Seated: 499   Standing: 2,400

Directions: **From West:** Leave M62 Jnc 27 Follow A650 towards Wakefield for 1.2miles turn left St. Andrews Ave. Ground 0.3 miles on left. **From East**: Leave M62 Jnc 28 follow A650 towards Bradford for 1.7 miles, turn right into St Andrews Ave.
Nearest Railway Station: Morley Low BR

Car Parking: 110 in & around ground

Admission: Season
Standing Adult £50, Family £100
Matchday
Standing Adults £5, Children/OAPs £2

Club Shop: Yes, Manager Mr. Gill Mitchell 0113 253 3487

Clubhouse: Weekdays 6-11, Sat 12-11, Sun 12-4 & 8-11
Three bars with snacks & bar meals available
Functions: Capacity 200
Contact Sheila Tonge 0113 253 3487

Training Nights: Tuesday & Thursday

PROGRAMME

Size: A5   Pages: 16   Price: £1
Editor: Peter Aveyard Tel: 0113 253 8193 (H)
e-mail: bruntcliffepete@cs.com

Advertising Rates - Mono
Page £300   1/2 page £175   1/4 page £100

Nick Sykes, Morley's captain, supported by fellow prop, Alan Benn, makes a determined drive forward against New Brighton.

NEW BRIGHTON FC

President	Dennis Morgan	c/o New Brighton FC Reeds Lane, Moreton, Wirral CH46 3RH.
		0151 677 2442
Chairman	Harry K Leyland	c/o New Brighton FC.
Hon. Secretary	Mrs B M Bowes	4 Murrayfield Drive, Moreton, Wirral CH46 3RS
		0151 678 2654(H) 0151 678 3278 (Fax) 07970 834298 (M)
		e-mail: Beryl.Bowes@btinternet.com
Hon. Treasurer	Paul Horner	1 Farndon Ave., Wallasey, Wirral CH45 3JX 0151 639 8606
Fixtures Secretary	B M Murphy	43 Brookfield Gardens, West Kirby, Wirral L48 4EL
		0151 625 8835 (H), 0151 708 7904 (B)
Press Officer	Geoff Stone	0151 625 6188 (H)
Director of Coaching	L Connor	c/o New Brighton FC.
Director of Rugby	A Saverimutto	c/o New Brighton FC.

For the third consecutive season since the elevation to National League Rugby, New Brighton found themselves in 3rd place. Once again we had led at the half way mark only to be overhauled in the run-in and, as always, losing to sides previously overcome with little effort.

That disappointment is now behind us and we congratulate Stourbridge for their consistency and Sedgley for their battling form after losing four early games. They will both enhance the standard of Division 2 and we look forward to rejoining them next year.

Our Tetley Cup campaign ended with an honourable defeat by London Welsh (17-32) after earlier scalps including Newbury (15-11). The Cheshire Cup was retained once again beating Winnington Park in the final. Plans for next season are well under way under the reins of the new Director of Rugby Alistair Saverimutto who is also re-siting his Wirral Rugby Academy at Reeds Lane. At the time of writing pre-season training has just started and faces both old and new are appearing in increasing numbers each week. We look forward to the new campaign with great appetite!

Finally we would like to commiserate with Aspatria and especially Walsall, who we believe had a raw deal at the hands of the "panel of experts". We trust they will soon be back! We also welcome Darlington Mowden Park, Scunthorpe, West Hartlepool and Blaydon to our league and look forward to meeting old and new friends in 2001/02.

Beryl Bowes, Hon. Secretary

NEW BRIGHTON

Comp.	Date	H/A	Opponents	Result & Score	Att	**15**	**14**	**13**	**12**	**11**
N3N	2-Sep	H	Sedgley Park	W 12-9	200	Butt	Brett/4p	Coast	Evans	Williams
N3N	9-Sep	H	Whitchurch	W 53-0	200	Butt/t	Brett/2t5cp	Coast/t	Evans/t	Williams
N3N	16-Sep	A	Tynedale	W 16-10	250	Butt	Brett/2p	Coast	Evans/t	Williams
N3N	30-Sep	A	Doncaster	L 3-11		Butt	Brett/p	Evans	Pennington	Williams
N3N	14-Oct	H	Liverpool St Helens	W 24-9	600	Butt	Brett/3cp	Coast/t	Evans	Johnson
N3N	28-Oct	A	Sandal	W 48-5		Butt	Brett/3c4p	Coast	Evans/2t	Johnson/t
N3N	11-Nov	H	Stourbridge	W 27-15	400	Pearson	Brett/2t2cp	Coast/t	Evans	Johnson
N3N	18-Nov	A	Walsall	W 13-10	325	Pearson/t	Brett/c2p	Coast	Pennington	Johnson
N3N	25-Nov	H	Bedford Athletic	W 31-7	250	Pearson/t	Brett/3c	Coast/t	Evans	Johnson
N3N	2-Dec	A	Dudley Kingwinsford	W 24-11	450	Pearson	Brett/c4p	Coast	Evans	Johnson
N3N	9-Dec	H	Morley	W 79-0	350	Mapp	Brett/t4c2p	Coast/t	Evans	Pearson/t
N3N	23-Dec	H	Dudley Kingwinsford**	W 32-13	350	Pearson	Brett/2cp	Coast/t	Evans/t	Johnson
N3N	6-Jan	H	Walsall	W 35-26		Mapp	Johnson	Coast	Brett/t3c3p	Pearson/t
N3N	13-Jan	A	Stourbridge	L 10-31	800	Mapp	van Scholr	Brett/t	Evans/t	Pearson
N3N	20-Jan	H	Sandal	W 35-28		Butt	Williams	Brett/cp	Evans/2t	Pearson
N3N	27-Jan	A	Aspatria*	W 36-20		Mapp	Pearson	Evans/t	Brett/2c4p	Johnson
N3N	3-Feb	H	Aspatria	W 45-8	300	Pearson	Brett/4c4p	Coast/t	Evans/2t	Johnson
N3N	10-Feb	A	Liverpool St Helens	W 21-17	250	Pearson	Brett/tc3p	Coast	Evans	Johnson
N3N	24-Feb	H	Doncaster	W 18-16		Pearson	Brett/c2p	Coast	Evans/t	Johnson
N3N	3-Mar	A	Nuneaton	L 8-17		Pearson	Williams	Evans	Brett/p	Johnson
N3N	24-Mar	A	Sedgley Park	L 10-26	1200	Mapp	Brett	Coast	Evans	Pearson
N3N	31-Mar	H	Nuneaton	W 37-0		Mapp	Williams/t	Evans	Brett/2cp	Pearson
N3N	14-Apr	A	Morley	W 31-18		Mapp	Brett/t3c	Evans/t	Coast	Williams
N3N	5-May	A	Bedford Athletic	L 20-23		Mapp	Pearson	Evans	Coast	Brett/cp
TBC	7-Oct	H	Leicester Lions	W 40-0		Butt	Brett/t2c2p	Coast/t	Evans/t	Johnson
TBC	21-Oct	H	Newbury	W 15-11		Butt	Brett/5p	Coast	Evans	Johnson
TBC	5-Nov	H	London Welsh	L 17-32		Pearson	Brett/2cp	Coast	Evans	Johnson

*after opponents name indicates a penalty try. Brackets after a player's name indicates he was replaced.
eg (a) means he was replaced by replacement code "a" and so on. / after a player or replacement name
is followed by any scores he made - eg /t, /c, /p, /dg or any combination of these*

EVER PRESENT

Geoff Jones, Steve Bellis, Paul Brett.

Most Appearances:

24	Geoff Jones, Steve Bellis, Paul Brett.
22	Emys Evans.
18	Marcus Coast, Tom Mapp.

PLAYERS USED

32 plus 1 as replacement only

MOST POINTS

Pts	Player	T	C	P	DG
258	P Brett	9	42	43	-
80	S Bellis	16	-	-	-
65	G Jones	13	-	-	-
35	M Coast	7	-	-	-
25	H Pearson	5	-	-	-
25	J Lamb	5	-	-	-

MATCH FACTS

10	9	1	2	3	4	5	6	7	8
Mapp	Hughes	Dorrington	Davies	Thomas	Fox	Allott	Jones	Brookman	Bellis
Mapp	Hughes	Gazzola	Taylor/t	Thomas	Fox/t	Allott	Jones	Brookman/t	Bellis
Mapp	Hughes	Dorrington	Taylor	Thomas	Allott	Fox	Jones	Brookman/t	Bellis
Mapp	Hughes	Dorrington	Taylor	Thomas	Allott	Fox	Jones	Brookman	Bellis
Mapp	Hughes	Dorrington	Davies	Dorrington	Fox	Campbell	Jones	Brookman/t	Bellis
Mapp	Hughes	Dorrington	Taylor	Thomas	Lamb	Campbell	Jones/2t	Brookman	Bellis
Butt	Hughes	Dorrington	Davies	Thomas	Fox	Campbell	Lamb	Jones/t	Bellis
Butt	Hughes	Gazzola	Davies	Thomas	Fox	Campbell	Lamb	Jones	Bellis
Butt	Hesketh	Gazzola	Taylor	Thomas	Allott	Campbell	Lamb	Jones/t	Bellis/2t
Butt	Hughes	Gazzola	Taylor	Thomas	Allott	Campbell	Lamb	Jones/2t	Bellis
Butt/t	Hesketh	Gazzola	Davies	Thomas	Allott	Fox/2t	Lamb/t	Jones/t	Bellis/4t
Butt	Hesketh	Gazzola	Davies	Thomas	Allott	Campbell	Lamb	Jones/t	Bellis
Butt	Hesketh	Gazzola	Taylor/t	Thomas	Allott	Campbell	Lamb	Jones	Bellis/t
Butt	Hesketh	Gazzola	Taylor	Thomas	Allott	Lamb	Jones	Jones	Bellis
Mapp	Bennett	Gazzola	Davies	Thomas	Allott	Campbell/t	Jones/t	Jones	Bellis/2t
Butt	Bennett	Dorrington	Davies	Gazzola	Lamb	Fox	Jones	Bellis/t	Jones/t
Mapp	Hughes	Dorrington	Taylor	Gazzola	Campbell	Fox	Lamb/t	Jones	Bellis/t
Butt	Bennett	Gazzola	Taylor	McCourt	Allott	Fox	Lamb	Jones	Bellis/t
Mapp	Hughes	Dorrington	Davies	McCourt	Fox	Campbell	Lamb	Jones	Bellis/t
Mapp/t	Hughes	Dorrington	Davies	McCourt	Fox	Campbell	Lamb	Bellis	Jones
O'Connor	Hughes	Dorrington	Taylor	Gazzola	Campbell	Stirrett	Jones	Brookman/t	Bellis/t
O'Connor/t	Hughes	Dorrington	Taylor/t	Gazzola	Stirrett	Campbell	Lamb/2t	Bellis	Jones/t
O'Connor	Morgan	Dorrington	Davies	Thomas/t	Campbell	Stirrett	Jones	Lamb/t	Bellis/t
Beauchamp	Morgan	Dorrington	Davies	Gazzola	Stirrett	Campbell	Lamb	Bellis/t	Jones/2t
Mapp	Hughes	Gazzola/t	Davies	Thomas	Allott	Campbell	Jones	Brookman	Bellis/t
Mapp	Hughes	Dorrington	Davies	Thomas	Fox	Campbell	Jones	Brookman	Lamb
Butt	Hughes	Dorrington	Taylor	Thomas	Fox	Campbell	Jones/2t	Brookman	Lamb

REPLACEMENTS   a - J Lyle   b - H Pearson   c - I Taylor   d - A Kettle

2000-01 HIGHLIGHTS

Paul Brett again topped the points scoring list and has now scored 560 in his two seasons at the club.

Paul was once again the leading scorer in the division.

No 8 Steve Bellis took the leading try scoring title this season from fellow back row man Geoff Jones and failed by just one to equal the club record of 17.

The three leading scorers were all ever presents for the club in league matches last season.

Lost just two of their first 19 matches of the season but two away defeats in successive matches against Nuneaton and Sedgley Park out paid to any hopes of a top two finish.

NEW BRIGHTON

LEAGUE STATISTICS *compiled by Stephen McCormack*

SEASON	Division	P	W	D	L	F	A	Pts Diff	Lge Pts	Lge Pos	Most Points	Most Tries
91-92												
92-93	NW 1	12	9	1	2	243	103	140	19	2		
93-94	NW 1	12	10	1	1	310	87	223	21	1p		
94-95	North 2	12	9	0	3	376	140	236	18	3		
95-96	North 2	12	10	1	1	232	105	127	21	1p		
96-97	North 1	21	14	1	6	484	381	103	29	3		
97-98	North 1	22	17	2	3	599	293	306	36	1p	243 Alex Guest	15 Ian Kennedy
98-99	N2N	26	20	0	6	703	329	374	40	3	159 Murray King	17 Ian Kennedy
99-00	N2N	26	21	0	5	784	283	501	42	3	302 Paul Brett	17 Geoff Jones
00-01	N3N	*24	19	0	5	668	336	332	38	3	258 Paul Brett	16 Steve Bellis

FACT FILE

Founded: 1875

Colours: Light blue, navy blue & white quarters/black/black
Change colours: White

Web site: www.Newbrightonrugby.co.uk

GROUND

Address:

Reeds Lane, Moreton, Wirral CH46 3RH
Tel: 0151 677 1873/2442   Fax: 0151 606 9745   e-mail: nbrugby@tesco.net
Capacity: 5,400   Seated: 400   Standing: 5,000

Directions:

M53 Junc 1 direction for New Brighton, 1st turning left (sign posted NBFC, Moreton).
After approx 1 mile turn left into Reeds Lane, ground entrance approx. 200 yards on left
Nearest Railway Station: Leasowe (Wirral Line)

Car Parking: 400 at ground

Admission: **Season** tickets - Adult £50.   **Matchday** - Adults £5. Children/OAPs £2.50

Clubhouse: Open 7 days a week
Functions: Capacity 300. Contact C Cattrall c/o Club

Club Shop: Yes

Training Nights: Tuesday & Thursday. Women: Wednesday

PROGRAMME Size: A5   Price: £1   Pages: 32
Editor: Ken Roberts email: Ken@kenrober.freeserve.co.uk
Advertising rates:
Colour - Full page £300
Mono - Full page £200, Half £120, Qtr £70

NUNEATON RFC

President	Keith Howells	Tel: 012476 348286
Secretary	Maggie Mander	7 Farriers Way, Crowhill, Nuneaton, Warks, CV11 6UZ
		Tel: 02476 381803 (H) 07808 734504 (Mob)
		e-mail: maggie@mander.softnet.co.uk
Treasurer	Mrs Susan Ryan	Tel: 02476 384482 (H) 02476 642226 (B)
Director of Rugby	Chris Tarbuck	Tel: 0961 128936 e-mail: tarby8@hotmail.com
1st XV Manager	Paul Vowles	Tel: 02476 736508 0777 5626679 (M)
Fixture Secretary	David Cadden	10 Henly Close, St Nicholas Park, Nuneaton. CV11 6HF
		Tel: 02476 326467 (H) 02476 205959 (B)
		e-mail: dcadden1@jaguar.com

The season started in the worst possible way with the loss of the club coach, Harry Roberts, who accepted a position with Coventry, and the loss of eight senior First XV players. We were very lucky, however, to find Chris Tarbuck who took on the position as director of rugby. Chris joined us from Coventry where he had been the previous season's captain and where he was considering whether he wished to remain as a player for another season. Luckily for us he decided to make a move into coaching.

When he joined The Nuns I am sure he was filled with despair. Having lost half of our squad he was forced to use our colts in the senior side. To their credit they have developed through the season and have become good and experienced squad members. Indeed, Gary Marshall became top try scorer of our league and was presented with an award at Banbury in June. Unfortunately Gary sustained a very serious injury during our fixture against Sandal towards the end of the season, when he collided with one of our own players and ended up with two broken ribs and a split kidney. He spent three weeks in hospital and is still under a consultant regarding the repair of his kidney. We await with patience to hear when he will be able to return to the club.

Chris Tarbuck did an excellent job with the team and built a very strong side during the season. This was reflected in our final fifth position and it has instilled great confidence for the forthcoming season. We were also the only team in our league to complete all of our fixtures which was quite an achievement due to the severe weather conditions and the impact of foot and mouth. There are several new players joining this season to strengthen the side even more, but unfortunately our team captain, Richard Moore, has elected to take a season off due to his business commitments. Rich confirms he will return to The Nuns for 2000-03. Mark Mitchell remains as club captain for a further year.

At our Annual Dinner, awards were presented to Craig Dutton - Player of the Year, Gary Marshall - Most Improved Player, Andy Goodall - Forward of the Year, Chris Atchinson - Extras Player of the Year (awarded for the third year in succession and he wants to know if he can keep it!), Tony Mears - Saracen of the Year, Philip Ryan - Colt of the Year and Paul Littlehales - Clubman of the Year. On top of this Gary Marshall, Jody Peacock and Chris Tarbuck were awarded players badges for playing in 24, 20 and 24 games respectively.

Back Row: Maggie Mander (Secretary), Paul Vowles (Team Manager), David Cadden (Fixtures Secretary), Andy Savage (Asst. Coach), Paul Rees, Stuart Gibson, Dave Lockey, Craig Court, Al Roberts, Stuart Pearman, James Coulsey, Andy Goodall, Chris Tarbuck (Director of Rugby), Keith Howells (President), Gail Gadden (Asst. Physio).
Front: Chris Warden (Team Manager's Asst.), Mark Mitchell (Club Captain), Gary Marshall, Jonathon Carter, Jodie Peacock, Rich Moore (Team Captain), Martin Shaw, Craig Dutton, Martin Smith, James Littlehales, Karen Stewart (Club Physio).

NUNEATON

Comp.	Date	H/A	Opponents	Result & Score	Att	15	14	13	12	11
N3N	2-Sep	A	Sandal	W 22-18	200	Peacock	Littlehales	Dutton/t	Bolstridge	Marshall
N3N	16-Sep	H	Stourbridge	L 5-46		Peacock	Marshall	Bolstridge	Littlehales	Smith(a/t)
N3N	23-Sep	A	Walsall	W 28-8	350	Peacock	Smith	Littlehales/2c3p	Dutton	Marshall/t
N3N	30-Sep	H	Bedford Athletic	W 22-13		Peacock	Marshall/t	Dutton/t	Littlehales/2cp	Smith
N3N	14-Oct	A	Dudley Kingwinsford	L 13-48	500	Peacock	Littlehales/c2p	Dutton	Marshall/t	Marshall
N3N	28-Oct	A	Aspatria*	W 18-15		Peacock/t	Baron	Marshall	Dutton	Marshall
N3N	4-Nov	H	Morley	W 50-27	250	Peacock/2t	Smith/t	Marshall	Dutton	Marshall/3t
N3N	11-Nov	A	Sedgley Park	L 3-57	250	Peacock	Smith	Marshall	Dutton	Marshall
N3N	18-Nov	H	Tynedale	W 29-9	150	Peacock	Smith/t	Marshall/t	Dutton	Marshall/t
N3N	25-Nov	A	Whitchurch	L 12-15	530	Peacock	Smith	Marshall	Dutton/t	Marshall
N3N	2-Dec	H	Doncaster	W 22-12	200	Coulsey	Smith	Marshall	Dutton	Marshall/2t
N3N	9-Dec	A	Liverpool St Helens	L 15-25	250	Coulsey	Smith/t	Marshall	Dutton	Marshall
N3N	23-Dec	A	Doncaster	L 11-38	800	Peacock	Baron	Marshall	Dutton	Marshall/t
N3N	6-Jan	A	Tynedale*	W 20-10		Peacock	Baron	Marshall	Dutton	Marshall
N3N	13-Jan	H	Sedgley Park	L 17-56	250	Coulsey	Smith	Marshall	Dutton	Marshall/t
N3N	20-Jan	H	Aspatria*	W 33-22		Peacock	Smith/t	Marshall	Dutton	Marshall/2t
N3N	27-Jan	A	Morley	L 16-26	400	Peacock	Smith	Marshall	Dutton/t	Marshall
N3N	3-Feb	H	Whitchurch	W 41-13		Reid	Baron/t	Littlehales	Dutton	Marshall/2t
N3N	10-Feb	H	Dudley Kingwinsford	W 29-0	200	Reid	Baron/t	Littlehales	Dutton	Marshall
N3N	24-Feb	A	Bedford Athletic	W 25-0		Reid	Baron/t	Littlehales	Dutton	Marshall/2t
N3N	3-Mar	H	New Brighton*	W 17-8		Reid	Baron	Marshall	Dutton	Marshall
N3N	10-Mar	H	Walsall	L 34-42		Peacock/c	Baron	Marshall	Dutton/c	Marshall/3t
N3N	17-Mar	A	Stourbridge	D 13-13	400	Peacock/c2p	Smith	Marshall	Dutton	Marshall
N3N	24-Mar	H	Sandal	W 53-17		Peacock/t	Smith/t	Marshall	Dutton	Marshall/t
N3N	31-Mar	A	New Brighton	L 0-37		Peacock	Smith	Marshall	Dutton	Baron
N3N	14-Apr	H	Liverpool St Helens	W 46-22		Peacock	Smith/t	Marshall	Dutton	Baron/2t
TBC	7-Oct	A	Liverpool St Helens	L 7-23		Peacock	Baron/t	Littlehales/c	Dutton	Marshall

*after opponents name indicates a penalty try. Brackets after a player's name indicates he was replaced.
eg (a) means he was replaced by replacement code "a" and so on. / after a player or replacement name
is followed by any scores he made - eg /t, /c, /p, /dg or any combination of these

EVER PRESENT Craig Dutton.

Most Appearances:
- 26   Craig Dutton.
- 24   Garry Marshall, Richard Moore, Chris Tarbuck.
- 23   Stuart Gibson.
- 21   Alan Roberts

PLAYERS USED

30 plus two as replacement only

MOST POINTS

Pts	Player	T	C	P	DG
139	W Masser	1	37	20	-
100	G Marshall	20	-	-	-
35	C Tarbuck	7	-	-	-
30	M Smith	6	-	-	-
30	A Baron	6	-	-	-

MATCH FACTS

10	9	1	2	3	4	5	6	7	8
Coulsey/2cp	Mitchell	Moore	Gibson	Court/t	Goodall	Roberts	Tarbuck/t	Nightingale	Rees
Dutton	Mitchell	Moore	Gibson	Court	Lockley	Roberts	Mitchell	Goodall	Tarbuck
Harrison	Carter	Moore	Gibson	Court	Lockley	Roberts	Mitchell	Nightingale/t	Tarbuck/t
Coulsey	Carter	Moore	Gibson	Court	Lockley/t	Roberts	Mitchell	Nightingale	Rees
Coulsey	Carter	Pearman	Gibson	Moore	Goodall	Roberts	Banks	Nightingale	Mitchell
Masser/c2p	Mitchell	Pearman	Gibson	Moore	Lockley	Goodall	Mitchell	Nightingale	Tarbuck
Masser/6cp	Mitchell	Moore	Snow	Pearman	Lockley	Roberts	Mitchell	Nightingale/t	Tarbuck
Masser/p	Mitchell	Pearman	Gibson	Moore	Lockley	Roberts	Banks	Nightingale	Tarbuck
Masser/3cp	Mitchell	Pearman	Gibson	Moore	Goodall	Roberts	Mitchell/t	Nightingale	Tarbuck
Coulsey/c	Mitchell	Pearman	Gibson	Court	Lockley	Roberts	Mitchell	Nightingale	Tarbuck/t
Masser/2cp	Mitchell	Moore	Gibson	Court/t	Goodall	Roberts	Mitchell	Nightingale	Tarbuck
Littlehales/cp	Mitchell	Moore	Gibson	Court	Goodall	Roberts	Mitchell	Nightingale	Tarbuck/t
Coulsey/2p	Bailey	Moore	Gibson	Court	Lockley	Roberts	Tarbuck	Goodall	Evans
Masser/2c2p	Bailey	Moore	Gibson	Court	Goodall/t	Roberts	Nightingale	Rees	Tarbuck
Masser/2cp	Bailey	Moore	Snow	Pearman	Goodall	Roberts	Banks/t	Rees	Tarbuck
Masser/2c3p	Mitchell	Pearman	Gibson	Moore	Goodall	Roberts	Banks	Rees	Tarbuck
Masser/c3p	Bailey	Pearman	Snow	Moore	Goodall	Roberts	Chaplin	Nightingale	Tarbuck
Masser/3c	Mitchell/t	Pearman	Gibson/2t	Moore	Goodall	Roberts	Mitchell/t	Chaplin	Tarbuck
Masser/3cp	Mitchell	Pearman/t	Gibson	Moore	Goodall	Roberts	Mitchell/t	Chaplin/t	Tarbuck
Masser/cp	Bailey/t	Pearman	Gibson	Moore	Goodall	Roberts	Mitchell	Chaplin	Tarbuck
Masser/2cp	Bailey/t	Moore	Gibson	Court	Goodall	Chaplin	Mitchell	Nightingale	Tarbuck
Mitchell	Bailey/t	Moore	Gibson	Court/t	Goodall	Chaplin	Mitchell	Nightingale	Tarbuck/t
Mitchell	Bailey	Pearman	Gibson	Court	Goodall	Lockley	Mitchell/t	Rees	Tarbuck
Masser/t4c	Mitchell	Moore	Gibson/t	Court	Goodall/t	Lockley	Mitchell/t	Rees/t	Tarbuck/t
Masser	Mitchell	Pearman	Gibson	Moore	Lockley	Roberts	Chaplin	Rees	Tarbuck
Masser/5c2p	Bailey	Moore	Gibson	Court/t	Lockley/t	Roberts	Banks	Chaplin	Tarbuck/t
Coulsey	Carter	Moore	Gibson	Court	Lockley	Roberts	Banks	Goodall	Rees

REPLACEMENTS   a - A Baron

Warwick Masser topped the points scorers list for the first time since 1995-96 with 139 points.

In the try scoring winger Garry Marshall smashed the record for tries in a season and finished with 20, this was seven better than the previous record set by Steve Carter.

Marshall also finished as leading try scorer in the division and joint leading try scorer in all the five National Leagues.

Centre Craig Dutton was the only ever present as the club used just 30 players to start matches, this was 10 less than the previous season.

NUNEATON

LEAGUE STATISTICS compiled by Stephen McCormack

SEASON	Division	P	W	D	L	F	A	Pts Diff	Lge Pts	Lge Pos		Coach		Captain
91-92	3	12	1	2	9	153	237	-84	4	12r	80	Vasile Ion	2	Colin Leake
92-93	D4N	12	2	0	10	138	269	-131	4	12				
93-94	D5N	12	4	1	7	122	200	-78	9	11				
94-95	D5N	12	4	0	8	129	161	-32	8	11				
95-96	D5N	12	4	1	7	176	329	-151	9	10	92	Warwick Masser	2	Darren Barry & Andy Brown, Paul Jones
96-97	D4N	26	8	1	7	457	667	-210	17	12	68	Marc Thomas & Gavin Henderson	9	Clive Bent
97-98	N2N	26	13	0	13	453	570	-117	26	7	141	Marc Thomas	7	Craig Court
98-99	N2N	26	14	2	10	596	533	66	30	5	135	Jez Harris	13	Steve Carter
99-00	N2N	26	11	1	14	610	665	-55	23	8	145	Marc Thomas	11	Steve Carter
00-01	N3N	26	15	1	10	597	605	-8	31	5	139	Warwick Masser	20	Gary Marshall

FACT FILE

Founded: 1879
Nickname: Nuns

Colours: Red with white & black
Change colours: Green, white, black

GROUND
Address: Liberty Way, Attleborough Fields, Nuneaton, Warks. CV11 6RR.
Tel: 01203 383206
Capacity (all standing) No limit

Directions: From M6 follow A444 to Nuneaton, follow ring road towards M69/A5. Ring road enters Eastborough Way, club just off mini round about
Nearest Railway Station: Nuneaton, 5 mins by taxi

Car Parking: Ample parking within the ground

Admission: Matchday - Adults £5, OAPs £2, Children £1

Clubhouse: Normal licensing hours
Functions: Capacity up to 100 (seated).
Bookings thro' Club Secretary

Club Shop: Open Matchdays & Sunday mornings.

Training Nights: Tuesday and Thursday.

PROGRAMME
Size: A5   Price: £1   Pages: 28 + cover
Editor: Maggie Mander, Club Sec.
ADVERTISING
Contact Maggie Mander

SANDAL RUFC

President	Henry Everett	31 Mount Crescent, Thornes, Wakefield WF2 8QG 01924 378987 (H)
Chairman	C R Hoyland	1 Moorhouse Lane, Haigh, nr Barnsley S74 4DD 01924 830572 (H)
Director of Rugby	Steve Ackroyd	c/o Sandal RUFC Home Tel: 01924 256004
Dir. of Youth Rugby	Steve Hodges	14 Carr Lane, Sandal, Wakefield WF2 6HJ 01924 255009 (H)
Hon. Secretary	Philip Harrison	46 Brandhill Drive, Crofton, Wakefield WF4 1PF 01924 863457 (H)
Press Officer	Philip Harrison	as Secretary
Fixtures Secretary	Colin Critchett	48 Sinclair Garth, Sandal, Wakefield WF2 6RE 01924 254329
Match Sec.& Referees	Malcolm Pashley	01924 255020

This has been a very difficult season for Sandal RUFC both on and off the field. We started the season full of optimism, but then we were affected by the worst injury list of our history. In only the third match of the campaign against Doncaster, we lost four players with long term injuries - Captain Mark Wolff, Jonlee Lockwood, Dean Lomas and Dan Smith. The injury list lengthened and up to Christmas we had only won three matches.

It was not until February that we started winning again when our injured players started to come back into form, but then we were fighting against relegation and the foot and mouth crisis.

We scored a double over Whitchurch and Walsall and were unable to play Aspatria and Tynedale so our fate was left in the hands of the task group. Our late performances were taken into account and we were awarded an extra half a point which enabled Sandal to maintain their National League status.

Our season was extended with a glorious run in the Yorkshire Cup, the oldest cup in world rugby, when we beat Wharfedale, Harrogate and Otley on the way to the semi final. We beat Doncaster in the semi leaving us with a difficult match against Middlesbrough in the final. We finally overcame our opponents after being behind four times in the match to win 26-24

Philip Harrison

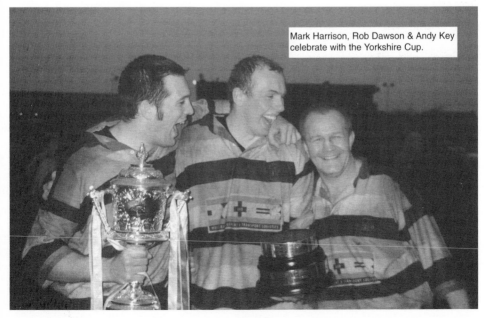

Mark Harrison, Rob Dawson & Andy Key celebrate with the Yorkshire Cup.

SANDAL

Comp.	Date	H/A	Opponents	Result & Score	Att	15	14	13	12	11
N3N	2-Sep	H	Nuneaton	L 18-22	200	Wolff/t	Barker	Lomas/c2p	Brindley	Munn
N3N	9-Sep	H	Tynedale	L 10-23		Wolff	Barker/t	Lomas/p	Brindley	Munn
N3N	23-Sep	A	Doncaster	L 33-55		Wolff	Greenhalgh	Lockwood/t	Lomas/2c	Barker/2t
N3N	30-Sep	A	Whitchurch	W 52-22	300	Brindley	Barker/2t	Palmer/t	Brindley/3t	Greenhalgh
N3N	14-Oct	H	Doncaster	L 11-53	250	Brindley	Doherty	Frazer	Palmer	Barker
N3N	28-Oct	H	New Brighton	L 5-48		Brindley/t	Doherty	Frazer	Barker	Elston
N3N	4-Nov	A	Liverpool St Helens	L 13-21	250	Brindley	Elston	Barker	Palmer	Doherty/t
N3N	11-Nov	H	Aspatria	L 15-29		Howarth	Elston	Palmer	Barker/t	White
N3N	18-Nov	A	Stourbridge	L 10-65	300	Elston	White	Barker	Howarth	Doherty
N3N	25-Nov	H	Walsall	W 39-30		Howarth/2t	Doherty/t	Barker	Stead	Elston/t
N3N	2-Dec	A	Bedford Athletic	L 19-24		Howarth/t	Houghton	Barker	Stead	Doherty/t
N3N	16-Dec	A	Morley	L 15-29	400	Wolff	Brindley	Barker/t	Stead	Doherty
N3N	23-Dec	H	Bedford Athletic	W 24-18		Wolff	Howarth/2t	Lockwood	Stead	Barker
N3N	6-Jan	H	Stourbridge	L 27-47		Wolff	Howarth	Lockwood	Barker/2t	Doherty
N3N	20-Jan	A	New Brighton	L 28-35		Wolff/2t	Doherty	Barker/2t	Lockwood	Howarth
N3N	27-Jan	H	Liverpool St Helens	L 22-34		Wolff/c	Howarth/2t	Lockwood	Barker	Doherty
N3N	3-Feb	A	Sedgley Park	L 16-47	250	Wolff	Lomas/t	Barker	Lockwood	Howarth/t
N3N	17-Feb	H	Dudley Kingswinsford	W 39-21		Wolff/t	Howarth	Barker	Brindley	Lomas
N3N	24-Feb	H	Whitchurch	W 22-17		Wolff	Howarth	Brindley/t	Barker	Lomas/2t
N3N	10-Mar	A	Dudley Kingswinsford	L 20-47	450	Wolff	Howarth	Brindley	Barker/2t	Doherty
N3N	17-Mar	H	Sedgley Park	L 19-66	300	Wolff/t	Howarth	Barker/t	Lomas/t	Brindley
N3N	24-Mar	A	Nuneaton	L 17-53		Brindley	Howarth/t	Barker	Lomas	Doherty
N3N	31-Mar	H	Morley	W 29-27		Wolff/t	Lomas/t	Barker/t	Brindley	Howarth/t
N3N	14-Apr	A	Walsall	W 37-35		Wolff/t	Howarth/2t	Barker	Brindley	Brindley
TBC	7-Oct	H	Tynedale	L 14-15						

** after opponents name indicates a penalty try. Brackets after a player's name indicates he was replaced.
eg (a) means he was replaced by replacement code "a" and so on. / after a player or replacement name
is followed by any scores he made - eg /t, /c, /p, /dg or any combination of these*

EVER PRESENT
Steve Dykes, Jamie Barker.

Most Appearances:

24	Steve Dykes, Jamie Barker.
21	Gary Swift.
19	Alex Ledger.
18	Dan Smith.

PLAYERS USED
39 plus three as replacement only

MOST POINTS

Pts	Player	T	C	P	DG
135	M Sales	1	38	18	-
75	J Barker	15	-	-	-
60	D Howarth	12	-	-	-
40	D Lomas	5	3	3	-
37	M Wolff	7	1	-	-

MATCH FACTS

10	9	1	2	3	4	5	6	7	8
Brindley	Wheeler	Goodwin	Swift	Fradgley(a/t)	Harrison	Barker	Dykes	Ledger	Smith
Sales/c	Wheeler	Goodwin	Swift	Kidd	Harrison	Barker	Dykes	Ledger	Smith
Sales/t2c	Wheeler	Witcombe	Swift	Kidd	Harrison	Barker	Smith	Ledger/t	Dykes
Sales/7cp	Wheeler	Goodwin	Swift	Witcombe	Potgieter	Harrison	Livermore	Ledger/t	Dykes
Brindley/2p	Wheeler	Kidd	Swift	Witcombe	Harrison	Barker	Livermore	Ledger/t	Dykes
Brindley	Wheeler	Kidd	Swift	Witcombe	Harrison	Barker	McIntosh	Ledger	Dykes
Brindley/p	Wheeler	Goodwin	Swift	Witcombe	Barker	Dawson	Dykes	Ledger	Smith/t
Brindley/cp	Wheeler	Goodwin	Swift	Witcombe	Barker	Dawson	Dykes	Ledger	Smith/t
Sales/cp	Wheeler	Kidd	Swift/t	Goodwin	Hargrave	Dawson	Dykes	Phillips	Smith
Sales/4c2p	Wheeler	Goodwin	Swift	Witcombe/t	Hargrave	Dawson	Dykes	Ledger	Smith
Sales/2c	Brindley	Goodwin	Swift	Witcombe/t	Hargrave	Dawson	Dykes	Ledger	Smith
Sales/cp	Wheeler	Goodwin	Swift	Witcombe/t	Dawson	Barker	Dykes	Ledger	Smith
Sales/3p	Wheeler	Kidd	Swift	Witcombe	Harrison	Dykes	Livermore/t	Ledger	Smith
Sales/cp	Harris	Witcombe	Swift	Kidd	Harrison	Dawson(b/t)	Livermore	Ledger	Dykes/t
Sales/4c	Bacon	Goodwin	Swift	Kidd	Dykes	Dawson	Livermore	Ledger	Smith
Sales	Bacon/t	Goodwin	Swift	Kidd	Harrison	Dawson	Dykes	Phillips	Smith/t
Brindley	Bacon/2p	Wilson	Swift	McSwiney	Dawson	Harrison	Key	Smith	Dykes
Sales/4c2p	Bacon/t(c/t)	Wilson	Swift	McSwiney	Harrison/t	Dawson	Dykes	Livermore	Smith/t
Sales/2cp	Bacon	Wilson	Swift	McSwiney	Harrison	Dawson	Dykes	Key	Smith
Sales/2c2p	Bacon	Wilson	Swift	McSwiney	Dawson	Harrison	Dykes	Ledger	Smith
Sales	Bacon/2c	McSwiney	Key	Wilson	Dawson	Dykes	Livermore	Ledger	Smith
Brindley/t	Bacon/c	McSwiney	Swift	Goodwin	Dawson	Dykes/t	Key	Ledger	Smith
Sales/3cp	Brindley	Wilson	Key	McSwiney	Dawson	Harrison	Lockwood	Ledger	Dykes
Sales/4c3p	Bacon	Wilson	Key/t	McSwiney	Dawson	Harrison	Lockwood	Ledger	Dykes

REPLACEMENTS   a - M Allchurch   b - D Smith   c - M Doherty

2000-01 HIGHLIGHTS

Outside half Mark Sales tops the points scorers in his first season at the club with 135 from 17 league appearances.

In the try scoring stakes centre Jamie Barker set a new club with 15 league tries. This beat the old record of 14 set by Mark Wolff two season ago.

Winger David Howarth also had a good season and ran in 12 tries from just 16 league appearances.

Only side they did the double against was Whitchurch where they were 52-22 winners away from home and 22-17 winners at home.

SANDAL

LEAGUE STATISTICS *compiled by Stephen McCormack*

SEASON	Division	P	W	D	L	F	A	Pts Diff	Lge Pts	Lge Pos	Coach	Captain
91-92	North 1	10	5	0	5	140	115	25	10	4	M Shuttleworth	M Hardcastle
92-93	North 1	12	6	1	5	205	129	76	13	4	M Shutleworth	M Hardcastle
93-94	North 1	12	9	0	3	219	131	88	18	2	M Shuttleworth	A Turton
94-95	North 1	12	8	3	1	227	126	101	19	1p	M Shuttleworth	A Turton

									Most Points			Most Tries
95-96	D5N	12	6	0	6	244	198	46	12	6	110 Mark Hardcastle	6 Mark Wolff
96-97	D4N	26	15	1	10	618	573	45	31	5	248 Mark Hardcastle	9 Andrew Wolff & Mark Wolff
97-98	N2N	26	13	1	12	485	547	-62	25*	8	268 Ian Shuttleworth	9 Ian Shuttleworth
98-99	N2N	26	13	0	13	697	611	86	26	7	246 Ian Shuttleworth	14 Mark Wolff
99-00	N2N	26	9	3	14	478	548	-70	21	10	97 Dean Lomas	8 Richard Wade
00-01	N3N	*24	7	0	17	542	868	-326	14	12	135 Mark Sales	15 Jamie Barker

FACT FILE

Founded: 1927
Nickname: The Milnthorpers

Colours: Maroon, gold & white hoops
Change colours: Gold with maroon & white hoops.

GROUND
Address: Milnthorpe Green, Standbridge Lane, Sandal, Wakefield, W. Yorks. WF27JD.
Tel: 01924 250661
Capacity: 1625   Seated: 75   Standing: 1500

Directions: From the M1, junction 39, take the A636 to Wakefield. After3/4 mile turn right at the roundabout into Ansdale Road, and after one mile the club will be found on the left.
Nearest Railway Station: Westgate, Wakefield.

Car Parking: 200 spaces are available within the ground.

Admission: Matchdays - Adults: £5 (incl. car park & programme)
Children/OAPs: £2.50.

Clubhouse: New clubhouse. open during normal licensing hours, two bars, bar meals available. Fitness centre.
Functions: Up to 120 can be catered for.

Club Shop: Open matchdays & Sundays.

Training Nights: Tuesday and Thursday.

PROGRAMME Size: A5   Price: With admission   Pages: 24 + cover

ADVERTISING RATES
Full page £200, 1/2 page £100 & 1/4 page £50

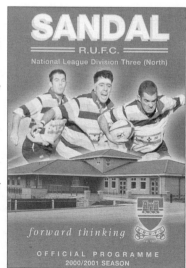

SCUNTHORPE R.U.F.C.

President	Pete Bright		
Chairman	Lew Clayton	2 Langley Drive, Bottesfor, N. Lincs.	
Secretary	Mick Hill	15 Peveril Ave., Scunthorpe DN17 1BQ	
		01724 403014 (B) 01724 359432 (H) 07730 803050 (M)	
		email: michael.hill@capara-merchant-bar.co.uk	
Fixture Secretary	Ray Wilson	70 Wiltshire Ave., Burton-on-Stather, N. Lincs.	01724 720915
Treasurer	Jim Lynch	3 Neath Road, Scunthorpe	01724 343678

As summer training unfolded so the changes in playing personnel also became apparent.

Those players from last season that were moving on were Billy Bragg (Army to Oxford), John Penn (university in Cardiff), Andy Wallhead (with injury) and Paul Sewell (Rugby Professional in Italy).

On the credit side, Mark Hyde returned from Doncaster and Rob Page from Hull Ionians. Tim Robinson signed following a four-year absence, which saw him plying his trade at Moseley, Nottingham and Camberley and a stint in New Zealand. Coming from the Colts, were Tom Foster, Luke Scargill and Gareth McSherry. Mick Coult decided to finish his professional Rugby League career and come back as player coach, supporting Liam Waldron.

The season started with a home league match against Burton-on-Trent on the 2nd September and a comfortable win. Victories also followed in the Tetley's at Ampthill on 9th Sept. and at Hereford in the league on the 16th Sept. This was followed by the first meeting of the season with Leicester Lions in the Tetley's at Leicester and a sobering defeat by 24-14 that told us much about the season to come. League wins followed against Newbold away (32-0), Stoke home (37-14), Broad Street away (26-16) and Camp Hill home (35-5) before the next meeting with Leicester Lions at home which The Greens won by 28-20.

The first defeat came away at Kenilworth 8-15 and was a surprise to everyone. After holding a 16 points to nil advantage against Longton at home, the best that was achieved was a 19-all draw. The league challenge got back on track with a 66-7 win at home to Banbury. An away win at Barkers Butts (28-5) signalled the end of the first half of the season with the wet weather starting to take effect due to cancellations.

The first match of the New Year brought a win at Camp Hill by 36-11. Victories followed at Stoke (18-6), at home to Kenilworth (40-27) and home to Newbold (48-3). It was crunch time on the 24th Feb. at Leicester Lions and a win by 17-16. Comfortable wins at home to Broad Street (55-5) and away at Burton (48-3) preceded a difficult encounter at Longton which finished with both sides again level on points, this time by 12 each. A big home win against Barkers Butts (71-10) was followed by an awkward away trip to Banbury where a win by 34-23 virtually ensured promotion. This was sealed with a 48-13 victory at home to Hereford.

The club is looking forward to the challenge of next season.

Skipper Phil Sidebottom (centre) congratulates his men after their win at Banbury virtually ensured promotion.
Photo courtesy of the Scunthorpe Eveneing Telegraph

SCUNTHORPE

Comp.	Date	Opponents	H/A	Result & Score	15	14	13	12	11
Mid 1	02/09	Burton	H	W 32-13	T.Foster/t	J.Astbury/t3c2p	M.Coult	M.Watterson	A.Dawson
Mid 1	16/9	Hereford	A	W 29-15	C.Conroy	J.Astbury/t3cp	M.Coult/t	M.Watterson	T.Foster
Mid 1	30/9	Newbold*	A	W 32-0	C.Conroy	J.Astbury/t3cp	M.Coult/t	M.Watterson/t	T.Foster
Mid 1	14/10	Stoke	H	W 37-14	C.Conroy	J.Astbury/t3c2p	M.Coult/t	A.Dawson/t	T.Foster
Mid 1	21/10	Broad Street	A	W 26-16	C.Conroy	J.Astbury/c3p	M.Coult/t	A.Dawson	T.Foster/2t
Mid 1	28/10	CampHill	H	W 35-5	C.Conroy	J.Astbury/3c3p	M.Coult	T.Foster	M.Watterson/t
Mid 1	04/11	Leicester Lions	H	W 28-20	C.Conroy/2t	J.Astbury/t2c3p	M.Coult	A.Dawson	T.Foster
Mid 1	11/11	Kenilworth	A	L 8-15	C.Conroy	J.Astbury/p	M.Coult	A.Dawson/t	T.Foster
Mid 1	18/11	Longton*	H	D 19-19	C.Conroy	J.Astbury/c4p	M.Coult	T.Foster	M.Watterson
Mid 1	25/11	Banbury	H	W 66-7	C.Conroy/2t	J.Astbury/3t5c2p	M.Coult/t	M.Watterson	T.Foster
Mid 1	9/12	Barkers Butts	A	W 28-5	C.Conroy	J.Astbury/2tc2p	M.Coult/t	M.Watterson	T.Foster
Mid 1	13/01	Camp Hill	A	W 36-11	T.Foster	J.Astbury/t4cp	M.Coult/t	K.Hadfield	M.Watterson/2t
Mid 1	27/01	Stoke	A	W 18-6	D.Blackburn	J.Astbury/tc2p	K.Hadfield	M.Watterson	T.Foster/t
Mid 1	03/02	Kenilworth*	H	W 40-27	T.Foster/t	J.Astbury/t5c	M.Coult	K.Hadfield	M.Watterson
Mid 1	10/02	Newbold	H	W 43-3	T.Foster/t	J.Astbury/t4cp	M.Coult	M.Watterson/t	K.Hadfield
Mid 1	24/02	Leicester Lions	A	W 17-16	T.Foster	J.Astbury/4p	M.Coult	K.Hadfield(a/t)	M.Watterson
Mid 1	03/03	Broad Street	H	W 55-5	T.Foster	J.Astbury/2t3c3p	M.Coult/t	M.Watterson/t	M.Sherwood/t
Mid 1	17/03	Burton	A	W 48-3	T.Foster/2t	J.Astbury/t4cp	M.Coult/t	M.Watterson	M.Sherwood/t
Mid 1	24/03	Longton	A	D 12-12	T.Foster	J.Astbury/4p	M.Coult	M.Watterson	M.Sherwood
Mid 1	31/03	Barkers Butts	H	W 71-10	T.Foster	J.Astbury/t8c	M.Coult	M.Watterson/5t	M.Sherwood/2t
Mid 1	14/04	Banbury	A	W 34-23	T.Foster/t	J.Astbury/t2c3p	M.Coult	M.Watterson	M.Sherwood
Mid 1	21/04	Hereford	H	W 48-13	T.Foster	J.Astbury/2t4c	M.Coult	M.Watterson/t	M.Sherwood/t
TBC p	09/9	Amptill	A	W 24-20	D.Blackburn	J.Astbury/tc4p	M.Watterson/t	A.Dawson	T.Foster
TBC 1	23/9	Leicester Lions	A	L 14-28	C.Conroy	J.Astbury/t3p	M.Coult	M.Watterson	T.Foster

*after opponents name indicates a penalty try. Brackets after a player's name indicates he was replaced.
eg (a) means he was replaced by replacement code "a" and so on. / after a player or replacement name
is followed by any scores he made - eg /t, /c, /p, /dg or any combination of these

EVER PRESENT

J Astbury, M Coult, G Lock, T Dunk, R Southee

MOST APPEARANCES

22   J Astbury, M Coult, G Lock, T Dunk, R Southee.
21   M Hyde, S Taylor

PLAYERS USED   25

MOST POINTS

Pts	Player	T	C	P	DG
343	J Astbury	21	60	39	-
60	M Watterson	12	-	-	-
50	T Foster	10	-	-	-
40	R Southee	8	-	-	-
35	M Coult	7	-	-	-
30	M Sherwood	6	-	-	-

MATCH FACTS

10	9	1	2	3	4	5	6	7	8
T.Robinson	G.Lock	P.Sewell	M.Hyde	S.Taylor	D.Stevens/t	T.Dunk	P.Sidebottom/t	S.Heath-Drury	R.Southee
T.Robinson	G.Lock	R.Page	M.Hyde	S.Taylor	P.Sidebottom	T.Dunk/t	R.Proctor/t	M.Dunk	R.Southee
T.Robinson	G.Lock	R.Page	M.Hyde	S.Taylor	P.Sidebottom	T.Dunk	R.Proctor	S.Heath-Drury	R.Southee
T.Robinson	G.Lock	R.Page	M.Hyde	S.Taylor	P.Sidebottom	T.Dunk	R.Proctor/t	S.Heath-Drury	R.Southee/t
T.Robinson	G.Lock	R.Page	M.Hyde	S.Taylor	P.Sidebottom	T.Dunk	R.Proctor	S.Heath-Drury	R.Southee
T.Robinson/3t	G.Lock	R.Page	J.Johal	S.Taylor	P.Sidebottom	T.Dunk	R.Proctor	S.Heath-Drury	R.Southee
T.Robinson	G.Lock	R.Page	M.Hyde	S.Taylor	P.Sidebottom	T.Dunk	R.Proctor	S.Heath-Drury	R.Southee
T.Robinson	G.Lock	R.Page	M.Hyde	S.Taylor	P.Sidebottom	T.Dunk	R.Proctor	S.Heath-Drury	R.Southee
T.Robinson	G.Lock	R.Page	M.Hyde	S.Taylor	P.Sidebottom	T.Dunk	R.Proctor	S.Heath-Drury	R.Southee
T.Robinson	G.Lock/t	R.Page	M.Hyde/t	S.Taylor	P.Sidebottom	T.Dunk/t	R.Southee	S.Heath-Drury(c/t)	M.Kelly
T.Robinson	G.Lock	R.Page	M.Hyde	N.Buttrick	P.Sidebottom	T.Dunk	R.Southee	S.Heath-Drury	M.Kelly/t
T.Robinson	G.Lock	R.Page	M.Hyde	S.Taylor	D.Stevens	T.Dunk	R.Southee	R.Proctor	M.Kelly
M.Coult	G.Lock	R.Page	M.Hyde	S.Taylor	D.Stevens	T.Dunk	R.Southee	S.Heath-Drury	M.Kelly
T.Robinson	G.Lock	R.Page/t	M.Hyde	S.Taylor	D.Stevens	T.Dunk	P.Sidebottom	S.Heath-Drury	R.Southee/2t
T.Robinson	G.Lock	R.Page/2t	M.Hyde/t	S.Taylor/t	P.Sidebottom	T.Dunk	R.Southee	S.Heath-Drury	M.Kelly
T.Robinson	G.Lock	R.Page	M.Hyde	S.Taylor	P.Sidebottom	T.Dunk	R.Proctor	S.Heath-Drury	R.Southee
T.Robinson	G.Lock	R.Page(b/t)	M.Hyde	S.Taylor	P.Sidebottom	T.Dunk/t	R.Proctor	S.Heath-Drury	R.Southee/t
T.Robinson	G.Lock	R.Page	M.Hyde/t	S.Taylor/t	D.Stevens	T.Dunk	P.Sidebottom	S.Heath-Drury	R.Southee/t
T.Robinson	G.Lock	R.Salmon	M.Hyde	S.Taylor	D.Stevens	T.Dunk	P.Sidebottom	S.Heath-Drury	R.Southee
T.Robinson	G.Lock	N.Buttrick	M.Hyde	S.Taylor/t	D.Stevens	T.Dunk	P.Sidebottom	S.Heath-Drury/t	R.Southee/t
T.Robinson	G.Lock	N.Buttrick	M.Hyde	S.Taylor/t	P.Sidebottom	T.Dunk	R.Southee/t	S.Heath-Drury/2t	M.Kelly
B.Sherwood	G.Lock	R.Page	M.Hyde/t	S.Taylor	P.Sidebottom	T.Dunk	R.Southee/t	S.Heath-Drury/2t	M.Kelly
T.Robinson	G.Lock	P.Sewell	M.Hyde	R.Page	P.Sidebottom	T.Dunk	R.Proctor	S.Heath-Drury	R.Southee
T.Robinson	G.Lock	R.Page	M.Hyde	S.Taylor	P.Sidebottom	T.Dunk	M.Dunk	S.Heath-Drury	R.Southee

REPLACEMENTS
a - M Sherwood   b - N Butterick   c - D Stevens

2000-01 HIGHLIGHTS

Right wing John Astbury had a fantastic season topping both the points and try scorers list.

He scored 343 points and ran in 21 tries.

He was one of five ever present players in the side and managed to score in every match.

He scored tries in 16 of Scunthorpe's 22 league matches scoring nine tries more than the next player on the list.

They suffered just one league defeat all season when going down 15-8 to Kenilworth, and they only once failed to score a try in a match when they drew 12-12 with Longton.

Longton were the only side they failed to beat as both matches ended in draws.

SCUNTHORPE

LEAGUE STATISTICS
compiled by Stephen McCormack

SEASON	Division	P	W	D	L	F	A	Pts Diff	Lge Pts	Lge Pos
91-92	M2E	10	3	1	6	113	134	-21	7	10
92-93	ME1	12	6	2	4	234	155	79	14	5
93-94	ME1	12	9	0	3	172	109	63	20	2
94-95	ME1	12	11	0	1	366	86	280	22	1p
95-96	M2	12	10	0	2	306	118	188	20	1p
96-97	M1	16	12	0	4	435	253	182	24	4
97-98	M1	16	10	0	6	415	279	136	20	4
98-99	M1	16	15	0	1	590	187	403	30	2
99-00	M1	16	11	0	5	364	206	158	22	2
00-01	M1	22	19	2	1	762	258	504	40	1p

FACT FILE

Founded: 1929
Nickname: The Greens
Colours: Green shirts with 2 narrow black bands bordered by 2 narrow white bands/black shorts/green & black hooped socks
Change colours: Red shirts with bands as above

Winger John Astbury races over to score a crucial try for the Greens in their match aagainst Banbury.
Photo courtesy of the
Scunthorpe Evening Telegraph

Ground:
Heslam Park, The Queensway, Scunthorpe
(entrance from Ashby Rd.)
Tel: 01724 843013
Capacity: 1000
Covered seating for 200 due this season.
Directions: End of M181 - A18 (Kingsway)
to 'Beefeater' Roundabout,
Turn right A159 -
300 metres on left sign post for 'Heslam Park'
Nearest Railway Station: Scunthorpe
Car Parking Spaces for 100 cars at ground
Admission Matchday: £4
Clubhouse Open evey day 12-2.30pm & 5-11pm
Club Shop Open Saturday lunchtime & Sunday morning
Training Nights Monday & Thursday
Colts: Wed   Women: Thur.

Programme Size: A4   Price: 50p
Editor: Mal Yates

SCUNTHORPE
RUGBY UNION FOOTBALL CLUB
MIDLAND LEAGUE ONE

TYNEDALE RFC

President	John Austin	Fourways, Cooks House, Hexham NE46 2LQ 01434 607349 (H) 01434 681616 (B)
Hon. Secretary	Bill Stewart	2 Beech Hill, Hexham NE46 3AG 01434 603970 (H)
Chief Executive	Andy Deacon	3 Burnside, Intake Way, Hexham NE46 1RU 01434 609750 (H) 0797 1526651 (M)
Ch. of Rugby	Alan Gledson	High Cowden, Birtley, Wark. NE48 3JE 01434 270303 (H)

After our superb promotion-winning year Tynedale looked forward to the 2000-2001 season with eager anticipation and confidence. There was, however, the realisation that it was going to be a difficult year; a number of players had retired or had left in the close season and the First XV squad at the start of the playing year lacked depth and experience.

The playing season started well. We won a number of league games and had a successful, if precarious, run in the Tetley Bitter Cup where we reached the Fourth Round for the first time in our history before going down to Worcester. The squad then suffered a series of injuries to important players and the long journeys to foreign parts with early starts in the depth of winter seemed to take their toll and appeared to affect the side's confidence. At one stage in the season the First XV squad only contained eight of the players who had been involved in our promotion year.

In February the Foot and Mouth epidemic hit the area and this disaster effectively ended all rugby for the season at Corbridge. A decision was taken by the management committee, and was reviewed each week, that no rugby matches and training would take place at Tynedale Park. It was agreed that the livelihood and welfare of the Tynedale farming community were of paramount importance. A number of members of the club were subsequently affected by the outbreak and it is sad to report that four members of the first Team squad had livestock culled during the crisis.

When our playing season finished we were lying in ninth place in the league. Players had returned after injury and we appeared to have regained confidence. With five of our eight remaining league games at home we were confident we would finish the season well. In all the circumstances we can be satisfied, but not complacent, about the team's performance this year.

For many of the younger Tynedale players, 2000-2001 was an important learning experience and they will be mentally and physically more robust as a result.

TYNEDALE

Comp.	Date	H/A	Opponents	Result & Score	Att	15	14	13	12	11
N3N	2-Sep	A	Liverpool St Helens	W 31-6	200	Mason	Roberts	Fletcher	Fleming	Holmes/t
N3N	9-Sep	A	Sandal	W 23-10		Shotton	Roberts	Fletcher	Fleming/t	Holmes
N3N	16-Sep	H	New Brighton	L 10-16	250	Mason	Roberts	Fletcher	Fleming	Holmes
N3N	30-Sep	H	Stourbridge	L 16-35		Mason	Roberts	Fletcher	Fleming	Holmes
N3N	14-Oct	A	Walsall	L 23-24	200	Mason	Holmes	Fletcher	Fleming	Walton/t
N3N	28-Oct	A	Dudley Kingwinsford*	D 13-13	250	Mason	Holmes	Fletcher	Fleming	Walton
N3N	11-Nov	H	Morley	W 9-5		Mason	Holmes	Fleming	Walton	Shotton
N3N	18-Nov	A	Nuneaton	L 9-29	150	Mason	Holmes	Fleming	Walton	Shotton
N3N	25-Nov	H	Sedgley Park	L 8-18	200	Holmes	Shotton/t	Fleming	Walton	Mason
N3N	2-Dec	A	Aspatria	W 26-8	100	Shotton	Mason	Fleming	Boston	Fitzgerald
N3N	9-Dec	A	Whitchurch	L 11-21	425	Shotton/t	Mason	Fleming	Boston	Fitzgerald
N3N	23-Dec	H	Aspatria*	W 33-20	200	Shotton	Holmes	Fleming	Boston	Fitzgerald
N3N	6-Jan	H	Nuneaton	L 10-20		Shotton	Fitzgerald	Fleming	Walton/t	Holmes
N3N	13-Jan	A	Morley	L 11-23		Shotton	Fitzgerald	Fleming	Walton	Holmes/t
N3N	27-Jan	A	Bedford Athletic	L 22-29	150	Shotton	Fitzgerald	Fleming	Boston/t	Moses/2cp
N3N	3-Feb	H	Bedford Athletic	W 24-0	200	Shotton	Fitzgerald	Boston	Fleming	Walton
N3N	17-Feb	H	Doncaster	L 0-6		Roberts	Fitzgerald	Boston	Fleming	Walton
N3N	24-Feb	A	Stourbridge	L 0-18	400	Moses	Walton	Boston	Fleming	Holmes
TBC	23-Sep	A	Halifax	W 19-0	200	Mason	Roberts	Fleming	Fletcher/t	Holmes
TBC	7-Sept	A	Sandal	W15-14		Mason	Roberts	Walton	Fleming	Holmes
TBC	21-Oct	H	Longton	W 23-0		Mason/t	Holmes	Fleming	Fletcher	Walton
TBC	4-Nov	H	Worcester	L 12-76	600	Fleming	Holmes/t	Fleming	Fletcher	Walton

*after opponents name indicates a penalty try. Brackets after a player's name indicates he was replaced.
eg (a) means he was replaced by replacement code "a" and so on. / after a player or replacement name
is followed by any scores he made - eg /t, /c, /p, /dg or any combination of these

EVER PRESENT	Gary Fleming, Keith Johnson

Most Appearances:

18	Gary Fleming, Keith Johnson.
17	Alan Moses, Simon Clayton-Hibbott.
16	Andrew Robson, Edward Parker.

PLAYERS USED

31 plus four as replacement only.

MOST POINTS

Pts	Player	T	C	P	DG
159	A Moses	1	11	43	1
35	S Clayton-Hibbott	7	-	-	-
15	E Holmes	3	-	-	-
10	A Murray	2	-	-	-
10	J SHotton	2	-	-	-
10	M Walton	2	-	-	-

MATCH FACTS

10	9	1	2	3	4	5	6	7	8
Moses/7p	Clayton-Hibbott/t	Fletcher	E Parker	Winter	K Johnson	Turnbull	Otuvaka	Robson	Lee
Moses/p	Clayton-Hibbott/2t	Fletcher	E Parker	Winter	K Johnson	Turnbull/t	Jewitt	Robson	Lee
Moses/cp	Clayton-Hibbott	R Parker	E Parker	Fletcher	K Johnson	Turnbull	Robson	Otuvaka/t	Lee
Moses/c3p	Clayton-Hibbott/t	Fletcher	E Parker	Winter	K Johnson	Turnbull	Jewitt	Robson	Lee
Moses/6p	Clayton-Hibbott	R Parker	E Parker	Fletcher	K Johnson	Johnson	Lee	Clarke	Jewitt
Moses/cpdg	Clayton-Hibbott	R Parker	Charlton	Winter	Turnbull	K Johnson	Robson	Murray	Jewitt
Moses/3p	Clayton-Hibbott	R Parker	E Parker	Winter	Clarke	Turnbull	Robson	Murray	Johnson
Moses/3p	Clayton-Hibbott	R Parker	E Parker	Winter	Turnbull	K Johnson	Robson	Murray	Jewitt
Moses/p	Clayton-Hibbott	R Parker	E Parker	Winter	Taylor	K Johnson	Bowen	Robson	Murray
Moses/c3p	Clayton-Hibbott/t	R Parker	E Parker	Fletcher	Taylor	K Johnson	Bowen	Robson/t	Murray/t
Moses/2p	Clayton-Hibbott	Johnson	E Parker	Fletcher	Taylor	K Johnson	Robson	Donton	Lee
Moses/t3c4p	Clayton-Hibbott/t	Fletcher	E Parker	Winter	Steadman	K Johnson	Robson	Donton	Murray
Moses/cp	Clayton-Hibbott	Fletcher	E Parker	Winter	K Johnson	Steadman	Robson	Ponton	Murray
Moses/2p	Clayton-Hibbott	Fletcher	E Parker	Winter	Turnbull	K Johnson	Robson	Otuvaka	Murray
Clayton-Hibbott	Holmes/t	R Parker	E Parker	Fletcher	K Johnson/t	Turnbull	Robson	Otuvaka	Murray
Moses/c4p	Clayton-Hibbott/t	R Parker	Charlton	Winter	Turnbull	K Johnson	Jewitt	Otuvaka	Murray/t
Fletcher	Holmes	R Parker	E Parker	Winter	Turnbull	K Johnson	Otuvaka	Robson	Murray
Fletcher	Clayton-Hibbott	Johnson	E Parker	Winter	Turnbull	K Johnson	Otuvaka	Robson	Short
Moses/c3pdg	Clayton-Hibbott	Fletcher	E Parker	Winter	Turnbull	K Johnson	Jewitt	Robson	Lee
Moses/3p2dg	Clayton-Hibbott	Fletcher	E Parker	Winter	K Johnson	Turnbull	Jewitt	Murray	Lee
Moses/2c2pdg	Clayton-Hibbott	R Parker	E Parker	Winter	Turnbull	K Johnson	Robson	Jewitt/t	Lee
Moses/c	Clayton-Hibbott	R Parker	E Parker	Winter	K Johnson	Turnbull	Robson	Murray	Jewitt(a/t)

REPLACEMENTS	a - M Lee

2000-01 HIGHLIGHTS

Alan Moses topped the scoring chart with 159 points from his 18 league matches. He also topped the points scoring as Tynedale won North One the previous season.

Scrum half Simon Clayton-Hibbott was again leading try scorer but this time with just seven tries, from 16 matches, compared to 13 the previous season.

TYNEDALE

LEAGUE STATISTICS compiled by Stephen McCormack

SEASON	Division	P	W	D	L	F	A	Pts Diff	Lge Pts	Lge Pos			
91-92	North1												
92-93	North1	12	9	0	3	323	111	212	18	2			
93-94	North1	12	7	0	5	255	168	87	14	5			
94-95	North1	12	4	1	7	184	154	30	9	11			
95-96	North1	12	7	1	4	212	163	49	15	5			
96-97	North1	22	14	1	7			225	29	3			
97-98	North1	22	13	2	7	510	332	178	28	5			
98-99	North1	22	15	0	7	573	298	275	30	3		**Most Points**	**Most Tries**
99-00	North1	22	22	0	0	710	221	489	44	1	246	Alan Moses	13 Simon Clayton-Hibbott & Epi Taione
00-01	N3N	*18	6	1	11	282	311	-29	13	8	159	Alan Mose	7 Simon Clayton-Hibbott

FACT FILE

Founded: 1876
Colours: Royal blue & white hoops/white/royal blue
Change colours: Navy blue, narrow yellow & white hoops/white/navy
Web site: www.tynedalerfc.co.uk

GROUND

Address: Tynedale Park, Station Rd., Corbridge, Northumberland NE45 5AY
Tel: 01434 632997   Office: Tel/Fax: 01434 632996
e-mail: tynedalerfc@hotmail.com
Capacity: Unlimited   Covered Seats: 350

Directions: From A69 westbound: 2nd exit at Styford roundabout (signed Corbridge) follow signs for Hexham. Cross single lane bridge to roundabout. First exit signed Gateshead.
250 yds to left fork into Station Road - 150 yards to entrance.

Nearest Railway Station: Corbridge, next to ground entrance

Car Parking: plentiful, within ground

Admission   Matchday: £4 adult.   Season: £50

Clubhouse: Open Mon & Thur 6.30-11, matchdays & Sun lunch. Private functions & special events.

Club Shop: Open on matchdays.
Contact Andy Deacon 01434 609750

Training Nights: Tuesday & Thursday, 7pm.

Programme   Size: A5   Pages: 8
Price: With admission
Editor: Keith Laidler
Advertising Rates: Contact Andy Deacon (Chief Executive)

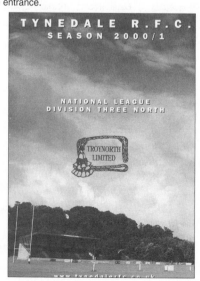

TYNEDALE R.F.C.
SEASON 2000/1

NATIONAL LEAGUE
DIVISION THREE NORTH

TROYNORTH LIMITED

WEST HARTLEPOOL RFC

President	Reg Turner
Chairman	Ron Greig
Vice Chairman	Stuart Murray
Coach	John Stabler
Club Secretary	Steve Smith
	Tel: 01423 536530 Fax: 01423 520125 Mob.: 07703 504730

All correspondence to: c/o West Hartlepool RFC, PO Box 132, Hartlepool TS25 5YW

While matters on the field did not improve in the 2000-1 season, there is cause for some optimism in the West ranks, albeit at a level in the national structure well below the heights of Premiership which the club played in 1998-99.

Now reliant on youth, several of the side are recent products of West's successful Junior system, as they found the bigger, more experienced forwards in National Two a little too good over an 80 minute period. There were a few chances of a win, such as an early game at Preston, home games against Lydney, Rosslyn Park surprisingly, and Camberley, who took the lead for the first time in injury time.

Generally, however, the side found itself always on the defensive, and, inevitably being starved of possession, they leaked points.

Teenager Mark Laycock impressed in his first senior season, playing in four different positions in the backs while Brett Cullinane's experience and determination ensured the forwards kept going throughout.

Plans are in the early stage to develop the current site in partnership with the Hartlepool Sixth Form College, a Clubhouse and three pitches being envisaged, to create a Centre of Excellence in the area

The club hopes to run a development side using last season's successful Colts while the Junior section, (the ambitious Under 16s toured New Zealand in the summer), will provide the talent for future seasons.

FACT FILE

Founded: 1881
Nickname: West

Colours: Green, red and white shirts, navy shorts, green socks
Change colours: Dark green - shirts, shorts and socks

GROUND
Address: Brinkburn, Blakelock Road, Hartlepool TS25 5PF
Capacity: 2,200   Seated: 700   Standing - uncovered: 1,500

Directions: A1/A19 proceeding north to A689 to Hartlepool. Turn left at the traffic lights as you enter the built-up area. Right at first junction (catcote Rd.) and continue for approx. 1.5 miles past schools on the left. Turn right at the traffic lights on shopping precinct, left at round about - Brinkburn (6th form College is 600 yds on left).
Nearest Railway Station: Hartlepool.
Car Parking: Yes at ground.

Admission :   (No concessions)
Matchday: £5   Season tickets: £50

Clubhouse: Restricted opening, matchdays from 12.30 onwards.

PROGRAMME   Not applicable

WEST HARTLEPOOL

Comp.	Date	H/A	Opponents	Result & Score	Att	15	14	13	12	11
N2	2-Sep	H	Fylde	L 3-16	285	Blades	Milne	Hutton	Thompson	Olugbode
N2	9-Sep	A	Wharfedale	L 14-51		Winney/2c	Blades	Milne	Hutton/2t	Olugbode
N2	16-Sep	H	Newbury	L 3-34		Winney/p	Olugbode	Hutton	Thompson	Milne
N2	23-Sep	A	Preston Grasshoppers	L 22-25	320	Winney/tc5p	Falkner	Milne	Hutton	Olugbode
N2	30-Sep	H	Rugby Lions	L 8-57		Winney/p	Laycock/t	Hutton	Hall	Olugbode
N2	14-Oct	H	Esher	L 5-47		Laycock	Olugbode	Hall	Hutton	Falkner
N2	28-Oct	H	Lydney	L 13-18		Winney/p	Laycock	Hutton	Milne	Olugbode
N2	4-Nov	A	Harrogate	L 0-60	250	Winney	Laycock	Hutton	Milne	Olugbode
N2	18-Nov	H	Rosslyn Park	L 31-43		Laycock/t	Olugbode	Milne	Hutton	Falkner
N2	25-Nov	N	Bracknell*	L 10-30		Laycock	Falkner	Hutton	Milne	Henderson
N2	9-Dec	A	Camberley	L 11-22	100	Laycock	Milne	Hutton	Thompson	Falkner
N2	16-Dec	A	Rosslyn Park	L 7-78		Laycock	Milne	Thompson	Hutton	Falkner
N2	23-Dec	H	Nottingham	L 5-45		Laycock/t	Falkner	Hutton	Milne	Thompson
N2	6-Jan	A	Lydney	L 8-58		Laycock	Clarke/t	Thompson	Hutton	Milne
N2	13-Jan	H	Harrogate	L 14-70	150	Falkner	Clarke	Thompson/2c	Hutton	Milne
N2	27-Jan	A	Kendal	L 0-92		Falkner	Clarke	Hutton	Thompson	Milne
N2	3-Feb	A	Nottingham	L 15-48		Laycock	Clarke	Thompson	Hutton	Milne
N2	10-Feb	A	Rugby Lions	L 0-69		Cuff	Falkner	Hutton	Milne	Clarke
N2	17-Feb	H	Kendal	L 11-42		Cuff	Clarke/t	Hutton	Milne	Falkner
N2	10-Mar	A	Newbury	L 3-53		Cuff	Clarke	Hutton	Milne	Thompson/p
N2	17-Mar	H	Wharfedale	L 18-44		Laycock	Clarke	Hutton	Milne/t	Cuff/t
N2	24-Mar	A	Fylde	L 0-27		Cuff	Falkner	Hutton	Milne	Clarke
N2	31-Mar	H	Camberley	L 17-21		Laycock/t	Clarke	Hutton	Milne	Cuff
N2	8-Apr	A	Esher	L 5-86	400	Cuff	Falkner	Milne	Foreman	Clarke
N2	14-Apr	A	Bracknell	L 0-76		Lilley	Cuff	Milne	Clarke	Falkner
N2	21-Apr	H	Preston Grasshoppers	L 17-54		Lilley/t	Cuff	Milne	Laycock/2t	Clarke
TBC	7-Oct	H	Longton	L 8-15						

after opponents name indicates a penalty try. Brackets after a player's name indicates he was replaced. eg (a) means he was replaced by replacement code "a" and so on. / after a player or replacement name is followed by any scores he made - eg /t, /c, /p, /dg or any combination of these

EVER PRESENT   None

Most Appearances
- 25 David Tighe, Chris Webb, Andrew Davies.
- 24 Allan Milne.
- 23 Brett Cullinane, Paul Hutton.
- 22 Mark Cholmondeley.

PLAYERS USED   42

MOST POINTS

Pts	Player	T	C	P	DG
63	J Stabler	1	8	14	-
38	T Winney	1	3	9	-
35	M Laycock	7	-	-	-
20	D Tighe	4	-	-	-
10	C Webb	2	-	-	-
10	G Clarke	2	-	-	-
10	P Hutton	2	-	-	-

MATCH FACTS

10	9	1	2	3	4	5	6	7	8
Winney/p	Tighe	Cullinane	Sawyer	Prest	Webb	Davies	Dolan	Hall	Armstrong
Haswell	Tighe	Prest	Cullinane	Cholmondeley	Webb	Davies	Dolan	Hall	Armstrong
Haswell	Tighe	Cullinane	Redston	Sinha	Webb	Davies	Hall	Ebbett	Armstrong
Haswell	Tighe	Whitlock	Cullinane	Cholmondeley	Webb	Davies	Ebbett	Bentely	Armstrong
Haswell	Tighe	Cullinane	Robinson	Cholmondeley	Webb	Davies	Ebbett	Bentely	Armstrong
Haswell	Tighe	Cullinane	Robinson	Cholmondeley	Webb/t	Davies	Wright	Ebbett	Bennett
Haswell	Tighe/2t	Cholmondeley	Robinson	Cullinane	Webb	Davies	Wright	Ebbett	Bennett
Haswell	Tighe	Cullinane	Robinson	Prest	Webb	Davies	Hall	Wright	Bennett
Stabler/2c4p	Tighe	Cholmondeley	Robinson	Cullinane/t	Webb/t	Davies	Wright	Ebbett	Bennett
Stabler/cp	Tighe	Cholmondeley	Robinson	Cullinane	Webb	Davies	Wright	Tones	Bennett
Stabler/2p	Tighe	Cullinane	Robinson	Cholmondeley	Webb	Davies	Ebbett/t	Wright	Bennett
Stabler/tc	Tighe	Cullinane	Robinson	Whitlock	Webb	Davies	Wright	Tones	Bennett
Stabler	Tighe	Cholmondeley	Robinson	Cullinane	Webb	Davies	Wright	Tones	Bennett
Stabler/p	Tighe	Cholmondeley	Robinson	Geritz	Davies	Webb	Wright	Ebbett	Bennett
Laycock/t	Tighe/t	Cholmondeley	Robinson	Geritz	Webb	Davies	Wright	Tones	Bennett
Laycock	Tighe	Cholmondeley	Robinson	Prest	Ince	Geritz	Webb	Laycock	Wright
Stabler/cp	Falkner	Cholmondeley/t	Robinson	Cullinane	Webb	Davies	Laycock/t	Tones	Wright
Laycock	Tighe	Cullinane	Robinson	Cholmondeley	Ince	Davies	Webb	Tones	Wright
Stabler/2p	Tighe	Cholmondeley	Cullinane	Cook	Webb	Davies	Whitehead	Tones	Wright
Laycock	Tighe	Cullinane	Robinson	Cholmondeley	Davies	Webb	Tones	Laycock	Wright
Stabler/c2p	Tighe	Cholmondeley	Robinson	Cullinane	Webb	Davies	Whitehead	Tones	Wright
Laycock	Tighe	Cholmondeley	Robinson	Cook	Webb	Davies	Cullinane	Tones	Wright
Stabler/2cp	Tighe	Cholmondeley	Robinson/t	Cook	Webb	Davies	Laycock	Tones	Cullinane
Stabler	Tighe/t	Cholmondeley	Robinson	Cook	Webb	Davies	Cullinane	Tones	Wright
Laycock	Tighe	Cholmondeley	Robinson	Cook	Ince	Davies	Cullinane	Tones	Wright
Walton/c	Tighe	Cholmondeley	Robinson	Cook	Webb	Davies	Cullinane	Tones	Wright

2000-01 HIGHLIGHTS

John Stabler topped the West Hartlepool scoring list for the first time since 1993-94 and finished the season just seven points short of 1,000 points in league rugby for the club.

The leading try scorer was Mark Laycock with seven which was the highest total for three years.

West have now lost 41 consecutive league matches going back to December 1999 when they won away at Orrell in Allied Dunbar Two.

At home you have to go back to March 1999 to find their last win. They have lost their last 29 home matches since they drew with Sale on the 28th March. Their last win was the match before when they beat Gloucester 33-32 on 14th March 1999

WEST HARTLEPOOL

LEAGUE STATISTICS
compiled by Stephen McCormack

SEASON	Division	P	W	D	L	F	A	Pts Diff	Lge Pts	Lge Pos	Most Points		Most Tries	
91-92	2	12	11	0	1	244	89	155	22	2p	118	John Stabler	7	John Wigley
92-93	1	12	3	0	9	149	236	-87	6	12r	89	John Stabler	3	Alan Brown
93-94	2	18	13	2	3	389	271	128	28	2p	103	John Stabler	7	John Wrigley
94-95	1	18	6	1	11	312	412	-100	13	9	93	Tim Stimpson	5	Paul Hodder
95-96	1	18	0	0	18	288	634	-346	0	10	110	Tim Stimpson	5	Tim Stimpson
96-97	1	22	3	0	19	382	795	-407	6	11r	126	Chris John	13	Steve John
97-98	P2	22	15	1	6	617	431	148	31	2p	241	Steven Vile	10	Emmett Farrell
98-99	P1	26	3	1	22	501	1007	-506	7	14r	240	Steven Vile	6	Steve John
99-00	P2	26	1	0	25	216	1114	-898	2	14r	64	James Lofthouse	3	Mark Thompson
00-01	N2	26	0	0	26	240	1266	-1026	0	14r	63	John Stabler	7	M Laycock

BIGGEST MARGINS

Home Win 54pts - 66-12 v Fylde 14.2.98
Away Win 45pts - 51-6 v Waterloo 11.4.98
Home Defeat 76pts - 0-76 v Bracknell 14.4.01
Away Defeat 92pts - 0-92 v Kendal 27.1.01

MOST CONSECUTIVE

Appearances 64 John Stabler 11.7.89-26.3.94
Matches scoring Tries 4 Owen Evans & Steve Cook
Matches scoring points 36 John Stabler
Victories 9
Defeats 41

MOST POINTS

Scored at Home 66 v Fylde 14.2.98
Scored Away 51 v Waterloo 11.4.98
Conceded at Home 91 v Harlequins 23.3.96
Conceded Away 93 v Rotherham 2.10.99

MOST TRIES

Scored in a match 10 v Fylde 14.2.98 (H)
Conceded in a match 14 v Harlequins/ Kendal-as above
plus Esher 8.4.2001

MOST APPEARANCES

by a forward 101 Phil Lancaster
by a back 105 (14) John Stabler

	MOST IN A SEASON	MOST IN A CAREER	MOST IN A MATCH	
Points	241 Steven Vile 97-98	693 John Stabler 87-01	26 Steven Vile	v Richmond 17.4.99 (H)
Tries	13 Steven John 96-97	32 Owen Evans 87-96	3 Owen Evans Peter Robinson John Wrigley	v Nuneaton 23.4.88 (H) v V. of Lune 2.3.91 (A) v Moseley 14.1.291 (H)
Conversions	33 Steven Vile 97-98	71 John Stabler 87-01	8 Steven Vile	v Fylde 14.2.98 (H)
Penalties	52 Steven Vile 98-99	141 John Stabler 87-01	7 Steven Vile	v Richmond 17.4.99 (H)
Drop Goals	3 John Stabler 88-89	8 John Stabler 87-97	2 Kevin Oliphant John Stabler	v V. of Lune 7.11.88 (A) v Sheffield 9.11.88 (H)

WHITCHURCH RFC

President	John Henry Wynn	Fenns Wood, Whitchurch, Shropshire. 01948 780343
Chairman	Paul Kaminski	21 Kingsway, Whitchurch SY13 1EH 01948 662536 (H), 01948 662889 (B)
Treasurer	Mark Smith	25 Smallbrook Rd., Whitchurch SY13 1BT. 01948 664894 07971 118980 (M)
Secretary	Graham Kendall	Hibernia, Mile Bank, Whitchurch SY13 4JY 01948 666632 (H), 0151 243 7831 (B) 0151 243 7800 (F) 07930 324524 (M)
Fixture Secretary	Paul Kaminski	21 Kingsway, Whitchurch SY13 1EH 01948 662536(H), 01948 662889 (B)
Marketing	Mike Dixon	Arden Fields, Ridley Hill Farm, Tarporley, Cheshire CW6 9RX 01829 260310

Our third season in the national leagues is not one to be looked upon with fondness.

We competed well against all opposition despite suffering some heavy defeats against the clubs at the top of our league. In the event the foot and mouth epidemic curtailed our campaign and, along with others, left us wondering how the season was to be decided.

We congratulate Stourbridge and Sedgeley Park on their well deserved promotion.

Our condolences, however, go to Aspatria and Walsall who, despite being unable to complete fixtures for perfectly valid reasons, have suffered relegation.

We wonder why the RFU could not see fit to extend the leagues for one season to avoid this.

Our thanks go to the 34 players who played for the First XV during our difficult league campaign, and to all our members and supporters for their patience.

Last, but not least, we thank our former coach `Ginger' Wills for his past commitment to this club and wish him success in his future career.

Graham Kendall

WHITCHURCH

Comp.	Date	H/A	Opponents	Result & Score	Att	15	14	13	12	11
N3N	2-Sep	A	Doncaster	L 21-64	265	Wynn	Aldersey	Brookshaw/t	Lutton	Edwards
N3N	9-Sep	A	New Brighton	L 0-53	200	Paton	Dodd	Wynn	Lutton	Edwards
N3N	16-Sep	H	Liverpool St Helens*	W 30-17	450	Brookshaw	Paton	Wynn	Lutton	Edwards
N3N	30-Sep	H	Sandal	L 22-52	300	Wynn	Paton/t	Brookshaw	Lutton	Edwards/t
N3N	14-Oct	A	Stourbridge	L 7-65	450	Lewis	Aldersey	Lutton/t	Marvell	Edwards
N3N	28-Oct	A	Bedford Athletic*	W 26-10		Lewis	Baker	Brookshaw	Lutton	Aldersey
N3N	4-Nov	H	Walsall	W 20-13	350	Lewis	Aldersey	Brookshaw	Lutton	Baker
N3N	11-Nov	H	Dudley Kingwinsford	W 13-11	300	Lewis	Aldersey	Brookshaw	Lutton	Edwards
N3N	18-Nov	A	Morley	W 23-13	400	Lewis	Aldersey/t	Brookshaw	Lutton	Edwards
N3N	25-Nov	H	Nuneaton	W 15-12	530	Lewis	Aldersey	Brookshaw	Lutton	Edwards
N3N	2-Dec	A	Sedgley Park	L 3-59	200	Canney/p	Aldersey	Antrobus	Lutton	Baker
N3N	9-Dec	H	Tynedale*	W 21-11	425	Canney/3c	Aldersey	Brookshaw/t	Lutton	Lewis
N3N	16-Dec	A	Aspatria	L 12-19		Canney/c	Baker	Aldersey	Lutton	McGaffney
N3N	23-Dec	H	Sedgley Park	L 14-39	415	Canney/2c	Aldersey	Brookshaw	Lutton	McGaffney
N3N	6-Jan	H	Morley	W 34-16		Lewis	Aldersey/2t	Brookshaw	Lutton/t	Baker/t
N3N	13-Jan	A	Dudley Kingwinsford	L 19-29		Lewis	Aldersey	Brookshaw	Lutton	Baker
N3N	27-Jan	A	Walsall	L 30-43		Lewis	Aldersey	Brookshaw	Lutton/t	Baker
N3N	3-Feb	A	Nuneaton	L 13-41		Lewis	Aldersey	Appleby	Lutton	Baker
N3N	10-Feb	H	Stourbridge	L 10-17	540	Lewis	Aldersey	Brookshaw	Lutton	Baker
N3N	24-Feb	A	Sandal	L 17-22		Brookshaw	McGaffney/t	Aldersey	Lutton	Baker
N3N	17-Mar	A	Liverpool St Helens	L 10-35		Lewis	Aldersey	Lutton	Marvell	Baker
TBC	23-Sep	H	Spalding	W 22-0	300	Wynn	Paton	Brookshaw	Lutton	Edwards
TBC	7-Oct	A	Fylde	L 11-16	300	Canney/2p	Lewis	Brookshaw	Lutton	Edwards

** after opponents name indicates a penalty try. Brackets after a player's name indicates he was replaced.
eg (a) means he was replaced by replacement code "a" and so on. / after a player or replacement name
is followed by any scores he made - eg /t, /c, /p, /dg or any combination of these*

Dean Lutton, John Canney.

Most Appearances:
21	Dean Lutton, John Canney.
20	Kevin Barber, Warren Howell, Tom Pemberton, Andy Short.,

PLAYERS USED

34 plus two as replacement only.

MOST POINTS

Pts	Player	T	C	P	DG
145	J Canney	1	34	24	-
25	P Appleby	5	-	-	-
25	P Mullock	5	-	-	-
20	T Pemberton	4	-	-	-
15	D Lutton	3	-	-	-
15	N Aldersey	3	-	-	-

MATCH FACTS

10	9	1	2	3	4	5	6	7	8
Canney/t3c	Mullock	Howell	Barber	Lear	Douglas	Pemberton/t	Short	Appleby	Charmley
Canney	Hares	Howell	Barber	Lear	Douglas	Pemberton	Short	Appleby	Charmley
Canney/2c2p	Mullock	Howell(a/t)	Barber	Lear/t	Charmley	Pemberton	Short	Appleby/t	Smith
Canney/2cp	Mullock	Howell	Barber	Lear	Leonard	Pemberton/t	Charmley	Charmley	Smith
Canney/c	Mullock	Hazelton	Barber	Howell	Charmley	Douglas	Smith	Short	Pemberton
Canney/3c	Mullock/t	Hazelton	Barber	Howell	Charmley	Pemberton/t	Short	Appleby	Smith/t
Canney/2c2p	Mullock	Hazelton	Barber	Howell	Charmley/t	Pemberton	Short	Appleby	Pemberton/t
Canney/c2p	Mullock	Hazelton	Barber	Howell	Charmley	Pemberton	Short	Appleby/t	Pemberton
Canney/2c3p	Mullock	Hazelton	Barber	Howell	Charmley	Pemberton	Owen	Short/t	Pemberton
Canney/cp	Mullock/t	Thompson	Barber	Lear	Charmley	Pemberton	Owen	Short	Pemberton/t
Wynn	Mullock	Howell	Barber	Thomas	Charmley	Pemberton	Short	Appleby	Pemberton
Wynn/t	Mullock	Howell	Barber	Lear	Charmley	Pemberton	Short	Appleby	Pemberton
Wynn	Mullock	Howell/t	Barber	Lear	Charmley/t	Pemberton	Short	Appleby	Pemberton
Knowles/t	Mullock	Howell	Barber	Lear	Charmley	Pemberton/t	Short	Appleby	Pemberton
Canney/2c	Mullock/2t	Howell	Bailey	Lear	Charmley	Pemberton	Short	Appleby	Pemberton
Canney/c4p	Mullock	Howell	Barber	Lear	Charmley(b/t)	Pemberton	Short	Appleby	Pemberton
Canney/3c3p	Mullock	Howell	Barber	Lear	Leonard	Pemberton	Short	Appleby/2t	Pemberton
Canney/c2p	Pemberton/t	Howell	Barber	Lear	Douglas	Pemberton	Short	Dutton	Pemberton
Canney/cp	Mullock/t	Hazelton	Barber	Howell	Leonard	Pemberton	Short	Appleby	Pemberton
Canney/2cp	Mullock	Howell	Barber	Lear	Leonard	Pemberton	Short	Appleby/t	Pemberton
Canney/cp	Mullock	Howell	Barber/t	Lear	Douglas	Pemberton	Charmley	Short	Pemberton
Canney/2cp	Mullock/2t	Howell	Barber	Lear	Leonard	Pemberton	Short	Appleby	Smith
Wynn	Mullock	Hazelton	Barber/t(c/t)	Howell	Douglas	Charmley	Smith	Short	Pemberton

REPLACEMENTS   a - G Hazleton   b - D Leonard   c - D Williams

2000-01 HIGHLIGHTS

John Canney topped the points scorers list for a third consecutive season for Whitchurch in National League rugby. He equalled his total set in 1998-99 with 145 points.

Scrum half Phil Mullock was joint leading try scorer with Paul Appleby with five tries. Mullock has now finished leading try scorer in each of Whitchurch's three seasons of National League rugby. Two of those seasons he has shared the title.

Canney was ever present for the second successive season and in all has played in 57 consecutive league matches. Since Whitchurch entered the National League he has played in 71 of his side's 73 matches.

The only other ever present last season was new centre Dean Lutton.

WHITCHURCH

LEAGUE STATISTICS compiled by Stephen McCormack

SEASON	Division	P	W	D	L	F	A	Pts Diff	Lge Pts	Lge Pos		Most Points		Most Tries
91-92	Mid 2W	10	4	1	5	132	139	-7	9	6				
92-93	Mid 2	11	4	0	7	156	130	26	8	9				
93-94	Mid 2	12	10	1	1	178	85	93	21	1p				
94-95	Mid 1	12	7	1	4	240	157	83	15	3				
95-96	Mid 1	12	5	1	6	197	171	26	11	8				
96-97	Mid 1	16	9	1	6	435	304	131	19	6				
97-98	Mid 1	16	16	0	0	537	210	327	32	1p				
98-99	N2N	26	9	1	16	450	559	-149	19	11	145	John Canney	7	Phil Mulock & Giles Hazelton
99-00	N2N	26	9	1	16	430	794	-364	19	11	90	John Canney	7	Phil Mullock
00-01	N3N	*21	8	0	13	357	636	-279	16	7	145	John Canney	5	Phil Mullock & Paul Appleby

FACT FILE

Founded: 1936

Colours: Red/white/red
Change colours: White

GROUND

Address: Edgeley Park, Whitchurch SY13 1EU
Tel: 01948 663316 Fax: 01948 665508
Capacity: Unlimited   Seated: None   Standing: Unlimited

Directions: Follow by-pass (A41/A49) to the south of the town. Opposite Sir John Talbot school, access via Edgeley Road (on right).
Nearest Railway Station: Whitchurch (5 mins walk)

Car Parking: Free parking on ground

Admission: Matchday - Adults £5   Concessions £3
Season Tickets - £40

Clubhouse: Regularly open
Functions: Yes. Contact Club

Club Shop: None

Training Nights: Tuesday & Thursday

PROGRAMME

Size: A5   Price: with entry   Pages: 16/20
Editor: Dr. Alan Hares 01630 652135

ADVERTISING RATES

Mono   Full page £100
Half £60   Qtr. £35

WHITCHURCH RUGBY CLUB

£5.00

RECORDS SECTION

DIVISION FOUR NORTH
(CURRENTLY NATIONAL DIVISION THREE NORTH)
Previously also Area League North & Division Five North

Relegated clubs' Match Facts for season 2000-01

The Last Ten Years
A breakdown showing the champions, runners-up, those relegated,
who scored most - points, tries, conversions, penalties & drop goals
in each of the last ten seasons in this division (or its equivalent)

All Time Team & Individual Records
A list of the various records for this division (or its equivalent)
since the start of the league system.

Ten Year Record
A grid showing those clubs who have been part of this division (or its equivalent),
and the league position they achieved for each of the last ten years

ASPATRIA

Comp.	Date	H/A	Opponents	Result & Score	Att	15	14	13	12	11
N3 N	2-Sep	H	Bedford Athletic	W 30-20	200	Thurlow/t	Wall	Chilton	Stoddart/2c2p	West
N3 N	9-Sep	H	Dudley Kingwinsford	L 13-20	175	Thurlow	West	Chilton	Stoddart/c2p	Wall
N3 N	30-Sep	A	Liverpool St Helens	L 10-19		Thurlow	West	Chilton	Stoddart/cp	Wall
N3 N	14-Oct	H	Morley	L 26-40	150	Stoddart/3c	Atkinson/t	Chilton/t	Wall	West
N3 N	21-Oct	A	Doncaster	L 20-43	650	Kasselman/t	Wall	Chilton	Stoddart/2c2p	Atkinson/t
N3 N	28-Oct	H	Nuneaton	L 15-18		Kasselman	Wall/t	Chilton	Stoddart/cp	Atkinson
N3 N	11-Nov	A	Sandal	W 29-15		Kasselman/t	Stoddart/tc4p	Chilton	Wall	Atkinson/t
N3 N	18-Nov	H	Sedgley Park	L 10-21	100	Kasselman	Stoddart/cp	Chilton	Wall	Atkinson
N3 N	25-Nov	A	Stourbridge	L 10-33	350	Kasselman	Atkinson	Chilton	Hay	West/t
N3 N	2-Dec	H	Tynedale	L 8-26	100	Stoddart/p	Atkinson	Chilton	Wall	West/t
N3 N	16-Dec	H	Whitchurch	W 19-12		Kasselman/t	Atkinson	Chilton	Wall	West
N3 N	23-Dec	A	Tynedale	L 20-33	200	Kasselman/t	Atkinson	Hay	Chilton	Wall/t(b/t)
N3 N	6-Jan	A	Sedgley Park	L 3-57		Thurlow	Wall	Kasselman	Hay	Atkinson
N3 N	20-Jan	A	Nuneaton	L 22-33		Kasselman	Woodcock/t	Chilton/2t	Wall	Atkinson
N3 N	27-Jan	H	New Brighton	L 20-36		Kasselman/t	Woodcock	Chilton	Wall	Haestrom
N3 N	3-Feb	A	New Brighton	L 8-45	300	Haestrom	Woodcock	Chilton	Wall	Atkinson
N3 N	17-Feb	A	Walsall	L 14-51		Woodcock	Bruhn	Haestrom	Wall	Atkinson
N3 N	24-Feb	H	Liverpool St Helens	W 30-19		Woodcock	Bruhn	Haestrom	Wall	Atkinson
TBC	23-Sept	A	Darlington	L 15-32						

* after opponents name indicates a penalty try. Brackets after a player's name indicates he was replaced.
eg (a) means he was replaced by replacement code "a" and so on. / after a player or replacement name
is followed by any scores he made - eg /t, /c, /p, /dg or any combination of these

REPLACEMENTS   a - G Andrews   b - P West

EVER PRESENT Jason Spires, Lee Wall, Derek Benson, Mark Bowe, Mike Burnett

MOST APPEARANCES

18	Jason Spires, Lee Wall, Derek Benson, Mark Bowe, Mike Burnett.
17	David Wilson

MOST POINTS

Pts	Player	T	C	P	DG
71	S Stoddart	1	12	14	-
49	S Wood	2	6	9	-
37	D Kasselman	5	-	4	-
25	D Benson	5	-	-	-

2000-01 HIGHLIGHTS

With Mike Scott going to play for Kendal in National Two it was Stephen Stoddart who topped the scoring list.

He did so with just 71 points as Aspatria were limited to only 18 matches in the league due to foot and mouth.

Three of their four wins were at home with the only away success coming at Sandal way back in November.

They did not play another match after they beat Liverpool St Helens in late February.

MATCH FACTS

10	9	1	2	3	4	5	6	7	8
Wood	Spires	Wall	Benson/t	Reay/2t	Wilson	Bowe	Brough	Burnett	Humes
Wood	Spires	Andrews	Benson	Long	Wilson	Bowe	Brough/t	Burnett	Humes
Wood	Spires	Wall	Kruger	Andrews	Wilson	Bowe	Benson	Burnett	Humes/t
Wood	Spires	Wall	Benson/t	Long(a/t)	Wilson	Bowe	Hay	Burnett	Humes
Wood	Spires	Long	Benson	Kruger	Wilson	Bowe	Hay	Burnett	Humes
Wood/t	Spires	Long	Benson	Kruger	Wilson	Bowe	Hay	Burnett	Humes
Wood	Spires	Kruger	Benson	Wall	Bowe	Brough	Hay	Burnett	Humes
Wood	Spires	Wall	Benson/t	Kruger	Bowe	Wilson	Hay	Burnett	Humes
Wood/cp	Spires	Wall	Benson	Andrews	Wilson	Bowe	Brough	Burnett	Humes
Wood	Spires	Long	Benson	Andrews	Wilson	Bowe	Hay	Burnett	Brough
Wood/3p	Spires	Wall/t	Benson	Andrews	Wilson	Bowe	Hay	Burnett	Humes
Wood/cp	Spires	Wall	Benson	Andrews	Wilson	Bowe	Brough	Burnett	Humes
Wood/p	Spires	Wall	Benson	Douglas	Wilson	Bowe	Burnett	Brough	Kruger
Wood/2cp	Spires	Andrews	Benson	Wall	Bowe	Wilson	Hay	Burnett	Humes
Wood/t2c2p	Spires	Andrews	Benson	Douglas	Bowe	Wilson	Hay	Burnett	Humes
Kasselman/p	Spires	Andrews	Benson/t	Wall	Bowe	Wilson	Brough	Burnett	Humes
Kasselman/3p	Spires	Andrews	Benson/t	Wall	Bowe	Wilson	Brough	Burnett	Humes
Kasselman	Spires	Andrews	Benson	Wall	Bowe	Wilson	Brough	Burnett	Humes

REVIEW

This season sees us join North One after having played in the National Leagues for many years.

We were very sorry for our club, players and the locality to lose this status.

The circumstances of our relegation will be discussed by many people for years to come. We had failed to play eight games due to Foot and Mouth, an outbreak which devastated our immediate area and North Cumbria in general.

A formula was applied which resulted in us being at the bottom of the table. This came at the end of a season beset by the fuel crisis, frozen pitches & flooding which affected many clubs nationally.

Yes, we feel bitter, but if only we had played like we did in February against Liverpool St. Helens earlier in the season we would not have found ourselves in the position we did.

Never mind, on and up is how we are now looking at things. We have an excellent team spirit and some new recruits so we hope to regain what was taken from us as soon as possible.

Several players have departed as is always the case and we wish them well, a couple have gone to Rugby League and some have just moved on.

We would like to wish everyone in National 3 North well for the forthcoming season and we'd like to thank all of those on the NCA Executive Committee who helped us enormously. We will be back.

AVRIL QUINN

WALSALL

Comp.	Date	H/A	Opponents	Result & Score	Att	15	14	13	12	11
N3 N	2-Sep	H	Dudley Kingwinsford	W 16-9	470	Crisp/2p	Shepherd	Wood	Mitchell	Beechy
N3 N	16-Sep	A	Morley	L 10-12	400	Crisp/cp	Shepherd	Wood/t	Mitchell	Beechy
N3 N	23-Sep	H	Nuneaton	L 8-28	350	Crisp/p	Allan	Wood	Shepherd	Beechy
N3 N	30-Sep	A	Sedgley Park*	L 7-25	300	Crisp/c	Ridgway	Shepherd	Towe	Beechy
N3 N	14-Oct	H	Tynedale	W 24-23	200	Crisp/c2p	Ridgway/t	Towe	Shepherd/t	Human
N3 N	28-Oct	H	Doncaster	L 5-17	250	Crisp	Ridgway	Towe	Shepherd	Human
N3 N	4-Nov	A	Whitchurch	L 13-20	350	Crisp/p	Human/t	Towe	Shepherd	Ridgway/t
N3 N	11-Nov	A	Liverpool St Helens	L 20-33	250	Shepherd	Ridgway	Wood	Towe/t	Human/t
N3 N	18-Nov	H	New Brighton	L 10-13	325	Ridgway	Human	Eastwood	Towe	Walker
N3 N	25-Nov	A	Sandal	L 30-39		Ridgway/t	Human/t	Mitchell	Towe	Walker
N3 N	16-Dec	A	Bedford Athletic	L 16-24	200	Marsh	Ridgway	Eastwood	Towe	Beechy/t
N3 N	23-Dec	A	Stourbridge	L 6-46	450	Crisp/2p	Marsh	Mitchell	Eastwood	Beechy
N3 N	6-Jan	A	New Brighton	L 26-35		Crisp/c3p	Human	Eastwood	Towe	Beechy/t
N3 N	13-Jan	H	Liverpool St Helens*	W 48-15		Crisp/3c3pdg	Human	Towe	Eastwood/t	Beechy/t
N3 N	27-Jan	H	Whitchurch	W 43-30		Crisp/2c3p	Human/t	Bambridge(a/2t)Towe		Marsh/t
N3 N	3-Feb	H	Stourbridge	L 22-25	500	Crisp/2cp	Beechy	Mitchell(b/t)	Shepherd	Human/t
N3 N	17-Feb	H	Aspatria*	W 51-14		Marsh/2t5c2p	Human	Shepherd	Eastwood/2t	Beechy/2t
N3 N	24-Feb	H	Sedgley Park	L 29-34	250	Marsh/3cp	Human	Towe/t	Eastwood/t	Beechy/t
N3 N	10-Mar	A	Nuneaton	W 42-34		Crisp/t3c2p	Beechy/2t	Towe	Eastwood/t	Marsh/t
N3 N	24-Mar	A	Dudley Kingwinsford	L 18-21	800	Crisp/c2p	Marsh/t	Towe	Eastwood	Beechy
N3 N	31-Mar	H	Bedford Athletic	L 10-15		Crisp	Marsh(c/t)	Towe	Eastwood	Beechy
N3 N	7-Apr	A	Doncaster	L 22-39		Crisp/t2cp	Beechy/t	Shepherd	Towe	Walker
N3 N	14-Apr	H	Sandal	L 35-37		Crisp/2c2p	Beechy/t	Wood	Eastwood	Walker/t
N3 N	21-Apr	H	Morley	W 27-13		Crisp/2cp	Shepherd	Eastwood/2t	Towe	Beechy/t
TBC	7-Oct	H	Dudley Kingswinford	L 17-21						

* after opponents name indicates a penalty try. Brackets after a player's name indicates he was replaced.
eg (a) means he was replaced by replacement code "a" and so on. / after a player or replacement name
is followed by any scores he made - eg /t, /c, /p, /dg or any combination of these

EVER PRESENT	Richard Lee	PLAYERS USED	36 plus two as replacement only

MOST APPEARANCES

24	Richard Lee.
23	Mark Gilbert.
22	Mike Crisp.
21	David Waite.
20	Karl Jones, Greg Harwood.

MOST POINTS

Pts	Player	T	C	P	DG
167	M Crisp	3	25	33	1
55	T Beechy	11	-	-	-
55	R Marsh	6	8	3	-
45	M Eastwood	9	-	-	-
35	E Saayman	7	-	-	-

MATCH FACTS

10	9	1	2	3	4	5	6	7	8
Harwood	Martin	Waite	Cox	Jones/t	Lee	Gilbert	Wilkinson	Dickson	Coleman
Harwood	Martin	Waite	Cox	Jones	Lee	Gilbert	Wilkinson	Bassett	Coleman
Harwood	Mitchell	Waite	Ramage	Jones	Lee	Gilbert/t	Bassett	Hitchen	Coleman
Harwood	Butler	Waite	Jones	Bradshaw	Lee	Gilbert	Heathcote	Hitchen	Wilkinson
Harwood	Butler/2p	Waite	Ramage	Jones	Godfrey	Gilbert	Lee	Tillott	Wilkinson
Harwood	Butler	Waite	Ramage	Jones	Godfrey	Heathcote/t	Lee	Tillott	Wilkinson
Harwood	Martin	Waite	Ramage	Nawarycz	Gilbert	Godfrey	Lee	Tillott	Wilkinson
Crisp/cp	Martin	Waite	Wooldridge	Bradshaw	Gilbert	Godfrey/t	Fitzgerald	Bassett	Lee
Crisp/cp	Martin	Waite	Ramage	Nawarycz	Gilbert/t	Godfrey	Lee	Fitzgerald	Wilkinson
Crisp/t2c2p	Martin	Waite	Ramage	Nawarycz	Godfrey/t	Gilbert	Lee	Fitzgerald	Wilkinson
Crisp/2p	Martin	Nawarycz	Wooldridge	Jones	Godfrey	Gilbert	Lee	Dawes	Saayman/t
Harwood	Martin	Waite	Wooldridge	Jones	Heathcote	Gilbert	Lee	Dawes	Saayman
Harwood	Martin/t	Waite	Wooldridge	Jones/t	Gilbert	Heathcote	Lee	Dawes	Saayman
Harwood	Martin	Waite	Wooldridge	Jones	Gilbert	Heathcote	Lee/t	Tillott	Saayman/2t
Harwood	Martin	Bradshaw	Wooldridge	Jones	Gilbert	Godfrey	Lee	Dawes	Saayman/2t
Harwood	Martin	Waite	Ramage	Jones	Gilbert	Godfrey	Lee	Coleman	Saayman/t
Harwood	Martin	Waite	Ramage	Jones	Godfrey	Gilbert	Lee	Dawes	Saayman
Harwood	Martin/t	Waite	Wooldridge	Jones	Gilbert	Godfrey	Lee	Tillott	Saayman
Harwood	Martin/t	Waite	Wooldridge	Jones	Gilbert	Godfrey	Lee	Tillott	Saayman
Harwood	Martin	Waite	Wooldridge	Jones/t	Coleman	Gilbert	Lee	Tillott	Saayman
Harwood/t	Butler	Waite	Wooldridge	Jones	Godfrey	Gilbert	Lee	Tillott	Saayman
Harwood	Butler	Lea	Wooldridge	Jones	Gilbert/t	Godfrey	Lee	Tillott	Saayman
Harwood	Butler	Waite	Wooldridge/t	Jones	Gilbert	Godfrey	Lee	Tillott(d/t)	Saayman/t
Harwood	Butler	Waite	Wooldridge	Jones/t	Godfrey	Gilbert	Lee	Dawes	Saayma

REPLACEMENTS   a - M Eastwood   b - R Marsh   c - M Wood   d - S Dawes

2000-01 HIGHLIGHTS

Mike Crisp was again top points scorer in his second season at the club.

Richard Lee was ever present for a second successive league campaign and has now played all 50 matches in the league since joining the club.

Winger Tom Beechy tops the try scoring list in his debut season for the club. He finished two clear of centre Mark Eastwood who was also a new signing for the club.

Richard Marsh scored 26 points in the 51-14 home win against Liverpool St Helens with two tries five conversions and two penalties.

THE LAST TEN YEARS   DIVISION 4 NORTH

1991-92	*Champions*	*Runners-up*	*Relegated*
	Aspatria	Hereford	Vale of Lune, Northern

Most Points: 127 Paul Grayson (Preston G)   Tries: 7 Jimmy Miller (Aspatria)
Penalties: 25 Paul Grayson (Preston G)   Conversions: 13 Andrew harrison (Aspatria)   D.Gs: 6 Paul Grayson (Preston G)

1992-93	*Champions*	*Runners-up*	*Relegated*
	Harrogate	Rotherham	Towcestrians

Most Points: 131 Ralph Zoing (Harrogate)   Tries: 9 Guy Easterby (Harrogate)
Steve Baker (Harrogate)
Penalties: 31 Simon Pennington (Stourbridge) Conversions: 28 Ralph Zoing (Harrogate)   D.Gs: N.A.

1993-94	*Champions*	*Runners-up*	*Relegated*
	Rotherham	Preston Grasshoppers	Bradford & Bingley, Durham City

Most Points: 118 Kevin Plant (Rotherham)   Tries: 8 John Dudley (Rotherham)
Penalties: 23 Richard Mills (Walsall)   Conversions: 22 Kevin Plant (Rotherham)   D.Gs: N.A.

1994-95	*Champions*	*Runners-up*	*Relegated*
	Walsall	Kendal	Hereford, Barkers' Butts

Most Points: 164 Richard MIlls (Walsall)   Tries: 11 Jon Rowe (Walsall)
Penalties: 31 Richard Mills (Walsall)   Conversions: 29 Richard Mills (Walsall)   D.Gs: N.A.

1995-96	*Champions*	*Runners-up*	*Relegated*
	Wharfedale	Worcester	Broughton Park

Most Points: 143 Alex Howarth (Wharfedale)   Tries: 10 Neil Hezeltine (Wharfedale)
Spencer Bradley (Worcester)
Penalties: 29 Alex Howarth (Wharfedale)   Conversions: 23 Alex Howarth (Wharfedale)   D.Gs: 3 Warwick Masser (Nuneaton)

1996-97	*Champions*	*Runners-up*	*Relegated*
	Worcester	Birmingham Solihull	Hereford, Stoke on Trent

Most Points: 317 Steve Kerry (Preston G)   Tries: 18 Nick Baxter (Worcester)
Penalties: 64 Steve Kerry (Preston G)   Conversions: 61 Tim Smith (Worcester)   D.Gs: 9 Steve Kerry (Preston G)

1997-98	*Champions*	*Runners-up*	*Relegated*
	Birmingham Solihull	Manchester	-

Most Points: 398 Steve Swindells (Manchester)   Tries: 21 Matt Hoskin (Manchester)
Penalties: 62 Steve Swindells (Manchester) Conversions: 91 Steve Swindells (Manchester) D.Gs: 4 Ian Shuttleworth (Sandal)
Rob Pound (Sheffield)

1998-99	*Champions*	*Runners-up*	*Relegated*
	Preston Grasshoppers	Stourbridge	Hinckley, Lichfield, Winnington Park

Most Points: 246 Ian Shuttleworth (Sandal)   Tries: 27 Michael Lough (Preston G.)
Penalties: Martin Emmett (Preston G.)   Conversions: Martin Emmett (Preston G.) D.Gs: 3 Ian Shuttleworth (Sandal)

99-2000	*Champions*	*Runners-up*	*Relegated*
	Kendal	Stourbridge	Sheffield

Most Points: 302 Paul Brett (New Brighton)   Tries: 22 Chris Hall (Morley)
Penalties: 55 Paul Brett (New Brighton)   Conversions: 53 Casey Mee (Kendal)   D.Gs: 2 Jamie Grayshon (Morley)

2000-01	*Champions*	*Runners-up*	*Relegated*
	Stourbridge	Sedgley Park	Walsall, Aspatria

Most Points: 258 Paul Brett (New Brighton)   Tries: 20 Garry Marshall (Nuneaton)
Penalties: Simon Worsley (Liverpool St Helens) Conversions: 50 Colin Stephens (Sedgley Park) D.Gs: 5 Simon Worlsey (Liverpool St H.)

TEAM RECORDS

ALL TIME RECORDS   DIVISION 4 NORTH

Highest score:	101	Manchester 101 Nuneaton 12, 25.4.98
Highest aggregate:	113	as above
Highest score by a losing side:	38	Nuneaton 40 Aspatria 38, 9.11.96
Highest scoring draw:	33	Nuneaton v Kendal, 25.1.98
Most consecutive wins:	19	Kendal 1999-2000
Most consecutive defeats:	18	Stoke-on-Trent 1996-97
Most points for in a season:	1029	Manchester 1997-98
Least points for in a season:	29	Birmingham Solihull 1988-89
Most points against in a season:	972	Hereford 1996-97
Least points against in a season:	67	Roundhay 1987-88
Most tries for in a season:	135	Stourbridge 1998-99
Most tries against in a season:	131	Hereford 1996-97
Least tries for in a season:		
Least tries against in a season:		
Most conversions for in a season:	98	Manchester 1997-98
Most conversions against in a season:	82	Hereford 1996-97
Most penalties for in a season:	73	Sheffield 1996-97
Most penalties against in a season:	60	Winnington Park 1996-97
Least penalties for in a season:		
Least penalties against in a season:		
Most drop goals for in a season:	10	Preston Grasshoppers 1996-97
Most drop goals against in a season:	8	Aspatria 1996-97

INDIVIDUAL RECORDS

ALL TIME RECORDS   DIVISION 4 NORTH

Most points in a season:	398	Steve Swindells (Manchester) 1997-98
Most tries in a season:	22	Chris Hall (Morley) 1999-2000
Most conversions in a season:	91	Steve Swindells (Manchester) 1997-98
Most penalties in a season:	64	Steve Kerry (Preston Grasshoppers) 1996-97
Most drop goals in a season:	9	Steve Kerry (Preston Grasshoppers) 1996-97
Most points in a match:	44	Jamie Morley, *Sheffield* v Lichfield 7.9.97
Most tries in a match:	6	Jason Slater, *Kendal* v Barkers Butts 14.1.95
Most conversions in a match:	10	Steve Swindells, *Manchester* v Nuneaton 25.4.98
		Kevin Plant, *Rotherham* v Durham 19.2.94
Most penalties in a match:	8	Steve Baker, *Stourbridge* v Hereford 26.1.91
Most drop goals in a match:	4	Steve Kerry, *Preston G.* v Aspatria 7.9.96

TEN YEAR RECORDS — DIVISION 4 NORTH

Club	91-92	92-93	93-94	94-95	95-96	96-97	97-98	98-99	99-00	00-01
Aspatria	1	-	-	-	-	10	9	10	12	14r
Barkers Butts	-	-	-	12	-	-	-	-	-	-
Bedford Athletic	-	-	-	-	-	-	-	-	9	10
Birmingham Solihull	-	-	9	10	3	2	1p	-	-	-
Bradford & Bingley	-	-	13	-	-	-	-	-	-	-
Broughton Park	-	-	-	-	13	-	-	-	-	-
Doncaster	-	-	-	-	-	-	-	-	6	4
Dudley Kingswinford	-	-	-	-	-	-	-	-	-	6
Durham City	10	8	12	-	-	-	-	-	-	-
Harrogate	7	1	-	-	-	-	-	-	-	-
Hereford	2	11	8	13	-	13	-	-	-	-
Hinckley	-	-	-	-	-	-	12	12r	-	-
Kendal	3	6	10	2	9	9	3	4	1p	-
Lichfield	5	5	7	5	12	11	13	13r	-	-
Liverpool St. Helens	-	-	-	-	-	-	-	-	13	9
Manchester	-	-	-	-	-	4	2p	-	-	-
Morley	-	-	-	-	-	-	-	-	7	11
New Brighton	-	-	-	-	-	-	-	3	3	3
Northern	13	-	-	-	-	-	-	-	-	-
Nuneaton	-	12	11	11	10	12	7	5	8	5
Preston Grasshoppers	4	3	2	3	8	3	4	1p	-	-
Rotherham	-	2	1	-	-	-	-	-	-	-
Sandal	-	-	-	-	6	5	8	7	10	12
Sedgley Park	-	-	-	-	-	-	5	8	5	2p
Sheffield	-	-	-	9	5	8	10	6	14r	-
Stoke on Trent	-	4	6	7	11	14	-	-	-	-
Stourbridge	6	9	5	6	7	6	6	2	2	1p
Towcestrians	9	13	-	-	-	-	-	-	-	-
Tynedale	-	-	-	-	-	-	-	-	-	8
Vale of Lune	13	-	-	-	-	-	-	-	-	-
Walsall	11	7	3	1	-	-	11	9	4	13r
Winnington Park	8	10	4	8	4	7	14	14r	-	-
Wharfedale	-	-	4	1	-	-	-	-	-	-
Whitchurch	-	-	-	-	-	-	-	11	11	7
Worcester	-	-	-	-	2	1	-	-	-	-

THREE SOUTH

LEAGUE TABLE SEASON 2000-01

	P	W	D	L	F	A	PD	Tries	Pens	PTS	Last 6 Matches W-D-L
Plymouth Albion	26	26	0	0	910	240	670	122	46	**52**	6-0-0
Launceston	26	20	1	5	777	391	386	102	45	**41**	4-1-1
Penzance & Newlyn	26	18	2	6	823	492	331	108	45	**38**	4-0-2
Barking	26	15	1	10	611	481	130	77	47	**31**	3-0-3
Redruth	26	14	1	11	691	595	96	88	41	**29**	4-0-2
North Walsham	26	12	1	13	550	458	92	62	55	**25**	2-0-4
Westcombe Park	26	12	0	14	550	660	-110	63	52	**24**	2-0-4
Clifton	26	10	1	15	509	628	-119	59	46	**21**	3-0-3
Blackheath	26	10	0	16	555	641	-86	72	38	**20**	4-0-2
Tabard	26	9	2	15	415	719	-304	51	35	**20**	1-0-5
Reading	26	9	1	16	462	643	-181	63	26	**19**	0-1-5
WestoN-super-Mare	26	7	1	18	370	691	-321	33	51	**15**	4-0-2
Basingstoke	26	7	1	18	333	686	-353	29	51	**15**	2-0-4
Cheltenham	26	7	0	19	492	723	-231	56	50	**14**	0-0-6

REVIEW OF THE SEASON

Plymouth Albion took the title impressively with a 100% record with 26 wins behind them. They were the leading scorers in the division and had the meanest defense, the perfect balance. Tom Barlow and Chris Atkinson kicked all the goals and Dan Ward-Smith topped the try scoring with a new club record of 20.

Launceston had an eventful first season in National League rugby. They finished as runners up to Plymouth Albion and went into a play-off with Sedgley Park for the right to go into National Two. The match was away from home and they were well beaten by the northern side. They had a high scoring season scoring plenty of tries. They also pushed Plymouth Albion hard in both their matches losing by just seven points on each occasion.

Penzance & Newlyn slipped one place from the previous season to third place in National Three South. They finished the season as second highest scorers behind Plymouth Albion but conceded twice as many points. They had the most exciting back division in the Division and were capable of scoring tries from anywhere on the pitch. Three of their backs scored 17 or more tries whilst Richard Newton came back to the club on loan from Cardiff and ran in 10 tries in no time whatsoever.

Barking finished fourth, but were seven points behind the team above them, which was a two place improvement on the previous season. Since winning promotion back in 1993-94 they have finished in the top six every season.

Redruth again finished fifth just two points behind fourth placed Barking. They faltered mid season with just two wins from a eight match run. They lost twice to Launceston but each time it was by five points or fewer. The only bad defeat they suffered was at Reading where they lost a high scoring match 47-35. Steve Larkins made a big contribution with over 200 points and Bede Brown dropped an impressive seven drop goals during the league campaign.

Sixth placed **North Walsham** dropped three places after finishing third in the two previous seasons. Walsham started the season reasonably well but after the turn of the year they went on a run of four defeats and a draw. Three teams, Plymouth Albion, Launceston and Westcombe Park, did the double over the East Anglian team. They did have a good defence and only the top two conceded fewer points than North Walsham.

Westcombe Park improved two places on the previous season and finished a highly creditable seventh in the National Three South division. They did not start the campaign to well with four successive defeats before they managed a win. They did do the double over North Walsham, which was an excellent achievement, which only Plymouth and Launceston managed.

Clifton made the most of the fixture list; they started the season well and finished it well but in the middle struggled with one win from nine league matches. They finished eighth which was a one-place drop on the last two seasons when they had come seventh. They did the double over Weston-super-Mare and Basingstoke. At home they had good home wins against Barking and North Walsham, sides who finished above them in the league.

Blackheath had a good opening day which ended an 18 match losing run they had carried over from the previous season. After that win they again went on a dreadful losing run. They lost 11 consecutive matches and were in deep trouble before starting the New Year win a win. They then put together an impressive run of nine wins from 14 matches and moved up the league table and away from relegation.

Tabard just escaped relegation by a single point as their form fell away at the end of the season. They finished 10th which is their lowest ever position in the division since winning promotion from London One back in 1992-93. They managed just one win in their last seven league matches. Early in the season they had good wins against North Walsham and Westcombe Park but failed to build on it and did not beat a side above them again all season.

Reading were unfortunate that four sides were relegated because two sides came down National Two and both went into National Three South. They fall out of the National leagues for the first time since 1992-93 when they were Champions in South West One. On the final day of the season they managed an excellent draw with third placed Launceston, if they could have won that match they would have been level with Tabard and a superior points difference would have seen them stay up. One point from their last six matches proved their downfall.

Weston super Mare put together some excellent late season form but by then it was to late and they were relegated out of the National Leagues despite finishing third bottom. This was because of the new play off system from the divisions below. They won four of the last five matches having managed just three wins in their first 21 matches of the season. They could not score enough points with only Basingstoke scoring fewer, no player scored over 100 points whilst the leading try scorer only scored four.

Basingstoke stayed just one season in National Three South after coming up with much promise. They could not score enough points and ended the season as the lowest scorers in the Division with just 333 points to their name. Their cause was not helped by the fact that they could not find a regular goal kicker with four players have a go during the season.

Cheltenham finished bottom of the table one point behind Basingstoke. They could score points but the conceded more than any other side in the division. They scored more points than the four sides immediately above them in the table. After putting together their best run of the season just after the New Year with three successive wins they lost form completely. They then went on a run of nine consecutive defeats, which saw them, drop, to the bottom of the table.

2000-2001
RECORD REVIEW
(Individual Records)

MOST POINTS - IN A SEASON

Fijian Nat Saumi moved into third place on the Divisions all time list after scoring 336 points for Penzance & Newlyn. Also moving into the top five is the Launceston full back Danny Sloamn who notched up 288 points in his first season at this level and helped his side to an impressive second place..

EVOLUTION OF RECORD

69	John Field	Askeans	1987-88
83	Simon Harvey	Clifton	1989-90
122	Melvin Badger	Weston-s-Mare	1990-91
129	Pete Russell	Havant	1991-92
133	Phil Belshaw	Reading	1993-94
176	Richard Perkins	Henley	1995-96
391	Nick Grecian	Newbury	1996-97

ALL-TIME RECORDS

391	Nick Grecian	Newbury	1996-97
351	Jon Gregory	Esher	1999-00
336	Nat Saumi	Penzance & New	2000-01
313	Jonathan Gregory	Esher	1998-99
288	Danny Sloman	Launceston	2000-01
264	Nick Churchman	Tabard	1996-97
260	Chris Atkinson	Plymouth	1999-00
256	Rob Thirlby	Redruth	1997-98
255	Tom Barlow	Plymouth	2000-01
253	James Shanahan	N Walsham	1997-98
248	Nick Thomson	Barking	1996-97
243	Derek Coates	Westcombe Park	1999-00
242	Nick Edmonds	Bridgwater & A	1997-98
239	Nick Churchman	Tabard	1997-98
230	Neil Coleman	Weston	1999-00

MOST TRIES - IN A SEASON

Penzance & Newlyn utility back Victor Olonga topped the 20 mark for the second successive season - the second man to achieve this in the history of National League rugby. He did though fall short of his total for last season but did finish joint leading scorer. He was joined on 20 by the Plymouth Albion No 8 Dan Ward-Smith - in his first season for the club.

EVOLUTION OF RECORD

7	John Willis	Redruth	1988-89
8	Melvin Badger	Weston-s-Mare	1990-91
9	Will Knight	Havant	1991-92
12	Steve Titcombe	Sudbury	1992-93
27	Brian Johnson	Newbury	1996-97
38	Richard Newton	Penzance & New	1999-00

ALL-TIME RECORDS

38	Richard Newton	Penzance & New	1999-00
27	Brian Johnson	Newbury	1996-97
25	Craig Davies	Newbury	1996-97
24	Victor Olonga	Penzance & New	1999-00
21	James Shanahan	North Walsham	1999-00
20	Victor Olonga	Penzance & New	2000-01
20	Dan Ward-Smith	Plymouth	2000-01
19	Tom Holloway	Newbury	1996-97
17	Robert Thirlby	Redruth	1997-98
17	Nat Saumi	Penzance & Newlyn	2000-01
17	Peter Redgrave	Penzance & Newlyn	2000-01
16	Nana Dontah	Esher	1998-99
16	James Shanahan	N Walsham	1998-99
16	Andy Carter	Met Police	1998-99
16	Jag Johal	Tabard	1999-00
15	Steve Walklin	Plymouth	1997-98
15	Mark Venner	Henley	1997-98
15	Michael Corcoran	Esher	1998-99
15	Steve Walklin	Plymouth	1999-00
15	Michael Corcoran	Esher	1999-00

MOST PENALTIES - IN A SEASON

Chris Atkinson's record of 59 was safe last season with Westcombe Park's Derek Coates topping the list with 46. That left him one clear of Launceston's Danny Sloman but three short of his best set in the previous season.

EVOLUTION OF RECORD

13	John Field	Askeans	1987-88
15	Simon Harvey	Clifton	1989-90
27	Rob Ashworth	Havant	1990-91
34	Phil Belshaw	Reading	1993-94
53	Nick Churchman	Tabard	1996-97
58	Jon Gregory	Esher	1998-99
59	Chris Atkinson	Plymouth	1999-00

ALL-TIME RECORDS

59	Chris Atkinson	Plymouth	1999-00
58	Jon Gregory	Esher	1998-99
53	Nick Churchman	Tabard	1996-97
53	Neil Coleman	Weston	1999-00
51	James Shanahan	N Walsham	1997-98
50	Nick Edmonds	Bridgwater & A	1997-98
50	Jon Gregory	Esher	1999-00
49	Derek Coates	Westcombe Park	1999-00
46	Derek Coates	Westcombe Park	2000-01
45	Carson Russell	Bracknell	1998-99
45	Danny Sloman	Launceston	2000-01

MOST CONVERSIONS - IN A SEASON

Nat Saumi moved into third place on the all time list for the division with 67 conversions. It was way of the leader Nick Grecian and 11 behind the second placed Jon Gregory. Danny Sloman again figured and moved into fourth place on the all time list.

EVOLUTION OF RECORD

9	John Field	Askeans	1987-88
10	Simon Harvey	Clifton	1989-90
16	Simon Blake	Redruth	1990-91
23	Pete Russelll	Havant	1991-92
28	Mike Hamlin	London Welsh	1992-93
100	Nick Grecian	Newbury	1996-97

ALL-TIME RECORDS

100	Nick Grecian	Newbury	1996-97
78	Jon Gregory	Esher	1999-00
67	Nat Saumi	Penzance & Newlyn	2000-01
59	Danny Sloman	Launceston	2000-01
55	Nat Saumi	Penzance & New	1999-00
52	Jon Gregory	Esher	1998-99
48	Robert Thirlby	Redruth	1997-98
46	Steve Larkins	Redruth	2000-01
42	Tom Barlow	Plymouth Albion	2000-01
39	Carson Russell	Bracknell	1998-99
38	Nick Thomson	Barking	1996-97
37	Mark Slevin	Met Police	1996-97
36	Jason Hoad	Camberley	1996-97
36	Tony Kingsmill	North Walsham	1999-00
36	Chris Atkinson	Plymouth	1999-00

MOST DROP GOALS - IN A SEASON

Redruth fly half Bede Brown dropped seven goals during his first season of League rugby and moved into third place on the all time list for the division.

EVOLUTION OF RECORD

2	Andy Perry	Havant	1987-88
	Andy Perry	Havant	1988-89
6	Simon Harvey	Clifton	1989-90
10	Simon Cattermole	Weston-s-Mare	1996-97
11	Nick Edmonds	Bridgwater & Alb.	1997-98

ALL-TIME RECORDS

11	Nick Edmonds	Bridgwater & Alb.	1997-98
10	Simon Cattermole	Weston-s-Mare	1996-97
7	Bede Brown	Redruth	2000-01
6	Simon Harvey	Clifton	1989-90
6	James Shanahan	N Walsham	1997-98
6	Stewart Whitworth	Redruth	1999-00

2000-01

NATIONAL THREE SOUTH

MOST POINTS

POINTS			T	C	P	DG
336	Nat Saumi	Penzance & New	17	67	39	-
288	Danny Sloman	Launceston	7	59	45	-
255	Tom Barlow	Plymouth A	12	42	32	5
228	Jon Martin	Clifton	7	32	41	2
215	Derek Coates	Westcombe Park	1	33	46	2
207	Steve Larkins	Redruth	8	46	25	-
192	Billy Murphy	Barking	3	27	40	1
166	Phil Watters	Cheltenham	7	13	35	-
152	Justin Azzopardi	Tabard	3	16	34	1
149	Phil Friel	N Walsham	4	24	27	-
134	Matt Senior	Reading	4	27	20	-
130	Jonathan Griffin	Blackheath	4	16	24	2
121	Bede Brown	Redruth	8	6	16	7
110	Chris Atkinson	Plymouth Albion	1	30	14	1
102	Mitch Hoare	Blackheath	4	20	13	1
100	Peter Redgrave	Penzance & New	17	3	3	-
100	Victor Olonga	Penzance & New	20	-	-	-
100	Dan Ward-Smith	Plymouth Albion	20	-	-	-

MOST PENALTIES

46	Derek Coates	Westcombe Park
45	Danny Sloman	Launceston
41	Jon Martin	Clifton
40	Billy Murphy	Barking
39	Nat Saumi	Penzance & New
35	Phil Watters	Cheltenham
34	Justin Azzopardi	Tabard
32	Tom Barlow	Plymouth Albion
27	Phil Friel	N Walsham
26	Neil Coleman	Weston
25	Steve Larkins	Redruth
24	Jonathan Griffin	Blackheath
23	Len Wilmot	N Walsham
20	Matt Senior	Reading

MOST DROP GOALS

7	Bede Brown	Redruth
5	Tom Barlow	Plymouth
2	Jon Martin	Clifton
2	Derek Coates	Westcombe Park
2	Jonathan Griffin	Blackheath
2	Ralph Knibbs	Clifton
1	Billy Murphy	Barking
1	Justin Azzoaprdi	Tabard
1	Chris Atkinson	Plymouth
1	Mitch Hoare	Blackheath
1	Neil Coleman	Weston
1	Matt Hart	Basingstoke
1	Paul Thirlby	Redruth
1	Steve Evans	Penzance & New
1	Carson Russell	Reading
1	Andrew Birkett	Penzance & New

MOST TRIES

20	Victor Olonga	Penzance & New
20	Dan Ward-Smith	Plymouth A
17	Peter Redgrave	Penzance & new
17	Nat Saumi	Penzance & New
15	Fred Lewis	Barking
14	Richard Thompson	Plymouth
14	Barnaby Kent	Clifton
13	Mark Fatialofa	Launceston
13	Andy Matchett	Plymouth A
13	Charles Abban	Blackheath
12	Jimmy Tucker	Launceston
12	Laka Waqaniere	Redruth
12	Tom Barlow	Plymouth A
11	Pat Sykes	Westcombe Park
11	Roger Thompson	Plymouth
10	Matt Bradshaw	Launceston
10	Dave Fitzgerald	Blackheath
10	Richard Newton	Penzance & New

MOST CONVERSIONS

67	Nat Saumi	Penzance & New
59	Danny Sloman	Launceston
46	Steve Larkins	Redruth
42	Tom Barlow	Plymouth A
33	Derek Coates	Westcombe Park
32	Jon Martin	Clifton
30	Chris Atkinson	Plymouth
27	Billy Murphy	Barking
27	Matt Senior	Reading
24	Phil Friel	N Walsham
20	Mitch Hoare	Blackheath
17	Matt Watts	Cheltenham
16	Justin Azzopardi	Tabard
16	Jonathan Griffin	Blackheath

NATIONAL DIVISION 3 SOUTH

FIXTURES 2001-02

Away Teams

HOME TEAMS	Barking (1)	Blackheath (2)	Camberley (3)	Cinderford (4)	Clifton (5)	Launceston (6)	Lydney (7)	North Walsham (8)	Old Colfeians (9)	Old Patesians (10)	Penzance/Newlyn (11)	Redruth (12)	Tabard (13)	Westcombe Park (14)
1 Barking		22.12	27.10	26.01	8.12	6.10	6.04	24.11	9.02	8.09	9.03	10.11	1.12	12.01
2 Blackheath	30.03		6.10	9.02	5.01	8.09	12.01	10.11	9.03	15.12	1.12	27.10	13.04	26.01
3 Camberley	2.02	16.02		6.04	20.10	5.01	8.12	22.09	30.03	19.01	17.11	1.09	3.11	16.03
4 Cinderford	3.11	20.10	15.12		2.02	30.03	1.12	16.02	13.04	17.11	5.01	16.03	19.01	22.09
5 Clifton	13.04	24.11	9.02	27.10		9.03	22.12	12.01	6.10	1.12	8.09	26.01	15.12	10.11
6 Launceston	16.02	16.03	24.11	22.12	22.09		10.11	1.09	12.01	2.02	3.11	8.12	20.10	6.04
7 Lydney	15.12	17.11	13.04	1.09	30.03	19.01		3.11	5.01	16.02	2.02	22.09	16.03	20.10
8 North Walsham	5.01	19.01	9.03	6.10	17.11	1.12	26.01		8.09	13.04	15.12	9.02	30.03	27.10
9 Old Colfeians	20.10	22.09	22.12	8.12	16.02	17.11	24.11	16.03		26.01	19.01	6.04	2.02	1.12
10 Old Patesians	16.03	6.04	10.11	12.01	1.09	27.10	6.10	8.12	26.01		9.02	24.11	22.09	22.12
11 Penzance & Newlyn	22.09	1.09	12.01	24.11	16.03	26.01	27.10	6.04	10.11	20.10		22.12	16.02	8.12
12 Redruth	19.01	2.02	1.12	8.09	3.11	13.04	9.03	20.10	15.12	5.01	30.03		17.11	16.02
13 Tabard	1.09	8.12	26.01	10.11	6.04	9.02	8.09	22.12	27.10	9.03	6.10	12.01		24.11
14 Westcombe Park	17.11	3.11	8.09	9.03	19.01	15.12	9.02	2.02	1.09	30.03	13.04	6.10	5.01	

BARKING RUFC

President	Gerald Mansfield	34 Spencer Road, Rainham, Essex RM13 8HB
		0207 260 4904 (B) 01708 551073 (H)
Club Secretary	Jim Marner	Meadow View, Kirkham Road, Horndon-on-the-hill, Essex SS17 8QE
		01708 858136 (B) 01268 490550 (H) 07957 328363 (M) 01708 858660 (F)
Treasurer	Debbie Weekes	Meadow View, Kirkham Road, Horndon-on-the-hill, Essex SS17 8QE
		0207 650 2301 (B) 01268 490550 (H) 07957 328363 (M)
Press Officer	Martin Dutt	70 Netherfield Gardens, Barking, Essex IG11 9TN
		020 8507 7308 (H&Fax) 07703 486375 (M) email: scoop@dutt.co.uk
1st XV Manager	Mark Diable	Highview, 21 Hillside Rd., Billericay, Essex CM11 2DA
		01277 657069 (H) 07764 182226 (M) email: mark.diable@ubsw.com
Director of Rugby	Dean Cutting	0208 502 6398 (H) 07939 155380 (M)
Director of Coaching	Mike Lovett	01708 224001 (H)
Coaching Staff	Eric Williams, Lee Stannard, Gary Cutting.	

Sixth place in their sixth season at this level in 99/00 was Barking's lowest finish, so they had to bounce back last season, which they did, finishing in fourth spot. But it could so easily have been higher were it not for the team's propensity to lose games that they should so easily have won.

A bright start saw the team open with three wins in a row before they suffered their first reverse, a 12-29 defeat at Clifton, the first of those games that got away as they reversed that defeat in February with a 50-18 victory, their biggest of the season.

A comfortable Tetley Bitter Cup victory against Tabard was followed by a nail-biting 20-18 victory over Launceston at Goresbrook before their Tetley Cup exit, 17-29 at the hands of Rosslyn Park. Another cliff-hanger saw a 17-17 home draw with Penzance, followed by a heartening 10-3 win at Eastern Counties rivals North Walsham.

Then came November, which always seems to be a bad month for Barking and this season was certainly no exception. A10-26 defeat at Plymouth was not unexpected, but the 20-27 defeat by Reading took their unbeaten home league record and this was followed by a 12-20 loss at Redruth.

December brought improvement with home and away wins over Tabard and victories at Westcombe Park and at home to Weston for a 100% month.

Reading were made to pay for their earlier audacity in winning at Goresbrook when they were beaten 37-3 in the return in January, a month which brought two of the closest games seen at Goresbrook all season as Plymouth scraped home 36-37 and then Barking came back from the dead to beat North Walsham 31-29.

February brought victories over Redruth and Clifton at home and their heaviest defeat of the season, 13-42 at Launceston, effectively ending their promotion challenge.

The team pose for a photograph with Mascot for the day, Sonny Ross, before their game against Reading. Photo: Kevin Webb

After winning at Cheltenham they suffered a string of defeats at home to Blackheath and at Basingstoke and Weston before rounding off their league programme with a further home defeat, this time at the hands of Westcombe Park.

To rub salt into the wounds a week later North Walsham won their Eastern Counties Cup semi final at Barking to end the season on a very low note – so watch out. The boys from the East End are looking to bounce back with a vengeance!

BARKING

Comp.	Date	H/A	Opponents	Result & Score	Att	15	14	13	12	11
N3S	2-Sep	H	Basingstoke	W 32-19		Wigley/t	McDonald	Lewis	Mahoney	Osunsami/2t
N3S	9-Sep	H	Cheltenham	W 23-10	300	Wigley	Gibson	Lewis/t	Mahoney	Osunsami
N3S	16-Sep	A	Blackheath	W 26-8	200	Murphy	McDonald	Lewis	Mahoney/t	Osunsami/t
N3S	30-Sep	N	Clifton	L 12-29		Wigley	McDonald/t	Lewis/t	Mahoney	Osunsami
N3S	14-Oct	H	Launceston	W 20-18	250	Gibson/t	McDonald	Eaton/t	Mahoney	Osunsami
N3S	28-Oct	H	Penzance & Newlyn	D 17-17		Murphy	Osunsami	Lewis	Mahoney	McDonald
N3S	4-Nov	A	North Walsham	W 10-3	250	Murphy	Osunsami	Lewis	Mahoney	McDonald
N3S	11-Nov	A	Plymouth Albion	L 10-26	1000	Lewis	McDonald	Eaton	Mahoney	Osunsami
N3S	18-Nov	H	Reading	L 20-27	200	Murphy/t	McDonald	Lewis	Mahoney	Gibson
N3S	25-Nov	A	Redruth	L 12-20	600	Murphy	McDonald	Eaton	Mahoney	Lewis
N3S	2-Dec	H	Tabard	W 21-3		Lawry	McDonald/t	Lewis	Mahoney	Osunsami
N3S	9-Dec	A	Westcombe Park	W 31-8	300	Lawry	McDonald	Gilmore	Mahoney	Lewis/3t
N3S	16-Dec	H	Weston super Mare	W 40-10	300	Lewis	McDonald/t	Gilmore/c	Mahoney/t	Osunsami/t
N3S	23-Dec	A	Tabard	W 29-19		Lewis	McDonald/2t	Stannard	Mahoney	Osunsami
N3S	6-Jan	A	Reading	W 37-3		Lewis/2t	Gibson	Stannard/t	Mahoney	Osunsami
N3S	13-Jan	H	Plymouth Albion	L 36-37		Lawry	McDonald	Stannard/t	Mahoney/t	Lewis
N3S	20-Jan	A	Penzance & Newlyn	L 13-16	800	Lewis	McDonald	Stannard/t	Mahoney	Gibson
N3S	27-Jan	H	North Walsham	W 31-29		Lawry	McDonald	Stannard	Mahoney	Lewis/t
N3S	3-Feb	H	Redruth	W 34-18		Lewis/t	McDonald	Stannard/t	Mahoney	Gibson/t
N3S	10-Feb	A	Launceston	L 13-42	420	Lewis/t	McDonald	Stannard	Mahoney	Gibson
N3S	24-Feb	H	Clifton	W 50-18		Lewis/t	McDonald/t	Stannard/2t	Mahoney	Martin/t
N3S	10-Mar	A	Cheltenham	W 25-15	200	Lewis/t	McDonald	Stannard	Eaton	Martin/t
N3S	17-Mar	H	Blackheath	L 15-20		Lewis/t	McDonald	Stannard	Eaton	Martin/t
N3S	24-Mar	N	Basingstoke	L 8-27		Lewis/t	Gibson	Stannard	Mahoney	Martin
N3S	31-Mar	A	Weston super Mare	L 16-22	200	Green/t	McDonald	Lewis	Mahoney	Gregory
N3S	14-Apr	H	Westcombe Park	W 30-17		Green	McDonald	Lewis/t	Mahoney	Gregory
TBC	21-Oct	H	Rosslyn Park	L 17-29		Lewis	McDonald/t	Eaton	Mahoney	Gibson

** after opponents name indicates a penalty try. Brackets after a player's name indicates he was replaced.
eg (a) means he was replaced by replacement code "a" and so on. / after a player or replacement name
is followed by any scores he made - eg /t, /c, /p, /dg or any combination of these*

EVER PRESENT — Pete Mahoney

Most Appearances:

26	Pete Mahoney.
25	Fred Lewis, Andy Eaton
24	Paul Everitt, Droston McDonald
23	Justin Murphy, Scott Knowles.

PLAYERS USED

31 plus one as a replacement only

MOST POINTS

Pts	Player	T	C	P	DG
192	B Murphy	3	27	40	1
75	F Lewis	15	-	-	-
52	D Gilmore	3	11	5	-
30	G Stannard	6	-	-	-
30	D McDonald	6	-	-	-

MATCH FACTS

10	9	1	2	3	4	5	6	7	8
Murphy/2cp	Eaton	Blenkinsop	Murphy/2t	Walker	Stone	Bailey	Martin	Everitt	Bury
Murphy/c2p	Eaton/t	Ambrose/t	Murphy	Walker	Stone	Bailey	Everitt	Knowles	Bury
Gilmore/3c	Eaton	Rate	Murphy	Walker/t	Burrow	Bailey/t	Everitt	Martin	Bury
Gilmore/c	Eaton	Rate	Murphy	Walker	Burrow	Bailey	Everitt	Knowles	Bury
Gilmore/2c2p	Cutting	Walker	Murphy	Rate	Burrow	Bailey	Stock	Knowles	Everitt
Gilmore/t	Eaton/c	Walker	Murphy(a/t)	Blenkinsop	Burrow	Bailey	Everitt/t	Knowles	Bury
Gilmore/tcp	Eaton	Ambrose	Murphy	Walker	Burrow	Bailey	Everitt	Knowles	Bury
Gilmore/tcp	Cutting	Ambrose	Murphy	Blenkinsop	Burrow	Bailey	Everitt	Knowles	Bury
Gilmore/cp	Eaton	Walker	Ambrose(b/t)	Rate	Burrow	Bailey	Everitt	Knowles	Stone/t
Gilmore/c	Cutting	Walker	Murphy	Rate/t	Burrow	Bailey	Everitt	Knowles/t	Stone
Murphy/c3p	Eaton	Ambrose	Murphy	Walker	Stone	Bailey/t	Everitt	Knowles	Bury
Murphy/3c	Eaton/t	Blenkinsop	Murphy	Ambrose	Burrow	Stone	Everitt	Knowles	Bury/t
Murphy/2c3p	Eaton/t	Orwell	Murphy	Ambrose	Burrow	Stone/t	Everitt	Knowles	Bury
Murphy/t3cp	Eaton	Walker	Ambrose	Blenkinsop	Stone	Bailey	Everitt	Knowles/t	Bury
Murphy/c5p	Eaton	Walker/t	Murphy	Blenkinsop	Stone	Burrow	Everitt	Knowles	Bury
Murphy/2c4p	Cutting	Blenkinsop/t	Murphy/t	Walker	Stone	Burrow	Everitt	Knowles	Bury
Murphy/c2p	Eaton	Walker	Murphy	Blenkinsop	Stone	Burrow	Everitt	Knowles	Bury
Murphy/2c4p	Eaton	Walker	Murphy/t	Blenkinsop	Stone	Burrow	Martin	Knowles/t	Bury
Murphy/4c2p	Eaton	Walker	Murphy	Blenkinsop	Stone	Burrow	Martin	Knowles	Stannard/t
Murphy/c2p	Eaton	Ambrose	Murphy	Blenkinsop	Stone	Stannard	Everitt	Knowles	Bury
Murphy/t3c2pdg	Eaton	Blenkinsop	Murphy	Walker	Stone	Burrow	Everitt/t	Knowles	Stannard
Mahoney	Cutting/2c2p	Blenkinsop	Murphy	Walker	Stone	Burrow	Everitt/t	Knowles	Stannard
Mahoney	Cutting	Blenkinsop	Murphy	Walker	Twydell/t	Bailey	Everitt	Knowles	Stannard
Murphy/p	Eaton	Blenkinsop	Murphy	Rate	Twydell	Bailey	Everitt	Knowles	Stannard
Murphy/2p	Eaton	Blenkinsop	Ambrose	Walker	Stone	Bailey/t	Everitt	Knowles	Stannard
Murphy/c6p	Eaton	Ambrose	Murphy	Walker/t	Stone	Twydell	Everitt	Martin	Stannard
Gilmore	Cutting/tc	Walker	Murphy	Ambrose	Burrow	Bailey	Everitt	Knowles	Bury/t

REPLACEMENTS   a - F Ambrose   b - J Murphy

2000-01 HIGHLIGHTS

Billy Murphy topped the points scorers list for the first time. He scored 172 points as he took over the kicking duties.

Fred Lewis set a new Barking record of 15 tries in a National League season. In 1996-97 C Tate and N Thomson both scored 14 tries as Barking finished third in the league.

Lewis also scored Barking's only hat trick of tries during the season - he did so in the away win at Westcombe Park in early December.

Centre/outside half Pete Mahoney was an ever present and played every minute of all the 26 league games.

BARKING

LEAGUE STATISTICS *compiled by Stephen McCormack*

SEASON	Division	P	W	D	L	F	A	Pts Diff	Lge Pts	Lge Pos		Coach		Captain
91-92	Lon 2N	10	7	1	2	187	140	47	15	2p		M Lovett		T Reader
92-93	Lon 1	12	6	1	5	183	171	12	13	7				
93-94	Lon 1	12	10	1	1	290	149	141	21	1p				
94-95	D5S	12	7	0	5	223	190	33	14	5		M Lovett		D Cutting
												Most Points		**Most Tries**
95-96	D5S	12	8	0	4	243	187	56	16	4	51	Lee Evans	6	P Green, C Tate, D Cutting
96-97	D4S	26	16	1	9	740	496	244	33	3	248	Nick Thompson	14	Chris Tate, N Thomson
97-98	N2S	26	19	0	7	762	450	312	38	3	69	Andy Tunningley	12	J Murphy, P Goodey
98-99	N2S	26	19	1	6	644	327	317	39	4	217	Justin Azzopardi	11	Scott Gregory
99-00	N2S	26	15	0	11	628	523	105	23	6	88	Justin Azzopardi	13	Scott Gregory
00-01	N3S	26	15	1	10	611	481	130	31	4	192	Billy Murphy	15	Fred Lewis

FACT FILE

Founded: 1930   **Colours**: Cardinal and grey   **Change colours**: Blue

GROUND

Address: Goresbrook, Gale St., Dagenham, Essex RM9 4TY

Tel: 0208 595 7324   **Website**: www.barkingrugby.com

Capacity: 2,000 - all uncovered standing

Directions: From Dartford Tunnel, follow A13 (London bound). Past the Ford works, continue for 2 miles to 2nd r'about (beneath a flyover). 4th exit and return back on A13 in opposite direction. The ground is half a mile on the left hand side.

From M11 - At end of M11 take A406 EAST bound towards the A13. Onto A13, signposted Dartford Tunnel, and ground is 4 miles on the left.

Nearest Railway Station: Becontree (District Line - Upminster direction).

Turn right on leaving the station into Gale Street. The ground is 1 mile on the left.

Car Parking: 200 spaces available at ground

Admission: Season Tickets (members only) £30.   Matchday (incl. programme): Members £3 Non-members: £5.00

Club Shop: Manager Adrian Peters 020 8550 0541

Clubhouse: Normal Licensing hours, snacks available.   Functions: Capacity 120.

Training Nights: Tuesdays & Thursday (seniors). Juniors: Monday & Wednesday

PROGRAMME   Size: A5   Price: With admission   Pages: 22 plus cover   Editor: Martin Dutt - Press Officer

Advertising Rates
Colour only
Full Page £250
Half Page £150

Scrum Half Andy Eaton crashed over for a try against Launceston.

Photo: Kevin Webb

The **Club**

BLACKHEATH RFC

President	Sir Hal Miller	Moorcroft Farm, Sinton Green, Worcester WR2 6NW
		01322 555906
Chairman		
Club Secretary	Barry Shaw	86 Crown Woods Way, Eltham, London. SE9 2NN.
		0208 850 7976 (H), 0208 850 7421 (Fax)
Fixtures Secretary	Jim Collett	8 Vanbrugh Fields, Blackheath, London. SE3 7TZ.
		0208 858 7571 (H), 0208 539 3348 (B)
Rugby Manager	Pat McCarthy	7 Beech Hill Road, London SE9 e-mail: plmccarthy@hotmail.com
General Manager	Albert Patrick	c/o Blackheath RFC. 0208 304 5161 (H) 07957 110528 (M)
Press Liaison	Jack Kay	c/o Blackheath RFC. 0208 858 8284 (H) 07971 580889 (M)
Head Coach	Chris Kibble	c/o Blackheath RFC. 0208 657 6212 (H) 07801 107562 (M)

"A game of two halves" is the oldest cliche in sport, but in Blackheath's case that was the exact story of their season. The first half of the campaign kicked off with a convincing 34-9 defeat of Weston-super-Mare followed by a good friendly win away to Nuneaton by 41-22 and spirits were high. The following eleven League games, however, read like the script of a horror movie. Defeat followed defeat despite the fact that Blackheath were always in the game and, in fact, led at half time in seven of the matches, the main exception being Plymouth who were always in control winning 41-0 at their place. Confidence or lack of it seemed to be the root of the problem plus several long-term injuries, notably to Ivan McKenzie, Mark Percival, Dave Morris and Alan Sharkey.

Come the New Year, and with plenty of morale boosting from coach Chris Kibble, a new tale unfolded. A good 27-10 victory over Cheltenham lit the blue touch paper and was followed by victories over Basingstoke and Westcombe Park, there was a hiccup against Redruth going down 23-35, but then came the match of the season at home to Penzance.

The powerful West Country outfit ran the club ragged in the first half leading 5-29 at the break and the writing seemed to be on the wall, but incredibly the home team fought back and in a heart stopping finale took the game 38-37. Everyone was now on a high and victories followed away to Barking and Reading. The club was now safe and the relaxed frame of mind showed when they went on to win the Middlesex Sevens at The Stoop beating Bracknell in the final 35-24 to climax a roller coaster of a season.

Jack Kay

Back Row: Jim Roques, Joe Bonner, Mark Hathaway, Mark Colgate, Chris Longman, Mark Percival.
Middle Row: Mike Williams, Don Shaw, Andy Wolstenholme, Albert Patrick (General Manager), Paul Goodey, Alan Knuckey, Chris Kibble (Head Coach), Chris Gianotti, Dave Glendinning, Tay Jackson, Chris Barber (Physio), Phil Ubee, Keith Green, Pat McCarthy (Rugby Manager).
Front: Jon Griffin, Rhys Powell, Mitch Hoare, Toby Booth (Capt.), Dave Fitzgerald, Charlie Abban, Tom Hadley.

BLACKHEATH

Comp.	Date	H/A	Opponents	Result & Score	Att	15	14	13	12	11
N3S	2-Sep	H	Weston super Mare	W 34-9	300	Hadley/t	Abban	Fitzgerald	Mullen	Sharkey
N3S	16-Sep	H	Barking	L 8-26	200	Hadley/p	Trace	Hoare	Fitzgerald/t	Abban
N3S	23-Sep	N	Clifton	L 18-38		Hadley	Abban/t	Fitzgerald/t	Mullen	Trace
N3S	30-Sep	H	North Walsham	L 14-29	250	Hadley	Trace	Fitzgerald/t	Mullen	Abban
N3S	14-Oct	A	Plymouth Albion	L 0-41	700	Hadley	Abban	Fitzgerald	Mullen	Razak
N3S	28-Oct	A	Westcombe Park*	L 22-30	400	Hadley	Hoare/2cp	Fitzgerald	Mullen	Sharkey
N3S	4-Nov	H	Redruth	L 22-48	180	Hadley	Sharkey	Fitzgerald/t	Mullen	Griffiths
N3S	11-Nov	H	Basingstoke	L 8-16		Hadley	Trace	Fitzgerald	Griffiths	Rea
N3S	18-Nov	A	Cheltenham	L 20-32	200	Hadley/t	Sharkey	Trace	Fitzgerald/t	Abban
N3S	25-Nov	H	Launceston	L 20-25	250	Hadley	Wharton	Trace	Fitzgerald	Abban/2t
N3S	2-Dec	A	Penzance & Newlyn	L 14-51	800	Hadley	Sharkey/t	Trace	Fitzgerald	Abban
N3S	16-Dec	A	Tabard*	L 22-40	200	Hadley	Sharkey	Trace	Fitzgerald/t	Abban
N3S	6-Jan	H	Cheltenham	W 27-10		Hadley	Abban/t	Fitzgerald	Hoare/tc	Griffiths
N3S	13-Jan	A	Basingstoke	W 43-12		Hadley	Sharkey/t	Hoare/5cp	Fitzgerald/2t	Abban/2t
N3S	20-Jan	H	Westcombe Park	W 25-14	600	Hadley	Trace/t	Hoare/p	Fitzgerald/t	Abban/2t
N3S	27-Jan	A	Redruth	L 23-35	400	Hadley	Abban	Fitzgerald	Hoare	Price
N3S	3-Feb	H	Penzance & Newlyn	W 38-37	400	Hadley	Trace/t	Hoare	Dutton/t	Abban/t
N3S	10-Feb	H	Plymouth Albion	L 13-19		Hadley	Trace	Hoare	Dutton	Abban
N3S	17-Feb	H	Reading	W 19-15		Hadley/t	Trace	Hoare	Fitzgerald	Abban
N3S	24-Feb	A	North Walsham	L 6-15	250	Hadley	Abban	Fitzgerald	Trace	Price
N3S	10-Mar	A	Clifton	W 40-0	140	Hadley/t	Trace/t	Griffiths	Mullen	Abban/t
N3S	17-Mar	A	Barking	W 20-15		Hadley	Abban/t	Fitzgerald	Goodey	Trace
N3S	31-Mar	H	Tabard	W 39-5		Hadley	Trace	Griffiths/t	Fitzgerald	Abban
N3S	7-Apr	A	Launceston	L 13-35	400	Hadley	Abban	Fitzgerald	Mullen	Powell
N3S	14-Apr	A	Reading	W 32-16		Hadley	Abban/2t	Fitzgerald/t	Trace/t	Griffiths/t
N3S	21-Apr	A	Weston super Mare	L 15-28		Hadley	Abban	Fitzgerald	Hoare/t	Trace
TBC	7-Oct	H	Swanagae	W 9-0		Hadley	Razak	Fitzgerald	Mullen	Abban
TBC	21-Oct	A	London Welsh	L 3-44	500	Hadley/p	Trace	Fitzgerald	Mullen	Sharkey

*after opponents name indicates a penalty try. Brackets after a player's name indicates he was replaced.
eg (a) means he was replaced by replacement code "a" and so on. / after a player or replacement name
is followed by any scores he made - eg /t, /c, /p, /dg or any combination of these

EVER PRESENT   Tom Hadley

Most Appearances:

26	Tom Hadley.
25	Dave Glendinning
23	Charles Abban, Dave Fitzgerald, Mitch Hoare, Darryl Vas.

PLAYERS USED

41 plus three as replacement only.

MOST POINTS

Pts	Player	T	C	P	DG
130	J Griffin	4	16	24	2
102	M Hoare	4	20	13	1
65	C Abban	13	=	=	=
50	D Fitzgerald	10	-	-	-
23	T Hadley	4	-	-	1

MATCH FACTS

10	9	1	2	3	4	5	6	7	8
Hoare/t4c2p	Percival/t	Vas	Elkinson	Roques	Ticehurst	Caughley	Booth	Goodey	Gleninning/t
Percival	Powell	Smith	McKenzie	Roques	Paul	Caughley	Booth	Goodey	Gleninning
Hoare/c2p	Powell	Smith	McKenzie	Roques	Temperley	Gleninning	Booth	Goodey	Walton
Hoare/3p	Powell	Bonner	McKenzie	Roques	Temperley	Paul	Walton	Goodey	Gleninning
Hoare	Powell	Vas	Morris	Roques	Temperley	Ruskin	Walton	Goodey	Gleninning
Price	Powell	Vas	Morris	Roques/t	Temperley	Ruskin	Booth	Goodey/t	Walton
Hoare/t2cp	Powell	Vas	Morris	Roques	Ticehurst	Ruskin/t	Booth	Goodey	Gleninning
Hoare/p	Powell	Vas	Morris	Roques	Temperley	Walton/t	Booth	Goodey	Gleninning
Hoare/cp	Powell	Bonner	Morris	Vas	Longman	Roques	Booth/t	Carroll	Gleninning
Hoare	Powell/t	Vas	Morris	Roques	Ruskin	Milnes	Walton/t	Booth	Gleninning
Hoare/2c	Powell	Vas	Morris	Bonner	Roques	Ruskin/t	Clarke	Wharton	Gleninning
Hoare/2cdg	Powell	Vas	Morris	Roques	Temperley	Ruskin	Walton	Booth/t	Gleninning
Griffin/t	Powell	Vas	Morris	Roques	Temperley/t	Ruskin/t	Walton	Booth	Gleninning
Griffin	Powell/t	Vas	Morris	Roques	Ruskin	Milnes	Temperley	Booth	Gleninning
Griffin/c	Percival	Penney	Morris	Vas	Colgate	Milnes	Temperley	Booth	Gleninning
Griffin/t2c3p	Percival	Vas	Morris	Penney	Longman	Colgate	Booth	Gianotti/t	Gleninning
Griffin/t2c3p	Percival	Penney/t	Morris	Vas	Colgate	Longman	Temperley	Gianotti	Gleninning
Griffin/c2p	Percival/t	Penney	Lane	Vas	Temperley	Colgate	Walton	Gianotti	Gleninning
Griffin/3p	Percival	Vas	Bonner	Roques	Milnes	Colgate	Temperley	Gianotti/t	Gleninning
Griffin/2p	Powell	Vas	Morris	Hathaway	Temperley	Milnes	Walton	Gianotti	Gleninning
Griffin/t3c2pdg	Percival/t	Hathaway	Lane	Penney	Temperley	Colgate	Walton	Booth	Gleninning
Griffin/4pdg	Percival	Penney	Bonner	Hathaway	Temperley	Colgate	Walton	Booth	Gleninning
Griffin/4c2p	Percival	Hathaway	Bonner/t	Roques	Colgate	Milnes	Booth/t	Goodey/t	Gleninning/t
Griffin/p	Percival/t	Vas	Bonner	Roques	Colgate	Milnes	Booth/t	Goodey	Gleninning
Griffin/2cp	Percival	Vas	Bonner	Hathaway	Colgate	Milnes	Booth	Goodey	Gleninning
Griffin/cp	Powell	Vas	Bonner	Hathaway	Longman	Colgate/t	Booth	Goodey	Gleninning
Hoare/3p	Powell	Vas	Morris	Roques	Ticehurst	Walton	Longman	Goodey	Gleninning
Price	Powell	Vas	Carroll	Lane	Temperley	Ruskin	Colgate	Goodey	Gleninning

2000-01 HIGHLIGHTS

After an opening day win against Weston, Blackheath then lost their next 11 league matches and looked doomed to relegation yet again.

However they managed to turn their season round and won eight of their next 11 matches to move up the table and out of the relegation zone.

Winger Charlie Abban did do well and notched up 13 tries to equal the club record for a league campaign.

Jonathan Griffin topped the points scoring with 130 points in just 14 matches after joining the club in the new year.

Nick Temperley receives his Man of the Match Award v North Walsham from Mick Skinner.
Nick was also voted forward of the year.

BLACKHEATH

LEAGUE STATISTICS *compiled by Stephen McCormack*

SEASON	Division	P	W	D	L	F	A	Pts Diff	Lge Pts	Lge Pos	Most Points		Most Tries	
91-92	2	12	4	0	8	140	266	-126	8	11	61	Neil Munn	2	Andy Mercer
92-93	2	12	4	2	6	142	231	-89	10	10r	97	Grant Eagle	5	Joe McIntyre
93-94	3	18	11	0	7	305	222	83	22	4	78	Stuart Burns	9	Mike Friday
94-95	3	18	12	2	4	299	190	109	26	2p	147	Sam Howard	5	Matt Griffiths
95-96	2	18	6	1	11	341	469	-128	13	7	153	Sam Howard	5	Mike Hanslip
96-97	2	22	7	0	15	412	641	-229	14	10	137	Chris Braithwaite	8	Mike Hanslip
97-98	P2	22	8	0	14	474	621	-147	16	9	84	Chris Braithwaite	13	John Clarke
98-99	P2	26	5	0	21	419	842	-423	10	13r	102	Campbell Aitken	12	John Clarke
99-00	N1	26	2	1	23	316	1037	-721	5	14r	48	Mitch Hoare	5	Nick Daniel
00-01	N3S	26	10	0	16	562	641	-79	20	9	130	Jon Griffin	13	Charles Abban

FACT FILE

Founded: 1858
Nickname: The Club

Colours: Red & black hoops, blue trim/black.
Change colours: Blue with red & black hoops/black.

GROUND

Address: The Rectory Field, Charlton Road, Blackheath. SE3 8SR.
Tel: 0208 293 0853 (office)   0208 858 1578 (clubhouse)   Fax: 0181 293 0854
Web site: www.blackheath-rugby.co.uk e-mail: blackheathrugby@LineOne.net
Capacity: 6,000   Seated: 572   Standing: 5,428

Directions: The entrance to the Rectory Field is approx 800 yards from the start of Charlton Road B210 at its junction with Stratheden Road/Westcombe Hill which is a turning off Shooters Hill Road A2. Nearest Railway Station: Blackheath (BR) or Westcombe Park (BR)

Car Parking: 250 spaces available on ground £3.
Off-street parking - 2 hours only, free

Admission:
Season   Adults £75   U17 Free   Matchday   £5

Club Shop: Yes. Manageress Mandy Allen 0208 293 5980

Clubhouse: Normal Licensing hours, light refreshments,
food from burger bar..
Available for private function hire 300 max. small bar 100

Training Nights: Tuesday & Thursday 7.30-9

PROGRAMME

Size: A5 Pages: 36 + cover   Price: £1
Editor Peter Brown, Mandy Allen & Debbie Ubee

ADVERTISING RATES (+VAT)
Colour   Full page £300, Half page £175

Blackheath Rugby Club
playing rugby since 1858
www.blackheathrugby.co.uk

OFFICIAL PROGRAMME

Blackheath v Westcombe Park
Saturday 20 January 2001
at 3.00pm

Blackheath Football Club
• Charlton Road • Blackheath • SE3 8SR

SEASON 2000 - 2001

CAMBERLEY RFC

President	Nick Carbury	9 Highgate Lane, Farnborough, Hants. GU14 8AF
		01252 548261 (H)
Chairman	Roger Chamberlain	'Harington', Kettlewell Hill, Horsell, Woking, Surrey GU21 4JJ
		01483 723832 (H)
Secretary	Alan Forfar	15 Old Rectory Gardens, Farnborough, Hampshire GU14 7BS
		01252 653715 (H)
Director of Finance	Neil Doody	The Forge, The Village, Finchampstead, Berks. RG40 4JN
		0118 973 4236 (H) 0118 973 0910 (F)
Fixtures Secretary	Bill Fletcher	01344 777701 (H)
Head Coach	Ian Pickup	99 Broadhurst, Ashstead, Surrey KT21 1QF
		01372 273141 (H) 07803 924419 (M)

After narrowly avoiding relegation in season 1999-2000, there was some expectation that, under new coach Ian Pickup, the club would fare better in National League Two this season. This scenario was endorsed following the first two league games of the season, which resulted in a narrow loss at Bracknell, and a good away win at Fylde. However, there then started a chapter of incidents from which the club never really recovered.

The first home game of the season, against Wharfedale, was lost to the fuel crisis and, after losses at Newbury and at home against Preston, due to severe flooding of our council controlled pitches, we were able to play just two games on our own pitch until mid March. "Home" games had to be played on local Army pitches and at Farnborough RFC, but the disruption and lack of continuity took a severe toll on the fortunes of the club. Successive wins in mid February at Preston and against Nottingham and Newbury led to some hope for survival, but the last six matches (many re-arranged) turned out to be against high flying clubs and we were not able to glean sufficient points to move away from the third from bottom position. Thus the club has become one of the first victims of the dreaded Regulation 9A and we have been relegated. Three losses against near neighbours Esher (one in the Tetley Bitter Cup) were perhaps crucial and the club was left to reflect upon the five or six games that were lost by a single score during the season.

Many encouraging things happened within the club during the season, with Ian Pickup quickly earning the respect of players and members alike, and, with several colts making fist XV debuts during the campaign, the club is well on its way to returning to the family club it has been in the past. No fewer than 51 players represented the first XV during the season and no less than seven place kickers were employed. The inability to field a settled side through injury, non-availability and suspensions was a major factor in the outcome of the season.

Despite all the difficulties experienced this season, one event placed everything into context. This was the sad and sudden death of chairman Peter Stevens in early February. All who have visited Camberley in the past few years will remember this amiable, white bearded character and will reflect with us the loss that the game of Rugby has suffered.

Camberley Action - LEFT: Angus Moncur against Newbury RIGHT: David Hughes against Rosslyn Park   Photos: Lee Crabb

CAMBERLEY

Comp.	Date	H/A	Opponents	Result & Score	Att.	15	14	13	12	11
N2	2-Sep	A	Bracknell	L 15-18		Allen	Cole/t	Kane	Davies	Moncur/t
N2	9-Sep	A	Fylde*	W 24-16	400	Gaynor	Allen	Kane	Davies	Moncur
N2	23-Sep	A	Newbury	L 13-34	300	Allen	Cole	Kane/t	Stafford/c2p	Moncur
N2	30-Sep	H	Preston Grasshoppers	L 8-33	200	Allen	Green	Kane	Stafford/p	Moncur
N2	14-Oct	H	Kendal	L 13-15	250	Allen	Green	Kane/t	Stafford/2p	Moncur
N2	28-Oct	H	Harrogate	W 16-15	150	Allen	Harbour	Kane	Lewis	Green
N2	11-Nov	A	Lydney	L 16-18	200	Allen	Harbour(a/t)	Kane/t	Lewis	Green
N2	25-Nov	A	Rosslyn Park	L 10-23	200	Kane	Allen/t	Lewis/cp	Davies	Green
N2	2-Dec	A	Rugby Lions	L 13-80	200	Kane	Allen	Lewis/c2p	Davies	Scott/t
N2	9-Dec	H	West Hartlepool	W 22-11	100	Kane	Allen	Lewis/2cp	Davies/2t	Green
N2	16-Dec	A	Nottingham	L 12-33	300	Kane	Allen	Lewis/tc	Davies	Green
N2	23-Dec	H	Lydney	W 32-3	200	Kane	Allen/t	Lewis/3c2p	Davies/t	Green
N2	6-Jan	A	Harrogate	L 5-49	400	Allen	Moncur/t	Davies	Kane	Harbour
N2	13-Jan	H	Esher	L 22-33	150	Allen/t	Green	Kane/2cp	Davies	Moncur
N2	3-Feb	H	Wharfedale*	L 24-30		Webb/2c	Allen	Dunckley	Saunders	Stewart/t
N2	10-Feb	A	Preston Grasshoppers	W 21-15	220	Webb/c3p	Stewart	Davies	Kane	Allen/t
N2	17-Feb	H	Nottingham	W 24-15		Webb/c2p	Green	Kane	Dunckley	Allen/t
N2	24-Feb	H	Newbury	W 23-16	200	Kane/t	Allen	Dunckley	Davies	Green
N2	3-Mar	A	Esher	L 10-27	250	Kane	Green/t	Davies	Lewis	Allen
N2	17-Mar	H	Fylde	L 24-28		Allen	Green/t	Dunckley	Davies	Stewart
N2	24-Mar	H	Bracknell	L 15-39		Webb	Green/t	Dunckley	Davies	Allen
N2	31-Mar	A	West Hartlepool	W 21-17		Webb/t3c	Green/t	Gaynor	Davies	Allen/t
N2	7-Apr	A	Kendal	L 5-24		Allen	Gaynor	Davies	Saunders	Stewart
N2	14-Apr	H	Rosslyn Park	L 10-23		Kane/t	Allen	Saunders	Davies	Gaynor
N2	21-Apr	H	Rugby Lions	L 12-69		Webb/c	Green	Kane	Stanton	Allen/t
N2	28-Apr	A	Wharfedale	L 16-49		Chapman	Stewart	Kane/p	Davies	Allen
TBC	7-Oct	H	Barnstaple	W 28-0	200	Allen	Smart/c2p	Fleming/t	Kane/p	Moncur/t
TBC	21-Oct	A	Esher*	L 24-38	350	Gaynor	Green	Fleming	Kane	Moncur

*after opponents name indicates a penalty try. Brackets after a player's name indicates he was replaced.
eg (a) means he was replaced by replacement code "a" and so on. / after a player or replacement name
is followed by any scores he made - eg /t, /c, /p, /dg or any combination of these

---

EVER PRESENT Ali Allen

Most Appearances:
26 .Ali Allen
24 Warren Milne, Mike Blackburn.
22 Phil Joyce.

PLAYERS USED

37 plus six as replacement only.

MOST POINTS

Pts	Player	T	C	P	DG
64	Howard Graham	4	7	7	3
42	Rob Smart	1	5	9	-
39	Scott Lewis	1	8	6	-
36	Steve Webb	1	8	5	-
35	Brad Kane	5	2	2	-
35	Ali Allen	7	-	-	-

MATCH FACTS

10	9	1	2	3	4	5	6	7	8
Smart/cp	Hughes	Davies	Cribb	Joyce	Canham	Blackburn	Milne	Kindon	Pickup
Smart/c4p	Hughes	Davies	Cribb	Joyce	Canham/t	Blackburn	Milne	Kindon	Pickup
Smart	Hughes	Waters	Cribb	Davies	Hayman	Blackburn	Milne	Kindon	Pickup
Lewis	Hughes	Blandin	Davies	Waters	Canham	Hayman	Milne	Kindon/t	Blackburn
Graham/c	Coulson	Waters	Cribb	Joyce	Canham	Blackburn	Claric	Kindon	Milne
Graham/c3p	Coulson	Waters	Jennings	Joyce	Pickup/t	Blackburn	Kindon	Clarke	Milne
Graham/2p	Coulson	Manthorpe	Jennings	Joyce	Pickup	Blackburn	Kindon	Clarke	Milne
Smart	Coulson	Waters	Gotting	Joyce	Blackburn	Canham	Milne	Claric	Hayman
Smart	Coulson	Waters	Jennings	Joyce	Canham	Blackburn	Kindon	Milne	Hughes
Graham	Coulson	Wllmot	Jennings	Waters	Milne	Blackburn	Scott/t	Clarke	Smith
Graham	Coulson/t	Wllmot	Gotting	Joyce	Blackburn	Soper	Scott	Clarke	Milne
Graham/t	Coulson	Wllmot	Gotting/t	Joyce	Pickup	Soper	Blackburn	Clarke	Hughes
Smart	Hughes	Wllmot	Gotting	Manthorpe	Blackburn	Pickup	Milne	Scott	Templeman
Graham/t	Hughes/t	Wllmot	Gotting	Joyce	Pickup	Blackburn	Scott	Clarke	Hughes
Graham/cdg	Hughes	Wllmot	Gotting	Joyce	Blackburn	Hayman	Milne/t	Hughes	Pickup
Graham	Smart	Wllmot	Gotting	Joyce	Pickup	Blackburn/t	Milne	Clarke	Stacey
Graham/2dg	Smart/t	Wllmot	Gotting	Joyce	Hayman	Blackburn	Milne	Clarke	Pickup
Graham	Smart/c2p	Wllmot	Gotting	Joyce	Pickup	Milne	Fleming(b/t)	Clark	Hughes/t
Graham	Smart/cp	Wllmot	Gotting	Joyce	Hayman	Pickup	Milne	Clarke	Hughes
Graham/t3cp	Coulson	Wllmot	Cribb	Joyce	Soper	Hayman	Milne	Blackburn	Pickup/t
Graham/cp	Hughes	Wllmot	Cribb	Joyce	Soper	Blackburn	Milne(c/t)	Clarke	Pickup
Graham	Baker	Wllmot	Cribb	Joyce	Hayman	Blackburn	Milne	Clarke	Pickup
Graham/t	Coulson	Wllmot	Cribb	Joyce	Hayman	Blackburn	Milne	Kindon	Pickup
Smart/cp	Hughes	Wllmot	Gotting	Joyce	Hayman	Blackburn	Milne	Kindon	Pickup
Gaynor/t	Baker	Wllmot	Gotting	Joyce	Milne	Blackburn	Kindon	Templeman	Pickup
Saunders/p	Baker	Wllmot	Gotting	Joyce	Hayman	Blackburn/t	Milne	Fleming/t	Cribb
Lewis/tc	Hughes	Waters	Davies	Joyce	Canham	Hayman	Blackburn	Kindon	Milne
Graham/t3cp	Coulson/t	Waters	Cribb	Joyce	Canham	Blackburn	Clarke	Kindon	Pickup

REPLACEMENTS a - D Scott   b - J Kindon   c - Fleming

2000-01 HIGHLIGHTS

They did manage three successive wins in February for the only time in two seasons.

They suffered their worst ever home defeat in terms of both most points against and biggest margin when losing 69-12 to Rugby Lions in April.

Their worst losing streak was four at the end of the season.

Ever present Ali Allen topped the try scorers with seven, two more than the next best achieved by Brad Kane.

Ben Stafford managed just three appearances but did extend his appearance record for for league matches 67.

CAMBERLEY

LEAGUE STATISTICS compiled by Stephen McCormack

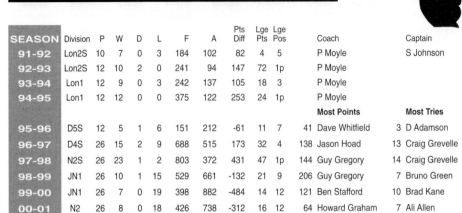

SEASON	Division	P	W	D	L	F	A	Pts Diff	Lge Pts	Lge Pos		Coach		Captain
91-92	Lon2S	10	7	0	3	184	102	82	4	5		P Moyle		S Johnson
92-93	Lon2S	12	10	2	0	241	94	147	72	1p		P Moyle		
93-94	Lon1	12	9	0	3	242	137	105	18	3		P Moyle		
94-95	Lon1	12	12	0	0	375	122	253	24	1p		P Moyle		
												Most Points		**Most Tries**
95-96	D5S	12	5	1	6	151	212	-61	11	7	41	Dave Whitfield	3	D Adamson
96-97	D4S	26	15	2	9	688	515	173	32	4	138	Jason Hoad	13	Craig Grevelle
97-98	N2S	26	23	1	2	803	372	431	47	1p	144	Guy Gregory	14	Craig Grevelle
98-99	JN1	26	10	1	15	529	661	-132	21	9	206	Guy Gregory	7	Bruno Green
99-00	JN1	26	7	0	19	398	882	-484	14	12	121	Ben Stafford	10	Brad Kane
00-01	N2	26	8	0	18	426	738	-312	16	12	64	Howard Graham	7	Ali Allen

FACT FILE

Founded: 1931

Colours: Black with amber collar.
Change colours: Yellow with black collar.

GROUND

Address: Watchetts Recreation Ground, Park Rd, Camberley, Surrey GU15 2SR
Tel: 01276 25395   Fax: 01276 25211
Capacity: 1,000   Seated: None   Standing: 1000 (uncovered)

Directions: M3 Jnc 4, follow signs for Frimley/Guildford. At 1st roundabout turn left, signed Camberley, one & a half miles to mini roundabout turn right into Park Rd.
Nearest Railway Station: Camberley

Car Parking: 500 nearby

Admission: Matchday £5 with programme

Club Shop: Open matchdays 12 noon - 5pm.
Contact Alex Boyden 01276 26200

Clubhouse: Mon - Fri 6-11, Sat. 11-11, Sun. 11-7.
Snacks available.
Functions   up to 90. Contact Lydia Rise 01276 25395.

Training Nights: Tuesday & Thursday

PROGRAMME   Size: A5   Pages: 24 + cover
Price: Included with admission
Editor: Alan Forfar 01252 653715

ADVERTISING RATES   Colour
Page   £500
1/2 Page   £300
1/4 Page   £150

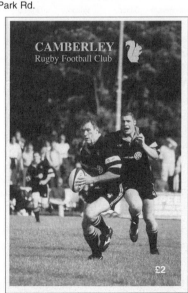

CINDERFORD RFC

President	Dave Field
Chairman	Rob Worgan
Treasurer	Barry Holmes
Club Administrator	Dennis Hargreaves Tel/Fax: 01594 825503
Director of Rugby	Dennis Hargreaves
Press Officer	Nigel Wilce 25, The Oakfield, Cinderford, Glos. GL14 2DA 01594 824017

```
c/o Cinderford RFC
Dockham Road
Cinderford
Glos. GL14 2AQ
Tel: 01594 822673  Fax: 01594 822400
```

A 24pts-10 play-off victory over Havant secured promotion after one of the longest and most successful seasons in Cinderford's history.

Despite problems caused by the foot & mouth outbreak the club managed to fulfil all but one of its league fixtures losing only once in SW1 - away to eventual champions Old Patesians who took the title on 'points difference'.

Old Pats also put us out of the Intermediate Cup but Cinderford gained sweet revenge by beating our old rivals by 14pts-13 in a thrilling Gloucestershire County Cup final. Outside-half Matt Sherratt dropped the winning goal after our opponents had taken the lead in the sixth minute of injury time.

Sherratt was the clubs leading points scorer with 271 in league and cup competitions while full back Mike Hart led the try list with sixteen. Hart, who joined from Western Counties (N) side Coney Hill during the close season, was a revelation. He proved to be both solid in defence and devastating in attack and was voted club 'Player of the Year' by his peers.

Cinderford,who were promoted from SW2(W) at the end of 98/99 stayed ahead of the game to achieve their goal of national league rugby one year earlier than anticipated in their three year plan.

While always trying to play fluid fifteen man rugby the side nevertheless played less expansively than in previous seasons. However their defensive record was an enviable one.

Cinderford, a blend of 'youth and experience' were well marshalled from the centre by former Gloucestershire captain Duncan Edwards. Director of Rugby Dennis Hargreaves was ably assisted by 'backs' coach Darryl Richards and former Gloucester favourite Bob (Dino) Phillips who has turned the forwards into a finely tuned unit.

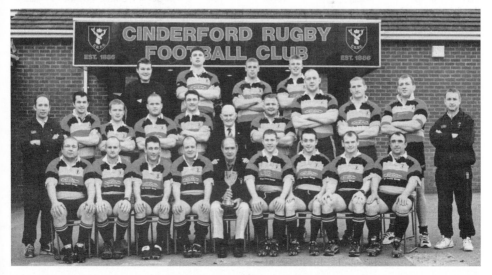

CINDERFORD

Comp.	Date	H/A	Opponents	Result & Score	15	14	13	12	11
SW1	02-Sep	A	Glos. O. B.	W 27-12	Hart	Verry	Edwards	Jewitt	Morris
SW1	23-Sep	A	Keynsham	W 39-20	Hart	Bedney	Edwards	Jewitt	Morris
SW1	30-Sep	H	Truro	W 24-06	Hart	Verry	Morgan	Jewitt	Bedney
Int Cup	07-Oct	A	Coney Hill	W 13-03	Hart	Verry	Edwards	Jewitt	Morris
SW1	14-Oct	A	Berry Hill	W 35-14	Hart	Verry	Bedney	Morgan	Morris
SW1	21-Oct	H	Dorchester	W 29-15	Hart	Verry	Bedney	Morgan	Morris
SW1	28-Oct	A	Bridgwater	W 43-03	Hart	Verry	Morgan	Jewitt	Morris
Int. Cup	04-Nov	A	Swindon	W 41-06	Hart	Verry	Morgan	Jewitt	Morris
SW1	11-Nov	H	Swanage	W 24-07	Hart	Verry	Edwards	Jewitt	Morris
SW1	25-Nov	A	Torquay	W 22-05	Hart	Morgan	Edwards	Bedney	Morris
Int Cup	02-Dec	A	Matson	W 33-08	Hart	Verry	Edwards	Jewitt	Morris
Co. Cup	03-Dec	H	Hucclecote	W 86-0	Hart	Verry	Morgan	Jewitt	Bedney
SW1	09-Dec	H	Old Patesians	W 15-10	Hart	Bedney	Edwards	Jewitt	Morris
SW1	16-Dec	H	Barnstaple	W 29-11	Hart	Verry	Edwards	Morgan	Bedney
SW1	23-Dec	H	Maidenhead	W 15-03	Jewitt	Verry	Edwards	Bedney	Morris
Int Cup	06-Jan	H	Chippenham	W 23-09	Hart	Verry	Morgan	Jewitt	Morris
SW1	13-Jan	H	Bridgwater	W 34-10	Hart	Verry	Edwards	Jewitt	Morris
Co. Cup	14-Jan	A	Glos. O. B.	W 30-05	Hart	Verry	Morgan	Jewitt	Bedney
SW1	20-Jan	A	Dorchester	W 28-10	Hart	Bedney	Edwards	Jewitt	Morgan
Int Cup	27-Jan	A	Old Patesians	L 06-16	Hart	Verry	Edwards	Jewitt	Morgan
SW1	17-Feb	A	Swanage	W 15-06	Hart	Bedney	Edwards	Jewitt	Morgan
Co. Cup	18-Feb	A	Matson	W 20-05	Hart	Bedney	Edwards	Jewitt	Morgan
SW1	24-Feb	H	Keynsham	W 28-16	Hart	Bedney	Edwards	Jewitt	Morgan
Co. Cup	05-Mar	A	Old Patesians	W 14-13	Hart	Bedney	Edwards	Jewitt	Morris
SW1	10-Mar	A	Maidenhead	W 34-14	Hart	Bedney	Edwards	Morris	Morgan
SW1	31-Mar	A	Old Patesians	L 10-16	Hart	Morgan	Edwards	Jewitt	Morris
SW1	07-Apr	H	Torquay	W 67-07	Hart	Morgan	Edwards	Jewitt	Morris
SW1	14-Apr	H	Berry Hill	W 17-12	Hart	Morgan	Edwards	Jewitt	Morris
SW1	28-Apr	A	Truro	W 25-17	Hart	Bedney	Morgan	Jewitt	Morris
SW1	12-May	A	Barnstaple	W 18-13	Hart	Verry	Edwards	Morgan	Bedney
Play Off	19-May	H	Havant	W 26-10	Hart	Verry	Edwards	Morgan	Bedney

EVER PRESENT   None

Most Appearances

30	Michael HART
29 + 2	Nicholas CUTHBERT
	Leon LIGGETT
27	Mark NICHOLLS
25 + 1	Kerry BOURNE

MOST POINTS

Pts	Player	T	C	P	DG
271	M. Sherratt	5	45	50	2
76	M. Roberts	1	22	8	1
60	M. Hart	16			
45	L. Liggett	9			
40	M.Bedney	8			
40	P. Verry	8			
35	A. Jewitt	7			
35	K. Bourne	7			
30	P. Hudson	6			

MATCH FACTS

10	9	1	2	3	4	5	6	7	8
Sherratt	Liggett	Broady	Kearsey	Martin	Cuthbert	Miles	Hudson	Bourne	Nicholls
Sherratt	Liggett	Broady	Kearsey	Martin	Cuthbert	Miles	Hudson	Bourne	Nicholls
Sherratt	Liggett	Broady	Kearsey	Martin	Cuthbert	Miles	Hudson	Bourne	Nicholls
Roberts	Liggett	Broady	Kearsey	Martin	Cuthbert	Gittins-Jones	Bennettt	Bourne	Nicholls
Sherratt	Liggett	Broady	Kearsey	Price	Cuthbert	Gittins-Jones	Hudson	Bourne	Nicholls
Sherratt	Liggett	Broady	Kearsey	Martin	Cuthbert	Gittins-Jones	Bennett	Bourne	Hudson
Sherratt	Liggett	Phillips	Kearsey	Martin	Cuthbert	Gittins-Jones	Hudson	Bourne	Nicholls
Sherratt	Liggett	Phillips	Kearsey	Martin	Cuthbert	Gittins-Jones	Hudson	Bourne	Nicholls
Sherratt	Liggett	Broady	Kearsey	Martin	Cuthbert	Gittins-Jones	Hudson	Bourne	Nicholls
Sherratt	Liggett	Broady	Poultney	Martin	Cuthbert	Miles	Hudson	Bourne	Nicholls
Sherratt	Liggett	Broady	Poultney	Martin	Cuthbert	Miles	Hudson	Bourne	Nicholls
Roberts	Liggett	Phillips	Gwilliam	Price	Williams	Gittins-Jones	Hudson	Wood	King
Sherratt	Liggett	Phillips	Poultney	Martin	Cuthbert	Gittins-Jones	Hudson	Bourne	King
Sherratt	Liggett	Broady	Kearsey	Martin	Cuthbert	Miles	King	Bourne	Nicholls
Sherratt	Liggett	Broady	Kearsey	Martin	Cuthbert	Miles	Hudson	Bourne	Nicholls
Sherratt	Liggett	Phillips	Poultney	Price	Cuthbert	Gittins-Jones	King	Bourne	Nicholls
Sherratt	Liggett	Broady	Poultney	Martin	Cuthbert	Miles	King	Bourne	Nicholls
Roberts	Arnott	Phillips	Poultney	Martin	Cuthbert	Gittins-Jones	King	Wood	Nicholls
Sherratt	Liggett	Broady	Poultney	Martin	Cuthbert	Miles	King	Bourne	Nicholls
Sherratt	Liggett	Phillips	Poultney	Martin	Cuthbert	Gittins-Jones	King	Bourne	Nicholls
Roberts	Liggett	Broady	Matthews	Price	Cuthbert	Miles	King	Mulraney	Nicholls
Sherratt	Arnott	Phillips	Poultney	Price	Miles	Gittins-Jones	Hudson	Wood	Nicholls
Sherratt	Liggett	Broady	Matthews	Martin	Cuthbert	Miles	Hudson	Bourne	Nicholls
Roberts	Liggett	Broady	Matthews	Martin	Cuthbert	Gittins-Jones	Hudson	Bourne	Nicholls
Roberts	Liggett	Phillips	Matthews	Martin	Cuthbert	Miles	Hudson	Bourne	Nicholls
Roberts	Liggett	Phillips	Matthews	Martin	Cuthbert	Miles	Hudson	Bourne	Nicholls
Roberts	Liggett	Broady	Matthews	Price	Cuthbert	Gittins-Jones	Hudson	Bourne	Nicholls
Sherratt	Liggett	Price	Matthews	Martin	Cuthbert	Gittins-Jones	King	Bourne	Miles
Roberts	Liggett	Broady	Matthews	Martin	Cuthbert	Miles	King	Bourne	Nicholls
Sherratt	Liggett	Phillips	Poultney	Price	Cuthbert	Gittins-Jones	Hudson	Mulraney	Nicholls
Sherratt	Liggett	Broady	Poultney	Martin	Cuthbert	Gittins-Jones	Hudson	Mulraney	Nicholls

REPLACEMENTS

Price (15)	Gittins-Jones (12)	Phillips (11)	Broady (8)
Miles (7)	Sherratt (7)	King (6)	Bedney (5)
Morgan (5)	Jewitt (3)	Verry (3)	Cuthbert (2)
Edwards (2)	Liggett (2)	Martin (2)	
Arnott	Bennett	Boseley	Bourne
Kibble	Matthews	Mulraney	
Roberts	Walding		

CINDERFORD

LEAGUE STATISTICS
compiled by Stephen McCormack

Right: Duncan Edwards pictured with the County Cup.

SEASON	Division	P	W	D	L	F	A	Pts Diff	Lge Pts	Lge Pos
91-92	SW1	10	8	0	2	180	87	93	16	2
92-93	SW1	12	5	0	7	170	269	-99	10	9
93-94	SW1	12	4	1	7	140	167	-27	9	9
94-95	SW1	12	3	2	7	141	178	-37	8	9
95-96	SW1	12	1	0	11	110	382	-272	2	13r
96-97	SW2w	22	15	0	7	481	373	108	30	3
97-98	SW2w	22	17	0	5	657	363	294	34	3
98-99	SW2w	22	19	2	1	621	181	440	40	1p
99-00	SW1	22	15	0	7	685	348	337	30	3
00-01	SW1	22	21	0	1	576	225	351	42	2p

Most Pts 271 Matthew Sherratt

Most Tries 16 Michael Hart

FACT FILE

Founded: 1886
Nickname:

Colours: Red, black & amber
Change colours: Black with red & amber centre hoops.

GROUND

Address   The Recreation Ground, Dockham Rd., Cinderford, Glos. GL14 2AQ
Tel: 01594 822673   **Tele/Fax:** 01594 822400

Capacity   2,000   Covered Seats: 300   Uncovered Standing: 2,700

Directions   From the A48 or A40 follow signs for Cinderford. In town centre, at mini-r'about, turn into Dockham Road, towards the County Store supermarket & the ground is just past the car park on the left.

Car Parking   100 free spaces at the ground

Admission: Matchday: £4.00

Clubhouse   Open 7-11pm weekdays & 12-11pm weekends
Club Shop   Open clubhouse hours

Training Nights Monday, Tuesday & Thursday evenings

PROGRAMME

  Size: A5   **Pages**: 26   **Price**: 50p
  Advertising: Contact Club Administrator

Cinderford RFC

Official Programme

Established 1886

Founded 1872

CLIFTON RFC

Chairman	Richard Clifton	24 Springwood Drive, Henbury, Bristol BS10 7PU 0117 950 6214 (H) 0117 950 0070 (B & Fax) 0385 220436 (M)
Commercial Manager	Terry Whatley	0117 900 4455 0117 950 2855 (Fax)
Secretary	Roger Bealing	13 Frobisher Road, Ashton, Bristol. BS3 3AU. 0117 963 1532 (H & Fax)
Rugby Chairman	John Raine	1 Shumack House, High Street, Pensford BS18 4NN 01761 490717 (H) 01761 221190 (B) 01761 221950 (Fax)
Fixtures & Press Secretary	Brian Ben Jordan	17 RoyalClose, Henbury, Bristol BS10 7XP 0117 950 4723 (H), 0117 950 2855 (Fax) 0117 903 1532 (B - Tues - Thur) e-mail: brainjordan@cableinet.co.uk
Director of Coaching	Mark Newall	35 Redwick Road, Pilning, Bristol BS35 4LG 01454 632068

Taking seven points in their first four games Clifton were looking forward to a successful season, but despite the hard work of the players and coaching staff it was not to be. They eventually finished in eighth position, but it was only after the final whistle in their last game of the season that they were assured of National League rugby for the twelfth successive season. A narrow victory over Weston in a fiercely fought contest eventually pulled them up the table, but, if they had lost this game by over 53 points, they would have only finished eleventh, a position from which Reading were relegated when the result of the play off was known.

The season started brightly with a first ever victory over Barking being the highlight of the opening month. Fly half Jonathan Martin was leading a talented set of backs with an abundance of pace on the wings and a fit pack capable of supplying quick second phase possession. When the firm grounds vanished with the arrival of the wet weather the back line lost some of its potency and the season developed a pattern of a victory followed by a run of defeats. The side gave an impressive display against the Pirates, but had victory snatched from them when the visitors scored a length of the field try in the final seconds. They also performed well against Launceston when, 22 points down at the break, they scored four second half tries, narrowly failing to catch the Cornishmen. The most dramatic game was the home fixture with North Walsham in which the lead changed hands twice in injury time and victory was obtained when Martin kicked a penalty from the touchline in atrocious conditions. The biggest disappointment was the away defeat at Cheltenham in a game we totally dominated, but credit must be given to the defence of the home side. The most pleasing performance was the away win at Tabard in which six excellent tries were scored.

Martin became the club's highest league points scorer in a season, while centre Barnaby Kent, who appeared in every game, raced over for fourteen tries. Back row man Eddie Smith and skipper Ralph Knibbs were models of consistency missing only one game while lock Nick Cooper missed only three.

The squad included several newcomers. Winger Graham Robertson successfully made the jump from Gloucester Two rugby, while the speed of Sam Beckerleg was a constant threat to defences. Adam Harvey proved to be a useful back row man while Craig Wymer, and towards the end of the season, Declan Bird provided cover at prop. It was pleasing to see Graham Hardy return after a major injury while former Bristol centre Simon Martin completed his rehabilitation from a knee injury, which almost forced him out of the game. Brendan Treacey was another who forced his way into the side on the strength of his performances in the Wanderers.

The future looks bright with the colts again winning the Bristol Colts Cup and under the direction of new Director of Rugby, Mark Newall, the club looks forward to a successful season.

CLIFTON

Comp.	Date	H/A	Opponents	Result & Score	Att	15	14	13	12	11
N3S	2-Sep	N	Tabard	D 24-24	200	Roberts	John	Knibbs	Kent/t	Ezulike
N3S	16-Sep	A	Weston super Mare	W 29-10	300	Randall	Ezulike	Knibbs/dg	Kent/2t	Robertson
N3S	23-Sep	N	Blackheath	W 38-18		Pritchard	John/t	Knibbs/t	Kent	Ezulike
N3S	30-Sep	N	Barking	W 29-12		Pritchard	John	Knibbs	Kent/t	Randall
N3S	14-Oct	A	North Walsham	L 6-19	250	Pritchard	John	Knibbs	Kent	Ezulike
N3S	28-Oct	A	Redruth	L 31-48	600	Pritchard/t	John/t	Knibbs	Kent/2t	Robertson
N3S	11-Nov	H	Westcombe Park	L 20-24	200	Pritchard	John	Knibbs	Kent/t	Robertson/t
N3S	18-Nov	A	Basingstoke	W 19-10		Pritchard	John	Knibbs	Kent	Robertson
N3S	25-Nov	H	Cheltenham	W 19-8		Pritchard	John/t	Knibbs	Kent	Robertson
N3S	2-Dec	A	Launceston	L 20-37	450	Pritchard	John	Knibbs	Kent	Randall/t
N3S	9-Dec	H	Penzance & Newlyn	L 14-20		Pritchard	John	Knibbs	Kent	Randall
N3S	16-Dec	A	Reading	L 12-30	200	Pritchard	John	Knibbs	Kent	Robertson
N3S	23-Dec	H	Launceston	L 25-29	150	Martin	John	Knibbs	Kent	Randall
N3S	6-Jan	H	Basingstoke	W 34-8		Martin/t	John/2t	Knibbs	Kent/2t	Beckerleg
N3S	13-Jan	A	Westcombe Park	L 19-34	250	Martin	Randall	Knibbs	Kent	Beckerleg/2t
N3S	20-Jan	H	Redruth	L 13-23	120	Martin	John	Knibbs	Kent	Beckerleg/t
N3S	27-Jan	A	Plymouth Albion	L 0-49	1200	Knibbs	John	Martin	Kent	Beckerleg
N3S	3-Feb	A	Cheltenham	L 6-9	200	Knibbs	John	Martin	Kent	Robertson
N3S	10-Feb	H	North Walsham	W 21-20		Knibbs	Robertson	Martin	Kent	Beckerleg
N3S	17-Feb	H	Plymouth Albion	L 12-37		Randall	Robertson	Knibbs	Kent	Beckerleg
N3S	24-Feb	A	Barking	L 18-50		Knibbs	Robertson/t	Martin	Kent/t	Randall
N3S	10-Mar	A	Blackheath	L 0-40	140	Randall	Robertson	Knibbs	Kent	John
N3S	31-Mar	H	Reading	W 31-19		Knibbs	John	Martin	Kent/3t	Robertson
N3S	14-Apr	A	Penzance & Newlyn	L 10-25	1000	Randall	John	Knibbs/tdg	Kent	Robertson
N3S	21-Apr	A	Tabard	W 41-12		Robertson/t	John/t	Martin	Kent	Beckerleg
N3S	28-Apr	H	Weston super Mare	W 18-13		Knibbs	John	Martin	Kent/t	Robertson/t
TBC 2	07-Oct	A	Cheshunt	L 12-18						

* after opponents name indicates a penalty try. Brackets after a player's name indicates he was replaced. eg (a) means he was replaced by replacement code "a" and so on. / after a player or replacement name is followed by any scores he made - eg /t, /c, /p, /dg or any combination of these

EVER PRESENT None

Most Appearances:
- 26 Barnaby Kent.
- 25 Ralph Knibbs, Eddie Smith.
- 24 Jon Martin.
- 23 Nick Cooper.

PLAYERS USED

28 plus three as replacements only.

MOST POINTS

Pts	Player	T	C	P	DG
228	J Martin	7	32	41	2
70	B Kent	14	-	-	-
30	C Wymer	3	-	5	-
30	D John	6	-	-	-

MATCH FACTS

10	9	1	2	3	4	5	6	7	8
Martin/3cdg	Lloyd	Hussey	Stephens	Wymer/t	Cooper	Franklin	Smith	Harvey/t	Amphlett
Martin/2c4p	Lloyd	Hussey	Stephens	Webster	Cooper	Franklin	Smith	Harvey	Tracey
Martin/t3c4p	Lloyd	Hussey	Stephens/t	Webster	Cooper	Franklin	Smith	Harvey	Amphlett
Martin/tc4p	Lloyd	Webster	Stephens	Wymer	Cooper	Franklin	Smith	Harvey/t	Amphlett
Martin/2p	Lloyd	Webster	Stephens	Wymer	Cooper	Roberts	Smith	Harvey	Amphlett
Martin/4cp	Lloyd	Hussey	Stephens	Wymer	Adams	Roberts	Smith	Harvey	Amphlett
Martin/tcp	Lloyd	Hussey	Stephens	Webster	Cooper	Roberts	Smith	Harvey	Amphlett
Martin/2pdg	Harraway	Webster/t	Stephens	Wymer	Cooper	Amphlett	Smith	Harvey	Burton/t
Martin/t2c	Harraway	Webster	Stephens	Wymer	Cooper	Amphlett	Burton	Harvey	Smith/t
Martin/5p	Lloyd	Webster	Stephens	Wymer	Cooper	Amphlett	Smith	Harvey	Burton
Martin/3p	Harraway/t	Hussey	Stephens	Webster	Cooper	Amphlett	Smith	Harvey	Burton
Martin/c	Lloyd/t	Hussey	Hardy	Webster	Cooper	Amphlett	Burton	Harvey/t	Smith
Martin/cp	Harraway	Hussey(b/t)	Hardy/t	Webster	Cooper	Amphlett/t	Smith	Tracey	Roberts(b/t)
Martin/t2c	Harraway	Hussey	Hardy	Webster	Cooper	Adams	Tracey	Harvey	Smith
Martin/t2c	Harraway	Hussey	Hardy	Webster	Adams	Amphlett	Tracey	Harvey	Smith
Martin/c2p	Harraway	Hussey	Stephens	Webster	Cooper	Amphlett	Tracey	Harvey	Smith
Martin	Harraway	Hussey	Stephens	Webster	Cooper	Amphlett	Hardy	Burton	Tracey
Martin/2p	Harraway	Hussey	Stephens	Webster	Cooper	Amphlett	Tracey	Burton	Smith
Martin/p	Harraway/t	Hussey	Stephens	Wymer/tp	Cooper	Amphlett	Tracey/t	Hardy	Smith
Martin	Harraway	Hussey	Stephens	Wymer/4p	Adams	Amphlett	Tracey	Hardy	Smith
Martin/c2p	Harraway	Hussey	Stephens	Webster	Cooper	Amphlett	Tracey	Hardy	Smith
Martin	Harraway	Wymer	Stephens	Bird	Cooper	Adams	Amphlett	Tracey	Smith
Martin/2c4p	Harraway	Hussey	Stephens	Wymer	Cooper	Adams	Amphlett	Tracey	Smith
Martin/c	Harraway	Webster	Stephens	Bird	Cooper	Adams	Hardy	Tracey	Smith
Martin/t4cp	Harraway/t	Hussey/t	Stephens/t	Webster	Cooper	Adams	Hardy	Tracey	Smith
Martin/c2p	Harraway	Webster	Stephens	Bird	Cooper	Adams	Hardy	Tracey	Smith

REPLACEMENTS   a - R Morgan   b - C Wymer

2000-01 HIGHLIGHTS

Jon Martin topped the points scorers list in his first full season for the club with 228, a new club record for a league season.

It beat the 222 that Simon Hogg scored back in 1993-94.

Martin was also second in the try scorers with seven but he was a long way behind the leader Barnaby Kent who scored 14 tries and just missed the club record of 16.

Ralph Knibbs missed just the one match and has played in 77 of Clifton's last 78 matches spread over three seasons.

Clifton struggled mid season and lost 11 out of 13 matches during this period.

CLIFTON

LEAGUE STATISTICS compiled by Stephen McCormack

SEASON	Division	P	W	D	L	F	A	Pts Diff	Lge Pts	Lge Pos	Most Points	Most Tries
91-92	D3	12	9	0	3	298	132	166	18		100 Simon Hogg	8 Matt Brain
92-93	D3	11	4	2	5	206	175	31	10		71 Simon Hogg	5 Mark Wyatt & Doug Woodman
93-94	D4	18	16	2	0	477	205	272	34	1p	222 Simon Hogg	16 John Phillips
94-95	D3	18	5	1	12	242	344	-102	11		116 Simon Hogg	4 Matt Brain & Mark Wyatt
95-96	D4	18	7	2	9	283	298	-15	16		87 Simon Hogg	5 Malcolm Crane
96-97	D3	30	4	0	26	518	1347	-829	8		80 Simon Hogg	13 Mark Buckingham
97-98	N2S	26	7	1	18	414	611	-197	15	11	58 Gareth Pugh	9 Janik Hendriksz
98-99	N2S	26	10	1	15	415	483	-68	21	7	153 Rhys Oakley	6 Alan Barnes
99-00	N2S	26	12	1	13	575	549	26	25	7	148 Rhys Oakley	9 Chris Randall
00-01	N3S	26	10	1	15	509	628	-119	21	8	228 Jonathan Martin	14 Barnaby Kent

FACT FILE

Founded: 1877
Nickname: The Club
Training Nights: Monday & Wednesday

Colours: Lavender, black and white hoops.
Change colours: White

GROUND

Address: Station Road, Cribbs Causeway, Henbury, Bristol BS10 7TP.
Tel: 0117 950 0445   Fax: 0117 950 2855   e-mail: brainjordan@cableinet.co.uk
Capacity: 2,500   Seated: 250   Standing: 2,250

Directions: Leave M5 at J17, taking dual carriageway A4018 towards Bristol (ignore signs to Regional Shopping Centre). Coaches go to 2nd r'about and take bus lane. Entrance to ground on right. Cars go on to next r'about (Old Crow P.H.) & return down other side of dual carriageway. Pass BP petrol station & take next left (signed Clifton RFC). Right at end of lane & ground entrance is on left. The way to ground is signed on dual carriageway.
Nearest Railway Station: Bristol Parkway, taxi 15 minutes

Car Parking: 250 spaces on the ground.

Admission: Season ticket - Adults To be decided
Matchday - Adults £5, OAPs £2.50, Children Free

Clubhouse: Normal licensing hours, bar meals available.
Functions: Capacity 150

Club Shop: Manager Stephanie Batterbury 01275 837523
or Mike Anderton

PROGRAMME Size: A5   Price: £1   Pages: 40 + cover.
Editor: Ben Jordan 0117 950 4723

Advertising Rates:
To be negotiated - contact club.

CLIFTON RUGBY
FOOTBALL CLUB

2000/2001 Season

Founded 1872

NATIONAL DIVISION
THREE SOUTH

LAUNCESTON RFC

President   John Fry   Thorne Farm, St. Giles on the Heath, Launceston PL15 9SA. 01566 784308

Secretary   Bill Gladwell   5 Hendra Tor View, Five Lanes, Launceston PL15 7RG
Tel: 01566 86864 (H) 0771 875 5823 (B/M) Fax: 01566 86818
e-mail: baggins@lrfc53.freeserve.co.uk

Fixture Secretary Mervyn Yeo   Whiterow Farm, Lewdown, Okehampton, Devon EX20 4QL 01566 783230

Treasurer   Dave Baker   Heightleigh, Tavistock Road, Launceston PL15 9HB 01566 773070

Match Secretary Graham Duke   Southbridge, Boyton, Launceston PL15 8NW   01566 785609

Launceston's first season in the national leagues proved to be very successful. After a long and tiring campaign, the season was completed with a play-off game away at Sedgley Park where they lost to a better drilled home side in a very entertaining match.

The road to the play-off was indeed a long one and had its moments along the way. The two games against Plymouth Albion proved to be a turning point in the All Blacks season. Both games saw Plymouth win by 13 points to 6 in two very closely fought encounters. Both the home and away games were staged in front of large crowds and only the magnificent Plymouth defence denied the All Blacks a share of the spoils.

The mid-season foot and mouth crisis caused some worrying moments for some players within the squad although the problems suffered here were less than those of the Northern division boys.

The squad remained fairly constant throughout although the F&M problems created some opportunities for emerging players. Top scorer was once again full-back, Danny Sloman, who could have been top scorer in the Division had some of his close calls gone over. Centre, Mark Fatialofa, Club captain, Jimmy Tucker and winger Matt Bradshaw were top try scorers for the club but back row players, Dean Shipton, Steve Dyer and Brett Luxton also featured highly in the scoring stakes. Director of Rugby, Roger Spurrell was delighted with the achievement and is laying plans for another assault on the league top spot. However, clubs like Blackheath and Cinderford will no doubt have something to say about his aspirations.

The pitch that was relayed at the end of the previous season stood up well to the rigours of this winter's campaign and is looking in even better shape for the next one. So it's back to the drawing board and 'here we go again!'   Bill Gladwell

Tight head, Steve Rush, in the thick of the action during the play off with Sedgley Park with, standing nearest the camera, Barry Lucas, hooker and at the back of the ruck, wing forward Dean Shipton.

411

LAUNCESTON

Comp.	Date	H/A	Opponents	Result & Score	Att	15	14	13	12	11
N3S	2-Sep	A	Redruth	W 34-29	700	Sloman/2t3cp	Bradshaw/t	O'Donnell	Fatialofa/t	Nancekivell
N3S	9-Sep	A	Basingstoke	W 30-17	200	Sloman/3c3p	Grimes	O'Donnell/t	Fatialofa/t	Nancekivell
N3S	30-Sep	H	Cheltenham	W 63-7	400	Sloman/t6c2p	Bradshaw/4t	O'Donnell	Fatialofa	Briskham/2t
N3S	14-Oct	A	Barking	L 18-20	250	Sloman/tc2p	Bradshaw	O'Donnell	Nancekivell	Briskham
N3S	28-Oct	H	Reading	W 37-0	400	Freestone	Cudmore	Sloman/3c2p	Nancekivell	Bradshaw
N3S	4-Nov	H	Westcombe Park	W 48-10	300	Freestone	Thorne/t	Sloman/t4c	Nancekivell/t	Bradshaw/2t
N3S	11-Nov	A	Tabard	W 26-13	200	Briskham	Bradshaw	Nancekivell	Sloman/2c4p	O'Donnell
N3S	18-Nov	H	Weston super Mare	W 51-5	320	Briskham(a/t)	O'Donnell	Sloman/3c	Nancekivell/2t	Bradshaw/t
N3S	25-Nov	A	Blackheath	W 25-20	250	Sloman/2c2p	O'Donnell	Fatialofa/t	Nancekivell	Bradshaw/t
N3S	2-Dec	H	Clifton	W 37-20	450	Sloman/3c2p	O'Donnell	Fatialofa/t	Nancekivell	Cudmore/2t
N3S	9-Dec	A	North Walsham	L 13-16	300	Sloman/c2p	O'Donnell	Fatialofa/t	Nancekivell	Bradshaw
N3S	16-Dec	H	Plymouth Albion	L 6-13	2000	Sloman/2p	Bradshaw	Fatialofa	Nancekivell	O'Donnell
N3S	23-Dec	A	Clifton	W 29-25	150	Sloman/3cp	Cudmore(b/t)	Fatialofa/t	Nancekivell	O'Donnell/t
N3S	6-Jan	A	Weston super Mare	W 35-25	200	Sloman/3c3p	Briskham/t(c/t)	Fatialofa	Nancekivell	Fry
N3S	13-Jan	H	Tabard	W 40-0	300	Sloman/4c	Nancekivell/t	Fatialofa/2t	Tucker/t	O'Donnell
N3S	27-Jan	H	Penzance & Newlyn*	W 31-5	2000	Sloman/3c	O'Donnell/t	Fatialofa	Nancekivell/t	Bradshaw/t
N3S	10-Feb	H	Barking	W 42-13	420	Birley/t6c	Bradshaw	Fatialofa	Nancekivell	O'Donnell
N3S	17-Feb	A	Penzance & Newlyn	L 20-43	2000	Sloman/2c2p	Bradshaw	Fatialofa	Nancekivell	O'Donnell
N3S	24-Feb	A	Cheltenham	W 31-19	200	Sloman/2c4p	O'Donnell/t	Nancekivell	Tucker	Briskham
N3S	17-Mar	A	Westcombe Park	W 24-10		Sloman/2c	O'Donnell	Tucker	Fatialofa/t	Nancekivell/t
N3S	24-Mar	N	Redruth	W 11-9	1000	Sloman/2p	Worsnip	Nancekivell/t	Tucker	Briskham
N3S	31-Mar	A	Plymouth Albion	L 6-13	3000	Worsnip	O'Donnell	Sloman/2p	Nancekivell	Briskham
N3S	7-Apr	H	Blackheath	W 35-13	400	Sloman/t2c2p	Cudmore	Fry	Nancekivell	Briskham
N3S	14-Apr	H	North Walsham*	W 16-15	400	Sloman/c3p	Worsnip	Fatialofa	Nancekivell	O'Donnell
N3S	21-Apr	A	Reading	D 28-28		Sloman/2c3p	Worsnip	Fatialofa/t	Nancekivell	O'Donnell/t
N3S	28-Apr	H	Basingstoke	W 41-3	325	Sloman/t4cp	Worsnip	Fatialofa/2t	Nancekivell/t	O'Donnell
TBC	23-Sep	N	Truro	W 26-0	400	Sloman/2c4p	Bradshaw/2t	O'Donnell	Fatialofa	Briskham
TBC	7-Oct	H	Gordano	W 40-0		Sloman/2t5c	Bradshaw(d/t)	Cudmore	Tucker	Briskham
TBC	21-Oct	A	Reading	L 25-31	250	Sloman/cp	Bradshaw	Nancekivell/t	Cudmore/t	Briskham
PO	26-May	A	Sedgley Park	L 23-40	1500	Sloman/2c3p	Gray/2t	Fatialofa	Nancekivell	Greatrix

*after opponents name indicates a penalty try. Brackets after a player's name indicates he was replaced.
eg (a) means he was replaced by replacement code "a" and so on. / after a player or replacement name
is followed by any scores he made - eg /t, /c, /p, /dg or any combination of these

EVER PRESENT

Steve Dyer, G Hutchings, B Luxton, Julian Wilce, Jimmy Tucker.

Most Other Appearances:
25 Eddie Nancekivell, Steve Rush, Danny Sloman.

PLAYERS USED

33 plus three as replacements only.

MOST POINTS

Pts	Player	T	C	P	DG
288	D Sloman	7	59	45	-
65	M Fatialofa	13	-	-	-
60	J Tucker	12	-	-	-
50	M Bradshaw	10	-	-	-
40	E Nancekivell	8	-	-	-

MATCH FACTS

10	9	1	2	3	4	5	6	7	8
Tucker	Chudleigh	Risdon	Lucas	Rush	Hutchings	Wilce	Wilcocks	Dyer/t	Luxton
Tucker/t	Chudleigh	Risdon	Lucas	Rush	Hutchings	Wilce	Wilcocks	Dyer	Luxton
Tucker/2t	Chudleigh	Shipton	Lucas	Rush	Hutchings	Wilce	Wilcocks	Dyer	Luxton
Tucker	Chudleigh	Risdon	Lucas	Rush	Hutchings	Wilce	Cameron	Dyer	Luxton/t
Tucker/t	Chudleigh/t	Risdon	Lucas	Rush	Hutchings	Wilce	Shipton	Dyer/2t	Luxton/t
Tucker	Chudleigh	Risdon/t	Lucas	Rush/t	Hutchings/t	Wilce	Shipton	Dyer	Luxton
Tucker/t	Chudleigh	Risdon	Lucas	Rush	Hutchings	Wilce	Shipton/t	Dyer	Luxton
Tucker	Chudleigh/t	Soby	Lucas	Rush/t	Hutchings	Wilce	Shipton/t	Dyer/t	Luxton/t
Tucker	Chudleigh/t	Soby	Lucas	Rush	Hutchings	Wilce	Shipton	Dyer	Luxton
Tucker	Chudleigh	Langridge	Lucas	Rush	Hutchings	Wilce	Shipton/t	Dyer/t	Luxton
Tucker	Chudleigh	Langridge	Lucas	Rush	Hutchings	Wilce	Shipton	Dyer	Luxton
Tucker	Chudleigh	Langridge	Lucas	Rush	Hutchings	Wilce	Shipton	Dyer	Luxton
Tucker/t	Chudleigh	Langridge	Lucas	Rush	Hutchings	Wilce	Boundy	Dyer	Luxton
Tucker	Chudleigh	Sobey	Lucas	Rush	Hutchings	Wilce	Cameron	Dyer	Luxton/2t
Birley/c	Chudleigh	Risdon	Lucas	Rush	Hutchings	Wilce/t	Boundy	Dyer/t	Luxton
Tucker/t	Chudleigh	Risdon	Lucas	Rush	Hutchings	Wilce	Shipton	Dyer	Luxton
Tucker/t	Chudleigh/t	Risdon	Lucas	Rush	Hutchings	Wilce	Shipton/2t	Dyer	Luxton/t
Tucker/t	Chudleigh	Risdon/t	Lucas	Rush	Hutchings	Wilce	Shipton	Dyer	Luxton
Birley	Chudleigh/t	Risdon	Lucas	Rush	Hutchings	Wilce	Shipton/t	Dyer	Luxton
Birley	Chudleigh	Risdon	Lucas	Rush	Hutchings	Wilce/t	Boundy	Dyer	Luxton/t
Birley	Chudleigh	Risdon	Lucas	Rush	Hutchings	Wilce	Shipton	Dyer	Luxton
Tucker	Chudleigh	Langridge	Lucas	Rush	Hutchings	Wilce	Shipton	Dyer	Luxton
Tucker/2t	Chudleigh	Rush/t	Lucas	Langridge	Hutchings	Wilce	Wilcocks/t	Dyer	Luxton
Tucker	Chudleigh	Rush	Meikle	Langridge	Hutchings	Wilce	Wilcocks	Dyer	Luxton
Tucker	Greatrix/t	Langridge	Meikle	Rush	Hutchings	Wilce	Wilcocks	Dyer	Luxton
Tucker	Greatrix/2t	Bolt	Lucas	Langridge	Hutchings	Wilce	Boundy	Dyer	Luxton
Tucker	Chudleigh	Sobey	Lucas	Rush	Tummon	Wilce	Wilcocks	Dyer	Luxton
Yates	Warren	Sobey	Lucas	Rush/t	Wilce	Tummon	Wilcocks	Cameron/t	Luxton/t
Tucker	Chudleigh/t	Risdon	Lucas	Soby	Hutchings	Wilce	Shipton/t	Dyer	Luxton
Tucker	Chudleigh	Bolt	Lucas	Rush	Hutchings	Wilce	Wilcocks	Dyer	Luxton

REPLACEMENTS   a - M Fatialofa   b - D Briskam   c - A Yates   d - P Thorne

2000-01 HIGHLIGHTS

Launceston were helped in their first season of National Rugby by having a settled side.
They had five ever presents and three more players who just missed a single match.

Danny Sloman led the way with 288 points including a creditable seven tries.

Centre Mark Fatialofa led the try scoring with 13 from just 17 league starts.

They lost five times all season - two of them were seven point losses to the Champions Plymouth Albion and another two were by two points and three respectivly to Barking and North Walsham away from home.

LAUNCESTON

LEAGUE STATISTICS *compiled by Stephen McCormack*

SEASON	Division	P	W	D	L	F	A	Pts Diff	Lge Pts	Lge Pos	Coach/ Most Points	Captain/ Most Tries
91-92	SW-WC											
92-93	SW-WC	12	11	0	1	317	75	242	22	2		
93-94	SW-WC	12	8	0	4	204	110	94	16	3		
94-95	SW-WC	12	12	0	0	438	90	348	24	1		
95-96	SW2	12	11	1	0	493	107	386	22	1		
96-97	SW1	22	18	0	4	752	324	328	36	2		
97-98	SW1	22	17	1	4	614	263	351	35	2		
98-99	SW1	22	20	0	2	1021	228	793	40	2		
99-00	SW1	21	19	0	2	693	266	427	38	1	Danny Sloman	
00-01	N3S	26	20	1	5	777	396	381	41	2	288 Danny Sloman	13 Mark Fatialofa

FACT FILE

Founded: 1948
Nickname: Cornish All Blacks

Colours: All black
Change colours: Red/white/green shirts

Ground Address: Polson Bridge, Launceston, Cornwall PL15 9QU - (No post please)
Tel: 01566 773406   Fax & e-mail: to Secretary
Capacity: 2,500   **Covered seating**: 220

Directions   M5 to Exeter, then A30 to Launceston.
After 45 minutes look for sign on left "Tavistock, Liftondown, Lifton" - turn left, down to T junction, left again, down hill to river Tamar, ground on the left.
Nearest Railway Station: Exeter 1hr, Plymouth 45 mins
Car Parking: Plenty at the ground

Admission: Matchday: Ground: Adults: £5.00 Children/OAP: £3   Stand: £4
Season tickets: Yes, price on application

Clubhouse: Open matchdays & training evenings.

Club Shop: Yes, selling replica kits, ties etc.   **Training Nights:** Tuesday & Thursday

Programme   **Size**: A5   **Pages**: 25   **Price**: £1   **Editor**: Bill Gladwell

Advertising: Contact John Dunn 01822 870300

Action from the play off with Sedgley Park, Launceston's No. 5 Julian Wilce on the break.

LYDNEY RFC

President	T C Bailey	Montrose, Highfield, Lydney, Glos. 01594 842287 (H)
Chairman	P J Price	Red Gables, 41a Park Road, Berry Hill, Coleford, Glos. 01594 834591 (H)
Secretary	A J Jones	5 Kimberley Close, Lydney, Glos. GL15 5AE 01594 842709 (H) Tel & Fax: (Club Office) 01594 843064
Treasurer	R A Jones	Sweetwater Cottage, Neds Top, Oldcroft, Glos. GL15 4NK 01594 845073 (B)
Fixture Secretary	R B Powell	S Kalni-Mesto, Parkhill, Whitecroft, Lydney, Glos. GL15 4PL 01594 562820 07810 157101 (M)

The arrival of a coaching team comprising Welsh and English Internationals Rhodri Lewis and Peter Kingston brought keen anticipation that 2000/01 would see a revival of our fortunes. Alas, it was not to be. The season was full of disappointment almost from the start, when we lost the first match at home to Preston and never really recovered, leaving us languishing among the bottom four teams for the rest of a truncated season.

The loss of Captain Nick Burnett at the turn of the year was a big blow, adding as it did to the problem of a lack of strength in depth, which is a perennial headache for a small club such as Lydney. Injury and unavailability took a severe toll on our limited 1st XV resources.

As if this were not enough, the foot and mouth epidemic descended on rural Gloucestershire with a vengeance. This brought about the abandonment of our last four fixtures on the advice of MAFF. We could not reasonably argue against the RFU decision that we should be relegated to Division 3 South along with Camberley.

As always we look forward to next season, when the coaching duties will be in the hands of three vastly experienced `old' players in the shape of Nick Nelmes, Julian Davis and Adrian Knox. We will probably need to look more to our local resources and the members, players and officials will as usual give their whole-hearted support to the club.

We say farewell to our popular chairman Peter Catlin and thank him for all his efforts over the past seasons. Phil Price takes over the reigns in his place and together with his committee will hope to see us meet and overcome the inevitable challenges in the months ahead.

Dave Dolan

LYDNEY

Comp.	Date	H/A	Opponents	Result & Score	Att.	15	14	13	12	11
N2	2-Sep	H	Preston Grasshoppers	L 9-22	500	Bennett	Smith	Holford	Hill	Vines
N2	9-Sep	A	Rugby Lions	L 10-35		Morgan/cp	Smith	Holford	Hill	Vines
N2	16-Sep	H	Kendal	W 20-16		Morgan/2c2p	Smith	Holford/t	Hill	Dunlop
N2	23-Sep	A	Esher	L 17-30	450	Johnson	Dunlop	Hill	Bennett	Vines
N2	30-Sep	H	Harrogate	L 3-24	200	Johnson	Vines	Hill	Holford	Dunlop
N2	14-Oct	A	Nottingham	L 22-44		Morgan	Vines	Bragg	Hill	Brookes
N2	28-Oct	A	West Hartlepool	W 18-13		Morgan/t	Holford	Ward/p	Bragg	Hill
N2	11-Nov	H	Camberley	W 18-16	200	Morgan	Holford	Bragg	Ward/c2p	Hill
N2	18-Nov	A	Fylde	W 18-13	450	Morgan	Holford	Bragg	Ward	Hill
N2	25-Nov	H	Wharfedale	L 0-9	400	Morgan	Holford	Bragg	Ward	Brookes
N2	9-Dec	A	Newbury	L 12-24		Morgan	Vines	Bragg	Hill	Brookes/t
N2	16-Dec	H	Fylde	L 9-13		Morgan	Vines	Bragg	Ward	Brookes
N2	23-Dec	A	Camberley	L 3-32	200	Johnson	Vines	Bragg	Ward	Hill
N2	6-Jan	H	West Hartlepool	W 58-8		Bendall	Dunlop	Holford	Ward/t	Brookes/2t
N2	13-Jan	A	Rosslyn Park	L 7-60		Morgan	Dunlop	Holford	Hill	Brookes
N2	20-Jan	H	Nottingham	L 21-28	400	Morgan	Moger	Holford	Hill	Brookes
N2	27-Jan	A	Bracknell	L 3-25		Morgan	Moger	Holford	Bragg	Vines
N2	3-Feb	H	Bracknell	L 8-36		Morgan	Moger	Holford	Bragg	Vines
N2	10-Feb	A	Harrogate	L 16-29	350	Bendall	Saville	Holford	Hill	Vines
N2	24-Feb	H	Esher	W 9-6		Bendall	Saville	Holford	Bragg	Vines
N2	10-Mar	A	Kendal	L 9-33		Saville	Dunlop	Bragg	Holford	Vines
N2	24-Mar	A	Preston Grasshoppers	L 18-50		Bendall/t	Saville	Holford	Bragg	Vines
TBC	07-Oct	A	Rosslyn Park	L 3-30		Morgan	Vine	Holford	Bragg	Hill

** after opponents name indicates a penalty try. Brackets after a player's name indicates he was replaced.
eg (a) means he was replaced by replacement code "a" and so on. / after a player or replacement name
is followed by any scores he made - eg /t, /c, /p, /dg or any combination of these*

<table>
<tr><td colspan="2">EVER PRESENT None</td></tr>
</table>

	EVER PRESENT	None		MOST POINTS					

EVER PRESENT None

Most appearances:
- 22   Paul Price.
- 19   Mark James.
- 18   Regan Torua

PLAYERS USED

37 plus six as replacement only.

MOST POINTS

Pts	Player	T	C	P	DG
70	S Ward	3	5	15	-
67	C Jones	-	11	15	-
23	S Morgan	1	3	4	-
15	N Burnett	3	-	-	-
15	D Jenkins	3	-	-	-
15	P Price	3	-	-	-

MATCH FACTS

10	9	1	2	3	4	5	6	7	8
Stack/3p	Turner	Price	Nelmes	James	Kiely	Roberts	Burnett	Jenkins	Torua
Davis	Turner	James	Nelmes	Horrell	Kiely	Roberts	Price	Jenkins/t	Torua
Jones	Davis	Price	Nelmes	James	Roberts	Kiely	Torua	Cadwallader/t	Burnett
Jones/2cp	Davis	Price	Nelmes	James	Kiely	Roberts	Torua	Cadwallader/t	Burnett/t
Morgan/p	Davis	Price	Nelmes	James	Kiely	Bashford	Evans	Torua	Burnett
Jones/2cp	Turner	Price	Nelmes	Horrell	Kiely	Bashford/t	Evans	Jenkins	Burnett
Williams	Collins	James	Price	Horrell/t	Kiely	Bashford	Evans/t	Torua	Burnett
Williams	Collins	James	Price	Horrell/t	Kiely	Bashford	Torua	Jenkins/t	Burnett
Williams/p(a/5p)	Collins	James	Price	Horrell	Kiely	Bashford	Evans	Torua	Burnett
Williams	Collins	Price	Nelmes	James	Kiely	Bashford	Evans	Torua	Burnett
Ward/c	Collins	Price	Horrell	James	Kiely/t	Bashford	Evans	Torua	Burnett
Jones/3p	Turner	James	Price	Horrell	Kiely	Bashford	Torua	Jenkins	Burnett
Jones/p	Collins	Price	Jenkins	James	Roberts	Bashford	Kiely	Torua	Burnett
Jones/6c2p	Collins/2t	James(b/t)	Price/t	Harris	Roberts	Bashford	Evans	Torua	Burnett/t
Ward/tc	Collins	Price	Jenkins	Harris	Roberts	Bashford	Evans	Torua	Kiely
Collins/p(a/t)	Turner/t	Price	Nelmes	James/t	Roberts	Kiely	Evans	Jenkins	Torua
Ward/p	Collins	Price	Nelmes	James	Roberts	Kiely	Evans	Jenkins	Stannard
Merrett/p	Collins	Harris	Price/t	James	Roberts	Bashford	Evans	Jenkins	Stannard
Ward/c3p	Collins	Price/t	Nelmes	James	Roberts	Bashford	Torua	Jenkins	Heaven
Ward/3p	Collins	Price	Nelmes	James	Roberts	Bashford	Evans	Torua	Stannard
Ward/3p	Collins	Price	Nelmes	James	Roberts	Bashford	Evans	Jenkins	Torua
Ward/tc2p	Collins	Price	Nelmes	James	Roberts	Bashford	Kiely	Jenkins	Evans
Merrett/p	Turner	James	Price	Mason	Kiely	Bashford	Evans	Jenkind	Burnett

REPLACEMENTS   a - C Jones   b - D Jenkins

2000-01 HIGHLIGHTS

Three of the six matches Lydney won were in a run at the end of October early November. Apart from that they managed just three other and won just two of their last 13 matches at the end of the season.

Failed to score tries in nine of the 22 matches that they played in their league campaign.

Stephen Ward was top points scorer with just 70 points, the lowest for the club in a league campaign since Andy Holford scored 70 points in 1994-95.

They did manage their biggest ever win when they thumped West Hartlepool 58-8, the 50 point winning margin erasing the 47 point win over Sidcup back in 1989.

LYDNEY

LEAGUE STATISTICS
compiled by Stephen McCormack

SEASON	Division	P	W	D	L	F	A	Pts Diff	Lge Pts	Lge Pos	Most Points		Most Tries	
91-92	3	12	2	0	10	91	261	-170	4	13	15	Andy Berry	3	Mark Fennell
92-93	D4S	12	8	0	4	187	170	17	16	3	102	Andy Halford	6	John Edwards
93-94	D5S	12	7	2	3	181	111	70	16	2	54	Andy Halford	5	Mike Stubbs & John Edwards
94-95	D5S	12	10	1	1	263	131	132	21	2	70	Andy Halford	7	Mike Stubbs
95-96	D5S	12	11	1	0	320	132	188	23	1	107	Robert Mills	6	Nick Nelmes & Julian Davis
96-97	D3	30	13	0	17	668	766	-98	26	10	275	Paul Morris	8	Mike Stubbs & Adrian Knox
97-98	JN1	26	5	0	21	361	575	-214	10	12	82	James Reid	7	Julian Davis
98-99	JN1	26	11	2	13	438	482	-44	24	8	104	Nick Paisley	7	L Smith/D Edwards
99-00	JN1	26	9	2	15	496	632	-136	20	10	248	Lee Osborne	6	Paul Price/ Charles Vine/Ross Armstrong
00-01	N2	*22	6	0	16	308	565	-257	12	13	70	Stephen Ward	4	by four players

FACT FILE

Founded: 1887
Nickname: Severnsiders
Website: romandelta.com/LydneyRFC

Colours: Black and white hoops
Change colours: Red

GROUND
Address: Regentsholm, Regent Street, Lydney, Glos GL15 5RN

Tel: 01594 842479 (Clubhouse)   Tel/Fax: 01594 843064 (Office)   email: best@romandelta.com
Capacity: 3,000 +   Seated: 490   Standing: 2,500 +

Directions: Turn off by-pass at either end and follow signs to Lydney. Turn into Swan Road (next to Swan Hotel) off the A48 in the centre of town. Straight on to the entrance to the recreation grounds, turn left inside ground.
Nearest Railway Station: Lydney BR (Approx. 1 mile)

Car Parking: Restricted on ground, spaces nearby

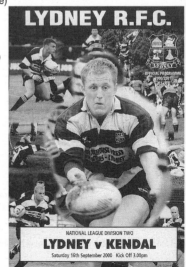

Admission: Not yet decided for 2001-02
(Last season)   Season   Adults £60   Children/OAPs £ 30
Matchday   Adults £6   Children/OAPs £3

Club Shop: None

Clubhouse: Open during normal licensing hours, with a range of snacks available on match days.
Functions: Contact Mrs Diane Emery 01594 841008 (H).

Training Nights: Tuesdays & Thursdays

PROGRAMME Size: A5   Pages: 32   Price: £1
Editor: Alan Keenan Tel: 01594 842228
Advertising Rates   (Mono)
Contact Gary McKelvey, Sponsorship Secretary 01594 844623
or Ann Sargent 01594 843064

LYDNEY R.F.C.

NATIONAL LEAGUE DIVISION TWO
LYDNEY v KENDAL
Saturday 16th September 2000 Kick Off 3.00pm

NORTH WALSHAM RFC

President T.B.A.

Chairman George Bradford 2 Bell Yard, Gunton Hall, Hanworth, Norwich NR11 7HJ
   Tel: 01263 768159 email: bradford3.freeserve.co.uk

Club Secretary Joe Hodges Church View, Town Street, Hickling, Norwich. NR12 0BQ
   Tel: 01692 598318 (H) email: joehodges@churchview-hickling.freeserve.co.uk

Press & Media Tony Marcantonio The White House, Southwood Road, Beighton,Norwich. NR13 3AB.
   01493 751837 (H) 07944 690042 (M) email: tony.marcantonio@ukgateway.net

Fixtures Secretary Richard Foulds Ian 2, Church Farm Cottage, Hautbois, Norwich NR12 7JW
   Tel: 01603 736584 (H) 07941 296560 (M) email: richardfoulds@talk21.com

After finishing third for two seasons in succession, sixth was a bit of a let down for the North Walsham faithful but in no way reflected the efforts put in by the players.

Five defeats by less than three points early in the new year effectively ended any chance of A top three finish but with a final run in of games against the top three there was no let up and all three were hard fought particularly the home game against Plymouth who had to pull out all the stops to preserve their well deserved undefeated tag.

As ever Walsham's geographical location made it hard for new coach Jon Curry to attract players to Scottow and the loss of James Shanahan to Bedford, Des Brett to Henley and James Sinclair and Dom Crossley to Norwich made the task no easier. Veteran lock John Morfoot was persuaded that retirement could wait another season (or two) and continued his partnership with Sam Tyler. Jeff van Poortvliet was an inspirational skipper on the field from open side and Kenny Dodds at No8 was top try scorer with 10.

In February a couple of new faces appeared in the line up when South Africans Len Wilmot (centre) and Gideon Rossouw (hooker) arrived at Scottow. Both slotted into the side and the life of the club quickly and proved valuable members on and off the field. Wilmot arrived at a time when Phil Friel was injured and took on the kicking duties finishing the season with an impressive 70% success rate.

North Walsham has always been a close knit outfit and as ever it was team spirit which kept them going during the lean spell when wins were hard to come by. Tony Marcantonio

North Walsham's No. 8, Kenny Dodds, breaks off the back of a scrum supported by Johhny Wyatt against Tabard

NORTH WALSHAM

Comp.	Date	H/A	Opponents	Result & Score	Att	15	14	13	12	11
N3S	2-Sep	H	Reading	W 28-7		Borrett/t	Kingsmill	Wyatt	Smith	Prema
N3S	9-Sep	H	Weston super Mare	W 41-3	300	Borrett	Brand	Smith	N Greenhall	Kingsmill/2c
N3S	16-Sep	A	Tabard	L 21-36	250	Borrett	Prema	C Greenhall	Smith	Brand
N3S	30-Sep	A	Blackheath	W 29-14	250	Brand	Kingsmill	Smith	N Greenhall	Prema
N3S	14-Oct	H	Clifton	W 19-6	250	Smith	Kingsmill	C Greenhall	N Greenhall/t	Prema
N3S	28-Oct	A	Plymouth Albion	L 14-20	900	Cooke	Lowles	C Greenhall	N Greenhall	Prema
N3S	4-Nov	H	Barking	L 3-10	250	Borrett	Cooke	C Greenhall	N Greenhall	Lowles
N3S	11-Nov	H	Redruth	W 26-5	250	Wyatt	Prema	C Greenhall/t	Fox	Ryan/t
N3S	18-Nov	A	Westcombe Park	L 10-13	250	Wyatt	Prema	C Greenhall/t	N Greenhall	Ryan
N3S	25-Nov	H	Basingstoke	W 25-3		Ryan/t	Kingsmill	C Greenhall/t	N Greenhall	Lowles
N3S	2-Dec	A	Cheltenham	W 32-12	200	Ryan	Rains	C Greenhall/t	N Greenhall	Lowles
N3S	9-Dec	H	Launceston	W 16-13	300	Borrett	Prema	C Greenhall	N Greenhall/dg	Lowles/t
N3S	16-Dec	A	Penzance & Newlyn	L 31-63	800	Lowles	Prema	C Greenhall	N Greenhall	Brand
N3S	23-Dec	H	Cheltenham	W 32-8	320	Borrett/t	Prema	C Greenhall/t	Kingsmill	Cooke/t
N3S	6-Jan	H	Westcombe Park	L 11-12	300	Ryan	Kingsmill	Youngs	C Greenhall	Lowles
N3S	13-Jan	A	Redruth	L 19-43	700	Walton	Brand/t	Borrett	Woodhouse	Lowles/t
N3S	27-Jan	A	Barking	L 29-31		Borrett/t	Lowles	C Greenhall/t	Woodhouse	Brand/t
N3S	3-Feb	A	Basingstoke	D 13-13		Borrett	Youngs	C Greenhall	Woodhouse	Brand
N3S	10-Feb	A	Clifton	L 20-21		Borrett/t	Ryan	N Greenhall	C Greenhall	Brand
N3S	24-Feb	H	Blackheath	W 15-6	250	Ryan	Cooke	Youngs	Wilmot/5p	Lowles
N3S	10-Mar	A	Weston super Mare	L 29-38	300	Borrett	Ryan/t	C Greenhall/t	Wilmot/2c5p	Lowles
N3S	17-Mar	H	Tabard	W 16-0	200	Ryan/t	Kingsmill	C Greenhall	Wilmot/c3p	Lowles
N3S	24-Mar	A	Reading	W 25-21	250	Borrett	Ryan	C Greenhall	Wilmot/2c2p	Lowles/t
N3S	31-Mar	H	Penzance & Newlyn	L 14-24		Borrett	Kingsmill	C Greenhall	Wilmot/3p	Ryan
N3S	7-Apr	H	Plymouth Albion	L 17-20		C Greenhall/t	Kingsmill	Youngs	Wilmot/4p	Borrett
N3S	14-Apr	A	Launceston	L 15-16	400	C Greennhall	Borrett/2t	Youngs	Wilmot/cp	Cooke
TBC	7-Oct	A	Old Colfeians*	W 21-17		Borrett	Prema	Smith/t	N Greenhall	Brand
TBC	21-Oct	A	Darlington MP	L 10-27		Cooke	Prema	C Greenhall	N Greenhall	Brand

*after opponents name indicates a penalty try. Brackets after a player's name indicates he was replaced.
eg (a) means he was replaced by replacement code "a" and so on. / after a player or replacement name
is followed by any scores he made - eg /t, /c, /p, /dg or any combination of these*

Most Appearances:
25 S Loose.
24 John Morfoot.
22 Sam Tyler.
21 Chris Greenhall.
20 Nick Greenhall, Chris Borrett.

PLAYERS USED

37 plus one as a replacement only

MOST POINTS

Pts	Player	T	C	P	DG
149	P Friel	4	24	27	-
81	L Wilmott	-	6	23	-
45	K Dodds	9	-	-	-
40	C Borrett	8	-	-	-
40	C Greenhall	8	-	-	-

MATCH FACTS

10	9	1	2	3	4	5	6	7	8
N Greenhall/t	Friel/2c3p	Loose	Woodhouse	Williams/t	Tyler	Morfoot	Baker	van Poortvliet	Dodds
Wyatt/2t	Friel/tc	Loose	Woodhouse	Williams	Tyler	Morfoot/t	Baker/t	van Poortvliet/t	Dodds/t
Wyatt	Friel/3c	Loose	Woodhouse	Scott	Tyler	Morfoot	Baker/t	van Poortvliet	Dodds/2t
Wyatt	Friel/c4p	Loose	Woodhouse/t	Williams	Tyler	Morfoot	Baker	Malone	Dodds/2t
Wyatt	Friel/c4p	Loose	Woodhouse	Williams	Morfoot	Tyler	Baker	van Poortvliet	Malone
Fox	Wyatt/3p	Loose	Hambling(a/t)	Scott	Morfoot	Tyler	Walters	Malone	Woodhouse
Wyatt	Friel/p	Loose	Woodhouse	Scott	Anthony	Tyler	Baker	Malone	Dodds
Borrett	Friel/c3p	Loose	Woodhouse/t	Scott	Morfoot	Tyler	Baker	van Poortvliet	Dodds
Borrett	Friel/cp	Loose	Woodhouse	Scott	Morfoot	Tyler	Baker	van Poortvliet	Dodds
Borrett/t	Friel/cp	Loose	Hambling	Scott	Morfoot	Tyler	Baker/t	van Poortvliet	Dodds
Borrett/t	Friel/t3c2p	Loose	Dodds/t	Scott	Morfoot	Tyler	Malone	van Poortvliet	Bensley
Fox/t	Friel/p	Brett	Hambling	Scott	Morfoot	Tyler	Malone	van Poortvliet	Baker
Borrett	Friel/t4cp	Loose	Hambling	Brett	Morfoot/t	Tyler/t	Malone/t	van Poortvliet	Baker
Fox	Friel/3c2p	Loose	Hambling	Brett	Morfoot	Tyler	Malone	van Poortvliet	Woodhouse/t
Fox	Friel/2p	Loose	Hambling	Scott	Morfoot	Furlong	Malone	van Poortvliet	Dodds/t
N Greenhall	Wyatt/2c	Loose/t	Hambling	Scott	Morfoot	Tyler	Malone	van Poortvliet	Dodds
N Greenhall	Friel/3cp	Loose	Byrne	Scott	Tyler	Morfoot	Malone/t	van Poortvliet	Bensley
N Greenhall	Friel/tp	Loose	Hambling	Scott	Mutimer	Tyler	Furlong/t	Malone	Dodds
Youngs/t	Wyatt/2c2p	Loose	Byrne	Leonard	Morfoot	Tyler	Malone	van Poortvliet	Furlong
N Greenhall	Wyatt	Loose	Byrne	Leonard	Morfoot	Anthony	Malone	van Poortvliet	Dodds
N Greenhall	Wyatt	Loose	Byrne	Leonard	Morfoot	Tyler	Malone	van Poortvliet	Dodds
N Greenhall	Wyatt	Loose	Rosseau	Leonard	Morfoot	Tyler	Malone	van Poortvliet	Dodds
Youngs/t	Wyatt	Loose	Rosseau	Leonard	Morfoot/t	Tyler	Malone	van Poortvliet	Dodds
Youngs	Wyatt	Loose	Rosseau	Leonard	Morfoot	Tyler	Malone	van Poortvliet	Dodds/t
N Greenhall	Wyatt	Loose	Rosseau	Leonard	Morfoot	Furlong	Woodhouse	van Poortvliet	Dodds
N Greenhall	Friel	Loose	Byrne	Leonard	Morfoot	Furlong	Rosseau	Dodds	Baker
Wyatt	Friel/c3p	Loose	Woodhouse	Williams	Morfoot	Tyler	Baker	Malone	Walters
Wyatt	Friel/cp	Loose	Woodhouse	Williams	Morfoot	Tyler	Baker	van Poortvliet/t	Dodds

REPLACEMENTS   a - K Dodds

2000-01 HIGHLIGHTS

Scrum half Phil Friel tops the scoring list for the second time in three seasons. Friel had his best season to date and scored 161 points

This was the highest total since James Shanahan scored 253 back in 1997/98.

In terms of try scored the utilty forward Kenny Dodds, who can play back row or hooker, topped the list with nine from 19 starts and one replacement appearance.

Won nine out of 13 at home but away from Norwich Road they managed just three wins.

NORTH WALSHAM

LEAGUE STATISTICS *compiled by Stephen McCormack*

SEASON	Division	P	W	D	L	F	A	Pts Diff	Lge Pts	Lge Pos		Coach	Captain
91-92	D4S	12	5	0	7	153	152	1	10	7		P Bryant	B Gardner
92-93	D4S	12	4	0	8	125	209	-84	8	11			
93-94	D5S	12	5	2	5	120	173	-53	12	8			
94-95	D5S	12	7	1	4	233	190	43	15	4		R Flatters	N Greenall
												Most Points	**Most Tries**
95-96	D5S	12	3	1	8	149	212	-63	7	11	51	Tony Kingsmill	3 Smith
96-97	D4S	26	10	1	15	426	605	-179	21	10	70	James Shanahan	10 Tom Rains
97-98	N2S	26	12	1	13	431	373	58	25	7	253	James Shanahan	8 James Shanahan Adain Brand
98-99	N2S	26	22	0	4	627	306	321	44	3	158	Phil Friel	16 James Shanahan
99-00	N2S	26	19	0	7	792	358	434	38	3	167	Tony Kingsmill	21 James Shanahan
00-01	N3S	26	12	1	13	550	461	89	25	6	149	Phil Friel	9 Kenny Dodds

FACT FILE

Founded: 1962   **Colours**: Green with 1wide black & 2 narrow white bands/black/green.
Nickname: Walsh   **Change colours**: All white   **Away colours:** Red, white and black
Web site: www.vikingrugby.com

GROUND
Address: Norwich Road, Scottow, Norwich, NR10 5BU
Tel: 01692 538808 (Office & Fax)   01692 538461 (Clubhouse)
e-mail: vikingrugby@lineout.net
Capacity: 1,000   Seated: 160   Standing: 1,000

Directions: From Norwich take B1150 to North Walsham, go through Coltishall towards N Walsham.
Ground is on left just past "Three Horseshoes" Pub
Nearest Railway Station: North Walsham

Car Parking: Ample at ground

Admission: Adults £5 inc programme

Clubhouse: Open matchdays & training nights.
Snacks & barmeals available
Functions   Capacity 80, contact David Robinson 01692 538808
Club Shop: Yes, contact Pat Narracott 01692 538808

Training Nights: Tuesday & Thursday 7.30pm

PROGRAMME
Size: A5   Price: With Entry
Pages: 44 + cover
Editor: Tony Marcantonio 01493 751837

ADVERTISING RATES
Contact David Robinson 01692 538808

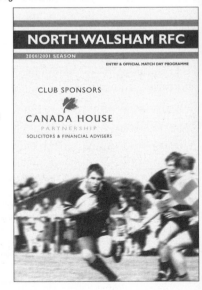

NORTH WALSHAM RFC
2000/2001 SEASON
ENTRY & OFFICIAL MATCH DAY PROGRAMME
CLUB SPONSORS
CANADA HOUSE
PARTNERSHIP
SOLICITORS & FINANCIAL ADVISERS

OLD COLFEIANS RFC

President	Moby Wale	31 Sackville Ave., Hayes, Bromley, Kent BR2 7JS	020 8325 0379 (H)	020 7837 2808 (B)
Chairman	Dick Hussey	5 The Avenue, Bickley, Bromley, Kent BR1 2BS	020 8290 5548 (H)	020 7240 3444 (B)
Secretary	Dai Andrew	80 Dallinger Rd., Lee, London SE12 0TH		
		020 8857 4036 (H) 020 8852 1250 (B) 07714 446871 (M)		
Treasurer	Clive Corlett	1 Lasseter Place, Vanburgh Hill, Blackheath, London SE3 7UX		020 8305 1261 (H)
Match Secretary	John Nunn	The Mount, 27 Westmount Rd., Eltham Park, London SE9 1JB		
		020 8850 1853 (H&F) 020 8265 7447 (H) 07989 449469 (M)		
Sponsorship Sec.	Clive Reffell	3 Prior St., Greenwich, London SE10 8SF	020 8853 1004 (H)	07788 444396 (M)
Press Secretary	Ray Phillips	39 Holme Lacey Rd., Lee, London SE12 0HD	020 8857 4049 (H)	020 8333 1941 (F)
1st XV Manager	Paul Wainman	22 Ryecroft Rd., Offord, Kent TN14 5LX		01959 524351 (H)

The Old Colfeians Rugby Club was founded in 1928 as a new section of the Old Colfeians Association to provide rugby football for former boys of the Colfes School. The club is still built around boys from Colfes School, where John Gallagher the former All Blacks full back is the master in charge of rugby. 50 percent of the first XV are ex-pupils with the team made up by friends from college or business. The Corinthian spirit still exists amongst players, officials and supporters and apart from training and physio support everyone contributes financially to the success of the rugby club. Incidentally, at the same venue soccer, cricket, squash, badminton, bowls, judo and netball all take place under the parent umbrella of the Old Colfeians Association.

League rugby started in London Three South East with promotion after two seasons to London Two South with further promotion in the 1991/92 season to London One, where the club has remained for eight seasons. After finishing in third place in 1999-2000 the last season was the finest in the club's history with 20 wins and two draws from the 22 league games. Old Colfeians not only won, but won well with forwards and three quarters combining to produce Fifteen man rugby of outstanding quality. The team scored over 100 tries with a points tally of 837 a margin in excess of 600 points above points conceded. After such a season with a six points margin between first and second place Old Colfeians deservedly became the first Old Boys club to reach National Leagues.

The season started with a fine victory over Staines, last year's runners-up, only for the team to draw the second game away to Thanet Wanderers, but this was the last set back until a drawn game against Staines in March proved only a temporary hitch. Highlights were double victories against Havant, runners-up, and Norwich who finished fourth. Although the victories were team efforts mention must be made of Matt Townsend, who scored 239 points (the highest in the league), Gavin Hurley with thirteen tries was equal highest try scorer and Dave Lewis ran in twelve tries. Steve Conlett and Matt Quilter played in all 25 cup and league games and skipper James Griffiths secured good line out ball and lead by example.

The team manager was Paul Wainman and the quality of the team effort was in no short measure due to fine coaching from Andy Smith and Jan Martin. The small number of players used was largely due to the fine physio support provided by Winston and his team.

In the cup we had two victories only to lose in the third game by a narrow margin to North Walsham. In the Kent Cup we lost in the semi-final to the eventual winners. Players and supporters alike realise that the season ahead in National League Three South will be a real challenge with stronger opposition and the increased commitment in time, travel and expense, but plans are well in hand to meet the challenge and to enjoy pastures new and to make new friends.

A jubilant Old Colfeians after their 36-13 away victory over Havant which virtually guaranteed promotion.

OLD COLFEIANS

Comp.	Date	H/A	Opponents	Result & Score	15	14	13	12	11
L1	02.09	H	Staines	W 43-16	Callard/t	Lewis D	Hurley/t	Powell/5cp(c)	Wicks
L1	16.09	A	Thanet Wanderers	D 20-20	Townsend/cp	Callard	Hurley/t	Louden/t	Wicks
L1	30.09	A	Harlow	W 50-20	Townsend/5t	Lewis D/2t	Hurley	Louden	Wicks/t
L1	14.10	H	Metropolitan Police	W 50-7	Townsend/4c4p	Lewis D/t	Hurley/2t	Louden	Wicks
L1	21.10	H	Cambridge	W 26-16	Townsend/2c4p	Lewis D/t	Hurley	Louden	Wicks
L1	28.10	A	Sutton & Epsom	W 33-21	Townsend/c7p	Callard	Lewis D	Louden	Wicks
L1	11.11	H	Thurrock	W 23-3	Townsend/3p	Lewis D/t	Hurley	Louden	Wicks
L1	18.11	A	Guildford & Godalming*	W 58-8	Townsend/6c2p	Wicks/2t(e/t)	Powell/t	Louden	Hurley/t
L1	25.11	H	Havant*	W 13-3	Townsend/c2p	Callard(n)	Powell	Louden	Hurley
L1	09.12	A	Norwich	W 27-11	Townsend/3c2p	Callard(e)	Powell	Louden	Hurley
L1	16.12	H	Guildford & Godalming*	W 65-0	Townsend/7c2p	Lewis D/t	Powell	Louden(d/t)	Hurley/3t
L1	13.01	H	Sutton & Epson	W 43-0	Townsend/2c3p	Lewis D(r)	Rutter(c/t)	Powell	Hurley
L1	27.01	A	Metropolitan Police	W 45-3	Townsend/t2c2p	Lewis D/4t	Rutter(g)	Louden	Hurley
L1	03.02	A	Thurrock	W 52-17	Townsend/t4cp(l/t3c)	Lewis D/2t	Powell (q/t)	Louden/t	Hurley/t
L1	10.02	H	Harlow	W 23-0	Hurley	Lewis D(m)	Rutter	Powell/c2p	Jarrett/t
L1	24.02	A	Winchester	W 32-10	Townsend(u/t)	Lewis D/2cp(f)	Rutter	Louden	Jarrett
L1	10.03	H	Thanet Wanderers	W 58-19	Townsend/5c5p	Lewis D	Rutter/t	Powell (d)	Hurley/2t
L1	17.03	A	Staines	D 12-12	Townsend/2p(d)	Lewis D/2p	Rutter	Powell	Hurley
L1	31.03	H	Norwich	W 28-8	Townsend/t2c2p	Lewis D/t	Rutter	Louden	Hurley(d)
L1	14.04	A	Havant	W 36-13	Townsend/3c	Lewis D/2t	Rutter/t	Powell/2t	Hurley/t
L1	21.04	H	Winchester	W 64-17	Townsend/6c4p	Lewis D/t(z)	Rutter/t	Powell/t	Hurley
L1	28.04	A	Cambridge	W 38-0	Townsend/t4c	Lewis D	Rutter	Powell	Hurley/2t
TBC	09.09	A	Slough	W 35-7	Townsend/3c3p	Callard/t	Lewis D(y)	Hurley	Wicks
TBC	23.09	H	Basingstoke	W 39-8	Townsend/5c2p	Callard(e)	Hurley	Louden	Wicks/3t
TBC	07.10	H	North Walsham	L 17-21	Townsend/4p	Lewis D/t	Hurley	Powell(j)	Wicks

** after opponents name indicates a penalty try. Brackets after a player's name indicates he was replaced.
eg (a) means he was replaced by replacement code "a" and so on. / after a player or replacement name
is followed by any scores he made - eg /t, /c, /p, /dg or any combination of these*

Steve Corlett (25)

Most Appearances
24 (1) Matt Quilter
23 (1) Gavin Hurley
23 James Griffiths, Warren Evans

PLAYERS USED

26 + 9 as replacement only

MOST POINTS

Pts	Player	T	C	P	DG
332	M Townsend	9	61	55	-
103	D Lewis	18	2	3	-
75	D Hurley	15	-	-	-
55	D Sargent	11	-	-	-
47	K Powell	4	6	3	-

MATCH FACTS

10	9	1	2	3	4	5	6	7	8
Chapman	Hyde	Quilter	Corlett/t	Tunnicliff/t	Sargent	Waden	Evans/t	Johnston(v)	Hubner
Chapman	Hyde/t	Quilter	Corlett	Tunnicliff	Sargent	Griffiths	Evans	Baker A	Walden(b)
Chapman(x/t)	Hyde	Hughes(h/t)	Corlett	Tunnicliff	Sargent	Griffiths	Evans/2t	Baker A	Walden
Whichello/t	Hyde	Quilter	Corlett	Hughes(k)	Griffiths	Walden	Evans/t	Baker A	Hubner/t
Rutter	Hyde	Quilter	Corlett	Tunnicliff	Griffiths	Walden	Evans/t	Baker A	Hubner(r)
Rutter	Hyde/t	Quilter	Corlett	Tunnicliff	Sargent/t	Griffiths	Evans	Baker A	Walden
Chapman(d)	Hyde/t	Quilter	Corlett	Tunnicliff	Sargent	Griffiths	Evans	Baker A	Walden/t
Rutter	Hyde	Quilter	Corlett	Tunnicliff(a)	Sargent/2t(r)	Griffiths	Evans	Baker A	Walden
Rutter	Hyde	Quilter	Corlett	Tunnicliff	Sargent	Griffiths	Evans	Baker A	Walden(b)
Chapman	Hyde	Quilter	Corlett	Tunnicliff/t	Sargent	Griffiths	Evans	Baker A/t	Walden/t(b)
Rutter	Hyde(d)	Quilter	Corlett	Hughes	Sargent/3t	Griffiths	Evans	Hubner(o)	Walden
Chapman/t	Hyde	Quilter	Corlett	Tunnicliff/t	Sargent/t	Griffiths	Evans	Baker A(r)	Walden
Chapman/t	Hyde/t	Quilter	Corlett	Hughes	Sargent	Griffiths	Evans(s)	Baker A	Walden
Chapman	Hyde	Quilter	Corlett	Hughes	Sargent	Griffiths(b)	Evans	Baker A	Walden
Chapman/t	Hyde/t	Quilter	Corlett	Hughes	Sargent(b)	Griffiths	Evans	Baker A	Walden
Chapman	Hyde/2t	Quilter	Corlett	Hughes(o)	Walden	Griffiths/t	Evans/t	Baker A	Hubner
Chapman/dg	Hyde	Quilter(a)	Corlett	Tunnicliff/t	Sargent/t	Griffiths	Evans(t)	Baker A(r)	Hubner
Chapman	Hyde	Quilter	Corlett	Tunnicliff	Sargent	Griffiths	Evans	Baker A	Hubner
Chapman	Hyde	Quilter/t	Corlett	Tunnicliff	Sargent	Griffiths	Evans(b)	Baker A(r)	Walden
Chapman	Lewis G	Quilter(a)	Corlett	Tunnicliff	Sargent	Griffiths	Evans	Johnston	Walden
Chapman/t	Lewis G	Quilter/t	Corlett	Tunnicliff(a)	Sargent/2t(b)	Griffiths	Evans	Johnston	Walden/t
Chapman	Lewis G	Quilter	Corlett	Tunnicliff(a)	Sargent	Griffiths	Evans	Johnston	Hubner/t(t/2t)
Chapman(x)	Hyde/t	Quilter	Corlett/t	Tunnicliff	Sargent/t	Griffiths	Hubner	Baker N	Walden
Chapman	Hyde(g)	Quilter	Corlett	Tunnicliff(a)	Sargent(b)	Griffiths	Evans	Baker A	Walden/t
Whichello	Hyde	Quilter	Corlett	Tunnicliff	Sargent	Griffiths	Hubner(n)	Baker A	Walden

REPLACEMENTS

a - Hughes	b - Hubner	c - Louden	d - Callard	e - Lewis D	f - Lewis G
g - Powell	h - Quilter	j - Rutter	k - Sargent	l - Rogers	m - Tilson
n - Davey	o - Tunnicliff	p - Chapman	q - Wicks	r - Johnston	s - Blackwell
t - Berry	u - Hurley	v - Senger	w - Baker N	x - Bowen	y - Gobir
z - Jarrett					

OLD COLFEIANS

LEAGUE STATISTICS compiled by Stephen McCormack

SEASON	Division	P	W	D	L	F	A	Pts Diff	Lge Pts	Lge Pos	Most Pts/ Coach	Most Tries/ Captain
91-92	L2s	10	8	1	1	226	110	116	17	1p		
92-93	L1	12	5	2	5	198	203	-5	12	12		
93-94	L1	12	5	0	7	166	221	-55	10	12		
94-95	L1	12	4	0	8	202	256	-54	8	12		
95-96	L1	12	4	0	8	138	241	-103	8	12		
96-97	L1	12	7	0	5	258	347	-89	12*	12		
97-98	L1	16	5	0	11	336	504	-168	10	13		
98-99	L1	16	9	1	6	310	316	-6	19	7		
99-00	L1	16	12	1	3	512	310	202	25	3		
00-01	L1	20	18	0	2	742	212	530	38	1p		

FACT FILE

Founded: 1928
Nickname:

Colours: Navy blue, burgundy, old gold & black bands/navy/navy
Change colours: Old gold with single narrow navy, burgundy & black bands

GROUND
Address

Horn Park, Eltham Road, Lee, London SE12

Tel: 0208 852 1181

Directions
Ground is in Eltham Road opposite Weigal Road, on the A20, 600 metres in the direction of Lee, Lewisham and London from the intersection of the A20 / A205 / South Circular Road. Nearest Railway Station: Lee 10-15 min. walk or Lewisham (then taxi).

Capacity 1000 - all uncovered standing
Car Parking 200 at club

Admission £3 including programme & parking..
Season tickets: Not available.

Clubhouse Open during normal licensing hours, 7 days. 2 bars.
Club Shop Open during home League and Cup games. Contact Josie Troke.

Training Nights Tuesday & Thursday

PROGRAMME
Size: A5
Pages: 24-28
Price: with admission
Editor: George Troke
Advertising: Page: £350   1/2 page £200

O C R F C
2 0 0 0   2 0 0 1

sponsored by
GMTV

OLD PATESIANS RFC

President	David Powell	Rigi, Western Rd., Cheltenham	01242 514980 (H)
Chairman	Ray Kingscott	94 Leckhampton RD., Cheltenham GL53 0BZ	
			01242 519569 (H) 07957 594032 (M)
Secretary	Steve Webley	56 Mead Rd., Cheltenham GL53 7DT	01242 244865 (H)
Treasurer	James Luxton	6 Littledown Rd., Cheltenham GL53 9LP	01242 260715 (H)
Fixture Secretary	Mark Knight	14b Canterbury Walk, Cheltenham GL51 5HG	
		01242 698756(H) 01242 271583 (B) 07719 857761 (M)	

The rugby club was formed in 1913 in Cheltenham for old boys of the local grammar school, founded by Richard Pate in the sixteenth century. It became a totally open club in the 1960s and is one section of the Patesians Sports and Social club.

When league rugby began the Pats were placed in Glos One and they stayed there until the 90/91 season when they won the league to enter Glos/Somerset. This league and the next one up, Western Counties, were won at the first attempt and then a period of consolidation followed in South West Two until 96/97 season when they were champions. A further consolidation took place with a struggle in 99/00 to stay in South West One.

New coaches were appointed in 00/01 and together with several players returning to the club and a couple of new faces the whole organisation was transformed. Not only did the First XV win the league (losing one match), but they also won the Intermediate Cup and just lost to a last kick of the game drop goal in the County Cup final. This was achieved with an amateur squad and the improvement was reflected in the Second XV coming third in the South West Merit Table and the U17 squad winning the County Cup for their age group.

The objectives of the club remain to try to provide enjoyable rugby for as many people who want to play at whatever level (last year there were four senior sides plus an occasional Vets) and to strive to be as successful as possible whilst maintaining the traditions of the game. The junior section will be expanding again for next season to include colts and at least one more age group and the Vets will play on a more regular basis.

For the season 01/02 we look forward to meeting old friends and rising to the challenge of the national league rugby.

L-R - **Back:** Neil Hyde (Touch Judge), Taff Powell (President), Pat Poulton (Team Manager), Pat Burford, Tony Robinson, Scott Miller, Chris Raymond, Dave Kingscott, Rich Harvey, Chris Penhale, Clive Organ, Ray Kingscott (Chairman), Ben Wilsdon, John Parker. **Middle:** Tim Field (Physio), Paul Sargison (2nd XV Coach/Manager), Mark Pearcey (Video Operator), Paul Bright, Dave Taylor, Will Morgan, Mark Bartlett, Pete Mitchell, Paul Morris (Asst. Coach), Mark Brooks (Aquatic porter), Dick Lewis, Ross Bissett. **Front:** Marcus Twinning (standing)(Aquatic porter), Jason Hyde, Barrie Davies, Dave Parry, Ralph Tucker (Captain), Chris Long, Ben Parker, Jon Steckbeck, Matt Dawson. **Seated:** Rob Kingscott, Sam Organ (Mascots).

OLD PATESIANS

Comp.	Date	H/A	Opponents	Result & Score	15	14	13	12	11
SW1	16.09	H	Bridgwater & Albion	W 29-0	Davies/t	Taylor(c)	Robinson/2c	Tucker	Parker/t
SW1	30.09	H	Maidenhead	W 46-5	Davies	Taylor/t	Robinson/4cp	Tucker	Parker/2t
SW1	14.10	A	Keynsham	W 37-5	Davies/t	Taylor	Tucker	Bartlett	Parker
SW1	21.10	H	Truro	W 41-6	Davies/t	Taylor/t	Tucker	Bartlett/t	Parker
SW1	28.10	A	Berry Hill	W 27-11	Davies	Taylor	Robinson	Tucker(o)	Parker
SW1	11.11	H	Dorchester	W 34-11	Davies	Taylor	Tucker/t	Bartlett	Parker
SW1	25.11	H	Swanage	W 40-5	Parker	Davies	Robinson/2t5c	Tucker	Taylor
SW1	09.12	A	Cinderford	L 10-15	Parker	Tucker	Robinson/cp	Bartlett	Davies
SW1	16.12	H	Bridgwater	W 24-19	Parker/t	Davies/t(x)	Tucker	Bartlett	Taylor/2t
SW1	13.01	H	Berry Hill	W 23-10	Parker	Davies/t	Robinson/p	Tucker	Taylor
SW1	20.01	A	Truro	W 24-16	Parker	Davies/t	Robinson/t2c	Tucker/t	Taylor/t
SW1	03.02	A	Torquay Athletic*	W 41-23	Parker/t	White/t	Robinson/2c	Tucker/t	Taylor
SW1	10.02	A	Maidenhead	W 21-3	Parker	White	Robinson/3c	Tucker	Taylor/t
SW1	17.02	H	Barnstaple	W 31-22	Parker(v)	White	Robinson/3c	Tucker/t	Taylor/2t
SW1	31.03	H	Cinderford	W 16-10	Parker	Taylor	Tucker	Bartlett	Bright/t
SW1	07.04	H	Keynsham	W 34-12	Parker	Davies/t	Tucker/t(11)	Bartlett	Taylor
SW1	14.04	A	Swanage*	W 40-5	Parker/t	White	Robinson/tcp	Tucker(11)	Taylor/2t
SW1	16.04	A	Dorchester	W 45-7	Robinson/5c	Davies/3t	Tucker(1/t)	Bartlett	Bright
SW1	05.05	A	Barnstaple	W 30.24	Parker/t	Bright	Tucker	Bartlett	Taylor
CC	18.11	A	Drybrook	W 25-8	Davies/t	Parker/t	Tucker	Bartlett	Robinson/2t
CC	07.01	H	Coney Hill	W 18-0	Parker/t	Davies	Tucker	Bartlett/t	Taylor
CC	18.02	A	Stroud	W 14-9	Parker(9)	Davies	Robinson	Bright	Taylor
CCF	05.03	H	Cinderford	L 13-14	Davies	Bright	Robinson/c2p	Tucker(10)	Taylor
IC	07.10	A	Old Centralians	W 43-0	Davies/3t	Taylor/t	Robinson/2c	Bartlett	Parker/t
IC	04.11	A	Cleve	W 41-12	Robinson/3c	Davies/t	Parker	Bartlett	Capie/2t
IC	02.12	H	High Wycombe*	W 96-12	Parker/t(x/t)	Davies	Robinson/t8c	Bartlett	Taylor/3t
IC	06.01	H	Woodford	W 39-12	Parker	White/t	Robinson/3c(h)	Lambert(1)	Capie/t
IC	27.01	H	Cinderford	W 16-10	Davies	White	Robinson/tcp	Tucker	Taylor
IC	24.02	A	Hertford	W 27-16	Davies	White	Tucker	Bright	Taylor
IC SF	17.03	H	Cleckheaton	W 34-7	Robinson/3cp	Davies	Tucker(o)	Taylor	Bright
IC Final	21.04	N	Blaydon	W 25-24	Robinson/2cp	Davies(12)	Tucker	Bartlett(11)	Taylor

* after opponents name indicates a penalty try. Brackets after a player's name indicates he was replaced.
eg (a) means he was replaced by replacement code "a" and so on. / after a player or replacement name
is followed by any scores he made - eg /t, /c, /p, /dg or any combination of these

EVER PRESENT	None

Most Appearances
Morgan	32
Raymond	31
Taylor	30

MOST POINTS

Pts	Player	T	C	P	DG
197	Robinson	10	57	11	-
100	Morgan	20			
80	Taylor	16			

MATCH FACTS

10	9	1	2	3	4	5	6	7	8
Steckbeck	Morgan	Long(e)	Newcombe	Mitchell	Kingscott/t(d)	Raymond	Burford	Parry/t	Dawson/t
Steckbeck	Morgan/t	Harvey	Newcombe(f)	Mitchell	Kingscott9d	Raymond	Burford	Parry/2t	Dawson(g)
Steckbeck	Morgan/t	Harvey	Hyde	Mitchell(l/t)	Kingscott(d)	Raymond	Burford/t2cp	Parry/t	Organ/t(m)
Steckbeck/t	Morgan	Harvey(l)	Hyde	Mitchell/t	Kingscott(d)	Raymond/t	Burford/3c(n)	Parry	Organ(m/t)
Steckbeck/t	Morgan/t	long/t	Hyde	Mitchell	Penhale(4)	Raymond	Burford	Organ/2t	Dawson
Armstrong	Morgan/3t	Harvey(t)	Hyde	Long	Penhale(u)	Raymond	Burford3cp(e)	Parry/t(n)	Organ
Steckbeck	Morgan/t	Harvey	Hyde	Long(t)	Penhale/t(s)	Raymond	Burford(n)	Parry	Organ/2t
Steckbeck	Morgan	Long(e)	Hyde	Mitchell	Kingscott(d)	Raymond	Burford	Parry/t	Dawson
Steckbeck/2c	Morgan	Harvey	Newcombe	Mitchell	Penhale	Raymond	Miller(f)	Parry(z)	Dawson
Steckbeck(x)	Morgan	Harvey(t/t)	Newcombe	Long	Penhale/t	Raymond	Burford/cp(4)	Organ	Dawson
Armstrong(v)	Morgan	Harvey(t)	Hyde	Long	Penhale(g)	Wilsdon	Burford	Raymond	Parry
Steckbeck	Morgan/t(6)	Long	Newcombe(f)	Mitchell/t	Penhale(4)	Raymond	Johnson	Parry/t	Burford/c
Steckbeck(x)	Morgan/2t	Harvey	Newcombe	Mitchell(l)	Kingscott(4)	Raymond	Burford	Parry	Dawson
Armstrong/2t	Morgan	Long(7)	Newcombe	Mitchell	Wisdon	Raymond	Miller(2)	Parry	Dawson
Steckbeck/2p	Morgan	Harvey(l)	Bisset	Mitchell	Kingscott	Raymond	Organ/t	Parry	Dawson
Armstrong	Morgan/t	Harvey(t)	Newcombe	Long	Kingscott/t	Raymond	Burford/t2c	Parry(g)	Dawson/t
Steckbeck	Morgan(8)	J Parker	Newcombe	Mitchell	Kingscott	Raymond/t	Organ	Miller	Dawson/t(l)
Armstrong/t	Morgan/t	Harvey(7)	Hyde	Long	Penhale	Raymond(4)	Burford	Parry/t	Dawson
Steckbeck/c2p(x/c)	Morgan	Harvey	Hyde	Long(t)	Penhale/t	Raymond	Organ	Parry(2)	Dawson/2t
Armstrong(v)	G Jones	Long	Hammett(r)	Mitchell(w)	Penhale	Kingscott(k)	Miller	R Jones	Parry/t
Steckbeck	Morgan(2)	Lake	Newcombe	Mitchell(w)	Wilsdon	Raymond	Hamilton/c2p	Bailey(3)	Dawson
Steckbeck	Morgan	Harvey	Hyde(r)	Long(t)	Penhale	Kingscott	Burford/3p	Johnson(8/t)	Organ
Armstrong(v)	Morgan	Harvey(t)	Newcombe	Long	Penhale(u)	Raymond	Burford(8/t)	Organ(n)	Dawson
Steckbeck/t(h/t)	Morgan	Harvey	Hyde(r)	Long	Kingscott	Penhale9k)	Burford/2c	Parry	Organ
Taylor/t	Morgan/t	Harvey/t	Hyde(r)	Mitchell(q)	Penhale	Raymond	Miller	Parry	Organ/t(s)
Steckbeck/3t	Morgan/2t	Harvey(l)	Newcombe	Mitchell	Kingscott	Raymond(b)	Miller	R Jones	Dawson/3t(y)
Armstrong	Morgan/t	Harvey	Hyde(2)	Long	Penhale/t	Kingscott(k)	Burford/2c2p	Parry	Organ
Steckbeck	Morgan	Harvey	Newcombe	Long(t)	Penhale	Raymond	Burford/2p	Parry(5)	Dawson
Armstrong/dg(v/c)	Morgan	Harvey(t)	Hyde	Long	Penhale/t	Raymond	Burford/c(n/t)	Organ/2t(5)	Dawson
Steckbeck(x)	Morgan/t	Harvey(l)	Newcombe(f)	Mitchell	Kingscott(z)	Raymond/t	Organ/t(n)	Parry/t	Dawson/t
Steckbeck/dg	Morgan/t	Long	Hyde	Mitchell(e)	Kingscott(d)	Raymond	Organ/2t(2)	Parry(n)	Dawson

REPLACEMENTS

a - Dixon	b - Hamilton	c - Fraine	d - Penhale	e - Harvey	f - Hyde
g - Organ	h - Tucker	k - Raymond	l - Long	m - Dawson	n - Miller
o - Bartlett	q - Lake	r - Bissett	s - R Jones	t - Mitchell	u - Kingscott
v - Steckbeck	w - Phillips	x - Armstrong	y - Bailey	z - Burford	
1 - Taylor	2 - Preece	3 - Woodward	4 - Wilsdon	5 - Johnson	6 - Wycherley
7 - J Parker	8 - Parry	9 - Capie	10 - White	11 - Bright	12 - B Parker

2000-01 HIGHLIGHTS

Playing at both Twickenham (Intermediate Cup Final) and Kingsholm in the same season.

Will Morgan, the club's leading try scorer, was also the leading try scorer in the league.

OLD PATESIANS

LEAGUE STATISTICS compiled by Stephen McCormack

SEASON	Division	P	W	D	L	F	A	Pts Diff	Lge Pts	Lge Pos
91-92	Gl 1	10	7	1	2	180	104	76	15	1p
92-93	G&S1	12	11	0	1	307	94	213	22	1p
93-94	WC	12	10	1	1	215	99	116	21	1p
94-95	SW2	12	7	0	5	288	167	121	12*	5
95-96	SW2	12	4	0	8	167	231	-64	8	10
96-97	SW2w	22	13	0	9	447	341	106	26	3
97-98	SW2w	22	19	0	3	485	257	228	38	1p
98-99	SW1	22	6	1	15	320	506	-186	13	9
99-00	SW1	22	8	1	13	386	583	-197	17	8
00-01	SW1	22	21	0	1	593	209	384	42	1p

FACT FILE

Founded: 1913
Nickname: The Pats

Colours: magenta, navy & white hoops
Change colours: Navy with white band

GROUND

Address   Clubhouse, Everest Rd., Leckhampton, Cheltenham. GL53 9LG
Tel: 01242 524633   Web site: www.old-pats.freeuk.com
Capacity   500 all uncovered standing
Directions
   From M5, J11a (Cirencester) towards Cirencester. Take exit A46 (Cheltenham/Stroud) towards Cheltenham. After approx. 1.5 miles turn right opposite Bell Inn signed Leckhampton. At mini r'about turn right then take 1st left (at Suzuki garage). Follow to end over crossroads and ground is thro' stone pillars at end.

   From M4, J15 & follow signs for Cheltenham past Swindon then Cirencester. At end of dual carriageway follow to r'about with Air Balloon PH. Turn right and immediate left signed Leckhampton/Cheltenham. Follow down steep hill & turn right just after 30mph sign into Old Bath Road. Follow for approx 400 yds to Wheatsheaf pub. Turn right & ground at the end thro' stone pillars.

Nearest Railway Station: Cheltenham, 3 miles
Car Parking   100 spaces at the ground

Admission   Matchday: £3.00 incl. programme.
Season tickets: Not available.
Clubhouse   Open every evening &
Sat. & Sun. lunchtime. Food available.
Available for hire, contact club 01242 524633
Club Shop   No

Training Nights   Tuesday & Thursday

PROGRAMME   **Size:** A5   **Pages:** 28
Price: With admission
Editor: Contact club
Advertising: Page £100; 1/2 page: £60; 1/4 page: £50

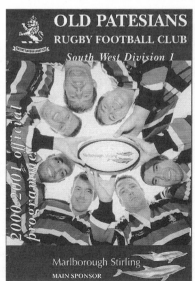

PENZANCE & NEWLYN RFC

President	Dicky Evans	
Chairman	Robin Turner	01736 367317
Club Administrator	Terry Drew	01736 351568
Chief Executive	Martin Scrase	01736 335315
Coaching Director	Kevin Moseley	01736 335311

c/o Penzance & Newlyn RFC,
Westholme, Alexandra Road, Penzance, Cornwall. TR18 4LY

Last season was our second in National Division 3 (South) and we ended it with a sense of under achievement, finishing third behind winners, Plymouth Albion, and our county rivals, Launceston. It was a case of a certain inconsistency during the middle of the season which saw our chances of a play-off spot slip away. After two campaigns of pushing for promotion, the pressure is really on this season to go one step further and achieve the top spot.

Our young squad, having gained two years' worth of valuable experience in this league, has been boosted by the arrival of new players to bolster the pack. The whole team will be keen to impose themselves on that, which is a much changed league, five clubs having departed and five others having joined. These new teams will certainly present fresh challenges to ourselves and the other established sides in our competition.

It is unlikely that our style of play will change evry much this season and we shall strive to play the exciting and entetaing type of rugby, which has become our trade mark. We trust that our top points scorers over the past two seasons, Nat Saumi, Victor Olonga and Richard Newton, will contrive to profit from much more user friendly ball delivery.

We look forward hugely to the challenges which await us this season in the league and, especially, in the Tetley's Bitter Cup. We have reached the Third Round in each of our previous two campaigns, losing narrowly to Moseley and Wakefield respectively. These were most prestigious games for us and we hope for more of the same this year. In true Pirates fashion, we shall extend the warmest of welcomes to our visitors, in the hope that all matches are played with the emphasis on running rugby and enjoyment for players and spectators alike.

Kevin Moseley

PENZANCE & NEWLYN

Comp.	Date	H/A	Opponents	Result & Score	Att	15	14	13	12	11
N3S	2-Sep	A	Plymouth Albion	L 0-19	1500	Saumi	Redgrave	Gadsdon	Evans	Richards
N3S	9-Sep	A	Westcombe Park	W 39-26	350	Saumi/2c4p	Redgrave	Gadsdon	Evans	Olonga/3t
N3S	16-Sep	H	Redruth	W 35-11	1500	Saumi/t3c3p	Olonga	Gadsdon/t	Evans	Redgrave/t
N3S	30-Sep	H	Basingstoke	W 28-17		Saumi/t4c	Redgrave/t	Gadsdon	Evans	Hawken
N3S	14-Oct	A	Cheltenham	W 40-24	250	Saumi/4c4p	Redgrave/t	Olonga/t	Gadsdon	Davies/t
N3S	28-Oct	A	Barking	D 17-17		Saumi/4p	Redgrave	Olonga	Gadsdon	Davies
N3S	11-Nov	A	Reading*	L 12-23	250	Saumi/c	Redgrave	Olonga	Gadsdon	Hawken
N3S	18-Nov	H	Tabard	D 24-24		Saumi/3cp	Redgrave	Gadsdon	Evans/2t	Hawken
N3S	25-Nov	A	Weston super Mare	W 17-14	250	Saumi/2cp	Redgrave	Gadsdon	Evans	Hawken/t
N3S	2-Dec	H	Blackheath*	W 51-14	800	Saumi/2t4cp	Redgrave	Olonga/2t	Gadsdon	Doyle
N3S	9-Dec	A	Clifton	W 20-14		Saumi/t2c2p	Redgrave	Olonga	Gadsdon	Hawken
N3S	16-Dec	H	North Walsham	W 63-0	800	Saumi/t9c	Redgrave/t	Olonga/3t	Gadsdon	Hawken
N3S	30-Dec	H	Weston super Mare	W 50-13	800	Saumi/t4c4p	Redgrave/t	Olonga/3t	Gadsdon	Hawken
N3S	6-Jan	A	Tabard	W 68-17	220	Hawken/t	Redgrave/t	Gadsdon	Saumi/2t6c3p	Newton/4t
N3S	13-Jan	H	Reading	W 48-12	800	Hawken/t	Redgrave/t	Saumi/t2c3p	Gadsdon	Newton/t
N3S	20-Jan	H	Barking	W 16-13	800	Hawken	Redgrave/t	Olonga	Gadsdon	Newton/t
N3S	27-Jan	A	Launceston	L 5-31	2000	Hawken/t	Redgrave	Saumi	Gadsdon	Newton
N3S	3-Feb	A	Blackheath	L 37-38	400	Hawken/2t	Redgrave	Olonga/2t	Evans/t	Newton
N3S	10-Feb	H	Cheltenham	W 58-0		Olonga/t	Redgrave/t	Hawken	Evans	Newton(b/t)
N3S	17-Feb	H	Launceston	W 43-20	2000	Hawken/t	Redgrave/3t	Gadsdon/t	Evans	Newton/2t
N3S	24-Feb	A	Basingstoke	W 53-18	350	Hawken/t	Redgrave/2t2c	Gadsdon/t	Evans/t	Newton/t
N3S	10-Mar	H	Westcombe Park	W 31-13	900	Hawken	Redgrave/t	Olonga/2t	Evans	Newton
N3S	17-Mar	A	Redruth	L 6-23	2000	Olonga	Redgrave	Gadsdon	Evans	Newton
N3S	24-Mar	H	Plymouth Albion	L 13-36	2000	Olonga	Hawken	Gadsdon	Bearman	Newton/t
N3S	31-Mar	A	North Walsham	W 24-14		Olonga/t	Redgrave/tc3p	Hawken	Bearman	Newton
N3S	14-Apr	H	Clifton	W 25-10	1000	Olonga/t	Redgrave/t	Saumi/tcp	Evans	Newton
TBC	21-Oct	H	Wakefield	L 22-26	1800	Saumi/t2cp	Redgrave	Olonga/t	Gadsdon	Davies

* after opponents name indicates a penalty try. Brackets after a player's name indicates he was replaced.
eg (a) means he was replaced by replacement code "a" and so on. / after a player or replacement name
is followed by any scores he made - eg /t, /c, /p, /dg or any combination of these

EVER PRESENT	None		MOST POINTS				
Most Appearances:			Pts	Player	T	C	P	DG
26	Steve Evans.		336	N Saumi	17	67	39	-
25	Peter Redgrave.		100	V Olonga	20	-	-	-
24	Chris Mills.		100	P Redgrave	17	3	3	-
23	Nat Saumi.		50	R Newton	10	-	-	-
22	Joe Bearman		41	S Evans	7	-	1	1
PLAYERS USED								
33 plus two as a replacement only.								

MATCH FACTS

10	9	1	2	3	4	5	6	7	8
Birkett	Beck	Harvey	Jenkin	Stewart	Carroll	Yelland	Durant	Penrose	Mills
Birkett/dg	Beck	Hood	Davey(a/t)	Nicholas	Carroll	Jarvis	Atkinson	Penrose	Mills
Birkett	Beck	Harvey	Davey	Nicholas	Carroll	Moseley	Atkinson	Penrose/t	Bearman
Olonga/t	Beck	Kevern	Jenkin	Nicholas	Carroll	Atkinson	Bearman/t	Jarvis	Mills
Evans	Beck/t	Hood	Davey	Nicholas	Carroll	Mills	Jarvis	Penrose	Bearman
Evans	Birkett	Harvey	Davey	Hood	Carroll	Mills	Durant/t	Penrose	Bearman
Evans	Beck	Harvey	Davey	Hood	Atkinson/t	Moseley	Durant	Penrose	Mills
Birkett	Beck/t	Harvey	Laity	Stewart	Carroll	Mills	Durant	Jarvis	Bearman
Birkett	Beck	Harvey	Laity	Stewart	Carroll/t	Mills	Atkinson	Jarvis	Bearman
Evans/t	Pascoe	Harvey	Laity	Hood	Carroll/t	Mills	Atkinson/t	Durant	Bearman
Evans	Pascoe	Harvey	Davey/t	Hood	Carroll	Mills	Atkinson	Penrose	Bearman
Evans/2t	Pascoe	Harvey/t	Laity/t	Hood	Carroll	Mills	Atkinson	Penrose	Bearman
Evans	Birkett	Hoskins	Laity	Nicholas	Carroll	Mills	Durant/t	Penrose	Bearman
Evans	Birkett/c	Harvey	Laity	Stewart	Carroll	Mills	Durant	Penrose	Bearman/t
Evans	Birkett	Harvey	Laity/t	Stewart	Carroll	Mills/t	Durant/t	Penrose	Bearman
Evans	Birkett/2p	Harvey	Laity	Stewart	Carroll	Mills	Durant	Penrose	Bearman
Evans	Birkett	Harvey	Davey	Stewart	Carroll	Mills	Durant	Penrose	Bearman
Saumi/3c2p	Birkett	Harvey	Davey	Nicholas	Carroll	Mills	Atkinson	Jarvis	Bearman
Saumi/4t5cp	Birkett/t	Harvey	Davey	Nicholas	Jarvis	Mills	Durant	Penrose	Bearman/t
Saumi/4c	Birkett	Harvey	Clackworthy	Stewart	Jarvis	Atkinson	Bearman	Penrose	Mills
Saumi/t4c2p	Birkett	Harvey	Clackworthy	Stewart	Jarvis	Atkinson	Durant	Penrose	Mills
Saumi/t4cp	Birkett	Harvey	Clackworthy	Hood	Jarvis	Atkinson	Bearman	Penrose	Mills
Saumi/2p	Birkett	Harvey	Clackworthy	Hood	Carroll	Atkinson	Bearman	Penrose	Mills
Evans/p	Pascoe	Harvey	Laity	Stewart	Carroll	Atkinson	Durant	Penrose/t	Mills
Evans/dg	Birkett	Harvey	Clackworthy	Stewart	Carroll	Atkinson	Durant	Penrose	Mills
Hawken	Pascoe	Hood	Laity(c/t)	Clackworthy	Carroll	Atkinson	Jarvis	Penrose	Bearman
Evans	Birkett	Hood	Davey	Nicholas	Carroll	Mills	Jarvis(d/t)	Penrose	Bearman

REPLACEMENTS   a - W Jenkin   b - P Gadsden   c - W Davey   d - A Durant

2000-01 HIGHLIGHTS

Nat Saumi topped the Division Three South points scoring charts with 336 points.

He has topped scored for The Pirates for the last three seasons but failed this season, by just three points, to break his own club record of 339 points set a couple of seasons ago in South West One.

The try scoring title went to Victor Olonga who for the second season running scored 20 tries but this time it was enough to top the list.

Last season's leading try scorer Richard Newton went off to Cardiff but did come back to play in the final 13 matches and rattled up 10 tries.

Plymouth were the only side to win at Westholme all season although Tabard did go away with a point in a 24 all draw.

PENZANCE & NEWLYN

LEAGUE STATISTICS compiled by Stephen McCormack

SEASON	Division	P	W	D	L	F	A	Pts Diff	Lge Pts	Lge Pos	Coach	Captain
91-92	Western Cos.	34	20	2	12	791	399	392	40	5	P Greaces	J Dean
92-93	Western Cos.	38	25	0	13	975	510	465	50	4	P Greaves	A Bick
93-94	Western Cos.	37	26	0	11	686	428	258	52	4	P Greaves	A Bick
94-95	Western Cos.	33	24	0	9	787	400	387	48	4	P Greaves	A Bick
95-96	Western Cos.	38	22	1	15	923	685	238	45	3p	R Tonkin	A Ellery
96-97	SW 2	31	25	0	6	1074	441	633	50	1p	R Tonkin	M Murrish
97-98	SW 1	39	26	1	12	1102	716	386	53	4	M Ring/P Johnson	M Murrish
98-99	SW1	32	26	0	6	1336	464	872	52	1p	P Johnson	A Bick

											Most Points	Most Tries
99-00	N2S	26	20	1	5	1055	479	576	41	2	204 Nat Saumi	38 Richard Newton
00-01	N3S	26	18	2	6	823	492	331	38	3	336 Nat Saumi	20 Victor Olonga

FACT FILE

Founded: 1945

Colours: Black, white & red hoops
Change colours: Black with red collar

Web site: www.pirates-rfc.co.uk

GROUND
Address: Westholme, Alexandra Road, Penzance, Cornwall. TR18 4LY
Tel: 01736 351568 / 364227   Fax: 01736 335319   e-mail: terry.drew@btclic.com
Capacity: 5,000   Seated: 560   Standing - Covered: 750 Uncovered: 3,690

Directions: Follow the sea road (via the harbour), past the Jubilee bathing pool to end of the promenade until mini roundabout at Beachfield Hotel, then turn right and the ground is 400 yards up on the left. Nearest Railway Station: Penzance, 250 yds from town centre

Car Parking: Limited at ground. Car Park on promenade for 300 cars. Off street parking available.

Admission: Season tickets - Adults £90 Sen. Citizens £50
Matchday - Standing: Adults £6, Sen. Cit./Students £3

Clubhouse: Open every eve. except Sun. & Mon. 7-11, Sun 12-3 & matchdays 12-11.
4 bars with snacks & bar meals available.
Corporate hospitality & Functions available.

Club Shop: At club - open during the week incl. matchdays

Training Nights: Tuesday & Thursday

PROGRAMME Size: A5   Price: 50p
Pages: 48   Editor: des Hosken

Advertising Rates (all + V.A.T.)
Page £300;   1/2 £160;   1/4 £90;   1/8 £50

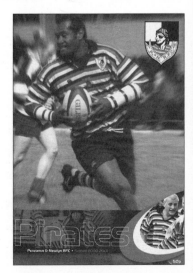

REDRUTH RFC

President	W J `Bill' Bishop OBE	Lafrowda, Tregolls Road, Truro TR1 1LE
Secretary	Roger Watson	Trelawny House, Fore St., Trelony, Truro TR2 5EX
		01872 530687 (H) 01872 530675 (B)
Fixtures Secretary	Denzil Williams	13 Boskennal Drive, Hayle, TR27 4DX
		01736 752795 (H)
Rugby Secretary	Simon Blake	Oakland, Albany Court, Redruth TR15 2NY
		01209 215401
Treasurer	Cyril Harding	Chy-an-Brea, Silver Hill, Perrannell Station, Truro TR3 7LP
		01872 863650
Press Officer	Steve Thompson	Trewartha, Blowing House Hill, Redruth TR15 3AG
		01209 212722 (H&F) 01209 314400 (B) 07801 309263 (M)

Even though we finished fifth in National League Three (South) for the second consecutive year we had a season of two halves. Eight games were lost in 2000 with 2001 bringing a marked change in fortunes; only a further three very close matches were lost, two of which were away to the sides which ended up first and second in the league. It clearly took a while for the introduction of players from Fiji and New Zealand to blend in with the rest of the team and produce results that their own commitment combined with the good work of the coaches deserved.

At the end of the season our Head coach was appointed county coach and a number of players were rewarded by being picked to play for Cornwall at Twickenham in a special invitation challenge match between the two previous County Champions.

Our colts won the Cornwall County Cup for the fourth year in succession and the fifteenth time in all - exactly half of the occasions on which it has been contested. Three of our colts are to be congratulated on their international selection - Adryan Winnan (fullback) England Schools, Guy Botterill (lock) England U18s and Julian Hosking (flanker) England U18s. Our under 9s and under 12s were both unbeaten although no festivals were played owing to the foot and mouth problems.

We were pleased to host the England `A' v France `A' international in April. With such a strong following for rugby in the county it is important that games of this standard continue to be played locally.

We were delighted that former colts captain Rob Thirlby was selected to represent England in the Rugby Sevens World Cup in Argentina in January and thrilled that another former colt, Phil Vickery, was selected for the Lions - our first former player to be so honoured since Richard Sharp in 1962.

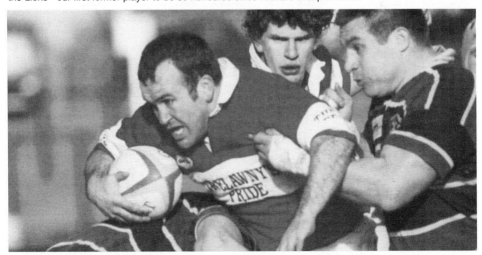

REDRUTH

Comp.	Date	H/A	Opponents	Result & Score	Att	15	14	13	12	11
N3 S	2-Sep	H	Launceston	L 29-34	700	Sincock	Veale	Hymans	Larkins/t3cp	Edyvean
N3 S	16-Sep	A	Penzance & Newlyn	L 11-35	1500	Sincock	Veale	Hymans	Larkins/2p	Edyvean
N3 S	23-Sep	H	Reading	W 29-22	700	Sincock	Veale	Hymans	Larkins/t2c4p	Parker
N3 S	30-Sep	A	Tabard	W 48-17		Sincock	Veale	Waqanivere/t	Larkins/t6c2p	Hymans/t
N3 S	14-Oct	H	Weston super Mare	W 30-6	600	Gomez	Sincock	Larkins/2c2p	Thirby/2t	Hymans/t
N3 S	28-Oct	H	Clifton	W 48-31	600	Gomez	Sincock	Larkins/5cp	Thirby	Hymans/2t
N3 S	4-Nov	A	Blackheath	W 48-22	180	Sincock/2t	Turnbull	Larkins/5c	Thirby/2t	Hymans
N3 S	11-Nov	A	North Walsham	L 5-26	250	Sincock	Turnbull	Larkins	Thirby/t	Hymans
N3 S	18-Nov	H	Plymouth Albion	L 19-30	1000	Sincock	Larkins/p	Hymans	Thirby	Gomez/t
N3 S	25-Nov	H	Barking	W 20-12	600	Sincock	Hymans	McCracken	Thirby/t	Gomez
N3 S	2-Dec	A	Westcombe Park	L 18-35	120	Sincock	Larkins	McCracken/t	Thirby	Hymans
N3 S	9-Dec	H	Basingstoke	L 15-18	650	Sincock/t	Larkins/t	McCracken	Thirby	Hymans
N3 S	16-Dec	A	Cheltenham	L 13-34	250	Sincock	Bushin	Thirby/t	McCracken	Larkins/t
N3 S	23-Dec	H	Westcombe Park	W 45-20	700	Sincock	Bushin/t	Thirby	McCracken	Larkins/t4c3p
N3 S	6-Jan	A	Plymouth Albion	L 10-30	2000	Sincock	Bushin	Thirby	McCracken	Larkins/cp
N3 S	13-Jan	H	North Walsham	W 43-19	700	Sincock	Bushin/2t	McCracken	Harris/2t	Larkins/4c(a/t)
N3 S	20-Jan	A	Clifton	W 23-13	120	Sincock	Bushin	McCracken	Gomez/t(b/t)	Veale/t
N3 S	27-Jan	H	Blackheath	W 35-23	400	Sincock	Veale	Gomez	McCracken/t	Larkins/t
N3 S	3-Feb	A	Barking	L 18-34		Sincock/2t	Veale	Gomez	McCracken	Larkins
N3 S	10-Feb	A	Weston super Mare	D 16-16	500	Sincock	Bushin	Gomez	McCracken	Larkins
N3 S	24-Feb	H	Tabard	W 32-0	500	Sincock/t	Larkins/3c2p	Thirby	Kirman	Edyvean
N3 S	10-Mar	A	Reading	L 35-47		Sincock	Larkins/2cp	Hymans	Kirman	Edyvean
N3 S	17-Mar	H	Penzance & Newlyn	W 23-6	2000	Larkins/2c2p	Bushin	Hymans	Kirman	Edyvean
N3 S	24-Mar	N	Launceston	L 9-11	1000	Larkins/3p	Veale	Hymans	Kirman	Sincock
N3 S	31-Mar	H	Cheltenham*	W 38-28	1000	Larkins/4c	Veale/t	Gomez	Kirman/t	Sincock
N3 S	14-Apr	N	Basingstoke	W 31-26	200	Larkins/3c	Veale/t	Hymans	Kirman/t	Sincock
TBC	7-Oct	H	Esher	L 10-14	700	Larkins/cp	Sincock	Waqanivere	Brown	Hymans

*after opponents name indicates a penalty try. Brackets after a player's name indicates he was replaced.
eg (a) means he was replaced by replacement code "a" and so on. / after a player or replacement name
is followed by any scores he made - eg /t, /c, /p, /dg or any combination of these

Most Appearances:
26	Tom Sincock, Neil Douch.
25	Ian Boase, Nick Croker, Jamie Knight.
24	Steve Larkins.
23	Simon O'Sullivan.

PLAYERS USED

27 plus eight as replacements only.

MOST POINTS

Pts	Player	T	C	P	DG
207	S Larkins	8	46	25	-
121	B Brown	8	6	16	7
60	L Waqanivere	12	-	-	-
43	P Thirlby	8	-	-	1
35	J Knight	7	-	-	-

MATCH FACTS

10	9	1	2	3	4	5	6	7	8
Thirby/t	Knight/t	Douch	Bush/t	Croker	O'Sullivan	Gray	Hawken	Boase	Waqanivere
Thirby	Knight	Douch	Bush	Croker	Hawken	Gray	Boase/t	Navin	Waqanivere
Thirby/dg	Knight/t	Douch	Bush	Croker	O'Sullivan	Gray	Navin	Boase	Hawken
Thirby	Knight	Douch	Bush/t	Croker	O'Sullivan/t	Gray	Navin	Boase/t	Hawken
Brown	Knight	Douch	Bush	Croker	O'Sullivan	Gray	Navin	Waqanivere	Hawken/t
Brown/t	Knight/t	Douch	Bush/t	Croker	O'Sullivan	Gray	Waqanivere/2t	Boase	Hawken
Brown/2tdg	Knight	Douch	Bush/t	Croker	O'Sullivan	Gray	Waqanivere	Boase	Hawken
Brown	Knight	Douch	Bush	Croker	O'Sullivan	Gray	Waqanivere	Boase	Hawken
Brown/t2dg	Knight	Douch	Bush	Croker	O'Sullivan	Gray	Navin	Boase	Hawken
Brown/2cpdg	Knight	Douch/t	Bush	Croker	Collins	Gray	Navin	Boase	Hawken
Brown/tc2p	Knight	Douch	Bush	Croker	O'Sullivan	Collins	Navin	Boase	Hawken
Brown	Knight	Douch	Clifton-Griffiths	Croker	O'Sullivan	Gray	Navin	Boase/t	Waqanivere
Brown/p	Knight	Douch	Clifton-Griffiths	Croker	O'Sullivan	Gray	Navin	Boase	Hawken
Brown/dg	Knight/t	Douch/t	Clifton-Griffiths	Croker	O'Sullivan	Gray	Navin	Boase	Waqanivere/t
Brown	Knight	Douch	Clifton-Griffiths	Croker	Waqanivere/t	Gray	Navin	Boase	Hawken
Brown/t	Knight/t	Douch	Bush	Croker	O'Sullivan	Gray	Navin	Boase	Waqanivere
Brown/c2p	Knight	Douch	Bush	Croker	O'Sullivan	Hawken	Navin	Boase	Waqanivere
Brown/t5p	Knight	Douch	Bush	Croker	O'Sullivan	Hawken	Navin/t	Boase	Waqanivere
Brown/c2p	Knight	Douch	Bush	Filde	O'Sullivan	Gray	Navin	Boase	Waqanivere
Brown/c3p	Knight	Douch	Clifton-Griffiths	Croker	O'Sullivan	Hawken	Navin	Boase	Waqanivere/t
Brown	Knight/t	Douch	Clifton-Griffiths	Croker	O'Sullivan	Hawken	Navin	Boase	Waqanivere/2t
Brown/tdg	Knight	Douch	Clifton-Griffiths	Croker	O'Sullivan	Hawken	Navin/t	Boase/2t	Waqanivere/t
Brown/dg	Sincock	Douch	Bush	Croker	O'Sullivan/t	Hawken	Navin	Boase	Waqanivere/t
Brown	Knight	Douch	Bush	Croker	O'Sullivan	Hawken	Navin	Boase	Waqanivere
Brown	Knight	Douch/t	Bush	Croker	O'Sullivan	Hawken	Navin	Boase	Waqanivere/2t
Brown/t	Knight/t	Douch	Bush	Croker	O'Sullivan	Hawken	Navin/t	Boase/t	Waqanivere
Thirby	Knight	Douch	Bush	Croker	O'Sullivan	Gray	Navin	Boase/t	Hawken

REPLACEMENTS   a - M Gomez   b - S Larkins

2000-01 HIGHLIGHTS

Steve Larkins tops the scoring for the second straight season and this time tops the 200 point mark.
It is the highest total since Rob Thirlby scored 256 in his final season before going on to greater things.

On the try scoring front new boy Luke Waqanivere ran out winner easily with 12 tries which was four more than the next best total.

Outside half Bede Brown dropped seven goals in the league campaign which was the second highest total in the National Leagues during the season.

After a bright start to the season Redruth won just one from six in the run up to Christmas, but steadied the ship in the new year to finish 5th place.

REDRUTH

LEAGUE STATISTICS compiled by Stephen McCormack

SEASON	Division	P	W	D	L	F	A	Pts Diff	Lge Pts	Lge Pos	Most Points		Most Tries	
91-92	D3	12	6	1	5	155	123	32	13	5	80	Kevin Thomas	2	by four players
92-93	D3	11	7	2	2	175	125	50	16	4	89	Kevin Thomas	6	Andy Knowles
93-94	D3	18	2	0	16	178	488	-310	4	10	71	Simon Blake	2	Mark Rose & Chris Whitworth
94-95	D4	18	6	2	10	309	387	-78	14	7	179	Simon Blake	4	Simon Blake
95-96	D4	18	7	2	9	358	392	-34	16	7	126	Stu Whitworth	8	Peter Congo
96-97	D3	30	7	0	23	565	1116	-551	14	15	120	Ian Morgan	10	Peter Congo
97-98	N2S	26	10	0	16	720	580	140	20	9	256	Rob Thirlby	17	Rob Thirlby
98-99	N2S	26	8	1	17	503	652	-151	17	11	175	Chris Sidwell	8	Steve Lakins
99-00	N2S	26	16	0	10	597	523	74	32	5	195	Steve Larkins	10	Jamie Knight
00-01	D3S	26	14	1	11	691	600	91	29	5	207	Steve Larkins	12	Luke Waquanivere

FACT FILE

Founded: 1875
Nickname: The Reds

Colours: Red with a green/yellow band
Change colours: Green with a red/yellow band

GROUND

Address: The Recreation Ground, Redruth, Cornwall TR15 1SY
Tel: 01209 215520   Fax: 01209 314438   web: redruth-rfc.cornwall.eu.org
Capacity: 15,000   Seated: 670   Standing: 14,330

Directions: A30 West through Cornwall, leave at Redruth exit over roundabout, down through council estate, 1/4 mile to crossroads, then left.
Nearest Railway Station: Redruth, walk thro Town Centre, down Green Lane grd at end, 10 mins

Car Parking: 50 on ground, 500 on Industrial Estate - free.

Admission: Season ticket -
Adults £75, OAP/children £45
Matchday -
Adults standing £6, seated £7, u16 Free

Clubhouse: Evenings 7-11, matchdays 12-11, Sun 12-2, 7-11.
Three bars, with snacks & bar meals available.
Functions catered for contact Social Committee

Club Shop: Open home matchdays.
Manageress Christina Thomas 01209 215520

Training Nights: Mondays & Wednesdays

PROGRAMME

Size: A5   Price: £1   Pages: 44
Editor: Nick Serpell 01579 348853
Advertising Rates
Full page £250, Half page £130, Qtr page £70

TABARD RFC

Chairman	Ross Hopcroft	100 Manor Road, Barton-le-Clay, Bedfordshire MK45 4WR
Secretary	Mrs P Mitchell	48 Hill Rise, Rickmansworth, Herts. WD3 2NZ 01923 490133
Fixtures Secretary	Mike Hodgkinson	1 West End Cottage, West End Rd., Kempston, West End, Bedford MK43 8RZ 01234 852582 (H) 01582 696287 (B)
1st XV Manager	Geoff Bird	1 Kendalls Close, Radlett, Herts 01923 852465 (H), 01923 852655 (B), 01923 852465 (Fax)
Director of Rugby	Ivor Jones	
Press Officer	Peter Cook	020 8207 5564 (H), 020 7250 7499 (B)

Tabard started the season with high hopes, but found that persistent injury problems played havoc with a season that started promisingly. The hopeful start saw a fight back to a 24 all draw against Clifton, having trailed 21-3 down with 20 minutes to go, and then a scintillating performance against North Walsham, 36-21, continued the high expectation. Unfortunately, two trips to the West Country, with weakened sides, saw heavy defeats against Plymouth and Redruth and Tabard then knew they were in for a hard season.

A good draw away at Penzance, again fighting back in the last 20 minutes and, a breakaway try against Reading, in atrocious conditions, were further highlights of the first part of the season. In the second half, Tabard gained revenge against Basingstoke, defeating them away. Reading also featured again in the second half of the season, when Tabard, needing one win from the last three games, beat them at Reading, 13-10, a result eventually proving crucial in the relegation stakes.

In the Tetley Bitter Cup competition, Tabard found themselves losing to old rivals Barking at the first hurdle, by 24-8.

Justin Azzopardi, playing at stand off to start with and full back later, was the highest points scorer in all games with 160, while scrum half Danny Kamo was the highest try scorer with seven. However, in the league and cup centre Cameron Langsford was the top try scorer with six.

Tabard also entered what was ostensibly their second team in the Hertfordshire Presidents Cup. Like last season, the entry was again rewarded with success, Tabard beating Albanians in a close final by an injury time penalty kick, making the final score 18-13. This victory meant that Tabard have now won this competition a record nine times.

Back row: A. Jorden, C. Wright, H. Hertz, P. Divers, B, Lane, K. Simpson. **Middle**: D. Choppin, A. Pinnock, M. Hanson, P. Webb, R. Sussoms, N. Turner, J. Turnbull, J. Johal, M. Evans, R. Matthews, R. Bromham, T. Andrews. **Front**: R. Woodward, I. McMullan, B. James, D. Moore, J. Sayers, M. Skinner, M. Collie, S. Greening, J. Nolan and S. Andrews.

TABARD

Comp.	Date	H/A	Opponents	Result & Score	Att	15	14	13	12	11
N3S	2-Sep	N	Clifton	D 24-24	200	Halbert/t2c	Turnbull	Pinnock	Dogbe	Dickinson/t
N3S	16-Sep	H	North Walsham	W 36-21	250	Skinner	Dickinson/t	Pinnock	Dogbe	Webb
N3S	23-Sep	A	Plymouth Albion*	L 17-58	1000	Skinner/c	Langford	Pinnock	Dogbe	Churchman/cp
N3S	30-Sep	H	Redruth	L 17-48		Skinner	Langford	Pinnock	Johal	Webb
N3S	14-Oct	A	Westcombe Park	W 23-21	250	Dudley	Dickinson/t	Langford	Pinnock	Turnbull/t
N3S	21-Oct	H	Basingstoke	L 15-22	180	Kruger	Dickinson	Langford	Pinnock	Turnbull
N3S	28-Oct	A	Cheltenham	W 19-14	200	Kruger	Dickinson	Langford	Pinnock	Turnbull/t
N3S	11-Nov	H	Launceston	L 13-26	200	Kruger	Dickinson	Langford	Turner	Turnbull
N3S	18-Nov	A	Penzance & Newlyn	D 24-24		Woodard	Dickinson/t	Langford/t	Turner	Turnbull
N3S	25-Nov	H	Reading	W 8-3	100	Dudley	Dickinson	Langford	Turner	McMullen/t
N3S	2-Dec	A	Barking	L 3-21		Kamo	Dickinson	Langford	Johal	McMullen
N3S	16-Dec	H	Blackheath	W 40-22	200	Kamo	Dickinson	Langford/t	Higgins	Turnbull(/t)
N3S	23-Dec	H	Barking	L 19-29		Kamo	McMullen	Langford	Higgins	Dickinson
N3S	6-Jan	H	Penzance & Newlyn*	L 17-68	220	Woodard	McMullen	Langford	Higgins	Dickinson
N3S	13-Jan	A	Launceston	L 0-40	300	Azzopardi	Dickinson	Langford	Dogbe	Turnbull
N3S	27-Jan	A	Basingstoke	W 29-19		Azzopardi(b/2t2c)	McMullen	Langford/2t	Pinnock	Turnbull
N3S	3-Feb	A	Weston super Mare	W 12-9		Turnbull	McMullen	Langford/t	Pinnock	Skinner/c
N3S	10-Feb	H	Westcombe Park	L 19-29	200	Turnbull	Dickinson/t	Langford	Pinnock	Skinner/2c
N3S	17-Feb	H	Cheltenham	W 29-20		Azzopardi/c4p	McMullen	Langford/t	Pinnock	Skinner
N3S	24-Feb	A	Redruth	L 0-32	500	Turnbull	McMullen	Chalmers	Williams	Skinner
N3S	10-Mar	H	Plymouth Albion	L 8-43		Azzopardi/p	McMullen/t	Webb	Pinnock	Skinner
N3S	17-Mar	A	North Walsham	L 0-16	200	Azzopardi	McMullen	Pinnock	Chalmers	Dogbe
N3S	31-Mar	A	Blackheath	L 5-39		Azzopardi	McMullen	Pinnock	Chalmers	Dogbe
N3S	7-Apr	A	Reading	W 13-10		Azzopardi/c2p	McMullen	Chalmers	Webb	Dogbe
N3S	14-Apr	H	Weston super Mare	L 13-20		Azzopardi/tc2p	McMullen	Langford	Chalmers	Pinnock
N3S	21-Apr	H	Clifton	L 12-41		Azzopardi	McMullen	Pinnock	Webb	Churchman/tc

TBC 2 7-Oct A Barking L 8-24

* after opponents name indicates a penalty try. Brackets after a player's name indicates he was replaced. eg (a) means he was replaced by replacement code "a" and so on. / after a player or replacement name is followed by any scores he made - eg /t, /c, /p, /dg or any combination of these

EVER PRESENT — None

Most Appearances:
- 24 Dick Malone.
- 22 Danny Kamo.
- 21 Justin Azzopardi.

PLAYERS USED

43 plus three as replacement only.

MOST POINTS

Pts	Player	T	C	P	DG
152	J Azzopardi	3	16	34	1
30	C Langford	6	-	-	-
25	J Dickinson	5	-	-	-
22	M Skinner	2	6	-	-
20	D Kamo	54	-	-	-

MATCH FACTS

10	9	1	2	3	4	5	6	7	8
Dudley	Skinner	Nolan	Pye	Collie	Malone	Lane	Johal/t	James(d/t)	Sayers
Azzopardi/2t2c4p	Kamo	Nolan	Pye	Collie	Malone	Lane	Johal/t	James	Sayers
Dudley/t	Kamo	Nolan	Instance	Collie	Sussum	Malone	Evans	Johal	Matthews
Azzopardi/2cp	Kamo/t	Nolan	Instance	Collie	Malone	Lane	Evans/t	Hanson	Sayers
Azzopardi/c2p	Kamo	Nolan	Sharp	Collie	Malone	Lane	Evans	Johal/t	Sayers
Azzopardi/5p	Kamo	Nolan	Sharp	Collie	Malone	Lane	Evans	Johal	Webb
Azzopardi/c4p	Kamo	Nolan	Sharp	Collie	Malone	Lane	Evans	Johal	Webb
Azzopardi/p	Kamo	Nolan	Sharp/t	Collie	Malone	Lane	Evans/t	Johal	Webb
Azzopardi/2c	Kamo/t	Nolan	Sharp	Collie	Malone	Finnie	Evans/t	Webb	Sayers
Azzopardi/p	Skinner	Nolan	Toeby	Sullivan	Malone	Lane	Cripps	Webb	Sayers
Azzopardi/p	Skinner	Nolan	Collier	Sullivan	Malone	Lane	Evans	Cripps	Sayers
Azzopardi/c5pdg	Skinner	Nolan	Pye	Bromham/t	Malone	Lane	Evans	Webb/t	Sayers
Azzopardi/2c	Skinner	Nolan	Pye	Bromham/t	Malone	Lane	Evans	Webb(c/t)	Matthews
Azzopardi/2cp	Skinner	Nolan	Pye	Bromham	Malone	Sussum	Lane	Webb	Matthews/t
Woodard	Kamo	Nolan	Pye	Bromham	Malone	Sussum	Lane	Sayers	Matthews
Woodard/t	Kamo	Nolan	Pye	Collie	Malone	Lane	Sayers	James	Matthews
Woodard	Kamo/t	Nolan	Pye	Collie	Malone	Sussum	Sayers	James	Matthews
Woodard	Kamo	Alstin	Pye	Collie	Malone/t	Sussum	Sayers/t	James	Matthews
Woodard	Kamo/t	Alstin	Pye	Collie	Malone	Sussum	Sayers/t	James	Webb
Woodard	Kamo	Alstin	Pye	Collie	Malone	Sussum	Evans	James	Sayers
Woodard	Kamo	Alstin	Pye	Collie	Malone	Sussum	Martin	James	Sayers
Woodard	Skinner	Alstin	Pye	Collie	Malone	Finnie	Lane	Evans	Martin
Woodard	Kamo	Webb	Pye	Collie/t	Malone	Sussum	Sayers	James	Martin
Woodard	Kamo	Webb	Pye	Collie	Malone	Finnie	Johal	James	Sayers/t
Woodard	Kamo	Bromham	Evenly	Webb	Sussum	Sayers	Johal	James	Webb
Woodard	Kamo(a/t)	Bromham	Evenly	Webb	Sussum	Sayers	Johal	James	Martin

REPLACEMENTS   a - D Moore   b - M Skinner   c - J Sayers   d - I McMullen   e - P Webb

2000-01 HIGHLIGHTS

Tabard had only three players who played in over 20 of their matches last season and used a total of 43 players in the 26 match league programme.

Having previously been top scorer at Barking for a couple of seasons Justin Azzopardi tops the Tabard list and so ends

Nick Churchmans 5 year run as Tabard's top scorer.

He notched up 152 points, the highest for three seasons at Tabard.

Tabard had their lowest ever finish since joining this league back in 1993-94.

TABARD

LEAGUE STATISTICS *compiled by Stephen McCormack*

SEASON	Division	P	W	D	L	F	A	Pts Diff	Lge Pts	Lge Pos		Coach		Captain
91-92	Lon 2N	10	9	1	0	167	59	108	19	1p		T Smithers		M Richards
92-93	Lon 1	12	10	1	1	230	127	103	21	1p				
93-94	D5S	12	6	2	4	183	136	47	14	3				
94-95	D5S	12	7	0	5	207	208	-1	14	6		I Jones		R Malone
												Most Points		**Most Tries**
95-96	D5S	12	4	1	7	195	244	-49	9	9	112	Nick Churchman	3	Giles Hewson Nick Churchman
96-97	D4S	26	10	3	13	511	557	-46	23	8	264	Nick Churchman	8	Nick Churchman
97-98	N2S	26	14	0	12	556	532	-24	28	6	239	Nick Churchman	11	Nick Churchman
98-99	N2S	26	9	1	16	461	501	-40	19	8	148	Nick Churchman	6	Andy Pinnock
99-00	N2S	26	11	1	14	550	627	-77	23	8	141	Nick Churchman	16	Jag Johal
00-01	N3S	26	9	2	15	415	721	-306	20	10	152	Justin Azzopardi	6	Cameron Langford

FACT FILE

Founded: 1951

Nickname: Tabs

Colours: Navy with broad yellow band edged with red.

Change colours: Dark green and white.

GROUND

Address: Cobden Hill, Radlett, Hertfordshire, WD7 7LN
Tel. Nos. 01923 855561
Capacity: 1,000   Seated: None Standing: 1,000

Directions: On A5183 Watling Street, from Elstree turn right after entry into Radlett, blind entrance by high brick wall nearly opposite "Cat & Fiddle" Pub.
Nearest Railway Station: Radlett

Car Parking: 250 spaces adjacent to ground

Admission: Adult standing £5, Children/OAPs Free
Season Ticket £40

Clubhouse: Matchdays & training eves only.
Bar meals available.
Functions: Contact Nick Gray 0831 668204

Club Shop: Open Saturdays only

Training Nights: Tuesday & Thursday

PROGRAMME Size: A5   Price: with entry
Pages: 16 + cover
Editor: Ross Hopcroft

ADVERTISING RATES (Colour)
Full page £400,
Half page £200, Qtr page £100

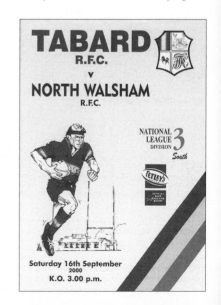

TABARD R.F.C.
v
NORTH WALSHAM R.F.C.

NATIONAL LEAGUE DIVISION 3 South

Saturday 16th September 2000
K.O. 3.00 p.m.

WESTCOMBE PARK RFC

President	Mike Payne	4 Bonchester Close, Chislehurst, Kent BR7 5HS 0208 402 6506 (H)
Chairman	John Yeates	Coppers, Farthing Street, Downe, Kent BR6 7JB
		01689 857495 (H) e-mail: yeates@waitrose.com
Secretary	Steve Scott	91 Court Road, Orpington, Kent BR6 0PU. 01689 87100 (H)
		07779 782629 (M) 020 7826 3035 (B) email: steve.scott2@btinternet.com
Treasurer	Terry Hadaway	Hilbre, Main Road, Knockholt, Kent TN14 7LD.
		01959 532067(H) 01233 898270 (B) email: t.hadaway@btinternet.com
Chairman of Rugby	John Bellinger	32A Courtyard, Eltham London SE9 5QE
Playing/Fixtures Sec.		020 8850 7280 (H) 020 7377 3060 (B) e-mail: Bellinger@aol.com
Chairman of Marketing/	Paul Cavalli	30 Warren Road, Orpington, Kent BR6 6HY. 01689 854618 (H) 01732 455456 (B)
Programme Editor		07836 570578 (M) 01732 741545 (F) e-mail: paulcavalli@westcombeparkrugby.co.uk
1st XV Manager	John Ward Turner	Westerham Lodge, Westerham Road, Keston Kent BR2 6DA 01689 854868 (B)
		07890 986682 (M) 01689 860246 (F) e-mail: pr@wardturner.co.uk
Match Secretary	Mrs Jackie Candish	6 Filmer Rd., Sevenoaks, Kent TN14 5AG. 01732 458848(H) 0207 300 5209(B)
Club Coaches	Fraser Thomson, 01689 607052 & Peter Danckert, 01622 663056	

Westcombe Park RFC was founded in 1904 and maintains the name of its original location on the fringes of Blackheath despite several moves before we settled in Orpington in 1937. We have now become very much a part of the Orpington/Bromley scene and among `Combe's objectives are the fostering of local sport at all levels and the strengthening of bonds between the club and the community.

This is our third year in National League Three South and it is a great credit to our players and our two coaches, Fraser Thomson and Peter Danckert, that we improved our position from ninth to seventh last season, and despite an horrendous injury list in the second half of this campaign we managed to pull off some notable wins. Particularly pleasing was the promise shown by our younger players. We look forward to continued success in 2001/02. Credit should also go to our Administration, for financial strains of National League status are considerable and it is partly through their efforts that our 1st XV thrives.

We have made many new friends in the last two years. Our loyal and growing band of supporters has been rewarded with excellent hospitality in many far flung parts of Southern England. The last game of the season against Barking saw the retirement of number eight `Pup' Harris. He had a distinguished rugby career with Blackheath, Wasps and the Barbarians, joining `Combe in 1997 and was an influential member of the team which saw the club rise from London 2 to National League status in two years.

We are very conscious of the importance of Mini and Junior rugby not only in promoting a great sport, but in building the future of `Combe. We are fortunate indeed to have so many good and enthusiastic coaches at all youth levels and also senior players willing to give up Sundays to aid their efforts. That Westcombe Park won the Kent Colts Cup this year convincingly against a strong Blackheath side is a great boost and we look forward to seeing some of our Colts in the senior sides this year and maybe in National League rugby before too long.

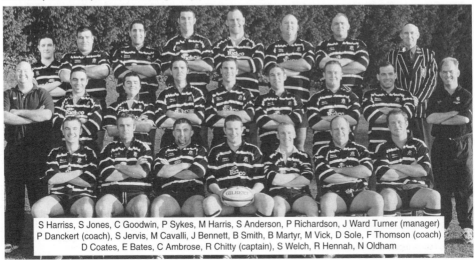

S Harriss, S Jones, C Goodwin, P Sykes, M Harris, S Anderson, P Richardson, J Ward Turner (manager)
P Danckert (coach), S Jervis, M Cavalli, J Bennett, B Smith, B Martyr, M Vick, D Sole, F Thomson (coach)
D Coates, E Bates, C Ambrose, R Chitty (captain), S Welch, R Hennah, N Oldham

WESTCOMBE PARK

Comp.	Date	H/A	Opponents	Result & Score	Att	15	14	13	12	11
N3S	2-Sep	H	Cheltenham	L 11-39	250	Smith/2p	Beckett	Bennett	Bates	Bailey
N3S	9-Sep	H	Penzance & Newlyn*	L 26-39	350	Coates/2c3pdg	Sykes	Bates	Jervis	Beckett
N3S	30-Sep	A	Reading	L 25-32	200	Coates/2c2p	Beckett/t	Bates	Jervis	Sykes/t
N3S	14-Oct	H	Tabard	L 21-23	250	Coates/c3p	Smith/t	Bennett	Bates	Sykes
N3S	21-Oct	A	Weston super Mare	W 26-14	200	Coates/3c	Smith/t	Bennett	Bates	Sykes
N3S	28-Oct	H	Blackheath	W 30-22	400	Coates/cp	Sykes/t	Bennett	Bates	Smith/3t
N3S	4-Nov	A	Launceston	L 10-48	300	Bennett	Sykes	Bates	Belcher	McCarthy/t
N3S	11-Nov	A	Clifton	W 24-20	200	Coates/3cp	Beckett	Bennett	Bates/t	Belcher
N3S	18-Nov	H	North Walsham	W 13-10	250	Coates/cpdg	Lawrence	Bennett	Bates	Bailey
N3S	25-Nov	A	Plymouth Albion	L 10-51	850	Coates/cp	Bailey	Bennett	Bates	Belcher
N3S	2-Dec	H	Redruth	W 35-18	120	Coates/t3c3p	Lawrence	Bennett	Bates/t	Sykes
N3S	9-Dec	H	Barking	L 8-31	300	Coates/p	Lawrence	Bennett	Bates	Sykes
N3S	16-Dec	A	Basingstoke	W 40-3	200	Coates/3c3p	Bailey	Sykes/t	Bates	Bennett
N3S	23-Dec	A	Redruth	L 20-45	700	Coates/2c2p	Belcher	Sykes	Bates	Bennett
N3S	6-Jan	A	North Walsham	W 12-11	300	Coates/4p	Daniel	Bates	Sykes	Smith
N3S	13-Jan	H	Clifton	W 34-19	250	Coates/2c5p	Smith	Bates/t	Sykes	Bailey/t
N3S	20-Jan	A	Blackheath	L 14-25	600	Coates/3p	Smith	Bates	Sykes/t	Belcher
N3S	27-Jan	A	Weston super Mare	L 5-15	200	Coates	Smith	Bates	Bennett/t	Tate
N3S	10-Feb	A	Tabard	W 29-19	200	Smith/t	Middleton	Bates/t	Sykes	Lawrence/t
N3S	24-Feb	H	Reading	W 36-27	250	Smith/c3p	Bennett/t	Bates	Sykes/2t	Belcher
N3S	3-Mar	H	Plymouth Albion	L 11-32	300	Smith/p	Tate	Bates	Sykes/t	Brennan
N3S	10-Mar	A	Penzance & Newlyn	L 13-31	900	Coates/c2p	Smith/t	Bates	Sykes	Middleton
N3S	17-Mar	H	Launceston	L 10-24		Coates/cp	Smith	Bates	Sykes	Bailey
N3S	24-Mar	A	Cheltenham	W 39-29	200	Coates/4c2p	Smith	Tate	Sykes/3t	Smith
N3S	31-Mar	H	Basingstoke	W 31-3		Coates/3p	Smith	Bates	Sykes/t	Lawrence/t
N3S	14-Apr	A	Barking	L 17-30		Coates/4p	Smith	Bates	Tate	Lawrence
TBC	7-Oct	A	Plymouth Albion	L 6-56	800	Coates/2p	Beckett	Bennett	Sykes	Smith

*after opponents name indicates a penalty try. Brackets after a player's name indicates he was replaced.
eg (a) means he was replaced by replacement code "a" and so on. / after a player or replacement name
is followed by any scores he made - eg /t, /c, /p, /dg or any combination of these*

EVER PRESENT
Simon Harriss (26)

Most Appearances:.
25 Elliott Bates.
22 Derek Coates, Simon Jones.
20 Pat Sykes, Shaun Welch.

PLAYERS USED
42 plus two as replacements only.

MOST POINTS

Pts	Player	T	C	P	DG
215	D Coates	1	33	46	2
55	P Sykes	11	-	-	-
55	B Smith	7	1	6	-
30	S Welch	6	-	-	-

MATCH FACTS

10	9	1	2	3	4	5	6	7	8
Jervis	Cavalli	Jones	Goldsmith	Anderson	Harriss	Colvin	Goodwin/t	Sole	Harris
Bober	Welch/t	Jones	Clarke	Hennah	Harriss	Richardson	Clifton	Spry	Goodwin
Cavalli	Welch	Jones	Vick	Ambrose	Harriss	Bussey	Goodwin/t	Spry	Harris
Cavalli	Welch	Jones/t	Vick	Anderson	Harriss	Bussey	Sole	Spry	Harris
Cavalli	Welch/2t	Jones	Vick	Anderson	Harriss	Bussey/t	Harris	Spry	Chitty
Cavalli	Welch	Jones	Vick	Anderson	Harriss	Richardson	Goodwin	Harris	Chitty/t
Cavalli	Welch	Jones	Vick	Anderson	Harriss	Richardson/t	Sole	Harris	Chitty
Cavalli/t	Welch	Jones	Vick	Ambrose	Harriss/t	Harris	Sole	Spry	Chitty
Cavalli	Welch	Jones	Vick	Ambrose	Harriss	Harris	Sole(a/t)	Goodwin	Chitty
Cavalli/t	Lawrence	Jones	Vick	Ambrose	Harriss	Bussey	Sole	Wisemans	Harris
Cavalli/t	Welch	Jones	Vick	Anderson	Harriss	Bussey	Sole	Goodwin/t	Harris
Cavalli	Welch/t	Jones	Vick	Ambrose	Harriss	Bussey	Sole	Goodwin	Harris
Cavalli	Lawrence	Jones	Vick	Anderson	Harriss/t	Harris/t	Sole	Goodwin/t	Chitty/t
Cavalli	Welch/t	Jones	Clarke	Campbell	Anderson/t	Harriss	Wisemans	Sole	Spry
Cavalli	Welch	Jones	Martyr	Anderson	Richardson	Harriss	Goodwin	Spry	Harris
Belcher	Cavalli	Jones	Martyr	Anderson	Harriss	Hayward	Goodwin/t	Spry	Harris
Cavalli	Welch	Jones	Martyr	Hennah	Hayward	Harriss	Goodwin	Spry	Harris
Belcher	Cavalli	Jones	Sole	Hennah	Richardson	Harriss	Oldham	Hayward	Goodwin
Coates/3cp	Welch	Jones/t	Martyr	Hennah	Harriss	Richardson	Oldham	Goodwin	Harris
Jervis	Welch	Hennah(b/t)	Archer	Anderson	Bussey	Harriss	Sole	Oldham/t	Hayward
Jervis/dg	Welch	Hennah	Archer	Anderson	Bussey	Harriss	Fotheringham	Oldham	Wisemans
Jervis	Welch	Hennah	Martyr	Anderson	Richardson	Harriss	Sole	Fotheringham	Oldham
Jervis	Welch/t	Hennah	Martyr	Archer	Richardson	Harriss	Sole	Oldham	Wisemans
Jervis	Lawrence	Hennah	Martyr	Jones	Harris/t	Harriss	Sole	Hayward	Wisemans/t
Jervis/tc	Welch	Jones	Martyr	Hennah	Harris	Harriss	Sole	Hayward	Wisemans/t
Jervis/t	Welch	Jones	Martyr	Anderson	Richardson	Harriss	Sole	Spry	Harris
Cavalli	Welch	Jones	Vick	Ambrose	Harriss	Bussey	Sole	Spry	Harris

REPLACEMENTS   a - N Spry   b - S Middleton

2000-01 HIGHLIGHTS

Derek Coates topped the Westcombe Park scoring charts with over 200 points for the second season running in National League rugby.

Pat Sykes led the try scoring with an impressive 11 tries, two more than the leading try scorer the season before.

Improved on last season and got some excellent results including doing the double over North Walsham.

Recovered well after losing their first four matches of the season. They then won eight of their next 12 to move rapidly up the table.

WESTCOMBE PARK

LEAGUE STATISTICS *compiled by Stephen McCormack*

SEASON	Division	P	W	D	L	F	A	Pts Diff	Lge Pts	Lge Pos	Coach	Captain
91-92	Lon 2S	10	8	0	2	214	130	84	20	3	C Chapman	F Thomson
92-93	Lon 2S	12	9	1	2	279	135	144	19	2	C Chapman	F Thomson
93-94	Lon 2S	12	10	1	1	259	130	129	21	2	F Thomson	P Harris
94-95	Lon 2S	12	7	1	4	228	177	51	15	4	F Thomson	G Mayor
95-96	Lon 2S	12	7	0	5	317	196	121	14	5	F Thomson	G Mayor
96-97	Lon 2S	12	7	0	5	414	228	186	14	4	F Thomson	J Hayday
97-98	Lon 2S	15	15	0	0	703	138	565	30	1p	F Thomson/D Vaughan	N Hayler
98-99	Lon 1	16	15	0	1	706	201	505	30	1p	F Thomson/P Danckert	R Chitty
											Most Points	**Most Tries**
99-00	N2S	26	11	0	15	550	706	-156	22	9	243 Derek Coates	9 Clark Goodwin
00-01	N3S	26	12	0	14	552	664	-112	24	7	215 Derek Coates	11 Pat Sykes

FACT FILE

Founded: 1904
Nickname: "Combe"

Colours: Navy blue, with white hoops, navy shorts
Change colours: White, with navy hoops, blue shorts

ADDRESS: Goddington Dene, Goddington Lane, Orpington, Kent BR6 9SX
Tel: 01689 834902   **Fax:** 01689 822116   **Web site:** www.westcombeparkrugby.co.uk
Capacity: 2000 standing

Directions: From M25 - exit at J4. At next round-about exit A244 (Orpington), at 40 MPH sign (2.8 miles from M25) turn right into Goddington Lane, opposite the Highway.
From A20 - Leave A20 at Crittall's Corner (Orpington A224). Take A224 to Orpington, Sevenoaks Way, Continue into Court Road, following sign, M25-Sevenoaks. After six sets of lights turn LEFT into Goddington Lane (opposite Volvo show room)
From Croydon - follow A232 into Orpington, over War Memorial roundabout, up Spur Road to A224. Turn Right into Court Road at lights, 1/4 mile turn Left into Goddington Lane.

Nearest Station: Orpington (Taxis/Buses), Chelsfield (10mins. walk)

Car Parking: 200, Special events: 2500

Admission: By programme

Club Shop: Open Saturdays & Sundays
Manager Jane Hadaway. 01959 532067

Clubhouse: Normal licensing hours, snacks and bar meals.
Functions Rooms available for up to 200
Contact House Manager: 01689 834902

Trianing Nights: Tuesdays and Thursdays.

PROGRAMME **Size:** A5 **Price:** £4.00 **Pages:** 20
Editor: Contact: Paul Cavalli
01689 854618 (H) 01732 455456 (B)
Advertising Rates
Full Page: £150.00,
1/2 page: £100.00 1/4 Page: £65.00 plus VAT

WESTCOMBE PARK RFC

RECORDS SECTION

DIVISION FOUR SOUTH
(CURRENTLY NATIONAL DIVISION THREE SOUTH)
Previously also Area League South & Division Five South

Relegated clubs' Match Facts for season 2000-01

Basingstoke	448-9
Cheltenham	450-1
Reading	452-3
Weston-super-Mare	454-5

Old Patesians celebrate after winning the Intermediate Cup at Twickenham.   Photo courtesy of The Cheltenham Newspaper Co. Ltd.

BASINGSTOKE

Comp.	Date	H/A	Opponents	Result & Score	Att	15	14	13	12	11
N3 S	2-Sep	A	Barking	L 19-32		Jones	Joseph	Hill	Taylor	Palmer/t
N3 S	9-Sep	H	Launceston	L 17-30	200	Jones	Joseph/t	Hill	Taylor	Palmer
N3 S	30-Sep	A	Penzance & Newlyn	L 17-28		Hilliard/t	Rees	Jones	Taylor	Joseph/t
N3 S	14-Oct	H	Reading	W 9-6		Hilliard	Rees	Jones	Taylor	Joseph
N3 S	21-Oct	A	Tabard	W 22-15	180	Hilliard	Joseph	Jones	Taylor	Nunn
N3 S	28-Oct	H	Weston super Mare	L 10-15	200	Hilliard	Hill	Taylor	Jones	Nunn
N3 S	4-Nov	A	Cheltenham	L 12-34	200	Joseph	Nunn	Jones	Taylor	Hill
N3 S	11-Nov	A	Blackheath	W 16-8		Joseph	Rees	Nunn/t	Taylor	Palmer
N3 S	18-Nov	H	Clifton	L 10-19		Joseph/t	Palmer	Taylor	Nunn	Rees
N3 S	25-Nov	A	North Walsham	L 3-25		Joseph	Rees	Jones	Taylor	Palmer
N3 S	2-Dec	H	Plymouth Albion	L 0-32		Joseph	Rees	Jones	Hill	Palmer
N3 S	9-Dec	A	Redruth	W 18-15	650	Elleston	Joseph	Nunn	Taylor	Palmer
N3 S	16-Dec	H	Westcombe Park	L 3-40	200	Palmer	Holmes	Nunn	Taylor	Joseph
N3 S	23-Dec	A	Plymouth Albion	L 6-72	1200	Elleston	Palmer	Jones	Taylor	Nunn
N3 S	6-Jan	A	Clifton	L 8-34		Elleston	Joseph	Nunn	Taylor	Palmer
N3 S	13-Jan	H	Blackheath	L 12-43		Waters	Palmer	Taylor	Nunn	Elleston
N3 S	27-Jan	H	Tabard	L 19-29		Lambert	Joseph	Nunn/t	Jones	Saunders
N3 S	3-Feb	H	North Walsham	D 13-13		Elleston	Nunn	Jones	Taylor	Saunders
N3 S	10-Feb	A	Reading	L 3-14	200	Dangerfield	Saunders	Jones	Taylor	Nunn
N3 S	17-Feb	A	Weston super Mare	W 14-8		Waters	Nunn	Jones	Taylor	Saunders/t
N3 S	24-Feb	H	Penzance & Newlyn	L 18-53	350	Palmer	Joseph	Jones	Taylor/t	Saunders/t
N3 S	17-Mar	H	Cheltenham	W 25-10		Waters/t	Palmer/t	Taylor	Jones	Jones/t
N3 S	24-Mar	H	Barking	W 27-8		Claffey	Jones/t	Taylor	Jones	Palmer/t
N3 S	31-Mar	A	Westcombe Park	L 3-31		Palmer	Holmes	Nunn	Taylor	Joseph
N3 S	14-Apr	H	Redruth	L 26-31	200	Claffey/c3p	Palmer	Jones	Taylor	Elleston/t
N3 S	28-Apr	A	Launceston	L 3-41	325	Dangerfield/p	Joseph	Jones	Nunn	Elleston
TBC	23-Sept	A	Old Colfians	L 3-39						

* after opponents name indicates a penalty try. Brackets after a player's name indicates he was replaced. eg (a) means he was replaced by replacement code "a" and so on. / after a player or replacement name is followed by any scores he made - eg /t, /c, /p, /dg or any combination of these

MOST APPEARANCES

25	Grant Taylor, Neal Taylor.
24	Paul Fisher
22	Richard Baker

PLAYERS USED

39 plus three as replacement only

MOST POINTS

Pts	Player	T	C	P	DG
66	M Hart	-	6	17	1
45	D Lambert	-	6	11	-
44	S Claffey	-	1	14	-
25	S Paynter	5	-	-	-
20	P MDella-Savina	4	-	-	-
15	R Joseph	3	-	-	-
15	J Palmer	3	-	-	-

MATCH FACTS

10	9	1	2	3	4	5	6	7	8
Hart/c3pdg	Rogers	Collins	Newsom	Hobden	Chapman	Taylor	Baker	Della-Savina	Hausermann
Hart/2cp	Rogers	Collins	Fisher	Orr	Chapman	Taylor	Reeve	Della-Savina/t	Hausermann
Hart/c	Rogers	Collins(a/t)	Fisher	Hobden	Taylor	Hudson	Baker	Della-Savina	Hausermann
Hart/3p	Cullum	Collins	Fisher	Orr	Chapman	Edwards	Baiger	Della-Savina	Taylor
Hart/c5p	Rogers/t	Collins	Fisher	Orr	Chapman	Edwards	Baker	Della-Savina	Taylor
Hart/cp	Rogers	Collins	Fisher	Hobden	Chapman	Edwards	Baker	Della-Savina/t	Taylor
Hart/4p	Rogers	Young	Fisher	Collins	Edwards	Chapman	Baker	Della-Savina	Taylor
Paynter/c3p	Cullum	Young	Fisher	Collins	Hausermann	Taylor	Baiger	Della-Savina	Reeve
Paynter/cp	Cullum	Young	Fisher	Collins	Morgan	Taylor	Baker	Della-Savina	Reeve
Paynter/p	Cullum	Young	Newsom	Bramhall	Chapman	Taylor	Reeve	Baker	Della-Savina
Taylor	Cullum	Young	Fisher	Bramhall	Chapman	Morgan	Baiger	Reeve	Taylor
Paynter/2p(b/c)	Cullum	Young	Fisher	Bramhall	Chapman	Morgan	Baker/t	Reeve	Taylor/t
Claffey/p	Rogers	Young	Fisher	Bramhall	Morgan	Chapman	Baker	Reeve	Taylor
Claffey/2p	Rogers	Young	Fisher	Bramhall	Morgan	Chapman	Baiger	Reeve	Taylor
Waters/p	Rogers	Young	Fisher/t	Bramhall	Chapman	Morgan	Baker	Reeve	Taylor
Claffey/4p	Cullum	Orr	Fisher	Bramhall	Chapman	Morgan	Reeve	Baiger	Taylor
Claffey/3p	Dean	Orr	Fisher	Bramhall	Chapman	Morgan	Baker	Della-Savina	Taylor/t
Lambert/c2p	Dean	Young	Fisher	Hobden	Morgan	Chapman	Baker	Della-Savina/t	Taylor
Lambert/p	Dean	Young	Fisher	Bramhall	Morgan	Hooker	Baiger	Della-Savina	Taylor
Lambert/3p	Dean	Young	Fisher	Bramhall	Morgan	Taylor	Baker	Della-Savina	St Bernard
Lambert/c2p	Dean	Young	Fisher	Bramhall	Morgan	Hooker	Baker	St Bernard	Della-Savina
Lambert/2c2p	Dean	Young	Fisher	Bramhall	Morgan	Hooker	St Bernard	Della-Savina	Taylor
Lambert/2cp	Dean/t	Young	Fisher	Bramhall	Morgan	Hooker	St Bernard	Della-Savina/t	Taylor
Claffey/p	Rogers	Young	Fisher	Bramhall	Morgan	Chapman	Baker	Reeve	Taylor
Lambert	Dean/t	Young	Fisher	Bramhall	Morgan	Chapman	Baker/t	Della-Savina	Taylor
Taylor	Dean	Young	Fisher	Bramhall	Morgan	Hooker	St Bernard	Della-Savina	Taylor

REPLACEMENTS   a - S Orr   b - T Jones

2000-01 HIGHLIGHTS

Basingstoke lasted just one season in the National League and now return to London One where they were for the previous five seasons.

Matt Hart topped scored with 66 points, the previous season he had scored 324 points to help Basingstoke to the London One title.

Basingstoke had four different players kick points during the season hence the low total for the leading points scorer.

Back row forward Phil Dela-Savina was the leading try scorer with four.

They did manage an excellent away win at Redruth and four of their seven wins came away from home.

CHELTENHAM

Comp.	Date	H/A	Opponents	Result & Score	Att	15	14	13	12	11
N3 S	2-Sep	A	Westcombe Park	W 39-11	250	Waters/t	Ainscow/t	Holder/t	Turner	Pitman
N3 S	9-Sep	A	Barking	L 10-23	300	Watters	Ainscow	Holder	Turner	Pitman
N3 S	30-Sep	A	Launceston	L 7-63	400	Waters	Ainscow	Holder	Bennell	Pitman
N3 S	14-Oct	H	Penzance & Newlyn	L 24-40	250	Fereday	Edwards	Holder	Bennell/t	Pitman
N3 S	28-Oct	H	Tabard	L 14-19	200	Fereday	Edwards	Holder	Turner	Ainscow
N3 S	4-Nov	H	Basingstoke	W 34-12	200	Fereday	Pitman	Holder/t	Turner	Edwards/t
N3 S	11-Nov	A	Weston super Mare	L 10-21	250	Fereday/t	Pitman	Holder	Morgan	Edwards
N3 S	18-Nov	H	Blackheath	W 32-20	200	Fereday	Edwards/t	Holder/t	Turner	Pitman
N3 S	25-Nov	A	Clifton	L 8-19		Watters/p	Edwards	Holder	Turner	Sarghini
N3 S	2-Dec	H	North Walsham	L 12-32	200	Fereday	Edwards	Holder/t	Turner	Sarghini
N3 S	9-Dec	A	Plymouth Albion	L 10-50	1000	Fereday(a/t)	Edwards	Pitman	Turner	Sarghini
N3 S	16-Dec	H	Redruth	W 34-13	250	Watters/2t	Edwards/t	Pitman	Turner	Sarghini
N3 S	23-Dec	A	North Walsham	L 8-32	320	Watters/p	Edwards	Pitman	Knight	Davies
N3 S	6-Jan	A	Blackheath	L 10-27		Watters/cp	Fereday/t	Turner	Holder	Pitman
N3 S	13-Jan	H	Weston super Mare	W 36-19	200	Fereday	Ainscow/t	Knight	Turner	Pitman
N3 S	27-Jan	H	Reading	W 33-22	150	Holder	Edwards/t	Knight	Turner/t	Davies/t
N3 S	3-Feb	H	Clifton	W 9-6	200	Holder	Edwards	Knight	Turner	Davies
N3 S	10-Feb	A	Penzance & Newlyn	L 0-58		Holder	Ainscow	Pitman	Turner	Edwards
N3 S	17-Feb	A	Tabard	L 20-29		Phillips	Spurway	Pitman	Holder	Edwards
N3 S	24-Feb	H	Launceston	L 19-31	200	Holder	Edwards	Pitman	Turner	Sarghini
N3 S	3-Mar	A	Reading	L 26-29		Holder/t	Edwards/t	Pitman	Turner	Davies
N3 S	10-Mar	H	Barking	L 15-25	200	Fereday	Edwards	Holder	Turner	Davies
N3 S	17-Mar	A	Basingstoke	L 10-25		Fereday	Edwards	Holder	Turner	Davies
N3 S	24-Mar	H	Westcombe Park	L 29-39	200	Fereday	Edwards	Holder	Turner	Ainscow
N3 S	31-Mar	A	Redruth	L 28-38	1000	Hanger	Davies	Holder	Turner/t	Edwards(c/t)
N3 S	14-Apr	H	Plymouth Albion	L 15-20		Watters/tcp	Ainscow	Holder	Pitman	Edwards
TBC	23-Sep	A	Gloucester Old Boys	W 32-17		Fereday/t	Edwards	Holder	Bennell	Pitman
TBC	7-Oct	A	Reading	L 8-49	300	Fereday	Ainscow/t	Holder	Bennell	Pitman

** after opponents name indicates a penalty try. Brackets after a player's name indicates he was replaced.
eg (a) means he was replaced by replacement code "a" and so on. / after a player or replacement name
is followed by any scores he made - eg /t, /c, /p, /dg or any combination of these*

MATCH FACTS

10	9	1	2	3	4	5	6	7	8
Watts/2c5p	Mudway	Gilder	Brown	Bayliss	Burton	Crabb	York	Clarke	Arthur/t
Watts/cp	Mudway/t	Gilder	Brown	Bayliss	Burton	Crabb	York	Clarke	Arthur
Watts/tc	Salter	Bayliss	Brown	Gilder	Burton	Crabb	York	Clifford	Clarke
Watts/t3cp	Mudway/t	Gilder	Hughes	Bayliss	Burton	Lodge	Rowe	Meadows	Arthur
Watts/3p	Salter	Bayliss	Brown	Gilder	Burton	Lodge	Clarke	Meadows	Arthur/t
Watts/t2c	Mudway/t	Bayliss	Brown	Gilder	Lodge	Arthur/t	York/t	Meadows	Clarke
Turner	Mudway/cp	Gilder	Hughes	Bayliss	Lodge	Crabb	York	Meadows	Arthur
Watts/3c2p	Mudway/t	Gilder	Ronaki/t	Bayliss	Lodge	Arthur	Clarke	Meadows	York
Phillips/t	Mudway	Gilder	Ronaki	Bayliss	Crabb	Lodge	Clarke	Meadows	York
Watts/tc	Mudway	Hurunui	Ronaki	Gilder	Arthur	York	Rowe	Meadows	Clarke
Watts/cp	Mudway	Gilder	Ronaki	Bayliss	Lodge	Arthur	Rowe	Meadows	York
Watts/3cp	Mudway/t	Gilder	Hughes/t	Bayliss	Crabb	Lodge	York	Meadows	Arthur
Watts	Mudway	Pitman	Waters	Gilder	Lodge	Crabb	York/t	Meadows	Arthur
Phillips	Mudway	Gilder	Hughes	Bayliss	Lodge	Crabb	York	Clarke	Arthur
Watters/2t2c4p	Mudway/t	Pitman	Hughes	Bayliss	Arthur	Lodge	Clarke	Bridgens	York
Watters/2c3p	Mudway/t	Pitman	Hughes	Bayliss	Lodge	Arthur	Clarke	Bridgens	York
Watters/3p	Mudway	Gilder	Francis	Bayliss	Lodge	Arthur	Clarke	Cooper	York
Watters	Salter	Gilder	Francis	Bayliss	Lodge	Arthur	Clarke	Cooper	York
Watters/5p	Turner/t	Gilder	Francis	Bayliss	Lodge	Arthur	Clarke	Rowe	York
Watters/c4p	Kelly	Pitman	Francis	Bayliss	Lodge	Crabb	York	Rowe/t	Arthur
Watters/3c	Kelly/t	Pitman	Ronaki	Bayliss	Crabb	Lodge	York/t	Rowe	Arthur
Watters/5p	Kelly	Pitman	Hughes	Bayliss	Lodge	Crabb	Rowe	Ronaki	York
Watters	Mudway	Pitman	Hughes	Bayliss	Crabb	Lodge	York/t	Ronaki	Arthur(b/t)
Watters/2c5p	Mudway	Pitman	Ronaki	Bayliss	Lodge/t	Arthur/t	Cooper	Rowe	York
Watters/tc2p	Mudway	Pitman	Ronaki/t	Bayliss	Lodge	Arthur	Cooper	Rowe	York
Phillips	Mudway	Pitman	Ronaki/t	Bayliss	Lodge	Crabb	Cooper	Clifford	York
Salter	Watts/t3c2p	Bayliss	Brown/t	Gilder	Burton	Crabb	York/t	Clarke	Meadows
Watts/p	Mudway	Bayliss	Hughes	Gilder	Lodge	Crabb	York	Clarke	Meadows

REPLACEMENTS a - P Watters b - N Rowe c - D Morgan

2000-01 HIGHLIGHTS

After six years in the division Cheltenham finally get relegated back into South West One.

Their first three seasons in this division they did well finishing in the top six each time, but since then though they have struggled.

Phil Watters topped the points scorers for a third consecutive season with his best total to date. His 166 beat his previous best by a single point.

Watters also finished joint top try scorer with seven tries along with scrum half Matt Mudway.

READING

Comp.	Date	H/A	Opponents	Result & Score	Att	15	14	13	12	11
N3 S	2-Sep	A	North Walsham	L 7-28		Senior	Brooks	Sly	Pokai/t	Couser
N3 S	23-Sep	A	Redruth*	L 22-29	700	Senior	Brooks	Sly	Pokai	Balzan
N3 S	30-Sep	H	Westcombe Park	W 32-25	200	Senior	Brooks	Sly	Pokai/t	Balzan/t
N3 S	14-Oct	A	Basingstoke	L 6-9		Senior	Wyatt	Sly	Pokai	Couser
N3 S	28-Oct	A	Launceston	L 0-37	400	Senior	Wyatt	Sly	Pokai	Balzan
N3 S	11-Nov	H	Penzance & Newlyn	W 23-12	250	Senior/c2p	Couser	Pokai	Wyatt	Goldie/t
N3 S	18-Nov	A	Barking*	W 27-20	200	Senior/2cp	Couser	Pokai	Wyatt	Goldie/t
N3 S	25-Nov	A	Tabard	L 3-8	100	Senior/p	Couser	Pokai	Wyatt	Goldie
N3 S	2-Dec	H	Weston super Mare	W 26-15	150	Senior/t3c	Couser/t	Pokai	Wyatt	Goldie/t
N3 S	16-Dec	H	Clifton	W 30-12	200	Senior/2c2p	Couser	Pokai/t	Wyatt	Goldie
N3 S	23-Dec	A	Weston super Mare*	W 23-15	250	Senior/c2p	Brooks/t	Couser	Wyatt	Goldie
N3 S	6-Jan	H	Barking	L 3-37		Brooks	Couser	Pokai	Wyatt	Goldie
N3 S	13-Jan	A	Penzance & Newlyn	L 12-48	800	Senior/c	Brooks	Pokai	Byre	Birchall
N3 S	27-Jan	A	Cheltenham	L 22-33	150	Senior/c	Pugh	Wyatt	Martin/t	Birchall
N3 S	3-Feb	H	Plymouth Albion	L 0-38	270	Senior	Birchall	Sly	Martin	Pugh
N3 S	10-Feb	H	Basingstoke	W 14-3	200	Senior/2c	Brooks	Donnolly	Sly	Sly
N3 S	17-Feb	A	Blackheath	L 15-19		Senior/t	Pugh	Donnolly	Sly	Brooks
N3 S	24-Feb	A	Westcombe Park	L 27-36	250	Senior/2c	Dyson/t	Donnolly	Sly	Pugh/p
N3 S	3-Mar	H	Cheltenham	W 29-26		Senior/2c	Pugh/t	Donnolly/t	Wyatt	Goldie
N3 S	10-Mar	H	Redruth	W 47-35		Senior/2c6p	Pugh	Grafton	Wyatt	Goldie
N3 S	17-Mar	A	Plymouth Albion	L 0-29	1200	Senior	Pugh	Grafton	Wyatt	Goldie
N3 S	24-Mar	H	North Walsham	L 21-25	250	Senior/3c	Pugh	Sly	Wyatt	Brooks
N3 S	31-Mar	A	Clifton	L 19-31		Senior/c4p	Pugh	Sly	Wyatt	Brooks
N3 S	7-Apr	H	Tabard	L 10-13		Senior/t	Pugh	Donnolly	Wyatt	Brooks
N3 S	14-Apr	H	Blackheath	L 16-32		Senior/2p	Pokai	Byre/t	Wyatt	Donnolly
N3 S	21-Apr	H	Launceston	D 28-28		Senior/t4c	Lynch	Donnolly	Sly	Byre
TBC	7-Oct	H	Cheltenham	W 49-8	300	Senior	Couser/t	Sly	Pokai/t	Balzan/t
TBC	21-Oct	H	Launceston*	W 31-25	250	Senior	Wyatt/t	Sly	Pokai/2t	Balzan
TBC	5-Nov	H	Rotherham	L 27-46	600	Senior	Balzan	Sly	Wyatt	Pokai/t

** after opponents name indicates a penalty try. Brackets after a player's name indicates he was replaced.
eg (a) means he was replaced by replacement code "a" and so on. / after a player or replacement name
is followed by any scores he made - eg /t, /c, /p, /dg or any combination of these*

MOST APPEARANCES

25	Mark Skrypec, Matt Senior
23	Jody Levett
22	Mark Vatcher.

PLAYERS USED

40 plus three as replacement only

MOST POINTS

Pts	Player	T	C	P	DG
134	M Senior	4	27	20	-
35	S Dyson	7	-	-	-
35	D McEwan	7	-	-	-
35	M Skrypec	7	-	-	-
27	C Russell	-	6	4	1

MATCH FACTS

10	9	1	2	3	4	5	6	7	8
Russell/c	Dyson	Guttridge	Perkin	Grierson	Vatcher	Skrypec	Levett	Conquer	Wilson
Russell/2cp	Dyson/t	Johnson	Kerr	Grierson	Vatcher	Stewart	Levett	Conquer	Holloway/t
Russell/3c2p	Dyson/t	Allen	Kerr	Grierson	Vatcher	Skrypec	Levett	Conquer	Holloway/t
Russell/pdg	Balzan	Allen	Kerr	Grierson	Vatcher	Skrypec	Levett	Stewart	Holloway
Russell	Dyson	Grierson	Kerr	Wightwick	Vatcher	Skrypec	Wilson	Salisbury	Holloway
Sly	Dyson	Allen	Kerr	Johnson	Skrypec	Vatcher/t	Levett	Stewart	Holloway/t
Sly	Dyson	Johnson	Kerr	Perkin/t	Skrypec	Vatcher	Levett	Stewart/t	Holloway
Sly	Dyson	Allen	Kerr	Perkin	Vatcher	Skrypec	Levett	Conquer	Holloway
Sly/t	Dyson	Allen	Kerr	Perkin	Vatcher	Skrypec	Levett	Conquer	Holloway
Wyatt	Dyson	Allen	Kerr	Perkin	Vatcher/t	Skrypec/t	Levett/t	Salisbury	Holloway
Wyatt	Grafton	Johnson/t	Kerr	Grierson	Vatcher	Skrypec	Levett	Salisbury	Holloway
Wyatt/p	Grafton	Allen	Kerr	Grierson	Vatcher	Skrypec	Levett	Salisbury	Holloway
Wyatt	Grafton	Johnson	Kerr	Grierson	Vatcher	Skrypec	Levett	Conquer	Holloway/2t
Sly	Dyson	Johnson	Kerr	Grierson/t	Vatcher/t	Skrypec/t	Levett	Conquer	Holloway
McEwan	Dyson	Johnson	Perkin	Wightwick	Sheppard	Skrypec	Salisbury	Hill	Stewart
McEwan	Dyson/t	Johnson	Kerr	Grierson	Vatcher	Skrypec/t	Salisbury	Levett	Stewart
McEwan/2t	Grafton	Wightwick	Perkin	Johnson	Vatcher	Skrypec	Conquer	Salisbury	Stewart
McEwan	Grafton	Knight-Barnard	Pemble	Wightwick	Vatcher/2t	Skrypec	Levett	Salisbury	Stewart/t
McEwan/t	Dyson/2t	Wightwick	Pemble	Grierson	Vatcher	Skrypec	Levett	Salisbury	Stewart
McEwan/2t	Dyson	Johnson	Pemble	Grierson	Vatcher/t	Skrypec/2t	Levett	Salisbury	Stewart
McEwan	Dyson	Wightwick	Pemble	Grierson	Sheppard	Skrypec	Levett	Salisbury	Stewart
McEwan	Dyson/t	Wightwick	Pemble	Grierson	Vatcher/t	Skrypec/t	Levett	Salisbury	Stewart
McEwan/t	Dyson	Wightwick	Perkin	Grierson	Pokai	Skrypec	Sheppard	McSherry	Levett
McEwan	Grafton	Johnson	Perkin	Grierson	Sheppard	Skrypec	Levett	Salisbury/t	Stewart
McEwan	Grafton	Johnson	Perkin	Wightwick	Vatcher	Skrypec	Levett	Salisbury	Stewart/t
McEwan/t	Grafton	Johnson	Perkin	Grierson	Vatcher	Skrypec/t	Levett	Salisbury/t	Stewart
Russell/3cp	Dyson/2t	Allen	Kerr/t	Grierson	Vatcher	Skrypec	Levett	Conquer	Holloway/2t
Russell/4cp	Dyson	Johnson	Perkin	Grierson	Vatcher	Skrypec	Levett	Stewart	Wilson
Russell/2cp	Dyson	Allen	Perkin(a/t)	Grierson	Vatcher	Skrypec	Levett/t	Stewart	Holloway/t

REPLACEMENTS　a - J Kerr

WESTON-super-MARE

Comp.	Date	H/A	Opponents	Result & Score	Att	15	14	13	12	11
N3 S	2-Sep	A	Blackheath	L 9-34	300	Taylor	Steele	Havard	Dickson	Rainey
N3 S	9-Sep	A	North Walsham	L 3-41	300	Taylor	Ross	Dickson	Havard	Rainey
N3 S	16-Sep	H	Clifton	L 10-29	300	Morris	Steele	Rainey	Denham	Ross
N3 S	30-Sep	H	Plymouth Albion	L 7-43	250	Dickson	Morris	Coleman/c	Havard/t	Rainey
N3 S	14-Oct	A	Redruth	L 6-30	600	Dickson	Steele	Rainey	Denham	Morris
N3 S	21-Oct	H	Westcombe Park	L 14-26	200	Sharp	Steele	Rainey	Forde	Morris
N3 S	28-Oct	A	Basingstoke	W 15-10	200	Sharp	McHale	Rainey/2t	Coleman/cp	Morris
N3 S	11-Nov	H	Cheltenham*	W 21-10	250	Denham	Rainey	Howells	Coleman/c3p	McHale
N3 S	18-Nov	A	Launceston	L 5-51	320	Denham	Garnham	Coleman	Havard	McHale/t
N3 S	25-Nov	H	Penzance & Newlyn	L 14-17	250	Garnham	McHale	Havard	Rainey	Denham
N3 S	2-Dec	A	Reading	L 15-26	150	Coleman/5p	McHale	Rainey	Havard	Steele
N3 S	16-Dec	A	Barking	L 10-40	300	Garnham/t	McHale/t	Rainey	Denham	Ross
N3 S	23-Dec	H	Reading	L 15-23	250	Garnham	Wiseman	Rainey	Denham	McHale
N3 S	30-Dec	A	Penzance & Newlyn*	L 13-50	800	Garnham	Wiseman/c2p	Rainey	Havard	McHale
N3 S	6-Jan	H	Launceston	L 25-35	200	Denham	Rainey	Havard	Coleman/c5pdg	Venn
N3 S	13-Jan	A	Cheltenham	L 19-36	200	Denham	Rainey	Havard	Coleman/c4p	Venn
N3 S	27-Jan	A	Westcombe Park	W 15-5	200	Taylor	Steele	Rainey/t	Venn	Morris
N3 S	3-Feb	H	Tabard	L 9-12		Morris	Steele	Venn	Coleman/3p	Rainey
N3 S	10-Feb	H	Redruth	D 16-16	500	Taylor	Steele	McCormack	Havard	Rainey
N3 S	17-Feb	H	Basingstoke	L 8-14		Taylor	Steele/t	Rainey	Havard	McHale
N3 S	24-Feb	A	Plymouth Albion	L 0-52	1100	Taylor	Webb	Rainey	McCormack	McHale
N3 S	10-Mar	H	North Walsham	W 38-29	300	Morris	Taylor	Havard	Rainey	McHale/2t
N3 S	31-Mar	H	Barking	W 22-16	200	Morris/t	Steele	McCormack/c5p	Havard	McHale
N3 S	14-Apr	A	Tabard	W 20-13		Morris	Steele	Havard	McCormack/2c2p	Rainey
N3 S	21-Apr	H	Blackheath	W 28-15		Morris	Rainey/t	Havard/t	McCormack/t3c	Steele
N3 S	28-Apr	A	Clifton	L 13-18		Morris	Steele	McCormack/c2p	McHale	Wiseman/t
TBC	23-Sep	H	Barnstaple	L 15-46		Dickson	Steele	Denham	Havard	Morris

*after opponents name indicates a penalty try. Brackets after a player's name indicates he was replaced.
eg (a) means he was replaced by replacement code "a" and so on. / after a player or replacement name
is followed by any scores he made - eg /t, /c, /p, /dg or any combination of these*

MOST APPEARANCES

24 Lee Hirons
23 Duncan Rainey
22 Mervyn Down
21 Paul Redman
19 Andy Glen, Andy Gunningham.

PLAYERS USED

40 plus three as replacement only

MOST POINTS

Pts	Player	T	C	P	DG
99	N Coleman	-	9	26	1
61	B McCormack	1	10	12	-
34	I Williams	2	3	5	1
20	P Reman	1	-	5	-
20	S McHale	4	-	-	-
20	D Bird	4	-	-	-
20	D Rainey	4	-	-	-

MATCH FACTS

10	9	1	2	3	4	5	6	7	8
Coleman/3p	Hirons	Steele	Bird	Gunningham	Pitt	Curry	Glen	Redman	Buller
Morris/p	Hirons	Mathias	Bird	Gunningham	Pitt	Curry	Cornish	Redman	Glen
Coleman/cp	Hirons	Gunningham/t	Bird	Down	Buller	Curry	Collins	Shepherd	Redman
Howells	Hirons	Gunningham	Burge	Down	Pitt	Glen	Simpson	Redman	Sparks
Venn	Hirons	Gunningham	Bird	Down	Glen	Pitt	Simpson	Redman/2p	Buller
Wiseman	Hirons	Gunningham	Bird/t	Down	Glen	Pitt	Simpson	Redman/3p	Buller
Venn	Hirons	Gunningham	Bird	Down	Glen	Pitt	Perry	Redman	Buller
Venn	Hirons	Gunningham	Bird/t	Down	Curry	Glen	Perry	Redman	Buller
Howells	Hirons	Gunningham	Bird	Down	Glen	Curry	Kerslake	Simpson	Buller
Coleman/2c	Hirons/t	Gunningham	Bird	Down/t	Glen	Buller	Kerslake	Simpson	Masina
Venn	Hirons	Gunningham	Bird	Down	Glen	Buller	Kerslake	Redman	Masina
Coleman	Hirons	Gunningham	Bird	Down	Glen	Pitt	Kerslake	Redman	Buller
Coleman/cp	Hirons	Gunningham	Bird/2t	Steele	Pitt	Buller	Kerslake	Redman	Masina
Venn	Hirons	Gunningham	Bird	Down	Pitt	Buller	Glen	Kerslake	Masina
Williams	Hirons	Gunningham	Bird	Down	Glen	Buller	Kerslake/t	Redman	Masina
Williams	Hirons	Gunningham	Bird	Down	Glen	Buller	Kerslake	Redman/t	Masina
Williams/tcp	Hirons	Gunningham	Bird	Down	Pitt	Buller	Kerslake	Redman	Masina
Williams	Hirons	Gunningham	Burge	Down	Pitt	Buller	Kerslake	Redman	Masina
Williams/tc3p	Hirons	Gunningham	Burge	Down	Buller	Glen	Kerslake	Redman	Masina
Williams/p	McCormack	Mathias	Burge	Down	Buller	Pitt	Kerslake	Redman	Masina
Williams	Hirons	Mathias	Burge	Matthews	Pitt	Glen	Kerslake	Redman	Masina
Williams/dg	McCormack/3c3p	Steele/t	Bird	Down	Pitt	Glen	Kerslake	Redman	Masina/t
Williams	Hirons	Steele	Bird	Down	Glen	Pitt	Kerslake	Redman	Masina
Williams	Hirons	Mathias/t	Burge	Down	Pitt	Glen	Kerslake	Simpson	Masina/t
Williams/c	Hirons/t	Steele	Burge	Down	Pitt	Curry	Kerslake	Simpson	Masina
Williams	Hirons	Steele	Burge	Down	Perry	Redman	Kerslake	Simpson	Masina
Coleman/cp	Hirons	Gunningham	Bird(a/t)	Down/t	Pitt	Buller	Collins	Shepherd	Redman

REPLACEMENTS   a - D Burge

After 11 years in this division Weston-super-Mare go back into South West One. This is a far cry from 1995-96 when they finished runners up the year after finishing third.

Neil Coleman again topped the points scoring list one short of 100, he did not play after 3rd February.

New scrum half Lee Hirons made the most appearances with 24.

Weston did manage to win four of their last five matches but the damage was already done - they lost 14 of their first 16 league matches.

THE LAST TEN YEARS   DIVISION 4 SOUTH

1991-92
Champions — **Havant**
Runners-up — Basingstoke
Relegated — Sidcup, Ealing

Most
Points: 129 Pete Russell (Havant)
Tries: 9 Will Knight (Havant)
Penalties: 24 Pete Russell (Havant)
Conversions: 23 Pete Russell (Havant)
D.Gs: 4 Paul Tincknell (Weston-s-Mare)

1992-93
Champions — **Sudbury**
Runners-up — London Welsh
Relegated — Thurrock

Most
Points: 123 Steve Dybler (Sudbury)
Tries: 12 Steve Titcombe (Sudbury)
Penalties: 31 Simon Pennington (Stourbridge)
Conversions: 28 Ralph Zoing (Harrogate)
D.Gs: N.A.

1993-94
Champions — **Reading**
Runners-up — Lydney
Relegated — Southend, Maidstone

Most
Points: 133 Phil Belshaw (Reading)
Tries: N.A.
Penalties: 34 Phil Belshaw (Reading)
Conversions: N.A.
D.Gs: 5 Paul Tincknell (Weston-s-Mare)

1994-95
Champions — **London Welsh**
Runners-up — Lydney
Relegated — Sudbury, Basingstoke

Most
Points: 119 Paul Thatcher (Weston-s-Mare)
Tries: N.A.
Penalties: 31 Paul Thatcher (Weston-s-Mare)
Conversions: N.A.
D.Gs: N.A.

1995-96
Champions — **Lydney**
Runners-up — Weston-s-Mare
Relegated — Camborne

Most
Points: 176 Richard Perkins (Henley)
Tries: 10 Richard Perkins (Henley)
Tommy Adams (Camborne)
Penalties: 28 Paul Thatcher (Weston-s-Mare)
Richard Larkin (Askeans)
Conversions: 27 Richard Perkins (Henley)
D.Gs: 4 Simon Cattermole (Weston-s-Mare)

1996-97
Champions — **Newbury**
Runners-up — Henley
Relegated — Berry Hill, Askeans, High Wycombe, Charlton Park

Most
Points: 391 Nick Grecian (Newbury)
Tries: 27 Brian Johnson (Newbury)
Penalties: 53 Nick Churchman (Tabard)
Conversions: 100 Nick Grecian (Newbury)
D.Gs: 10 Simon Cattermole (Weston-s-Mare)

1997-98
Champions — **Camberley**
Runners-up — Henley
Relegated — -

Most
Points: 256 Rob Thirlby (Redruth)
Tries: 17 Rob Thirlby (Redruth)
Penalties: 51 James Shanahan (N. Walsham)
Conversions: 48 Rob Thirlby (Redruth)
D.Gs: 11 Nick Edmonds (Bridgwater)

1998-99
Champions — **Bracknell**
Runners-up — Esher
Relegated — Havant

Most
Points: 313 Jonathon Gregory (Esher)
Tries: 16 Nana Dontah (Esher), Andy Carter (Met Police),
& James Shanahan (N. Walsham)
Penalties: 58 Jon Gregory (Esher)
Conversions: 52 Jon Gregory (Esher)
D.Gs: 3 by five players

99-2000
Champions — **Esher**
Runners-up — Penzance & Newlyn
Relegated — Bridgwater, Norwich & Met. Police

Most
Points: 351 John Gregory (Esher)
Tries: 38 Richard Newton (Penzance & Newlyn)
Penalties: 59 Chris Atkinson (Plymouth A.)
Conversions: 78 John Gregory (Esher)
D.Gs: 6 Stewart Whitworth (Redruth)

2000-01
Champions — **Plymouth Albion**
Runners-up — Launceston
Relegated — Basingstoke, Cheltenham, Reading & Weston-s-M

Most
Points: 336 Nat Saumi (Penzance & Newlyn)
Tries: 20 Dan Ward-Smith (Plymouth A.)
& Victor Olonga (Penzance & N.)
Penalties: 46 Derek Coates (Westcombe P.)
Conversions: 67 Nat Saumi (Penzance & N.)
D.Gs: .7 Bede Brown (Redruth)

ALL TIME RECORDS — TEAM RECORDS — DIVISION 4 SOUTH

Highest score:	**136**	Penzance & Newlyn 136 Met Police 6, 15.04.00
Highest aggregate:	**142**	as above
Highest score by a losing side:	**34**	Redruth 34 Otley 41, 21.9.96
Highest scoring draw:	**25**	Henley v Metropolitan Police, 5.4.97
Most consecutive wins:	**26**	Plymouth Albion 2000-01
Most consecutive defeats:	**28**	Metropolitan Police 1998-99/1999-2000
Most points for in a season:	**1170**	Newbury 1996-97
Least points for in a season:	**64**	Maidstone 1989-90
Most points against in a season:	**1308**	Met Police 1999-2000
Least points against in a season:	**61**	Reading 1993-94
Most tries for in a season:	**167**	Newbury 1996-97
Most tries against in a season:	**188**	Met Police 1999-2000
Least tries for in a season:		
Least tries against in a season:		
Most conversions for in a season:	**103**	Newbury 1996-97
Most conversions against in a season:	**95**	Charlton Park 1996-97
Most penalties for in a season:	**66**	Camberley 1997-98
Most penalties against in a season:	**65**	Plymouth Albion 1997-98
Least penalties for in a season:		
Least penalties against in a season:		
Most drop goals for in a season:	**14**	Bridgwater 1997-98
Most drop goals against in a season:	**8**	Metropolitan Police 1997-98

ALL TIME RECORDS — INDIVIDUAL RECORDS — DIVISION 4 SOUTH

Most points in a season:	**385**	Nick Grecian (Newbury) 1996-97
Most tries in a season:	**38**	Richard Newton (Penzance & Newlyn) 1999-00
Most conversions in a season:	**96**	Nick Grecian (Newbury) 1996-97
Most penalties in a season:	**59**	Chris Atkinson (Plymouth) 1999-2000
Most drop goals in a season:	**11**	Nick Edmonds (Bridgwater) 1997-98
Most points in a match:	**41**	Nat Saumi, *Penzance* v Met Police 15.4.00
Most tries in a match:	**7**	Richard Newton, *Penzance* v Met Police 15.4.00
Most conversions in a match:	**13**	Nat Saumi, *Penzance* v Met Police 15.4.00
Most penalties in a match:	**7**	Carson Russell, *Bracknell* v N Walsham 27.3.99
		Jon Gregory, *Esher* v Tabard 18.03.00
Most drop goals in a match:	**4**	Simon Cattermole, *Weston-s-M.* v Berry Hill 16.11.96

TEN YEAR RECORDS — DIVISION 4 SOUTH

SEASONS

Club	91-92	92-93	93-94	94-95	95-96	96-97	97-98	98-99	99-00	00-01
Askeans	-	-	-	-	8	14	-	-	-	
Barking	-	-	-	5	4	3	3	4	6	4
Basingstoke	2	5	11	13	-	-	-	-	-	13r
Berry Hill	-	7	7	11	5	11	-	-	-	
Blackheath	-	-	-	-	-	-	-	-	-	9
Bracknell	-	-	-	-	-	-	-	1p	-	
Bridgwater & Albion	-	-	-	-	-	-	8	10	12r	
Camberley	-	-	-	-	7	4	1p	-	-	
Camborne	6	4	4	8	13	-	-	-	-	
Charlton Park	-	-	-	-	-	13	-	-	-	
Cheltenham	-	-	-	-	6	5	5	13	11	14r
Clifton	-	-	-	-	-	-	11	7	7	8
Ealing	13	-	-	-	-	-	-	-	-	-
Esher	-	-	-	-	-	-	4	2	1	-
Havant	1	-	-	-	-	-	12	14r	-	-
Henley	-	-	-	9	3	2	2p	-	-	-
High Wycombe	5	8	9	10	10	12	-	-	-	-
Launceston	-	-	-	-	-	-	-	-	-	2
London Welsh	3	2	6	1	-	-	-	-	-	-
Lydney	-	3	2	2	1	-	-	-	-	-
Maidstone	8	12	13	-	-	-	-	-	-	-
Metropolitan Police	10	9	10	7	12	7	14	5	14r	
Newbury	-	-	-	-	-	1	-	-	-	-
North Walsham	7	11	8	4	11	10	7	3	3	6
Norwich	-	-	-	-	-	-	-	6	13r	-
Penzance & Newlyn	-	-	-	-	-	-	-	-	2	3
Plymouth Albion	-	-	-	-	-	6	13	12	4	1
Reading	-	-	1	-	-	-	-	-	-	11r
Redruth	-	-	-	-	-	-	9	11	5	5
Sidcup	12	-	-	-	-	-	-	-	-	-
Southend	11	6	12	-	-	-	-	-	-	-
Sudbury	4	1	-	12	-	-	-	-	-	-
Tabard	-	-	3	6	9	8	6	8	8	10
Thurrock	-	13	-	-	-	-	-	-	-	-
Westcombe Park	-	-	-	-	-	-	-	-	10	7
Weston-super-Mare	9	10	5	3	2	9	10	9	9	12r

NORTHERN DIVISION

A complete club index appears at the back of the book.
This shows which Division and league each club is in for the 2001-02 season

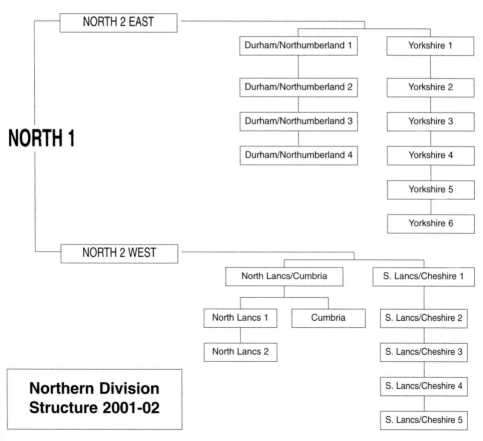

Northern Division Structure 2001-02

NORTHERN DIVISION OFFICIALS 2001-2002

North   **Chairman**
Mike Lord
68 Hoole Street,
Chester. CH2 3NL
Tel: 01244 312702
Fax: 01244 347988
07801 283506 (M)

North   **Hon Secretary**
Les Bentley
32 Moorhead Terrace,
Shipley,
West Yorkshire. BD18 4LB
Tel: 01274 585460
Fax: 01274 591245

North   **Northumberland Rep**   North   **Cheshire rep**
North Competitions Committee rep   **Asst Treasurer - Fines**
Dudley Gibbs   Richard Hazelhurst
'Sandyford',   217 Dickens Lane
Healey,   Poynton
Northumberland. NE44 6BA   Stockport SK12 1SS
Tel: 01434 682496   Tel: 01625 874485 (H)
Fax: 01434 682019   0161 406 6086 (B)
                                              Fax: 0161 406 6084

North   **Hon Treasurer**   North   **Yorkshire rep**
                Durham rep
Dave Thompson   Mike Smith
12 Aldsworth Close,   The Lowe, Wainstalls, Halifax,
Springwell,   West Yorkshire HX2 7TR
Gateshead NE9 7PG   Tel: 01422 882879
Tel: 0191 416 9839 (H)   Fax: 01422 882879
07778 809125 (M)   07850 233019 (M)

North   **Lancashire rep**   North   **Cumbria rep**
North 2 West   **League Secretary**   **Asst Treasurer - offshore**
Ivon Hodgson   Jack Hamer
Kimberley End,   55 Rush Green Road,
22 Capesthorn Close,   Lymm,
Holmes Chapel,   Cheshire. WA13 9PS
Cheshire. CW4 7EW   Tel: 01925 755584
Tel: 01477 533406

                              North 2 West   **League Secretary**
                              Ivon Hodgson
LEAGUE SECRETARIES   Kimberley End,
                              22 Capesthorn Close,
                              Holmes Chapel,
                              Cheshire. CW4 7EW
                              Tel: 01477 533406

North 1   **League Secretary**   **North 2 East**   **League Secretary**
Alan Johnson   Alan Bentley
6 Rugby Drive, Tytherington,   15 Sycamore Drive, Cleckheaton,
Macclesfield, Cheshire SK10 2DJ   West Yorkshire DB19 6AP
Tel/Fax 01625 614697   Tel: 01274 869364 (H)
                                              01274 861101 (B)

North Lancs 1 **League Secretary**
Colin Barton
4 Oulderhill Drive, Rochdale,
Lancashire OL11 5LB
Tel: 01706 350312

North Lancs 2 **League Secretary**
Bill Hopkinson
Far Hey Head Farm, Littleborough,
Rochdale Lancs OL15 9NS
Tel: 01706 379879

North Lancs - Cumbria **League Secretary**
Ian Scott Brown
7 Pendle View, Grindleton,
Nr Clitheroe, Lancashire BB7 4QU
Tel: 01200 440102

Cumbria **League Secretary**
Frank Sheppard
74 Meadow Field, Gosforth,
Cumbria CA20 1HX
Tel: 01946 725327

South Lancs Cheshire 1 **League Secretary**
Mike Massey
Fieldside, Grange Road, Bowden,
Cheshire WA14 3EE
Tel: 0161 9282997

South Lancs Cheshire 2 **League Secretary**
Brian Minor
45 Gorton Street, Peel Green, Eccles,
Manchester M30 8LX
Tel: 0161 2885324

South Lancs Cheshire 3 **League Secretary**
Vic Thomas
5 Portree Close, Winton, Eccles,
Manchester M30 8LX
Tel: 0161 7887274

South Lancs Cheshire 4 **League Secretary**
Peter Riley
27 Grappenhall Road, Stockton Heath,
Warrington, Cheshire WA4 2AH
Tel: 01925 6044896

South Lancs Cheshire 5 **League Secretary**
Ken Potter
54 Tennyson Drive, Ormskirk,
Lancashire L39 3PL
Tel: 01695 571176

Durham Northumberland 1 **League Secretary**
Gordon Gravil
6 Grampian Way, Thorne,
South Yorkshire DN8 5YL
Tel: 01405 813642

Durham Northumberland 2 **League Secretary**
Tony Brown
22 Mill Crescent, Hebburn,
Tyne & Wear NE31 1UQ
Tel: 0191 4693716

Durham Northumberland 3 **League Secretary**
Joyce Baty
5 Brooklands, Ponteland,
Northumberland NE20 9LZ
Tel: 01661 823527

Durham Northumberland 4 **League Secretary**
John Ker
4 Anlaby Close, Billingham,
Cleveland TS23 3RA
Tel: 01642 560536

Yorkshire 1 **League Secretary**
Trevor Graveson
Attermire House, Castle Hill,
Settle BD24 9EU
Tel: 01729 823559

Yorkshire 2 **League Secretary**
Bill Cooper
Moorcroft, Lucy Hall Drive,
Baildon, West Yorkshire BD17 5BG
Tel: 01274 584355

Yorkshire 3 **League Secretary**
Ron Lewis
17 Harewood Drive, Wrenthorpe,
Wakefield, Yorkshire WF2 0DS
Tel: 01924 299874

Yorkshire 4 **League Secretary**
Jim Cooper
8 Otterwood Bank, Foxwood Hill,
Acomb, Yorkshire YO24 3JS
Tel: 01904 797858

Yorkshire 5 **League Secretary**
Graham Mapplebeck
46 Cranmore Crescent, Belle Isle,
Leeds LS10 4AN
Tel: 0113 270 4935

Yorkshire 6 **League Secretary**
Kathleen McNally
28 Cherry Tree Road, Armthorpe,
Doncaster, Yorks DN3 2HP
Tel: 01302 834252

NORTH ONE

2000-01 LEAGUE TABLE

	P	W	D	L	PF	PA	PD	Pts	
Darlington Mowden Park	20	20	0	0	719	163	556	40	
Blaydon	21	19	0	2	588	306	282	38	
Bradford & Bingley	22	12	0	10	503	392	111	24	
Macclesfield	21	12	0	9	403	293	110	24	
Driffield	21	12	0	9	476	388	88	24	
Sheffield	22	12	0	10	387	310	77	24	
Chester	22	11	1	10	517	393	124	23	
Hull Ionians	22	8	0	14	399	516	-117	16	
*Middlesbrough	21	8	1	12	472	402	70	15	-2
Wigton	15	5	0	10	184	235	-51	10	
Stockton	21	4	0	17	220	724	-504	8	
*Northern	22	1	0	21	245	991	-746	-2	-4

2001-02 FIXTURE GRID

	Aspatria	Bradford & Bingley	Chester	Darlington	Driffield	Halifax	Hull Ionians	Macclesfield	Middlesbrough	Sheffield	West Park St Helens	Wigton
Aspatria		09.03	29.09	06.04	26.01	08.12	05.01	08.09	27.10	17.11	20.10	23.02
Bradford & Bingley	22.09		13.04	26.01	02.03	27.10	09.02	17.11	05.01	06.10	16.03	22.12
Chester	02.03	08.12		17.11	06.10	26.01	27.10	05.01	06.04	09.02	22.09	16.03
Darlington	22.12	10.11	12.01		16.03	06.10	02.03	02.02	09.02	22.09	13.04	01.12
Driffield	10.11	29.09	23.02	08.09		06.04	08.12	09.03	17.11	05.01	02.02	20.10
Halifax	13.04	02.02	10.11	23.02	22.12		22.09	20.10	02.03	16.03	01.12	12.01
Hull Ionians	01.12	20.10	02.02	29.09	13.04	09.03		23.02	16.03	22.12	12.01	10.11
Macclesfield	16.03	12.01	01.12	27.10	22.09	09.02	06.10		26.01	02.03	22.12	13.04
Middlesbrough	02.02	01.12	22.12	20.10	12.01	29.09	08.09	10.11		13.04	23.02	09.03
Sheffield	12.01	23.02	20.10	09.03	01.12	08.09	06.04	29.09	08.12		10.11	02.02
West Park St Helens	09.02	08.09	09.03	08.12	27.10	05.01	17.11	06.04	06.10	26.01		29.09
Wigton	06.10	06.04	08.09	05.01	09.02	17.11	26.01	08.12	22.09	27.10	02.03	

ASPATRIA RUFC

Founded: 1875

Secretary: Avril Quinn, 1 Beacon Close, Aspatria, CA5 3HU
016973 21610 (H) 016973 31234 (B) 016973 32749 (Fax) E-mail: avrilq@excite.com
Director of Rugby: Melvyn Hanley, 7 King Street, Aspatria, Cumbria, CA5 3AD.
016973 20328 (H), 01946 815111 (B), 01946 815082 (Fax)
President: Norman Lazonby, Croft House, Dubwath, Bass Lake, Cumbria 01768 776363
Chairman: John Heyworth   **Treasurer:** Barney Clegg 016973 20285   **County Representative:** David Wilson
Fixture Secretary: P Gray 016973 21760   **Team Secretary:** M Ray 016973 21313
Ground Address: Bower Park, Station Road, Aspatria, Cumbria Tel: 016973 20420   Website: www.aspatriarufc.com
Capacity: 2,250 Seated: 250   Standing: 2,000
Directions: M6 Junc 41, B5305 to Wigton. Left in Wigton Town Centre - 2 miles left onto by-pass. 7 miles to Aspatria - left in town centre towards station   Nearest Railway Station: Aspatria, right out of station, club 100yds on right
Car Parking: 200 at ground, 200 nearby   **Admission:** tba
Clubhouse: Normal licensing hours. Snacks & bar meals available match days only
Club Shop: Open 2-5 matchdays Contact Mary Hanley 016973 20328
Colours: Black & red hoops/black **Change colours:** Black shirts/white
Training Nights: Tuesday & Thursday   **Nickname:** Black/reds
Programme Size: A5   Price: 50p   Pages: 56   Editor: Avril Quinn
Advertising Rates Mono only Full page £100, Half page £50, Qtr £25

Aspatria RUFC - Back Row: Fred Story (Main Sponsor), Mark Bowe, Alex Reay, Tom Wall, Paul Hay, Lee Wall, Paul West, David Humes, Paul Brough, Lee Chilton Ian Sewell (Story Construction). Front: Ashley Barton, David Wilson, Mike Burnett, Steve Wood, Derek Benson (Capt.), Jason Spires, Steve Stoddart, Graham Andrews, Jason Thurlow.

BRADFORD & BINGLEY R.F.C.

President Michael Woodward 10 Fox Hill Close, Queensbury, Bradford BD13 2JP 01274 881253
Secretary John Gray White House, Street Lane, East Morton BD20 5SE 01274 510636
Fixture Secretary Barry Shinn 20 Heaton Drive, Eldwick BD16 3DN 01274 563791
Chairman Will Arthur 12 Park Hill Close, Bradford BD8 0DG 01274 487083
League Contact as Secretary, see above

Ground **Address:** Wagon Lane, Cottingley Bridge, Bingley, W. Yorks. BD16 1LT
Tel: 01274 775441   Fax: 01274 775442   Website: www.townwebs.syol.com/towns/bingley/rfc.html
Directions: M62 onto M606 to Bradford ring road, right to 2nd roundabout, left onto A650 for 5 miles to Bingley, right by Beckfoot School onto Wagon Lane, ground 200 yards along.
Nearest Railway Station: Bingley   **Car Parking:** Approx. 300 spaces at ground
Admission Matchday Adult £3; OAP & Student £1.50 u18 Free
Club Shop Contact Tim Richmond 01274 563919

Programme Size: A5   Pages: 24   Price: With admission   Editor: Steve Oddy 01274 563254
Advertising: Contact Stuart Booth 01274 569567 (H) 01274 569558 (B) Dave Narey 01274 511129 (H) 01274 690100 (B)
Colours: Red, amber & black hoops/black   **Change colours:** All black
Training Nights: Tuesday & Thursday   **Nickname:** 'The Bees'

NORTHERN

CHESTER R.U.F.C.

Founded: 1925

President	C Cawthorn	21 Oaklands Avenue, Tattenhall, Chester CH3 9QU	Tel: 01829 770498
Chairman	W Evans	12 Orchard Croft, Guilden Sutton, Chester CH3 7SL	Tel: 01244 300515
Treasurer	D Gray	Applegarth, Little Heath Rd., Chester CH3 7AH	
Hon. Secretary	P Rhodes	The Hollies, off Carriage Drive, Frodsham, Cheshire WA6 6EF	
		Tel: 01928 731485	
Fixture Sec.	C Cawthorn	21 Oaklands Avenue, Tattenhall, Chester CH3 9QU	Tel: 01829 770498
Director of Rugby	J Booth	The Old School House, Acres Rd., Bebington, Cheshire	

GROUND   **Address:** Hare Lane, Littleton, Chester CH3 7DB   Tel: 01244 336017
Website: www.chester-rufc.com
Capacity: 1,000   Covered Seating: 500
Directions: From the A55 - the Chester outer ring road - take the A51and then the first left into Hare Lane.
Car Parking: Included with admission **Nearest Railway Station:** Chester
Admission: Matchday £3   Season tickets: Not available
Clubhouse: Open Tues., Wed. & Thur. Sat. & Sun. & for private functions.
Club Shop: Open matchdays & Sundays.
Programme: **Size:** A5   **Price**: Incl. with admission   Advertising: Contact A Rees 01244 675352
Training Nights: Tuesday & Thursday
Colours: Red shirts, black shorts   **Change colours:** Blue shirts, black shorts

DARLINGTON RFC

Founded: 1863

President	Eric Rogers	45 Barratt Rd., Darlington DL3 8LA	01325 468560
Chairman	Andrew Foster	45 Hartford Rd., Darlington DL3 8HF	01325 466501
Club Secretary	Peter Sanderson	School House, Chapel St., Middleton One Row, Darlington DL2 1DA	
			01325 332986
Fixtures Secretary	David Gardner,	'Shieldaig', Boldron Lane, Startford, Barnard Castle, Co.Durham. DL12 9AP	
		email: davidandsusangardener@tesco.net	01833 630742
Treasurer	Frank Nelson	1 Mayfield, Barnard Castle, Co. Durham DL12 9AR	01833 638307
League Contact:	Tommy Miller	51 First Ave., Colburn, Catterick Garrison DL9 4RL	01748 832700

GroundAddress: Blackwell Meadows, Grange Road, Darlington. DL1 5NR Tel: 01325 363777 Fax: 01325 363888
Capacity: 2,150   Seated: 150   Uncovered Standing: 2000   Web site: www.darlingtonrfc.co.uk
Directions: From south take A66, DRFC directly off Blands Corner roundabout.
        From north take A68 to Darlington and continue to A66 junction at Blands Corner r'about at Blackwell
Car Parking: Spaces for 200 cars & 4 coaches at ground.   Nearest Railway Station: Darlington Bank Top
Clubhouse: Open Mon-Sat 11-11pm and Sunday 12-10.30pm   **Club Shop:** Open weekends **Admission:** N/A
Training Nights: Monday & Thursday (seniors)
Programme: Size: A4   Price: With admission   Pages: 10
Colours: Scarlet with black & white Hoop   **Change colours:** Black & white quarters

DRIFFIELD F.C.

Founded: 1926

President	Mike Sellers	Low Kaythorpe, Rudston, Driffield YO25 0JD	Tel: 01262 420237
Chairman	John Harrison	9 Parsonage Close, Nafferton, Driffield YO25 0LH	Tel: 01377 253032
Hon. Secretary	Colin Seabrook	'Lilleygarth', Main Street, Skerne, Driffield YO25 9HS	Tel: 01377 253690
Fixture Sec.	John Leason	15 Albion Street, Driffield. YO25 6PZ	Tel: 01377 254036
Director of Rugby	Stuart Cooper	1 Orchard Drive, Middleton, Driffield YO25 9UW	

Ground Address   Kelleythorpe, Driffield, E. Yorks. YO25 9DW Tel: 01377 256598
         Capacity: Unlimited - all uncovered standing

Directions: From M62 follow A614 to the strat of the Driffield by-pass. Ground opposite.
         From York take A166 to Driffield by-pass then right along by-pass for half mile. Ground on left.
         Nearest Station: Driffield, 1 mile from ground.
         Car Parking: Unlimited car parking at ground.

Admission: Matchday £3.00 including programme. No season tickets available.
Clubhouse: Open Tues & Thurs evs., matchdays & Sun morning.   **Club Shop:** Open Sunday morning.
Colours: Blue/black/white   **Change colours:** All red   **Training Nights:** Tuesday & Thursday
Programme: **Size:** A5   **Pages**: 20   **Price**: With admission   **Editor**: John Harrison (Chairman)
         Advertising: Contact editor

HALIFAX R.U.F.C.

Founded: 1919

President	David Brook MBE, MA	Hall Park House, Hall Park Rd., Walton, Wetherby Tel: 01937 843939
Chairman	Peter Smith	Torrington, 446 Burnley Road, halifax HX2 7LW Tel/Fax: 01422 360143
Treasurer	Chris Mellor	37 Harewood Ave., Highroad Well, Halifax HX2 0LU Tel: 01422 362619
Secretary	Mike Smith	The Lowe, Wainstalls, Halifax, West Yorkshire. HX2 7TR
& League Contact		Tel: 01422 882879 (H) 07850 233019 (Mobile) Email: thelowe@aol.com
Fixture Secretary	Glyn Kenyon	18 Watkinson Road, Illingworth, Halifax, HX2 9DB
		Tel: (H) 01422 245193 Email: glyn@kenyon.freeserve.co.uk

Ground   Standeven Memorial Ground, Ovenden Park, Keighley Road, Ovenden, Halifax, West Yorks. HX2 8AR
Tel: 01422 365926

Capacity: 5000   **Seated:** 200   **Standing:** Covered - 300   Uncovered - 4500

Directions   From Halifax town centre, take the main road to Keighley (A629), HRUFC is approx 2.5 miles from the town centre on right behind Moorside Junior School   **Car Parking:** on the ground

Admission   Matchday £4 incl. programme & car park   **Nearest Railway Station:** Halifax

Clubhouse   Open training evenings & matchdays   **Club Shop:** Open as clubhouse

Colours   Dark blue, light blue and white hoops   **Change colours:** All blue

Training Nights   Tuesday & Thursday evenings   **Nickname:** "Fax"

Programme   **Size:** A5   **Price:** with admission   **Pages:** 68   **Editor:** Mike Smith (Secretary)
Advertising: Contact Chairman at home address

HALIFAX RUFC

HULL IONIANS R.U.F.C.

Founded: 1989

President	B Appleyard	c/o the club
Chairman	R Gosling	c/o the club
Secretary	Peter G Hewitt	24 Melton Road, North Ferriby, E. Yorks. HU14 3ET
		Tel: 01482 633626 e-mail: peterghewitt@hotmail.com
Director of Rugby	Saun Carty	c/o the club
League Contact	Karl Hornsey	
Ground Address	Brantingham Park, Brantingham Road, Elloughton, Brough, E. Yorks. HU15 1HX	

Tel: 01482 667342 Fax: 01482 666695   Capacity: 2,500 Covered Seating: 225

Directions: Take M62 East. Becomes A63. Take first exit. Follow signs to Brough. After 1 mile take left turn to Brantingham (2nd of two left turns)). At T junction turn right. Club 1/2 mile on RHS.
Nearest Railway Station: Brough **Car Parking:** Spaces for 120 cars (+ overflow if reqd.)

Admission: Matchday £3

Clubhouse: Open 7 days. 2 bars, 3 sponsors' rooms, gym, sports hall & solarium. Functions catered up to 200

Club Shop: Open training days & matchdays.

Programme   Size: A5   Pages: 30   Price: inclusive with admission.
Editor: Karl Hornsey   Advertising: Contact Craig Bone

Colours: White shirts with red & green trim   **Change colours:** Blue shirts
Training Nights: Tuesday & Thursday   **Nickname:** "I"s

MACCLESFIELD R.U.F.C.

Founded: 1877

President	M E Richardson	High Ash Farm, Wildboarclough, Macclesfield SK10 2E	01260 500964
Chairman	I Wooldridge	23 Cherington Crescent, Macclesfield SK11 8LA	01625 618777
Secretary	Anton Woolford	2 Church Lane, Sutton Lane Ends, Macclesfield. SK11 0DS	01260 253390
Treasurer	Alan Johnson	6 Rugby Drive, Tytherington, Macclesfield SK10 2JD	01625 614697 Tel/Fax

e-mail: ajohnco@macc61.freeserve.co.uk

Ground Priory Park, Priory Lane, Prestbury, Macclesfield, Cheshire SK10 4AF
Tel: 01625 827899 Fax: 01625 827899
Capacity: 5,500 Covered Seating: 200

Directions About 1 mile west of Town Centre on the B5087 - Macclesfield to Alderley Edge road, adjacent to Leisure Centre.
Nearest Railway Station: Macclesfield (in town centre) **Car Parking**: Spaces for 250 cars at ground

Admission: £3.50 including programme

Clubhouse: Open Saturdays & Sundays & every night except Wed. & Sunday

Club Shop: Open Saturady & Sunday & Tues & Thursday evenings.

Programme: Size: A5 Pages: 32 Price: £1 Editor: G A Allen
Advertising: O/S Back Cover £350 I/S Back Cover £160 Full page: £100 1/2 Page £

Colours: Blue and white hoops **Change colours:** Red/black/white vertical stripes

Nickmame: The Silkmen **Training Nights:** Tuesday & Thursday

MIDDLESBROUGH R.U.F.C.

Founded: 1872

President: Mike Wright 01642 275759 (H) **Chairman:** Walter Hibbert 01429 297947 (H)

Secretary Don Brydon 20 Westwood Ave., Linthorpe, Middlesbrough, TS5 5PY Tel/Fax: 01642 819954(H)

Fixture Secretary John Haddon 5 Wycherley Avenue, Linthorpe, Middlesbrough.
Tel 01642 - 821126 (H) 677181 (B) 606458 (Fax)

Director of Rugby John Dixon, 11 Pavilion Close, Seaton Carew, Hartlepool TS25 2PE Tel: 01429 276874 (H)

Press Officer Mike Read Orchard House, Thimbleby, Northallerton, DL6 3PY.
Tel: 01609 883525 (H) 01642 242753 (B) 01642 246326 (Fax)

Match Secretary Andy Murray Tel 01287 637803

League Contact Results/player registration - Keith Bircham 01642 882332 (H) All other matters - Secretary

Ground Acklam Park, Green Lane, Acklam, Middlesbrough, TS5 7SL. Tel 01642 818567

Directions A19 take A1130 exit to Middlesbrough. Left at small r/about, right at bollards to Croft Ave, straight
across traffic lights to Green Lane, club 600 yards on R. Nearest Railway Station: Middlesbrough

Car Parking: Yes - Ample - Free **Admission** Matchday £3.00

Club Shop Yes open Tues/Wed/Thurs evenings & Sunday morning

Clubhouse Open every evening, plus Thurs-Sunday lunch time with bar meals available

Colours: Maroon with two gold hoops/Maroon **Change Colours:** Sky Blue **Training Nights:** Tuesday & Thursday

Programme Size A5 - Pages 28 - Price with admission - Editor Don Brydon Tel 01642 819954(H)
Advertising Walter Hibbert, 50 Lufton Avenue, Hartlepool, TS26 9QW. Tel 01429 297947

SHEFFIELD R.U.F.C.

Founded: 1902

Chairman Bill Campbell c/o Sheffield RUFC, Administration Office, Abbeydale Park Sports Club,
Abbeydale Rd. South, Sheffield S17 3LG 01142 367023 (H)

President Steve Newsome c/o Sheffield RUFC

Club Secretary William Oliver Cumberland House, Cumberland Street, SheffieldS1 4PT
0114 255 6817 (H), 0114 249 5501 (B), 0114 279 8804 (Fax)

Internal Admin Richard Fedyk 0114 236 4785 (H), 01332 262951(B), 01332 262846 (Fax)

Club Coach John Adams c/o Sheffield RUFC

Fixtures Secretary Neil Adgie 663 Manchester Rd., Sheffield S10 5PR 0114 230 4588 (H)

League Contact Neil Adgie as above

Ground Address: Abbeydale Park Sports Club, Abbeydale Road South, Sheffield. S17 3LG Tel 0114 236 7011
Capacity: 1200 Seated: 200 Standing: 1000 Website: sheffieldrufc.co.uk

Directions: The club is on the A621 (Bakewell to Baslow road) out of Sheffield. Nearest Station: Sheffield (BR)

Car Parking: 200 spaces are available at the club. Admission: Matchday Adult £4 (OAPs £2)

Clubhouse: Normal Licensing hours, snacks, bar meals & restaurant. Club Shop: Open matchdays only.

Colours: Blue & white hoops/navy blue/red. **Change colours:** Red/navy blue/red.

Training Nights: Tuesday and Thursday at 7pm

Programme Size: A5 Price: with admssion Pages: 20 + cover Editor: John Phillips 0114 236 7930 (H)
Advertising - Full page £250, 1/2 page £125

WEST PARK (ST. HELENS) R.F.C.

Founded: 1947

President	Tony Rigby	1 Pentire Ave., Windle, St. Helens	01744 26803
Chief Executive	Malcolm Worsley	Old Lodge Farm, Burtonwood, Cheshire	01925 225845
Deputy Executive	John Bradbury	104 Mossbank rd., St. Helens WA11 7DG	01744 733578
Director of Finance	Norman England	'Caleb View', 71 Dingle Rd., Upholland WN8 0EW	01695 622665
Director of Administration	John B Fletcher	'Cellduminn', 7 Kings Rd., Taylor Park, St. Helens WA10 3HT	

01744 755895 (H) 01744 617372 (B & Fax)
email: jean-fletcher@talk21.com

Ground Address   West Park RFC, Redrocks, Prescot Road, St. Helens WA10 3AG
Tel: 01744 26138 **Fax:** 01744 617372 **website:** westparkrfc.co.uk **email:** jean-fletcher@talk21.com
Capacity   1000   Covered Seating: 20   Standing: Covered - 250   Uncovered - 730
Directions: M62 off at J6 & take M57 towards Liverpool docks & Southport. Turn off at Prescot sign (Knowsley Safari Park sign) and follow signs to St. Helens. After passing the "Grapes' PH, West Park is approx. 1/2 mile on left.
Car Parking: 150 spaces at ground, a further 150 next door in Carmel College   **Nearest Railway Station:** Hatto Heath
Admission: Matchday £3   **Clubhouse:** Open every evening except Sunday   **Club Shop:** thro' Dir. of Admin..
Colours: Green & gold hooped shirts, green shorts **Change colours:** All red **Training Nights:** Tuesday & Thursday
Programme: **Size:** A5   **Pages:** 20**Price:** with admission**Editor:** J B Fletcher
Advertising: 1/4 page £50 1/2 page: £100 Page: £200 - all + VAT - contact J B Fletcher

West Park (St. Helens) RFC - the winners of North 2 West pictured at Vale of Lune having secured the title.

WIGTON R.U.F.C.

Founded: 1882

President	M Sunter	Kathy's Cottage, 6 Riverside, Caldbeck.	Tel: 01697 478081 (H)
Chairman	A H Robson	2 Station Hill, Wigton, Cumbria	Tel: 01697 342310 (H)
Hon. Secretary	Alan Lynch	Parsonbridge, Westward, Wigton, Cumbria CA7 8NH	Tel: 01697 343436 (H)
Fixture Secretary	Trevor Richardson	26 Mount Pleasant Gardens, Wigton, Cumbria	Tel: 01697 345590
Treasurer	Robert Hird	Oxrigg Farm, Westward, Wigton	Tel: 01697 344969
League Contact	A H Robson	As above	

Ground   **Address:** Lowmoor Road, Wigton, Cumbria CA7 9QT   Tel: 01697 342206 Fax: 01697 343436
Capacity: Unlimited   Covered seats: 100
Directions: M6 (North), take Junction 41 sign-posted Wigton, or A595 Carlisle to Cockermouth - both roads bring you to Wigton Junction. Follow road for half a mile, club is on the left.
Nearest Station: Wigton
Car Parking: Unlimited car parking at ground.
Admission   Matchday: £3   Season Ticket: £50
Clubhouse: Open 7 nights per week, 2 bars and usual facilities. **Club Shop:** Yes
Colours: Green shirts/white shorts   **Change colours:** All white
Training Nights: Monday & Wednesday   **Nickname:** The Greens
Programme: Size: A5 Pages: 6 Price: With admission   Advertising: Contact R Aird, 01697 344969

NORTHERN DIVISION FINAL LEAGUE TABLES 2000-01

North 2 East

	P	W	D	L	PF	PA	PD	Pts	-
Halifax	21	20	1	0	883	146	737	41	
Darlington	21	19	0	2	852	213	639	38	
Goole	21	14	1	6	400	325	75	29	
Huddersfield	20	12	1	7	470	270	200	25	
Redcar	20	10	1	9	380	359	21	21	
Bridlington	21	8	1	12	293	418	-125	17	
Old Crossleyans	21	8	1	12	228	494	-266	17	
Alnwick	16	8	0	8	297	274	23	16	
Beverley	21	7	1	13	355	435	-80	15	
Morpeth	17	6	2	9	287	358	-71	14	
West Park Bramhope	22	3	2	17	135	694	-559	8	
York	21	0	1	20	121	715	-594	1	

North 2 West

	P	W	D	L	PF	PA	PD	Pts	-
West Park St Helens	22	19	0	3	616	263	353	38	
Aldwinians	21	14	2	5	462	314	148	30	
Winnington Park	21	12	1	8	425	329	96	25	
Vale of Lune	22	12	0	10	412	370	42	24	
*Stockport	22	11	1	10	462	418	44	21	2
Caldy	21	10	1	10	373	363	10	21	
Lymm	21	10	1	10	375	368	7	21	
Broughton Park	22	10	0	12	472	531	-59	20	
Altrincham Kersal	22	9	2	11	342	465	-123	20	
*Blackburn	21	8	0	13	366	462	-96	14	2
Penrith	16	6	0	10	196	282	-86	12	
Widnes	21	1	0	20	301	637	-336	2	

North Lancs/Cumbria

	P	W	D	L	PF	PA	PD	Pts	-
Workington	20	20	0	0	626	140	486	40	
Carlisle	21	17	0	4	627	254	373	34	
Rochdale	18	12	1	5	365	219	146	25	
Blackpool	19	12	0	7	502	298	204	24	
Rossendale	19	11	1	7	341	215	126	23	
Oldham	19	9	0	10	376	262	114	18	
Netherhall	19	8	0	11	335	271	64	16	
Kirkby Lonsdale	16	7	0	9	289	280	9	14	
Cockermouth	19	6	1	12	232	560	-328	13	
*Calder Vale	19	4	0	15	178	637	-459	6	2
*Fleetwood	19	3	0	16	182	594	-412	4	2
*Egremont	16	1	1	14	165	488	-323	1	2

North Lancs 1

	P	W	D	L	PF	PA	PD	Pts	-
De La Salle	21	20	1	0	580	124	456	41	
Tyldesley	21	19	1	1	719	201	518	39	
Bury	22	13	1	8	411	340	71	27	
Trafford MV	22	13	0	9	415	294	121	26	
Old Bedians	21	9	1	11	205	318	-113	19	
Bolton	22	9	0	13	404	436	-32	18	
Burnage	22	9	0	13	365	402	-37	18	
Didsbury Toc H	22	9	0	13	347	488	-141	18	
Eccles	22	8	1	13	250	375	-125	17	
Heaton Moor	22	8	0	14	301	378	-77	16	
Ashton-under-Lyne	22	8	0	14	297	419	-122	16	
Broughton	21	2	1	18	211	730	-519	5	

North Lancs 2

	P	W	D	L	PF	PA	PD	Pts	-
Lytham	16	14	1	1	466	126	340	29	
Thornton Cleveleys	16	12	1	3	402	145	257	25	
Littleborough	16	11	2	3	376	99	277	24	
Colne & Nelson	16	10	0	6	259	180	79	20	
North Manchester	15	8	1	6	289	250	39	17	
*Chorley	16	5	1	10	170	318	-148	9	2
Carnforth	15	4	0	11	147	330	-183	8	
Lostock	16	2	2	12	116	471	-355	6	
Clitheroe	14	0	0	14	80	386	-306	0	

Cumbria

	P	W	D	L	PF	PA	PD	Pts	-
Vickers Sports	18	15	1	2	563	157	406	31	
St Benedict's	17	15	1	1	458	109	349	31	
Millom	21	13	0	8	442	348	94	26	
Windermere	17	9	1	7	362	266	96	19	
*Creighton	19	10	1	8	367	342	25	19	2
Keswick	18	8	1	9	320	259	61	17	
*Furness	18	10	1	7	281	318	-37	17	4
Moresby	14	7	0	7	251	215	36	14	
*Greengarth	15	7	0	8	156	241	-85	12	2
*Ambleside	13	7	0	6	141	256	-115	12	2
Upper Eden	14	3	0	11	168	268	-100	6	
*Silloth	15	2	0	13	171	428	-257	2	2
Whitehaven	19	0	0	19	74	547	-473	0	

South Lancs/Cheshire 1

	P	W	D	L	PF	PA	PD	Pts	-
Birkenhead Park	22	20	0	2	762	222	540	40	
Warrington	22	18	0	4	536	258	278	36	
Wigan	22	14	1	7	434	209	225	29	
Aspull	21	13	1	7	361	236	125	27	
St Edward's O.B.	22	11	0	11	380	321	59	22	
Birchfield (Lancs)	22	10	1	11	315	408	-93	21	
Wilmslow	21	10	0	11	286	415	-129	20	
Vagabonds (I.O.M.)	21	8	0	13	326	402	-76	16	
Northwich	22	8	0	14	276	435	-159	16	
Leigh	22	7	0	15	252	445	-193	14	
Oldershaw	22	5	0	17	273	491	-218	10	
*Ashton on Mersey	21	4	1	16	146	505	-359	3	6

South Lancs/Cheshire 2

	P	W	D	L	PF	PA	PD	Pts	-
Dukinfield	22	20	0	2	641	242	399	40	
Ormskirk	22	19	0	3	703	223	480	38	
Southport	22	18	1	3	595	330	265	37	
Wirral	21	14	0	7	477	352	125	28	
Trentham	21	14	0	7	380	273	107	28	
Ellesmere Port	22	8	1	13	282	437	-155	17	
Sandbach	22	7	0	15	248	464	-216	14	
Wallasey	22	6	1	15	214	417	-203	13	
Moore	22	5	2	15	304	561	-257	12	
Crewe and Nantwich	20	5	1	14	195	379	-184	11	
*St Mary's O.B. (Lancs)	21	5	0	16	318	466	-148	8	2
*Newton-le-Willows	19	4	0	15	250	463	-213	6	2

South Lancs/Cheshire 3

	P	W	D	L	PF	PA	PD	Pts	-
Anselmians	16	14	0	2	452	191	261	28	
Runcorn	15	13	0	2	347	189	158	26	
Sefton	16	11	0	5	309	168	141	22	
Hoylake	14	9	1	4	311	174	137	19	
Ruskin Park	15	7	0	8	269	295	-26	14	
Marple	16	5	0	11	208	328	-120	10	
Douglas (I.O.M.)	15	4	1	10	234	352	-118	9	
Congleton	16	3	0	13	148	350	-202	6	
Eagle	15	2	0	13	139	370	-231	4	

South Lancs/Cheshire 4

	P	W	D	L	PF	PA	PD	Pts	-
Orrell Anvils	17	15	0	2	609	141	468	30	
Bowdon	15	13	1	1	505	115	390	27	
Prenton	13	10	1	2	380	119	261	21	
Liverpool Collegiate O.B.	16	9	3	4	306	159	147	21	
Helsby	17	10	0	7	309	228	81	20	
Parkonians	17	6	0	11	203	414	-211	12	
Halton	16	5	0	11	175	335	-160	10	
Port Sunlight	17	5	0	12	178	404	-226	10	
Vulcan	13	1	1	11	101	386	-285	3	
*Capenhurst	17	2	0	15	140	605	-465	2	2

South Lancs/Cheshire 5

	P	W	D	L	PF	PA	PD	Pts
Oswestry	12	11	0	1	486	105	381	22
Manchester Wanderers	12	9	0	3	326	138	188	18
Mossley Hill A.C.	12	8	0	4	205	126	79	16
Holmes Chapel	11	6	0	5	236	196	40	12
Prescot	11	3	0	8	131	258	-127	6
Waterloo Vikings	12	3	0	9	185	389	-204	6
Lucas Merseyside	12	1	0	11	87	444	-357	2

Durham/N'thm'land 1

	P	W	D	L	PF	PA	PD	Pts	
*Westoe	22	21	0	1	666	232	434	40	2
Percy Park	22	15	0	7	491	357	134	30	
Durham City	22	14	1	7	500	385	115	29	
Consett	22	14	0	8	470	322	148	28	
*Hartlepool Rovers	22	13	0	9	459	385	74	24	2
Horden	22	12	0	10	540	473	67	24	
West Hartlepool TDSOB	22	9	1	12	355	343	12	19	
Ryton	22	9	1	12	379	373	6	19	
Ashington	22	9	0	13	419	467	-48	18	
Gateshead	22	7	0	15	278	564	-286	14	
Winlaton Vulcans	22	6	0	16	262	442	-180	12	
*Medicals	22	1	1	20	314	790	-476	1	2

Durham/N'thm'land 2

	P	W	D	L	PF	PA	PD	Pts
Gosforth	21	19	0	2	644	180	464	38
Billingham	22	17	0	5	626	275	351	34
North Shields	22	17	0	5	519	206	313	34
Houghton	22	13	0	9	374	352	22	26
Hartlepool	22	11	2	9	379	429	-50	24
Sunderland	22	11	0	11	472	523	-51	22
Whitby	18	10	0	8	310	193	117	20
Acklam	22	10	0	12	312	299	13	20
Whitley Bay Rockcliff	21	7	0	14	264	498	-234	14
Wallsend	22	5	1	16	257	496	-239	11
Blyth	21	4	1	16	226	529	-303	9
Novocastrians	21	2	0	19	212	615	-403	4

Durham/N'thm'land 3

	P	W	D	L	PF	PA	PD	Pts	
Guisborough	21	18	0	3	528	174	354	36	
Barnard Castle	21	18	0	3	557	215	342	36	
Ponteland	22	18	0	4	443	233	210	36	
Seaton Carew	21	16	0	5	537	268	269	32	
Bishop Auckland	21	12	1	8	454	335	119	25	
*Seghill	22	9	0	13	233	418	-185	16	2
West Hartlepool Amat.	22	7	1	14	284	369	-85	15	
Chester le Street	19	7	0	12	291	326	-35	14	
Jarrovians	21	6	0	15	160	550	-390	12	
Wearside	21	5	1	15	299	453	-154	11	
Wensleydale	14	2	1	11	184	271	-87	5	
*Durham Constabulary	21	3	0	18	174	532	-358	4	2

Durham/N'thm'land 4

	P	W	D	L	PF	PA	PD	Pts
Yarm	12	10	1	1	340	88	252	21
Newton Aycliffe	11	9	1	1	305	171	134	19
South Tyneside College	11	8	0	3	360	119	241	16
Richmondshire	12	6	0	6	110	286	-176	12
Seaham	12	3	0	9	118	280	-162	6
Hartlepool B.B.O.B.	12	2	0	10	132	232	-100	4
Hartlepool Athletic	12	2	0	10	89	278	-189	4

* denotes points deducted in right hand column

Yorkshire 1

	P	W	D	L	PF	PA	PD	Pts	
Cleckheaton	22	21	0	1	613	197	416	42	
Wheatley Hills	22	16	0	6	352	238	114	32	
Selby	22	14	2	6	388	309	79	30	
Yarnbury	22	12	2	8	401	321	80	26	
Old Brodleians	22	13	0	9	415	338	77	26	
Pontefract	22	13	0	9	414	339	75	26	
North Ribblesdale	22	10	0	12	364	375	-11	20	
Pocklington	22	10	0	12	359	404	-45	20	
Hull	22	6	2	14	315	531	-216	14	
Huddersfield Y.M.C.A.	22	6	1	15	345	420	-75	13	
Keighley	22	5	0	17	251	485	-234	10	
Ripon	22	2	1	19	242	502	-260	5	

Yorkshire 2

	P	W	D	L	PF	PA	PD	Pts	
Scarborough	22	20	0	2	670	152	518	40	
Sheffield Tigers	22	17	1	4	527	298	229	35	
Leodiensians	22	17	0	5	579	403	176	34	
West Leeds	22	11	2	9	382	422	-40	24	
Hemsworth	22	11	1	10	361	353	8	23	
Dinnington	22	10	1	11	379	501	-122	21	
Northallerton	22	9	1	12	340	381	-41	19	
Castleford	22	8	2	12	388	351	37	18	
Ilkley	22	7	2	13	347	448	-101	16	
*Roundhegians	22	8	0	14	347	438	-91	14	2
Bradford Salem	22	5	2	15	286	416	-130	12	
*Wath on Dearne	22	3	0	19	255	698	-443	2	4

Yorkshire 3

	P	W	D	L	PF	PA	PD	Pts	
York Railway Institute	22	17	1	4	569	213	356	35	
Skipton	22	17	1	4	557	216	341	35	
Malton and Norton	22	17	1	4	637	303	334	35	
Heath	22	16	1	5	446	240	206	33	
Old Otliensians	22	11	2	9	267	265	2	24	
Leeds Corinthians	22	9	3	10	321	292	29	21	
Halifax Vandals	22	9	2	11	299	396	-97	20	
Barnsley	22	9	1	12	390	487	-97	19	
Bramley Phoenix Park	22	9	0	13	337	440	-103	18	
Moortown	22	6	2	14	304	413	-109	14	
Sheffield Oaks	22	3	0	19	160	630	-470	6	
Hullensians	22	2	0	20	244	636	-392	4	

Yorkshire 4

	P	W	D	L	PF	PA	PD	Pts	
Stocksbridge	20	17	1	2	490	136	354	35	
Old Rishworthians	19	15	1	3	598	151	447	31	
Hessle	19	15	1	3	468	162	306	31	
Knottingley	20	11	0	9	400	273	127	22	
Wetherby	20	10	0	10	278	374	-96	20	
Baildon	19	8	2	9	296	335	-39	18	
Mosborough	20	8	2	10	222	416	-194	18	
Old Modernians	20	7	1	12	312	340	-28	15	
Stanley Rodillians	20	6	0	14	176	410	-234	12	
Thornensians	20	3	0	17	177	679	-502	6	
*Edlington Granby	17	3	0	14	111	252	-141	4	2

Yorkshire 5

	P	W	D	L	PF	PA	PD	Pts
Wakefield Cougars	18	17	1	0	648	120	528	35
Danum Phoenix	18	14	0	4	529	211	318	28
Aireborough	18	12	0	6	440	229	211	24
Marist	18	11	1	6	434	149	285	23
Ossett	18	11	0	7	301	189	112	22
Sheffield Medicals	18	7	0	11	327	495	-168	14
Hornsea	18	6	0	12	285	410	-125	12
Adwick le Street	18	5	1	12	261	415	-154	11
Rotherham Clifton	18	5	0	13	180	611	-431	10
Wickersley Exel	18	0	1	17	154	730	-576	1

Yorkshire 6

	P	W	D	L	PF	PA	PD	Pts
Rawmarsh	14	12	1	1	431	125	306	25
Wharfedale Rams	14	12	0	2	406	91	315	24
Knaresborough	14	11	1	2	383	143	240	23
Garforth	14	6	0	8	203	224	-21	12
Withernsea	14	4	0	10	160	348	-188	8
Nestle Rowntree	14	3	0	11	218	374	-156	6
Wibsey	13	3	0	10	126	329	-203	6
Thirsk	13	3	0	10	93	386	-293	6

469

NORTHERN DIVISION FIXTURE GRIDS 2001-2002

North 2 East

	Alnwick	Bridlington	Cleckheaton	Goole	Huddersfield	Morpeth	Northern	Old Crossleyans	Redcar	Stockton	Westoe	Wheatley Hills
Alnwick		16.03	22.09	06.10	08.12	06.04	05.01	27.10	09.02	02.03	26.01	17.11
Bridlington	08.09		02.03	09.02	06.04	22.09	08.12	26.01	27.10	06.10	17.11	05.01
Cleckheaton	09.03	29.09		27.10	08.09	06.10	06.04	17.11	26.01	09.02	05.01	08.12
Goole	23.02	20.10	02.02		29.09	17.11	09.03	08.12	05.01	10.11	06.04	08.09
Huddersfield	13.04	22.12	16.03	02.03		05.01	17.11	09.02	06.10	22.09	27.10	26.01
Morpeth	22.12	09.03	23.02	12.01	01.12		10.11	08.09	13.04	02.02	29.09	20.10
Northern	01.12	13.04	22.12	22.09	12.01	26.01		06.10	02.03	16.03	09.02	27.10
Old Crossleyans	02.02	10.11	12.01	13.04	20.10	16.03	23.02		22.12	01.12	09.03	29.09
Redcar	20.10	02.02	10.11	01.12	23.02	08.12	29.09	06.04		12.01	08.09	09.03
Stockton	29.09	23.02	20.10	26.01	09.03	27.10	08.09	05.01	17.11		08.12	06.04
Westoe	10.11	12.01	01.12	22.12	02.02	02.03	20.10	22.09	16.03	13.04		23.02
Wheatley Hills	12.01	01.12	13.04	16.03	10.11	09.02	02.02	02.03	22.09	22.12	06.10	

North 2 West

	Aldwinians	Altrincham Kersal	Birkenhead Park	Blackburn	Broughton Park	Caldy	Lymm	Stockport	Vale of Lune	Warrington	Winnington Park	Workington
Aldwinians		05.01	20.10	23.02	27.10	17.11	09.03	29.09	26.01	06.04	08.09	08.12
Altrincham Kersal	01.12		12.01	10.11	16.03	22.12	20.10	02.02	13.04	29.09	23.02	09.03
Birkenhead Park	09.02	17.11		29.09	06.10	26.01	08.09	09.03	27.10	08.12	06.04	05.01
Blackburn	06.10	26.01	02.03		22.09	27.10	06.04	08.09	09.02	05.01	08.12	17.11
Broughton Park	02.02	08.09	23.02	09.03		13.04	01.12	22.12	12.01	20.10	10.11	29.09
Caldy	12.01	06.04	10.11	02.02	08.12		23.02	20.10	01.12	09.03	29.09	08.09
Lymm	22.09	09.02	16.03	22.12	05.01	06.10		13.04	02.03	26.01	17.11	27.10
Stockport	02.03	27.10	22.09	16.03	06.04	09.02	08.12		06.10	17.11	05.01	26.01
Vale of Lune	10.11	08.12	02.02	20.10	17.11	05.01	29.09	23.02		08.09	09.03	06.04
Warrington	22.12	02.03	13.04	01.12	09.02	22.09	10.11	12.01	16.03		02.02	06.10
Winnington Park	16.03	06.10	22.12	13.04	26.01	02.03	12.01	01.12	22.09	27.10		09.02
Workington	13.04	22.09	01.12	12.01	02.03	16.03	02.02	10.11	22.12	23.02	20.10	

North Lancs/ Cumbria

	Blackpool	Carlisle	Cockermouth	De La Salle	Kirkby Lonsdale	Netherhall	Oldham	Penrith	Rochdale	Rossendale	St Benedict's	Tyldesley
Blackpool		29.09	02.02	10.11	08.12	06.04	20.10	12.01	01.12	23.02	08.09	09.03
Carlisle	02.03		13.04	22.12	26.01	06.10	01.12	16.03	22.09	12.01	09.02	27.10
Cockermouth	27.10	08.12		02.03	22.09	26.01	08.09	06.10	09.02	06.04	17.11	05.01
De La Salle	26.01	06.04	29.09		06.10	17.11	09.03	09.02	27.10	08.09	05.01	08.12
Kirkby Lonsdale	13.04	10.11	09.03	23.02		08.09	22.12	02.02	12.01	01.12	29.09	20.10
Netherhall	22.12	23.02	10.11	12.01	16.03		02.02	01.12	13.04	20.10	09.03	29.09
Oldham	09.02	05.01	16.03	22.09	06.04	27.10		02.03	06.10	08.12	26.01	17.11
Penrith	17.11	08.09	23.02	20.10	27.10	05.01	29.09		26.01	09.03	08.12	06.04
Rochdale	05.01	09.03	20.10	02.02	17.11	08.12	23.02	10.11		29.09	06.04	08.09
Rossendale	06.10	17.11	22.12	16.03	05.01	09.02	13.04	22.09	02.03		27.10	26.01
St Benedict's	16.03	20.10	12.01	01.12	02.03	22.09	10.11	13.04	22.12	02.02		23.02
Tyldesley	22.09	02.02	01.12	13.04	09.02	02.03	12.01	22.12	16.03	10.11	06.10	

North Lancs 1

	Bolton	Burnage	Bury	Calder Vale	Didsbury Toc H	Eccles	Fleetwood	Heaton Moor	Lytham	Old Bedians	Thornton Cleveleys	Trafford MV
Bolton		06.04	06.10	02.03	27.10	16.03	05.01	26.01	22.09	09.02	17.11	08.12
Burnage	22.12		12.01	02.02	08.09	09.03	10.11	29.09	23.02	13.04	20.10	01.12
Bury	23.02	17.11		10.11	08.12	20.10	09.03	06.04	02.02	05.01	08.09	29.09
Calder Vale	29.09	27.10	26.01		05.01	23.02	08.09	08.12	20.10	17.11	06.04	09.03
Didsbury Toc H	02.02	16.03	13.04	01.12		10.11	23.02	09.03	12.01	22.12	29.09	20.10
Eccles	08.09	22.09	09.02	06.10	26.01		08.12	17.11	02.03	27.10	05.01	06.04
Fleetwood	01.12	26.01	22.09	16.03	06.10	13.04		09.02	22.12	02.03	27.10	12.01
Heaton Moor	10.11	02.03	22.12	13.04	22.09	12.01	20.10		01.12	16.03	23.02	02.02
Lytham	09.03	06.10	27.10	09.02	17.11	29.09	06.04	05.01		26.01	08.12	08.09
Old Bedians	20.10	08.12	01.12	12.01	06.04	02.02	29.09	08.09	10.11		09.03	23.02
Thornton Cleveleys	12.01	09.02	16.03	22.12	02.03	01.12	02.02	06.10	13.04	22.09		10.11
Trafford MV	13.04	05.01	02.03	22.09	09.02	22.12	17.11	27.10	16.03	06.10	26.01	

North Lancs 2

	Ashton-under-Lyne	Broughton	Carnforth	Chorley	Clitheroe	Colne & Nelson	Garstang	Littleborough	Lonsdale Wanderers	Lostock	North Manchester	West Park Warriors
Ashton-under-Lyne		08.09	27.10	29.09	23.02	09.03	20.10	26.01	08.12	05.01	17.11	06.04
Broughton	16.03		26.01	01.12	13.04	12.01	22.12	22.09	09.02	06.10	02.03	27.10
Carnforth	02.02	10.11		22.12	09.03	01.12	23.02	12.01	29.09	08.09	13.04	20.10
Chorley	02.03	05.01	06.04		16.03	08.12	22.09	06.10	26.01	27.10	09.02	17.11
Clitheroe	06.10	08.12	22.09	08.09		06.04	02.03	09.02	17.11	26.01	27.10	05.01
Colne & Nelson	22.09	17.11	05.01	13.04	22.12		16.03	02.03	27.10	09.02	06.10	26.01
Garstang	09.02	06.04	06.10	09.03	29.09	08.09		27.10	05.01	17.11	26.01	08.12
Littleborough	10.11	09.03	17.11	23.02	20.10	29.09	02.02		06.04	08.12	05.01	08.09
Lonsdale Wanderers	13.04	20.10	02.03	10.11	12.01	02.02	01.12	22.12		22.09	16.03	23.02
Lostock	01.12	23.02	16.03	02.02	10.11	20.10	12.01	13.04	09.03		22.12	29.09
North Manchester	12.01	29.09	08.12	20.10	02.02	23.02	10.11	01.12	08.09	06.04		09.03
West Park Warriors	22.12	02.02	09.02	12.01	01.12	10.11	13.04	16.03	06.10	02.03	22.09	

Cumbria

	Ambleside	Creighton	Egremont	Furness	Greengarth	Keswick	Millom	Moresby	Silloth	Upper Eden	Vickers Sports	Whitehaven	Windermere
Ambleside		06.10	22.09	16.02	27.10	06.04	02.03	22.12	02.02	01.09	19.01	16.03	08.12
Creighton	23.02		26.01	13.04	05.01	20.10	01.12	12.01	23.03	09.02	09.03	10.11	29.09
Egremont	09.03	17.11		19.01	08.12	29.09	02.02	09.02	13.04	23.02	23.03	20.10	08.09
Furness	20.10	22.12	01.12		23.03	09.02	12.01	06.04	08.09	10.11	29.09	26.01	23.02
Greengarth	09.02	06.04	12.01	01.09		10.11	22.12	08.09	09.03	26.01	23.02	01.12	20.10
Keswick	05.01	16.02	02.03	27.10	02.02		06.10	23.03	17.11	16.03	08.12	22.09	13.04
Millom	29.09	19.01	10.11	08.12	13.04	23.02		26.01	05.01	20.10	08.09	09.02	09.03
Moresby	13.04	08.12	27.10	05.01	16.03	01.09	17.11		02.03	22.09	02.02	06.10	19.01
Silloth	10.11	01.09	22.12	16.03	22.09	26.01	06.04	29.09		01.12	20.10	12.01	09.02
Upper Eden	23.03	27.10	06.10	02.02	17.11	08.09	16.02	09.03	19.01		13.04	02.03	05.01
Vickers Sports	01.12	22.09	01.09	02.03	06.10	12.01	16.03	10.11	16.02	22.12		06.04	26.01
Whitehaven	08.09	02.02	16.02	17.11	19.01	09.03	27.10	23.02	08.12	29.09	05.01		23.03
Windermere	12.01	02.03	16.03	06.10	16.02	22.12	22.09	01.12	27.10	06.04	17.11	01.09	

NORTHERN

South Lancs/Chesire 1

	Aspull	Birchfield (Lancs)	Dukinfield	Leigh	Northwich	Oldershaw	Ormskirk	St Edward's O.B.	Vagabonds (I.O.M.)	Widnes	Wigan	Wilmslow
Aspull		05.01	02.02	20.10	08.12	06.04	08.09	29.09	17.11	10.11	09.03	23.02
Birchfield (Lancs)	01.12		10.11	02.02	06.04	08.09	09.03	23.02	08.12	12.01	29.09	20.10
Dukinfield	27.10	26.01		29.09	17.11	05.01	08.12	08.09	06.10	09.02	06.04	09.03
Leigh	09.02	27.10	02.03		26.01	17.11	05.01	06.04	22.09	06.10	08.12	08.09
Northwich	13.04	22.12	12.01	10.11		09.03	29.09	20.10	16.03	01.12	23.02	02.02
Oldershaw	22.12	16.03	01.12	12.01	22.09		23.02	02.03	02.03	13.04	20.10	10.11
Ormskirk	16.03	22.09	13.04	01.12	02.03	06.10		10.11	09.02	22.12	02.02	12.01
St Edward's O.B.	02.03	06.10	16.03	22.12	09.02	27.10	26.01		05.01	22.09	17.11	13.04
Vagabonds (I.O.M.)	12.01	13.04	23.02	09.03	08.09	29.09	20.10	01.12		02.02	10.11	22.12
Widnes	26.01	17.11	20.10	23.02	05.01	08.12	06.04	09.03	27.10		08.09	29.09
Wigan	22.09	02.03	22.12	13.04	06.10	09.02	27.10	12.01	26.01	16.03		01.12
Wilmslow	06.10	09.02	22.09	16.03	27.10	26.01	17.11	08.12	06.04	02.03	05.01	

South Lancs/Chesire 2

	Anselmians	Ashton on Mersey	Crewe and Nantwich	Ellesmere Port	Moore	Runcorn	Sandbach	Southport	St Mary's O.B. (Lancs)	Trentham	Wallasey	Wirral
Anselmians		13.04	22.09	16.03	12.01	01.12	10.11	20.10	23.02	22.12	02.03	02.02
Ashton on Mersey	08.12		05.01	17.11	23.02	20.10	29.09	08.09	06.04	26.01	27.10	09.03
Crewe and Nantwich	09.03	01.12		22.12	10.11	12.01	02.02	23.02	29.09	13.04	16.03	20.10
Ellesmere Port	08.09	12.01	06.04		02.02	10.11	20.10	29.09	09.03	01.12	08.12	23.02
Moore	17.11	06.10	26.01	27.10		02.03	08.09	08.12	05.01	09.02	22.09	06.04
Runcorn	05.01	09.02	17.11	26.01	29.09		09.03	06.04	08.12	27.10	06.10	08.09
Sandbach	26.01	02.03	27.10	09.02	16.03	22.09		05.01	17.11	06.10	06.04	08.12
Southport	09.02	16.03	06.10	02.03	13.04	22.12	01.12		27.10	22.09	26.01	12.01
St Mary's O.B. (Lancs)	06.10	22.12	02.03	22.09	01.12	13.04	12.01	02.02		16.03	09.02	10.11
Trentham	06.04	10.11	08.12	05.01	20.10	02.02	23.02	09.03	08.09		17.11	29.09
Wallasey	29.09	02.02	08.09	13.04	09.03	23.02	22.12	10.11	20.10	12.01		01.12
Wirral	27.10	22.09	09.02	06.10	22.12	16.03	13.04	17.11	26.01	02.03	05.01	

South Lancs/Chesire 3

	Bowdon	Congleton	Douglas (I.O.M.)	Eagle	Hoylake	Marple	Newton-le-Willows	Orrell Anvils	Ruskin Park	Sefton
Bowdon		29.09	23.02	17.11	27.10	12.01	02.02	13.04	16.03	08.12
Congleton	09.03		16.03	12.01	02.02	27.10	06.10	17.11	08.12	13.04
Douglas (I.O.M.)	06.10	22.09		09.03	17.11	08.12	27.10	02.02	13.04	12.01
Eagle	22.12	10.11	29.09		06.04	22.09	01.12	23.02	26.01	20.10
Hoylake	26.01	20.10	22.12	08.12		13.04	10.11	16.03	23.02	29.09
Marple	10.11	26.01	06.04	16.03	01.12		22.12	29.09	20.10	23.02
Newton-le-Willows	20.10	23.02	26.01	13.04	12.01	17.11		08.12	29.09	16.03
Orrell Anvils	01.12	22.12	20.10	06.10	22.09	09.03	06.04		10.11	26.01
Ruskin Park	22.09	06.04	01.12	27.10	06.10	02.02	09.03	12.01		17.11
Sefton	06.04	01.12	10.11	02.02	09.03	06.10	22.09	27.10	22.12	

South Lancs/ Chesire 4

	Capenhurst	Halton	Helsby	Liverpool Coll. O.B.	Manchester Wanderers	Oswestry	Parkonians	Port Sunlight	Prenton	Vulcan
Capenhurst		22.09	06.04	20.10	23.02	22.12	26.01	29.09	01.12	10.11
Halton	16.03		01.12	23.02	29.09	10.11	20.10	06.04	22.12	26.01
Helsby	08.12	13.04		29.09	16.03	26.01	23.02	22.12	10.11	20.10
Liverpool Collegiate O.B.	02.02	06.10	09.03		27.10	06.04	22.12	10.11	22.09	01.12
Manchester Wanderers	06.10	09.03	22.09	26.01		01.12	10.11	20.10	06.04	22.12
Oswestry	17.11	12.01	27.10	08.12	13.04		16.03	23.02	02.02	29.09
Parkonians	27.10	02.02	06.10	17.11	12.01	22.09		01.12	09.03	06.04
Port Sunlight	09.03	08.12	17.11	12.01	02.02	06.10	13.04		27.10	22.09
Prenton	13.04	17.11	12.01	16.03	08.12	20.10	29.09	26.01		23.02
Vulcan	12.01	27.10	02.02	13.04	17.11	09.03	08.12	16.03	06.10	

South Lancs/ Chesire 5

	Burtonwood	Holmes Chapel	Lucas Merseyside	Mossley Hill A.C.	Prescot	Waterloo Vikings
Burtonwood		12.01	08.12	27.10	17.11	13.04
Holmes Chapel	10.11		06.10	22.09	09.03	22.12
Lucas Merseyside	06.04	23.02		22.12	01.12	20.10
Mossley Hill A.C.	26.01	16.03	17.11		12.01	29.09
Prescot	22.12	29.09	13.04	10.11		23.02
Waterloo Vikings	01.12	17.11	02.02	09.03	06.10	

Durham Northumberland 1

	Ashington	Billingham	Consett	Durham City	Gateshead	Gosforth	Hartlepool Rovers	Horden	Percy Park	Ryton	West Hartlepool TDSOB	Winlaton Vulcans
Ashington		29.09	13.04	23.02	10.11	12.01	20.10	22.12	01.12	16.03	02.02	09.03
Billingham	02.03		16.03	02.02	01.12	13.04	10.11	22.09	22.12	09.02	12.01	06.10
Consett	08.12	08.09		09.03	20.10	02.02	29.09	05.01	10.11	17.11	23.02	06.04
Durham City	06.10	27.10	22.09		13.04	22.12	12.01	02.03	16.03	26.01	01.12	09.02
Gateshead	26.01	05.01	09.02	08.12		02.03	06.04	27.10	06.10	22.09	08.09	17.11
Gosforth	17.11	08.12	27.10	06.04	29.09		08.09	26.01	09.02	06.10	09.03	05.01
Hartlepool Rovers	09.02	26.01	02.03	17.11	22.12	16.03		06.10	22.09	05.01	13.04	27.10
Horden	06.04	09.03	01.12	29.09	02.02	10.11	23.02		12.01	08.12	20.10	08.09
Percy Park	05.01	06.04	26.01	08.09	23.02	20.10	09.03	17.11		27.10	29.09	08.12
Ryton	08.09	20.10	12.01	10.11	09.03	23.02	01.12	13.04	02.02		22.12	29.09
West Hartlepool TDSOB	27.10	17.11	06.10	05.01	16.03	22.09	08.12	09.02	02.03	06.04		26.01
Winlaton Vulcans	22.09	23.02	22.12	20.10	12.01	01.12	02.02	16.03	13.04	02.03	10.11	

NORTHERN

Durham Northumberland 2

	Acklam	Barnard Castle	Blyth	Guisborough	Hartlepool	Houghton	Medicals	North Shields	Sunderland	Wallsend	Whitby	Whitley Bay Rock.
Acklam		20.10	29.09	23.02	01.12	12.01	02.02	10.11	22.12	09.03	13.04	08.09
Barnard Castle	09.02		06.10	13.04	10.11	16.03	22.12	02.02	12.01	01.12	22.09	02.03
Blyth	02.03	23.02		01.12	02.02	22.12	13.04	20.10	10.11	12.01	16.03	22.09
Guisborough	06.10	08.12	05.01		08.09	27.10	09.02	06.04	09.03	29.09	26.01	17.11
Hartlepool	05.01	26.01	27.10	16.03		02.03	22.09	17.11	13.04	22.12	06.10	09.02
Houghton	17.11	08.09	06.04	02.02	29.09		10.11	09.03	23.02	20.10	05.01	08.12
Medicals	27.10	06.04	08.12	20.10	09.03	26.01		08.09	29.09	23.02	17.11	05.01
North Shields	26.01	27.10	09.02	22.12	12.01	22.09	16.03		01.12	13.04	02.03	06.10
Sunderland	06.04	17.11	26.01	22.09	08.12	06.10	02.03	05.01		16.03	09.02	27.10
Wallsend	22.09	05.01	17.11	02.03	06.04	09.02	06.10	08.12	08.09		27.10	26.01
Whitby	08.12	09.03	08.09	10.11	23.02	01.12	12.01	29.09	20.10	02.02		06.04
Whitley Bay Rockcliff	16.03	29.09	09.03	12.01	20.10	13.04	01.12	23.02	02.02	10.11	22.12	

Durham Northumberland 3

	Bishop Auckland	Chester le Street	Jarrovians	Newton Aycliffe	Novocastrians	Ponteland	Seaton Carew	Seghill	Wearside	Wensleydale	West Hartlepool Am.	Yarm
Bishop Auckland		06.10	05.01	26.01	22.09	17.11	02.03	13.04	22.12	27.10	09.02	16.03
Chester le Street	23.02		08.12	09.03	12.01	29.09	01.12	20.10	02.02	08.09	06.04	10.11
Jarrovians	01.12	13.04		20.10	02.02	10.11	12.01	22.12	09.03	29.09	08.09	23.02
Newton Aycliffe	10.11	22.09	09.02		22.12	02.02	16.03	12.01	01.12	06.10	02.03	13.04
Novocastrians	09.03	17.11	27.10	06.04		08.09	26.01	29.09	23.02	08.12	05.01	20.10
Ponteland	12.01	02.03	26.01	27.10	16.03		22.09	01.12	13.04	09.02	06.10	22.12
Seaton Carew	29.09	05.01	17.11	08.09	10.11	09.03		23.02	20.10	06.04	08.12	02.02
Seghill	08.12	09.02	06.04	17.11	02.03	05.01	06.10		16.03	26.01	27.10	22.09
Wearside	06.04	27.10	22.09	05.01	06.10	08.12	09.02	08.09		17.11	26.01	02.03
Wensleydale	02.02	16.03	02.03	23.02	13.04	20.10	22.12	10.11	12.01		22.09	01.12
West Hartlepool Amateurs	20.10	22.12	16.03	29.09	01.12	23.02	13.04	02.02	10.11	09.03		12.01
Yarm	08.09	26.01	06.10	08.12	09.02	06.04	27.10	09.03	29.09	05.01	17.11	

Durham Northumberland 4

	Durham Constabulary	Hartlepool Athletic	Hartlepool B.B.O.B.	Richmondshire	Seaham	Shildon Town	S. Tyneside College
Durham Constabulary		26.01	17.11	12.01	29.09	23.02	16.03
Hartlepool Athletic	27.10		08.12	17.11	13.04	22.09	12.01
Hartlepool B.B.O.B.	22.12	06.04		01.12	20.10	26.01	23.02
Richmondshire	10.11	22.12	13.04		23.02	20.10	29.09
Seaham	09.03	01.12	02.02	06.10		06.04	17.11
Shildon Town	06.10	16.03	27.10	02.02	08.12		13.04
South Tyneside College	22.09	10.11	06.10	09.03	22.12	01.12	

NORTHERN

Yorkshire 1

	Beverley	Hull	North Ribblesdale	Old Brodleians	Pocklington	Pontefract	Scarborough	Selby	Sheffield Tigers	West Park Bramhope	Yarnbury	York
Beverley		08.12	05.01	29.09	23.02	27.10	20.10	09.03	06.04	08.09	17.11	26.01
Hull	13.04		22.09	10.11	12.01	02.03	01.12	02.02	23.02	20.10	16.03	22.12
North Ribblesdale	01.12	09.03		02.02	10.11	16.03	12.01	20.10	29.09	23.02	22.12	13.04
Old Brodleians	02.03	26.01	27.10		16.03	06.04	22.09	08.12	17.11	05.01	09.02	06.10
Pocklington	06.10	17.11	26.01	08.09		22.09	02.03	06.04	05.01	08.12	27.10	09.02
Pontefract	02.02	29.09	08.09	22.12	09.03		23.02	01.12	20.10	10.11	13.04	12.01
Scarborough	09.02	05.01	17.11	09.03	29.09	06.10		08.09	08.12	06.04	26.01	27.10
Selby	22.09	27.10	09.02	13.04	22.12	05.01	16.03		26.01	17.11	06.10	02.03
Sheffield Tigers	22.12	06.10	02.03	12.01	01.12	09.02	13.04	10.11		02.02	22.09	16.03
West Park Bramhope	16.03	09.02	06.10	01.12	13.04	26.01	22.12	12.01	27.10		02.03	22.09
Yarnbury	12.01	08.09	06.04	20.10	02.02	08.12	10.11	23.02	09.03	29.09		01.12
York	10.11	06.04	08.12	23.02	20.10	17.11	02.02	29.09	08.09	09.03	05.01	

Yorkshire 2

	Castleford	Dinnington	Hemsworth	Huddersfield Y.M.C.A.	Ilkley	Keighley	Leodiensians	Northallerton	Ripon	Skipton	West Leeds	York R. I.
Castleford		22.09	08.09	06.10	17.11	08.12	06.04	26.01	09.02	05.01	27.10	02.03
Dinnington	09.03		22.12	02.02	29.09	10.11	01.12	08.09	12.01	20.10	13.04	23.02
Hemsworth	16.03	06.04		02.03	26.01	05.01	08.12	27.10	06.10	17.11	09.02	22.09
Huddersfield Y.M.C.A.	23.02	27.10	29.09		08.12	08.09	09.03	05.01	26.01	06.04	17.11	20.10
Ilkley	12.01	02.03	10.11	13.04		20.10	02.02	22.09	22.12	23.02	16.03	01.12
Keighley	13.04	26.01	01.12	16.03	09.02		12.01	06.10	22.09	27.10	02.03	22.12
Leodiensians	22.12	05.01	13.04	22.09	27.10	17.11		09.02	02.03	26.01	06.10	16.03
Northallerton	10.11	16.03	02.02	01.12	09.03	23.02	20.10		13.04	29.09	22.12	12.01
Ripon	20.10	17.11	23.02	10.11	06.04	09.03	29.09	08.12		08.09	05.01	02.02
Skipton	01.12	09.02	12.01	22.12	06.10	02.02	10.11	02.03	16.03		22.09	13.04
West Leeds	02.02	08.12	20.10	12.01	08.09	29.09	23.02	06.04	01.12	09.03		10.11
York Railway Institute	29.09	06.10	09.03	09.02	05.01	06.04	08.09	17.11	27.10	08.12	26.01	

Yorkshire 3

	Barnsley	Bradford Salem	Bramley Phoenix Park	Halifax Vandals	Heath	Hessle	Leeds Corinthians	Malton and Norton	Old Otliensians	Roundhegians	Stocksbridge	Wath on Dearne
Barnsley		08.12	17.11	26.01	27.10	05.01	22.09	06.04	08.09	06.10	02.03	09.02
Bradford Salem	13.04		09.02	06.10	02.03	27.10	26.01	12.01	01.12	16.03	22.12	22.09
Bramley Phoenix Park	12.01	20.10		22.09	16.03	23.02	02.03	02.02	10.11	13.04	01.12	22.12
Halifax Vandals	10.11	23.02	09.03		22.12	29.09	16.03	20.10	02.02	01.12	12.01	13.04
Heath	02.02	29.09	08.09	06.04		09.03	08.12	23.02	20.10	12.01	10.11	01.12
Hessle	01.12	02.02	06.10	02.03	22.09		09.02	10.11	12.01	22.12	13.04	16.03
Leeds Corinthians	09.03	10.11	29.09	08.09	13.04	20.10		01.12	22.12	02.02	23.02	12.01
Malton and Norton	22.12	17.11	27.10	09.02	06.10	26.01	05.01		13.04	22.09	16.03	02.03
Old Otliensians	16.03	05.01	26.01	27.10	09.02	17.11	06.04	08.12		02.03	22.09	06.10
Roundhegians	23.02	08.09	08.12	05.01	17.11	06.04	27.10	09.03	29.09		20.10	26.01
Stocksbridge	29.09	06.04	05.01	17.11	26.01	08.12	06.10	08.09	09.03	09.02		27.10
Wath on Dearne	20.10	09.03	06.04	08.12	05.01	08.09	17.11	29.09	23.02	10.11	02.02	

NORTHERN

Yorkshire 4

	Baildon	Danum Phoenix	Hullensians	Knottingley	Moortown	Mosborough	Old Modernians	Old Rishworthians	Sheffield Oaks	Stanley Rodillians	Wakefield Cougars	Wetherby
Baildon		20.10	12.01	13.04	02.02	08.09	09.03	01.12	10.11	29.09	23.02	22.12
Danum Phoenix	09.02		16.03	22.09	22.12	02.03	01.12	10.11	02.02	06.10	13.04	12.01
Hullensians	17.11	08.09		05.01	10.11	08.12	20.10	29.09	09.03	06.04	02.02	23.02
Knottingley	08.12	09.03	01.12		12.01	06.04	02.02	23.02	29.09	08.09	10.11	20.10
Moortown	27.10	06.04	26.01	17.11		05.01	23.02	09.03	08.09	08.12	20.10	29.09
Mosborough	16.03	29.09	13.04	22.12	01.12		10.11	20.10	23.02	09.03	12.01	02.02
Old Modernians	22.09	05.01	09.02	27.10	06.10	26.01		06.04	08.12	17.11	02.03	08.09
Old Rishworthians	05.01	26.01	02.03	06.10	22.09	09.02	22.12		17.11	27.10	16.03	13.04
Sheffield Oaks	26.01	27.10	22.09	02.03	16.03	06.10	13.04	12.01		09.02	22.12	01.12
Stanley Rodillians	02.03	23.02	22.12	16.03	13.04	22.09	12.01	02.02	20.10		01.12	10.11
Wakefield Cougars	06.10	08.12	27.10	26.01	09.02	17.11	29.09	08.09	06.04	05.01		09.03
Wetherby	06.04	17.11	06.10	09.02	02.03	27.10	16.03	08.12	05.01	26.01	22.09	

Yorkshire 5

	Adwick le Street	Aireborough	Edlington Granby	Hornsea	Marist	Ossett	Rawmarsh	Rotherham Clifton	Sheffield Medicals	Thornensians	Wharfedale Rams
Adwick le Street		13.04	23.02	16.03	20.10	22.12	09.03	10.11	02.02	01.12	12.01
Aireborough	08.12		09.03	17.11	29.09	05.01	06.04	20.10	23.02	10.11	02.02
Edlington Granby	06.10	22.09		26.01	12.01	02.03	09.02	13.04	01.12	16.03	22.12
Hornsea	08.09	12.01	10.11		01.12	13.04	29.09	09.03	22.12	02.02	23.02
Marist	09.02	02.03	17.11	05.01		06.10	27.10	22.12	13.04	22.09	16.03
Ossett	06.04	01.12	29.09	08.12	23.02		08.09	02.02	20.10	12.01	10.11
Rawmarsh	22.09	22.12	20.10	02.03	02.02	16.03		12.01	10.11	13.04	01.12
Rotherham Clifton	26.01	09.02	08.12	22.09	06.04	27.10	17.11		08.09	06.10	02.03
Sheffield Medicals	27.10	06.10	05.01	06.04	08.12	09.02	26.01	16.03		02.03	22.09
Thornensians	05.01	26.01	08.09	27.10	09.03	17.11	08.12	23.02	29.09		20.10
Wharfedale Rams	17.11	27.10	06.04	06.10	08.09	26.01	05.01	29.09	09.03	09.02	

Yorkshire 6

	Burley	Garforth	Knaresborough	Pontefract Pythons	Thirsk	Walkington Rovers	Wibsey	Wickersley Exel	Withernsea
Burley		02.02	13.04	09.03	16.03	12.01	27.10	06.10	08.12
Garforth	20.10		29.09	26.01	22.12	08.12	13.04	10.11	23.02
Knaresborough	01.12	09.03		06.04	10.11	02.02	06.10	22.09	22.12
Pontefract Pythons	29.09	27.10	08.12		23.02	17.11	12.01	02.02	16.03
Thirsk	22.09	17.11	12.01	06.10		09.03	08.12	27.10	13.04
Walkington Rovers	10.11	06.04	20.10	22.12	29.09		22.09	01.12	26.01
Wibsey	26.01	01.12	23.02	10.11	06.04	16.03		22.12	20.10
Wickersley Exel	23.02	12.01	16.03	20.10	26.01	13.04	17.11		29.09
Withernsea	06.04	06.10	17.11	22.09	01.12	27.10	02.02	09.03	

CLUBS

ACKLAM RUFC
Ground Address: Talbot Park, Saltersgill Avenue, Middlesborough, Cleveland
Tel: 01842 321397
Brief Directions: Leave A19 at A174 towards Redcar. Leave Marton slip road and turn left through lights and left again into Broadwell Road.Follow signs to Saltersgill Pavilion.
Club Secretary: K.J.Heath, 43 Ash Green, Coulby Newham, Middlesbrough TS8 0UW. Tel No: 01642 590927
Fixtures Secretary: Jim Ward, 108 Guisborough Road, Nunthorpe, Middlesborough, TS7 0JD. Tel No : 01642 319302.
Club Colours: Black, green and white
League: Durham/Northumberland 2

ADWICK-LE-STREET RUFC
Ground Address: Church Lane Playing Fields, Adwick-le-Street, Doncaster, South Yorkshire Tel: 01302 723550 (HQ Foresters Arms)
Brief Directions: 4 miles north of Doncaster on A638 Wakefield Road. Just off south bound A1 (Doncaster turn off at Redhouse) Ground directly opposite Adwick Railway Station.
Club Secretary: R J Terry, 7 Cranfield Drive, Skellow, Doncaster, South Yorkshire. DN6 8RS Tel: (H) 01302 727580 (W) 01977 669201
Fixtures Secretary: M A Leach-Flanagan, 31 Alexandra Road, Bentley, Doncaster, South Yorkshire. Tel: (H) 01302 872429
Club Colours: Navy with White/Royal Hoops
League: Yorkshire 5

AIREBOROUGH RUFC
Ground Address: Nunroyd Park, Yeadon, Leeds, LS19 Tel: 01943 878299
Brief Directions: From Leeds follow signs for Airport. Then for Guiseley - Club is approx 1 mile from Jct 600 R/about on the A65 - Leeds/Ilkley Road.
Club Secretary: M Harper, 32 Aire View, Yeadon, West Yorkshire
Tel: (H) 01132 504219 (W) 01132 505151
Fixtures Secretary: Mr Paul Markie, 1 Hillside Rise, Guiseley, Leeds LS20 9DJ
Tel: (H) 01943 879363 (W) 01274 693622
Club Colours: Maroon and white hoops - Black shorts
League: Yorkshire 5

ALDWINIANS RUFC
Ground Address: Audenshaw Park, Droylsden Road, Audenshaw, Manchester. M34 5SN
Tel: 0161 301 1001
Brief Directions: East of Manchester, at the junction of the A662 /635 Nr. Snipe Retail Park.

Club Secretary: Mr. Chris Daly, 60 Green Lane, Hollingworth, Hyde, Cheshire. SK14 8JQ Tel: (P&F) 01457 762402 Email: cldaly@aol.com
Fixtures Secretary: Alan Whalley, 190 Greenside Lane, Droylsden, Manchester. M35 6RR. Tel: (H) 0161 355 5922 (W) 0161 223 1353 Ext 246
Club Colours: Red and white narrow hoops. Blue shorts/socks
League: North 2 West

ALNWICK RUFC
Ground Address: Greensfield, St James, Alnwick, Northumberland Tel: 01665 602342
Brief Directions: A1 slip (South) of Alnwick signed Alnwick from N/castle, after slip 1st left, club 300 yds on left. From Edinburgh, after slip straight over cross roads, Greensfield Ave as above
Club Secretary: Mr. R. Todd, Linden House, Lesbury, Alnwick, Northumberland, NN66 3QW Tel: 01665 830898
Fixtures Secretary: John Answorth Tel: (H) 01665 605196
Club Colours: Royal blue jersey with gold lion rampant badge,white shorts
League: North 2 East

ALTRINCHAM (KERSAL) RFC
Ground Address: Stelfox Avenue, Timperley, Altrincham, Cheshire Tel: 0161 972 9157
Brief Directions: M56 J3, take road towards Altrincham, after 3 miles 3rd exit off roundabout, Stelfox Ave 100 yds on right
Club Secretary: Edward Frankland, 59 Station Road, Goostrey, Cheshire CW4 8PJ
Tel: 0161 833 5215 (W)
Fixtures Secretary: George Brugnoli, 231 Brooklands Road, Sale, Greater Manchester. Tel: (H) 0161 973 0194 (W) 0385 261743
Club Colours: Black, red & white hoops
League: North 2 West

AMBLESIDE
Ground Address: Galava Park, Borrans Road, Ambleside, Cumbria LA22 0UL.
Tel: 015394 32536
Brief Directions: A591 Kendal to Ambleside. Take Coniston, Hawkshead road at Traffic Lights - ground half mile on left after lights.
Club Secretary: Mrs. Jeanette. Irwin, Flat 2, Orrest Drive, Windermere LA23 2LF.
Tel No: 015394 42025
Fixtures Secretary: Nick. Fecitt, Hart Head Farm, Rydal, Ambleside, Cumbria.
Tel No: (H) 015394 33772
Club Colours: Black & Amber.
League: Cumbria

ASHINGTON J.W. RFC
Ground Address: Recreation Ground, Ellington Road, Ashington, Northumberland
Tel: 01670814123
Brief Directions: 1 mile north west of Ashington town centre on A1068. Map available on request
Club Secretary: Albert Armstrong, 25 Dundale Drive, Cramlington, Northumberland. NE23 2GA.
Tel: (H) 01670 736891 (W) 01670 533303
Fixtures Secretary: A Armstrong as above plus:-
e-mail: aarmstrong@northumberland.gov.uk
Club Colours: Royal blue and amber hoops, white shorts.
League: Durham/Northumberland 1

ASHTON ON MERSEY RUFC
Ground Address: Banky Lane, off Carrington Lane, Ashton on Mersey, Cheshire
Tel: 0161 973 6637
Website: aomrufc.co.uk
Brief Directions: M63 J63 Carrington Spur, towards Carrington, right at lights, left at T junction, club 300 yards on right
Club Secretary: Mike McCarthy, 111 Woodlhouse Lane, Sale, Cheshire. M33 4LF
Tel No: 0161 962 7641
Fixtures Secretary: Pat.Stokes. 26 Oldfield Road, Sale, Cheshire M33 2AQ
Tel: (H) 0161 282 3245
Club Colours: Maroonshirts with navy shorts and maroon and white socks
League: South Lancs & Cheshire 2

ASHTON-UNDER-LYNE RFC
Ground Address: St Albans Avenue, Ashton-Under-Lyne, Lancashire. OL6 8TU
Tel: 0161 330 1361
Website: aulrfc@supanet.com
Brief Directions: Town centre, Henrietta Street to Broadoak Hotel, through mini R/about to St Albans Avenue
Club Secretary: Mr Dennis Gee, 26 Burnedge Lane, Grasscroft, Oldham. OL4 4EA
Tel: (H) 01457 872823
Fixtures Secretary: Paul Newton., 6 The Ladysmsith, Ashton-under-Lyne, OL6 9AR Tel No: 0161 339 8931 - Email: pannewton@aol.com
Club Colours: Red, black and amber hoops,black shorts, red socks
League: North Lancs 2

ASPULL RFC
Ground Address: Aspull Rugby Football Club, Woodshaw Park, Woods Road, Aspull, Wigan, Lancs., WN2 1PL. Tel: 01942 831611
Brief Directions: M61 Jtn 6, follow signs for Aspull & Wigan on B5239. At T/Jtn turn left onto B5238 to Wigan.1st left is Woods Road - club at the end.
Club Secretary: Graham Bennett, 11 Prestbury Avenue, Marus Bridge, Wigan, Lancs. WN3 6SG.
Tel: 01942 824297.
Email: gbennett15@hotmail.com
Fixtures Secretary: Geoff Gregson, 26 Lyndon Avenue, Shevington, Wigan, Lancs., WN6 8BT.
Tel: (H) 01257 421421 - Fax - 01257 473595
Club Colours: Sky and navy hoops
League: South Lancs & Cheshire 1

BAE BARROW RUFC
(formerly Vickers Sports)
Ground Address: BAE Systems Sports Club, Hawcoat Lane, Barrow in Furness, Cumbria
Tel:01229 825296/823366
Website: www.vcfc.co.uk
Brief Directions: M6 Jct 36. Follow A590 to Barrow. From West Coast A591. Follow signs to Barrow. From west turn left at Strawberry Hotel on Abbey Road. From East turn right - club 300m on left Hancoat Lane.
Club Secretary: Alan Troughton, 188 Yarlside Road, Barrow-in-Furness, Cumbria,
Tel: 01229 838023
Fixtures Secretary: Norman Smith, 3 Old Farm Close,Barrow-in-Furness, Cumbria. 0EYBarrow in Furness, Cumbria Tel: 01229 828234
Club Colours: Maroon and white shirts.
League: Cumbria

BAILDON RUFC
Ground Address: Jenny Lane, Baildon, Shipley, West Yorks. BD17 6RS
Tel: 01274 582644
Brief Directions: A650 to centre of Shipley, follow Baildon signs in village centre, roundabout 3rd exit then left on Jenny Lane
Club Secretary: Mr G Porter, 100 Cliffe Avenue, Baildon, BRadford. BD17 6PD.
Tel: 01274 419596
Fixtures Secretary: Mr M Bradney, 1 Sandhurst St., calverley, Pudsey LS28 5RN
Tel: 0113 255 3497   07710 616814 (M)
Club Colours: Red, white and black hoops
League: Yorkshire 4

BARNARD CASTLE RUFC
Ground Address: The Clubhouse, 7 Birch Road, Barnard Castle, Co Durham DL12 8JR
Ground: The Demesnes(off Newgate).
Tel: 01833 631766
Brief Directions: Head into Town centre. At Market Cross follow signs for Bowes Museum. Take L. turn at Catholic Church (Birch Road). Clubhouse is on left (approx 100 yds)
Club Secretary: Tim Worley, 17 Newgate, Barnard Castle, Co Durham. DL12 8NQ
Tel: (H) 01833 637608   (W) 01833 690305
Fixtures Secretary: Mr. David Jackson c/o Headlam Hall Hotel, Headlam, Nr. Darlington, Co. Durham, DH2 3HA. Tel: 01325 730238
Club Colours: All black. Change Black & Red
League: Durham/Northumberland 2

BARNSLEY RUFC
Ground Address: Shaw Lane, Barnsley, South Yorkshire. S70 6HZ
Tel: 01226 203509 Website: barnsleyrufc.co.uk
Brief Directions: M1 J37, towards Barnsley, through 1st major lights, 2nd turning right into Shaw Lane, ground on right after school
Club Secretary: Mick Marshall, 4 Westbourne Grove, Barnsley. S75 1AE
Tel: (H) 01226 321721 - Email:
mick.marshall@barnsleyrufc.co.uk
Fixtures Secretary: Steve Lumb, 21 Haigh Moorway, Royston, Barnsley, S71 4EG.
Tel: 01226 726542
Club Colours: Red, white and blue irregular hoops
League: Yorkshire 3

BEVERLEY RUFC
Ground Address: Beaver Park, Norwood, Beverley. East Yorishire, HU17 9HT
Tel: 01482 870306
Brief Directions: Through Beverley centre, follow signs for Hornsea, ground is just before rail level crossing behind Lady Le Gros pub
Club Secretary: Andrew Winter, 4 The Vineyards, Leven, Beverley, East Yorkshire, HU17 5LD.Tel: (H) 01964 543981
Email: andrewwinter@leven93swinternet.co.uk
Fixtures Secretary: Rob Jenner, 42 Normandy Avenue, Beverley, East Yorkshire, HU17. Tel: (H) 01482 868944 - E-mail: robert-jenner@hotmail.com
Club Colours: Green, brown and white
League: Yorkshire 1

BILLINGHAM RUFC
Ground Address: Greenwood Road, Billingham, TS23 4AY.   Tel No: 01642 563057
Website: billingham rufc.co.uk
Brief Directions: From A19, leave for A1027 Follow signs to Belasis Hall Technology Park - left at park entrance R/about - beyond Tech. Park on right hand side.
Club Secretary: John Ker, 4 Anlaby Close, Billingham. TS23 3RA   Tel: (H) 01642 560536
Email: jn ker004@aol.com
Fixtures Secretary: Hadyn Beckwith, 5 Gorton Close, Billingham, TS23 2TF
Tel No : 01642 560649
Club Colours: Green and thin white hoopsand white shorts.
League: Durham/Northumberland 1

BIRCHFIELD (LANCS) RUFC
Ground Address: Albright & Wilson Recreational Club, Birchfield Road, Widnes, Cheshire. WA8 0TB
Tel: 0151 424 3222
Brief Directions: From M62 Junct. 7, follow A57 (Warrington) . Turn right at first set of lights, then right at T junction, 1st left at roundabout onto Birchfield Rd. Ground is 250 yds on the right.
Club Secretary: Stuart Ashton, 11 Eltham Close, Widnes, Cheshire. WA8 3RG
Tel: (H) 0151 424 6344
Fixtures Secretary: Kevin McDonnell, 20 Newlyn Gardens, Penketh, Warrington. WA5 2UX.
Tel: (H) 01925 722440 (W) 0151 424 4109 (M) 0802 400333
Club Colours: Maroon and black
League: South Lancs & Cheshire 1

BIRKENHEAD PARK FC
Ground Address: The Upper Park, Park Road North, Birkenhead. CH41 8AA
Tel: 0151 652 4646
Brief Directions: M53 J1, follow signs for Bidston and Birkenhead centre. Straight on at R/about with church in centre. Take 1st right after Aldi Supermarket into Park Road North. Ground is on left.
Club Secretary: Peter Greville, 2 Howbeck Close, Oxton, Prenton, Birkenhead CH43 6TH
Tel: 0151 653 6070 (W)
Fixtures Secretary: Bob Hardman, 32 Shamrock Road, Claughton, Birkenhead.
Tel: (H) 0151 652 5204
Club Colours: Red, white and blue
League: North 2 West

BISHOP AUCKLAND RUFC
Ground Address: West Mills Playing Fields, Bridge Road, Bishop Auckland, Co Durham. DL14 7PA Tel: 01388 602922
Brief Directions: Follow signs for Crook. Avoid new road over viaduct. Take old road down hill past Newton Cap pub. Turn off left before River Wear.
Club Secretary: Ajmair Singh, 156 Collingwood Street, Coundon, Bishop Auckland, Co. Durham, DL14 8LL. Tel: 07980 146696 (M)
Fixtures Secretary: Ron Williamson, 19 Waddington Street, Bishop Auckland, Co Durham, DL14 6HG Tel: 01388 600059 (H)
Club Colours: Navy and sky blue hoops
League: Durham/Northumberland 3

BLACKBURN RUFC
Ground Address: Ramsgreave Drive, Blackburn, Lancs. BB1 8NB   Tel: 01254 247669 -
Brief Directions: M6 J31, follow A677 for 5 miles to County Hotel. Turn left (Yew Tree Drive) - Ground is 1.5 miles on left.
Club Secretary: John Beeston, Forge Cottage, 43 Belthorn Rd, Belthorn, Blackburn BB1 2NN Tel No: 01254691093 Email:
john.beeston@pmm.co.uk
Fixtures Secretary: Andy Whalley, 5 Heys Court, Oswaldtwistle, Accrington, Lancs, BB5 3BN Tel No: 01772 741 181
Club Colours: Royal Blue shirts + white band, blue shorts, red and white socks
League: North 2 West

BLACKPOOL RUFC
Ground Address: Fleetwood Road, Norbreck, Blackpool, Lancashire
Tel: 01253 853308
Club Website: wwblackpool-rugby.co.uk
Brief Directions: M55 J4, right onto A583, right onto Whitegate Drive (still A583), bear right onto Devonshire Rd B5214, club on right 0.5 mile past Red Lion pub
Club Secretary: Cliff Wainscott, 15 Stafford Avenue, Poulton-Le-Fylde, Lancashire. FY6 8BJ
Tel: (H) 01253 885151
Fixtures Secretary: M Spowart, 3 Plymouth Rd., Blackpool. FY3 7JS
Tel No: 01253 393448
Club Colours: Red & blue squares
League: North Lancs & Cumbria

BLYTH RFC
Ground Address: Blyth Cricket, Rugby & Tennis Club, Plessey Road, Blyth, Northumberland Tel: 01670 352063
Website:
www.users.globalnet.co.uk/~mcorner/rugby.htm
Brief Directions: Take A1 north of Newcastle and turn off onto A19. After 2 miles take A189 (North) and then turn off towards Blyth on A1061. Follow town centre signs and turn left onto A193, turn left into Plessey Road.
Club Secretary: Dave Grey, 12 Winchester Avenue, Blyth, Northumberland,
BE24 2EY. Tel: 01670 369591
Email: dave.grey@bt.com
Fixtures Secretary: Alan Raffle, 51 Druridge Drive, Newsham Farm Estate, Blyth, Northumberland, NE24 4QR Tel: 01670 366002
Club Colours: Black and green hoops, black shorts
League: Durham/Northumberland 2

BOLTON RUFC
Ground Address: Mortfield Pavilion, Avenue Street, Bolton. BL1 3AW
Tel: 01204 363710
Brief Directions: Head out of Bolton on Chorley Old Road, signposted near Morrisons supermarket
Club Secretary: Robert Killiner. 9 Kittiwake Road, Heapey, Chorley, Lancs. PR6 9BA.
Tel: 01257 268107
Email: rob@cyclone-imaging.co.uk
Fixtures Secretary: David Patchett
Badger Cottage, 2 Richmal Terrace, Ramsbottom, Bury BL0 9EN Tel: (H) 017064 826298
Club Colours: Red and white hoops, black shorts and red socks.
League: North Lancs 1

BOWDON RUFC
Ground Address: Clay Lane Sports Club, Clay Lane, Timperley, Altrincham, Cheshire, WA15 7AF. Tel: 0161 980 8321

Brief Directions: M56 J6, follow signs to Hale, after 1.5 turn right at lights onto Delahays Rd, through next set of lights, after 0.5 mile up Thorley Lane turn right at Mini R/about on to Clay Lane. Club on left.
Club Secretary: Myles Kitchener
67 Crofton Avenue, Timperley, Altrincham, Cheshire, WA15 6BZ
Tel: 0161 973 3003H
Email: kitch@kitchiner.freeserve.co.uk
Fixtures Secretary: Frank Norton, 36 Green Walk, Timperley. Altrincham, Cheshire, WA15 6JN.
Tel: 0161 980 8195H - Email: fsjn@hotmail.com
Club Colours: Claret, white and black
League: South Lancs & Cheshire 3

BRADFORD SALEM RFC
Ground Address: Shay Lane, Heaton, Bradford. BD9 6SL Tel: 01274 496430
Brief Directions: From Bradford centre take A650 (Towards Keighley) along Manningham Lane. Left at 'The Park' (pub) and up hill turn right at top, past shops into Shay Lane. Ground is 100 yds on left.
Club Secretary: Mr. B. D. Strachan, 272 Leaventhorpe Lane, Thornton, Bradford, BD13 3BJ.
Fixtures Secretary: John Dobson
Tel: (H) 01274 487517
Club Colours: Royal blue, gold, black hoops, black shorts, blue socks
League: Yorkshire 3

BRAMLEY PHOENIX PARK RFC
Ground Address: The Warrels, Grosmont Terrace, Warrels Road, Bramley, Leeds. LS13 3NY Tel: 0113 257 7787
Club Secretary: Andrew Hurdley, Hall Farm, Hall Road, Little Preston, Leeds.
LS26 8UT Tel: (H) 0113 286 0131
Fixtures Secretary: T Smith c/o The Club
Club Colours: Green, black and gold, black shorts
League: Yorkshire 3

BRIDLINGTON RUFC
Ground Address: Dukes Park, Queensgate, Bridlington Tel: 01262 676101
Brief Directions: Follow signs to Bridlington, 1st traffic lights keep in n/s lane, right at roundabout, left at next lights, ground is 0.25 mile on right
Club Secretary: Gordon Morrice, Woodside House, 11 Martongate, Bridlington. YO16 6TS Tel No: 01262 676101 Email:
gordon@g.morrice.fsbusiness.co.uk
Fixtures Secretary: John Waller, 12 Hustler Road, Bridlington, East Yorkshire. Yo16
Tel No 01262 603476
Club Colours: Navy & Amber Hoops.
League: North 2 East

BROUGHTON PARK FC
Ground Address: G.MP. Sports & Social Club,Hough End Centre, Mauldeth Road West, Manchester M217SX Tel No: 0709 207 0268
Brief Directions: From M60 Jct 5 or M56 Jct# get on A5103 towards Manchester. After 21/2 miles turn left at Princess Pub into Mauldeth Road. Ground is 1/2 mile on left .
Club Secretary: Rob Loveday, 2 Devonshire Road, Heaton Moor, Stockport SK4 4EF. Tel No: 0161 947 9157 Email: secretary@broughton-park.co.uk
Fixtures Secretary: Tom Barber, 48 Pauldon Road, Manchester M23 8PD
Tel: (H) 0161 998 8936 (W) 0161 226 2501
Club Colours: Black and white hoops
League: North 2 West

BROUGHTON RUFC
Ground Address: Yew Street, Broughton, Salford. M7 9HL Tel: 0161 743 0902
Club Secretary: R. Ashton, 62 Milnthorpe Street, Salford, Manchester, M6 6DJ.
Fixtures Secretary: Peter Raymond Smith, 33 Kirtley Avenue, Monton Green, Eccles, Manchester, M30 9PU
Tel: (H) 0161 788 8098 (W) 0161 908 6075
Club Colours: Blue with yellow, red, yellow stripe midway
League: North Lancs 2

BURLEY RFC
Ground Address: The Club House, Abbey Road, Leeds. LS5 3NG   Tel: 0113 275 7400
Brief Directions: Travel out of Leeds on the A65 past Kirkstall Abbey. Club House on left after and opposite Vestergate Pub.
Club Secretary: R.K.N.Jones, 377 Burley Road, Leeds, West Yorkshire, LS4 2SP
Tel: 01132 742769
Fixtures Secretary: John Sanderson 3 Southolme Close, Leeds LS5 3LP
Tel: (H) 01132 787772
Club Colours: Maroon and white
League: Yorkshire 6

BURNAGE RFC
Ground Address: Varley Park, Battersea Road, Heaton Mersey, Stockport. SK4 3EA
Tel: 0161 432 2150
Brief Directions: J.1 on M60 1st left onto A5145, 1st Left after Crown Pub into Station Road, bends to right into Battersea Road - Club at bottom.
Club Secretary: Rick Hine, 23 Litchfield Street, Reddish, Stockport, SK5 6BQ.
Tel: 0161 666 0890
Fixtures Secretary: Dave Harper, 11 Fulmer Gardens , Bamford, Rochdale OL11 5RB
Tel: 01706 632232
Club Colours: Black
League: North Lancs 1

BURTONWOOD
Ground Address: Alder Lane, Burtonwood
Brief Directions: From M6 J22 or M62 J9 proceed to Winwick Island then take A49 towards Newton, at traffic lights turn left onto Hollins Lane and follow road to Burtonwood. Pitches on left hand side.
Club Secretary: John Harper, 8 Camborne Road, Burtonwood, Warrington, WA5 4LX.
Tel: 01925 221559 (H)
Fixtures Secretary: John Harper - as above
League Contact: John Harper - as above
Club Colours: Red & black quarters
League: South Lancs & Cheshire 5

BURY RFC
Ground Address: Bury Sports Club, Radcliffe Road, Bury, Lancashire.   Tel: 0161 764 1528
Brief Directions: Leave M602 at J.17 follow A56 towards Bury. After 4 miles turn left at T/lights into Radcliffe Road. Club 20yds on right.
Club Secretary: G J Hilton, 66 Twiss Green Lane, Culcheth, Warrington, Cheshire WA3 4DQ
Tel: (H) 01925 762119
Fixtures Secretary: M. Kennedy,15 Beeston Close, Bolton, Lancs. Tel: 01204 597891
Club Colours: Red, gold and blue hoops, navy blue shorts, red stockings
League: North Lancs 1

CALDER VALE RUFC
Ground Address: Holden Road, Reedley, Burnley, Lancashire. BB10 2LE
Tel: 01282 424337
Brief Directions: M65 J12, right to to Brierfield, through one set of traffic lights, Holden Road on left approxa quarter mile by Oaks Hotel
Club Secretary: Mr W K Seed, 30 Moorland Drive, Brierfield, Nelson. BB9 5ER
Tel: (H) 01282 614172
Fixtures Secretary: Mr M Wilton, 93 Talbot Drive, Brier Cliffe, Burnley, Lancs. BB10 2RT
Tel: (H) 01282 457963
Club Colours: Royal blue and gold hoops
League: North Lancs 1

CALDY RFC
Ground Address: Paton Field, Telegraph Road, Lower Caldy Crossroads, Caldy, Wirral.
Tel: 0151 625 8043
Brief Directions: M53-Jcnt 1 - B5139 West Kirby - A540
Club Secretary: R. B. Flashman, 26 Milton Crescent, Heswall, Wirral CH60 5ST
Tel: 0151 342 5300
Fixtures Secretary: K Doolan, 41 Woodbank Road, Whitby, Ellesmere Port, CH65 6PX. Tel: (H) 0151 348 0119
Club Colours: Sable, claret, gold and silver quarters
League: North 2 West

CAPENHURST RUFC
Ground Address: BNFL Sports Ground, Capenhurst, Chester, CH1 6ER.
Tel: 0151 3473494
Brief Directions: From Liverpool M53, A41 turn R. at lights to Capenhurst, L. at R/about, over railway bridge past BNFL Wks. Ground on R. From Warrington/Cheshire M56 to end R. at R/about, L. to Capenhurst. T-Jncn turn L. Past BNFL Ground on R.
Club Secretary: Ted Roberts, 8 Chichester Street, Chester, CH1 4AD.   Tel: 01244 378789
Email: ted.roberts@ukgateway.net
Fixtures Secretary: Dave Basnett, 21 St Stephens Rd, Prenton, Birkenhead, Wirral. CH1 4AD. Tel No: 0151 608 1980
Email: ted.roberts@ ukgateway.net
Club Colours: Blue & White
Change Blue & white
League: South Lancs & Cheshire 4

CARLISLE RFC
Ground Address: The Rugby Ground, Warwick Road, Carlisle, Cumbria.
Tel: 01228 521300
Brief Directions: M6 J43 on A69, head towards Carlisle, through 3 sets of lights,
turn right after 200yds into ground after 3rd set.
Club Secretary: N J Laycock, 90 Greystone Road, Carlisle. Cumbria, CA1 2DD
Tel: (H & F) 01228 523447 - Email:
nlaycock@freenet.co.uk
Fixtures Secretary: D D Morton, 14 Naworth Drive, Lowry Hill, Carlisle, Cumbria, CA3 0DD.
Tel/Fax: 01228 532447 - Email:
mortwas82@aol.com
Club Colours: Red, white & blue irregular hoops, blue shorts, red socks
League: North Lancs & Cumbria

CARNFORTH RFC
Ground Address: Carnforth High School, Kellet Road, Carnforth, Lancashire
Brief Directions: From M6 J.35, Turn right turn at T/Jct. school .5 mile on right
Club Secretary: Paul Jackson, 72 Morecambe Road, Lancaster,Lancs. LA1 5TA
Tel No: 01524 847143
Email: jacko@mcbe.fsnet.co.uk
Fixtures Secretary: Steve Vose, 2 Lindow Square, Lancaster, Lancs., LA1 1SE.
Tel: 01524 382385
Club Colours: Green and black hoops, black shorts, green socks
League: North Lancs 2

CASTLEFORD RUFC
Ground Address: Willow Bridge Lane, Whitwood, Castleford   Tel: 01977 554762
Brief Directions: M62E towards Hull, exit J31, 2nd turn left off roundabout, approx 1 mile through traffic lights, ground on right hand side

Club Secretary: M.Connell, 30 Church Avenue, Swillington , Leeds, LS26 8QH
Tel: (H) 0113 286 5231 Email: mconnell@arch-chemicals.com
Fixtures Secretary: D.Price, 10 Langdale Avenue, Outwood, Wakefield WF1 3TX
Tel No: 01924 825434
Club Colours: Red and blue quarter shirts, blue shorts.hoops
League: Yorkshire 2

CHESTER-LE-STREET RFC
Ground Address: Donald Owen Clarke Centre, Riverside Park, Chester-Le-Street, Co. Durham
Tel: 0191 3871995
Brief Directions: Take A1(M) to Chester-Le-Street, follow directions to County Cricket Ground, Rugby Club is situated adjacent to ground in the Donald Owen Clarke Centre.
Club Secretary: Mr. David Kilkenny, 64 Highfield Rise, Chester-Le-Street, Co. Durham, DH3 3UX.
Tel: (H) 0191 3888357
Fixtures Secretary: Graham Rodger, 3 Fife Avenue, Chester-Le-Street, Co. Durham
Tel: (H) 0191 389 1713
Club Colours: Blue shirts and shorts, red socks - Change Yellow Shirts, Blue shorts, Red socks.
League: Durham/Northumberland 3

CHORLEY
Ground Address: Brookfields, Chancery Road, Astley Village, Chorley, Lancashire PR71XP. Tel: 01257 268806
Brief Directions: Exit M61 J.8 towards Chorley acorss 1st R/about. Right at 2nd R/about past hospital on left. Left at next R/about into Chancery Road. Club on the right after 200 yards.
Club Secretary: Sean Riches, 12 Middlewood Close, Eccleston, Chorley, Lsncs PR7 5QG
Tel: (H) 01257 450651
Fixtures Secretary: Dave Nickeas, 7 Morris Close, Stokes Hall, Leyland, Lancs., PR5 2FD.
Tel: (H) 01772 451171
Club Colours: Black and white hoops, Red
League: North Lancs 2

CLECKHEATON RUFC
Ground Address: The Pavilion, Moorend, Cleckheaton, West Yorkshire. BD19 3UD
Tel: 01274 873410
Brief Directions: Off J.26 M62 - take road to Dewsbury and in 200 yards turn left into Cleckheaton Sports Club.
Club Secretary: Mr. C. Wharton, 8 Ingfield, Oakenshaw, Bradford, West Yorks., BD12 7EF. -
Tel: 01274 674870
Fixtures Secretary: Peter Lawton, 5 York Place, Cleckheaton, West Yorks.,
BD19 3PA. Tel: 01274 864155
Club Colours: Red and white hoops, black shorts
League: North 2 East

CLITHEROE RFC
Ground Address: Littlemoor Park, Littlemoor Road, Clitheroe, Lancs   Tel: 01200 422261
Brief Directions: A59 Turn off to Clitheroe on A671 (Town centre). Turn Right into Littlemoor Road, just after 30 MPH sign.
Club Secretary: Andrew Burrill, 7 Shays Drive, Clitheroe.
Tel: 01200 424434
Fixtures Secretary: Philip Isherwood, 160 Chatburn Road, Clitheroe.
Tel: (H) 01200 423781
Club Colours: Maroon and gold shirts with blacvk shorts and maroon socks
League: North Lancs 2

COCKERMOUTH RUFC Ltd
Ground Address: `Grasmoor', Strawberry How, Cockrmouth, Cumbria, CA13 9QT.
Tel: 01900 824884
Brief Directions: Leave by-pass along Lampugh Rd and Station St. Turn L. 50yards past Shell F/Stn on Right into Lorton Rd. .5 mile pass cemetry oin left turn left into Strawberry How - 100 yds club driveway on right (then open fields!).
Club Secretary: Chris Garrard, "Bent Dyke", Bent Ash Lonning Eaglesfield, Nr Cockermouth, Cumbria. CA13 0SF
Tel: (H) 01900 822835
Fixtures Secretary: A Quarry, 14 Collinfield, Kendal, Cumbria.
Tel: (H) 01539 731640
Club Colours: Black and amber hoops, black shorts
League: North Lancs & Cumbria

COLNE & NELSON RUFC
Ground Address: Holt House, Harrison Drive, Colne, Lancashire, BB8 9SF
Tel: 01282 863339
Brief Directions: At end of M65follow Skipton signs. Through traffic lights and left at large round-about and on the top of the hill.
Club Secretary: Keith Thornton, 261 Brunshaw Road, Burnley, Lancs. BB10 4QR
Tel: (W) 01282 717673
Fixtures Secretary: H. Lambert, 13 Townley Street, Colne, Lancs, BB8 9LF
Tel: 01282 860095
Club Colours: All black
League: North Lancs 2

CONGLETON RUFC
Ground Address: Clubhouse, Hankinson's Field, 78 Park Street, Congleton, Cheshire. CW12 1EG
Tel: 01260 273338
Website: confgleton-rufc.co.uk
Brief Directions: Follow signs to Leisure centre. Pitch along side. Clubhouse 50m up hill.
Club Secretary: Dennis Thorley, 46 Bladon Crescent, Alsager, via Stoke-on-Trent. ST7 2BG.
Tel: (H) 01270 878293.
Email: dennis.thorley@iclwaj.co.uk

Fixtures Secretary: Ken Williams, 2 Sprink Lane, Buglawton, Congleton, CW12
Tel: (H) 01260 279202
Club Colours: Red, white, red, black 3" hoops,black shorts
League: South Lancs & Cheshire 3

CONSETT & DISTRICT RFC
Ground Address: Belle Vue Park, Medomsley Road, Consett, Co Durham
Tel: 01207 590662 (admin) or 503600
Clubhouse: The Demi., Albert Rd., Consett Tel: 01207 590662
Brief Directions: Behind and to the side of Consett Civic Centre only 400m from centre of Consett. Full details on website.
Club website: www.derwntside.org.uk/community/demi
Club Secretary: Barry Cook,37 Queens Road, Blackhill, Co.Durham. DH8 0BL
Tel: 01207 500624 e-mail: cooklbaz@aol.com
Fixtures Secretary: Robert Brough, Sowerby House, St Ives Road, Leadgate, Consett Co Durham. DH8 7PZ Tel 01207 501951
e-mail: schaboom@hotmail.com
Club Colours: Black and amber hoops with red trim and black shorts and socks
League: Durham/Northumberland 1

CREIGHTON RUFC
Ground Address: Carrs Field, Caxton Road, off Newtown Road, Carlisle   Tel: 01228 521169
Brief Directions: Follow signs to hospital, 500m past hospital on right - sign to Industrial Estate.
Club Secretary: David J Thomlinson, 146 Moorhouse Road, Carlisle, Cumbria, CA2 7QR - Email: djt@halton-soal.co.uk
Tel: (H) 01228 535111   (W) 01228 524379
Fixtures Secretary: Ian Langley, Kiln Green House, Aikton, Wigton, CA7 0HY.
Tel: 01697 344900
Club Colours: Navy blue, red collars and cuffs, white shorts, red sock
League: Cumbria

CREWE AND NANTWICH RUFC
Ground Address: Crewe Vagrants Sports Club, Newcastle Road (A500), Willaston, Nantwich, Cheshire. CW5 7EP
Tel: 01270 569506
Brief Directions: Situated on A500, opposite The Horseshoe pub, 2 miles east of Nantwich and 6 miles from J16 M6
Club Secretary: Alan Jones, 9 Gingerbread Lane, Nantwich, Cheshire. CW5 6NH
Tel: (H & W) 01270 625737
Fixtures Secretary: Bob Christie,127 A Welsh row , Nantwich CW5 5ET
Tel: (H) 01270 629637 (after 8 p.m.) (W) 01270 624160
Club Colours: Black Jersey with broad white band
League: South Lancs & Cheshire 2

DE LA SALLE (SALFORD) RUFC
Ground Address: Lancaster Road, Salford 6
Tel: 0161 789 2261
Brief Directions: Sth: off M602 Eccles Jcn 2 follow Salford past Hope Hsptl on rt, next lights left onto Lancaster Rd. From Nth: A580 East Lancs Rd towards Salford, right at Lancaster Rd, club halfway on right
Club Secretary: Paul Barrett, 24 Delbooth Avenue, Flixton, Manchester M41 8SD
Tel No: 0161 746 8199
Email: the - barrett @delboothj.fsnet.co.uk
Fixtures Secretary: Jim Collins, 8 Oakwood Drive, Salford
Tel: (H) 0161 281 3761 (W) 0161 775 7928
Club Colours: Red and gold quarters
League: North Lancs & Cumbria

DIDSBURY TOC H RFC
Ground Address: Ford Lane, Didsbury, Manchester   Tel: 0161 446 2146
Brief Directions: From A34 follow signs for Didsbury to Shell garage. Left on to Dene Road immediate left to Ford Lane - down to bottom.
Club Secretary: Mrs. Geraldine Harris, 17 Edenhall Avenue, Burnage, Manchester, M19 2BG. Tel: 0161 224 1251
Fixtures Secretary: Peter Bradley, 8 Barnard Avenue, Heaton Moor, SK4 4EP.
Tel: 0161 432 0496
Club Colours: Black and amber hoops
League: North Lancs 1

DINNINGTON RUFC
Ground Address: Lodge Lane, Dinnington, Sheffield, South Yorkshire. S31 7PB
Tel: 01909 562044
Brief Directions: M1 J.31 Take A57 towards Worksop. Turn left B6060 2nd Traffic Lights after one and a half miles turn left on Lodge Lane.
Club Secretary: Bill Gilbody, 16 Devonshire Drive, North Anston, Sheffield. S25 4AQ. Tel: (H) 01909 562997 Email:bill@thegilbodys.co.uk
Fixtures Secretary: As Secretary.
Club Colours: Blue, gold, black and white hoops. Change: All green
League: Yorkshire 2

DONCASTER PHOENIX RUFC
(formerley Danum Phoenix)
Ground Address: Castle Park, Armthorpe Road, Doncaster. DN2 5QB. Tel: 01302 831388
Brief Directions: From M18 J4 to Doncaster, left at 2nd R/about, right at next R/about. Ground 1 mile on left. From A1M, A630 into Doncaster, anti-clockwise round ring road 1st R/about right.
Club Secretary: Will Hircock, 10 Guinevere Drive, South Elmsall, Pontefract WF9 2WB
Tel: 0776 993 0274
Fixtures Secretary: Graham Kitchen, 18 Broadway, Dunscroft, Doncaster, DN7 4AA.
Tel: (H) 01302 844700
Club Colours: Black with red & yellow band on chest
League: Yorkshire 4

DOUGLAS (I.O.M.) RUFC
Ground Address: The Clubhouse, Port-E-Chee, Douglas, Isle of Man Tel: 01624 676493
Brief Directions: Leave Douglas via Peel Road to Quaterbridge, ground on right. FROM AIRPORT. Head for Douglas turn left at Quarterbridge roundabout, ground on the Right.
Club Secretary: P E Garrett,9 Birch Hill Grove,Onchan , Douglas, Isle of Man IM3 4EJ
Tel No 01624 629037
Fixtures Secretary: TGethin Taylor,17 Keeil Pharkk Pack, Glen Vine, Isle of Man IM4 4EW
Tel No: 01624 851180
Club Colours: Maroon with gold band
League: South Lancs & Cheshire 3

DUKINFIELD RUFC
Ground Address: Blocksages Playing Fields, Birch Lane, Dukinfield, Cheshire
Tel: 0161 343 2592
Brief Directions: On B6170 between Hyde and Ashton-under-Lyne, next to the baths
Club Secretary: Mr. C. Hadley, 3 Milton Close, Dukingfield, Cheshire, SK16 5DZ.
Fixtures Secretary: Alan Hilton, Old St,Georges Vicarage, Pennine View, Heyrod, stalybridge, Cheshire. Tel: (H) 0161 338 3410
Club Colours: Royal blue and gold hoops
League: South Lancs & Cheshire 1

DURHAM CITY RFC
Ground Address: Hollow Drift, Green Lane, Durham City. DH1 3JU
Tel: 0191 386 1172 Website: durhamcityafc.co.uk
Brief Directions: Take A1M, then A690, straight across 1st roundabout, left at next roundabout, left at traffic lights, after 300 yards turn left into Green Lane, opposite Durham Prison
Club Secretary: Mr R Elston, c/o club
Tel: (H) 0191 386 3245
Fixtures Secretary: Mr J Thompson c/o club
Tel: (H) 01388 528071
Club Colours: Blue and gold hoops, blue shorts with blue and gold socks.
League: Durham/Northumberland 1

DURHAM CONSTABULARY RUFC
Ground Address: Durham Constabulary Police HQ, Aykley Heads, Durham.DL1 5TT
Tel: 0191 3864929
Brief Directions: Situated to the north of Durham City, follow signs for County Hall and then Police Headquarters
Club Secretary: Mr Peter Davis, 44 Hauxley Drive, Chester-le-Street, Co. Durham, DH2 3TE Tel: (H) 0191 3890848
Email: peterdavis@bronyaur.fsnet.co.uk
Fixtures Secretary: M.Taylor, 79 Willowtree Avenue, Gilesgate Moor, Durham DH!1DZ
Tel: 0191 3865562
Club Colours: Royal blue and gold quarters, black shorts
League: Durham/Northumberland 4

EAGLE RUFC

Ground Address: Eagle Sports, Thornton Road, Great Sankey, Warrington
Tel: 01925 632926 Sat. Emergencies Tel: 0976 288560
Brief Directions: A57 west from Warrington towards Liverpool onto the dual carriageway, where road splits at roundabout take left hand road (A562) and at lights turn left into Thornton Rd
Club Secretary: Mark Simmons, 3 Dorchester Road, Great Sankey, Warrington, WS5 1XZ.
Tel: 01925 492689
Fixtures Secretary: Dave Unsworth, 20 Keith Avenue, Warrington. Tel: (H) 01925 727565
Club Colours: Black and white
League: South Lancs & Cheshire 3

ECCLES RFC

Ground Address: Gorton Street, Peel Green, Eccles, M30 7LZ Tel: 0161 789 2613
Brief Directions: M63 J2 towards Eccles, Gorton Street 2nd on left
Club Secretary: A C Brunt, 12 Woodstock Drive, Worsley, Manchester. M28 2WW
Tel: (H) 0161 794 4114
e-mail: andybrunt@hotmail.com
Fixtures Secretary: Alan Chettoe, 7,Pelton Avenue, Wardley, Manceater M27 9QT
Tel: 0161 661 1158
Club Colours: Navy & white hoops, white shorts
League: North Lancs 1

EDLINGTON AND GRANBY RUFC

Ground Address: Granby Road WMC, Broomhouse Lane, Edlington, Doncaster, South Yorkshire
Brief Directions: A1(M) J36, A630 in direction of Rotherham for 0.25 mile, left at traffic lights, then 2nd left, right at T junction, Granby club and ground are 0.25 mile on left
Club Secretary: Keith Richards, 5 Markham Square, Edlington, Doncaster, South Yorkshire, DN12
Fixtures Secretary: Colin Ford, 56 Roberts Road, Edlington, Doncaster, DN12 1JG.
Club Colours: Yellow shirts, black shorts and socks
League: Yorkshire 5

EGREMONT RUFC

Ground Address: Bleech Green, Egremont, Cumbria Tel: 01946 820645
Brief Directions: M6 J36, follow A595 north towards Workington, Egremont is approx 4 miles south of Whitehaven
Club Secretary: Mr Luke Murphy, 13 Sunnyside, Castle Croft, Egremont, Cumbria. CA22 2BS
Tel: 01946 822261
Fixtures Secretary: Mr. L. Oliver, Mellbreak, Bookwell, Egremont, Cumbria.
Tel: 01946 822443
Club Colours: Black and amber
League: Cumbria

ELLESMERE PORT RUFC

Ground Address: The Whitby Sports & Social Club, Chester Road, Whitby, Ellesmere Port, Cheshire. Tel: 0151 200 7050 or 7080
Brief Directions: M6, M56, M53 J.10. A5117 to Strawberry Pub R/about 4th off. Ground in .75 mile
Club Secretary: Mr.A.R.J. Dale, 12 Archers Way, Great Sutton, Ellesmere Port, Cheshire, CH66 2RY
Tel: 0151 200 1860 - Fax: 0151 2001860
Fixtures Secretary: Mr. G. Fenion, 19 Belgrave Drive, Ellesmere Port, Cheshire, CH65 7EJ.
Tel: 0151 357 3841 - Fax: 01244 287561
Club Colours: Black w/ 2 single red/yellow hoops
League: South Lancs & Cheshire 2

FLEETWOOD RUFC

Ground Address: `Broadwaters', Melbourne Avenue, Fleetwood, Lancs, FY7 8AY
Tel: 01253 874774 - Fax: 01253 779556
Brief Directions: M55, J3 (Blackpool) to Fleetwood/Kirkham follow, A585 to Fleetwood, 1st exit off r'about at Nautical Coll., sharp left at tram tracks into the Crescent, round to Melbourne Ave.
Club Secretary: C.Smith, 46 The Strand, Rossall, Fleetwood FY7 8NR Tel No: 01253 874725
Email: csmith@cybermil.uk.com
Fixtures Secretary: A,Thompson, 67 Levens Drive, Poulton -le-Fylde, Lancs. FY6 8EZ
Tel: 01255 882121 (H) - 01253 392957 (W)
Club Colours: Green and gold hoops
League: North Lancs 1

FURNESS RUFC

Ground Address: Strawberry Grounds, Abbey Road, Barrow-in-Furness, Cumbria
Tel: 01229 825226
Brief Directions: At 3rd R/about on Dalton bypass take L. exit for hospital. At mini R/about turn R. onto Abbey Road after approx 1 mile turn L. into Croslands Park Road, entrance 100 yards on R.
Club Secretary: I. McAllister, 14 Jesmond Avenue, Barrow in Furness, Cumbria, LA13 9AW.
Tel: 01229 839806
Fixtures Secretary: D. Troughton, Greystones House, Greystones Lane, Dalton in Furness, Cumbria, LA15 8PX. Tel: 01229 462586
Club Colours: Blue and white hoops
League: Cumbria

GARFORTH RUFC

Ground Address: Garforth Community College, Lidgett Lane, Garforth, Leeds. LS25 1LJ
Brief Directions: A63 Leeds to Selby Road, left into Lidgett Lane, school on right, thro' main gate, to changing facilities at back of school buildings
Club Secretary: George Shaw, 34 Rose Court, Garforth, Leeds. LS25 1NS
Tel: (H) 0113 286 7193 (W) 01274 732707
Fixtures Secretary: Jonathan Fallas, 14 FirtreeAvenue, Garforth, Leeds, LS25 2JN.
Tel: 0113 2863042 - Mobile: 07788 591717
Club Colours: Red, yellow, blue & black quarters
League: Yorkshire 6

NORTHERN

GARSTANG
League: North Lancs 2
For further details contact:
North Lancs 2 League Secretary
Bill Hopkinson, Far Hey Head Farm, Littleborough,
Rochdale Lancs OL15 9NS
Tel: 01706 379879

GATESHEAD RFC
Ground Address: Hedley Lawson Park,
Eastwood Gardens, Low Fell, Gateshead. NE9
5UB Tel: 0191 4200207
Brief Directions: Travelling north A167 into
Gateshead, pass 2 sets main lights, turn right
Joicey Rd, 2nd left Eastwood Gdns. Travelling
south A167, left Springfield Hotel, phone box turn
left
Club Secretary: M A Nunn, 30 Limetrees
Gardens, Low Fell, Gateshead.
NE9 5BE Tel: (H) 0191 4203089
Fixtures Secretary: Dr.W.D,Hetherington, 97
Kells Lane, Lowfell, Gateshead NE9 5XX.
Tel (H) 0191 4219487
Club Colours: Red,Navy and sky narrow hoops ,
white shorts
League: Durham/Northumberland 1

GOOLE RUFC
Ground Address: Westfield Bank Sports
Complex , Westfield Lane, Hook, Goole, North
Humberside. DN14 5PW Tel: 01405 762018
Brief Directions: M62 J36, straight through 2 sets
of traffic lights, continue on road out of Goole,
right towards Hook just before Boothferry bridge
into Westfield Lane
Club Secretary: I R Higgins, 14 The Meadows,
Howden, Goole, North Humberside. DN14 7DX
Tel: (H) 01430 430037 (W) 01405 768621
Fixtures Secretary: P Shand, 4 Kings Close,
Pontefract, West Yorks WF8 3PD
Tel: (H) 01977 780652 (W) 01977 703357
Club Colours: Gold shirt with navy band, navy
shorts
League: North 2 East

GOSFORTH RFC
Ground Address: Bullocksteads Sports Ground,
Ponteland Road, Kenton Bank Foot, Newcastle-
upon-Tyne NE13 8AH Tel: 0191 286 0088
Website: www.gosforthfc.fsnet.co.uk
Brief Directions: Turn off A1 at Airport sign, fol-
low B6918 westwards for approx 1 mile. Ground is
on right hand side of Ponteland Road.
Club Secretary: Trevor Hogg, 11 Launceston
Close, Kingston Park, Newcastle-upon-Tyne. NE3
2XX Tel: (H) 0191 2711120
Email: t.hogg@tesco.net
Fixtures Secretary: Malcolm Bell, 3 Lansdowne
Gardens, Stakeford, Northumberland NE62 5LF.
Tel: 01670 851652
Club Colours: Green and white hoops, white
shorts, hooped socks.
League: Durham/Northumberland 1

GREEN GARTH RUFC
Ground Address: Greengarth Hostel, Holmbrook,
Cumbria   Tel: 01946 725800
Club Secretary: Robert Eales, 20 Wholehouse
Road, Scale, Cumbria. CA20
Tel: (H) 019467 28734
Fixtures Secretary: Steven Edgare
Tel: (H) 019467 841534
Club Colours: Maroon and gold
League: Cumbria

GUISBOROUGH RUFC
Ground Address: Belmangate, Guisborough,
Cleveland. TS14 7BB   Tel: 01287 632966
Website: www.geocities.com/grufc
Brief Directions: Leave A19 at A174 Jctn. to
Marton. Turn R. into A171 to Guisborough via
Nunthorpe at Swans Corner. Through town to
T/lights - Bow St., Whitby Road, Belmangate Jctn
- over to club just prior to Bridge.
Club Secretary: Jonty Weastell, 18 Sudbury,
Marton, Middlesbrough, TS8 9XZ.
Tel: 01642 317200 (H) 01642 230800 (B).
Email: jonny.weastell@ssp.surveysors.co.uk.
Fixtures Secretary: J. Weastell, as above
Club Colours: Black and amber trim. Change
Green & white hoops
League: Durham/Northumberland 2

HALIFAX VANDALS RUFC
Ground Address: Warley Town Lane, Warley,
Halifax, West Yorkshire   Tel: 01422 831704
Brief Directions: From Halifax head towards
Burnley. At King Cross junction take a right to
Warley. Left at top of road then left to Warley vil-
lage.Ground opposite Maypole public house.
Club Secretary: S.Beard, 2 Woodside Terrace,
Halifax , West Yorkshire. HX3 6ER
Tel No: 01422 333099
Email: steohen.neard@hotmail.com
Fixtures Secretary: Stephen Beard
Tel: 01422 353099
Club Colours: Blue & white thin hoops, navy shorts
League: Yorkshire 3

HALTON RUFC
Ground Address: Widnes Recreation Club,
Liverpool Road, Widnes, Cheshire
Tel: 0151 424 2355/50
Brief Directions: Frm M62 J7, A57 W'ington, rt at
1st lights, rt at T jcn, rt after 4th pelican, rt at
lights, club on lft. Frm R'corn Brge, towncentre
slip, under flyover, lft at r'bout, over next r'bout, rt
at lights, club on lft
Club Secretary: S.G.Dennett. 267 Lunts Heath
Road,Widnews, CheshireWA8 5BB
Tel: 01514243978 (H) 07050 191715 (W)
Email: stedennett@supanet.com
Fixtures Secretary: D.Dyer, 19 Clincton Close,
Widnes, Cheshire WA8 8JP
Tel No: 0151 424 6944
Club Colours: Blue with gold and green band.
League: South Lancs & Cheshire 4

HARTLEPOOL ATHLETIC RFC
Ground Address: Oakesway Estate, Hartlepool, Co Durham. TS24 0RE   Tel: 01429 274715
Brief Directions: Leave A19 at A179 Hartlepool turn off, follow signs for Headland, ground 3 miles from A19
Club Secretary: Jim Ainslie, 10 Regent Street, Hartlepool, Co Durham. TS24 0QN
Tel: (H) 01429 260003
Fixtures Secretary: John Bentham, 22 Tempest Rd., Hartlepool, Co.Durham.
TS24 9QH Tel: (H) 01429 281012
Club Colours: Sky blue/ white/ royal blue
League: Durham/Northumberland 4

HARTLEPOOL BOYS BRIGADE OLD BOYS RFC
Ground Address: Old Friarage, Headland, Hartlepool (Field only)   Tel: 0793 2585037M
Brief Directions: A19 take A179 Hartlepool exit, over 4 R/abouts left at T Jnct, take l eft fork at `Mural', left at Fire Station, right onto seafront, ground on left after tennis courts.
Club Secretary: G K Faint, 11 Nesbyt Road, Hartlepool. TS24 9NB   Tel: (H) 01429 265674
Fixtures Secretary: I Mulrooney, 6 Carr Street, Hartlepool, TS26 8RE   Tel: 01429 272254
Club Colours: Black with broad white band, black shorts
League: Durham/Northumberland 4

HARTLEPOOL RFC
Ground Address: Mayfield Park, Easington Road, Hartlepool. TS24 9BA   Tel: 01429 266445
Brief Directions: Leave A19 north of town on A179 over 2 roundabouts, right at 3rd, ground 500m on left
Club Secretary: Dave Jones, 14 Turnberry Grove, Hartlepool TS27 3PX
Tel: (H) 01429 231125
Email: davjones@supanet.com
Fixtures Secretary: Ken Thompson, 10 Boswell Grove, Hartlepool.   Tel: (W) 01642 279880
Club Colours: Black and white
Change Colours: Maroon and White
League: Durham/Northumberland 2

HARTLEPOOL ROVERS
Ground Address: The Friaridge, Low Warren, Westview Road, Hartlepool,
TS24 0BP Tel: 01429 267741
Brief Directions: Take A19 to the A179 turn off. Follow A1049 (Bypass Hartlepool) for 4 miles to the headland.
Club Secretary: Bill Dale, 21 Knapton Avenue, Billingham, Stockton-on-Tees.
TS22 5DJ Tel: (H) 01642 863791
Fixtures Secretary: Tony Lowe, Alma House, Junction Rd., Stockton-on-Tees. TS20 1PJ. Tel: (H) 01624 530697
Club Colours: White shirts, black shorts, red socks
League: Durham/Northumberland 1

HEATH RUFC
Ground Address: North Dean, Stainland Rd, West Vale, Halifax. HX4 8LS   Tel: 01442 372920
Brief Directions: M62 J24, follow Halifax signs at bottom of hill (end of dual c'way), turn left towards Stainland, clubhouse approx 500m on left through used car lot
Club Secretary: Peter Burton,
10 Castle Lane, Ripponden, Sowerby Bridge, West Yorks. HX6 4JY   Tel No: 01422 824847
Fixtures Secretary: John Ingham,
1 George Street, Greetland, Halifax, West Yorkshire, HX4 8DH.   Tel: 01422 371045
Club Colours: Emerald, gold and claret
League: Yorkshire 3

HEATON MOOR RUFC
Ground Address: Green Lane, Heaton Moor, Stockport SK4 2NF.   Tel: 0161 432 3407
Brief Directions: M60 Jct. 1 to Stockport. A5145 towars Didsbury. At top of hill, turn right at T/lights into Bankhall Road. Turn right at next set of lights into Green Lane. Club 250yds on left.
Club Secretary: D. N. Todd, 7 Warwick Road, Heaton Chapel, Stockport, Cheshire, SK4 4NQ.
Tel: 0161 432 0943H - 0161 374 3000W
Email: davidtodd@lycos.co.uk
Fixtures Secretary: M.J. Jeskins, 5 Hazel Drive, Moss Nook, Manchester, M22 5LY.
Tel Nos: 0161 436 4807H - 0161 485 4372W
Club Colours: Black, red and amber
League: North Lancs 1

HELSBY RUFC
Ground Address: Helsby Sports and Social Club, Chester Rd, Helsby, Cheshire Tel: 01928 722267
Brief Directions: Head west along M56 J14, left at roundabout, continue for 1 mile to lights, go straight ahead and pass the Helsby Arms pub, club is next turning on left (opposite petrol station).
Club Secretary: C.Johnson, Greenfields, Primrose Lane, Alvaney, Cheshire WA6 9BS. Tel: 01928 724180(H).
Email: chris.j.johnson@dtosorigin-it.co.uk
Fixtures Secretary: A Ryder, 64 Chester Road, Helsby, Warrington, Cheshire
Tel: (H) 01928 723733
Club Colours: Black and gold hoops
League: South Lancs & Cheshire 4

HEMSWORTH RUFC
Ground Address: Moxon Fields, Lowfield Road, Hemsworth, Pontefract, West Yorkshire. WF9 4JT
Tel: 01977 610078
Brief Directions: Pontefract Road from Town cen-tre turn right after passing Hemsworth School.
Club Secretary: M ark Roberts, The Elms, Stockingate, South Kirkby, Pontefract. WF9 3QX
Tel: (H) 01977 644379
Fixtures Secretary: N.Jennings, 8 Churchfield Terrace, Cudworth, Barnsley.
Club Colours: Navy quarters/ navy/ navy
League: Yorkshire 2

HESSLE RUFC
Ground Address: Livingston Road, Hessle, Hull, East Yorkshire   Tel: 01482 643430
Brief Directions: Turm right off clive Sullivan Way at `Sainsburys'. At mini R/about turn right and then left into Livingston Road. Club lm on left.
Club Secretary: Nick Whitaker,77 West Grove,Askew Avenue, Hull HU4 6RQ
Tel: 01482 576091
Fixtures Secretary: P K Denton
Tel: (H) 01482 561338
Club Colours: Green, black and white irregular hoops
League: Yorkshire 3

HOLMES CHAPEL RUFC
Ground Address: A P Sports & Social Club, Brookl;ands, Holmes Chapel, CW4 8BE
Tel: 01477 532018
Brief Directions: Ground is on A54 (Holmes Chapel -Congleton Rd) on outskirts of village just beyond Railway Station
Club Secretary: Martin Cummins, 4 Portree Drive, Holmes Chapel, Cheshire CW4 7JB
Tel No: 01477 534617
Fixtures Secretary: John Leary
Tel: (H) 01606 554614 (W) 01606 562816
Club Colours: Blue and gold hoops
League: South Lancs & Cheshire 5

HORDEN WELFARE RFC
Ground Address: Welfare Park, Northumberland Street, Horden, Peterlee, County Durham
Tel: 0191 5863501
Brief Directions: A19 into Peterlee, follow signs for Horden, left onto Sunderland Rd, turn right at Bell Hotel, 100 yards to club house
Club Secretary: Joseph Watson, `Clairemont', Sunderland Rd., Horden, Peterlee, Co. Durham. SR8 4PF. Tel No: 0191 5861042
Fixtures Secretary: Robert Brownless, 31 Manor Way, Peterlee, Co. Durham.
Tel: 0191 5864454
Club Colours: Claret & Blue
League: Durham/Northumberland 1

HORNSEA RUFC
Ground Address: The Hollis Recreation Ground, Westwood Avenue, Hornsea, East Yorkshire. HU18 1BB Tel: 01964 534181
Brief Directions: Leave Hornsea on Atwick and Bridlington road. Turn left after 300m onto Westwood Avenue, opposite school playing fields.
Club Secretary: Ian Rodmell, 100 Parliament Street, Norton, Halton, North Yorkshire. YO17 9HE Tel No: 01653 698605
Fixtures Secretary: Roger Mc Latchie, 18 Shaftsbury Avenue, Hornsea, East Yorks, HU18 1LX. Tel: (H) 01964 534497
Club Colours: Black with green and white hoops
League: Yorkshire 5

HOUGHTON RUFC
Ground Address: Dairy Lane, Houghton le Spring, Tyne & Wear   Tel: 0191 5841460
Brief Directions: Situated on A1052, Houghton to Chester-le-Street road, opposite Houghton Police Station, 0.25 mile west of A690
Club Secretary: Mrs. Lorraine Walls
38 Hopgarth Gardens, Chester-Le-Street, Co. Durham, DH3 3RH   Tel: 0191 3883642
Fixtures Secretary: John Felton, 37 Larchwood, Harraton, Washington, Tyne & Wear, NE38 9BT.
Tel: (H) 0191 4161467
Club Colours: Black shirts with white hoop, black shorts, black socks
League: Durham/Northumberland 2

HOYLAKE RUGBY RFC
Ground Address: Melrose Avenue, Hoylake, Wirral, Merseyside, CH47 3BU
Tel: 0151 632 2538
Website: www.hoylake.net
Brief Directions: Turn at R/about in Hoylake towards Railway Station after .25 mile, turn lft down Carham Lane
Club Secretary: Stirling K. Dutton, 10 Hadfield Avenue, Hoylake, Wirral, CH47 3DJ.
Tel: 0151 632 0379
Email: stirling.dutton@excite.co.uk
Fixtures Secretary: John Kellaway, 43 Dovedale Road, Hoylake, Wirral, CH47.
Tel: 0151 632 5742
Club Colours: Red, green and white hoops
League: South Lancs & Cheshire 3

HUDDERSFIELD RUFC
Ground Address: Lockwood Park, Brewery Drive, Lockwood, Huddersfield. HD1 3UR
Tel: 01484 469801/452809
Brief Directions: Leave Huddersfield town centre on A616 signed Holmfirth, 0.75 mile straight across lights on B6108 signed Meltham, left after 300yds into ground
Club Secretary: Ian D Cleave, 2 Clough Way, Fenay Bridge, Huddersfield, W.Yorks HD8 0JL
Tel: 01484 306045
Fixtures Secretary: Brian Swift Tel: 01484 469801 (H) 07713 607906 (M)
Club Colours: Claret, gold and white.
League: North 2 East

HUDDERSFIELD YMCA RUFC
Ground Address: Lawrence Batley Sports Centre, Laund Hill, Huddersfield. HD3 4YS Tel: 01484 654052
Brief Directions: From west: M62 J23, follow Huddersfield signs, ground 0.5 mile on left. From east: M62 J24, Rochdale sign at r'bout, along A643 for 1 mile, left at r'bout, ground 0.5 mile left
Club Secretary: Ian Leask, 3 Cheviot Way, Upper Hopton, Mirfield, West Yorkshire. WF14 8HW Tel: (H) 01924 508642 (W/F) 01924 508641
Fixtures Secretary: Brian Castle, 10 Hauchs Road, Quarmby, Huddersfield HD3 4YS

Tel: 01484 656120 (H) 01484 433836 (W)
Club Colours: Red and black hoops, black shorts, red and blacksocks
League: Yorkshire 2

HULL RUFC
Ground Address: Haworth Park, Emmott Road, Beverley High Road, Hull. HU6 7AB
Tel: 01482 802119
Brief Directions: The ground is East of Beverley High road (A1079) and is signed from t he main road.
Club Secretary: D J Ward, 78 St Margarets Avenue, Cottingham, Hull. HU16 5NB
Tel: (H) 01482 842292 (W) 01482 325242
Fixtures Secretary: Steve Watson, 236 Bracknell Avenue, Hull HU5 4QG
Tel: 01482 341946
Club Colours: Black with gold and red band
League: Yorkshire 1

HULLENSIANS RUFC
Ground Address: Springhead Lane, Springfield Way, Anlaby Common, Hull
Tel: 01482 505656 Website: www.hullensians.org.uk
Brief Directions: A63 to Hull. Turn off at Ferriby follow signs for Anlaby. Travel along Boothferry Road, left along First Avenue, right at the end, sharp left at R/about 1st right Springhead Lane.
Club Secretary: Peter Francis Jones, 5 Sherwood Drive, Anlaby Common, Hull, HU4 7RG. Tel: 01482 354975
Fixtures Secretary: Tim Robinson, 79 Huntley Drive, Chanterlands Avenue, Hull. HU5 4DP Tel: (H) 01482 844707
Club Colours: Red and black
League: Yorkshire 4

ILKLEY RUFC
Ground Address: Stacks Field, Denton Road, Ilkley, West Yorkshire. LS29 0AD
Tel: 01943 607037
Brief Directions: From lights in town, turn towards the river down Brook Street, the ground is visible 300 metres on right
Club Secretary: J.K. Bernard, 36 Dale View,Ilkley, West Yorks. LS29 9BP
Tel No: 01943 602945
Fixtures Secretary: David Duxbury, 12 Broadfield Way, Addingham , Ilkley LS29 0TJ
Tel No: 07071 224432
Club Colours: Red, white and black hooped shirts ,white shorts
League: Yorkshire 2

JARROVIANS RUFC
Ground Address: Lukes Lane Estate, Hebburn, Tyne & Wear Tel: 0370 964 113
Brief Directions: North end of A1(M)/A194(M), continue north along A194, at 1st roundabout turn left, then immediate right, follow road along full length, ground on right

Club Secretary: Albert Ritson, 5 Belsfield Gardens, Monkton Jarrow, Tyne & Wear NE32 5QP Tel: 0191 4893866
e-mail: geordie1946@hotmail.com
Fixtures Secretary: Dave King., 53 Peterborough Way, Fellgate Estate, Jarrow, Tyne & Wear Tel: (H) 0191 4891611
Club Colours: Black and amber hoops
League: Durham/Northumberland 3

KEIGHLEY RUFC
Ground Address: Skipton Road, Utley, Keighley, West Yorkshire. BD20 6DX
Tel: 01535 602174
Brief Directions: Access to ground is from former A629 from Keighley to Skipton, ground is on right travelling north just on outskirts of town. NB no access from present A629 Aire V'ly rd
Club Secretary: M T Greaves, Holmlea, Summerhill Lane, Steeton, Keighley, West Yorkshire. BD20 6RX Tel: (H) 01535 653192 (W) 01535 605646
Fixtures Secretary: J Midgley Tel: 01535 214545 (W) 01535 605311
Club Colours: Scarlet, white and green hoops
League: Yorkshire 2

KESWICK RFC
Ground Address: Davidson Park, Tithebarn Street, Keswick, Cumbria
Tel: 017687 72823
Brief Directions: Leave A66 follow signs for Borrowdale. Turn right at Caterite Supermarket and immediate right again 50m beyond entrance to supermarket car park. Club is 50 yards on right.
Club Secretary: David Etherden, Keswick Bridge Timeshare, Station Road, Keswick, Cumbria, CA12 4NL. Tel: 017687 78277H - 73591W
Fixtures Secretary: Alan F. Gray, 49 Blencathra Street, Keswick, Cumbria, CA12 4XB
Tel: 017687 73051
Club Colours: Green. blue & yellow hoops, White shorts, Red socks.
League: Cumbria

KIRKBY LONSDALE RUFC
Ground Address: The Club House, Underley Park, Kirkby Lonsdale, via Carnforth, Cumbria, Lancs
Tel: 015242 71780
Brief Directions: M6 J36, 1st left turn signpost town centre, keep left sign KL RUFC Old Hutton, 0.5 mile turn right
Club Secretary: Richard Harkness, Meadowgarth, Fairbank, Kirkby Lonsdale, Via Carnforth, Cumbria, Lancs., LA6 2BD
Tel: (H) 015242 71137
Fixtures Secretary: W. Whewell, Field Edge, Heron Syke, Burton in Kentdal, LA6 1LG.
Tel: 01524 782049 - Fax: 01524 782935
Club Colours: Red, black and amber hoops and socks, black shorts
League: North Lancs & Cumbria

KNARESBOROUGH RUFC
Ground Address: Hay-A-Park, Park Lane, off Chain Lane, Knaresborough
Tel: 01423 866811
Brief Directions: Follow A59 to centre of Knaresborough, at traffic lights by Board Inn turn north, away from Calcutt (signpost), take 2nd right, at school, follow on to end of road.
Club Secretary: Antony Merrin, 73 West End Avenue, Harrogate, North Yorkshire HG2 9BX
Tel: 01423 569245
Fixtures Secretary: Steve McGrail, 33 Westville Oval, Harrogate, N.Yorks.
Tel: 01423 522521
Club Colours: Blue and gold hooped shirts, navy shorts and socks
League: Yorkshire 6

KNOTTINGLEY RUFC
Ground Address: Knottingley RUFC, Howards Field, Marsh Lane, Knottingley.
WF11 9DE Tel: 01977 672438
Brief Directions: Onto A645 main road toward Knottingley, turn off at town hall/St Botolophs Church, follow road 500m past Cherry Tree pub, turn left just before lights at bridge to Howards Field
Club Secretary: Adrian Carley, 50 Womersley Road, Knottingley, West Yorkshire
Tel: (H) 01977 677690
Fixtures Secretary: John Alexander
Tel: (H) 07899 732757
Club Colours: Blue & white shirts/ blue/ blue
League: Yorkshire 4

LEEDS CORINTHIANS RUFC
Ground Address: Nutty Slack, Middleton District Centre, Leeds. 10-4RA Tel: 0113 2711574
Brief Directions: M62 J28 to Leeds or M1 city centre to Dewsbury follow signs for A653, turn onto Middleton ringroad at Tommy Wass pub, right at 1st r'bout and go to rear of supermarket onto shale track to club
Club Secretary: Andrew Parker,16 Forsythia Avenue, East Ardsley, Wakefield.
WF3 2HT. Tel: 01924 823675
Fixtures Secretary: Graham Mapplebeck,46 Cranmore Crescent, Belle Isle , Leeds LS10 4AN
Tel: (H) 0113 2704935 (W) 0113 2457205
Club Colours: Black , gold and white.
League: Yorkshire 3

LEIGH RUFC
Ground Address: Round Ash Park, Hand Lane, Pennington, Leigh WN7 3NA
Tel: 01942 673526
Website:www. leighrufc .co.uk
Brief Directions: At the top of Hand Lane, which is off St. Helens Road in the Pennington area of Leigh.
Club Secretary: Alan J. Westwell, 140 Chestnut Drive South, Leigh, Lancs. WN7 3JY
Tel: 01942 671017

Fixtures Secretary: Tom Hughes, 2 Launceston Drive, Hindley Green, Wigan, Lancs.
Tel: (H) 01942 257427
Club Colours: Black and amber
Change Black and white
League: South Lancs & Cheshire 1

LEODIENSIAN RUFC
Ground Address: Crag Lane (off King Lane), Alwoodley, Leeds. LS17 5PR
Tel: 0113 2673409 Website: www. leodiensian.co.uk
Brief Directions: Leeds ringroad (outer) to Moortown Sainsburys, from Sainsburys travel away from Leeds on King Lane for 0.75 mile, ground on left hand side
Club Secretary: Iain Batchelor, 1 Sunningdale Green, Allwoodley, Leeds LS17 7SQ.
Tel: 0113 2681197 Email: secrtary@leodiensian.co.uk
Fixtures Secretary: Michael Crook Tel: (H) 01132 260455 (W) 01535 636116
Club Colours: Navy blue and gold
League: Yorkshire 2

LITTLEBOROUGH RUFC
Ground Address: Deep Lane, Rakewood, Hollingworth Lake, Littleborough, Lancashire.
OL15 0AP Tel: 01706 370220
Brief Directions: From Littleborough centre, under railway bridge. right turn signs for Hollingworth Lake. Turn between lake and Fisherman Pub, straight down lane 800yds on right.
Club Secretary: Stephen Blackburn, 2 Mount Avenue, Hurstead, Ridale,Lancs. OL12 9QE
Tel No: 01706 375489
Fixtures Secretary: Brent Pollitt, 36 Charlotte Street, Rochdale, Lancs. Tel No: 01706 341732
Club Colours: Black, yellow and green
League: North Lancs 2

LIVERPOOL COLLEGIATE OLD BOYS RUFC
Ground Address: Liverpool Cricket Club, Aigburth Rd., Grassendale, Liverpool.19
Brief Directions: M62 Follow Queens Drive to Aigburth Road (Ohone secretary if further details are needed)
Club Secretary: F.Carrol, 10 Mather Avenue, Allerton, Liverpool L18 5HS
Tel No: 0151 724 4756
Fixtures Secretary: L.Brown.24 Salisbury Road, Cressington Park, Liverpool L19 0PJ
Tel No: 0776 9585140
Club Colours: Light blue, dark blue quarters
League: South Lancs & Cheshire 4

LONSDALE WANDERERS
League: North Lancs 2
For further details contact:
North Lancs 2 League Secretary
Bill Hopkinson, Far Hey Head Farm, Littleborough, Rochdale Lancs OL15 9NS
Tel: 01706 379879

LOSTOCK RFC
Ground Address: Lostock Lane, Lostock, Bolton, Lancashire
Brief Directions: M61 J6, turn right at roundabout on A6027 towards Horwich, 1 mile on turn right before traffic lights, ground on left (Back of BAC car park.
Club Secretary: R Fletcher, 19 Shaftesbury Avenue, Lostock, Bolton Lancs., BL6 4AP
Tel: (H) 01204 698362
Fixtures Secretary: B.Jubb, 5 Lower Makinson Fold, Horwich, Bolton, Lancs., BLG 7PD
Tel: 01204 696998
Club Colours: All Black
League: North Lancs 2

LUCAS MERSEYSIDE RUFC
Ground Address: Walton Sports Centre, Walton Hall Ave, Walton, Liverpool 4
tel: 0151 523 3472
Brief Directions: The ground is situated at the very end of the A580 East Lancs Road, Liverpool.
Club Secretary: Peter Earle, 38 Mayfair Ave, Bowring Park, Liverpool 14 0JZ
Tel: 0151 489 5399
Fixtures Secretary: Ian Jennings, 13 Swanside Avenue, Liverpool 14   Tel: 0151 228 1684
Club Colours: Blue & Green Hoops with black shorts and socks.
League: South Lancs & Cheshire 5

LYMM RFC
Ground Address: Beechwood,Crouchley Lane, Lymm, Cheshire. WA13 0AT Tel: 01925 753212
Website: www.lymmrfc.free-on-line.co.uk
Brief Directions: M6 J20 to Lymm, 1.5 miles right at T junction, 0.5 mile turn right into Crouchley Lane, club 200 yds on right
Club Secretary: Mr. G. Kennedy, 3 Northway, Lymm, Cheshire, WA13 9AT Tel: 01925 754995
Fixtures Secretary: Chris Monks, 8 Newlands Road, Stockton Heath, Warrington WA4 2DS
Tel: (H) 01925 262904
Club Colours: Black, green, white
League: North 2 West

LYTHAM
Ground Address: Woodlands Memorial ground, Blackpool Road, Ansdell, Lytham St Annes, Lancashire. Fy8 4EL   Tel No: 01253 734 733
Brief Directions: Follow Lytham St Annes signs on B5230 at end of M55 then B5261 onto Queensway. Ground is three miles on left opposite 'Blossoms' public house and R.C.church.
Club Secretary: Sean Townsend, 26 Badgers Walk East, Lytham St Annes, Lancashire FY8 4BS
Tel No: 01253 737649
Fixtures Secretary: Grahame Benstead, 19 Wellington St, Lytham St Annes, Lancashire. FY8 5BZ   Tel No: 01253 736922
Club Colours: Claret , gold and white
League: North Lancs 1

MALTON & NORTON RUFC LTD
Ground Address: The Gannock, Old Malton, Malton, North Yorkshire, YO17 0EY.
Tel: 01653 694657
Website: www-norton-rfu.co.uk.
Brief Directions: From A64 York to Scarborough - take bypass and enter Malton on the Pickering road A169, club is on left after mini R/about. From Malton head towards Old Malton and club is on right
Club Secretary: Bill Laidler, `Ashdale', Beacon Park, Second Avenue, Pickering, North Yorks., YO18 8AH. Tel: 01751 472228.
Email: laidler@wlaidler.fsnet.co.uk.
Fixtures Secretary: As Club Secretary above.
Club Colours: Red, black and white hoops
League: Yorkshire 3

MANCHESTER WANDERERS RUFC
Ground Address: Grove Park, Grove Lane, Cheadle Hulme, Cheshire, SK8 7NB.
Brief Directions: From North-East: Exit 3 from M60. South on A.34 (signed Wilmslow) for 2.5 miles. At second R/about exist left on B5095. Ground is on the left 400-500 yards. From South-West: M6 to M56 (Manchester Airport). To A.34 South to B5095 Bramhall.
Club Secretary: Peter Luxton, 33 Bowdan Avenue, Hazel Grolve, Stockport, Cheshire, SK7 4LH. Tel: 0161 2851023
Fixtures Secretary: Cliff Williams, 45 Drive, Marple, Stockport, Cheshire. Tel: 0161 449 8325
Club Colours: Red & white quarters
League: South Lancs & Cheshire 4

MARIST RUFC
Ground Address: Cranbrook Avenue, Cottingham Road, Hull Tel: 01482 859216
Brief Directions: From M62 follow signs for Universities, then continue to Cranbrook Avenue along Cottingham Road
Club Secretary: Graham Barnett, 84 Eastfield Road, Hull, HU4 6DX.
Fixtures Secretary: Ralph Ayre, 92 Aukland Ave, Cottingham Rd, Hull HU6 Tel: (H) 01482 804166
Club Colours: Blue & white
League: Yorkshire 5

MARPLE RUFC
Ground Address: Wood Lane Playing Fields, Wood Lane, Marple, Stockport, Cheshire,
Brief Directions: Club House at Wood Lane Playing Fields. A626 into Marple, turn right into Cross Lane at Bowling Green Pub, turn right into Wood Lane. At Otters Lodge pub, go to end of road, club house on left at field.
Club Secretary: Stuart Budd, 143 Woodville Drive, Marple, Stockport, SK6 7RD.
Tel: 07968 089569 Email: stuart.bould@brfc.com
Fixtures Secretary: N Hawkley, 109 Woodville Drive, Marple , Stockport, SK6 7RD
Tel: 0161 366 0110
Club Colours: Red and black
League: South Lancs & Cheshire 3

NORTHERN

MEDICALS RFC
Ground Address: Cartington Terrace, Heaton, Newcastle Tel: 0191 2761473
Club Secretary: D.W.Reeve, 3 Station Road North, Forest Hall, Newcastle NE12 0AR.
Fixtures Secretary: Dr A Ramshaw, 19 Douglas Avenue, Gosforth, Newcastle NE3 4XD
Club Colours: Maroon with white shorts, maroon & white socks
League: Durham/Northumberland 2

MIDDLESBROUGH RUFC
Ground Address: Acklam Park, Green Lane, Middlesborough
Tel: 01642 818567
Brief Directions: A19, A11330 exit to M'bro, immediate left at fork, right at bollards onto Croft Ave, straight over traffic lights onto Green Lane, club 400yds on right
Club Secretary: Don Brydon, 20 Westwood Ave, Linthorpe, Middlesborough. TS5 5PY
Tel: (H) 01647 819954 (W) 01642 264047
Fixtures Secretary: J. Haddon, 5 Wycherley Avenue, Linthorp, Middlesbrough TS5 5HH
Tel: (H) 01287 637803
Club Colours: Maroon shirts, white shorts
League: North 1

MILLOM RUFC LTD
Ground Address: Wilson Park, Haverigg, Millom, Cumbria. LA18 4LU
Tel: 01229 770401
Brief Directions: Follow the coast road from the Harbour Hotel. Carry on past Inshore Rescue, the club is 150yds on the right
Club Secretary: G E Whitfield, 13 Willowside Park, Haverigg, Millom, Cumbria. LA18 4PT
Tel: (H) 01229 774876
Fixtures Secretary: Ian Shovelton, 10 Buttermere Drive, Millom, cumbria, LA18 4PL
Tel: (H) 01229 773743
Club Colours: Blue and white
League: Cumbria

MOORTOWN RUFC
Ground Address: Moss Valley, King Lane, Alwoodley, Leeds, West Yorkshire
Tel: 0113 2678243
Brief Directions: From the ring road turn up past the entrance to Sainsburys, 1.5 miles turn right onto The Avenue, 0.5 mile turn right into Far Moss
Club Secretary: Graham Spark, 7 Hall Cliffe Grove, Horbury, Wakefield. WF4 6DE.
Tel: (H) 01924 242753 e-mail: graham@gpspark screaming.net
Fixtures Secretary: Nick Webb, 8 Adel Wood Drive, Adel, Leeds. LS16 8ES
Tel: 0113 2677833 e-mail: nwebb@speedprint.co.uk
Club Colours: Maroon with green and white hoops, blue shorts.
League: Yorkshire 4

MORESBY RUFC
Ground Address: Walkmill Park, Old Pit Road, Moresby Parks, Whitehaven, Cumbria
Tel: 01946 695984
Brief Directions: M6 Junction 40 (Penrith) A66 for 35 miles. Turn left onto A595 for approx 7 miles, then left up Swallow Brow. Ground is approx 2 miles.
Club Secretary: Thomas Callan, 15 Burton High Close, Harras Moor Park, Whitehaven, Cumbria CA28 6SD Tel: 01946 694583
Fixtures Secretary: Syd Bray, 19 Sneckyeat Road, Hensingham, Cumbria Tel: 01946 694199
Club Colours: Red shirts, white shorts
League: Cumbria

MORPETH RFC
Ground Address: Grange House Field, Mitford Road, Morpeth. NE61 1RJ Tel: 01670 512508
Brief Directions: North from Newcastle on A1 from Morpeth centre travelling north, left after telephone exchange onto Mitford Road, entrance on right past the school
Club Secretary: Ken Fraser, Solway House, De Merley Road, Morpeth. NE61 1HZ
Tel: (H) 01670 511208 (W) 01670 353016 (W)
e-mail: fraser@ macmillan-ctc.org.uk
Fixtures Secretary: Bill Hewitt, The Birches, Lane End Farm, Felton, Northumberland NE65 9NY Tel: (H) 01670 787755
Club Colours: Red, white & navy irregular hoops
League: North 2 East

MOSBOROUGH RUFC
Ground Address: Mosborough WMC, Station Road, Mosborough, Sheffield, S20.
Tel: 0114 248 5546
Brief Directions: M1 J30, take A616 towards Sheffield, at 2nd set of lights turn right, clubhouse on left 50m.
Club Secretary: Miss Louise Cameron, 8 Stone Street,Mosborough, Sheffield. S20 5AA
Tel: 0114 2489873
Email: louise.cameron@dfee.gov.uk
Fixtures Secretary: John Staton, 10 Westfield Crescent, Mosborough, Sheffield S20 5AQ
Tel: 01142 489705
Club Colours: Black and red
League: Yorkshire 4

MOSSLEY HILL RUFC
Ground Address: Mossley Hill Athletic Club, Mossley Hill Road, Liverpool 18
Tel: 0151 7244377
Brief Directions: From M62 take ring road towards Liverpool Airport. Turn left onto Allerton Road, right onto Rose Lane (at Tescos) Ground is behind Mossley Hill Church at top of Rose Lane.
Club Secretary: Andy Pealing, 48 Heathfield Park, Widnes, Cheshire. WA8 9WY.
Tel: 0151 423 1821
Fixtures Secretary: John Parr, 30 Ridgtor Road, Liverpool 25   Tel: (H) 0151 428 7625
Club Colours: Maroon and gold quarters
League: South Lancs & Cheshire 5

NETHERHALL
Ground Address: Netherhall Park, Netherhall Road, Maryport
Brief Directions: A66 to Cockermouth Head to Workington, right at roundabout for Maryport, turn left off bypass head into Maryport, right at lights A596 to Carlisle, club 400yds on right
Club Secretary: Paul Bartlett, 66 Garborough Close, Crosby, Maryport. CA15 6RZ
Tel: (H) 01900 818420
Fixtures Secretary: L Rumney
Tel: (H) 01900 811440
Club Colours: Claret and gold
League: North Lancs & Cumbria

NEWTON AYCLIFFE RUFC
Ground Address: Newton Aycliffe Sports Club, Moore Lane, Newton Aycliffe, Co. Durham. DL5 5AG Tel: 01325 312768
Brief Directions: Enter Newton Aycliffe on Central Ave, at the roundabout turn L. on Shafto Way take 3rd L. (Creighton Rd) then lst R. Moore Lane, carry on to end of the road. Opposite Wacky Warehouse A167
Club Secretary: Mrs. Sue Adams, 35 Holly Hill, Shildon, Co. Durham, DL4 2DB.
Tel: 01388 774669 or 07973 306629
Fixtures Secretary: Mr Charles Heslop, 35 Holly Hill, Shildon, Co. Durham, DL4 2DB.
Tel: 01388 774669
Club Colours: Gold, Maroon and Green Hoops
League: Durham/Northumberland 3

NEWTON-LE -WILLOWS RUFC
Ground Address: Crow Lane East, Newton-le-Willows, Merseyside
Tel: 01925 224591
Brief Directions: M6 J23, take signs for Newton A49, continue down Ashton Rd (A49) until mini roundabout with Oak Tree pub on right, right into Crow Lane, club 300 yds on right
Club Secretary: David Hughes, 127 Birley St., Newton-le-Willows, Merseyside Wa12 9UN.
Tel no: 01925 221304
Fixtures Secretary: Steve Kruger, 2 Camelot Close, Newton-le-Willows, Merseyside.
Tel No: 01925 221937
Club Colours: Royal blue and gold hoops
League: South Lancs & Cheshire 3

NORTH MANCHESTER & OLDHAM COLLEGES RUFC
Ground Address: Greengate/Victoria Avenue East, Moston, Manchester
Tel: 0161 682 9234
Club Secretary: Brian H Stott, 8 Barlea Avenue, New Moston, Manchester. M40 3WL
Tel: (H) 0161 682 0541 (W) 0161 681 1582
Fixtures Secretary: Jason Malone
Tel: (H) 0161 653 5020
Club Colours: Green, black and white hoops
League: North Lancs 2

NORTH RIBBLESDALE RUFC
Ground Address: Grove Park, Lower Greenfoot, Settle, North Yorkshire Tel: 01729 822755
Brief Directions: Leave A65 at roundabout on southern outskirts of town, into town turning right at Falcon Manor Hotel, ground 0.25 mile on left
Club Secretary: Chris Sharpe, Flat 2, 34 Duke Street, Settle, North Yorks, BD24 9AN. Tel: 01535 636694 Email: cvsharpe@lineone.net
Fixtures Secretary: D. Brown, 4 East view, Settle, North Yorks., BD24 9AU.
Tel Nos: 01729 824041 (H) 07812958940 (M)
Club Colours: Royal blue and white.
League: Yorkshire 1

NORTH SHIELDS RFC
Ground Address: Preston Playing Fields, Preston Village, North Shields, Tyne & Wear
Tel: 0191 257 7352
Brief Directions: From Tyne Tunnel (south) or A1/A19 (north) take A1058, follow signs for Tynemouth, club is situated next to Tynemouth Swimming Baths
Club Secretary: David Daniels, 1 Highcross Road, North Shields, Tyne & Wear, NE30 3JG.
Tel: (H) 0191 252 6395 (W) 0191 253 1329
Fixtures Secretary: A,G, Shield, 9 Cresswell Avenue, North Shields, Tyne & Wear NE29 9BQ
Tel No: 0191 259 0402
Club Colours: Royal blue and white hoops
League: Durham/Northumberland 2

NORTHALLERTON RUFC
Ground Address: Brompton Lodge, Northallerton Road, Brompton, Northallerton, N. Yorks. DL6 2PZ
Tel: 01609 773496
Brief Directions: Brompton Road. Left at filling station. Club 1/4 mile on left.
Club Secretary: David Middlemiss, 13 Quaker Lane, Northhallerton, Yorks.
Tel: (H) 01609 779945
Email: david.middlemiss@genie.co.uk
Fixtures Secretary: Alan Bradley, 15 Borrowby Ave., Northallerton, N. Yorkshire.
Tel: (H) 01609 772743
Club Colours: Green, amber and white
League: Yorkshire 2

NORTHERN FOOTBALL CLUB
Ground Address: McCracken Park, Great North Road, Gosforth, Newcastle upon Tyne. NE3 2DG
Tel: 0191 236 3369
Brief Directions: From south & west, A1 western bypass north, take 'city north/Gosforth B1318' for 0.75 mile, ground on left. From north take B1318 from A1, ground 0.75 mile on left
Club Secretary: R M Gibson, c/o Northern FC
Fixtures Secretary: Richard Kain, 13 Polworth Road, Brunton park, Newcastle upon Tyne NE3 5ND Tel: (H) 0191 217 0362
Club Colours: Navy, Red and White shirts, navy shorts, red socks
League: North 2 East

NORTHERN

NORTHWICH RUFC
Ground Address: Moss Farm Reception Centre, Moss Farm, Moss Road, Winnington, Northwich, Cheshire. Tel: 01606 79984
Brief Directions: Follow directions from Northwich town centre to swimming pool
Club Secretary: Dave Sargeant, 12 Sydney Street, Greenbank, Northwich, CW8 4AP. Tel: (H) 01606 783335 - Wmail: dsargey@hotmail.com
Fixtures Secretary: Paul Hughes, 14 Woodland Road, Hartford, Northwich, CW8 1NS
Tel: (H) 01606 76817
Club Colours: All black
League: South Lancs & Cheshire 1

NOVOCASTRIANS RFC LTD
Ground Address: Sutherland Park, The Drive, High Heaton, Newcastle upon Tyne.
NE7 7SY Tel: 0191 2661247
Website: www.novocastriansrfc.co.uk
Brief Directions: From A19 or Newcastle Central Motorway take A6127M and A1058 signed Newcastle - Tynemouth. Exit on slip road A188 to Killingworth. NVOS. RFC signs at The Drive. Club on left.
Club Secretary: Brian Chater, 100 Malvern Road, Preston Grange, North Shields, Tyne & Wear. NE29 9ES Tel: (H) 0191 2576885
Fixtures Secretary: Bob Fay
Tel: (H) 0191 4873393 (W) 0191 3862714
Club Colours: Red, black and white hoops
League: Durham/Northumberland 3

OLD ANSELMIANS RUFC
Ground Address: Malone Field, Eastham Village Road, Eastham, Wirral, Cheshire.
Tel: 0151 327 1613
Brief Directions: M53 J5, take A41 towards Birkenhead, take 1st road on right into the village stay on that road until you come to the ground on the left hand side.
Club Secretary: Trevor Petterson, 102 Princes Boulevard, Higher Bebbington, Wirral, Cheshire, CH63 5LP. Tel: 0151 608 1540.
Email: petterst@email-msn.co.uk
Fixtures Secretary: Tony McArdle, 18 Greenbank Drive, Heswall, Wirral, Cheshire, CH61 5UF.
Tel: 0151 342 1470
Club Colours: Blue, gold and white
League: South Lancs & Cheshire 2

OLD BEDIANS RFC
Ground Address: Underbank Farm, Millgate Lane, East Didsbury, Manchester. M20 5QX
Tel: 0161 445 8862
Club Secretary: Ian Wilson, 7 Brooklands Close, Denton, Manchester. M34 3PL
Tel: (H) 0161 445 8862 (W) 0161 287 7760 (Fax) 0161 287 7761
Fixtures Secretary: G Tucker
Tel: (H) 0161 445 2358
Club Colours: Navy blue shirts, white shorts
League: North Lancs 1

OLD BRODLEIANS RUFC
Ground Address: Woodhead, Denholme Gate Road, Hipperholme, Halifax
Tel: 01422 202708
Brief Directions: M62 J26, follow A58 signs to Halifax, after 3.75 miles turn right at Hippodrome lights, continue up hill for 0.5 mile, club on left about 250 yds after Shell petrol station
Club Secretary: Mr Simon Heaton, Sutcliffe Wood Farm, Woodbottom Lane, Hove Edge, Brighouse. HD6 2QW Tel: (H) 01484 721628
Email: sheaton@heaton-valnes.co.uk
Fixtures Secretary: Mr M Hey, 2 Sunnybank Cres., Sowerby Bridge, Halifax.
Tel: (H) 01422 839614
Club Colours: Black, red and white shirts, black shorts
League: Yorkshire 1

OLD CROSSLEYANS RUFC
Ground Address: Standeven House, Broomfield Avenue, Halifax, West Yorkshire. HX3 0JF Tel: 01422 363000
Brief Directions: M62 Exit 24. A629 towards Halifax at 4th set of lights. Left at A646 towards Rochdale /Burnley. Left at second mini round-about. (Birdcage Lane).
Club Secretary: Richard A Davies, 4 Warley Dene, Holme Road, Warley, Halifax, West Yorks. HX2 7RS Tel: (H) 01422 832218
Fixtures Secretary: Derek Ainley, 1 Savile Heath, Manaor Heath Road, Halifax.
Tel: (H) 01422 368233
Club Colours: Blue, white and amber
League: North 2 East

OLD MODERNIANS RUFC
Ground Address: The Clubhouse, Cookridge Lane, Cookridge, Leeds, West Yorkshire. LS16 7ND Tel: 0113 267 1075
Brief Directions: A660 north from Leeds until 1/4 mile past junction with A6120 ring road at Lawnswood. Fork left at Cookridge, ground 2 miles on right
Club Secretary: J.C,Bracewell, 8 Holly Park, Huby, Leeds, LS17 0BT
Tel No: 01423 734782
Fixtures Secretary: D Carter Tel: (H) 0113 267 9718
Club Colours: Red and black hoops shirts and socks, black shorts
League: Yorkshire 4

OLD OTLIENSIANS RUFC
Ground Address: Chaffer's Field, Pool Road, Otley, West Yorkshire LS21
Tel: 01943 461476
Brief Directions: From Otley town centre, take A659 to Harrogate, turn right at Smiths Garden Centre, follow sign to clubhouse
Club Secretary: David Beardsley, 56 Birdcage Court, Otley, West Yorkshire, LS21 3HH. Tel: 01943 466362

NORTHERN

Fixtures Secretary: Adrian Normanton, 26 Roseberry Crescent, Great Ayton, Middlesborough, TS9 6ER Tel: 01642 723199H 01642 467144W
Email: adrian.normanton@corusgroup.com
Club Colours: Navy blue, royal blue and white narrow hoops
League: Yorkshire 3
Contact: Brian Webster, 6 Holt Gardens, Church Lane, Adel, Leeds, LS16 8HP. Tel: 01132 678618

OLD RISHWORTHIAN RUFC
Ground Address: The Clubhouse, Copley, Halifax, West Yorkshire. HX3 0UG
Tel: 01422 353919 Website: www.singlevision.co.uk/orrufc
Brief Directions: M62 J24 follow signs to Halifax, down Long Hill to Dual Carriageway at 1st set of lights turn left over mini R/about signed Sowerby Bridge, enter Copley, turn left at Volunteer pub, club on left in half a mile.
Club Secretary: D W Butler, Keepens, Shaw Lane, Holywell Green, Halifax. HX4 9DH. Tel: (H) 01422 371672 (W)0113 204 3300
Email: lovebutler@singlevision.co.uk
Fixtures Secretary: R Wadsworth, Abbotsroyd Cottage, Rochdale Rd, Barkisland, Halifax, West Yorks. Tel: (H) 01422 822113 (W) 01484 845740
Club Colours: Maroon, white and black hoops
League: Yorkshire 4

OLDERSHAW RUFC
Ground Address: Belvidere Recreation Ground, Belvidere Road, Wallasey, Cheshire.
Tel: 0151 638 4379
Brief Directions: J.1 M53 to New Brighton, turn 2nd R. after golf club, 2nd L. into Grove Rd, turn R. at traffic lights. Ground is half mile on right hand side.
Club Secretary: Mr. A. P. Grabe, 19 Beresford Road, Wallasey, Cheshire, CH45 0JJ.
Tel: 0151 5131470H - 0151 5129535W.
Fixtures Secretary: Mr Peter Purland. 63 Croxteth Road, Liverpool, L8 3SF.
Tel: 0151 733 4854 H
Club Colours: Navy blue with gold hoops
League: South Lancs & Cheshire 1

OLDHAM RUFC
Ground Address: Manor Park, Bryth Road, Bardsley, Oldham. OL8 2TJ
Tel: 0161 624 6383
Brief Directions: Off the main A627 Oldham to Ashton road, behind Bardsley Church
Club Secretary: T J Brown, 12 Tilton Street, Oldham. OL1 4JA
Tel: (H) 0161 620 1878 (W) 0161 624 4167
Fixtures Secretary: T Park, 79 Crofton Avenue, Timperley, Cheshire
Tel: 0161 962 0781 (H) 0161 624 4167(W)
Club Colours: Red and white hoops , navy shorts
League: North Lancs & Cumbria

ORMSKIRK RUFC
Ground Address: Green Lane, Ormskirk, Lancs. L39 1ND   Tel: 01695 572523
Brief Directions: Adjacent A59 at junction with A570 opposite the Fiveways Pub.
Club Secretary: R.A.Spencer, 62 New Lane, Aughton, Ormskirk, Lancs. L394UD.
Tel: 01695 421186
Fixtures Secretary: A.Barton. Tel : 01257 253051 (H) 0771 3974981(M)
Club Colours: Dark green with light green and navy blue hoops
League: South Lancs & Cheshire 1

ORRELL ANVILS
Ground Address: Edge Hall Road, Church Street, Wigan, WN5 8TL. Tel: 01942 623193
Brief Directions: M6, Junction 26, follow signs for Orrell club.
Club Secretary: Eric Wilkinson, 60 Winstanley Road, Billinge, Wigan, WN5 7XD.
Tel: 01695 622813 - Email: eric@wilconet.freeserve.co.uk
Fixtures Secretary: Mel Parker, 2 Warrington Road, Golborne-le-Dale, Newton-le-Willows. Tel: 01925 226679
Club Colours: Black & Amber
League: South Lancs & Cheshire 3

OSSETT RUFC
Ground Address: Ossett Cricket and Athletic Club, Springmill, Queens Terrace, Ossett, West Yorkshire Tel: 01924 273618
Club website: www.users.totalise.co.uk~ossett-rufc
Brief Directions: M1 J40, A638 to Wakefield, right at 1st lights, turn right up to Spring Mill after 0.5 mile
Club Secretary: P.A.Taylor, 10 Grange Drive, Ossett, W.Yorks WF5 0SH
Tel: 01924 276800 e-mail: tays@tinyonline.co.uk
Fixtures Secretary: I Whitehead, 20 Westfield Street, Ossett, W.Yorks WF5 8JE.
Tel: 01924 274345
Club Colours: Black shirts with narrow red and white hoops, black shorts
League: Yorkshire 5

OSWESTRY RFC
Ground Address: Park Hall, Oswestry
Tel: 01691 652949
Brief Directions: From Chester area take A483/A5 .Turn left at A495 ,next left150 meteres. Club is at end of lane
Club Secretary: Jim Pickard, 12 Hampton Rise, Oswestry, Shropshire SY11 1ST
Tel No: 01691 654899
Fixtures Secretary: Mark Hemming, Oakfield House, Morda House, Oswestry SY11 2AU. Tel No : 01691 652912
Club Colours: Black and red hoops, black shorts and red socks
League: South Lancs & Cheshire 4

PARKONIANS RUFC

Ground Address: H Martin Curphey Memorial Ground, Holm Lane, Oxton, Birkenhead, Wirral, Merseyside. L43 2HU   Tel: 0151 652 3105
Brief Directions: M53 J3, A552 for Birkenhead, turn off into Holm Lane at the Swan Hotel, club is 200m on left
Club Secretary: Mr P L Mullen, 8 Deerwood Crescent, Little Sutton, South Wirral. L66 1SE
Tel: (H) 0151 339 1270 (W) 0151 448 6280
Fixtures Secretary: Mr E Potter
Tel: (W) 0151 609 0202
Club Colours: Maroon, blue and white
League: South Lancs & Cheshire 4

PENRITH RUFC

Ground Address: Winters Park, Penrith, Cumbria CA11 4RG.
Tel: 01768 863151 (Secretary) - 01768 843462 (Steward)
Brief Directions: M6 J40, A66 east for 0.5 mile, A686 east for 0,5 mile, PRUFC on left just past Police HQ
Club Secretary: Keith Davis, Ivy Bank, 59 Lowther Street, Penrith, Cumbria. CA11 7UQ
Tel: (H) 01768 866089
Fixtures Secretary: Willie Mounsey, The Luham, Edenhall, Penrith, Cumbria.
Tel: (H) 01768 881202
Club Colours: Myrtle green and white hoops
League: North Lancs & Cumbria

PERCY PARK RFC

Ground Address: Percy Park RFC, The Clubhouse, Preston Avenue, North Shields, Tyne & Wear. NE29 Tel: 0191 2575710
Brief Directions: From A19 (north or south) take A1058 Coast road signed East Tynemouth & North Shields. Turn right onto Preston North Road immediately after Swimming Baths and 3rd left is Preston Avenue where the ground is on the left.
Club Secretary: A C Baker, 30 The Garth, Winlaton, Tyne & Wear. NE21 6DD
Tel: (W) 0191 4144869 (Fax) 0191 4148672
Fixtures Secretary: Andy Donaghy, 71 Davison Avenue, Whitley Bay, Tyne & Wear, NE26 3ST.
Tel: 0191 2534689
Club Colours: Black and white hoops
League: Durham/Northumberland 1

POCKLINGTON RUFC

Ground Address: Percy Road, Pocklington, East Yorkshire. YO4 2QB   Tel: 01759 303358
Brief Directions: Pocklington is situated 13 miles east of York off the A1079 towards Hull, ground located near town centre
Club Secretary: Ian Johnston, Fern Lea, 39 Percy Road, Pocklington, East Yorks.. YO4 2LZ
Tel: (H) 01759 302967
Fixtures Secretary: Adrian Wilson
Tel: (H) 01759 305014
Club Colours: Navy and white quarters
League: Yorkshire 1

PONTEFRACT PYTHONS

League: Yorkshire 6
For further details contact
Yorkshire 6 League Secretary
Kathleen McNally, 28 Cherry Tree Road, Armthorpe, Doncaster, Yorks DN3 2HP
Tel: 01302 834252

PONTEFRACT RFC

Ground Address: Moor Lane, Carleton, Pontefract, West Yorkshire. WF8 3RX
Tel: 01977 702650
Brief Directions: Exit A1 at Darrington, follow signs for Pontefract, 2 miles to Moor Lane which is 1st left after 30mph sign on outskirts of Pontefract
Club Secretary: S.J.Trigg, 52 Hadleigh Rise, Pontefract, West Yorkshire. WF8 4SJ
Tel: 01977 703786
Fixtures Secretary: D.L.Handle, 7 Mill Hill Close, Darrington, Pontefract
Tel No: 01977 704615
Club Colours: All royal blue.
League: Yorkshire 1

PONTELAND RFC

Ground Address: Ponteland Leisure Centre, Callerton Lane, Ponteland, Northumberland. NE20 9EG   Tel: 01661 825441
Brief Directions: From north or south, enter village via A696, at lights by Diamond Inn turn to follow river, entrance to Sports Centre 150 yards on left just after zebra crossing
Club Secretary: D.Whaley, 72 Cheviot View, Ponteland, Northumberland. NE20 9BW
Tel No: 01661 820425
Fixtures Secretary: T.W.Snaith, 17 Glebe Crescent, Forest Hall, Newcastle, NE12 7JR.. Tel No: 0191 2689315
Club Colours: Maroon shirts with a black and white hoop, white shorts, maroon socks with a white top
League: Durham/Northumberland 3

PORT SUNLIGHT RFC LTD

Ground Address: Leverhulme Playing Fields, Green Lane, Bromborough, Wirral Ch62 3PU Tel: 0151 334 3677
Website: portsunlightrfc.merseyside.orghttp://
Brief Directions: A41 Bromborough at T/light turn into Old Hall Road, at R/about 3rd exit into Riverwood Road, take 1st right into lane signed PSRFC
Club Secretary: Mrs Louise Outram, 30 June Avenue. Bromborough, Wirral Ch62 6EB. Tel No: 0151 334 2349
Emailk: greystones@tingworld.co.uk
Fixtures Secretary: Alan Corfe, 10 Brinley Close, Bromborough, Wirral. CH62 6EB
Tel NO: 0151 327 5732
Club Colours: Black and white narrow hoops
League: South Lancs & Cheshire 4

PRENTON RUFC
Ground Address: The Clubhouse, Prenton Dell, Prenton Dell Road, Prenton, Wirral, Merseyside. L43 3BS   Tel: 0151 608 1501
Brief Directions: M53 Jct 3 Follow signs to Birkenhead. Pass under railway bridge(A551) 200 yds sign for golf range, Preston Dell Rd with club entrance half a mile on right.
Club Secretary: Mr. C. McHugh, 85 Arrowe Park Road, Upton, Wirral, Merseyside, CH49 0UG.
Fixtures Secretary: Paul Bennett, 2 Aston Wood Road, Birkenhead L42 6DJ
Tel : 0151 7644 9775
Club Colours: Maroon, gold and black
League: South Lancs & Cheshire 4

PRESCOT
Ground Address: Rainhill High School, Warrington Road, Rainhill
Brief Directions: From M62, J7 take road to Rainhill. School is situated on right hand side.
Club Secretary: Kevin O'Keefe, 39 French St., St. Helens WA10 3DT
Tel: 01744 616683 (H) 01695 50123 (B)
Fixture Secretary: John Carney, 54 Leslie Rd., St. Helens.   Tel: 01744 752715 (H)
Club Colours:
League Contact: John Carney, as above
League: South Lancs & Cheshire 5

RAWMARSH RUFC
Ground Address: Rawmarsh Leisure Centre, Barbers Avenue, Rawmarsh, Rotherham, South Yorkshire Tel: 01709 719952
Brief Directions: From Sheffield or Doncaster approach the Rotherham ring road.Take A630 and enquire at Mushroom Garage.
Club Secretary: Eric Perkins, 21 Harding Avenue, Rawmarsh, Rotherham, South Yorkshire, S62 7ED. Tel: 01709 526786
Fixtures Secretary: Eric Perkins, 21 Harding Avenue, Rawmarsh, Rotherham.
Tel: (H) 01709 526786
Club Colours: Black, maroon and amber hoops. Change: Black & amber.
League: Yorkshire 5

REDCAR RUFC
Ground Address: McKinlay Park, Green Lane, Redcar. TS10 3RW
Tel: 01642 482733 (FAX) 01642 480830
Brief Directions: From A19 take A174 east towards Saltburn, take 2nd left (B1269), over level crossing, 1st right to coast road, continue to Green Lane on right at end of houses
Club Secretary: Hugh Bernard,97 Oak Road, Redcar TS10 3PS   Tel No; 01642 486688
Email: hhhb97@hotmail.com
Fixtures Secretary: Dave Pearson, 36 Henry Street, Redcar, Cleveland
Tel: 01642 473786
Club Colours: Black and Red
League: North 2 East

RICHMONDSHIRE RUFC
Ground Address: The Playing Fields, Theakston Lane, Richmond, North Yorkshire. DL10 4LL
Tel: 01748 850515
Brief Directions: A6136 out of Richmond, pass bus station approx 500 yards turn right, club situated on left approx 100 yards from junction
Club Secretary: Mr Russell Lord, 12 Whitefields Walk, Richmond, North Yorkshire. DL10 7DE Tel: (H) 01748 824273 (W) 01904 525844
Fixtures Secretary: Bob Dixon
Tel: (H) 01748 825360
Club Colours: Red, yellow and white hoops
League: Durham/Northumberland 4

RIPON RUFC
Ground Address: Mallorie Park, Ripon, North Yorkshire. HG4 2QD   Tel: 01765 604675
Brief Directions: Mallorie Park is off main Ripon - Pateley Bridge Road, follow signs for Pateley Bridge via Skellbank
Club Secretary: M P P Viner,Golden Hill House, Barton le Willows, York YO60 7PD
Tel: 01653 619282 (H) 07799408223 (M)
Email: mijovin963@supanet.com
Fixtures Secretary: A W Proud, 1 Ure Bank Terrace, Ripon, North Yorkshire, HG4 1JG
Tel: (H) 01765 605474 (W) 0113 292 6846 (M) 0467 318069
Colours: White, light & dark blue narrow hoops
League: Yorkshire 2

ROCHDALE RUFC
Ground Address: Moorgate Avenue, Bamford, Rochdale, Lancs. OL11 5LU
Tel: 01706 46863
Brief Directions: From Rochdale: B6222 to Bury past Cemetary Hotel, Moorgate Ave 3rd on right. From M62: J20 A627(M) to Rochdale, over 2nd r'bout B6452 left into B6222 at Cemetary Hotel
Club Secretary: John McManus, 27 Hunstanton Drive, Brandlesholme, Bury, Lancs. BL8 1EG
Tel: (H) 0161 761 4371 (W) 0161 740 4993 (F) 795 8094
Fixtures Secretary: Michael Deasey
Tel: (H) 01706 356094 (W) 01706 353208
Club Colours: Maroon and white hoops
League: North Lancs & Cumbria

ROSSENDALE RFC
Ground Address: Marl Pits Sports Centre, Newchurch Road, Rawtenstall, Rossendale, Lancashire Tel: 01706 229152
Brief Directions: A56, onto Newchurch Road at the market. Ground 1 mile up on the leflt.
Club Secretary: Alec Graham, Long MNeadow, 636 Newchurch Road, Rawtenstall, BB4 9HG.
Tel: 01706 225078
Fixtures Secretary: T erence Kelly, 111 Broadway, Haslingden, Lancs.
Tel: 01706 217361
Club Colours: Maroon and white
League: North Lancs & Cumbria

NORTHERN

ROTHERHAM CLIFTON
Ground Address: Change at Rotherham Rugby Club and play on Hemingthorpe PLaying Fields.
Brief Directions: M1 Jct 33. Follow Rotherway for 1/2 mile to roundabout. Take 2nd exit for Bawtry.AtTraffic lights straight on up hill to roundabout. First left to town centre and ground is 1 mile on right.
Club Secretary: Paul C Richardson, 22 Boswell Street, Broom, Rotherham S65 2ED. Tel No: 01709 517823
Fixtures Secretary: As above
Club Colours: Maroon & Sky Blue Hoops, navy blue shorts.
League: Yorkshire 5

ROUNDHEGIANS RUFC
Ground Address: Memorial Ground, Chelwood Drive, Roundhay, Leeds. LS8 2AT
Tel: 0113 266 7377
Brief Directions: A61 to junction with Street Lane, follow Street Lane towards Roundhay Park, Chelwood Drive is a road off Street Lane
Club Secretary: D.J.Matthews, 32 Woodhall Road, Calverley, Leeds LS28 5PP
Tel: 0113 2557623
e-mail: david @ flankers.freeserve.co.uk
Fixtures Secretary: Stafford Smart,Laurendene, Harrogate Rd.,Huby, Leeds.W17 0EF
Tel No: 01423734803
Club Colours: Green, black and white hoops
League: Yorkshire 3

RUNCORN RFC
Ground Address: Halton Sports, Murdishaw Avenue, Runcorn. WA7 6HP
club website: www.runcornrfc.co.uk
Brief Directions: M56,A56,A533, Runcorn,Murdishaw,Halton Arms Pub off Murdishaw Avenue.
Club Secretary: Jeff Gore, 26 Tarnbeck, Norton, Runcorn, Cheshire WA7 6SF
Tel: (H) 01928 712284
e-mail: jeffgore@saltunion.com
Fixtures Secretary: Tony Elliot. Tel No: 01928 715091
Club Colours: Blue and white hoops & blue and white quarters
League: South Lancs & Cheshire 2

RUSKIN PARK RUFC
Ground Address: Ruskin Drive, St Helens, Merseyside   Tel: 01744 22893
Brief Directions: Turn off A580 onto A570 towards St Helens. Travel approx one mile and turn right into Dentons Green Lane. Ruskin Drive is 400 yards on left.
Club Secretary: Brian Ball, 10 Broadway, Eccleston, St.Helens, Lancs WA10 5DE
Tel No: 01744 611955
Email: b.j.ball@btinternet.com
Fixtures Secretary: Barry Loftus, Prescot Road, St Helens, Merseyside.   Tel No: 01744 608578

Email: barry.loftus@btclick.com
Club Colours: Blue with black and white band
League: South Lancs & Cheshire 3

RYTON RFC
Ground Address: Main Road, Barmoor, I Ryton, Tyne & Wear. NE40 3AG
Tel: 0191 413 3820
Brief Directions: On B6317 road to the west of Ryton, B6317 Ryton Road signposted from A695
Club Secretary: Gordon Wright, 57 Middle Row, Stargate, Ryton ,Tyne & Wear NE40 3EE
Tel 0191 4131986 Mobile 07931 860858
Email: gordon.wright1@btinternet.com
Fixtures Secretary: Ian Nesbitt, 118 Middle Drive, Ponteland, Newcastle upon Tyne NE20 9DW
Tel: 01661 823629
Club Colours: Royal blue or green
League: Durham/Northumberland 1

SANDBACH RUFC
Ground Address: Bradwall Road, Sandbach, Cheshire. CW11 9AP   Tel: 01270 762475
Website: www.sandbachrufc.co.uk
Brief Directions: M6 J17, follow signs for Sandbach, turn right by Texaco garage. Turn right on to Offley Rd, turn right signed Bradwall, club 400 yards on right
Club Secretary: Andy Maddock, 40 Mortimer Drive, Sandbach, Cheshire. CW11 4HS
Tel: (H) 01270 759538
Email: secretary @sandbachrufc.co
Fixtures Secretary: George Elphick, Biddulph Park Farm, Troughstones Road, Biddulph, Staffordshire, ST8 7SJ. Tel No: 01782 510751
Club Colours: Green and red
League: South Lancs & Cheshire 2

SCARBOROUGH RUFC
Ground Address: The Clubhouse, Scalby Road, Scarborough, North Yorkshire. YO12 6EE
Tel: 01723 363039
Brief Directions: Main Whitby Road out of Scarborough, approx 2 miles
Club Secretary: Mrs S E Hanson, c/o The Clubhouse, Scalby Road, Scarborough, North Yorkshire, YO12 6EE. Tel: (W) 01723 363039
Fixtures Secretary: J. B. Beanland c/o club address. Tel: (H & Fax) 01723 367023
Club Colours: Maroon, navy and white
League: Yorkshire 1

SEAHAM RUFC
Ground Address: New Olrive Playing Fields Club, 27 Cornelia Terrace, Seaham, Co Durham
Tel: 0191 581 2331
Brief Directions: Come down A19 or A1, follow signs for Seaham, once in Seaham follow signs for harbour and ask for directions to club (everyone knows where it is)
Club Secretary: Mrs Carol Pinter, 37 Stavordale St., Dawdonn, Seaham Co.Durham SR 7 7LS
Tel: (W) 01915 815836

Fixtures Secretary: Alan Mason
Tel: (H) 0191 520 0282 (W) 0191 279 4342
Club Colours: Red jersey, white shorts, red socks
League: Durham/Northumberland 4

SEATON CAREW RUFC
Ground Address: Seaton Carew Sports Club
,Hornby Park, Elizabeth Way, Seaton Carew,
Hartlepool. TS25 2AZ Tel: 01429 260945
Brief Directions: From A19 take A689 to
Hartlepool, right at Owton Lodge pub onto B1276
to Seaton Carew seafront area, turn right and go
along seafront past golf club, club on right in
Elizabeth Way.
Club Secretary: Paul McManus, 9 Ruswarp
Grove, Seaton Carew, Hartlepool. TS25 2BA Tel:
(H) 01429 296327 (W) 01429 268821
Fixtures Secretary: Andrew Sedgwick. Tel Nos:
01429 261995 (H) 01429 266544 (W) 01429
524411(Fax)
Club Colours: Maroon and amber hooped shirts&
socks, black shorts
League: Durham/Northumberland 3

SEFTON RUFC
Ground Address: Thornhead Lane, Leyfield
Road, West Derby, Liverpool. L12 9EY
Tel: 0151 228 9092
Brief Directions: End of M62 take A5058 towards
Bootle, at A57 turn right, left at lights, right in front
of hospital, left at Bulldog pub (Leyfield Road),
right into lane by electricity substation
Club Secretary: Roy Spencer, 8 Stoneycroft
Close, Liverpool L13 0AT.Tel: (H) 0151 228 9833
Fixtures Secretary: B Houghton
Tel: (H) 0151 428 3740
Club Colours: Red and white hooped
shirts/socks, blue shorts
League: South Lancs & Cheshire 3

SEGHILL RFC
Ground Address: Welfare Park, Seghill,
Cramlington, Northumberland
Tel: 0191 2370414
Brief Directions: A19 through Tyne Tunnel, take
sliproad for Seghill, right at junction, left at next
junction, right at mini r'bout then 2nd left, right at T
junction, car park 150yds on right
Club Secretary: Sheila Burgess, 19 Chester
Grove, Seghill, Northumberland. Ne23 7TR Tel
No: 0191 2374056
Fixtures Secretary: Geoffrey Fenwick, 20
Wheatfield Grove, Benton , Newcastle
Tel: (H) 0191 2665146
Club Colours: Scarlet and black hooped shirts
and socks, white shorts
League: Durham/Northumberland 3

SELBY RUFC
Ground Address: Sandhill Lane, Leeds Road,
Selby. YO8
Tel: 01757 703608 Website: www.selbyrufc.org
Brief Directions: Situated off Sandhill Lane, 1

mile west of town centre off A63 Leeds road
Club Secretary: G.Adamson,70 Parkways, Selby,
N.Yorks. YO8 9BB   Tel No 01757 706125
Fixtures Secretary: J.Phillips, Greystones,
Chapel Street, Hillam,Leeds LS25 5HP
Tel Nos: 01977 680437 (H) 01757 213344 (W)
Club Colours: Green, red and gold narrow hoops
League: Yorkshire 1

SHEFFIELD MEDICALS RUFC
Ground Address: University Ground, Warminster
Road, Norton, Sheffield.
Brief Directions: M1 J33 to Sheffield A630. 2
miles turn left A6102 to Bochum Parkway. Take
3rd Exit off R/about onto Norton Avenue. Over
next R/about onto Hemsworth Road, Warminser
Road 6th right
Club Secretary: Jonathon Cowley,16 The Nook,
Crookesmoor, Sheffield, S10 1EJ
Tel No: 0114 268 3200
Email: jbcowley@hotmal.com
Fixtures Secretary: Adan Hogg, 9 Brick Street,
Crookes, Sheffield. S10 1WR
Tel: 0771 235 9442
Club Colours: Navy & sky blue with white hoops.
Change: Navy & Burgundy with white hoops
League: Yorkshire 5

SHEFFIELD OAKS RUFC
Ground Address: Malin Bridge Sports and Social
Club, 22A Stannington Rd, Malin Bridge, Sheffield.
S6 5TA Tel: 01142 345349
Brief Directions: M1 J36 into Sheffield (north),
A61 to Hillsborough Ground, 1st available right
after Hillsborough Ground, Bradfield Rd, to Holme
Lane, left at end of Holme Ln, 1st right after petrol
station
Club Secretary: Kay Grayson,13 Hill Close,
Stannington, Sheffield S6 6BH
Tel No: 0114 2339209
Fixtures Secretary: Glyn Davies, 12 Malin Road,
Stannington, Sheffield, S6 5FG.
Tel: (H) 01142 2335829
Club Colours: Royal blue with gold hoops
League: Yorkshire 4

SHEFFIELD TIGERS RUFC
Ground Address: Dore Moor, Hathersage Road,
Sheffield. S17 3AB   Tel: 0114 236 0075
Website: www.sheffieldtigers.co.uk
Brief Directions: About 5 miles south west of
Sheffield city centre on the A625 signed
Hathersage. Ground just after Dore Moor Inn.
Club Secretary: Alick Bush, 210 Bradway Road,
Sheffield. S17 4PE
Tel: (H) 0114 2361129 (W) 0114 2716950
e-mail; alickb@chsheff-tr.trent.nhs.uk
Fixtures Secretary: Mick Rothenburg,65
Westwick Rd.,Sheffield S8 7BU
Tel No: 0114 274 0378 Email:
m.rothenburg@amserve.net
Club Colours: Maroon & gold hoops, black shorts
League: Yorkshire 1

SHILDON TOWN RUFC
Ground Address: Shildon Sunnydale Leisure Centre Tel: 01388 777340
Brief Directions: Please phone fixtures secretary
Club Secretary: Patrick Lewis, 11 Co-operative Street, Shildon, Co. Durham DL4 1DA
Tel: 07940 309237
Fixtures Secretary: Peter Plews, 14 Alexandra Street, Shildon, Co. Durham DL4 2EY
Tel: 01388 777334
Club Colours: Red and Green Quarters
League: Durham/Northumberland 4

SILLOTH RUFC
Ground Address: Old Marshalling Yard,Eden Street, Silloth, Cumbria.CA5 4HE
Tel: 016973 32299
Brief Directions: Lies in the centre of town
Club Secretary: David Henderson, 8 Beaconsfield Terrace, Silloth, Cumbria. CA5 4HE
Tel: (H) 016973 31076
Fixtures Secretary: Richard Smith
Tel: (H) 016973 31936
Club Colours: Green and black hoops
League: Cumbria

SKIPTON RFC
Ground Address: Coulthurst Memorial Grounds, Carleton New Road, Skipton, N Yorks. BD23 2AZ
Tel: 01756 793148
Brief Directions: Locate Skipton Railway Station - opposite car park, turn onto Carleton New Road, club 1st right after railway bridge
Club Secretary: Andrew Clark, 33 High St.,Gargrave, North YorKs BD23 3RA
Tel No: 01758 749565 (H) 07836 560140 (M)
Fixtures Secretary: Paul Tyson, 24 Rombalds Drive, Skipton.BD23 2SP
Tel; 01756 797661 or 0421 979143
Email: tysontiny@aol.com
Club Colours: Cardinal red shirts, black shorts
League: Yorkshire 2

SOUTH TYNESIDE COLLEGE RUFC
Ground Address: Grosvenor Road, South Shields, Tyne & Wear
Tel: 0191 427 3500
Brief Directions: Travel to south side of Tyne Tunnel, take road to South Shields, travel to Westhoe area of South Shields, ground adjacent to S.T. College
Club Secretary: R Smith, 87 Colman Avenue, South Shields, Tyne & Wear. NE34 9AG
Tel: (H) 0191 4242101 (W) 0191 4273571
Fixtures Secretary: C Moule
Tel: (H) 0191 3887548 (W) 0191 4273577
Club Colours: Black with 2 red and 1 gold hoop
League: Durham/Northumberland 4

SOUTHPORT RUFC
Ground Address: Waterloo Road, Hillside, Southport, Merseyside, PR8 4QW
Tel: 01704 569906
Brief Directions: Enter town on A570 turn left at Scarisbrick Hotel in town centre. Leave town on main Liverpool road A565. Ground on right down the hill from Mersey Rail Hillside
Club Secretary: Mrs. Ann Shorrock, 32d Lulworth Road, Birkdale, Southport, PR8 2BQ.
Tel: 01704 562340
Fixtures Secretary: Mrs Margaret Jackson, 43 Kenilworth Road, Ainsdale, Southport, PR8 3PH.
Tel: (H) 01704 578362.
Email: jacksongfw@aol.com
Club Colours: Red, black, amber
League: South Lancs & Cheshire 2

ST BENEDICTS RFC
Ground Address: Newlands Avenue, Mirehouse, Whitehaven, Cumbria,
Club House attached to St.Benedicts Social Club, Meadow Rd. Mirehouse, Whitehaven, Cumbria.
Brief Directions: M6 to jct 40 (Penrith) A66 to A595 to Whitehaven-Barrow by pass and Pelican garage.Straight on to hospital over rouindabout then 1st rt down hill to green. Club by church.
Club Secretary: Stephen House, 12 Castlerigg Close, Mirehouse, Whitehaven, Cumbria. CA28 9RJ
Fixtures Secretary: Ian Maguire. 9 Grisedale Close, Mirehouse, Whitehaven, Cumbria. CA28 8DF
Club Colours: Black, emerald and amber.
League: North Lancs & Cumbria

ST EDWARDS OLD BOYS RUFC
Ground Address: Bishops Court, North Drive, Sandfield Park, West Derby, Liverpool. L12 2AR
Tel: 0151 228 1414
Brief Directions: To end of M62, traffic lights, right onto Queens Drive (A5080), downhill through lights, right at next lights onto Alder Rd, left onto Eaton Rd, playing fields on left
Club Secretary: Simon J Smith, 107 Church Road, Woolton, Liverpool. L25 6OB
Tel: (H) 0151 428 2799 (W) 0151 227 3869
Fixtures Secretary: B Reilly, 130 Quarry Street, Woolton, Liverpool, L25
Tel: (H) 0151 428 3296 (W) 0151 283 3300
Club Colours: Royal blue with gold band
League: South Lancs & Cheshire 1

ST MARYS OLD BOYS RUFC
Ground Address: Sandy Lane, off Gorsey Lane, Hightown, Merseyside   Tel: 0151 929 2020
HQ: 17 Moor Lane, Crosby. L23   0151 924 1774
Brief Directions: Gorsey Lane is off a small road linking Little Crosby and Hightown, and can be reached from the A565 heading from Liverpool or Southport
Club Secretary: Laurence Doherty, 1 Marlborough Rd, Great Crosby, Liverpool L23 3DD
Tel NOs: 0151 931 4200 (H) 0151 924 3926 (W)
Fixtures Secretary: Mr Peter Moore
Tel: (H) 017048 78537
Club Colours: Maroon, yellow and blue hoops
League: South Lancs & Cheshire 2

STANLEY RODILLIANS RUFC
Ground Address: Manley Park, Lee Moor Road, Stanley, Wakefield, West Yorkshire. WF3 4EF
Tel: 01924 823619
Brief Directions: M62 J30, head towards Wakefield, turn right opposite Gordons Tyres, top of hill turn right, past double junction on left, turn left just after Lee Moor pub
Club Secretary: M.Thompson, 23 Cyprus Mount, Wakefield, West Yorks. WF1 2RS
Tel No: 01924 217970
Fixtures Secretary: I Young
Tel: (H) 0113 282 6743 (W) 01742 671131
Club Colours: Green, black and white
League: Yorkshire 4

STOCKPORT RUFC
Ground Address: Memorial Ground, Headlands Road, Bramhall, Stockport, Cheshire.SK7 3AN
Tel: 0161 439 2150 http://wwwstockportrugby
Brief Directions: Contact Fixture Secretary
Club Secretary: Michael Drew, c/o Cardwell & Drew Ltd., 8 Hawthorn Lane, Wilmslow, Cheshire, SK9 5DD. Tel: 01625 539037
Email: mike@cardwell-draw.damon.co.uk
Fixtures Secretary: M J Wroe, 62 Kennerley Rd, Davenport, Stockport, SK2 6EY
Tel: (H) 0161 484 0838
Club Colours: Red, white and green hoops
League: North 2 West

STOCKSBRIDGE RUFC
Ground Address: Stone Moor Road, Bolsterstone Tel: 0114 288 5078
Club House - 634 Manchester Road, Stocksbridge, Sheffield S36 1DY.
Brief Directions: Ground: Just outside village of Bolsterstone.   Club House: Just outside centre of Stocksbridge, opposite fire station.
Club Secretary: Mick Gribbins, 7 Hole House Lane, Stocksbridge, Sheffield S36 1BN
Tel: 0114 2884995
Fixtures Secretary: Keith Moore, 1 Marsden Road, Stocksbridge, Sheffield S36 5EE
Tel Nos: 0114 2886570 (H) 0794 6802051 (M)
Club Colours: Royal blue with two white hoops
League: Yorkshire 3

STOCKTON RFC
Ground Address: Norton (Teesside) Sports Complex, Station Road, Norton, Stockton, Cleveland. TS20 1PE Tel: 01642 554031
Brief Directions: From A19 take A1027 to Norton, at roundabout turn right into Station Rd, 60 yds on turn right, travel to end, clubhouse on left before Norton Tavern for dressing rooms
Club Secretary: Eric Smalley, 10 Derwent Close, Redmarshall, Stockton on Tees TS21 1HS
Tel: (H) 01642 630742
Fixtures Secretary: Brendon Thornton
Tel: (H) 01642 895825
Club Colours: Red / white / royal blue
League: North 2 East

SUNDERLAND RFC
Ground Address: Ashbrooke West Lawn, Sunderland, Tyne & Wear. SR2 7HH
Tel: 0191 528 4536
Brief Directions: A19 tow'ds Sunderland, exit Durham/S'land jcn, east 2.5 mls on Durham Rd to Barnes Htl, right then left into Qn Alex'a Rd, over 1st r'bout, 1st left W'bank Rd, left Ashbrk Rd, club 200yds left
Club Secretary: Mr J C Martin, 11 Roker Park Terrace, Sunderland, Tyne & Wear. SR6 9LY
Tel: (H) 0191 567 7045
Fixtures Secretary: Mr A Scott-Gray
Tel: (H) 0191 522 6188
Club Colours: Red,black & Gold hoops, white shorts
League: Durham/Northumberland 2

THE GENTLEMEN OF MOORE RUFC
Ground Address: The Clubhouse, Moss Lane, Off Runcorn Road, Moore, Warrington. WA4 6UU
Tel: 01925 740473
Brief Directions: M56 J11 follow A56 towards Warrington, straight over R/about, left at 1st set of traffic lights along Runcorn Road for 2 miles, right on `S' bend into Moss Lane in Moore Village
Club Secretary: John Stockton, 3 Hayes Lane, Appleton, Warrington, Cheshire. WA4 3DA.
Tel: (H) 01925 266025
Email: johnstockton@cwcom.net
Fixtures Secretary: S J Woollacott, 2 Knutsford Road, Grappenhall, Warrington, WA4 2JZ.
Tel: 01925 266576.
Email: wollacott.sj@bigfoot.com
Club Colours: Black with broad gold band. Change Red with black collars/cuffs.
League: South Lancs & Cheshire 2

THIRSK
League: Yorkshire 6
For further details contact
Yorkshire 6 League Secretary
Kathleen McNally, 28 Cherry Tree Road, Armthorpe, Doncaster, Yorks DN3 2HP
Tel: 01302 834252

THORNENSIANS RUFC
Ground Address: Clubhouse, Coulman Road, Thorne, Doncaster, South Yorkshire
Tel: 01405 812746
Brief Directions: M18 J6 signed Thorne, 1 mile to town, left at traffic lights, right at crossroads, left at Church, club on left past school
Club Secretary:
c/o Clubhouse, Thornensians RUFC
Tel No: 01405 812746(H)
Fixtures Secretary: S.J.Gravil,
49 King Edward Rd, Thorne, Doncaster DN8 4DE.
Tel: 01405 816539
Club Colours: Blue, black and white hoops
League: Yorkshire 5

THORNTON CLEVELEYS RUFC
Ground Address: Fleetwood Road North, Thornton Cleveleys, Lancashire
Tel: 01253 854104
Brief Directions: J3 M55 A585 to Fleetwood, follow A585 for 6 miles to second roundabout take 4th exit into Fleet Road. Ground is 1.5mile on left.
Club Secretary: Dr. Philip Horsfield, 336 Fleetwood Road North, Thornton Cleveleys, Lancs FY5 4LQ. Tel No: 01253 868537
Email: phorsfield@talk21.com
Fixtures Secretary: Martin Long Tattenham, Derby Road, Poulton-le-Fylde. Tel: 01253 895222
Club Colours: Black, red, and amber
League: North Lancs 1

TRAFFORD (METROVICK) RFCC
Ground Address: Macpherson Park, Finney Bank Road, Sale, Cheshire. M33 1LR
Tel: 0161 973 7061
Brief Directions: M63 J7, head for Altrincham, at 1st traffic lights turn right (Glebelands Rd), Finney Bank Rd is 0.5 mile along on right
Club Secretary: Mr. D. Moore, 19 Gredle Close, Urmston, Trafford, Manchester, M41 9RL.
Fixtures Secretary: Mr M Pringle, Flat 4, 109 Edge Lane, Stretford, Manchester M32 8PU
Tel: (H) 0161 286 1775 (W) 0161 877 7760
Club Colours: Black and white hoopes
League: North Lancs 1

TRENTHAM RUFC
Ground Address: New Inn Lane, Trentham, Stoke-on-Trent, Staffs. Tel: 01782 642320
Brief Directions: M6 J15, A500 towards Stoke-on-Trent, A34 south signs to Trentham, at Trentham Gardens R/about tunr left onto Longton road, then 4th left into New Inn Lane, Approx 1\3rd mile on right.
Club Secretary: Mrs Jane Procter, Holly House, Barn Court, Clayton, Newcastle, Staffs ST5 4N. Tel: 01782 623292
Email: michaelpehollyhouse78.freeserve.co.uk
Fixtures Secretary: Mr Michael Procter. As above
Club Colours: Green and white hoops
League: South Lancs & Cheshire 2

TYLDESLEY RUFC
Ground Address: St George's Park, Astley Street, Tyldesley M29 8HG
Tel No: 01942 882967
Website: tyldesleyrugby.com
Brief Directions: Follow A572 into Tyldesley centre where Astley Street is the main road facing the town square.
Club Secretary: Mr H Hughes, 81 Astley Street, Tyldesley, Lancashire, M29 7BA.
Tel No : 01942 513334
Email: howard.3.hughes@bt.com
Fixtures Secretary: Mr A W Jones, 363 Manchester Road, Astley, Manchester M29 7DX
Tel: (H) 01942 876938 (W) 01942 883348
Club Colours: Royal blue shirts, white shorts
League: North Lancs & Cumbria

UPPER EDEN RUFC
Ground Address: Pennine Park, Westgarth Road, Kirkby Stephen, Cumbria CA17 4DW
Tel: 017683 71585
Brief Directions: M6 J38, 12 miles to Kirkby Stephen, turn left by Spar shop (Westgarth), straight on to top of estate. A66 turn off at Brough, 4 miles to K. Stephen, right just after shop
Club Secretary: N. Marston, Meadow Barn, Oxenthwaite, Barras, Kirby Stephen, Cumbria CA17 4ES
Tel No : 017683 41179
Fixtures Secretary: D.Metcalfe, 17 The Crescent, Kirby Stephen, Cumbria Ca17 4AF
Tel No: 017683 71795
Club Colours: Black and white hoops
League: Cumbria

VAGABONDS (I.O.M.) RUFC
Ground Address: Mike Hailwood Centre, Glencrutchery Road, Douglas, Isle of Man. IM2 6DA   Tel: 01624 661996
Website: vagabonds.iofm.net
Brief Directions: From Douglas Promenade head uphill at the T/lights. Across the 1st T/lights, then turn right at the 2nd T/lights. The ground is on the right past the TT Grandstand.
Club Secretary: Peter Barlow, 22 Betely Woiods Avenue, Douglas, Isle of Man, IM2 7DA. Tel: 01624 621324 - Email: jugs@ukonline.co.uk
Fixtures Secretary: David Watterson, 7 Castlemere Apartmebnts, Central Prom, Douglas, Isle of Man IM2 4LJ   01624 670398
Club Colours: White with black & yellow band
League: South Lancs & Cheshire 1

VALE OF LUNE RUFC
Ground Address: Powder House Lane, Lancaster. LA1 2TT
Tel: 01524 64029 / 63151
Website www.btinternet.com/~valeoflune
Brief Directions: M6 J34 for Lancaster, follow signs for A589 Morecambe, approx 0.5 mile, turn right down Scale Hall Lane, turn left at T/junction, ground 100yds on right
Club Secretary: Peter Atkinson, 12 Moorside Road, Brook House, Lancaster, LA2 9PJ.
Tel: (H) 01524 770152 / (F) 01524 771877
Fixtures Secretary: Fred Swarbrick, Oxendale Farm, Wyresdale Road, Lancaster, LA1 3JJ. Tel: (H) 01524 37601
Club Colours: Cherry and white hoops
League: North 2 West

VULCAN RUFC
Ground Address: The Sports Ground, Wargrave Road, Newton-le-Willows, Merseyside
Tel: 01925 224180
Brief Directions: Wargrave Rd is a continuation of Victoria Rd which is off Crow Lane West (A572)
Club Secretary: Ronnie Evans, 132 Park Road South, Newton-le-Willows, WA12 8QD
Tel: 01925 270051

NORTHERN

Fixtures Secretary: Mike Holland, 4 Wayfarers Drive, Newton-Le-Willows, Merseyside, WA12 Tel: (H) 01925 229201
Club Colours: Black and amber/ black / black
League: South Lancs & Cheshire 4

WAKEFIELD COUGARS RUFC
Ground Address: Wakefield Cougars RUFC, College Grove, Eastmoor Road,Wakefield. WF1 3RR Tel : 01924 374801
Brief Directions: M1 Jct41. Take A650 to City centre. Left at Queen Elizabeth GS to Wakefield Rd.Ground 250 yds.M62 Jct30 .A642 to centre. Rt at Lights after hospital to Eastmoor Rd.Grd 300yds.
Club Secretary: Alex Judson, 2 Windsor Crescent, Wrenthorpe, Wakefield WF1 2BS Tel: (H) 01924 361358 (M) 0976 976153
Fixtures Secretary: Bill Halstead
Tel: (H) 01274 872710 (Fax) 01274 865975
Club Colours: Black & Gold. Alternative Red.
League: Yorkshire 4

WALKINGTON ROVERS
Ground Address: Walkington Playing Field, Walkington, Beverely, East Yorkshire.
Brief Directions: South or West: Head for Humber Bdg at R'abt turn L. for Beverley A164 stay on this road passed Willerby- Skidby-Cottingham. After Skidby/Cottingham R'abt sign on L. for Walkington (abt 2M) turn L & go to Traffic Lightd turn L into Village. Turn L before pond Autherd Garth follow Signpost to Playing Field. From North head for Beverley Racecourse go up hill to R'abt take 2nd left to Walkington go to Traffic Lights turn R. into village then follow directions as above.
Club Secretary: Dave Lee, 57 Canada Drive, Cherry Burton, East Yorkshire. Tel: 01964 550500
Fixtures Secretary: Andy Taylor, Dockside House, Earles Road, Hedon Road, Hull, E. Yorks, HU9 1UD. 07866 372424M
Club Colours: Red & white hoops, blue collar & cuffs
League: Yorkshire 6

WALLASEY RUFC
Ground Address: Cross Lane, Leasowe Road, Wallasey, Wirral, Merseyside.
CH45 8NS Tel: 0151 638 1486
Website: rugby-club.org.uk or wallaseyrufc.cjb.net
Brief Directions: Exit 1 on M53 towards Wallasey, take 2nd slip road to A551, turn right at lights
Club Secretary: J A Burton, 14 Seaview Lane, Irby, Wirral, Merseyside. CH61 3UL
Tel: (H) 0151 648 4341 (W) 0151 639 6508
Fixtures Secretary: A Rae, 8 Inchcape Rd, Wallasey, Wirral, Merseyside CH45 8JR
Tel: (H) 0151 638 6903
Club Colours: Red, black, white hoops
League: South Lancs & Cheshire 2

WALLSEND RFC
Ground Address: Benfield Community Association Sam Smiths Pavilion, Benfield School Campus, Benfield Road, Walkergate, Newcastle. NE6 4NU Tel: 0191 265 9357.
Brief Directions: Just off A1058 Newcastle-Tynemouth (Coast rd), turn on to C127 to Benfield School, club at rear of school
Club Secretary: Brian J Thirlaway, 29 Belmont Close, Battle Hill Estate, Wallsend, Tyne & Wear. NE28 9DX Tel: (H) 0191 234 4877
Fixtures Secretary: Stuart Robinson, 5 Dinsdale Avenue, Kings Estate, Wallsend
Tel: 0191 262 7485
Club Colours: Myrtle green jerseys with gold trim
League: Durham/Northumberland 2

WARRINGTON RUFC
Ground Address: Bridge Lane, Appleton, Warrington Tel: 01925 264591
Brief Directions: J20 M6. Follow A50 Warrington 2m. At lights turn left, after 1 1/2 mls 2 sets of lights, left at 2nd set, under bridge first right into Bridge Lane, .1/4m on right.
Club Secretary: G.P.Robinson, 25 Victoria Avenue, Grappenhall, Warrington WA42XU
Tel No: 01925 489213
Email: gavin.robinson@ quista.net
Fixtures Secretary: P.Broadbent, 22 Victoria Avenue, Grappenhall, Warrington. WA4 2PD.
Tel No 01925 261959
Club Colours: Red, white and green
League: North 2 West

WATERLOO VIKINGS FC
Ground Address: St. Anthonys Road, Blundellsands, Liverpool, L23 8TW.
Tel: 0151 924 4552
Brief Directions: Same as Waterloo FC
Club Secretary: M Flett, Lanvollon, 17 Fulwood Park, Aigburth, Liverpool L17 5AD
Tel: 0151 728 7807 (H) 0151 489 2139 (B)
Fixtures Secretary: John Rimmer, 2 Chapel Meadow, Longton, Preston, PR4 5NR.
Tel: 01772 885000 (W) 01772 614277 (H) 01772 203702 (Fax).
Club Colours: Red, green & black hoops
League Contact: Brian Taylor, 28 College Avenue, Crosby, L23 0SS.
Tel: 0151 928 9912 (H) 0468 245280 (M)
League: South Lancs & Cheshire 5

WATH-UPON-DEARNE RUFC
Ground Address: Moor Road, Wath-Upon-Dearne, Rotherham   Tel: 01709 872399
Brief Directions: Moor Road is adjacent to Wath Swimming Baths on the main Rotherham to Barnsley (A630) road
Club Secretary: Mr S Poxton, 19 Packham Way, Wath-upon-Dearne, Rotherham, S Yorks S63 6BR
Tel: (H) 01709 874154 (W) 01226 282549
Fixtures Secretary: Mr S Corns
Tel: (H) 01709 874911
Club Colours: Blue with maroon and gold bands
League: Yorkshire 3

WEARSIDE RUFC
Ground Address: Fulwell Quarry Reclamation Site, Newcastle Road, Sunderland, Tyne & Wear.
Brief Directions: Leave A19, follow A184 (Newcastle Rd) into Sunderland passing Regal Greyhound Stadium on left, turn right at round-about to changing rooms
Club Secretary: S. F. Thompson, 87 Beach Road, South Shields, Tyne And Wear. NE 33 2LZ
Tel: (H) 0191 497 5013
Fixtures Secretary: William Johnston, 14 Manila Street, Hendon, Sunderland. Tel: 0191 552 3559
Club Colours: Royal blue and scarlet hoops
League: Durham/Northumberland 3

WENSLEYDALE RUFC
Ground Address: Cawkill Park, Wensley Road, Leyburn, North Yorkshire. DL8 5AR
Tel: 01969 623067 Website: wensleydalerufc.com
Brief Directions: Leave Leyburn on the Hawes/Wensley Road (A684) the club is one mile west of Leyburn on the left.
Club Secretary: Graham Jameson, 7 Fearby Rd., Masham, Ripon, N.Yorks. HG4 4ES
Tel: 01765 689185 (H)
Email: graham@bellfieldwest .com
Fixtures Secretary: Brian Carlisle, Hoppers Estate Agents, Central Chambers, Keyburn, N. Yorkshire. DL8 5BD
Tel: 01969 622936 / 01969 663570
Club Colours: Black and yellow hoops
League: Durham/Northumberland 3

WEST HARTLEPOOL AMATEUR RFC
Ground Address: Hartlepool Sixth Form College, Catcote Road, Hartlepool, Cleveland.
Brief Directions: Entering Hartlepool on A689 turn left at 1st set of T/lights into Truro Drive. At T/Jnt then left into Catcote Road. Ground Approx. 2 miles on right hand side.
Club Secretary: Tony Wilson, 27 Suggitt Street, Hartlepool, Cleveland, TS26 8PY.
Tel: 01429 279322H - 07788 972827M
Fixtures Secretary: Graham Frankland, 39 Parklands Way, Hartlepool, Cleveland.
Tel: 01429 261716
Club Colours: Royal Blue with Red & White
League: Durham/Northumberland 3

WEST HARTLEPOOL
TECHNICAL DAY SCHOOL OB RUFC
Ground Address: Grayfields, Wiltshire Way, Hartlepool Tel: 01429 233548
Brief Directions: From A19 take A179 to Hartlepool, right at roundabout, continue for approx 2 miles, left into estate, right at T junction, club on left after 0.5 mile
Club Secretary: D Bramley, 63 Hutton Avenue, Hartlepool, TS26 9PP Tel: (H) 01429 263157
Email: david.bramley@which.net
Fixtures Secretary: A Cheshire, 9 Elmwood Place, Hartlepool. Tel: (H) 01429 262939
Club Colours: Blue and white
League: Durham/Northumberland 1

WEST LEEDS RUFC
Ground Address: Blue Hill Lane, Wortley, Leeds. LS12 4NZ
Tel: 0113 2639869
Brief Directions: From M621 to Leeds outer ring road take A6110 and turn right at second round-about . After Ringways, turn right at lights follow road leftt at Fawcett Lane and club is half a mile on left
Club Secretary: Jill Broadbent, 21 Butterbowl Road, Leeds. LS12 5JE
Tel: (H) 0113 279 6220 (W) 0113 2436700
Fixtures Secretary: Colin Edwards, 59 Moorfield, Guildersome, LS27 7BW.
Tel: (H) 0113 2522487
Club Colours: Navy, old gold and white
League: Yorkshire 2

WEST PARK BRAMHOPE RUFC
Ground Address: The Sycamores, Bramhope, Leeds. LS16 9JR
Tel: 0113 2671437
Brief Directions: From Leeds city centre take A660 sign posted Skipton & Otley, at Bramhope village turn left at roundabout direct to Club
Club Secretary: Rob Storey, 7 Moseley Wood Way, Cookridge, Leeds, LS16 7HN.
Tel: 0113 2675266
Fixtures Secretary: Phil March, 202 Moseley Wood Gardens, Cookridge, Leeds, LS16 7JE. Tel: 0113 226 8246
Club Colours: Black and gold
League: Yorkshire 1

WEST PARK WARRIORS
League: North Lancs 2
For further details contact:
North Lancs 2 League Secretary
Bill Hopkinson, Far Hey Head Farm, Littleborough, Rochdale Lancs OL15 9NS
Tel: 01706 379879

WESTOE RFC
Ground Address: Dean Road, South Shields, Tyne & Wear. Tel: 0191 456 1506
Brief Directions: Map available
Club Secretary: J R Wells, 240 Mowbray Road, South Shields. NE33 3NW
Tel: (H) 0191 4552260
Fixtures Secretary: D Allen, 118 Harton House Road (E), South Shields, NE34 6DZ
Tel: (H) 0191 4569531 (W), 0191 456115
Club Colours: Red, sky and dark blue hoops
League: North 2 East

WETHERBY RUFC
Ground Address: Grange Park, Wetherby, West Yorkshire, LS22
Tel: 01937 582461 Website: wetherbyrugby.com
Brief Directions: From Wetherby town centre head for A1 south, pass Police station on left, to R/about, 2nd exit for A1 south, cross A1 and take left turn into Grange Park.
Club Secretary: Mark Lonsdale, 9 Darnborough

Street, York YO23 1AN
Tel No : 01904 626772
Email: mark.lonsdale@scbfew.co.uk
Fixtures Secretary: Richard Watts, 43 St. James Street, Wetherby, West Yorks LS22 5RS
Tel: 01937 584446
Club Colours: Red and white hoops, white shorts
League: Yorkshire 4

WHARFEDALE RAMS RUFC
Ground Address: Wharfeside Avenue, Threshfield, Skipton, N. Yorks, BD23 5ND
Tel: 01756 752547
Brief Directions: Take B6265 from Skipton, signed Grassington, after 8 miles turn right after Old Hall Inn in Threshfield, left after 400 metres down Wharfeside Avenue.
Club Secretary: Dave Lovell, 2 Brackenley Crescent, Embsay, Skipton, N. Yorks, BD23 6PO.
Tel: 01756 795804
Fixtures Secretary: Michael Harrison, Old Hall Stables, threshfield, Skipton, N. Yorks, BD23 5PL.
Tel: 01756 752777
Club Colours: Emerald green shirts
League: Yorkshire 5

WHEATLEY HILLS DONCASTER RUFC
Ground Address: Wheatley Hills Sports Ground, Brunel Road, York Road Industrial Estate, Doncaster. DN5 8PT Tel: 01302 781472
Brief Directions: A638, behind B & Q depot, on Wakefield Road, 1 mile from town centre.
Club Secretary: A. R. Dunkerley, 1 Mayfields, Scawthrope, Doncaster, Yorkshire, DN5 7UA. Tel: 01302 782214 (H) 01302729793 (W)
Email: dunk@beargarden.freeserve.co.uk
Fixtures Secretary: Chris Whitehouse, 11A Hillfold, South Elmsall, Pontefract, WF9 2BZ.
Tel No: 01977 644303 (H) 08707 415151 (W)
Club Colours: Maroon, gold & white broad hoops
League: North 2 East

WHITBY HARLEQUINS RUFC
Ground Address: Showfield, White Leys Road, Whitby, North Yorkshire. YO21 1L8
Tel: 01947 602008
Brief Directions: North West side of river, towards Sandend off Stakesby Road
Club Secretary: Mr F Howarth, 18 Lime Grove, Whitby, North Yorks YO21 1LP
Tel: (H) 01947 600692
Fixtures Secretary: Mr T Cook
Tel: (H) 01947 600614
Club Colours: Maroon and black
League: Durham/Northumberland 2

WHITEHAVEN RUFC
Ground Address: The Playground, Richmond Terrace, Whitehaven, Cumbria. CA28 7QR. Tel: 01946 695253
Brief Directions: Behind the Whitehaven Sports Centre and next to Jacksons Timber Yard.
Club Secretary: Mr E McConnell, 38 Loop Road South, Whitehaven, Cumbria. CA28 7SE.

Tel: (H) 01946 692225
Fixtures Secretary: As above.
Club Colours: Maroon and white hoops
League: Cumbria

WHITLEY BAY ROCKCLIFF RFC
Ground Address: Lovaine Avenue, Whitley Bay, Tyne & Wear. NE25 8RW
Tel: 0191 2513704
Brief Directions: Travelling downhill on Hillheads Rd. past the Ice rink, turn 2nd right (club signed) along Lovaine Avenue, 2nd right into club.
Club Secretary: Martin Page, 25 Hillcrest, Whitley Bay, Tyne And Wear, NE25 9AD. Tel: (H) 0191 2510748
Fixtures Secretary: Mr D Bennett, 4 Millfield Gardens, Tynemouth, Tyne And Wear.
Tel: (H) 0191 2572174
Club Colours: Cardinal and gold shirts
League: Durham/Northumberland 2

WIBSEY RUFC
Ground Address: Northfield Road, Wibsey, Bradford. BD6
Tel: 01274 671643
Brief Directions: From top of M606 take 2nd exit towards Odsal roundabout, take 4th exit at side of Police station, 0.75 mile on left joined onto White Swan pub
Club Secretary: Steve Rose,236 Poplar Grove, Great Horton, Bradford BD7 4HU
tel: 01274 406546
Fixtures Secretary: Bob Wood
Tel: 01274 571810 (H) 0794 136 4204 (M)
Club Colours: Red and green hoops
League: Yorkshire 6

WICKERSLEY EXEL
Ground Address: Wickersley Comprehemsive School, Bawtry Road, Wickersley, Rotherham
Brief Directions: M18 Junction 1. Follow sign for Rotherham. Ground on left just before footbridge.
Club Secretary: David Trueman, 12 Larch Road, Maltby, Rotherham, S66 8AZ. Tel: 01709 817971
Fixtures Secretary: Steve Houghton, 150 Pear Tree Ave., Bramley, Rotherham, S. Yorks.S66 2NF
Tel Nos: 01709 531758 (H) 0498 825644(M)
Club Colours: Blue and gold
League: Yorkshire 6

WIDNES RUFC
Ground Address: Heath Road, Widnes, Cheshire. WA8 7NU   Tel: 0151 424 2575
Brief Directions: From M62 exit at J7, A57 to Warrington, right at 1st lights, right at junction up to roundabout, 1st left-Birchfield Rd, down to 1st major lights, right, right at 2nd lights, 1st right, club on left
Club Secretary: Alan Evans, 238 Mill Lane, Bold, Widnes,Lancs. Tel: (H) 0151 424 3443
Fixtures Secretary: Raymond Heapey
Tel: (H) 0151 424 6565
Club Colours: Red and black hooped jerseys
League: South Lancs & Cheshire 1

WIGAN RUFC
Ground Address: Douglas Valley, Wingates Road, Leyland Mill Lane, Wigan. WN1 2SA
Tel: 01942 242556
Brief Directions: M6 J27, follow signs to Standish, take A49 towards Wigan, 2 miles, 1st left after Cherry Gardens Hotel into Leyland Mill Lane, then signposted
Club Secretary: Graham Heeley, 9 Water Drive, Standish, Wigan WN6 0EH Tel No: 01257 421465
Email: heeley@aol.com
Fixtures Secretary: David Clarke
Tel: (H) 01942 207771
Club Colours: Black and white irregular hoops
League: South Lancs & Cheshire 1

WILMSLOW RUFC
Ground Address: Memorial Ground, Kings Road, Wilmslow. SK9 6JF   Tel: 016625 522274
Brief Directions: Kings Road is off the A538 - Wilmslow to Altrincham, approx 4 miles from the M56 junction, on the left as you enter the town.
Club Secretary: J.Fletche,6 Highlands Drive, Offerton, Stockport SK2 5HX
jffletcher@ukonline.co.uk
Fixtures Secretary: J. Harries, 'Gwynant', 39 Wallingford Road, Wilmslow SK9 3JT
Tel No: 01625 524359 (H)
e-mail: texukltd@dialstart.net
Club Colours: Sky blue w/ maroon & white hoops
League: South Lancs & Cheshire 1

WINDERMERE RUFC
Ground Address: Dawes Meadow, Longlands, Bowness on Windermere, Cumbria. LA23 3AS
Tel: 015394 43066
Brief Directions: Drive towards Bowness & the lake from Windermere, coming in to Bowness, right just before cinema, right again past the bowling club, clubhouse is on the right.
Club Secretary: J C Stephenson, 46 Craig Walk, Windermere. LA23 2JT   Tel: (W) 015394 45448
Fixtures Secretary: K E Williams, 40A Main Rd, Windermere, LA23 1DY Tel: (H) 015394 42389
Club Colours: Amber and black
League: Cumbria

WINLATON VULCANS RFC
Ground Address: Axwell View Playing Fields, Winlaton, Blaydon-on-Tyne. NE21 6EU
Tel: 0191 4142502
Brief Directions: From A1 take exit past Metro Centre signed Swalwell, take signs for Blaydon, just past Blaydon Pool turn left, continue up Shibdon Bank for 0.5 mile, club on left
Club Secretary: Steve Foley, 62 Silverdale Drive, Winlaton Blaydon-on-Tyne NE216EN
Tel: 0191 4146894 (H) 0191 2112015 (W)
Fixtures Secretary: Ian Bilclough, 7A Tyne Street, Winlaton, Blaydon-on-Tyne
Tel: (H) 0191 4147723
Club Colours: Black shirts with white collar
League: Durham/Northumberland 1

WINNINGTON PARK RFC
Ground Address: Burrows Hill, Hartford, Northwich, Cheshire. Tel: 01606 74242
http://homepages.tesconet.com/~winpark
Brief Directions: 1 mile from Hartford turn off A556, signed Hartford, neat BlueWeaver Bridge, turn right at Church, left at the lights, right at T.Jct. Then next left, Barrows Hill Ground 2nd on right.
Club Secretary: Mr. J.C.W. Dowqnham, 216 London Road, Northwich, Cheshire, CW9 8AQ.
Tel: 01606 48962H - 01565 633294W
Fixtures Secretary: Mr. C. F. Gleave, Westerley, West Road, Weaverham, Northwich, CW8 3HH.
Tel: 01606 853999H - 01925 752016W
Club Colours: Royal and Navy Blue
League: North 2 West

WIRRAL RFC
Ground Address: The Memorial Ground, Thornton Common Road, Clatterbridge, Wirral, Merseyside, CH63 4JU. Tel: 0151 334 1309
Brief Directions: M53 J4. Follow signs for Willaston & Naston. Straight ahead at R/about. Left at 1st crossroads.
Club Secretary: Graeme Roberts, 19 Thornton Road, Higher Bebington, Wirral, Merseyside, CH63 5PN. Tel: 0151 608 9643
Email: graeme.roberts@huytonroberts.fsnet .co.uk
Fixtures Secretary: Alan Hignett, 22 Argyle Avenue, Eastham, Wirral, Merseyside.
Tel: (H) 0151 327 1309
Email: alanr@hignotts.freeserve.co.uk
Club Colours: Maroon and white hoops
League: South Lancs & Cheshire 2

WITHERNSEA RUFC
Ground Address: Plough Inn, Northside Roadl, Hollym, Nr. Withernsea, Hull, East Yorkshire. HU19 2RS   Tel: 01964 612049
Brief Directions: Through Hull on to the A1033 to Withernsea, go through Patrington and next village is Hollym. Turn left at crossroads.
Club Secretary: Mr A C Ellis, Seaside Lane, Tunstall,Roos, Nr Hull, HU 12 0JQ
Fixtures Secretary: Mr R K Thompson, 3 Oak Avenue, Withernsea, Hull, HU19 2PE
Tel: 01964 613722
Club Colours: White and blue hoop
League: Yorkshire 6

WORKINGTON RFC
Ground Address: Ellis Sports Ground, Mossbay Road, Workington. CA14 3XZ Tel: 01900 602625
Brief Directions: Adjacent to B5296, 0.5 mile south of town centre, 1st right after traffic lights at T A Centre
Club Secretary: M J Heaslip, 32 Elizabeth St, Workington. CA14 4DB   Tel: (H) 01900 66339 (W) 01946 591542 (F) 01946 590929
Email: michael.heaslip@cumbriacc.gov.uk
Fixtures Secretary: K.Greenhow, 34 Udale Court, Moorclose, Workington.   Tel: 07718 330117
Club Colours: Black and white hoops
League: North 2 East

YARM RFC
Club Secretary: Mr. C. M. Hoggart, 5 Honister Walk, Egglescliffe, Stockton on Tees, TS16 9DR.
Fixtures Secretary: As above
League: Durham/Northumberland 3

YARNBURY (HORSFORTH) RFC
Ground Address: Brownberrie Lane, Horsforth, Leeds Tel: 0113 2581346
Brief Directions: Follow signs on Leeds outer ring road (A6120) to Horsforth. Turn north onto Low Lane at T junction turn left then third exit off the roundabout
Club Secretary: Paul Trigg, 3 Moorland Gardens, Moortown, Leeds. LS17 6JT
Tel: (H) 0113 2251389
Fixtures Secretary: John Riley, 65 Broadgate Lane, Horsforth, Leeds, LS18 5AB
Tel: (H) 0113 2589131 (W) 01924 441818
Club Colours: Blue, black & white uneven hoops
League: Yorkshire 1

YORK RAILWAY INSTITUTE RUFC
Ground Address: Railway Institute Sports Ground, New Lane, Acomb, York. YO2 4NU
Tel: 01904 798930

Brief Directions: From A1237 York ringroad, take B1224 signposted Acomb for 1.5 miles, after the Church of the Latter Day Saints on right, take the 1st on the right (New Lane), sports ground at end
Club Secretary: Bryn D Bates, 16 Beech Place, Strensall, York. YO32 5AS
Tel: 01904 491296 (H) 01904 622112 (W)
Fixtures Secretary: W F Cooper, Moorcroft, Lucy Hall Drive, Baildon, Shipley Tel: (H) 01274 584355
Club Colours: Royal blue and white hoops
League: Yorkshire 2

YORK RUFC
Ground Address: Clifton Park, Shipton Road, York YO3 6RE   Tel:01904 623602
Brief Directions: Turn south off York outer ring road (A10) towards city centre on A19 from Thirsk, club situated on right after about 1.75 miles
Club Secretary: Brian McClure, 15 Stubden Grove, York. YO30 4UY   Tel: (H) 01904 691026
e-mail: bmcc1999@aol.com
Fixtures Secretary: Colin Ventress, 1 Barnfield Way, Copmanthorpe, York YO23 3RT
Tel No: 01904 704793
Club Colours: Green, black and white hoops
League: Yorkshire 1

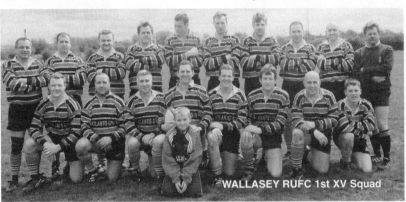

WALLASEY RUFC 1st XV Squad

PONTELAND RFC
The club's millennium photgraph The u.18s were playing away and missed the photocall.

BIRKENHEAD PARK
The winning team from the
Barbados Sevens last summer.

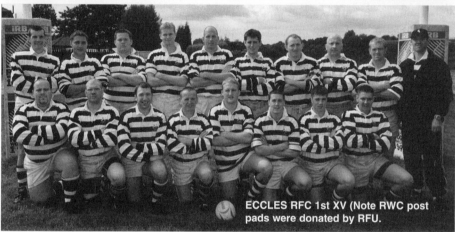

ECCLES RFC 1st XV (Note RWC post
pads were donated by RFU.

TRENTHAM RFC

MIDLAND DIVISION

A complete club index appears at the back of the book.
This shows which Division and league each club is in for the 2001-02 season

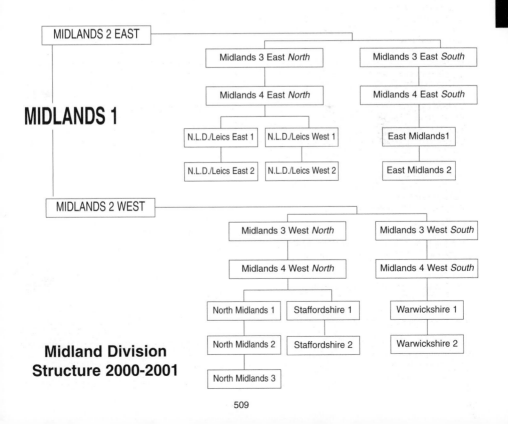

MIDLANDS 1

MIDLANDS 2 EAST

Midlands 3 East *North*

Midlands 3 East *South*

Midlands 4 East *North*

Midlands 4 East *South*

N.L.D./Leics East 1

N.L.D./Leics West 1

East Midlands1

N.L.D./Leics East 2

N.L.D./Leics West 2

East Midlands 2

MIDLANDS 2 WEST

Midlands 3 West *North*

Midlands 3 West *South*

Midlands 4 West *North*

Midlands 4 West *South*

North Midlands 1

Staffordshire 1

Warwickshire 1

North Midlands 2

Staffordshire 2

Warwickshire 2

North Midlands 3

**Midland Division
Structure 2000-2001**

MIDLANDS LEAGUES OFFICIALS 2001-2002

David I Robins   **Chairman**
The Clubhouse, Upper Chase Rd, Malvern WR14 2BU
Tel: 01684 564826 (H) Tel: 01684 560247 (B)
Fax: 01684 893125
Email: dir-int@dir-int.demon.co.uk

Mike Bracey   Midland 1   League Sec
154 Manor Road, Barton-le-Clay, Bedford MK45 4NU
Tel: 01582 881237 (H)

Brian Johnston   Midland 2 West   League Sec
9 Nursery Close, Atworth, Melksham Wilts SN1Z 8HX
Tel: 01225 790658 (H) Tel: 0207 9180410 (B)
Fax: 01249 442865

Bob Ingledew   Midland 2 East   League Sec
15 Martin Close, Bedford MK41 7JY
Tel: 01234 407521
Email: bingledew@ntlworld.com

Nigel Banwell   Midland 3 West (North)   League Sec
16 Riverside Close, Upton upon Severn,
Worcester WR8 0JN
Tel: 01684 592046 (H)
Email: nigelbanwell@hotmail.com

Keith Dale   Midland 3 West (South)   League Sec
14 St Anthony's Drive, Newcastle, Staffs ST5 2JE
Tel: 01782 615770 (H) Fax: 01782 615235

Philip Osborne   Midland 3 East (North)   League Sec
Ashthorne, Teeton Rd, Ravensthorpe,
Northampton NN6 8EJ
Tel: 01604 770772 (H) Tel: 01327 705785 (B)

Clive Elliott   Midland 3 East (South)   League Sec
9 Wavertree Close, Cosby, Leics LE9 1TN
Tel: 0116 284 1746 (H) Tel: 01788 544 508 (B)
Fax: 01788 568711
Email: cliveelliott56@netscapeonline.co.uk

Alan Humphreys   Midland 4 West (North)   League Sec
26 Low Fold Close, St Johns, Worcester WR2 5UE
Tel: 01905 422522 (H)

Martin Dolphin   Midland 4 West (South)   League Sec
10 Canonbie Lea, Madeley, Telford,
Shropshire TF7 5RL
Tel: 01952 684904 (H) Tel: 01952 294424 (B)
E-mail: martin@dolphin.mc.fsnet.co.uk

David Trubee   Midland 4 East (North)   League Sec
42 Charnwood Drive, Ripley, Derbyshire DE5 3TB
Tel: 01773 512719 (H)
Email: dtrubee@dircon.co.uk

MIDLAND

Kevin Curtis
21 Potton Road, St Neots, Huntingdon,
Cambs PE19 2NP
Tel: 01480 3900066 (H)
Email: Kevin.curtis@ntlworld.com

Midland 4 East (South) League Sec

John McNally
490 Brook Lane, Moseley, Birmingham B13 0BZ
Tel: 0121 604 6180 (H)
Tel: 0121 783 7232 (B) Fax: 0121 789 8306

North Midlands 1 League Sec

Terry Wheeler
14 Wollescote, Pedmore, Stourbridge,
W Midlands DY9 7JJ
Tel: 01384 832647 (H) Tel: 0121 423 4000 (B)

North Midlands 2 & 3 League Sec

Jason Swingewood
48 Appledore Grove, Packmoor, Stoke-on-Trent ST6 6XH
Tel: 01782 816213 (H) Tel: 0151 955 6835 (B)

Staffordshire 1 & 2 League Sec

Ray Roberts
261 Alwyn Rd, Bilton, Rugby, Warks CV22 7RP
Tel: 01788 810276 (H) Tel: 01788 816520 (B)
Email: rayrobwark@aol.com

Warwickshire 1 & 2 League Sec

Henri Ginvert
5 The Paddock, Markfield, Leics LE6 9RR
Tel: 01530 242761 (H) Tel/Fax: 01534 249621 (B)
Mobile: 0385 724989
E-mail: henri.ginvert@eaglestar.co.uk

NLD/Leics 1 (West) League Sec

Tim Bembridge
5 Blackthorn Lane, Boston, Lincs, PE21 9BG
Tel: 01205 351973 (H) 0773 116513 (M) 01509 842283 (Fax)

NLD/Leics 1 (East) League Sec

David Miller
37 Rosemary Drive, Alvaston, Derby DE24 0TA
Tel: 01332 755935 (H) Tel: 01332 260144 (B)
Email: milleradmiller@aol.com

NLD/Leics 2 (West) League Sec

David H Murphy
The Old Carpenters Arms, 32 High St, Little Bytham,
Grantham, Lincs NG33 4QX
Tel: 01780 410692 (H)

NLD/Leics 2 (East) League Sec

Peter Howard
Caudle View,Church Lane, Thorpe, Langton,
Leics LE16 7TR
Tel: 01858 545227 (H) Tel: 01455 610747 (B)

East Midlands 1 League Sec

Dr Chris Rowan
17 Blethan Drive, Huntingdon, Cambridgeshire, PE18 6GN
Tel: 01480 892838 (B) 01480 434959 (H)
Email: chris.rownl@ntlworld.com ; rowanc@wkong.huntingdon.com

East Midlands 2 League Sec

MIDLAND

MIDLAND ONE

2000-01 LEAGUE TABLE

	P	W	D	L	PF	PA	PD	Pts
Scunthorpe	22	19	2	1	762	258	504	40
Leicester Lions	22	19	0	3	574	183	391	38
Longton	22	15	3	4	545	255	290	33
Broadstreet	22	14	0	8	474	394	80	28
Kenilworth	22	10	0	12	339	446	-107	20
Hereford	22	10	0	12	330	439	-109	20
Camp Hill	22	9	1	12	269	335	-66	19
Banbury	22	9	0	13	448	517	-69	18
Barkers Butts	22	8	0	14	391	533	-142	16
Newbold	22	7	0	15	310	497	-187	14
Burton	22	5	0	17	240	586	-346	10
Stoke on Trent	22	4	0	18	287	526	-239	8

MIDLAND

2001-02 FIXTURE GRID	Banbury	Barkers Butts	Broadstreet	Camp Hill	Dunstablians	Hereford	Kenilworth	Leicester Lions	Longton	Luctonians	Malvern	Walsall
Banbury		16.03	22.09	06.10	02.03	09.02	27.10	26.01	17.11	05.01	08.12	06.04
Barkers Butts	08.09		26.01	17.11	22.09	02.03	05.01	06.10	08.12	09.02	06.04	27.10
Broadstreet	09.03	10.11		29.09	12.01	01.12	23.02	13.04	20.10	22.12	02.02	16.03
Camp Hill	23.02	12.01	02.03		01.12	13.04	20.10	22.12	02.02	16.03	10.11	22.09
Dunstablians	29.09	09.03	17.11	05.01		06.10	08.12	09.02	06.04	27.10	08.09	26.01
Hereford	20.10	29.09	05.01	08.12	23.02		06.04	27.10	08.09	26.01	09.03	17.11
Kenilworth	02.02	01.12	06.10	09.02	13.04	22.12		16.03	10.11	22.09	12.01	02.03
Leicester Lions	10.11	23.02	08.12	06.04	20.10	02.02	08.09		09.03	17.11	29.09	05.01
Longton	12.01	13.04	09.02	27.10	22.12	16.03	26.01	22.09		02.03	01.12	06.10
Luctonians	01.12	20.10	06.04	08.09	02.02	10.11	09.03	12.01	29.09		23.02	08.12
Malvern	13.04	22.12	27.10	26.01	16.03	22.09	17.11	02.03	05.01	06.10		09.02
Walsall	22.12	02.02	08.09	09.03	10.11	12.01	29.09	01.12	23.02	13.04	20.10	

BANBURY

Founded: 1925

Hon. Secretary:	Bryan A Davies,	34 Horton View, Banbury. OX16 9HP Tel: 01295 262027
President:	Roy Evans,	Whineray, Thorpe Rd., Chacombe, Oxon. 01295 710853
Chairman:	Neil Chapman	156 Oxford Road, Banbury, Oxon. OX16 9BA 01295 258337
Player/Coach	Martin Hobley	64 Burwell Drive, Witney, Oxon. OX8 7LY 01865 252381
Fixtures Secretary:	Roger Croft	1 Daisy Hill Farm Cottage, Duns Tew, Oxford OX6 4JS. 01869 347124
League Contact:	As Fixture Secretary above.	

Ground Address: Bodicote Park, Oxford Road, Banbury, Oxon. Tel/Fax: 01295 279000
Capacity: 3,400   Covered Seating: 366   Uncovered Standing: 3,000
Directions: M40 Junct. 11. Follow the signs to Town Centre, Hospital, Adderbury A4260. The ground is situated 1.5 miles past the hospital on the A4260 towards Adderbury on the left.
Nearest Railway Station: Banbury
Car Parking: 500 +spaces available on the ground.   **Clubhouse:** Yes   **Club Shop:** Open matchdays only.
Admission: £3 with programme for league matches. Season tickets are available.
Programme: Size: A5   Pages: 24   Price: with admission   Editor: Norman Lacey
Advertising rates: Full page £100
Colours: Navy & white hooped shirts, navy shorts   **Change colours:** Red, with single navy & white hoop, navy shorts
Training Nights: Monday & Thursday   **Nickname:** Bulls

BARKERS' BUTTS RFC

Founded: 1947

President	R Anderson	22 Washbrook Lane, Coventry CV5 9EG	Tel: 02476 526633
Chairman	R A White	36 Westcotes, Coventry CV4 9BD	Tel: 02476 469875
Sponsorship Sec.	R Berisford	9 Macauley Road, Coventry CV2 5FD	Tel: 02476 441162
Hon. Secretary	H Roberts	84 Keresley Road, Coventry CV6 2JD	Tel: 02476 333244
Fixture Secretary	B Lester	7 Tiverton Road, Coventry CV2 3ED	Tel: 02476 443605
League Contact	R G Coward	c/o Barkers' Butts RFC (see below)	

Ground: Pickford Grange Lane, Allesley, Coventry CV5 9AR Tel: 01676 522192 Fax: 01676 523470
Capacity: 1000 - all uncovered standing.   Website: barkersbutts.co.uk
Directions: From Birmingham A45 - take Meriden turn - turn right at 3rd roundabout.
From Coventry A45 - take Meriden slip road, after 200 yds turn left - ground 300 yds on right.
Nearest Railway station: Birmingham International or Coventry
Car Parking: 200 spaces available at ground
Matchday admission: £2
Clubhouse: Open Mon.-Fri. 7-11pm, Sat. 12-11 & Sun 12-4 **Club Shop:** Open 1-5 Sat & 12-2 Sun.
Colours: Royal blue and amber   **Change colours:** All red   Training Nights: Tuesday & Thursday
Programme: Size: A3   Pages: 32   Price: £1   Editor: J Saltmarsh
Advertising: £125 full page £75 half page

BROADSTREET RFC

Founded: 1929

President	D Branston	114 Earle Court, Bell Green, Coventry CV7 7GX 02476 663866
Chairman	G Watts	15 Coopers Walk, Bubbenhall, Coventry CV8 3JB 02476 301838 (H) 02476 633336 (B)
Secretary	C J McGinty	14 Glendower Ave., Whoberley, Coventry CV5 8BE
		02476 679261 (H) 00353 7323155 (H) 00353 7323349 (F) 07801 869730 (M)
Coach	R Harcourt	69 Heather Road, Binley Woods, Coventry CV3 2DD 02476 542788 (T/F) 07887 884932 (M)
Fixture Secretary	D Wilkinson	4 Court Leet, Binley Woods, Coventry CV3 2DD 02476 543548 (H)
		Web site: www.jweb.indirect.co.uk/bspages

Ground Ivor Preece Field, Rugby Rd., Binley Woods, Coventry CV3 2AY   Web Site: broadstreet-rfc.co.uk
Tel: 02476 541068 (Manager) 02476 541069 (Fax) 02476 541070 (Clubhouse)
Capacity: 2,250   Covered Seating: 250   **Admission:** Matchdays - £3 including programme.
Directions M6 J2. Follow signs for Warwick, Stratford & Banbury along the Coventry Eastern By-pass (A46).
At the Morrisons / TGI Friday roundabout, signed Binley Woods & Coventry, take the left turn to Binley Woods (A428). The ground is immediately on your left.
Nearest Railway Station: Coventry   **Car Parking:** 150 spaces on ground.
Clubhouse: Every eve. & lunchtimes. Available for private functions. **Club Shop:** Matchdays & normal trading hours.
Programme: Size: A5   Pages: 32 + cover   Price: with admission   Editor: C J McGinty (Sec.)
Colours: White with red & green bands, navy shorts.   **Change colours:** Red with white & green bands, navy shorts
Training Nights: Tuesday & Thursdays 6.45pm.   **Nickname:** `The Street'

CAMP HILL R.F.C.

Founded: 1893

Chairman	Martin Crutchley	0121 745 4454 (H/B)
Treasurer	R L Lewin	
Secretary	Phil Moylan	47 Fallowfield Avenue, Hall Green, Birmingham B28 0NN
		Tel: 0121 243 2478 (H) 07958 248934 (M) e-mail: secretary@chrfc.com
Fixture Secretary	Graham Scutt	130 Longmore Road, Shirley, Solihull, West Mids. Tel: 0121 744 4495
League Contact	Phil Moylan (see above)	

Ground: Haslucks Green Rd, Shirley, Solihull, West Mids. B90 2EF Tel: 0121 744 4175 Fax: 0121 745 6499
Website: www.chrfc.com   email: enquiries@chrfc.com
Capacity: 400 - all uncovered standing

Directions: M42 J4 - A34 towards Birmingham for approx. 3 miles. Thro' Shirley to main traffic lights - turn left - club signposted 400 yds on left. **Nearest Railway station:** Shirley, 10 minute walk
Car Parking: 100 spaces at ground

Admission £3 including matchday programme
Clubhouse Open training nights and matchdays. **Club Shop:** Open with clubhouse
Colours: Royal blue   **Change Colours:** All red
Training Nights: Tuesday and Thursday (Seniors & Ladies) Sunday (Minis & Juniors)   **Nickname:** 'Camps'
Programme **Size:** A5   **Pages:** 40   **Price:** With admission   **Editor:** Phil Moylan (as above)
Advertising: Contact Editor

DUNSTABLIANS RUFC

Founded: 1948

President	Ross Barrington	20 Ringshall, Little Gaddesden, Berkhamsted, Herts HP4 1ND	01442 843464
Chairman	Steve Butler	12 Church Rd., PulloxHill, Beds. MK45 5HE	01525 716343
Secretary	Paul Freeman	36 Lincoln Way, Harlington, Dunstable, Beds., LU5 6NQ.	01525 750852
Treasurer	Tim Allsop	58 Holywell Rd., Studham, Dunstable, Beds. LU6 2PD	01582 873095
Fixtures Secretary	Dai Gabriel	19 Hillyfields, Dunstable, Beds. LU6 3NS	01582 606262
League Contact	Paul Freeman (as above)		

Ground **Address:** Bidwell Park, Bedford Road, Houghton Regis, Dunstable, Beds. LU5 6JW.
Tel: 01582 866555   email: secretary@dunstablians-rufc.org.uk   www.dunstablians-rufc.org.uk
Capacity: 400 all uncovered standing
Directions: M1 J12 through Toddington, ground is 2-3 miles on left on double bend before Houghton Regis or North out of Dunstable on A5, turn right after roundabout to Thorn, at end of road, ground is opposite.
Car Parking: 100+ cars at ground   Nearest Railway Station: Leagrave, Luton or Harlington
Admission: Matchday £3
Clubhouse: Two bars, changing rooms, kitchen & showers. **Club Shop:** Yes
Training Nights: Tuesday & Thursday
Programme: Size: A5 Price: with admission Pages: 32 Editor: Steve Butler (as above) Advertising: Contact Editor
Colours: Red, black, silver **Change colours:** All black **Nickname:** "Ds"

HEREFORD R.F.C.

Founded: 1870

Secretary	Peter Greenow, Hackford House, Dinedor Cross, Hereford HR2 6PD
	Tel: 01432 870874 (H)
Fixture Secretary	Fred Walsh, 32 Chandos Street, Whitecross, Hereford
	Tel: 01432 351560 (H) 07970 012544 (Mob)
Treasurer	A Whitfield, 47 Pengrove Road, Hereford HR2 1PT
	Tel: 01432 359770 (H) 01432 274544 (B)

Ground Wyeside, Hereford HR4 9UT Tel: 01432 273410

Directions Follow the ring road to Ross-on-Wye, turn right before the bridge over the River Wye, first left after 'The Antelope' into Broomy Hill, first left again into a narrow lane, the club is on the riverside.

Club Colours Red and black

KENILWORTH R.F.C.

Founded: 1924

President	Chris Holmes	36 Lunn Ave., Kenilworth CV8 2DS 01203 713313
Chairman	Chris Elgar	7 Wordsworth Drive, Kenilworth CV8 2TB 01926 852587
Secretary	Wille Whitesmith	4 Glasshouse Lane, Kenilworth CV8 2AJ 01926 859465 (H)
		e-mail: willie@iges.co.uk
Treasurer	John Davies	24 Thirlestone Close, Kenilworth CV8 2DW 01926 857962
Fixtures Secretary	Graham Billinger	7 Saville Grove, Kenilworth Kenilworth CV8 2PR 01926 851914

Ground   Jack Davies Memorial Ground, Glasshouse lane, Kenilworth CV8 2AJ
Tel: 01926 853945 Fax: 01926 851394 website: www.westmids.co.uk/kenilworthrugby
Capacity: Unknown
Directions   A452 off A46. At roundabout take third exit onto Birches lane; ground is about 1/2 mile on the right.
Nearest Railway station: Coventry   Car Parking: Plenty at the ground
Admission   Charges vary   No season tickets are available
Clubhouse   Tue, Wed & Thur 7-11pm, Fri 6-11pm, Sat 12-12, Sun 12-3pm   **Club Shop:** Open as clubhouse
Colours: Yellow & blue/dark blue   **Change colours:** All red
Training Nights: Tues, Wed & Thur.   **Nickname:** "Kens"
Programme   Size: A5   Pages: 20+   Price: Varies   Editor: Chris Holmes 01203 713313
Advertising: Page: £100   Half: £60   Quarter: £35

LEICESTER LIONS R.F.C.

Founded 1999

Westleigh (Founded 1904) & Wigston (Founded 1946) merged 1999

Secretary   Haydn Evans, c/o Thirteen Amp Ltd., Units 1-4, Brunel Rd., Hinckley, Leics. LE10 0AA
Tel: 01455 251411   e-mail: hevans@13-amp.co.uk
Fixture Secretary   Chris Barker, 29 Oliver Court, 329 London Rd., Leicester LE2 2PQ
Tel: 0116 270 2278 e-mail: chris@barker-leicsfreeserve.co.uk
League Contact   Roger Hill, 24 Welford Road., Blaby, Leics. LE8 4FS
Tel: 0116 277 2494 Fax: 0116 278 8089 mob. 07710 645033

Ground: Westleigh Park, Lutterworth Road, Blaby, Leicestershire LE8 3DP Tel: 0116 277 1010
Directions: M1/M69 J21, take B4114 to Narborough, left at Foxhunter r'about (Toby Carvery), right at next r'about, straight over next r'about & left at next (4th) r'about, ground 150 yds on left.
Admission   By programme
Programme   Price: £2   Size: A5   Pages: 20
Clubhouse   Open Mon & Thur, matchdays & Sun am.
Training Nights Monday and Thursday.
Colours   Black, white and purple quarters

LONGTON R.F.C.

Founded: 1952

President	Martin Hamer	
Chairman	Brent Rawlings	20 Fernlea Grove, Weston Coyney, Stoke-on-Trent, Staffs. ST3 5HT 01782 335317
Secretary	Dr. John Till	The Old Barn, Peacock Lane, Hanchurch, Stoke-on-Trent ST4 8RZ
		e-mail: JRandS@till2.fsnet.co.uk 01782 657660 (H)
Fixture Secretary	Ian Wright	41 Sackville St., Basford, Stoke-on-Trent ST4 6HU 01782 616903 (T&Fax)
League Contact	Tim Tams	c/o D Passmore Ltd., Unit 2, Alderflat Drive, Newstead Estate, Stoke-on-Trent ST4 8XB
		01782 646918 (B) 01889 567832 (H)
Coach	Bob Edbrooke	
Ground		Roughcote Lane, Caverswall, Stoke-on-Trent, Staffs. ST11 9EG Tel: 01782 394449
		Capacity: 250 - all uncovered standing

Directions: Roughcote Lane is off the A520, 2 miles north of the A500/A520 intersection at Meir, to the east of Stoke-on-Trent.
Nearest Railway station: Stoke-on-Trent   Car Parking: Plenty on ground
Admission: to be arranged
Clubhouse: Open matchdays & training nights   **Club Shop:** Limited amount of merchandise available from clubhouse
Colours: Black and amber, black shorts   **Change colours:** Blue & white
Training Nights: Tuesday & Thursday
Programme: Size: A5   Pages: Vary   Price: £1

MIDLAND

LUCTONIANS RFC

Founded: 1948

Chairman	David Thomas, Old Hall, Newtown, Leominster, Herefordshire. 01568 615472 (H) 01568 612977 (B)
Club Secretary	Huw Davies, The Bell House, Kingsland, Leominster, Herefordshire. HR6 9RU.
	e-mail:club@luctonians.freeuk.co Tel: 01568 708450 (H) 01432 362130 (W)
Treasurer	Richard Powell, Lower Newton, Weobley, Hereford. 01544 318340 (H&B)
Fixtures Secretary	Simon Green-Price, c/o the club Tel: as ground, plus mobile 07967 806678
League Contact	Simon Green-Price (as above)

Ground   **Address**: Mortimer Park, Hereford Road, Kingsland, Leominster, Herefordshire. HR6 8JS
Tel: 01568 709080 Fax: 01568 708169   email: cluboffice@luctonians.co.uk   Website: luctonians.co.uk
Capacity: Ample, all uncovered standing
Directions: 4 miles north west of Leominster off the A44 in the village of Kingsland, opposite the Monument Inn.
Car Parking: 200+ at ground   Nearest Railway Station: Leominster
Admission: £2 including programme
Clubhouse: Open Sat, Sun & training nights   **Club Shop:**   Yes, within clubhouse.
Programme: Size: A5   Price: £1 (incl. with ground admission)   Pages: 20   Advertising: Contact Editor
Editor: Rod Hawnt, Kingsfield Ho., Trevern, Marden, Herefordshire HR1 3EX 01568 797867 (H) 01885 483789 (B)
Training Nights: Tuesday & Thursday   **Nickname:** 'Lucs'
Colours: Black with white hoops, black shorts & socks.   **Change colours:** All green

MALVERN

Club Secretary	Simon Phillips, The Chantry, 2 Camphill Road, Worcester WR5 2HE. Tel: 01905 767887
	e-mail: simonphillips@fountaincourt.com
Fixtures Secretary	W Pomeroy, 50 Barnards Green Road, Malvern. WR14 3LW
	Tel: (H) 01684 562279. e-mail: wpomeroy@dera.gov.uk
GroundAddress:	Spring Lane, Malvern Link, Worcester. WR14 1AJ Tel: 01684 573728
Directions:	Turn left at Texaco garage on approaching Malvern from Worcester on A449. Ground is on right.
Colours:	Maroon, gold and light blue hoops, navy shorts

WALSALL R.F.C.

Founded: 1922

President	D E Horton	c/o Walsall RFC, Broadway Ground, Delves Rd,Walsall WS1 3JY
Chairman	Barry J Bodilly	55A Highgate Road, Walsall. 01922 645330 (H)
Club Secretary	Steve Lewis	15 Coppyhall Grove, Aldrdge WS9 8RP 01922 451569 (H) 01922 613310 (Fax)
Fixtures Secretary	Tim Day	20 Daffodil Place, Walsall. WS5 3DN 01922 611729(H), 01922 613310 (Fax)
Press Officer	Howard Clews	4 Binbrook Rd, Short Heath, Walsall. WV12 4TW 01902 631947 (H), 01922 613310 (F)
Director of Coaching	Arnie Evans	0121 353 1017 (H), 0121 378 1288 (B)

GroundAddress: Broadway Ground, Delves Road, Walsall WS1 3 JY   Tel: 01922 626818   Fax 01922 613310
Capacity: 2,250 Seated: 250   Standing: 2,000
Directions: From NE (A38.A461) almost into Town centre, take ring Rd left, ground 2 miles on right.
From NW (M6) Jnc 9, go left and bear right at lights onto ring road, ground on left after 2miles.
From South, head for M6 Jct 7, take A34 Walsall, after 2 miles left onto ring road, ground half mile on right.
Nearest Railway Station: Walsall BR 1.5 miles, hourly bus or taxi.
Car Parking: 100 adjacent to Clubhouse, 200 within 5 mins walk. **Admission**: Match £5, inc programme, Members £3
Clubhouse: Matchdays 12-11. Eves (except Wed), 8-11Sun. 12-4.30. Snacks & bar meals available.
Club Shop: Yes, contact Club Secretary   **Training Nights:** Tuesday & Thursday
ProgrammeSize: A5   Price: Included in entryPages: 36 plus coverEditor: Howard Clews 01902 631947
Advertising RatesMono Full Page £150, Half £75
Colours: Scarlet/black/scarlet   **Change colours:** Royal blue & amber/blue/blue & amber

MIDLAND DIVISION FINAL LEAGUE TABLES 2000-01

Midlands 2 East

	P	W	D	L	PF	PA	PD	Pts	-
*Dunstablians	22	22	0	0	950	195	755	42	2
Wellingborough	22	18	0	4	575	323	252	36	
Luton	22	15	1	6	510	264	246	31	
Kettering	22	14	1	7	572	306	266	29	
Syston	22	13	0	9	451	451	0	26	
Mansfield	22	10	1	11	370	380	-10	21	
Huntingdon	22	9	2	11	296	406	-110	20	
Lincoln	22	9	0	13	308	453	-145	18	
Ampthill	22	5	4	13	310	487	-177	14	
Nottingham Moderns	22	6	0	16	323	554	-231	12	
Leighton Buzzard	22	5	0	17	266	675	-409	10	
Stockwood Park	22	1	1	20	171	608	-437	3	

Midlands 2 West

	P	W	D	L	PF	PA	PD	Pts	-
Malvern	22	19	2	1	595	239	356	40	
Luctonians	22	18	1	3	522	251	271	37	
Bromsgrove	22	16	2	4	623	232	391	34	
Hinckley	22	17	0	5	621	262	359	34	
Sutton Coldfield	22	12	0	10	356	366	-10	24	
Old Laurentians	22	11	0	11	455	458	-3	22	
Derby	22	9	1	12	377	447	-70	19	
Newport	22	7	1	14	376	601	-225	15	
Wolverhampton	22	7	0	15	283	420	-137	14	
Selly Oak	22	6	0	16	293	421	-128	12	
Belgrave	22	4	0	18	235	593	-358	8	
Lichfield	22	2	1	19	218	664	-446	5	

Midlands 3 East (North)

	P	W	D	L	PF	PA	PD	Pts	-
Spalding	18	16	1	1	671	138	533	33	
Ilkeston	18	15	0	3	659	201	458	30	
Market Bosworth	18	13	1	4	510	198	312	27	
Newark	18	13	0	5	304	256	48	26	
Stoneygate	18	10	0	8	320	406	-86	20	
Loughborough	18	7	1	10	229	392	-163	15	
Glossop	18	5	1	12	212	433	-221	11	
Oadby Wyggestonians	18	3	0	15	188	447	-259	6	
*Long Eaton	18	4	0	14	253	502	-249	4	4
Paviors	18	1	2	15	134	507	-373	4	

Midlands 3 West (North)

	P	W	D	L	PF	PA	PD	Pts	-
Shrewsbury	18	16	0	2	480	163	317	32	
Stafford	18	13	0	5	433	223	210	26	
Aston Old Edwardians	18	13	0	5	367	247	120	26	
Leek	18	10	0	8	268	327	-59	20	
*Old Halesonians	18	10	1	7	450	295	155	19	2
Kidderminster	18	9	1	8	348	279	69	19	
Old Yardleians	18	9	1	8	332	301	31	19	
Telford	18	4	0	14	226	354	-128	8	
Birmingham Exiles	18	4	0	14	162	548	-386	8	
Newcastle (Staffs)	18	0	1	17	140	469	-329	1	

Midlands 4 East (North)

	P	W	D	L	PF	PA	PD	Pts	-
Matlock	18	17	0	1	718	154	564	34	
Market Rasen	18	14	0	4	443	213	230	28	
Ashbourne	18	14	0	4	435	283	152	28	
Grimsby	18	8	1	9	247	288	-41	17	
Amber Valley	18	7	2	9	185	299	-114	16	
Buxton	18	6	1	11	271	416	-145	13	
Mellish	18	6	1	11	218	388	-170	13	
Belper	18	4	2	12	167	311	-144	10	
*Ashfield	18	6	1	11	312	353	-41	9	4
Worksop	18	3	2	13	186	477	-291	8	

Midlands 4 West (North)

	P	W	D	L	PF	PA	PD	Pts	-
Bridgnorth	18	15	0	3	407	176	231	30	
Dixonians	18	13	1	4	440	191	249	27	
Burntwood	18	9	2	7	288	198	90	20	
Tamworth	18	10	0	8	242	268	-26	20	
Ludlow	18	9	1	8	248	278	-30	19	
Handsworth	18	9	0	9	359	245	114	18	
Old Saltleians	18	8	1	9	293	243	50	17	
Willenhall	18	7	2	9	186	286	-100	16	
*Edwardians	18	4	1	13	191	232	-41	7	2
Warley	18	2	0	16	117	654	-537	4	

Midlands 3 East (South)

	P	W	D	L	PF	PA	PD	Pts	-
South Leicester	18	18	0	0	707	161	546	36	
Stewarts & Lloyds	18	16	0	2	410	191	219	32	
Northampton Old Scouts	18	11	0	7	415	327	88	22	
Towcestrians	18	10	0	8	321	356	-35	20	
Peterborough	18	9	0	9	399	332	67	18	
Long Buckby	18	8	1	9	304	338	-34	17	
Northampton Mens Own	18	5	1	12	375	475	-100	11	
Vipers	18	5	0	13	205	561	-356	10	
Old Northamptonians	18	4	0	14	271	434	-163	8	
Lutterworth	18	3	0	15	229	461	-232	6	

Midlands 3 West (South)

	P	W	D	L	PF	PA	PD	Pts	-
Stratford-Upon-Avon	16	13	0	3	532	145	387	26	
Leamington	16	11	1	4	352	191	161	23	
Keresley	16	11	0	5	332	249	83	22	
Old Coventrians	16	10	0	6	349	231	118	20	
Nuneaton Old Edwardians	16	9	0	7	305	287	18	18	
Bedworth	16	7	1	8	295	260	35	15	
Old Leamingtonians	16	5	2	9	223	346	-123	12	
Evesham	16	2	0	14	187	349	-162	4	
*Kings Norton	16	2	0	14	91	608	-517	2	2

Midlands 4 East (South)

	P	W	D	L	PF	PA	PD	Pts	-
Kibworth	18	15	0	3	509	170	339	30	
Melton Mowbray	18	12	1	5	402	214	188	25	
Loughborough Students	18	11	0	7	422	192	230	22	
*Kesteven	18	10	2	6	282	237	45	20	2
*Northampton Casuals	18	10	1	7	282	256	26	19	2
Leicester Forest	18	9	1	8	225	272	-47	19	
Coalville	18	8	0	10	292	260	32	16	
Stamford	18	5	0	13	210	501	-291	10	
*West Bridgford	18	5	0	13	202	466	-264	6	4
Sleaford	18	2	1	15	205	463	-258	5	

Midlands 4 West (South)

	P	W	D	L	PF	PA	PD	Pts	-
Silhillians	18	15	1	2	439	183	256	31	
Pershore	18	15	0	3	413	181	232	30	
Droitwich	18	14	0	4	395	181	214	28	
Southam	18	13	0	5	331	206	125	26	
Cleobury Mortimer	18	9	1	8	240	269	-29	19	
Berkswell & Balsall	18	7	2	9	235	203	32	16	
*Dunlop	18	6	0	12	233	328	-95	10	2
Trinity Guild	18	3	1	14	265	409	-144	7	
Redditch	18	3	0	15	251	374	-123	6	
Stoke Old Boys	18	2	1	15	158	626	-468	5	

* denotes points deducted in right hand column

MIDLAND

East Midlands 1

	P	W	D	L	PF	PA	PD	Pts	-
Biggleswade	20	17	0	3	606	220	386	34	
Bugbrooke	20	14	1	5	446	212	234	29	
Northampton BBOB	20	14	1	5	407	199	208	29	
Brackley	20	11	0	9	463	327	136	22	
Wellingborough O.G.	20	10	1	9	458	415	43	21	
Bedford Queens	20	10	1	9	292	397	-105	21	
Daventry	20	10	0	10	388	364	24	20	
Rushden & Higham	20	8	1	11	369	345	24	17	
Deepings	20	5	1	14	236	615	-379	11	
St Ives (Midlands)	20	4	1	15	241	538	-297	9	
Bedford Swifts	20	3	1	16	224	498	-274	7	

East Midlands 2

	P	W	D	L	PF	PA	PD	Pts	-
Kempston	18	14	1	3	663	139	524	29	
Westwood	18	14	1	3	573	152	421	29	
Biddenham	18	13	0	5	405	175	230	26	
Corby	18	12	1	5	360	229	131	25	
*Northampton Heathens	18	8	0	10	279	517	-238	14	2
Thorney	18	6	0	12	175	414	-239	12	
*St Neots	18	10	0	8	363	266	97	8	12
Vauxhall Motors	18	3	0	15	212	452	-240	6	
*Brixworth	18	1	0	17	66	626	-560	-2	4
*Oundle	18	7	1	10	323	449	-126	-5	20

NLD/Leics 1East

	P	W	D	L	PF	PA	PD	Pts	-
Oakham	18	18	0	0	560	94	466	36	
East Retford	18	14	0	4	376	177	199	28	
Boston	18	12	0	6	299	150	149	24	
Southwell	18	11	1	6	300	235	65	23	
Keyworth	18	9	0	9	276	331	-55	18	
Nottinghamians	18	7	1	10	299	289	10	15	
Boots Athletic	18	5	0	13	244	328	-84	10	
Cotgrave	18	4	1	13	140	307	-167	9	
*Barton & District	18	6	0	12	273	374	-101	6	6
Cleethorpes	18	2	1	15	111	593	-482	5	

NLD/Leics 2 East

	P	W	D	L	PF	PA	PD	Pts	-
North Kesteven	15	13	0	2	454	87	367	26	
Stamford College	16	11	0	5	283	143	140	22	
Skegness	13	10	0	3	269	121	148	20	
Gainsborough	16	8	0	8	232	256	-24	16	
Appleby Frodingham	15	6	0	9	249	241	8	12	
Bingham	15	6	0	9	197	251	-54	12	
Horncastle	16	6	0	10	235	449	-214	12	
Yarborough Bees	13	4	0	9	175	308	-133	8	
Bourne	13	2	0	11	111	349	-238	4	

NLD/Leics 1 West

	P	W	D	L	PF	PA	PD	Pts	-
Old Newtonians	20	17	1	2	532	147	385	35	
Melbourne	20	15	1	4	530	262	268	31	
Nottingham Casuals	20	15	0	5	582	216	366	30	
Aylestone St James	20	15	0	5	429	177	252	30	
Bakewell Mannerians	20	13	0	7	266	227	39	26	
Leesbrook	20	8	1	11	288	503	-215	17	
Dronfield	20	8	0	12	342	327	15	16	
East Leake	20	8	0	12	285	332	-47	16	
Castle Donington	20	5	0	15	251	395	-144	10	
Rolls Royce	20	4	1	15	213	679	-466	9	
Tupton	20	0	0	20	118	571	-453	0	

NLD/Leics 2 West

	P	W	D	L	PF	PA	PD	Pts	-
Aylestonians	12	12	0	0	352	63	289	24	
Ashby	12	9	0	3	338	139	199	18	
Chesterfield	12	9	0	3	259	132	127	18	
Ollerton	12	5	1	6	171	335	-164	11	
*Meden Vale	12	3	1	8	120	207	-87	5	2
*Hope Valley	12	2	0	10	92	301	-209	2	2
*University Of Derby	12	1	0	11	115	270	-155	-4	6

North Midlands 1

	P	W	D	L	PF	PA	PD	Pts	-
Ledbury	14	13	0	1	361	153	208	26	
Stourport	13	12	0	1	277	125	152	24	
Veseyans	12	6	0	6	146	160	-14	12	
Five Ways O.E.	13	6	0	7	194	310	-116	12	
Upton On Severn	14	4	1	9	184	249	-65	9	
Bishops Castle & O.V.	12	4	0	8	226	145	81	8	
Bromyard	10	3	0	7	146	177	-31	6	
Old Griffinians	14	2	1	11	186	401	-215	5	

North Midlands 2

	P	W	D	L	PF	PA	PD	Pts	-
Tenbury	16	15	0	1	305	126	179	30	
Yardley & District	16	11	3	2	405	117	288	25	
Aldridge	16	10	2	4	292	185	107	22	
Bournville	16	8	3	5	225	188	37	19	
Clee	16	7	4	5	211	113	98	18	
*Birmingham C.S.	16	6	1	9	212	196	16	11	2
Harborne	16	4	1	11	114	358	-244	9	
Bloxwich	16	3	1	12	178	335	-157	7	
*Birchfield	16	0	1	15	73	397	-324	-1	2

North Midlands 3

	P	W	D	L	PF	PA	PD	Pts	-
Solihull	12	11	0	1	683	89	594	22	
Worcester Wanderers	12	11	0	1	560	91	469	22	
Bredon Star	12	6	0	6	297	259	38	12	
Essington	12	6	0	6	165	220	-55	12	
Kynoch	12	5	1	6	153	302	-149	11	
Greyhound	12	1	1	10	69	504	-435	3	
Chaddesley Corbett	12	1	0	11	43	505	-462	2	

Staffordshire 1

	P	W	D	L	PF	PA	PD	Pts	-
Wednesbury	12	9	1	2	338	74	264	19	
Wheaton Aston	12	9	0	3	295	114	181	18	
Uttoxeter	12	8	0	4	255	106	149	16	
Linley	12	6	0	6	158	168	-10	12	
Whittington	12	5	0	7	224	267	-43	10	
GEC St. Leonards	12	4	0	8	129	212	-83	8	
Rugeley	12	0	1	11	48	506	-458	1	

Staffordshire 2

	P	W	D	L	PF	PA	PD	Pts	-
Cannock	12	10	1	1	443	39	404	21	
Gnosall	12	8	2	2	308	155	153	18	
Barton under Needwood	12	7	1	4	222	162	60	15	
Stone	12	6	1	5	184	163	21	13	
Market Drayton	12	4	1	7	98	254	-156	9	
Michelin	12	1	3	8	103	369	-266	5	
Eccleshall	12	1	1	10	89	305	-216	3	

Warwickshire 1

	P	W	D	L	PF	PA	PD	Pts	-
Earlsdon	18	17	0	1	432	134	298	34	
Coventry Welsh	18	13	0	5	315	232	83	26	
Marconi Coventry	18	12	0	6	311	170	141	24	
*Shipston On Stour	18	11	1	6	339	212	127	21	2
Manor Park	18	9	0	9	194	224	-30	18	
Spartans (Midlands)	18	8	1	9	272	237	35	17	
Alcester	18	7	0	11	272	291	-19	14	
Rugby St Andrews	18	5	0	13	178	317	-139	10	
*Claverdon	18	5	0	13	214	357	-143	8	2
Pinley	18	2	0	16	149	502	-353	4	

Warwickshire 2

	P	W	D	L	PF	PA	PD	Pts	-
Standard	14	13	0	1	285	89	196	26	
Old Wheatleyans	14	10	1	3	356	155	201	21	
Coventry Technical	14	10	1	3	257	138	119	21	
Atherstone	14	8	0	6	391	204	187	16	
Harbury	14	6	0	8	299	308	-9	12	
*Coventry Saracens	14	5	0	9	122	354	-232	8	2
Old Warwickians	14	2	0	12	142	260	-118	4	
*Coventrians	14	1	0	13	120	464	-344	-4	6

MIDLAND DIVISION FIXTURE GRIDS 2001-2002

Midlands 2 East

	Ampthill	Hinckley	Huntingdon	Ilkeston	Kettering	Lincoln	Luton	Mansfield	South Leicester	Spalding	Syston	Wellingborough
Ampthill		17.11	22.09	16.03	02.03	09.02	27.10	26.01	06.10	05.01	08.12	06.04
Hinckley	12.01		09.02	13.04	22.12	16.03	26.01	22.09	27.10	02.03	01.12	06.10
Huntingdon	09.03	20.10		10.11	12.01	01.12	23.02	13.04	29.09	22.12	02.02	16.03
Ilkeston	08.09	08.12	26.01		22.09	02.03	05.01	06.10	17.11	09.02	06.04	27.10
Kettering	29.09	06.04	17.11	09.03		06.10	08.12	09.02	05.01	27.10	08.09	26.01
Lincoln	20.10	08.09	05.01	29.09	23.02		06.04	27.10	08.12	26.01	09.03	17.11
Luton	02.02	10.11	06.10	01.12	13.04	22.12		16.03	09.02	22.09	12.01	02.03
Mansfield	10.11	09.03	08.12	23.02	20.10	02.02	08.09		06.04	17.11	29.09	05.01
South Leicester	23.02	02.02	02.03	12.01	01.12	13.04	20.10	22.12		16.03	10.11	22.09
Spalding	01.12	29.09	06.04	20.10	02.02	10.11	09.03	12.01	08.09		23.02	08.12
Syston	13.04	05.01	27.10	22.12	16.03	22.09	17.11	02.03	26.01	06.10		09.02
Wellingborough	22.12	23.02	08.09	02.02	10.11	12.01	29.09	01.12	09.03	13.04	20.10	

Midlands 2 West

	Bromsgrove	Burton	Derby	Newbold	Newport	Old Laurentians	Shrewsbury	Stafford	Stoke on Trent	Stratford-Upon-Avon	Sutton Coldfield	Wolverhampton
Bromsgrove		08.09	26.01	22.09	06.10	08.12	17.11	02.03	05.01	09.02	06.04	27.10
Burton	16.03		22.09	02.03	26.01	17.11	06.10	09.02	27.10	05.01	08.12	06.04
Derby	10.11	09.03		12.01	13.04	20.10	29.09	01.12	23.02	22.12	02.02	16.03
Newbold	09.03	29.09	17.11		09.02	06.04	05.01	06.10	08.12	27.10	08.09	26.01
Newport	23.02	10.11	08.12	20.10		09.03	06.04	02.02	08.09	17.11	29.09	05.01
Old Laurentians	13.04	12.01	09.02	22.12	22.09		27.10	16.03	26.01	02.03	01.12	06.10
Shrewsbury	12.01	23.02	02.03	01.12	22.12	02.02		13.04	20.10	16.03	10.11	22.09
Stafford	29.09	20.10	05.01	23.02	27.10	08.09	08.12		06.04	26.01	09.03	17.11
Stoke on Trent	01.12	02.02	06.10	13.04	16.03	10.11	09.02	22.12		22.09	12.01	02.03
Stratford-Upon-Avon	20.10	01.12	06.04	02.02	12.01	29.09	08.09	10.11	09.03		23.02	08.12
Sutton Coldfield	22.12	13.04	27.10	16.03	02.03	05.01	26.01	22.09	17.11	06.10		09.02
Wolverhampton	02.02	22.12	08.09	10.11	01.12	23.02	09.03	12.01	29.09	13.04	20.10	

Midlands 3 East North

	Belgrave	Glossop	Loughborough	Market Bosworth	Market Rasen	Matlock	Melton Mowbray	Newark	Nottingham Moderns	Stoneygate
Belgrave		22.09	29.09	22.12	10.11	01.12	20.10	23.02	06.04	26.01
Glossop	16.03		23.02	20.10	29.09	10.11	22.12	26.01	01.12	06.04
Loughborough	09.03	06.10		01.12	22.12	06.04	26.01	20.10	22.09	10.11
Market Bosworth	17.11	02.02	13.04		23.02	27.10	16.03	08.12	12.01	29.09
Market Rasen	12.01	09.03	17.11	06.10		02.02	08.12	13.04	27.10	16.03
Matlock	13.04	12.01	08.12	26.01	20.10		29.09	16.03	17.11	23.02
Melton Mowbray	02.02	17.11	27.10	22.09	06.04	09.03		12.01	06.10	01.12
Newark	06.10	27.10	02.02	06.04	01.12	22.09	10.11		09.03	22.12
Nottingham Moderns	08.12	13.04	16.03	10.11	26.01	22.12	23.02	29.09		20.10
Stoneygate	27.10	08.12	12.01	09.03	22.09	06.10	13.04	17.11	02.02	

MIDLAND

Midlands 3 East South

	Kibworth	Leighton Buzzard	Long Buckby	Northampton Mens Own	Northampton Old Scouts	Peterborough	Stewarts & Lloyds	Stockwood Park	Towcestrians	Vipers
Kibworth		16.03	29.09	23.02	20.10	26.01	10.11	22.12	01.12	06.04
Leighton Buzzard	22.09		10.11	29.09	22.12	23.02	01.12	20.10	06.04	26.01
Long Buckby	09.03	12.01		17.11	06.10	13.04	02.02	08.12	27.10	16.03
Northampton Mens Own	06.10	09.03	22.12		01.12	20.10	06.04	26.01	22.09	10.11
Northampton Old Scouts	02.02	17.11	23.02	13.04		08.12	27.10	16.03	12.01	29.09
Peterborough	27.10	06.10	01.12	02.02	06.04		22.09	10.11	09.03	22.12
Stewarts & Lloyds	12.01	13.04	20.10	08.12	26.01	16.03		29.09	17.11	23.02
Stockwood Park	17.11	02.02	06.04	27.10	22.09	12.01	09.03		06.10	01.12
Towcestrians	13.04	08.12	26.01	16.03	10.11	29.09	22.12	23.02		20.10
Vipers	08.12	27.10	22.09	12.01	09.03	17.11	06.10	13.04	02.02	

Midlands 3 West North

	Aston Old Edwardians	Bridgnorth	Dixonians	Kidderminster	Leek	Lichfield	Old Halesonians	Old Yardleians	Selly Oak	Telford
Aston Old Edwardians		29.09	23.02	16.03	20.10	26.01	10.11	22.12	01.12	06.04
Bridgnorth	09.03		17.11	12.01	06.10	13.04	02.02	08.12	27.10	16.03
Dixonians	06.10	22.12		09.03	01.12	20.10	06.04	26.01	22.09	10.11
Kidderminster	22.09	10.11	29.09		22.12	23.02	01.12	20.10	06.04	26.01
Leek	02.02	23.02	13.04	17.11		08.12	27.10	16.03	12.01	29.09
Lichfield	27.10	01.12	02.02	06.10	06.04		22.09	10.11	09.03	22.12
Old Halesonians	12.01	20.10	08.12	13.04	26.01	16.03		29.09	17.11	23.02
Old Yardleians	17.11	06.04	27.10	02.02	22.09	12.01	09.03		06.10	01.12
Selly Oak	13.04	26.01	16.03	08.12	10.11	29.09	22.12	23.02		20.10
Telford	08.12	22.09	12.01	27.10	09.03	17.11	06.10	13.04	02.02	

Midlands 3 West South

	Bedworth	Birmingham Exiles	Evesham	Keresley	Leamington	Nuneaton Old Edwardians	Old Coventrians	Old Leamingtonians	Pershore	Silhillians
Bedworth		23.02	16.03	29.09	20.10	26.01	10.11	22.12	01.12	06.04
Birmingham Exiles	06.10		09.03	22.12	01.12	20.10	06.04	26.01	22.09	10.11
Evesham	22.09	29.09		10.11	22.12	23.02	01.12	20.10	06.04	26.01
Keresley	09.03	17.11	12.01		06.10	13.04	02.02	08.12	27.10	16.03
Leamington	02.02	13.04	17.11	23.02		08.12	27.10	16.03	12.01	29.09
Nuneaton Old Edwardians	27.10	02.02	06.10	01.12	06.04		22.09	10.11	09.03	22.12
Old Coventrians	12.01	08.12	13.04	20.10	26.01	16.03		29.09	17.11	23.02
Old Leamingtonians	17.11	27.10	02.02	06.04	22.09	12.01	09.03		06.10	01.12
Pershore	13.04	16.03	08.12	26.01	10.11	29.09	22.12	23.02		20.10
Silhillians	08.12	12.01	27.10	22.09	09.03	17.11	06.10	13.04	02.02	

Mildlands 4 East North

	Amber Valley	Ashbourne	Buxton	East Retford	Grimsby	Kesteven	Long Eaton	Loughborough Students	Melbourne	Paviors
Amber Valley		16.03	29.09	23.02	20.10	26.01	10.11	22.12	01.12	06.04
Ashbourne	22.09		10.11	29.09	22.12	23.02	01.12	20.10	06.04	26.01
Buxton	09.03	12.01		17.11	06.10	13.04	02.02	08.12	27.10	16.03
East Retford	06.10	09.03	22.12		01.12	20.10	06.04	26.01	22.09	10.11
Grimsby	02.02	17.11	23.02	13.04		08.12	27.10	16.03	12.01	29.09
Kesteven	27.10	06.10	01.12	02.02	06.04		22.09	10.11	09.03	22.12
Long Eaton	12.01	13.04	20.10	08.12	26.01	16.03		29.09	17.11	23.02
Loughborough Students	17.11	02.02	06.04	27.10	22.09	12.01	09.03		06.10	01.12
Melbourne	13.04	08.12	26.01	16.03	10.11	29.09	22.12	23.02		20.10
Paviors	08.12	27.10	22.09	12.01	09.03	17.11	06.10	13.04	02.02	

Midlands 4 East South

	Biggleswade	Bugbrooke	Coalville	Leicester Forest	Lutterworth	Northampton Casuals	Oadby Wyggestonians	Oakham	Old Newtonians	Old Northamptonians
Biggleswade		16.03	29.09	23.02	20.10	26.01	10.11	22.12	01.12	06.04
Bugbrooke	22.09		10.11	29.09	22.12	23.02	01.12	20.10	06.04	26.01
Coalville	09.03	12.01		17.11	06.10	13.04	02.02	08.12	27.10	16.03
Leicester Forest	06.10	09.03	22.12		01.12	20.10	06.04	26.01	22.09	10.11
Lutterworth	02.02	17.11	23.02	13.04		08.12	27.10	16.03	12.01	29.09
Northampton Casuals	27.10	06.10	01.12	02.02	06.04		22.09	10.11	09.03	22.12
Oadby Wyggestonians	12.01	13.04	20.10	08.12	26.01	16.03		29.09	17.11	23.02
Oakham	17.11	02.02	06.04	27.10	22.09	12.01	09.03		06.10	01.12
Old Newtonians	13.04	08.12	26.01	16.03	10.11	29.09	22.12	23.02		20.10
Old Northamptonians	08.12	27.10	22.09	12.01	09.03	17.11	06.10	13.04	02.02	

Midlands 4 West North

	Burntwood	Cleobury Mortimer	Handsworth	Ludlow	Newcastle (Staffs)	Old Saltleians	Tamworth	Wednesbury	Wheaton Aston	Willenhall
Burntwood		16.03	29.09	23.02	20.10	26.01	10.11	22.12	01.12	06.04
Cleobury Mortimer	22.09		10.11	29.09	22.12	23.02	01.12	20.10	06.04	26.01
Handsworth	09.03	12.01		17.11	06.10	13.04	02.02	08.12	27.10	16.03
Ludlow	06.10	09.03	22.12		01.12	20.10	06.04	26.01	22.09	10.11
Newcastle (Staffs)	02.02	17.11	23.02	13.04		08.12	27.10	16.03	12.01	29.09
Old Saltleians	27.10	06.10	01.12	02.02	06.04		22.09	10.11	09.03	22.12
Tamworth	12.01	13.04	20.10	08.12	26.01	16.03		29.09	17.11	23.02
Wednesbury	17.11	02.02	06.04	27.10	22.09	12.01	09.03		06.10	01.12
Wheaton Aston	13.04	08.12	26.01	16.03	10.11	29.09	22.12	23.02		20.10
Willenhall	08.12	27.10	22.09	12.01	09.03	17.11	06.10	13.04	02.02	

MIDLAND

MIDLAND

Midlands 4 West South

	Berkswell & Balsall	Coventry Welsh	Droitwich	Dunlop	Earlsdon	Kings Norton	Ledbury	Southam	Stourport	Woodrush
Berkswell & Balsall		01.12	29.09	23.02	06.04	10.11	16.03	22.12	26.01	20.10
Coventry Welsh	13.04		26.01	16.03	20.10	22.12	08.12	23.02	29.09	10.11
Droitwich	09.03	27.10		17.11	16.03	02.02	12.01	08.12	13.04	06.10
Dunlop	06.10	22.09	22.12		10.11	06.04	09.03	26.01	20.10	01.12
Earlsdon	08.12	02.02	22.09	12.01		06.10	27.10	13.04	17.11	09.03
Kings Norton	12.01	17.11	20.10	08.12	23.02		13.04	29.09	16.03	26.01
Ledbury	22.09	06.04	10.11	29.09	26.01	01.12		20.10	23.02	22.12
Southam	17.11	06.10	06.04	27.10	01.12	09.03	02.02		12.01	22.09
Stourport	27.10	09.03	01.12	02.02	22.12	22.09	06.10	10.11		06.04
Woodrush	02.02	12.01	23.02	13.04	29.09	27.10	17.11	16.03	08.12	

Notts/Lincs/ Derbys/Leic. 1 East

	Boston	Keyworth	Mellish	North Kesteven	Nottinghamians	Skegness	Sleaford	Southwell	Stamford	West Bridgford
Boston		16.03	29.09	23.02	20.10	26.01	10.11	22.12	01.12	06.04
Keyworth	22.09		10.11	29.09	22.12	23.02	01.12	20.10	06.04	26.01
Mellish	09.03	12.01		17.11	06.10	13.04	02.02	08.12	27.10	16.03
North Kesteven	06.10	09.03	22.12		01.12	20.10	06.04	26.01	22.09	10.11
Nottinghamians	02.02	17.11	23.02	13.04		08.12	27.10	16.03	12.01	29.09
Skegness	27.10	06.10	01.12	02.02	06.04		22.09	10.11	09.03	22.12
Sleaford	12.01	13.04	20.10	08.12	26.01	16.03		29.09	17.11	23.02
Southwell	17.11	02.02	06.04	27.10	22.09	12.01	09.03		06.10	01.12
Stamford	13.04	08.12	26.01	16.03	10.11	29.09	22.12	23.02		20.10
West Bridgford	08.12	27.10	22.09	12.01	09.03	17.11	06.10	13.04	02.02	

Notts/Lincs/ Derbys/Leic. 1 West

	Ashby	Ashfield	Aylestone St James	Aylestonians	Bakewell Mannerians	Belper	Dronfield	Leesbrook	Nottingham Casuals	Worksop
Ashby		16.03	29.09	23.02	20.10	26.01	10.11	22.12	01.12	06.04
Ashfield	22.09		10.11	29.09	22.12	23.02	01.12	20.10	06.04	26.01
Aylestone St James	09.03	12.01		17.11	06.10	13.04	02.02	08.12	27.10	16.03
Aylestonians	06.10	09.03	22.12		01.12	20.10	06.04	26.01	22.09	10.11
Bakewell Mannerians	02.02	17.11	23.02	13.04		08.12	27.10	16.03	12.01	29.09
Belper	27.10	06.10	01.12	02.02	06.04		22.09	10.11	09.03	22.12
Dronfield	12.01	13.04	20.10	08.12	26.01	16.03		29.09	17.11	23.02
Leesbrook	17.11	02.02	06.04	27.10	22.09	12.01	09.03		06.10	01.12
Nottingham Casuals	13.04	08.12	26.01	16.03	10.11	29.09	22.12	23.02		20.10
Worksop	08.12	27.10	22.09	12.01	09.03	17.11	06.10	13.04	02.02	

Notts/Lincs/Derbys/Leic. 2 East

	Appleby Frodingham	Barton & District	Bourne	Cleethorpes	Gainsborough	Horncastle	Meden Vale	Ollerton	Stamford College	Yarborough Bees
Appleby Frodingham		22.09	09.03	06.10	02.02	27.10	12.01	17.11	13.04	08.12
Barton & District	16.03		12.01	09.03	17.11	06.10	13.04	02.02	08.12	27.10
Bourne	29.09	10.11		22.12	23.02	01.12	20.10	06.04	26.01	22.09
Cleethorpes	23.02	29.09	17.11		13.04	02.02	08.12	27.10	16.03	12.01
Gainsborough	20.10	22.12	06.10	01.12		06.04	26.01	22.09	10.11	09.03
Horncastle	26.01	23.02	13.04	20.10	08.12		16.03	12.01	29.09	17.11
Meden Vale	10.11	01.12	02.02	06.04	27.10	22.09		09.03	22.12	06.10
Ollerton	22.12	20.10	08.12	26.01	16.03	10.11	29.09		23.02	13.04
Stamford College	01.12	06.04	27.10	22.09	12.01	09.03	17.11	06.10		02.02
Yarborough Bees	06.04	26.01	16.03	10.11	29.09	22.12	23.02	01.12	20.10	

Notts/Lincs/Derbys/Leic. 2 West

	Anstey	Bingham	Boots Athletic	Castle Donington	Chesterfield	Cotgrave	East Leake	Hope Valley	Rolls Royce	Tupton
Anstey		16.03	29.09	23.02	20.10	26.01	10.11	22.12	01.12	06.04
Bingham	22.09		10.11	29.09	22.12	23.02	01.12	20.10	06.04	26.01
Boots Athletic	09.03	12.01		17.11	06.10	13.04	02.02	08.12	27.10	16.03
Castle Donington	06.10	09.03	22.12		01.12	20.10	06.04	26.01	22.09	10.11
Chesterfield	02.02	17.11	23.02	13.04		08.12	27.10	16.03	12.01	29.09
Cotgrave	27.10	06.10	01.12	02.02	06.04		22.09	10.11	09.03	22.12
East Leake	12.01	13.04	20.10	08.12	26.01	16.03		29.09	17.11	23.02
Hope Valley	17.11	02.02	06.04	27.10	22.09	12.01	09.03		06.10	01.12
Rolls Royce	13.04	08.12	26.01	16.03	10.11	29.09	22.12	23.02		20.10
Tupton	08.12	27.10	22.09	12.01	09.03	17.11	06.10	13.04	02.02	

East Midlands 1

	Bedford Queens	Brackley	Daventry	Deepings	Kempston	Northampton BBOB	Rushden & Higham	St Ives (Midlands)	Wellingborough O.G.	Westwood
Bedford Queens		09.03	01.12	06.04	22.09	06.10	20.10	26.01	22.12	10.11
Brackley	29.09		22.12	01.12	06.04	22.09	23.02	20.10	10.11	26.01
Daventry	13.04	17.11		27.10	12.01	02.02	08.12	16.03	23.02	29.09
Deepings	08.12	13.04	26.01		17.11	12.01	16.03	29.09	20.10	23.02
Kempston	16.03	08.12	10.11	22.12		13.04	29.09	23.02	26.01	20.10
Northampton BBOB	23.02	16.03	20.10	10.11	01.12		26.01	22.12	29.09	06.04
Rushden & Higham	02.02	06.10	06.04	22.09	09.03	27.10		10.11	01.12	22.12
St Ives (Midlands)	27.10	02.02	22.09	09.03	06.10	17.11	12.01		06.04	01.12
Wellingborough O.G.	17.11	12.01	06.10	02.02	27.10	09.03	13.04	08.12		16.03
Westwood	12.01	27.10	09.03	06.10	02.02	08.12	17.11	13.04	22.09	

MIDLAND

MIDLAND

East Midlands 2

	Bedford Swifts	Biddenham	Corby	Northampton Heathens	Oundle	St Neots	Thorney	Vauxhall Motors
Bedford Swifts		01.12	12.01	10.11	13.04	20.10	09.03	29.09
Biddenham	06.04		02.02	20.10	12.01	29.09	10.11	08.09
Corby	27.10	06.10		22.09	23.02	06.04	08.09	08.12
Northampton Heathens	08.12	26.01	09.03		06.10	08.09	29.09	17.11
Oundle	17.11	27.10	29.09	02.02		09.03	20.10	06.04
St Neots	26.01	23.02	01.12	16.03	22.09		13.04	27.10
Thorney	22.09	08.12	16.03	23.02	26.01	17.11		06.10
Vauxhall Motors	23.02	16.03	10.11	13.04	01.12	12.01	02.02	

North Midlands 1

	Bishops Castle & O.V.	Bromyard	Edwardians	Five Ways O.E.	Redditch	Tenbury	Upton On Severn	Veseyans	Warley	Yardley & Distric
Bishops Castle & O.V.		16.03	29.09	23.02	20.10	26.01	10.11	22.12	01.12	06.04
Bromyard	22.09		10.11	29.09	22.12	23.02	01.12	20.10	06.04	26.01
Edwardians	09.03	12.01		17.11	06.10	13.04	02.02	08.12	27.10	16.03
Five Ways O.E.	06.10	09.03	22.12		01.12	20.10	06.04	26.01	22.09	10.11
Redditch	02.02	17.11	23.02	13.04		08.12	27.10	16.03	12.01	29.09
Tenbury	27.10	06.10	01.12	02.02	06.04		22.09	10.11	09.03	22.12
Upton On Severn	12.01	13.04	20.10	08.12	26.01	16.03		29.09	17.11	23.02
Veseyans	17.11	02.02	06.04	27.10	22.09	12.01	09.03		06.10	01.12
Warley	13.04	08.12	26.01	16.03	10.11	29.09	22.12	23.02		20.10
Yardley & District	08.12	27.10	22.09	12.01	09.03	17.11	06.10	13.04	02.02	

North Midlands 2

	Aldridge	Birmingham C.S.	Bloxwich	Bournville	Clee	Harborne	Old Griffinians	Solihull	Worcester Wanderers
Aldridge		16.03	29.09	23.02	20.10	26.01	10.11	22.12	01.12
Birmingham C.S.	22.09		10.11	29.09	22.12	23.02	01.12	20.10	06.04
Bloxwich	09.03	12.01		17.11	06.10	13.04	02.02	08.12	27.10
Bournville	06.10	09.03	22.12		01.12	20.10	06.04	26.01	22.09
Clee	02.02	17.11	23.02	13.04		08.12	27.10	16.03	12.01
Harborne	27.10	06.10	01.12	02.02	06.04		22.09	10.11	09.03
Old Griffinians	12.01	13.04	20.10	08.12	26.01	16.03		29.09	17.11
Solihull	17.11	02.02	06.04	27.10	22.09	12.01	09.03		06.10
Worcester Wanderers	13.04	08.12	26.01	16.03	10.11	29.09	22.12	23.02	

North Midlands 3

	Bewdley	Birchfield	Bredon Star	Chaddesley Corbett	Erdington	Essington	Greyhound	Kynoch
Bewdley		16.03	29.09	23.02	20.10	26.01	10.11	22.12
Birchfield	22.09		10.11	29.09	22.12	23.02	01.12	20.10
Bredon Star	09.03	12.01		17.11	06.10	13.04	02.02	08.12
Chaddesley Corbett	06.10	09.03	22.12		01.12	20.10	06.04	26.01
Erdington	02.02	17.11	23.02	13.04		08.12	27.10	16.03
Essington	27.10	06.10	01.12	02.02	06.04		22.09	10.11
Greyhound	12.01	13.04	20.10	08.12	26.01	16.03		29.09
Kynoch	17.11	02.02	06.04	27.10	22.09	12.01	09.03	

Staffordshire 1

	Cannock	GEC St. Leonards	Linley	Uttoxeter	Whittington
Cannock		12.01	01.12	23.02	26.01
GEC St. Leonards	22.09		10.11	26.01	13.04
Linley	16.03	23.02		22.12	22.09
Uttoxeter	10.11	20.10	13.04		16.03
Whittington	20.10	22.12	12.01	01.12	

Staffordshire 2

	Barton under Needwood	Eccleshall	Gnosall	Market Drayton	Michelin	Rugeley	Stone
Barton under Needwood		27.10	13.04	01.12	26.01	22.09	09.03
Eccleshall	23.02		01.12	09.03	22.12	12.01	20.10
Gnosall	08.12	16.03		12.01	10.11	20.10	23.02
Market Drayton	16.03	10.11	06.10		08.12	23.02	22.09
Michelin	20.10	22.09	09.03	13.04		01.12	12.01
Rugeley	22.12	06.10	26.01	27.10	16.03		08.12
Stone	10.11	26.01	27.10	22.12	06.10	13.04	

Warwickshire 1

	Alcester	Manor Park	Marconi Coventry	Old Wheatleyans	Rugby St Andrews	Shipston On Stour	Spartans (Midlands)	Standard	Stoke Old Boys	Trinity Guild
Alcester		20.10	26.01	16.03	22.12	01.12	06.04	29.09	23.02	10.11
Manor Park	02.02		08.12	17.11	16.03	12.01	29.09	23.02	13.04	27.10
Marconi Coventry	27.10	06.04		06.10	10.11	09.03	22.12	01.12	02.02	22.09
Old Wheatleyans	22.09	22.12	23.02		20.10	06.04	26.01	10.11	29.09	01.12
Rugby St Andrews	17.11	22.09	12.01	02.02		06.10	01.12	06.04	27.10	09.03
Shipston On Stour	13.04	10.11	29.09	08.12	23.02		20.10	26.01	16.03	22.12
Spartans (Midlands)	08.12	09.03	17.11	27.10	13.04	02.02		22.09	12.01	06.10
Standard	09.03	06.10	13.04	12.01	08.12	27.10	16.03		17.11	02.02
Stoke Old Boys	06.10	01.12	20.10	09.03	26.01	22.09	10.11	22.12		06.04
Trinity Guild	12.01	26.01	16.03	13.04	29.09	17.11	23.02	20.10	08.12	

Warwickshire 2

	Atherstone	Claverdon	Coventrians	Coventry Saracens	Coventry Technical	Harbury	Old Warwickians	Pinley	Warwick
Atherstone		20.10	16.03	29.09	23.02	26.01	10.11	22.12	01.12
Claverdon	02.02		17.11	23.02	13.04	08.12	27.10	16.03	12.01
Coventrians	22.09	22.12		10.11	29.09	23.02	01.12	20.10	06.04
Coventry Saracens	09.03	06.10	12.01		17.11	13.04	02.02	08.12	27.10
Coventry Technical	06.10	01.12	09.03	22.12		20.10	06.04	26.01	22.09
Harbury	27.10	06.04	06.10	01.12	02.02		22.09	10.11	09.03
Old Warwickians	12.01	26.01	13.04	20.10	08.12	16.03		29.09	17.11
Pinley	17.11	22.09	02.02	06.04	27.10	12.01	09.03		06.10
Warwick	13.04	10.11	08.12	26.01	16.03	29.09	22.12	23.02	

MIDLAND

MIDLAND

ALCESTER RFC
Ground Address: Birmingham Road, King's Coughton, Alcester, Warwickshire.B49 5QF
Tel: 01789 764061
Brief Directions: The Ground is situated on the West side of the A435 between Studley and Alcester approx. 1 mile north of Alcester at Kings Coughton.
Club Secretary: Mr. F. D. Billingsley, Foxton House, Willoughby Close, Kings Coughton, Alcester, B49 5QJ.
Fixtures Secretary: Alan Brookes, 20 Alauna Avenue, Alcester, Warwicks., B49 6AN.
Tel: (H) 01789 764076
Club Colours: Red and black. Black shorts
League: Warwickshire 1

ALDRIDGE RFC
Ground Address: Bourne Vale, Little Hardwick Road, Aldridge, West Midlands WS9 0SQ.
Tel: 0121 353 2856
Website: aldridgerfc.freeserve.co.uk
Brief Directions: Sign posted off Little Hardwick Road. Situated at the end of Bourne Vale.
Club Secretary: Mark Field, 47 Canberra Road, Walsall WS5 3NN   Tel: (H) 01922 637588
e-mail; mark@field5536.freeserve.co.uk
Fixtures Secretary: Alex Reed, 2 Coppice View Road, Sutton Coldfield, West Midlands B73 6UE.
Tel: (H) 0121 243 8599
Club Colours: Black, Maroon & Gold hoops, black shorts
League: North Midlands 2

AMBER VALLEY RUFC
Ground Address: Pye Bridge, Lower Somerscotes, Alfreton, Derbyshire DE55 1NF.
Tel: 01773 541308
Brief Directions: M1 J28 follow A38 towards Derby, 2 miles B600 to Somerscotes, follow B600 towards Selston club 2 miles on left.
Club Secretary: Andrew Clarke, 98 Hickton Road, Swanwick, Alfreton, Derbyshire, DE55 1AG
Tel: 01773 605785
Email: aclarke15@compuserve.com
Fixtures Secretary: Andy Pickworth, 53 Ashton Close, Swanwick, Alfreton, Derbyshire, DE55 1HG.   Tel: 012773 528845
Club Colours: Black, gold/maroon hoops, Black shorts
League: Midlands 4 East (North)

AMPTHILL & DISTRICT
Ground Address: Dillingham Park, Woburn Street, Ampthill, Bedfordshire. MK45 2HX.
Tel: 01525 403303
Website: www.ampthillrufc.com
Brief Directions: Ground on right approaching Ampthill from Woburn
Club Secretary: Mrs. Helene E Wright,74 Willow Way, Ampthill, Bedfordshire, MK45 2SP.
Tel: 01525 754551 Email: ampthill@freeuk.com
Fixtures Secretary: Mrs G Lindsey -Davis,20 The Cedars, Ampthill, Beds.
Tel No: 01525 757124
Club Colours: Maroon and amber
League: Midlands 2 East

ANSTEY RFC
Ground Address: Bennion Road, Beaumont Leys or Link Road, Anstey. Phone to confirm 07973 561289 / 07769 831905 / 07930 418049 Both off A46 - M1 J.21A or J.22
Website: www.ansteyrfc.co.uk
Brief Directions: See Website - Bennion Road off A5630. Changing Room rear of Swimming Baths near Beaumont Leys shopping centre. Link Road - Changing rooms at Martin High School
Club Secretary: Alan Chapman, 1 Groby Road, Anstey, Leics, LE7 7FN.
Tel: 0116 2217727 Email: ac@alanchapman.com
Fixtures Secretary: Ian Pollock, 14 Pinewood Close, Leicester, LE4 1ER   Tel: 0116 236 7364
Club Colours: Black with red & green chevron
League: NLD/Leics 2 West
League Contact: As Secretary

APPLEBY FRODINGHAM RFC
Ground Address: Brumby Hall Social Club, Ashby Road, Scunthorpe.
Tel: 01724 276259
Brief Directions: Off M180 (Scunthorpe). Right at 1st R/about, 3rd turning off 2nd R/about. Left at next R/about onto Ashby Road, Brumby Hall 100yds on left.
Club Secretary: Rob Garner, 26 Glanville Avenue, Scunthorpe, Lincs DN17 1DE.
Tel: 07957 934878
Fixtures Secretary: Andy Graves, 69 Glanville Avenue, Scunthorpe, Lincs, DN17.
Tel: 01724 276259
Club Colours: Black and White.
Change Red and White
League: NLD/Leics 2 East

ASHBOURNE RUFC
Ground Address: The Recreation Ground, Cokayne Avenue, Ashbourne. DE6 1EJ
Brief Directions: A52 Derby/Ashbourne. The ground is visible coming down the Derby Hill to your right.
Club Secretary: Peter J Fuller, Ednaston Lodge Farm, Ashbourne, Derby. DE6 3BA.
Tel: (H) 01335 360381
Email: fullerful4et@supanet.com
Fixtures Secretary: Andrew Bailey, Ednaston Hall, Athbourne, Derby.
Tel: 01335 343432
Club Colours: Gold & blue hoops
League: Midlands 4 East (North)

ASHBY RFC

Ground Address: Nottingham Road, Ashby, Leicester, LE65 1DJ
Tel: 01530 413992
Brief Directions: M42 junction 13, signposted Ashby (A50), right at next roundabout, signposted Lount Breedon (A453)
Club Secretary: John Mitchell, 50 Pennine Way, Ashby, Leicester LE65 1EW.
Tel: (H) 01530 415284
Fixtures Secretary: J Grimsley,
Tel: (H) 01530 414531
Club Colours: Maroon and light blue hoops with navy blue shorts
League: NLD/Leics 1 West

ASHFIELD

Ground Address: Moor Lane Community Centre, Moor Lane, Mansfield, Notts. NG15 5SF
Brief Directions: A38 into Mansfield to McDonalds island, 3rd exit,through three sets of lights. Moor Lane on right just after speed cameras, ground on right.
Club Secretary: Stephen Trainer,
12 Belfry Close, Broadlands Park,
Kirkby in Ashfield, Notts. NG17 8NS
Tel: 01623 400411H / 0115 977 3279W
Fixtures Secretary: John Chambers, 12 Berry Hill Lane, Mansfield, Nottingham NG18 4BQ.
Tel: 01623 641391
Club Colours: Navy, amber and red hoops with black sleeves
League: NLD/Leics 1 West

ASTON OLD EDWARDIANS FC

Ground Address: Sunnybank Avenue, Perry Common, Birmingham. B44 0HP
Tel: 0121 373 5746
Brief Directions: Off College Road (A453) approx half way between A452 and B4138. Seat garage located on corner of A453 and Sunnybank Avenue.
Club Secretary: Mrs G.M. Grundy,
31 Frederick Rd, Sutton Coldfield, Birmingham, West Midlands, B73 5QN.
Tel: 0121 354 5840
Fixtures Secretary: Mr Tony Stafford,
54 Station Rd, Marston Green, Solihull, West Midlands, B37 7BA.
Tel: (H) 0121 684 2653.
Email: a.stafford@blueyonder.co.uk
Club Colours: Red, white and green hooped jerseys, white shorts
League: Midlands 3 West (North)

ATHERSTONE RFC

Ground Address: Ratcliffe Road, Atherstone, Warks
Tel: 01827 714934
Brief Directions: Drive into town centre, turn at Midland Bank into Ratcliffe Road, clubhouse approx 0.75 mile down on left

Club Secretary: David Boal, Thurmaston House, 74 South Street, Atherstone, Warks. CV9 1DZ
Tel: (H) 01827 713145
Fixtures Secretary: Ian Calder, 19 Station Road, Polesworth, Tamworth, Staffs B78 1EL.
Tel: 01827 331981
Club Colours: Black and White
League: Warwickshire 2
League Contact: As Secretary

AYLESTONE ST JAMES RFC

Ground Address: Covert Lane, Scraptoft, Leicester
Tel: 01162 419202
Brief Directions: Out of Leicester on A47 Uppingham Rd, left into Scraptoft Lane, top of lane go directly on to Covert Lane, 2nd clubhouse on left
Club Secretary: C. J. Gamble, 24 Firfield Avenue, Birstall, Leicestershire, LE4 4DR.
Fixtures Secretary: P Chapman
Tel: (H) 01162 431826
Club Colours: Blue and white hoops, navy shorts
League: NLD/Leics 1 West

AYLESTONIANS RFC

Ground Address: Knighton Lane East, Leicester.
Tel: 0116 2834899
Club Secretary: Clive Cooper, 31 Rockingham Close, Leicester
Tel: (H) 0116 2250610
Email: c.cooper11@ ntlworld.com
Fixtures Secretary: John Rouse, 16 Brentwood Avenue, Finham, Coventry CV3 6FN
Tel No: 0247 641 0418
Club Colours: Red, white and navy blue hoops with navy horts
League: NLD/Leics 1 West
League Contact: As Fixture Secretary

BAKEWELL MANNERIANS RUFC

Ground Address: The Showground, Coombs Road, Bakewell, Derbyshire
Brief Directions: Follow the `Agricultural Centre' signs from the A6. The pitch is on the right in front of the centre. Changing is at the Pavilion across the river via the footbridge.
Club Secretary: Martin Pearce,Manor House Farm, Over Haddon, Bakewell, Derbyshire. DE45 1JE   Tel No: 01629 814706
Email: jmpprop@aol.com
Fixtures Secretary: Rod Bell, Nether Croft, Eaton Place, Baslow, Derbys. DE45 1RW.
Tel: 01246 583564
Club Colours: Navy, light blue and white hoops, navy shorts
League: NLD/Leics 1 West

BARTON & DISTRICT RUFC
Ground Address: Mill Lane, Barton, North Lincolnshire.
Tel: 01464 531119
Brief Directions: To Barton, Right at mini round-about, through Barton market place, out of Barton approx 1 1/2 miles to Barrow, right at roundabout next sharp right into ground.
Club Secretary: T Phipps, 4 West Alridge, Barton-on-Humber
Tel: (H) 01652 632373 (W) 01724 847888
Fixtures Secretary: Graham Briggs, 99 Farthings Road, Barton.
Tel: 01652 634187 (H)
Club Colours: Red and white hoops
League: NLD/Leics 2 East

BARTON-UNDER-NEEDWOOD
Ground Address: Holland Sports & Social Club, Efflinch Lane, Barton-Under-Needwood, Staffs
Tel: 01283 712937
Club Secretary: G. Steen, 8 Gawain Grove, Stretton, Burton on Trent, Staffs DE13 0GN.
Tel: (H) 0585 098257
Fixtures Secretary: N. Rigby, 67 Arden Road, Barton-Under-Needwood, Staffs DE13 8LE.
Tel: (H) 01283 716528 (W) 0121 3537833
League: Staffordshire 2

BEDFORD QUEENS RUFC
Ground Address: c/o Bedford Atletic, (Ground share), Putnoe Wood, Wentworth Drive, Bedford, MK41 8QA.
Tel: 01234 350874
Brief Directions: From Bedford City Centre, take A428 Goldington Road towards Cambridge. Take B660 Kimbolton Road towards Kimbolton for 1.75 miles, turn right onto Wentwoth Drive. Ground .5 mile on left.
Club Secretary: Jason Cracknell, 105 Dudley Street, Bedford, MK40 3SZ.
Tel: 07976 559506 Email: cracks@dialstart.net
Fixtures Secretary: Andy Radnor, No. 133, Ireland, SG17 5QL.
Tel: (H) 01462 816175
Club Colours: Maroon & white hoops, navy blue, maroon & white topped socks.
League: East Midlands 1
League Contact: As Fixtures Secretary

BEDFORD SWIFTS RUFC
Ground Address: Bedford Athletics Stadium, Barkers Lane/Newnham Avenue, Bedford, MK41 9SA
Tel: 01234 351115 Website: www.bedford.swifts.co.uk
Brief Directions: From M1 J.13 A421 signed Cambridge, at end of Bedford By Pass, left to A428 into Bedford, follow signs to Bedford Leisure Centre Aspects or Bedford Athletic Stadium. From A1, A428 west to Birmingham & Northampton on outskirts of Bedford follow the same direction signs to facilities.

Club Secretary: Trevor N Stewart, 64 Ravensden Rd, Renhold, Bedford MK41 0JY.
Tel: (H) 01234 771828
Fixtures Secretary: Matthew Norris, Flat 5, 1 Dynevor Road, Bedford, MK40 2DB.
Tel: (H) 01234 327862
Club Colours: Gold and royal blue hoops, navy shorts
League: East Midlands 2
League Contact: Mr. P. Briggs, 6 Fleming Close, Thorpe Grange, Biddenham, Beds, MK40 4QJ
Tel: 01234 345321

BEDWORTH RUFC
Ground Address: Rectory Fields, Smarts Road, Bedworth. CV12 0BP
Tel: 02476 312025
Brief Directions: M6 J3. Bedworth turn off A444 Bypass, left at the bottom of slip road then left at Cross Keys pub into Smarts Road
Club Secretary: David Hatfield, 14 Asydnall Road, Longlord, Coventry, CV6 6BW
Tel: 02476 362399
Fixtures Secretary: Tom Murphy, 7 Larkim Close, Bulkington, Bedworth, CV12 9PB.
Tel: 02476 315892
Club Colours: Emerald Green jerseys, white shorts
League: Midlands 3 West (South)

BELGRAVE RFC
Ground Address: Belgrave Pastures, Thurcaston Road, Abbey Lane, Leicester.
Tel: 0116 2663033
Brief Directions: Ground situated where A6 Loughborough Road meets the Abbey Lane, opposite Mcdonalds
Club Secretary: Michael John Goddard, Grange Court, 271A Birstall Road, Birstall, Leics. LE4 4DJ
Tel: (H) 0116 2677383 (W) 0802 263676
Fixtures Secretary: Kevin Hick
Tel: (H) 0116 2608617 (W) 0116 2739501
Club Colours: Red and black hoops, black shorts
League: Midlands 3 East (North)

BELPER RUFC LTD
Ground Address: Herbert Strutt School Fields, Derby Road, Belper, Derbyshire.
Website: www.brufc.freeuk.
Brief Directions: Ground is off A6 in Belper between Safeways supermarket and Babbington Hospital - near town centre.
Club Secretary: Ian Davison, 42 Royston Drive, Lower Kilburn, Belper.DE56 0EL
Tel No: 01773 821112
Fixtures Secretary: Mike Phelan, 5 Derby Road, Lower Kilburn, Belper, Derbyshire.
Tel: 01332 780203 Email: mike.caroline@lineone.net
Club Colours: Black and white hoops
League: NLD/Leics 1 West

MIDLAND

BERKSWELL & BALSALL RFC
Ground Address: Honiley Road, Meek End, Nr. Balsall Common, Coventry
Brief Directions: From Birmingham or Balsall Common follow main road to Warwick A4111 (Not road to Kennilworth). Ground approx I mile on right with entrance in Honiley Road.
Club Secretary: Mrs Lesley Fahy, 7 Dalmeny Road, Westwood Heath, Coventry, CV4 8AX.
Tel: 02476 474093
Fixtures Secretary: Mr Keith Ballinger, 340 Kenilworth Rd., Balsall Common, Coventry CU7 7ER.
Tel: 01676 533020
Club Colours: Red and black shirts, black shorts
League: Midlands 4 West (South)

BEWDLEY
League: North Midlands 3
For further information contact:
North Midlands 2 & 3 League Secretary
Terry Wheeler, 14 Wollescote, Pedmore, Stourbridge, W Midlands DY9 7JJ
Tel: 01384 832647 (H) Tel: 0121 423 4000 (B)

BIDDENHAM RFC
Ground Address: The Pavilion, Deep Spinney, Biddenham, Beds.
Website: www.biddenham/rugbyclub.co.uk
Brief Directions: On entering Biddenham from A428. R/about turn right follow the road along. Pavilion in front of you.
Club Secretary: Jonathon Gambold, 22 Days Lane, Biddenham, MK40 4AE
Tel No: 01234 347247
Email: jonathon.gambold@internet.com
Fixtures Secretary: Jez Bird, 24 Banbury Close, Wokingham, Berkshire, RG41 2YS.
Tel: 07968 977482
Club Colours: Bottle green and cream quarters, Bottle green shorts and socks.
League: East Midlands 2
League Contact: Phil Mann, 24 Church End, Renhold, MK41 0LU
Tel: 01234 772438

BIGGLESWADE RUFC
Ground Address: Langford Road, Biggleswade, Beds. SG18 9RA
Tel: 01767 312463
Website: http:// www.members.tripod.com/biggleswaderfc
Brief Directions: On the A6001 Biggleswade to Henlow Road, approx 1 mile from Biggleswade by the Broom turn off, on the right hand side coming from Biggleswade
Club Secretary: Mike Williams, 8 Laurel Way, Ickleford, Hitchin, Herts. SG5 3UP.
Tel: (H) 01462 624925 (W) 01462 443091

Fixtures Secretary: Mike Pearson,1 Marlowe Court, Eaton Ford, St Neots, Cambs.PE19 7LG
Tel: (H) 01480 385077
Email: biggleswade.rugby@ntlworld.com
Club Colours: Navy with red hoop
League: Midlands 4 East (South)
League Contact: As Fixture Secretary

BINGHAM RFC
Ground Address: The Town Pavilion, Brendan Grove, Wynhill, Bingham, Notts.
Tel: 01949 832874
Brief Directions: A46/A52 roundabout, take Bingham exit then 1st left (town pavilion sign), left at T jct. Down hill, left Brendon Grove still following pavilion signs.
Club Secretary: John Perry, 29 Cogley Lane, Bingham, Notts. NG13 8DD
Tel: 01949 875231 Email: jperry.goem@regions.gsi.gov.uk
Fixtures Secretary: Graham Mason, 5 Church Close, Bingham, Notts.
Tel: 01949 875771
Club Colours: Green/red, white
League: NLD/Leics 2 West
League Contact: Barry Stewart, 62 Carnarvon Close, Bingham, Notts.
Tel: 01949 875128

BIRCHFIELD RUFC
Ground Address: UCE Sports Ground, Moor Lane, Witton, Birmingham, B6 7AA.
Tel: 0121 356 2142
Brief Directions: M6 J7 A34 towards Birmingham, A452 towards Sutton Coldfield, ground on Kiingstanding road B4138 1/2mile from A453 junction. B'ham A-Z Ref 5B page 48
Club Secretary: John Wingate, 9 Eaton Wood, Pype Hayes, Birmingham, B24 0NW.
Tel: 07811 864592 (M) Email: john@jwingate.fsnet.co.uk
Fixtures Secretary: Robert Chapman, 44 Olton Croft, Acocks Green, B'ham, B27 6PG.
Tel: (H) 0121 604 3694
Club Colours: Black with green hoop on arm, black shorts and socks
League: North Midlands 3
League Contact: As Secretary

BIRMINGHAM CITY CIVIL SERVICE RFC
Ground Address: Old Damson Lane, Elmdon, Solihull, West Midlands
Directions: Opposite Birmingham Airport on A45
Club Secretary: R. G. Webb, 51 Ladbrooke Road, Solihull, West Midlands, B91 3RW.
Tel: 0121 705 2812
Fixtures Secretary: Karl Smith.
Tel: 01526 60251
Club Colours: Red and White shirts, blue socks and red socks
League: North Midlands 2

BIRMINGHAM EXILES
Ground Address: Catherine de Barnes Lane, Bickenhill, Solihull, West Midlands B92 0DX.
Tel: 01675 442995
Brief Directions: Leave M42 at J.6 then leave A45 Coventry Road at Birmingham Airport junction and take Catherine de Barnes Lane exit.
Club Secretary: M. Whateley, 19 Wimbourne Road, Sutton Coldfield, West Midlands B76 2SU
Tel: 0121 687 5169 (W) 0121 378 3446 (H)
Fixtures Secretary: P.Bates, 69 Woodlands Way, Chelmsley Wood, B'ham. B37 6RN
Tel Nos: 0121 788 1081 (H) 07802 350854 (M)
Club Colours: Blue and Red hoops, navy blue shorts
League: Midlands 3 West (South)

BISHOPS CASTLE & ONNY VALLEY RFC
Ground Address: Love Lane, Bishops Castle, Shropshire
Brief Directions: On Eastern edge of town off the A484 Shrewsbury to Clun Road
Club Secretary: D. Bryan Jones, c/o Halls, Church Street, Bishops Castle, Shropshire
Tel No: 01588 638755
Fixtures Secretary: R. Jones, Hayford Farm, Westbury, Shrewsbury, Shropshire
Tel No: 01743 884248
Club Colours: Green and red
League: North Midlands 1

BLOXWICH RFC
Ground Address: Bloxwich Sports Club, Stafford Road, Bloxwich. WS3 3NJ
Tel: 01922 405891
Brief Directions: 0.25 mile outside Bloxwich Town on A34 to Cannock, entrance between houses on left marked by black and white posts, 100yds past traffic lights
Club Secretary: Mr Anthony Allen, 16 Sorrel Close, Featherstone, Staffs. WV10 7TX.
Tel: (H) 01902 739835 (W) 01902 864726
Fixtures Secretary: Paul Coyne c/o club.
Club Colours: Green with black and white chest hoops and black shorts
League: North Midlands 2

BOOTS ATHLETIC RUFC
Ground Address: Boots Athletic Club, Holme Road, Lady Bay, West Bridgford, Notts
Tel: 01159 9492388
Brief Directions: Follow signs to either Trent Bridge Cricket or Nottingham Forest, the Athletic Grounds are at the junction of Lady Bay Bridge and Trent Boulevard.
Club Secretary: Graham Atkinson, 42 Ashness, Gamston, Notts NG2 0QW
Tel No: 0115 969 6367

Fixtures Secretary: Carl Wharmby, 6 Eley Close, Ilkeston, Derbyshire, DE7 9JV.
Tel: 0115 944 7571
Club Colours: Dark blue and light blue quarters
League: NLD/Leics 2 West

BOSTON RFC
Ground Address: Great Fen Road, Wyberton, Boston, Lincs. PE21 7PB
Tel: 01205 362683 Website: www.boston-rufc.org
Brief Directions: Quarter of a mile west of Boston on A1121 next to airfield
Club Secretary: M.R.Keightley, 25 Manor Gardens, Boston, Lincs. PEE21 6JG
Tel No: 01205 364755
Fixtures Secretary: Mr T Bembridge, 5 Blackthorne Lane, Boston, Lincs. PE219BG
Tel No: 01205 351973
Email: tim@tbembridge.freeserve.co.uk
Club Colours: Royal blue & white hoops shirts and socks with blue shorts
League: NLD/Leics 1 East

BOURNE RUFC
Ground Address: Milking Nook Drive, Splading Road, Bourne, Lincs.
Tel: 01778 393346
Brief Directions: Take the Spalding road out of Bourne and the ground is on the right after one and a half miles.
Club Secretary: Martin Hunter, 16 Rochester Court, Bourne, Lincs.
Tel: 01778 423 259
Fixtures Secretary: As Secretary.
Club Colours: Navy Blue with broad gold band and navy blue shorts
League: NLD/Leics 2 East

BOURNVILLE RFC
Ground Address: Rowheath, Heath Road, Bournville, Birmingham. B30
Tel: 0121 475 0480
Brief Directions: A38 out of B'ham city centre, after approx 5 miles turn left into Oaktree Ln and follow signs for Cadbury World, turn right into Maryvale Rd, ground 0.5 mile on left
Club Secretary: Keith Smith, 1 Whitley Rd., Northfield, Birmingham B31 3BD
Tel: 0121 6801269 (H) - 077596 79397 (M)
Fixtures Secretary: Eamon Harkin, 18 Landsdowne Rd., Studley, Warwicks. B807RB
Tel: 01527 853241 (H) 0796 8440875 (M)
Club Colours: Blue, maroon and gold shirts, blue shorts
League: North Midlands 2

MIDLAND

BRACKLEY RUFC

Ground Address: Fine Lady Fields, Nightingale Close, Brackley, Northants. NN13 6PN.
Tel: 01280 700685 Website:
www.brackleyrufc.co.uk
Brief Directions: A43 Northampton, go towards Town Centre, take 4th turn right (opp. Bell Inn). Bear right at mini R/about. Turn left at next R/about, then right at nedt R/about - club on left.
Club Secretary: Alan Jukes,
The Old Ale House, The Square, Moreton Pinkney, Northants, NN11 3SH.
Tel: 01295 768915.
Email: ajukes@aol.com
Fixtures Secretary: Mike Harper, Horwell Farm, Baynards Green, Bicester, Oxon.OX6 9SQ.
Tel: 01869 345821
Club Colours: Royal blue and white quarters, blue shorts, blue & white socks.
League: East Midlands 1
League Contact: As Secretary

BREDON STAR RFC

Ground Address: Bredon Playing Fields, Kemerton Road, Bredon, Nr Tewkesbury, Glos.
Tel: 01684 772831
Brief Directions: From Jct 5 of M5 take A46 to Evesham.Left after 2 miles at traffic lights onto B4079. Left at T junction in village and car park is 50 yards on right before Nissan garage.
Club Secretary: Ms Rachel brown, Pamington Farm, Ashchurch, Tewkesbury, Glos. GL208LX
Tel: 01684 772396
Fixtures Secretary: Neil Evans,
Apple Orchard, Chapel Lane, Kinsham, Tewkesbury GL20 8HS
Tel: (H) 01684 772645 (W) 0973 171451
Club Colours: Red and black shirts with black shorts
League: North Midlands 3

BRIDGNORTH RFC

Ground Address: The Bull, Bridge Street, Bridgnorth, Shropshire. WV15 5AA
Tel: 01746 762796
Website: www.bridgnorth-rugby.co.uk
Brief Directions: Severn Park off A442 Bridgnorth to Telford Road. Clubhouse adjacent to Old Bridge Low Town. Parking at Falcon Pub car park.
Club Secretary: S.N. Rossiter-Stread,
8 Lower Forge, Eardington,
Bridgnorth, WV16 5LQ.
Tel: 01746 764286 (H) 01952 811500 (W)
Email: samrs@breathemail.net
Fixtures Secretary: Alun Stoll, Ty'r Ysgol, Vicarage Road, Penn, Wolverhampton, Staffs.
Tel: 01902 558355
Club Colours: All black
League: Midlands 3 West (North)

BROMSGROVE RFC

Ground Address: Finstall Park, Finstall Road, Bromsgrove, Worcs. B60 3DH
Tel: 01527 874690 Website:
www.bromsgrovefc.co.uk
Brief Directions: Situated between Aston Fields and Finstall on Finstall Road (B4184), Bromsgrove
Club Secretary: Robin J Davies,
Drovers Barn, 4 Naunton Farm Barns,
Holt Heath, Worcs WR6 6NG
Tel: 07866 155686 (M) 01905 621808 (H)
Email: robin.davies@inter-alliance.com
Fixtures Secretary: Ralph M Gordon., 66 Hanbury Road, Stoke Heath, Bromsgrove, Worcs.
Tel: (H & W) 01527 832003
Email: rmgordon@btclick.com
Club Colours: White jerseys with red/black/red hoops, white shorts
League: Midlands 2 West

BROMYARD RFC

Ground Address: The Clive Richards Sports Ground, Instone, Tenbury Road, Bromyard.
Tel: 01885 483933
Brief Directions: From Bromyard, take the B4214 towards Tenbury Wells, the ground is on the right hand side, approx 0.5 mile from the town
Club Secretary: Deborah J Piggot,
Upper Brockington, Bredenbury, Bromyard, Hereford, HR7 4TH.
Tel: (H) 01885 483322
Email: deborahpiggott@compuserve.com
Fixtures Secretary: Simon Irwin,
2 Pinetree Cottages, Tedstone Wafre, Bromyard, Hereford, HR7 4QD.
Tel: (H) 01885 488322
Club Colours: Green with gold band, black shorts
League: North Midlands 1

BUGBROOKE RUFC

Ground Address: The Playing Fields, Pilgrims Lane, Bugbrooke, Northants
Tel: 01604 831137
Brief Directions: A45 from Northampton towards J16 M1 at Kislingbury R/abt. Turn L. for Rugbrook. Go through village on same road almost at other end for Bugbrooke Community Centre. Turn left in there.
Club Secretary: Bryn Curtis c/o J.Curtis, West End, Bugb rooke, Northants.
Tel No: 01604 830317 (H) 07884 116678 (M)
Fixtures Secretary: Mr Staff Hurlston,
97 Mount Pleasant, Harpole, Northants NN7 4DL.
Tel: (H) 01604 831184
Club Colours: Bottle green & yellow quarters, green, green & yellow hoops
League: Midland 4 East (South)

BURNTWOOD RUFC
Ground Address: The North Shore, Church Street, Chasetown, Staffordshire, WS7 8XE.
Tel: 01543 676651
Brief Directions: From A5 follow directions to Chasetown Clubhouse at end of Church St. Club is next to Chasetown Football Club.
Club Secretary: Kevin Cantrill, 39 Hunter Avenue, Burntwood, Staffs. WS79AQ.
Tel: 01543 672737
Fixtures Secretary: Mark Bourne, 27 Willett Avenue, Burntwood, Staffordshire WS7 8FJ.
Tel: 01543 675918
Club Colours: Scarlet, Emerald & white hoops, black shorts.
League: Midlands 4 West (North)

BURTON RFC
Ground Address: Peel Croft, Lichfield Street, Burton upon Trent, Staffs. DE14 3RH.
Tel: 01283 564510
Website: burtonrugbyclub.co.uk
Brief Directions: In the centre of Burton, adjacent to Safeways supermarket
Club Secretary: J D Lowe, 20 The Chevin, Stretton, Burton upon Trent, DE13 0XU
Tel/Fax: (H) 01283 534422
Fixtures Secretary: J D French, 193 Newton Rd., Burton upon Trent , DE15 0TU
Tel: 01283 548774
Club Colours: White with black diagonal band
League: Midlands 2 West
League Contact: J Edwards, 18 Byron Road, Swadlincote, Derbys. DE11 0DD.
Tel: 01283 221855

BUXTON RUFC
Ground Address: Fairfield Centre, Victoria Park Road, Buxton, Derbyshire
Tel: 01298 24081
Brief Directions: Follow A6 Stockport, up Fairfield Rd. 1st R. Queens Rd becomes Bench Rd, left at T jcn with Victoria Park Rd, Centre on left after Royal Forresters
Club Secretary: David Robson, 20 Errwood Avenue, Buxton, Derbyshire SK17 9BD
Tel: (H) 01298 22432 (W) 01298 26121 Ext 125
Fixtures Secretary: Lorraine Trevis Brown, 6 New Road, Whaley Bridge, Derbyshire, SK23 7JG.
Tel: (H) 01663 73504 (W) 01298 23195
Club Colours: Blue, red and gold hoops, blue shorts
League: Midlands 4 East (North)

CANNOCK RUFC
Ground Address: The Morgan Ground, Stafford Road, Huntingdon, Staffordshire. WS12 4NU
Tel: 01543 467906
Club Secretary: Mr. B. Fletcher, 43 Ampleforth Drive, The Meadows, Stafford, ST17 4TE

Fixtures Secretary: Phil Pearson
Tel: (H) 01889 575 167 (W) 0121 544 2387
Club Colours: Blue and gold hoops
League: Staffordshire 1

CASTLE DONINGTON RUFC
Ground Address: The Spittal Pavilion, The Spital, Castle Donington, Derbyshire
Tel: 01332 812214 (pub)
Brief Directions: Travel into Donington from A6 turning right into the Spittal after the Tudor Inn, ground is situated 400yds on right
Club Secretary: A Hackett, 88 Station Road, Castle Donnington, Derbys. DE74 2NL
Tel No: . 01332 853344 e-mail; moose@ donington-demon.co uk
Fixtures Secretary: Alan Hampson, 77 Station Rd Castle Donington, Derby.
Tel: (H) 01332 812314
Club Colours: Red & black quarters, black, red & black
League: NLD/Leics 2 West

CHADDESLEY CORBETT
Ground Address: Chaddesly Corbett Sports Club, Longmore, Fox Lane, Chaddesley Corbett
Website: ccrfc.co.uk
Brief Directions: On A448 between Kidderminster & Bromsgrove. Do not enter village, turning to ground is on sharp corner between The Fox P.H. and Rowberrys farm shop. Signed CCRFC - turn right from Kidderminster, left from Bromsgrove.
Club Secretary: Nigel Evans, Cherry Tree House, Mustow Green, Nr. Kidderminster, DY10 4LQ.
Tel: 01562 777070
Fixtures Secretary: M Page, 8 The Green, Chaddesley Corbett, DY10 4PZ
Tel: 01562 777700
Club Colours: Green & Blue Quarters with blue shorts and green socks.
League: North Midlands 3

CHESTERFIELD RUFC
Ground Address: The Rugby Field, Stonegravels, Sheffield Road, Chesterfield, Derbyshire.
Tel: 01246 232321
Brief Directions: M1 J29, follow signs to Chesterfield town centre A61 to Sheffield (old road, not bypass), ground is on left 1 mile from town centre
Club Secretary: D. J. Taylor, 7 Hallfields Rise, Shirland, Alfreton, Derbyshire, DE55 6DH.
Tel: 0115 9895223W 01773 836138H
e-mail: duncan.taylor@nelsons-solicitors.co.uk
Fixtures Secretary: Steve Allford, 3 Lincoln Street, Chesterfield, Derbys. S40 2TW
Tel: 01246 297053H 07759 489384M
Club Colours: Red and white hoops, white shorts
League: NLD/Leics 2 West

MIDLAND

CLAVERDON RFC
Ground Address: Ossetts Hole Lane, Yarningale Common, Claverdon, Warwicks. CV35 8HN.
Tel: 01926 843133
Brief Directions: Off A4189 Warwick to Henley in Arden.
Club Secretary: Basil Sayer, Croft Cottage, 162 High Street, Henley-in-Arden, Soloihull B95 5BN
Tel No: 01564 795714
Email: big@basil.junglelink.co.uk
.**Fixtures Secretary:** Lindsey Shaw, 23 Castle Close, Henley in Arden, Solihuiull, B95 5LR.
Tel: 01789 41411 x4598 (W)
Club Colours: Red and white
League: Warwickshire 2

CLEE HILL RFC
Ground Address: Golden Lion, 2 Lion Lane, Tenbury Road, Clee Hill, Ludlow, Shropshire.
Tel: 01584 890262
Brief Directions: Between Ludlow and Cleobury Mortimer on A4117. Take B4214 to Clee Hill (signposted Tenbury Wells). Ground approx. I mile on right hand side.
Club Secretary: Mrs. Penny Cooper, Studley Cottage, Clee Hill, Nr. Ludlow, Shropshire, SY8 3NP.
Tel: 01584 890990
Fixtures Secretary: Harvey Stevens, 17 Crestwood Avenue, Kidderminster, Worcs. DY11 6JS
Tel: 01562 637384
Club Colours: Maroon & Navy Blue quarters, Blue shorts
League: North Midlands 2

CLEETHORPES RUFC
Ground Address: Lucarleys Club, Wilton Road, Cleethorpes, N E Lincs.
Tel: 01472 812936
Brief Directions: Follow signs for Tesco superstore, ground is first turning right past Tesco.
Club Secretary: Simon Regan, 8 Robson Road, Cleethorpes, N.E.Lincolnshire. DN35 5SY
Tel: 01472 317605
Fixtures Secretary: John Walsham,38 Richmond Road,, Cleethorpes, N.E. Lincs.
Tel: (H) 01472 699322
Club Colours: Blue & Gold hoops
League: NLD/Leics 2 East

CLEOBURY MORTIMER RFC
Ground Address: Cleobury Mortimer Sports & Social Club,, Love Lane, Cleobury Mortimer, Kidderminster, Worcs DY14 8PE
Tel: 01299 271448
Brief Directions: To Cleobury along main street, then turn right just before the Three Horseshoes pub, left at mini roundabout, car park and ground 100 yards on left

Club Secretary: Tim Wright, Candleford, Larks Rise, Cleobury, Mortimer DY148JJ
Tel No: 01299 271702 Email: cmrfc@hotmail.com
Fixtures Secretary: Kath Phillips, Orchard House, Ludlow, Roadf, Cleobury Mortimer DY14 8DU Tel No: 01299 270381
Club Colours: Red and green quarters, black shorts
League: Midlands 4 West (North)

COALVILLE RFC
Ground Address: Memorial Ground, Broomleys Road, Coalville, Leicester
Tel: (H) 01530 812090
Brief Directions: Leave M1 at Junction 22. Coalville is signposted on A511. Go over four roundabouts and then turn left at fifth roundabout and Coalville RFC is 100 yards on right.
Club Secretary: Peter Smith, 50 Parkdale, Ibstock, Leics LE67 6JW
Tel: (H) 01530 262113 (W) 01530 832085
Fixtures Secretary: Glyn Harding, 115 High Street, Ibstock, Leicester LE67 6JQ
Tel: 01530 262200 (H & W)
Club Colours: Navy blue with amber stripe, Navy blue shorts
League: Midlands 4 East (South)

CORBY RFC
Ground Address: Northen Park, Rockingham Road, Corby, Northants, NN17 2AE
Tel: 01536 204466
Brief Directions: Located at the junction of the A6003 (Corby to Oakham Road) and the A6116 (Rockingham Road) Corby.
Club Secretary: Clayton Nunn, 20 Dovedale Road, Corby, Northamptonshire, NN17 1LP.
Tel: 01536 395933
Fixtures Secretary: Charles Sanders, 21 Brunswick Gardens, Corby, NN18 9ER
Tel: 01536 396287
Club Colours: Red and white quarters, blue
League: East Midlands 2
League Contact: As Secretary

COTGRAVE COLLIERY RUFC
Ground Address: Cotgrave Community Centre, Woodview, Cotgrave, Nottingham.
Tel: 0115 9892916
Brief Directions: Cotgrave lies in triangle boarded by A52 Nottingham/ Grantham Rd, A46 Leicester/Newark Rd & A606 N'ham - Melton Mowbray Rd, Community Centre is opposite the Miners Welfare
Club Secretary: I.Johns, 3 Lakeside Avenue, Sawley, Nottingham.
Tel No: 0115 849702
Fixtures Secretary: T.Wood, 14 Willowdene, Cotgrave, Nottingham
Tel: 0115 9894518
Club Colours: Claret and blue quarters
League: NLD/Leics 2 West

COVENTRIANS RFC
Ground Address: Black Pad, off Yelverton Road, Radford, Coventry. CV6 4NW
Tel: 074 7668 2885
Brief Directions: M6 J3 onto A444 to Coventry, right at 2nd roundabout to Holbrooks, at next 2nd roundabout Yelverton Road is 50yds on right
Club Secretary: Jeff Daniell, 116 Mill Farm Park, Marston Jabbett, Bedworth Warwicks CV12 9SF.
Tel: 024 76 37 3470
Fixtures Secretary: As Secretary
Club Colours: Royal blue and white quarters
League: Warwickshire 2

COVENTRY SARACENS
Ground Address: Bredon Avenue, Binley, Coventry, CV6 2AR
Tel: 01203 453557
Brief Directions: From A46 (Eastern bypass) take A428 to Coventry City Centre for approx 1 mile, left into Bredon Ave, ground approx 200 mtrs on left
Club Secretary: Brian Craner, 71 Westhill Road, Coundon, Coventry. CV6 2AD
Tel: (H) 024 76590280
Email: briancraner@supanet.com
Fixtures Secretary: Steven Hancox, 21 Anne Crescent, Willenhall, Coventry, CV3 3GX.
Tel: 024 76306217
Club Colours: Black with red and green V
League: Warwickshire 2

COVENTRY TECHNICAL RFC
Ground Address: Mitchell Avenue, Canley, Coventry
Tel: 01203 471733
Brief Directions: The club is only 5 mins from A45 Flethhampstead Highway, northbound take right turn into Charter Ave, southbound left at island by Canley fire and police station
Club Secretary: Mrs A Wallis-Power, 27 Nod Rise, Mount Nod, Coventry CV5 7HU
Tel: 024 7647 4040
Email: a.power@warwick.ac.uk
Fixtures Secretary: Kurtis Gunn, 62 Pantolf Place, Newbold, Rugby CV21 1HR
Tel: 01788 333692
Club Colours: Green, gold and brown
League: Warwickshire 2

COVENTRY WELSH RFC
Ground Address: Burbages Lane, Longford, Coventry. CV6 6AY
Tel: 01203 360303
Brief Directions: M6 J3, take bypass road A444 to next roundabout and the right hand turn at roundabout is Burbages Lane
Club Secretary: Jean Williams, 173 Good Years End Lane, Bedworth, Nuneaton, Warks. CV12 0HU.
Tel: (H) 01203 364596

Fixtures Secretary: Gary Greenway
Tel: (H) 01203 315403
Club Colours: Red shirts, black shorts
League: Midlands 4 West (South)

DAVENTRY RFC
Ground Address: Stefen Hill, Western Avenue, Daventry, Northants. NN11 4ST
Tel: 01327 703802
Brief Directions: M1 J16, A45 west to Daventry, upon reaching Daventry, straight over roundabout heading for Daventry town centre, 3rd road on left and the ground is facing you
Club Secretary: Peter Weckerman, 3 Portland Close, Daventry, Northants NN11 4SQ.
Tel: (H) 01327 311151
Fixtures Secretary: Graham Woodliffe, Old Barn House, The Green, Badby, Daventry, Northants, NN11 3AF.
Tel: (H) 01327 703496 (W) 01327 305137
Email: gwoodlif@ford.com
Club Colours: All black
League: East Midlands 1

DEEPINGS RUFC
Ground Address: Linchfield Road, Deeping St James, Peterborough
Tel: 01778 345228 Website: deepings.com/rugby
Brief Directions: R'bout Market Deeping (Jcn of A15/A16) take A16 towards Spalding, through town until sight footbridge, left at Xroads before bridge, immediate right thro' gates to ground
Club Secretary: Brian Kirby, 29 Tattershall Drive, Market Deeping, Peterborough PE6 8BS
Tel: (H) 01778 343048 (W)07720538600 (M)
e-mail: kirby 01.b@care4free.net
Fixtures Secretary: Colin Astley ,34 Thackers Way,Deepings St James, Peterborough PE6 8HP Tel No: 07944 985021
Club Colours: Green, black and gold hoops
League: East Midlands 1

DERBY RFC
Ground Address: The Pavilion, Kedleston Road, Derby. DE22 2TF
Tel: 01332 344341
website:derbyrugbyfootballclub.com
Brief Directions: Off A38 at Markeaton Park towards University of Derby campus - ground half a mile further on the left
Club Secretary: John L Archer, 5 Dunvegan Close, Stenson Fields, Derby DE24 3AL.
Tel: 07932 308584 (M) 01332 769300 (H)
Email: johnlarcher@supanet,com
Fixtures Secretary: John Dickens, 57 Wheeldon Avenue, Derby.
Tel: 01332 341546(H), 07944 833319
         (M) 01332 702502 (W)
Club Colours: Black and amber hoops, black shorts
League: Midlands 2 West

MIDLAND

DIXONIANS RFC
Ground Address: 31A Fountain Road, Edgbaston, Birmingham. B17 8NJ
Tel: 0121 434 3313
Brief Directions: From Five Ways Biringham A456 direction Kidderminster in 1.5 miles turn right Fountain Road/Stanmore Road
Club Secretary: Vivian Shingler, Timberhonger House, Timberhonger, Bromsgrove, Worcestershire. B61 9ET
Tel: (H) 01527 861686
Fixtures Secretary: David Hall
Tel: (H) 0121 378 2839
Club Colours: Maroon, green & black, black, green
League: Midlands 3 West (North)

DROITWICH RFC
Ground Address: Hanbury Road, Droitwich Spa, Worcs., WR9 8PR.
Tel: 01905 771919
Website: www.droitwichfc.co.uk
Brief Directions: M5 J5, A38 towards Droitwich, turn towards town centre. At traffic lights turn left into Hanbury Road, club 2 miles on left.
Club Secretary: Mr. P. Hopkins, 7 Chilham Place, Worcester, WR4 0LH.
Email: philip hopkins1@virgin.net
Fixtures Secretary: Richard Latham, 3 Isaacs Way, Droitwich, Worcs. WR9 8UZ.
Tel: (H) 01905 794638 - (W) 0121 5853033
Club Colours: Black and gold hoops
League: Midlands 4 West (South)

DRONFIELD RUFC
Ground Address: Gosforth School, Carr Lane, Dronfield-Woodhouse, Dronfield.
Brief Directions: From north (Sheffield) into Dronfield, right at Coach & Horses, bear right under bridge, follow road at top of hill turn left (Stubley Drive), turn into school car park
Club Secretary: Robert Machin, 2 Hatton Close, Dronfield, Woodhouse S18 5RW
Tel: 01246 411453
Fixtures Secretary: Verdon McCauliffe, 56 Highfield, Road, Dronfield S18 6UW
Club Colours: Red shirts, black shorts
League: NLD/Leics 1 West

DUNLOP RFC
Ground Address: Dunlop Sports and Social Club, Burnaby Road, Radford, Coventry.
Tel: 01203 662394
Website: www.dunloprfc.co.uk
Brief Directions: M6 J3, take 4th exit to Coventry, along bypass, over roundabout, right at 2nd roundabout, left at 3rd roundabout, turn right into Burnaby Rd, ground .5 mile on right
Club Secretary: Mrs Kim Challis, 24 Birchfield Road, Counden, Coventry. CV6 2BD.
Tel: (H) 024 7633 7152
email: kim@challis1959.fsnet.co.uk

Fixtures Secretary: Mr John Ormsby, 5 Postbridge Road, Styvechale, Coventry CV3 5AG.
Tel:(H) 24 7641 0313
Club Colours: Black and amber hoops, black shorts
League: Midlands 4 West (South)

EARLSDON RFC
Ground Address: Mitchell Avenue, Canley, Coventry. CV4 8DY.
Tel: 01203 464467
Brief Directions: Along A45 to Police and Fire Stations, follow signs to Canley & Warwick University
Club Secretary: J Ward, 18 Wainbody Avenue, Green Lane, Coventry, CV3 6DB
Tel: (H) 01203 419729 or 024 76 419729
Fixtures Secretary: A.Barker, 29 Palmerston Rd., Earlsdon, Coventry CV5 6FM.
Tel: 02476 711321
Club Colours: Red and white
League: Midlands 4 West (South)

EAST LEAKE RFC
Ground Address: Costock Road Playing Fields, Costock Road, East Leake, Loughborough, Leicestershire
Brief Directions: A60 N'gham tow'ds L'boro, right at Costock tow'ds E. Leake, ground on right. M1 J24, A6 tow'ds L'boro, left onto A6006 tow'ds Rempstowe, left where signed, thro' village, club on right
Club Secretary: Audrey Pridmore, 6 Ashby Road,Keyworth, Derbys. DE74
Tel No: 01509 670246
email: audrey100@totalise.co.uk
Fixtures Secretary: Nigel Kendall, 28 Salisbury Avenue, East Lake, Loughborough, Leics. LE12 6NJ
Tel No: 01509 856735
Club Colours: Maroon and white hoops, black shorts
League: NLD/Leics 2 West

EAST RETFORD RUFC
Ground Address: Ordsall Road, Retford, Nottinghamshire
Tel: 01777 703234
Brief Directions: From A1, join B620 from Worksop, past Ranby prison on left, through Babworth crossroads, right at mini roundabout, ground .5 mile on right
Club Secretary: E M Henderson, 51 Trent Street, Retford, Notts. DW22 6NG
Tel: (H) 01777 706987
Fixtures Secretary: I. McComb, 125 Ordsall Road, Retford, Nottinghamshire.
Tel No: 01777 701092
Club Colours: Emerald and amber hoops, navy blue shorts
League: Midlands 4 East (North

ECCLESHALL RUFC
Ground Address: Baden Hall Farm, Near Eccleshall.
Tel: 01785 851495
Brief Directions: From centre of Eccleshall follow A519 (Newcastle), take right fork after leaving town, past Drake Hall then follow signs to Baden Hall on right
Club Secretary: K. E. Levitt, 46 Old Road, Stone, Staffs. ST15 8HR
Tel: (H) 01785 818234
Tel: (W) 01925 836105
Fixtures Secretary: I. Bradford, 1 Buckmaster Avenue, Clayton, Newcastle, Staffs. ST5 3AJ
Tel: (H) 01782 632256 (W) 01782 823447
Club Colours: Yellow with green & black band, black shorts.
League: Staffordshire 2

EDWARDIAN FC
Ground Address: The Memorial Ground, Streetsbrook Rd, Solihull, West Mids. B90 3PE
Tel: 0121 744 6831
Brief Directions: M42 J.4. Follow A34 towards Birmingham. Turn right into Olton Road. At lights straight over into ground.
Club Secretary: Peter Dean, 25 Glascote Close, Shirley, Solihull, West Midlands B90 2TA
Tel: 0121 744 3776
Fixtures Secretary: Steve Abercrombie, 35 Green Lane, Shirley, Solihull, West Midlands B90 1AP
Tel: 0121430 7508
Club Colours: Old gold, claret and navy irregular hoops, navy shorts
League: North Midlands 1
League Contact: Paul Price, 88 Stonor Road, Hall Green, Birmingham, B28 0QR
Tel: 0121 745 8745

ERDINGTON RFC
Ground Address: Spring Lane Playing Fields, Kingsbury Road, Erdington, Birmingham 23.
Tel: 0121 373 7597
Club Secretary: Derek Owen, 129 Bradbury Road, Solihull, West Midlands. B92 8AL.
Tel: (H) 0121 706 4699 (W) 0121 654 4022
Fixtures Secretary: Keith Robinson
Tel: (H) 0121 351 2740
Club Colours: White shirts with single blue hoop
League: North Midlands 3

ESSINGTON RUFC (merged with Wulfrun)
Ground Address: High Hill Centre, High Hill, Essington, Wolverhampton, West Midlands. WV11 2DW. Tel No: 01922 492795
Brief Directions: M6 J.11 A462 for 3 miles. Traffic lights turn right, Upper Snyde Lane - .75 mile - club on left.

Club Secretary: M.R. Chandler, 32 Coppice Rd., Walsall Wood, Walsall, West MIdlands. WS9 9BL.
Tel: 01543 820611
Email: handmchandler@aol.com
Fixtures Secretary: G.Smith, 7 Oakwood Close, Essington, Wolverhampton, West Midlands WV11 2DQ.
Tel: 01922 400222
Club Colours: Black shirts and shorts with red socks.
League: North Midlands 3

EVESHAM RFC
Ground Address: Evesham Sports Club, Albert Road, Evesham, Worcs
Tel: 01386 446469
Brief Directions: A435 south - over railway bridge, Albert Road is 2nd right off High Street, Evesham, go to end to Evesham Sports Club
Club Secretary: Carol Horseman, 3 Green Hill Gardens, Evesham, Worcs.
Tel No: 01386 423603
Fixtures Secretary: S. Nettel, 43 Prin ces Road, Evesham, Worcs., WR11 4GQ.
Tel: (H) 01386 456111
Club Colours: Navy and maroon hoops
League: Midlands 3 West (South)

FIVE WAYS OLD EDWARDIANS FC
Ground Address: Masshouse, Ash Lane, Hopwood, Birmingham
Tel: 0121 445 4909
Website: fivewaysoe.freeserve.co.uk
Brief Directions: M42 J2, signpost to Birmingham reach roundabout to Birmingham, 100yds before garage on right turn right into Ash Lane, club on right at end of lane
Club Secretary: Richard Lisseter, 138 Chatsworth Road, Halesowen, West Midlands. B62 8TH
Tel: (H) 0121 559 6549 (W) 0121 550 1724
Email: rlissiter@aol.com
Fixtures Secretary: Derek Earl, 88 Westminster Road, Selly Oak, Birmingham B29 7RS
Tel: 0122 248 1222
Club Colours: Navy blue and amber
League: North Midlands 1

GAINSBOROUGH RUFC
Ground Address: Castle Hills School, The Avenue, Gainsborough
Brief Directions: Follow signs for Leisure Centre, the school is next to it
Club Secretary: T Tanner, 11 Northolme, Gainsborough, Lincs. DN21 2QN
Tel: (H) 01427 610768 (W) 01246 451245
Fixtures Secretary: Howard Russel
Tel: (H) 01427 628265 (W) 01724 276221
Club Colours: 1st team:black shirt & shorts/2nd team:black & yellow qrtrs.
League: NLD/Leics 2 East

MIDLAND

GEC ST LEONARDS RUFC
Ground Address: GEC Protection and Control, GEC St Leonards Social Club, St Leonards Avenue, Stafford, Staffs.
Tel: 01785 258070
Club Secretary: J A Waibley, 26 Hall Close, Stafford, Staffs. ST17 4JJ
Tel: (H & W) 01785 253201
Fixtures Secretary: Mr I McLeod
Tel: (H) 01889 579365 (W) 0860 694548
Club Colours: Black with a gold hoop
League: Staffordshire 1

GLOSSOP RUFC
Ground Address: Hargate Hill Lane, Charlesworth, Glossop, SK13 5HG.
Tel: 01457 864553
Brief Directions: Through Glossop on A57, take A626 signed Marple, ground is 1.5 miles on left
Club Secretary: Alastair May, 6 Kinder Grove, Romiley, Stockport. SK6 4EU
Tel: (H) 01457 864553
Fixtures Secretary: Phil Littlewood, Oakmount, 76 Dinting Road, Glossop.
Tel: 01457 867168
Club Colours: Royal blue shirts, black shorts
League: Midlands 3 East (North)

GNOSALL RUFC
Ground Address: Gnosall Cricket Club, Brookhouse Road, Gnosall, Stafford.
Tel No: 01785 823500
website: gnosallrugby.org.uk
Brief Directions: A518 (Stafford & Telford road), from Stafford to mini R/about, village centre, straight over is Brookhouse Road, 1st left down track by Play Area.
Club Secretary: Mrs Anne Timmins, Norden Newport Road, Gnosall, Stafford. ST20 0BN.
Tel: 01785 823 431
Email: anne.timmins@btinternet.com
Fixtures Secretary: Stuart Davies, 27 Cranmore Grove, Aston Lodge, Stafford. ST15 XD
Tel No: 01785 817846
Club Colours: Green & black quarters, black shorts.
League: Staffordshire 2

GREYHOUND RFC
Ground Address: Hereford City Sports Ground, Grandstand Road, Hereford HR2 7RL
Tel: 01432 371733
Brief Directions: Turn off A49 Leominster Road. The ground is on the opposite side to the Hereford Leisure Centre.
Club Secretary: Allan Braithwaite, 1 Marlbrook Road, Red Hill, Hereford HR2 7PU
Tel: (H) 01432 371733
Fixtures Secretary: Nigel Greening, 9 Old School Lane, Hereford, HR1 1EU
Tel: (H) 01432 356579
Club Colours: Light Blue with Navy Blue band.
League: North Midlands 3

GRIMSBY RUFC
Ground Address: The Pavillion, Springfield Road, Scartho, Grimsby, North East Lincolnshire. DN33 3JF.
Tel: 01472 878594
Brief Directions: From M180/A180, take A1136, left at roundabout, right at Toothill roundabout, left at Bradley crossroads, right at Nuns corner, right fork, 1st right
Club Secretary: Mr T Horswood, 5 Ferriby Lane, Grimsby. DN34 3NU.
Tel: 01472 872416 e-mail: terry.horswood@lor.co.uk
Fixtures Secretary: John Waudby,25 Park Drive, Grimsby N.E.Lincs. DN320EFT
Tel: 01472 500135 e-mail: john.waudby@gbr.conoco.com
Club Colours: Royal blue shirts & black shorts.
League: Midlands 4 East (North)

HANDSWORTH RUFC
Ground Address: Charles Lewis Memorial Ground, 450 Birmingham Rd, Walsall, WS5 3JP.
Tel: 0121 357 6427
Brief Directions: M6 J7, take A34 towards Walsall, ground at bottom of hill at end of dual carriageway on left
Club Secretary: Alec Hardy, 6 Freemount Square, Great Barr, Birmingham. B43 5QT
Tel: (H) 0121 358 6612
Fixtures Secretary: As Secretary above
Club Colours: Red and white hoops, black shorts.
League: Midlands 4 West (North)

HANFORD RFC (Formally Michelin)
Ground Address: Hanford Cricket & Rugby Club, Church Lane, Hanford, Stoke-on-Trent, Staffs, ST4 8QP.
Tel: 01782 641442
Brief Directions: M6 J.15, A500 towards Stoke, 1st exit (signed Trentham) turn right at R/about. Immediate left after Petrol Station. 1st left into club.
Club Secretary: Craig Boulton, 11 Whatmore St., Smallthorne, Stoke-on-Trent, Staffs, ST6 1SH.
Tel: 01782 851281
Fixtures Secretary: Brian Davies, 15 Stanley Grove, Badderley Green, Stoke on Trent, Staffs., ST2 7SA.
Tel: (H) 01782 545085
Club Colours: Navy Blue & Gold Hoops
League: Staffordshire 2

HARBORNE RFC
Ground Address: Playing Fields, Metchley, Park Road, Harborne, Birmingham
Tel: 0121 427 2690
Brief Directions: From Birmingham city centre follow signs to Harborne (3 miles) Ground to south of High Street

Club Secretary: Anthony Steel. 7 Stableford Close, Harborne, B'ham. B32 3XL.
Tel: 0121 427 6627
Fixtures Secretary: Simon Parker, 56 Farm Road, Rowley Regis, West Midlands.
Tel: (H) 0121 532 4780 e-mail: simon parker 65@netmail.com
Club Colours: Black & green hoop with red stripe.
League: North Midlands 2

HARBURY RFC
Ground Address: Waterloo Fields, Middle Road, Harbury, Leamington Spar, Warwickshire.
Tel: 01926 613462
Brief Directions: 1 mile off Fosse Way, 2 miles north of junction of Fosse Way with B4100 (Banbury-Warwick Road) between J.12 and J.13 M40
Club Secretary: Peter Rollason, 27 Farm Street, Harbury, CV33 9LR.
Tel: 01926 613422
email: prollason@telco4u.com
Fixtures Secretary: Jerry Birbeck, 22 Campion Terrace, Leamington Spa, Warks.
Tel: (H) 01926 424053
Club Colours: Red &White Hoops, Black Shorts and socks
League: Warwickshire 2

HINCKLEY RFC
Ground Address: Leicester Road, Hinckley, Leicestershire, LE10 3DR.
Tel: 01455 615010 - Fax: 01455 615050
Brief Directions: From M69 take A5 towards Tamworth. Right at 1st R/about. Follow road over 3 R/abouts then turn right at 4th. The club is 300 metres on the right.
Club Secretary: John Bennett, Beechrome, Ivydene Close, Earl Shilton LE9 7LR
Tel No: 01455 843874
email: John @James-Ben nett.co.uk
Fixtures Secretary: Trevor Williams, 94 Druid Street, Hinckley, Leicestershire, LE10 1QQ.
Tel: 07939 351866 - or c/o club numbers
Club Colours: Black and Amber, Black shorts.
League: Midlands 2 East

HOPE VALLEY RUFC
Ground Address: Castleton Playing Fields, Hollowford Road, Castleton, Derbyshire (No mail to this address)
Tel: (c/o The Peak Hotel) 01433 620247
Brief Directions: From Sheffield A625 through Hathersage and Hope to Castleton, 100 metres past Peak Hotel turn right into Back St, ground is 500 metres on right
Club Secretary: Mrs K Copley, 21 Michlow Drive, Bradwell, Hope Valley S33 9GA
Tel No: 01433 621669
email: kim@coppo22.freeserve

Fixtures Secretary: M. Smith, 27 Old Road, Whaley Bridge, High Peak. SK23 7HS
Tel: 01663 734591
email: smiffy-coppo 22.freeserve.co.uk
Club Colours: Purple, green and white quarters, black shorts
League: NLD/Leics 2 West

HORNCASTLE
Ground Address: Horncastle Playing Fields, The Wong, Horncastle, Lincolnshire.
Brief Directions: To centre of Horncastle traffic lights, take Boston direction 200yds turn right follow signs to playing field.
Club Secretary: Mick Jenkinson, 2 The Crescent, Horncastle, Lincolnshire LN9 6EZ.
Tel: 01507 525183
Fixtures Secretary: David Stow, 7 Mareham road, Horncastle, Lincs.
Tel: 01507 522128
Club Colours: Green and gold quarters black shorts
League: NLD/Leics 2 East

HUNTINGDON & DISTRICT RFC LTD
Ground Address: Hinchingbrooke School, Brampton Road, Huntingdon, Cambs.PE18 6BN
website: www.huntingdonrufc.co.uk
Brief Directions: Heading into Huntingdon from A14 or A1, Hinchingbroke School is adjacent to Hinchingbroke Hospital on the left.
Club Secretary: Mrs S Morgan, 17 Pages Way, Brampton, Huntingdon PE28 4UR
Tel; No: 01480 383625
Fixtures Secretary: Mrs. I. Tack, 37 Egremont Road, Hardwick, Cambridge.
Tel: -1954 211140
Email: mrstefiracing.co.uk
Club Colours: Emerald Green shirts, navy blue shorts, green and green socks
League: Midlands 2 East

ILKESTON RUFC
Ground Address: The Stute, Hallam Fields Road, Ilkeston, Derbys. DE7 4AZ
Tel: 0115 9323244
Website: www.ilkeston-stute.co.uk
Brief Directions: M1 Exit 25, A52 to Nott'ham. Left at 2nd round't (A6007) Ilkeston Rd. At mini round't, A6007 now Stapleford Rd. Left at T jct to A609.Left at garage toThurman St/Corpor'n Rd,T jct left
Club Secretary: Michael Green, 62 Northen Drive, Trowell, Nottingham NG9 3QL
e-mail: michael.green@marconi.com
Tel No: 0115 9170740 (H) 0115 9064709 (W)
Fixtures Secretary: Colin Fox, 39 Nursery Hollow, Ilkeston, Derbys. DE7 4LO
Tel: (H) 0115 9308421 (M) 0802 714518
Club Colours: Blue, green and white hoops, green shorts and socks.
League: Midlands 2 East

MIDLAND

KEMPSTON RFC
Ground Address: Sports Club,134 High Street, Kempston, Beds. MK42 7BN
Tel: 01234 852499
Brief Directions: Head towards Kempston. Find Sainsburys, go down hill past Citroen Garage on right , stay on this road and club is on right before you go out of Kempston
Club Secretary: Rob Burnage, 8 King Street, Kempston, Bedford MK42 8BN
Tel: 01234 301477H - 01438 354111W
Email: robert.burnage@hotmail.com
Fixtures Secretary: Chris Pitts, 34 Park Road, Kempston, Beds. MK42 8NZ
Tel: 01234 840921
Club Colours: Red & Black Quarters. Change: Yellow
League: East Midlands 1

KERESLEY RFC
Ground Address: The John E. Radford Fields, Burrow Hill Lane, Chorley, Nr Coventry. CV7 8BE.
Tel: 01676 540082
Brief Directions: Situated off Bennetts Road North, just past Keresley Village
Club Secretary: John Frawley,
37 The Crescent, Keresley, Coventry.
Tel: 024 7633 7537
email: jwfrawley@ hotmail.com
Fixtures Secretary: A Atkins, 2 Carpenters Close, Burbage, Hinckley, LE10 2RB.
Tel: 01455 456956
Club Colours: Royal blue, scarlet and white, navy shorts
League: Midlands 3 West (South)

KESTEVEN RUFC
Ground Address: Wood Nook, High Dyke, Grantham, Lincs.
Tel: 01476 564887
Brief Directions: A52 out of Grantham towards Spalding, past the R.A.F. camp then right at roundabout (B6403). Club on right about 400 yards.
Club Secretary: Bill Berridge, 60 Belton Grove, Grantham, Lincs. NG33 5AA
Tel: 01476 590561
Fixtures Secretary: Rob Cole.
Tel: 01476 401194
Club Colours: Black shirts, white shorts
League: Midlands 4 East (North)

KETTERING RFC
Ground Address: Waverley Road (off Pipers Hill Road), Kettering, Northants NN15 6NT.
Tel: 01536 485588
Brief Directions: A14 J10, turn onto A6 to Kettering, at second traffic lights turn right, first left and first left again into Waverley Road, Ground is at end of road
Club Secretary: Mrs L Blatchly, c/o The Club.

Fixtures Secretary: Rob Bowley,
Messuage Farmhouse, 10 Lower Benefield, Peterborough PE8 5AF.
Tel: (H) 01832 205382
Club Colours: Royal Blue and white irregular hoops, navy shorts
League: Midlands 2 East

KEYWORTH RFC
Ground Address: The Pavilion, Willoughby Lane, Widmerpool, Nottingham NG12 5BU.
Tel: 0115 937 5579
Brief Directions: A606 from Nottingham to Melton Mowbray. Turn right at Widmerpool cross roads. Turn left at end of road, then 2nd left to Willoughby, ground is on the right hand side.
Club Secretary: R.W. Baker, 14 Orchard Way, Wymeswold, Leics. LE12 6SW
Tel: 01509 881473
Fixtures Secretary: A.Evans, 6 East Close, Keyworth, Nottingham, NG12 5GN
Tel N o: 0115 846 0795
Club Colours: Black with gold hoops, black shorts.
League: NLD/Leics 1 East

KIBWORTH RUFC
Ground Address: Northampton Road, Market Harborough, Leicestershire
Tel: 01858 464210
Brief Directions: From town centre, follow signs for Leisure Centre, club on right as you enter centre. From M1, M6, A14, follow A508 to Market Harborough, ground on left as entering town
Club Secretary: David R Coe, Flat 1, 58-60 Station Road, Desborough, Kettering, Northants NN142RS
Tel: (H) 01536 762482 (W) 01536 464188
e-mail: david.r.coe@talk21.com
Fixtures Secretary: As Secretary
Club Colours: All Black
League: Midlands 3 East (South)

KIDDERMINSTER CAROLIANS RFC
Ground Address: Marlpool Lane, Kidderminster, Worcs. DY11 4HP
Tel: 01562 740043
Brief Directions: Follow signs from Kidderminster ringroad to Bridgnorth, at end Proud Cross Ringway is Jackson pub, Marlpool Lane is to one side, ground 400m from pub
Club Secretary: Keith Skirving,43 Leawood Grove, Kidderminster, Worcs. DY11 6JT.
Tel: (H) 01562 747482
email:san.kela@talk21.com
Fixtures Secretary: Mr Tim Carder, 218 Puxton Drive, Kidderminste, Worcs.DY11 5HJ
Tel: (H) 01562 747910 (W) 01902 774217
Club Colours: Black with gold hoops and Black shorts
League: Midlands 3 West (North)

KINGS NORTON RFC
Ground Address: Ash Lane, Hopwood,
Birmingham. B48 7BB
Tel: 0121 445 3340
Brief Directions: Near exit 2 from the M42, take
Birmingham road and turn down Ash Lane, ground
on right
Club Secretary: G S C Maciver,
11 Chapel Walk, Kings Norton,
Birmingham B30 3LW.
Tel: (H) 0121 459 2279
Fixtures Secretary: N.Osborne.
Tel No: 01564 822831
Club Colours: Red and gold hoops, black shorts,
red socks
League: Midlands 4 West (South)

KYNOCH RFC
Ground Address: Holford Drive, Perry Barr,
Birmingham. B42 2TU
Tel: 0121 356 4369
Brief Directions: Ms Carole Gibbs, 46 Church
Hill, Wednesbury, West Midlands, WS10 9DG.
Tel: 0121 456 8267 Day - 0121 556 8796 Eve.
Email: carole.gibbs@mills-reeve.com
Club Secretary: Paul Sturch,
132 Brantley Rd., Witton, Birmingham B67 DP.
Tel: 0121 6862648
Fixtures Secretary: Ray Jones, 23 Blounts Rd,
Erdington, Birmingham, B23 7DE
Tel: (H) 0121 382 0310
Club Colours: Black and white hoops
League: North Midlands 3

LEAMINGTON RUFC
Ground Address: Moorefields, Kenilworth Road,
Blackdown, Leamington Spa, Warwickshire. CV32
6RG Tel/Fax: 01926 425584
Brief Directions: Join A46 Warwick bypass (from
North M6, J2, from South M40, J15). Leave
bypass at Leamington/Kenilworth junction. Take
A452 towards Leamington 1 mile, ground on left
Club Secretary: John Lyons,
3 Denewood Way, Kenilworth, CV8 2NY.
Tel: 01926 855787
email: john@lyons99,freeserve.co.uk
Fixtures Secretary: Tony Grimes,
White Hall, Long Itchington, Rugby, CU23 8PU
Tel: (H) 01926 813501
Club Colours: Royal blue with single scarlet and
gold hoop
League: Midlands 3 West (South)

LEDBURY RFC
Ground Address: Ross Road Playing Field, Ross
Road, Ledbury, Herefordshire, HR8 2LP.
Tel: 01531 631788
Brief Directions: Get off Exit 2 of the M50. Take
A417 to Ledbury for 4 miles. Take left turn at
R/about down by-pass. Next R/about take A449 to
Ross-on-Wye, 100yds on right.

Club Secretary: Jill Matthews,40 Bank Crescent,
Ledbury, Herefordshire. HR8 1AD
Tel: 01531 633958H 07779 662567M
email: j122ym123@aol.com
Fixtures Secretary: Trevor Humphreys, 10
Challinor Close, Ledbury, Herefordshire
Tel; 07808 987846M 00353 429387435W
Club Colours: Black and white hoops
League: Midlands 4 West (South)

LEEK RUFC
Ground Address: Post & Times Park, St
Edwards, Cheddleton, North Staffs.
Tel: 01538 361770
Brief Directions: Leek RFC is located within the
grounds of St Edwards Hospital, Cheddleton situ-
ated south of Leek on the A520
Club Secretary: Andrew Chandler, 22 Shirburn
Road, Leek, North Staffs. ST136LE
Tel No: 01538 381045
email : achandle @celestica.com
Fixtures Secretary: Daniel Hunt, 4 Southbank St.
Leek, Staffs STT13 5LN
Tel: 01538 388526
Club Colours: Blue and white hoops, blue, blue
League: Midlands 3 West (North)

LEESBROOK RUFC
Ground Address: Asterdale Sports Centre,
Borrowash Road, Spondon, Derby. DE21 7PH.
Tel: 01332 668656
Brief Directions: M1 J25, 3rd turn marked
Spondon. From city centre take A52, take turning
marked Spondon (Ntm Old Road)
Club Secretary: John Burns, 160 Cole Lane,
Borrowash, Derby, DE72 3GP
Tel: (H) 01332 674216
Fixtures Secretary: Peter Dodd,14 Sunny Cres.,
Chaddesden, Derby DE21 6QN
Tel: 01332 662144
Club Colours: Black, with green and blue band,
black shorts and socks.
League: NLD/Leics 1 West

LEICESTER FOREST RFC
Ground Address: Hinckley Road, Leicester
Forest East, Leicester LE3 3PJ
Tel: 0116 2387136
website: leicesterforestrfc.com
Brief Directions: Ground is off the main A47
Leicester. Hinckley road 1.5 miles from the
Leicester Forest Services on the M1.
Club Secretary: Kate Coles, 45 Beechwood
Avenue, Leicester Forest East, Leicester LE3 3PL
Tel No: 0116 2338881
Fixtures Secretary: Tony Thraves, 5 Lynmouth
Drive, Wigston, Leicester, LE18 1BP.
Tel: 0116 210 0980. (H0 09762 59882 (M)
email: lfrfc@aol.com
Club Colours: Dark Blue and Light Blue shirts
with blue shorts
League: Midlands 4 East (South)

MIDLAND

LEIGHTON BUZZARD RFC
Ground Address: Wright's Meadow, Leighton Road, Stanbridge, Leighton Buzzard, Beds. LU7 9HR.
Tel: 01525 371322
Brief Directions: North: M1 J13, A507 through Woburn, South: M1 J9, then A5 to Dunstable, A505 to Aylesbury, 2nd turn right, Club 1 mile on right
Club Secretary: D Horace, 2 Loyne Close, Leighton Buzzard, Beds, LU7 7YR.
Tel: 01525 375048
Fixtures Secretary: A. Perrey, 22 The Coppins, Ampthill, Beds, MK45 2SN.
Tel: 01525 403812
Club Colours: Navy blue & white hoops
League: Midlands 3 East (South)

LICHFIELD RUFC
Ground Address: Cooke Fields, Tamworth Road, Lichfield, WS14 9JE
Tel: 01543 263020
website: www.lichfieldrugby.co.uk
Brief Directions: Take A51 from Lichfield to Tamworth for approx one mile. Ground behind Horse & Hockey public house.
Club Secretary: Roger Fathers, 75 Spring Lane, Whittington, Lichfield, Staffs.
WS14 9NA. Tel No; 01543 433118
Email: roger@textileassemblies.co.uk
Fixtures Secretary: Steve Barr, 2 Barley Croft, Whittington Lichfield, Staffs., WS14 9LY
Tel No: 01543 432605.
email: stevebarruk@yahoo.com
Club Colours: Myrtle green, navy, red
League: Midlands 3 West (North)
League Contact: As Fixture Secretary

LINCOLN RFC
Ground Address: Lindum Sports Ground, St Giles Avenue, Wragby Road, Lincoln.
Tel: 01522 526592
Brief Directions: Head for Cathedral, club is located on Wragby Road in the `Upilll' area of Lincoln.
Club Secretary: Huw M. Edwards, 60 Bailgate, Lincoln. LN1 3AL.
Tel: 01522 534849
Email: huw.edwards@langleys.co.uk
Fixtures Secretary: Simon Gregory, 4 St. Johns Road, Lincoln.
Tel: 01522 829203
Club Colours: Red/green/white bands, green
League: Midlands 2 East

LINLEY & KIDSGROVE RUFC
Ground Address: Ski Centre, Bathpool Park, West Morland Avenue, Kidsgrove, Stoke-on-Trent.
Brief Directions: M6 J16, A500 towards Stoke-on-Trent, 2nd junction A34 Kidsgrove, follow signs for the Ski Centre

Club Secretary: Jason Swingewood, 48 Appledore Grove, Packmoor, Stoke-on-Trent. ST6 6XH
Tel: H 01782 816213 W 0151 9556835
e-mail: jason@jswingewood.freeserve.co.uk
Fixtures Secretary: Michael Cunningham.
Tel: 01782 638725
Club Colours: Green and gold quarters
League: Staffordshire 1

LONG BUCKBY RFC
Ground Address: Station Road, Long Buckby, Northamptonshire
Tel: 01327 842222
Brief Directions: 0.25 mile from market square, along Station Road towards Daventry
Club Secretary: Rob McNally, 30 Pakfield Road, Long Buckby, Northampton. NN6 7QJ
Tel No: 01327 842912
email: rob.mcn@orange.net
Fixtures Secretary: S Ruddlesden
Tel: (H) 01327 842933
Club Colours: Emerald green
League: Midlands 3 East (South)

LONG EATON RFC
Ground Address: West Park, Long Eaton, Nottingham. (non postal)
Tel: 0115 946 0907
Brief Directions: M1 Jct 25. Follow signs to Long Eaton. Then West Park Leisure Centre. Club is based next to Leisure Centre.
Club Secretary: Mrs P Hickinbottam, P.O. Box 5830, Long Eaton, Nottingham NE10 1LX
Fixtures Secretary: Chris Brookes, 82 Thoresby Road, Long Eaton, Nottingham, NG10 3NP.
Tel: 0115 9468485H, 01773 540707W, 07941 041333M
Club Colours: Royal blue and white hoops with blue shorts.
League: Midlands 4 East (North)

LOUGHBOROUGH RFC
Ground Address: The Clubhouse, Derby Road Playing Fields, Loughborough (not a postal address).
Tel: 01509 216093
Brief Directions: Turn onto Bishop Meadow Road. At Bishop Meadow R/about (A6) turn left at Pay Less DIY. First right then first left
Club Secretary: Steve Hughes, 6 MacLean Avenue, Loughborough, Leicestershire LE11 5xx
Tel: (H) 01509 558955
Email: stev.hughes @ balfourrail.co.uk
Fixtures Secretary: Mick Payne, 59 Birdhill Road, Woodhouse Eaves, Leics.
Tel: 01509 890947
Club Colours: Navy Blue and old gold
League: Midlands 3 East (North)

LOUGHBOROUGH STUDENTS
Ground Address: Loughborough University, Leics. LE11 3TU
Tel: 01509 632009 (Athletic Union)
Brief Directions: M1 J21, head towards Loughborough along Ashly Rd, follow directions into University, 1st XV pitch immediately on left
Club Secretary: Mr. J. Saker, Management Develop Centre, Loughborough University, Loughborough, Leicestershire, LE11 3TU.
Fixtures Secretary: Glynn James, 31 Melbourne Road, Stamford, Lincs., PE9 1UD.
Tel: (H) 01780 51793
Club Colours: White and maroon
League: Midlands 4 East (North)

LUDLOW RFC
Ground Address: MEB Ground, The Linney, Ludlow. SY8 1EE
Tel: 01584 875762
Brief Directions: Approaching Ludlow town centre from north, turn R. just after Honda Equipe, follow narrow road for .5 mile, club on right behind football pitch
Club Secretary: David Francis, Milford Top Cottage, Diddlebury Craven Arms, Shropshire SY7 9JX.   Tel: 01584 841296
Fixtures Secretary: Rob Flemons
Tel: (H) 01568 780334
Club Colours: Red shirts, black shorts
League: Midlands 4 West (North)

LUTON RFC
Ground Address: Newlands Road, Luton, Beds.
Tel: 01582 720355
Website: www.lutonrugby.com
Brief Directions: M1 J10, take spur to roundabout, turn right, 200m turn right again, ground 1km on left
Club Secretary: Phil Wilson, 17 Burghley Close, Flitwick, Bedford. MK45 1TF
Tel: (H) 01525 713409 (W) 01480 452451 x 6771
Fixtures Secretary: Martin Alexander
Tel: (H) 01582 598581 (W) 01582 22333
Club Colours: Green ,red and black.
League: Midlands 2 East

LUTTERWORTH RFC
Ground Address: Ashby Lane, Bitteswell, Nr Lutterworth, Leics LE17 4SQ.
Tel: 01455 557329
Brief Directions: Approx 1.5 miles north off Lutterworth on A426 take left turn at small cross roads (signed to Lutterworth RFC)
Club Secretary: Colin Hudson, "Spring Bank", Ashby Lane, Bitteswell, Lutterworth, Leics. LE17 4SQ.
Tel: 0l788 860442
Fixtures Secretary: Chris Payne, Cawder Ghyll, Main Street, Shawell, Nr. Lutterworth, Leics.
Tel: (H) 01788 860442
Club Colours: Red, green and white hoops
League: Midlands 4 East (South)

MANOR PARK RFC
Ground Address: Griff & Coton Sports Club, Heath End Road, Stockingford, Nuneaton, Warks.
Tel: 02476 386798
Brief Directions: M1-M6 J3, A444 Nuneaton, keep left at George Elliot Hospital, into Heath End Road, turn into Griff & Coton Sports Ground on right
Club Secretary: W J Newcombe, 489 Heath End Road, Stockingford, Nuneaton, Warks. CV10 7HD.
Tel: (H) 02476 374476
Fixtures Secretary: S Atkinson, 10 East Avenue, Bedworth.
Tel: (H) 02476 730606
Club Colours: Red and black hooped jerseys, black shorts and socks
League: Warwickshire 1

MANSFIELD RUFC
Ground Address: Eakring Road, Mansfield, Notts, NU18 3EN
Tel: 01623 649834
website: www.mansfieldrugby.co.uk
Brief Directions: From Mansfield Town centre take A617 towards Neward. Travel 2 miles, turn left towards Ollerton. Travel 1 mile to T/lights turn right onto Eakring Road.
Club Secretary: S.Troman, 44 Leadale Crescent, Mansfield Woodhouse, Notts NG19 9HL
Tel: 01623 652993
Fixtures Secretary: Simon Harrison,12 Lime Tree Place, Rainworth , Notts.
Tel: 01623 792145
Club Colours: Blue and white hoops, navy shorts with royal blue socks.
League: Midlands 2 East

MARCONI COVENTRY RFC
Ground Address: Marconi Sports Pavilion, Allard Way, Coventry, CV2 1HS.
Tel: 024 7656 2831
website: gptrfc.freeserve.co.uk
Brief Directions: From M6 J2 join A46. After approx 2 miles right at r'about. Left at next r'about. Right at lights, right at next lights, then left at 2nd set of lights. Ground 300 yds on the left.
Club Secretary: Brett Naylor, 177 Tennyson Road, Poets Corner, Coventry, CV2 3JD.
Tel: 024 7627 8547 (H)
email: brett.naylor@marconi.com
Fixtures Secretary: Roger Wood, 67 John McGuire Crescent,Coventry, CV32 2QH
Tel: 02476 459379
Club Colours: Red, green & blue hoops, blue shorts.
League: Warwickshire 1

MIDLAND

MARKET BOSWORTH RFC
Ground Address: Cadeby Lane, Cadeby, Market Bosworth, Nuneaton. CV13 0BE.
Tel: 01455 291340 www.pdcnet.org.uk/mbrfc
Brief Directions: Off the A447, Hinckley to Ibstock Road, turn at signs for Cadeby and follow lane in direction of Market Bosworth
Club Secretary: G. Donnelly, 23 Norfolk Road, Desford, Leicester. LE9 9HR
Tel: 01455 823522
Fixtures Secretary: Robert Harding, 73 Elmesthorpe Lane, Earl Shilton, Leicester. LE9 7PT Tel No: 01455 442637
Club Colours: Blue and gold hoops, black shorts
League: Midlands 3 East (North)

MARKET DRAYTON RFC
Ground Address: Greenfields Sports Ground, Greenfields Lane, Market Drayton, Shropshire, TF9.
Brief Directions: Turn into town centre from the Gingerbread Man pub. Greenfields is signposted 300m from the R/about on the righthand side of the bridge.
Club Secretary: Mark Sheridan, 15 Prospect Road, Market Drayton, Shropshsire, TF9 3AP.
Tel: 07968 285670M - 01630 654810
Email: mark.sheridan@niab.com
Fixtures Secretary: Dave Gould, 16 Pendral Close, Tern Hill, Market Drayton, Shropshire, TF9 2ET.
Tel: 01630 638777
Club Colours: Black/Green trim
League: Staffordshire 2

MARKET RASEN AND LOUTH RUFC
Ground Address: Willingham Road, Market Rasen, Lincs., LN8 3RE
Tel: 01673 843162
Brief Directions: Situated I mile out of Market Rasen heading east towards Louth on A631 on the right hand side, just passed De Aston Secondary School
Club Secretary: Nicholas Pope, 41 Church Street, Middle Rasen, Market Rasen, Lincs., LN8 3TR
Fixtures Secretary: P. Dixon, Springfield, High Street, Glentham, Lincs., LN2 3EA.
Tel: 01673 878222 -
email: pjbdixon@glentham60.freeserve.co.uk
Club Colours: Red and green 2" hoops
League: Midlands 3 East (North)

MATLOCK RUFC
Ground Address: Cromford Meadows, Cromford, Matlock, Derbyshire
Tel: 01629 822821
Brief Directions: Turn off A6 at Cromford towards Crich/Holloway, Ground 100yds on right
Club Secretary: Bob Grindrod, 2 George Road, Matlock, Derbyshire
Tel No: 01629 56741

Fixtures Secretary: D Pearson, Greyfriars, Bakewell Road, Matlock, Derbys.
Tel: (H) 01629 55440
Club Colours: Royal blue, gold & grey quarters, navy blue shorts, royal blue
League: Midlands 3 East (North)

MEDEN VALE RFC
Ground Address: Welbeck Colliery Welfare, Elkersley Road, Meden Vale, Mansfield, Notts.
Tel: 01623 842267
Brief Directions: From A60 turn towards Meden Vale, follow road until petrol station then turn left up the hill, take 2nd left into car park
Club Secretary: Mike Heaton, 5 Budby Crescent, Meden Vale, Mansfield, Notts.
Tel: (H) 01623 846076   (W) 0115 9476091
Fixtures Secretary: David Ellison, 7 Priory Gardens, Swanwick, Derbyshire DE55 1DU.
Tel: (H) 01773 609040 (W) 01283 539211
Club Colours: Red with black collars
League: NLD/Leics 2 East

MELBOURNE RFC
Ground Address: Melbourne Recreation Ground, Cock Shut Lane, Melbourne, Derbys. DE73 1DG.
Tel: 01332 863674
Brief Directions: From M1, A453 to Melbourne. From Derby/Uttoxeter, A514 to Melbourne. Then B587 to Recreation Ground
Club Secretary: David Kent, 39 Thorpedowns Road, Church Gresley, Swadlingcote Derbyshire, DE11 9RB Tel No: 01283 552510
Fixtures Secretary: Ms. Jo Cherry, 5 George Street, Melbourne, Derbys. DE731FS
Tel: (H) 01332 863930
Club Colours: Bottle green shirts and white shorts
League: Midland 4 East (North)

MELLISH RFC
Ground Address: War Memorial Ground, Plains Road, Mapperley, Nottingham NG3 5RT.
Tel: 0115 926 6653
Brief Directions: Ground situated on west side of B684 opposite The Travellers Rest, 2 miles east of the turn off the A614 and 2 miles north of the Plains squash club (national grid ref: 605463)
Club Secretary: Bob Knowles, 20 Spring Lane, Lambley, Nottingham, NG4 4PH.
Tel: 0115 931 2037
email: knowles@lambley20.freeserve.co.uk
Fixtures Secretary: Syd Harris, 2 Tilstock Court, Watnall, Nottingham, NG16 1JZ
Tel: (H)0115 938 5456
Club Colours: Green, black, gold hooped jerseys, black shorts and socks
League: NLD/Leics 1 East

MELTON MOWBRAY RFC
Ground Address: Burton Road, Melton Mowbray, Leics. LE13 1DR   Tel: 01664 63342
website: www.mmrfc.freeserve.co.uk

Brief Directions: Leave Melton Mowbray via the A606 to Oakham. Access is on the left past King Edward VII Upper School.
Club Secretary: Hugh Middleton, 10 New Road, Burton Lazars, Leics. LE14 2UU.
Tel No: 01664 563792
email: middleton-hugh@hotmail.com
Fixtures Secretary: Steve. Kerr - 30 Dorothy Avenue, Melton Mowbray, Leics. LE13 0LB
Tel: 01664 850954
Club Colours: Maroon, white, maroon
League: Midlands 3 East (North)

NEWARK RFC
Ground Address: Kelham Road, Newark, Nottinghamshire
Tel: 01636 702355
Brief Directions: From A1, A46 Newark bypass, ground is on Kelham Road on the road marked to Kelham on the right. From A46, take Newark bypass, left at roundabout, ground on right
Club Secretary: J.E. Rimmer, Old Vicarage, Chapel Lane, Coddington, Newark NG24 0PW.
Tel: 01636 640352
Fixtures Secretary: Owen Mathias, North Muskham Prebend, Church St., Southwell, Notts. NG 25 0HQ
Tel No: 01636 815808 Fax: 01636 815747
Club Colours: Navy blue with single hoop and white shorts.
League: Midlands 3 East (North)

NEWBOLD-ON-AVON RFC
Ground Address: The Clubhouse, Parkfield Road, Newbold-on-Avon, Rugby. CV21 1EZ
Tel: 01788 565811 Web site:
www.newboldrfc.co.uk
Brief Directions: M6, J1 to Rugby. After 1/2 mile, at large landscaped r'about turn right (3rd exit) to Newbold village (1.5 miles). At crossroads, Parkfield Road is straight over, clubhouse 100 metres on the right.
Club Secretary: R. Hall, 8 Belmont Rd., Rugby.CV22 5NZ
Tel: 01788 334757
Fixtures Secretary: Paul E Bale, 135 Norman Rd., Rugby CV21 1DW.
Tel: 01788 560014 (H) 569750 (B) e-mail:
paul.bale@virgin.net
Club Colours: Red and black quarters
League: Midlands 2 West
League Contact: Fixture Secretary as above

NEWCASTLE (STAFFS) RUFC
Ground Address: Pavilion Ground, Lilleshall Road, Clayton, Newcastle-under-Lyme, Staffordshire. ST5 3BX
Tel: 01782 617042
Brief Directions: M6 J15 to Newcastle, turn L. at 1st R/about, straight over next R/about, R. at next R/about down Stafford Ave. 3rd Rd on L. Lilleshall Road - past Cricket Ground on R.

Club Secretary: Dave Ellerton, 45 The Plaisaunce, Westlands, Newcastle, Staffs. ST5 3RZ.
Tel: 01782 614276 e-mail: davidfe@ freenet-name.co.uk
Fixtures Secretary: Jeff Scholes, 51 Emery Avenue, West;lands, Newxaste, Staffs. ST5 2JF Tel No: 01782 617840
Club Colours: Maroon and white hoops, black shorts & socks.
League: Midlands 4 West (North)

NEWPORT (SALOP) RUFC
Ground Address: The Old Showground, Forton Road, Newport, Shropshire
Tel: 01952 810021
Brief Directions: From the bypass, take turning to Newport on the roundabout that also signs to Shrewsbury, the ground is on the right
Club Secretary: David W. H. Rees, Valhalla, 19 Granville Avenue, Newport, Shropshire TF16 7DX
Tel No: 01952 404228
Email: david.rees@jones and ferriday.co.uk
Fixtures Secretary: David Vasilionka,25 Norbroom Drive, Newport, Shropshire.
Tel No: 01952 810755 (H) 01952 428743 (W)
Club Colours: Maroon and white hoops with white shorts and maroon socks.
League: Midlands 2 West

NORTH KESTEVEN RUFC
Ground Address: Pavilion Club (rear of Memorial Hall), Newark Road, North Hykeham, Lincoln.
Brief Directions: From A46 south of Lincoln, go towards Lincoln, look for Memorial Hall sign on left opposite North Kesteven School and Sports Centre
Club Secretary: Chris Moon, 5 Mount Lane, Welton, Lincs. LN2 3TQ
Tel No: 01673 861873
Fixtures Secretary: Nigel Thomas, 192 Hykeham Road, Lincoln. LN6 8AR
Tel No: 01522 696666
Club Colours: Black jersey, white, red and green hoops, black shorts
League: NLD/Leics 1 East

NORTHAMPTON BOYS BRIGADE O.B. RUFC
Ground Address: St Andrews Mill, St Andrews Road, Northampton. NN1 2PQ
Tel: 01604 632460
Brief Directions: M1 J15A, follow signs for town centre, left at 1st lights just past 'Saints' Northampton RFC, cross 3 sets of lights, left into St Andrews Rd, Ground entrance by Texaco garage
Club Secretary: Mrs. Helen Bolden,15 Berry Lane, Wootton, Northampton. NN46JU
Tel: 01604 766949
Fixtures Secretary: Tony Bolden:same details as Secretary above.
Club Colours: Light blue, dark blue and maroon hoops with black shorts
League: East Midlands 1

MIDLAND

NORTHAMPTON CASUALS RFC
Ground Address: Rushmills House, Old Bedford Road, Rushmills, Northampton, NN4 7AA.
Tel: 01604 36716
Brief Directions: At J15 of M1 take A508 to Northampton and then 4th slip road and take A428 to Bedford. At first roundabout go right round and back towards Northampton, then take first left.
Club Secretary: John Wearing,145 Obelisk Rise, Kingsthorpe, Northampton. NN2 8TX
Tel No: 01604 844882
Email: john. wearing@virgin .net
Fixtures Secretary: M D Askew, 60 Minton Rd, Kingsthorpe, Northampton
Tel: (H) 01604 454283
Club Colours: Black with amber band
League: Midlands 4 East (South)

NORTHAMPTON HEATHENS RFC
Ground Address: The Racecourse, East Park Parade, Northampton.   Tel: 01604 39250
Club Secretary: Mr. D. G. Hodgkinson, 5 Pine Trees, Weston Favell, Northampton, NN3 3ET
Fixtures Secretary: Derek Hodgkinson
Tel: (H) 01604 416442
League: East Midlands 2

NORTHAMPTON MENS OWN RFC
Ground Address: Stoke Road, Ashton, Northampton. NN72JN
Tel: 01604 862463
Brief Directions: M1 J15, take A508 to Milton Keynes for 2.5 miles, through Roade village, take next left turning at crossroads, after 1 mile, signed Ashton, ground 0.5 mile on right
Club Secretary: John Goold, 38 Millway, Duston, Northampton. NN5 6ES   Tel: (H) 01604 756297
Fixtures Secretary: Ernie Dalby
Tel: (H) 01604 870609 (W) 01332 252132/0802 765527
Club Colours: White shirts with blue hoop and black shorts.
League: Midlands 3 East (South)

NORTHAMPTON OLD SCOUTS RFC
Ground Address: Rushmere Road, Northampton. NN1 5RY
Tel: 01604 633639
Brief Directions: Mi Jct 15 head towards N'ton. Signs to town centre/Bedford.2nd exit off r'about after slip road into Rushmere Rd. Club is first building on left
Club Secretary: Bob Letty, 49 Barley Hill Road, Northampton
Tel: 01604 493727
e-mail: bob@spherepartnership.co.uk
Fixtures Secretary: Keith Shurville,41 Churchill Avenue, Northampton. NN3 6RY
Tel: 01604 494374(H) 07721 368477(M)
e-mail: shurv-rugby@hotmail.com
Club Colours: Red, green, gold & navy hooped shirts, navy shorts.
League: Midlands 3 East (South)

NOTTINGHAM CASUALS RFC
Ground Address: Canal Side, Meadow Road, Beeston Rylands, Nottingham. NG9 1JG.
Tel: 0115 925 0135
website: www.rugby-club.co.uk
Brief Directions: M1 J25, A52 to Nottingham, after 2nd roundabout, right at 2nd lights, straight across 2 crossroads, continue till road makes sharp right, over bridge, turn left
Club Secretary: Andy Crowther, 18 Longleat Crescent, Chilwell, Nottingham. NG9 5EU
Tel: 0115 9678390
email: onzc@clara.net
Fixtures Secretary: Lech Kluk, 46 Springfiield Avenue, Sandiacre, Nottingham NG10 5LZ
Tel: 0115 946 2846 e-mail: uktrain@aol.com
Club Colours: Maroon ,black and white with black shorts.
League: NLD/Leics 1 West

NOTTINGHAM MODERNS RFC
Ground Address: Ferryfields, Main Road, Wilford Village, Nottingham, NG1 7AA.
Tel: 0115 981 1374
Brief Directions: On the banks of the Trent, 10 minutes walk from Nottingham City centre. On A453 by Clifton Bridge.
Club Secretary: Keith Straughan, 44 Longdale Road, Daybrook, Nottingham N65 6ES
Tel No: 0115 9262891
Fixtures Secretary: Alistair Clark,17 Mountsorrel Drive, Abbet Park, West Bridgford, Nottingham.
Tel No: 0115 9819207
Club Colours: Red and white hoops
League: Midlands 3 East (North)

NOTTINGHAMIANS
Ground Address: Adbolton Lane, West Bridgford, Nottingham   Tel: 0115 9811372
Brief Directions: M1 jct 24, A453 to A52, the Nottingham ring road. Follow signs to Holme Pierrepont (National Water Sports centre)
Club Secretary: David Hampson, 36 Longleat Crescent, Chilwell, Nottingham, NG9 5EU.
Tel: (H) 0115 9258395
email: hampson@longleat36.fsnet.co.uk
Fixtures Secretary: Matthew Draper, 3 Crescent Avenue, Careton, Nottingham NG43JQ.
Tel: 0115 9874533
Club Colours: Black, white and purple quarters with black shorts and socks.
League: NLD/Leics 1 East

NUNEATON OLD EDWARDIANS RFC
Ground Address: Weddington Road, Nuneaton, Warwickshire CV10 0AL   Tel: 024 76386778
Brief Directions: Off M6 J3: follow A444 into and through Nuneaton, on left leaving town. Off A5 at A444 junction: A444 into Nuneaton for 2 miles, ground on right
Club Secretary: Ken McBride, 4 Kendal Close, Nuneaton, Warwicks. CV11 6ES
Tel: 02476 34 7370 (H) and 01455 232 784 (W)

Fixtures Secretary: John Burdett, 5 Henley Close, Nuneaton, Warwicks. CV11 6HF.
Tel: 024 76347257 (H) 024 76341231 (W)
Club Colours: Red and white hoops, black shorts
League: Midlands 3 West (South)

OADBY WYGGESTONIAN RFC
Ground Address: Oval Park, Wigston Road, Oadby, Leicester
Tel: 0116 2714848
Brief Directions: M1 J21, follow Leicester South and East for 4 miles to A50, turn right, left at roundabout, ground 0.5 mile on left
Club Secretary: Jim Kilgallen, 75 Leicester Road, Oadby, Leicester. LE2 4DP
Tel: (H) 0116 2713987 (W) 0116 285 8032
Fixtures Secretary: Tony Bayley, 27 Dover House, Dover St., Leicester.
Tel: (H & W) 0116 255 3787
Club Colours: Black, white and gold hoops, black shorts
League: Midlands 4 East (South)

OAKHAM RFC
Ground Address: The Showground, Barleythorpe Road, Oakham, Rutland
Tel: 01572 724206
Brief Directions: Take the A606 Oakham to Melton Mowbray and ground is on left.
Club Secretary: Peter Bateman, 26 Well Street, Langham, Oakham, Rutland. LE15 7JS
Tel: (H) 01572 723850 (H) 01572 756143 (W)
ee-mail: rut.preervation@bt click.com
Fixtures Secretary: Peter Bateman - as above.
Club Colours: Black shirts with single amber band
League: Midlands 4 East (South)
League Contact: As Secretary

OLD COVENTRIANS RFC
Ground Address: Tile Hill Lane, Coventry. CV4 9DE
Tel: 02476 715273
Website: ocrfc.freeserve.co.uk
Brief Directions: Tile Hill Lane is at the Junction of A45 and B4101
Club Secretary: Phil Gill, 27 Glebe Crescent, Kenilworth, CV8 1JA
Tel No: 01926 858634 e-mail: phil-gill@ok.ibm.com
Fixtures Secretary: Colin Hart, 7 Staverton Close, Mount Nod, Coventry CV5 7LF
Tel: 02476 469463
Club Colours: Black, red and gold shirts with black shorts.
League: Midlands 3 West (South)

OLD GRIFFINIANS RFC
Ground Address: West MIdland Transport Stadium, Billesley Common, Wheelers Lane, Kings Heath, Birmingham B13 0ST
Tel: 0121 687 2465
Brief Directions: M42 J3, take A435 into B'ham, at Kings Heath turn right into Wheelers Lane and follow signs for Indoor Tennis Centre (B'ham A-Z page 106, grid ref C2)
Club Secretary: Rick Adie, 33 Middlemore Road, Northfield, Birmingham. B31 3UD.
Tel: (H) 0121 624 7504 (H) 0121 453 1778 (W)
Fixtures Secretary: Bernard Malin, 59 Spiceland Road, Northfield, Birmingham B311NL.
Tel: 0121 475 3788 (H)
Club Colours: All Black
League: North Midlands 2

OLD HALESONIANS RFC
Ground Address: Wassell Grove, Hagley, Stourbridge. DY9 9JD
Tel: 01562 883036
Brief Directions: Wassell Grove is signposted on the A456, 4 miles from junction 3 of the M5
Club Secretary: Mr Mike Churchill, 10 Parkfield Road, Halesowen, West Mids. B62 0HL.
Tel: 0121 602 3797
Fixtures Secretary: Mr Ian Glendinning, 31 Middleacre Road, Bartley Green, West Mids. B32
Tel: 0121 603 5639
Colours: Royal blue, amber & gold irregular hoops
League: Midlands 3 West (North)

OLD LAURENTIAN RFC
Ground Address: Fenley Field, Lime Tree Avenue, Rugby. CV22 7QT
Tel: 01788 810855
Website: oldlaurentian RFC.co.fc
Brief Directions: From A45 take A4071 turn right into Alwyn Road. right again into Lime Tree Ave. or M6 Leicester Road, Bilton Road, Bilton Village, left into Alwyn Road and right into Lime Tree Ave.
Club Secretary: Alan Willis, 45 Frobisher Road, Rugby, CV22 7HS.
Tel: 01788 813481 email: awillis@jaguar.com
Fixtures Secretary: Vic Smith, 180 Norton Leys, Hillside, Rugby, CV22 5RY.
Tel: 01788 812255   email: vsmith8@ford.com
Club Colours: Maroon, green and gold
League: Midlands 2 West

OLD LEAMINGTONIANS RFC
Ground Address: The Crofts, Bericote Road, Blackdown, Leamington Spa. CV32 6QP
Tel: 01926 424991
website: www.olrfc.co.uk
Brief Directions: From A46 take A452 towards Leamington Spa, after 600 yards take left fork towards Cubbington, ground .75 mile on right
Club Secretary: Dennis Fisher, 14 New Street, Cubbington, Leamington Spa CV32 7LA.
Tel: (H) 01926 778639 e-mail: jananden@tesco.uk
Fixtures Secretary: Martyn Rawbone
Tel: (H) 01926 497464 (before 9pm) (W) 0121 698 4021
Club Colours: Blue and gold hoops, navy shorts
League: Midlands 3 West (South)

OLD NEWTONIANS RFC
Ground Address: Hinckley Road (A47), Leicester Forest East, Leicester
Tel: 0116 2392389
Brief Directions: Follow main A47 to Hinckley out of Leicester, pass Red Cow pub on right, continue along A47 for 1 mile ground on right
Club Secretary: Geoff. Clark, 250 Wigston Lane, Aylestone, Leicester. LE2 8DH
Tel: (H) 0116 2832309
Fixtures Secretary: Peter Muggleton, 18 Roman Road, Birstall, Leicester, LE4 4BG.
Tel: 0116 2676739
Club Colours: Navy (white, green, red) central band, navy shorts
League: Midlands 4 East (South)

OLD NORTHAMPTONIANS RFC
Ground Address: Sports Field, Billing Road, Northampton.   Tel: 01604 634045
Website: www.oldnorthamptonians-rfc.co.uk
Brief Directions: Follow signs for Northants County Cricket Ground and District of Abington
Club Secretary: Michael Parsons, 65 Porlock Close, Northampton. NN5 6BS
Tel No: 01604 755887
email: mjpipparson@aol.com
Fixtures Secretary: Simon James, 7 Chipsey Avenue, Northampton. NN1 5SE
Tel No: 01604 639860
Club Colours: Cardinal red, navy, gold hoops navy shorts
League: Midlands 4 East (South)

OLD SALTLEIANS RFC
Ground Address: Watton Lane, Water Orton, Coleshill, Birmingham. B46 1PJ
Tel: 0121 748 3380
Brief Directions: Junction of Gilson Road/Watton Lane, off A446, near Coleshill
Club Secretary: Colin Gardner, 26 Julius Drive, Coleshill, North Warwickshire, B46 1HL. 01675 465050 (H) 0121 233 2323 (W)
Fixtures Secretary: Nik Wilkins,
14 Mercury Close, Catesby Grange, Daventry, Northants NN11 5HW
Tel No: 01327 878785 (H) 0121 333 3305 (W)
Club Colours: Red and yellow hooped shirts, navy shorts, red, yellow and blue socks
League: Midlands 4 West (North)

OLD WARWICKIAN RFC
Ground Address: Sports Ground, Hampton Road, Warwick
Tel: 01926 496295
Brief Directions: Follow road out of Warwick towards Henley in Arden pass the Warwick Horse Race Stadium and ground is on the right after bypass
Club Secretary: Patrick Wing, 57 Broadeers Road, Knowle, Solihull, West Midlands. B93 9OG
Tel: (H) 01564 779947
e-mail: patrickwing@yahoo.co.uk

Fixtures Secretary: Andrew Marshall,
33 Borrowoale Rd,Leamington Spa, Warwicks. CV32 6AY
Tel: (H) 01926 881499 (M) 0421 556098
Club Colours: Maroon and white hoops
League: Warwickshire 2

OLD WHEATLEYANS RFC
Ground Address: Norman Place Road, Coundon, Coventry
Tel: 024 76334 888
Brief Directions: At J9 on Coventry ring road, take A4170 (Radford Rd), after 1.5 miles turn left into Norman Place Rd, entrance is at the far end of road, on left
Club Secretary: Andrew Hibberd, 59 Frilsham Way, Allesley Park, Coventry. CV5 9LJ.
Tel: (H) 01203 711955 (W) 01203 563166
Email: andy-hibbard@lineone.net
Fixtures Secretary: Graham Paine, 2 Craven Street, Chapel Fields, Coventry CV5 8DU
Tel: 024 766 79864
Club Colours: Blue, maroon and gold
League: Warwickshire 1

OLD YARDLEIANS RFC
Ground Address: Tilehouse Lane, Shirley, Solihull, West Midlands
Tel: 0121 744 3380
Brief Directions: From north, M42 J4, Stratford Road, Dog Kennel Lane, Dickens Heath Road, Tythebarn Lane, Tilehouse Lane. From south, M42 J3 Alcetter Lane, Station Road, Lowbrook Lane, Tilehouse Lane.
Club Secretary: Ian Wallace, 54 Geraldine Road, Yardley, Birmingham. B25 8BD
Tel: 0121 604 2168
Fixtures Secretary: Shannon Killarney, 112 Fabian Crescent, Shirley, Solihull, West Midlands. B90 2AD.
Tel: 0121 733 7116
e-mail: shannontk.msn.com
Club Colours: Old gold, maroon and green
League: Midlands 3 West (North)
League Contact: As Fixtures Secretary

OLLERTON RFC
Ground Address: Boughton Sports Field, Church Road, Boughton, Newark, Notts
Brief Directions: From A614 take A6075 through New Ollerton and Boughton, turn left on apex of right hand bend at Harrow Inn, 200 yds right at Church, follow lane to the back of houses Church Lne
Club Secretary: Dave Price,
Lathkill, Harrow Farm, Tuxford Road, Boughton, Newark, Notts. NG22 9JZ.
Tel: (H) 01623 860871
e-mail; daipri@lathkill.freeserve.co.uk
Fixtures Secretary: D.Wilford
Tel No: 01623 824120
Club Colours: Yellow and blue hoops Change Colours : Black
League: NLD/Leics 2 East

MIDLAND

OUNDLE RFC LTD
Ground Address: Occupation Road, Oundle, Peterborough
Tel: 01832 273101
Brief Directions: From Peterborough, cross bridge, turn right by garage, turn right then right again down single track road
Club Secretary: Duncan Hook, 12 Wyatt Way, Oundle, Peterborough, Cambs. PE8 4HE.
Tel: (H) 01832 275407
Email: duncan.hook@farming.co.uk
Fixtures Secretary: Andrew Kendall, 30 Sydons Close, Oundle, Peterborough, Cambs., PE8 4QJ.
Tel No: 01832 274760
Club Colours: Red and white hoops on black with black shorts.
League: East Midlands 2

PAVIORS RFC
Ground Address: The Ron Rossin Ground, Burntstump Hill, Arnold, Nottingham NG5 8PG
Tel: 0115 9630384
Website: paviorsfc.co.uk
Brief Directions: A614 from Nottingham to Doncaster, 2 miles north of city turn left onto Burntstump Hill, first left pass the school on left to Rugby Club
Club Secretary: Ruth Boulton, The Barnacles, 40 St. Andrews, Grantham, Lincs., NG31 9PE.
Tel: 01476 401977
Email: tomas-boulton@hotmail.com
Fixtures Secretary: Len Hines, 6 Beverley Gardens, Gelding, Nottingham NG4 3LF.
Tel: (H) 0115 9563379
Club Colours: Green with red bands, green or blue shorts
League: Midlands 4 East (North)

PERSHORE RFC
Ground Address: Piddle Park, Mill Lane, Wyre Piddle, Pershore, Worcestershire.
Tel: 01386 554105
Website: www.prfc.co.uk
Brief Directions: Between Worcester and Evesham on B4538, turn off main road in middle of village on the corner by the War Memorial, club 0.5 mile down the lane
Club Secretary: David Snell, 22 Churchfields, Bishop Cleeve, Cheltenham GL52 8LL
Tel No: 01242 678032
Fixtures Secretary: David Kelly.
Tel: 01386 554307
Club Colours: Black shirts with two scarlet hoops, black shorts
League: Midlands 3 West (South)

PETERBOROUGH RUFC
Ground Address: Second Drove, Fengate, Peterborough. PE1 5XA
Tel: 01733 69413
Brief Directions: See website : or leave A1 or A47.Take Parkways to East of City, following signs for Fengate Industries

Club Secretary: Ms Barbara Johnson, 4 Middleham Close, Peterborough PE2 8XG.
Tel: 01733 894854 H
E-mail: scihedges.jhuntsch.peterbro.uk
Fixtures Secretary: Mel Proud, 64 Ramsey Road, Warboys, Cambs. PE173RW
Tel: (H) 01487 822951
Club Colours: Red, silver, gold
League: Midlands 3 East (South)

PINLEY RFC
Ground Address: The Croft, Wyken Croft, Coventry
Tel: 01203 602059
Club Secretary: Mr. T. L. Nutting, 299 Ansty Road, Wyken, Coventry, CV3 3FN.
Fixtures Secretary: B Lester
Tel: (H) 01203 443605
Club Colours: Red and black quarters
League: Warwickshire 2

REDDITCH RFC
Ground Address: Bromsgrove Road, Redditch
Brief Directions: Bromsgrove Highway - Birchfield Road - Bromsgrove Road
Club Secretary: Brian Carr, 60 Wychbury Rd., Quarry Bank, Brierley Hill, West Mids. DY5 2XX.
Tel:(H) 01384 79092 (W) 013884 422494
Fixtures Secretary: Paul Thurston, 18 Crendon Close, Stuclley, Warks.
Tel: (H) 01527 854802
Club Colours: Light and dark blue hoops, dark shorts
League: North Midlands 1

ROLLS ROYCE RFC
Ground Address: Merrill Way, Allenton, Derby
Brief Directions: Contact Secretary
Club Secretary: C.J.Ellans, 39 Keyhaven Close, Derwent Heights, Derby. DE21 4SQ
Tel No : 01332 720844
email: chris.ellans@ rolls-royce.com
Fixtures Secretary: Mr. T. Jenkins, 5 Woodland Road, Derby, DE22 1GF.
Tel: 01332 298564
Club Colours: Maroon and sky blue quarters, black shorts, maroon socks
League: NLD/Leics 2 West

RUGBY ST ANDREWS RFC
Ground Address: Hillmorton Grounds, Ashlawn Road, Rugby.   Tel: 01788 542786
Brief Directions: Ashlawn Road runs between Dunchurch (A45) and Hillmorton (M1-Northampton) A428
Club Secretary: Patricia Lee, 29 Faraday Road, Rugby CV22 5ND
Tel: (H) 01788 333393
email: pat .lee@rugby.god.ulk
Fixtures Secretary: Richard Hopley,13 Alfred St., Rugby, Warwicks.   Tel No: 01788 330664
Club Colours: Sky & navy quarters navy shorts.
League: Warwickshire 1

MIDLAND

RUGELEY RUFC
Ground Address: Rugeley Youth Centre, Burnthill Lane, Rugeley, Staffs., WS15 2HS
Tel: 0421 449869
Brief Directions: A460 towards Hednesford, 1st right into Burnthill Lane. 50 yards on right, Rugeley Youth Centre.
Club Secretary: Ian McLeod, 6 Raven Road, Yoxall, Burton on Trent, Staffs., DE13 8PY.
Tel: 01543 472864
Email: ian@combinationboilerservices.co.uk
Fixtures Secretary: Ian Bailey, 2 Ingleside, Rugeley, Stafffs, WS15 2SZ.
Tel: 0421 449869
Club Colours: Gold shirts and black shorts
League: Staffordshire 2

RUSHDEN AND HIGHAM RFC
Ground Address: Manor Park, Bedford Road, Rushden, Northants, NN10 0SA.
Tel: 01933 312071
website: rhrufc.co.uk/rugby
Brief Directions: On main A6 Bedford side of Rushden, on the left leaving Rushden and the right when approaching Rushden from Bedford
Club Secretary: Steve Miles, Kialanga, The Green, Orlingbury, Kettering, Northants. NN14 1JA.
Tel: 01933 400123 (H).
Email: steve.miles@haematology.demon.com
Fixtures Secretary: Tristan Clee, 121 Torrington Crescent, Wellingborough, Northants, NN8 5ET.
Tel: 01933 675973
email: tc@ocscourier.com
Club Colours: Black and white hoops, black shorts, yellow & white socks
League: East Midlands 1

SELLY OAK RFC
Ground Address: Holders Lane, Moseley, Birmingham Tel No: 0121 472 0939
Website: tcsclub.force 9.co.uk
Brief Directions: From Edgbaston Cricket Ground turn right into Russell Road, proceed until right turn into Moor Green Lane, Holders Lane is 1st right
Club Secretary: Simon Walster, 52 Wheats Avenue, Harborne, Birmingham B17 0RJ.
Tel: 0121 604 8726
Fixtures Secretary: Nick Lally, 78 Reservoir Road, Selly Oak, Birmingham B28 6TF
Tel Nos: 0121 603 1493 (H) 0771 892 6682 (M)
Club Colours: Blue and white hoops with red spangles and blue shorts
League: Midlands 3 West (North)

SHIPSTON ON STOUR RFC
Ground Address: Mayo Road, Shipston on Stour, Warwicks
Tel: 01608 662107
Brief Directions: On A3400, through Shipston, turn opposite hospital and follow signs.

Club Secretary: Richard H Slatter, Woodhills Farm, Todenham, Moreton in Marsh, Gloucestershire. GL56 9PH
Tel: (H) 01608 650453 (W) 01608 650453
Fixtures Secretary: Rob Hawkins
Tel: (H) 01608 682216
Club Colours: All black. Change: Yellow
League: Warwickshire 1

SHREWSBURY RUFC
Ground Address: Sundorne Castle, Uffington, Shrewsbury. SY4 4RR
Tel: 01743 353380
website: www.shrewsburyrufc@ freeserve.net
Brief Directions: Follow M54/A5 extension from north or south to Shrewsbury, exit bypass at roundabout, marked B5062 Haughmond Abbey, ground 800 mtrs on left
Club Secretary: Graham S Jackson, 99 Highfields, Shrewsbury. SY2 5PJ
Tel: (H) 0771 544 7016
Fixtures Secretary: Glyn Jones, 10 Copthorne Park, Copthorne, Shrewsbury, Shropshire.
Tel: 01743 360194
Club Colours: Sky blue and navy blue narrow hooped shirts, navy shorts
League: Midlands 2 West

SILHILLIANS RUFC
Ground Address: Warwick Road, Copt Heath, Knowle, Solihull, West Midlands
Tel: 01564 777680
Brief Directions: J5 M42, then towards Knowle, ground 50yds on left hand side
website: www.silhillians.com
Club Secretary: G R Loader, 12 Stubbs Road, Penn, Wolverhampton, West Midlands. WV3 7DF.
Tel: 07702 632218
Fixtures Secretary: John Griffin, 17 Bridge Meadow Drive, Knowle, Solihull, B93 9QG.
Tel: 01564 775409
Club Colours: Maroon and blue shirts, blue shorts
League: Midlands 3 West (South)

SKEGNESS RFC
Ground Address: Wainfleet Road Playing Fields, Skegness
Tel: 01754 765699
Brief Directions: A153 turn right for town centre, 0.5 mile turn right at Highwayman pub, ground across A52
Club Secretary: Alan Hawkes, Grunters Grange, East Keal, Spilsby. PE23 4AY.
Tel: (H) 01790 752788 - FAX: 01790 754611
Email: skegrfc@aol.com
Fixtures Secretary: John Harris, 13 Jenkins Close, Beacon Park Estate, Skegness.
Tel: (H) 01754 765797
Club Colours: Royal blue and white hoops, navy shorts
League: NLD/Leics 1 East

SLEAFORD RFC
Ground Address: Sleaford RFC, East Road Ground, Ruskington Road, Sleaford, Lincs.
Tel: 01529 303335
website: www.sleaford-rfc.freeserve.co.uk
Brief Directions: One mile north east of Sleaford on the A153 Skegness road, at the junction with the A17 Sleaford by-pass.
Club Secretary: Scott Cooyer, Damask, 17 The Sidings, Roskington, Sleaford. NG34 9GM
Tel No: 01526 833036
email: Rrscollyer@aol.com
Fixtures Secretary: George Marsh, 37 Meadow Field, Sleaford, Lincs.
Tel: (H) 01529 303859
Club Colours: Red and black hoops, black shorts., red socks
League: NLD/Leics 1 East

SOLIHULL
League: North Midlands 2
For further information contact:
North Midlands 2 & 3 League Secretary
Terry Wheeler, 14 Wollescote, Pedmore, Stourbridge, W Midlands DY9 7JJ
Tel: 01384 832647 (H)   Tel: 0121 423 4000 (B)

SOUTH LEICESTER RFC
Ground Address: Welford Road, Wigston, Leicester, LE18 1TE   Tel: 011 2882066
Brief Directions: M1/M69 J21, head east on ringroad towards Oadby & Wigston, take A50 towards Northampton, ground at the final round-about of the built up area of Wigston
Club Secretary: Henri Ginvert, 5 The Paddock, Markfield,Leicester LE67 9RR
Tel: 01530 242761 (H) 01530 249621 (FAX)
e-mail: henri.ginvert@uk.zurich.com
Fixtures Secretary: J. Pinnock 197 Little Glen Road, Glen Parva, Leicester LE2 9TX.
Tel: 07050 153252
Club Colours: Green and white hoops
League: Midlands 2 East

SOUTHAM
Ground Address: Kineton Road, Southam, Nr. Rugby, Warwickshire Tel: 01926 813674
Brief Directions: Take Leamington road (A425) off Southam by-pass (A423). Left at next round-about, past Ind. Estate. Ground on right.
Club Secretary: Ivan Harvey,
Rookery Nook, Priors Hardwick, Nr. Rugby, Warwickshire. CV23 8SL
Tel: (H) 01327 260709
Fixtures Secretary: Paul Broadway, 37 Barcus Close, Southam, Leamington Spa, Warwicks.
Tel: 01926 815118
Club Colours: Navy blue jerseys, white hoops with white shorts.
League: Midlands 4 West (South)

SOUTHWELL RUFC
Ground Address: Pentelowes, Park Lane, Southwell, Notts. NG25 0LA
Website: www.southwellrugby.co.uk
Brief Directions: On entering into Southwell follow signs to the recreation centre. The rugby club is behind the recreation centre.
Club Secretary: Andrew Smith, 66 Easthorpe, Southwell, Notts. NG25 0HZ
Tel No: 01636 812869
Fixtures Secretary: Phil Gordon, Beggars Behind, Main Street, Morton, Southwell, Notts.
Tel: (H) 01636 830485
Club Colours: Maroon and navy blue quarters
League: NLD/Leics 1 East

SPALDING RFC
Ground Address: Memorial Field, St Thomas' Road, Spalding, Lincs.   Tel: 01775 725191
Brief Directions: From north, south & east, exit bypass at town centre sign, 1st left over river, immediate right, left into St Thomas Rd, From west, in town, 1st right after railway crossing
Club Secretary: Peter Jullien, Sunnyside House, 21 The Parkway, Spalding, Lincs. PE11 3EE.
Tel: 01775 712376 (H) 07967 807495 (M)
Fixtures Secretary: Martin Beecham, 48 West Elloe, Spalding, Lincs. PE11 2BH
Tel: 01775 722356 (H) 07887 821173 (M)
Club Colours: Maroon and blue hoops
League: Midlands 2 East

SPARTANS RUFC
Ground Address: Coppice Lane, Middleton, Nr Tamworth, Staffordshire. B78 2BS.
Tel: 0121 308 5857
Brief Directions: Club is situated by the junction of A446 and Coppice Lane, 0.25 mile on the Colehill side of the A453 at Bassetts Pole
Club Secretary: Tim Hesketh,108 Somerset Rd., Erdington, Birmingham B23 6NH
e-mail: tim.hesketh@willenhallsteel.co.uk
Fixtures Secretary: John Whiting,
33 Whiston Grange, Moorgate, Rotherham S.Yorkshire. S60 3BG   Tel: 01709 372265 (H 01709 842201 (W)   0831 118191 (M)
Club Colours: Black shirts and black shorts
League: Warwickshire 1

ST IVES RUFC
Ground Address: Somersham Road, St Ives, Cambs. PE27 3LY Tel No 01480 464455
Website: www.stivesrufc.co.uk
Brief Directions: Follow signs to St Ives off A14 follow by pass (B1040) to Ramsey and ground is on left approx .5 mile from St Ives.
Club Secretary: Chris Ford, 3 The Aisled Barn, The Green, Hilton, Cambs. PE28 9NR
Tel: 01480 831862   email: thefords@ic24.net
Fixtures Secretary: Gillian Price, 32 Laburnum Way, St Ives, Cambs. PE27 3YW
Tel: 01480 381742
Club Colours: Royal B lue, black
League: East Midlands 1

MIDLAND

ST NEOTS RUFC
Ground Address: The Common, St Neots. Cambs. PE19 1HA   Tel: 01480 474285
Brief Directions: Follow signs for Little Paxton from town centre, ground on left as you leave St Neots (1 mile from Town centre)
Club Secretary: D.Young, 3 Constable Drive, Eaton Ford, St. Neots, Cambs. PE19 3RH
Fixtures Secretary: D.Warmington
Tel No: 01954 718153
Club Colours: Light blue with navy blue hoops.
League: East Midlands 2

STAFFORD RUFC
Ground Address: County Ground, Castlefields, Newport Road, Stafford. ST16 1BG.
Tel: 01785 211241
Website: www. staffordrugby club.co.uk
Brief Directions: M6 J13, A449 to Stafford for 1.5 miles, turn on left marked Rowley Park Westway, continue to junction with Newport Rd, turn right, Club 500 yds on left
Club Secretary: P.L.Hill, 39 Rising Brook, Stafford. ST17 0PV
Tel: (H) 01785 259583
Fixtures Secretary: B Bowen, 6 Fallowfield, Wildwood, Stafford ST17 4QU
Tel: 01785 603961
Club Colours: Black and amber hooped jerseys, black shorts
League: Midlands 2 West

STAMFORD COLLEGE OLD BOYS RFC
Ground Address: Stamford College, Drift Road, Stamford, Lincs
Brief Directions: Follow signs to Stamford College, ground behind Leisure Centre
Club Secretary: James Gerever, 77 Radcliffe Rd., Stamford,Lincs. PE91AU
Tel No: 01780 766849
 e-mail: james.gerever@adas.co.uk
Fixtures Secretary: Ray Bates. 55 Millfield Road, Deeping St James, Lincs. PE6 8QX.
Tel: 01778 348644
e-mail: rbates@aptelecom.com
Club Colours: Red and green hoops
League: NLD/Leics 2 East

STAMFORD RUFC
Ground Address: Hambleton Road, Stamford, Lincs   Tel: 01780 752180
Brief Directions: Take Oakham/Melton Mowbray exit from A1, turn towards Stamford, approx 500 yds right turn into Lonsdale Rd, approx 200 yds fork left into Hambleton Rd
Club Secretary: Andrew Jones, 36 Empingham Road, Stamford, Lincs. PE9 2RH
Tel No: 07967 398838
Fixtures Secretary: T.B.A.
Club Colours: Purple, black and white shirts, black shorts
League: NLD/Leics 1 East
League Contact: As Secretary

STANDARD RFC
Ground Address: Tanners Lane off Tile Hill Lane, Coventry CV4 9BD   Tel No 024 76675186
Brief Directions: From A45 to Tile Hill Lane to Tile Hill Village. Tale Tanners Lane and Ground is 100 yds on left.
Club Secretary: Chris Hughes, 108 Earlsdon Avenue South, Coventry. CV5 8DN
Tel: (H) 024 76679552 -
email: chris.hughes@waa.co.uk
Fixtures Secretary: Melvyn O'Neill, 87 Demontfort Way, Cannon Park, Coventry CV4 7DU   Tel No: 024 766 90600
Club Colours: Dark blue, sky blue and white hoops with blue shorts
League: Warwickshire 1

STEWARTS & LLOYDS RFC
Ground Address: Occupation Road, Corby, Northants. NN17 1EH.   Tel: 01536 400317
Brief Directions: From Kettering, A6003 towards Oakham, right at roundabout at top of Rockingham Hill, .75 mile, turn right past Game Bird Pub into Occupation Rd, 1st right into ground
Club Secretary: J M Thompson, 5 Howe Crescent, Corby, Northants. NN17 2RY
Tel: (H) 01536 202433(M) 07970 783253 (Fax) 01536 202433   Email: malc.s-l.rfc@talk21.com
Fixtures Secretary: Alan Brooks., 22 Lister Close, Corby, Northants. NN17 1XR
Tel Nos: 01536 266901H 07977 825071M & 01536 266901Fax
Club Colours: Black shirts and shorts with black & white socks.
League: Midlands 3 East (South)

STOCKWOOD PARK RFC
Ground Address: Stockwood Park, London Road, Luton, Beds. LU1 4BH
Tel: 01582 728044
Website: www.stockwoodparkrfc.co.uk
Brief Directions: M1 J10, left at end of slip road, left at 1st set of traffic lights into Stockwood Park, Club on right
Club Secretary: M.A.Lovell, 4 Westlecote Gardens, Luton, Beds. LU2 7DR
Tel No: 01582 401091
Email: lovell.ma@barclays.net
Fixtures Secretary: J.Carroll, 41 Wychwood Avenue, Luton, Beds.   Tel No: 01582 655527
Club Colours: Red with yellow hoop, navy, red
League: Midlands 3 East (South)

STOKE OLD BOYS RFC
Ground Address: A G Gale Field, Brookvale Avenue, Binley, Coventry. CV3 2RF.
Tel: 024 7645 3631
website: stokeoldboysrfc.co.uk
Brief Directions: Off Binley Road, closest landmark is Binley Fire Station, 40 yards out of town
Club Secretary: Peter Newman, 30 Cliffordbridge Road, Coventry CV3 2DZ Tel No: 024 76611275
email: peterknewman@aol.com

MIDLAND

Fixtures Secretary: Dave Henly, 104 Hermitage Road, Wyken, Coventry. CV2 5GE
Club Colours: Maroon and white hoops.
League: Warwickshire 1

STOKE on TRENT RUFC
Ground Address: Hartwell Lane, Barlaston, Stoke on Trent, ST15 8TL Tel: 01782 372807
Brief Directions: From M1: A38 to A50. Left at lights (A520) at town outskirts. Take Rd. to Barlaston after 3m.Club 1m on left. From M6 leaveJ15 (A34 South) to Barlaston, club on right
Club Secretary: David V Potts, Oaks Cottage, Moddershall Oaks, Nr Stone, Staffs. ST15 8TG.
Tel: 01782 373309 (H) 01782 715555 (B)
Fixtures Secretary: Eric Hardistry, 29 Kingston Drive, Stone, Staffs ST15 0JH
Tel: 01785 813641(H)
Club Colours: Dark blue with light blue hoops
League: Midlands 2 West
League Contact: D R Hodgson, 16 Farrier Close, Aston Lodge, Stone, Staffs. ST15 8XP.
Tel: 01782 844144 (B) 01785 818275 (H)

STONE RUFC
Ground Address: Bibby's Social Club, Tilling Drive, Walton, Stone.
Tel: 01785 810206
Brief Directions: From A34 take B5026 to Eccleshall. Take first L. `Tilling Drive', Ground is at end of Tilling Drive.
Club Secretary: Fiona Foster, 17 Granville Terrace, Stone, ST15 9DF.
Tel: 01785 615591
Fixtures Secretary: Matt Upton, 11 St. Michael's Mount, Stone, ST15 8PZ.   Tel: 01785 605598
Club Colours: Maroon & Green Quarters, Black shorts
League: Staffordshire 2

STONEYGATE FC
Ground Address: Covert Lane, Scraptoft, Leics. LE7 9SP
Tel: 0116 2419188
Brief Directions: A47 east out of Leicester (Signposted Peterborough), left at lights (Coles Nurseries) into Station La, turn right at bottom onto Covert Lane.
Club Secretary: S Morris, 203 Evington Lane, Leicester. LE5 6DJ
Tel: (H) 0116 2735927 (W) 0116 2628596
Fixtures Secretary: M C Herbert
Tel: (H) 0116 2202324 (W) 0116 255 2694
Club Colours: Red, white and navy blue.
League: Midlands 3 East (North)

STOURPORT RFC
Ground Address: The Playing Fields, Walshes Meadow, Dunley Road, Stourport-on-Severn, Worcestershire, DY13. Tel: 01299 822210
Brief Directions: From Stourport Town Centre, cross River Severn Bridge, turn immediate left towards Leisure Centre, ground straight ahead at end of road, club in view
Club Secretary: Terry Harding,
`The Oaks', Wilden Top, Stourport-On-Severn, Worcs, DY13 9JQ.
Tel: 01299 878071
email: caninetuf@aol.com
Fixtures Secretary: Eddie Osborn,
52 Stagborough Way, Lickhill, Stourport, Worcs. DY13 8TU
Tel No: 01299 871439
Club Colours: Yellow chevron on blue, blue shorts and socks
League: Midlands 4 West (South)

STRATFORD UPON AVON RFC
Ground Address: Pearcecroft Loxley Road, Stratford upon Avon
Tel: 01789 297796
Brief Directions: Central Stratford, off Tiddington Road, alongside river on southern bank
Club Secretary: Charles Beighton, 15 Wetherby Way, Kings Acre,Stratford Upon Avon, Warwickshire, CV37 9LU Tel No: 01789 415462
Fixtures Secretary: Ian Fathers, 61 Loxley Rd, Stratford upon Avon, Warwicks. CV37 7DP
Tel Nos: 01789 205715 (H) 07733 101549 (M)
Club Colours: Black and white hooped jerseys with black shorts and socks.
League: Midlands 2 West

SUTTON COLDFIELD RFC
Ground Address: Walmley Road, Walmley, Sutton Coldfield
Tel: 0121 351 5323
Brief Directions: M6 J5 take A452 (Brownhills) at Bagot Arms pub, then right onto B4148 to Walmley. Or A38 at A453 to Sutton Coldfield - T/lights left to Walmley.
Club Secretary: Ian Larsen, 29 Willmott Road, Four Oaks, Sutton Coldfield BT5 5NR.
Tel: (H) 0121 308 6176
Email: ian@scrfc.fsnet.co.uk
Fixtures Secretary: John McElhannan, Four Oaks, Sutton Coldfield
Tel No: 0121 241 1178
Club Colours: Emerald green, white shorts
League: Midlands 2 West

SYSTON RUGBY FOOTBALL CLUB
Ground Address: Barkby Road, Queniborough, Leicester
Tel: 0116 2601223
Brief Directions: Off A607 Melton Mowbray road (Ring secretary for map)
Club Secretary: M.Scott, 2 Pembroke Avenue, Syston, Leicester LE7 2BZ
Tel: 0116 2603756
Fixtures Secretary: I Thorpe, 12 Perseverance Road, Birstall, Leics. LE4 4AU
Tel: (H) 0116 2677950
Club Colours: Navy and saxe (light blue) hooped shirts, navy shorts
League: Midlands 2 East

MIDLAND

TAMWORTH RUFC
Ground Address: Wigginton Lodge, Wigginton Park, Tamworth, Staffs
Tel: 01827 68794
Brief Directions: Head north out of town towards Burton, left turn into Thackeray Drive, right at T junction, 1st left, 1st left to park
Club Secretary: Michael Hobbs, 227 Hockley Road, Tamworth, Staffs
Tel: (H) 01827 288602
Fixtures Secretary: Gordon Penley
Tel: (H) 01827 285211
Club Colours: Maroon, black and white
League: Midlands 4 West (North)

TELFORD HORNETS RFC
Ground Address: Town Park, Hinnshay Road, Dawley, Telford. TF4 3NZ
Tel: 01952 505440
Brief Directions: M54, J4 for town centre, 2nd exit at roundabout, 1st exit next roundabout onto A442, continue to Cattlefield, 4th exit at roundabout to Dawley, 4th right, club .75 mile on left
Club Secretary: Mrs Linda Potts, 17 Ellesmere Court, Newport, Shropshire. TF10 7SD
Tel No: 01952 418801 (H & Fax.)
e-mail; lin@blue yonder.co.uk
Fixtures Secretary: Gareth Evans, 14 Andreas Drive, Muxton, Telford TF2 8SF
Tel: 0467471693 (M) 01952273888 (W)
Club Colours: Black and gold chest band
League: Midlands 3 West (North)

TENBURY RFC
Ground Address: Penlu, Worcester Road, Tenbury Wells, Worcs. WR15 8AY
Tel: 01584 810456
Brief Directions: Next to Tenbury Hospital
Club Secretary: Mr M Spicer, 19 Castle Close, Tenbury Wells, Worcs. WR15 8AY.
Tel: (H) 01584 819541
Fixtures Secretary: Mark Morgan, Deepcroft Farmhouse, Newnham Bridge, Tenbury Wells, Worcs.
Tel: (H) 01584 781412
Club Colours: Green and black Hoops
League: North Midlands 1

THORNEY RUFC
Ground Address: Crowland Road, Thorney, Peterborough, Cambs.
Clubhouse: Thorney Ex-Servicemens Club, Station Road, Thorney, Cambs. PE6 0QE.
Tel: 01733 270283
Brief Directions: A47 from Peterborough towards Wisbech, at traffic lights in Thorney Village turn left. Changing rooms situated l.5 miles outside village on Crowland Road.
Club Secretary: Louis Deplancke, 7 Headlands Way, Whittlesey, Peterborough, Cambs., PE7 1RL
Tel: 01733 204893
Email: louis@dep135.freeserve.co.uk

Fixtures Secretary: As Secretary
Club Colours: Navy and gold quarters
League: East Midlands 2

TOWCESTRIANS RFC
Ground Address: Greens Norton Road, Towcester, Northamptonshire. NN12 8AW.
Tel: 01327 350141
Brief Directions: From A43/A5 junction roundabout take exit for Greens Norton and Blakesley, ground situated approx 1 mile on right
Club Secretary: Richard Titmuss, 67 Clare Crescent, Towcester, Northants NN12 6QQ.
Tel: 01327 358031
email: r.titmuss@tesco.net
Fixtures Secretary: Bob Price, Kilnyard, Park Lane, Gayton, Towcester, Northants. NN7 3HB
Tel No: 01604 858795
Club Colours: Maroon with white edged amber band, black shorts, maroon socks
League: Midlands 3 East (South)

TRINITY GUILD RFC
Ground Address: Rowley Road, Baginton, Coventry
Tel: 01203 305928
Brief Directions: From north, follow A45 west of Coventry, follow airport signs. From south, follow A45 from M45. From west, follow A46 to A45
Club Secretary: D H Williams, 122 Grange Road, Longford, Coventry. CV6 6DA.
Tel: (H)02476 725075 (W)01203 666655 Ext 2420
Fixtures Secretary: K Lightowler
Tel: (H) 024 76 725075
Club Colours: Maroon, old gold and dark navy hoops
League: Warwickshire 1

TUPTON RUFC
Ground Address: The Recreation Ground, North Side, Tupton, Chesterfield
Tel: (Tupton Social Club) 01246 862002
Brief Directions: From Chesterfield south A61 to Tupton, left at roundabout into Queen Victoria Road, then 2nd left into North Side
Club Secretary: Bob Curry, 190 Queen Victoria Road, Tupton, Chesterfield S42 6DW
Tel: (H) 01246 862059 - (M) 0976 538682
Fixtures Secretary: I. Bulloch.
Tel: (H) 01246 238920 (M) 07977 413389
Club Colours: Navy blue with 3 gold hoops, blue, blue
League: NLD/Leics 2 West

UPTON-UPON-SEVERN RFC
Ground Address: Collingshurst Meadow, Old Street, Upton-upon-Severn.
Tel: 01684 594445
Brief Directions: Opposite Upton-upon-Severn Church in the main street of the town. 10 miles south of Worcester and 7 miles north of Tewkesbury on the A38 trunk road

MIDLAND

Club Secretary: Paul Pickering,
11 The Farrington Suite, Norton Barracks, Norton,
Worcester. WR5 2PA
Tel: 01905 355534
Fixtures Secretary: As Above
Club Colours: Black and white quarters, black
shorts
League: North Midlands 1

UTTOXETER RFC
Ground Address: Oldfields Sports Centre,
Springfield Road, Uttoxeter, Staffs.
Tel: 01889 564347
Brief Directions: From the centre of Uttoxeter,
take Stone Road, after 200 yards right into
Springfield Road. After 50 yards turn right.
Club Secretary: Ian Bould, 23 New Road,
Uttoxeter, Staffs. ST14 7DD
Tel: 01889 564313
email: i.bould@hotmail.com
Fixtures Secretary: Jason Cabrera, 72 Bentley
Road, Uttoxeter Staffs ST14 7EN
Tel: 01889 564483
email: mel.cabrera@freeserve.co.uk
Club Colours: Navy blue with red, white, yellow
hoops, navy, red with blue top
League: Staffordshire 1
League Contact: As Secretary

VAUXHALL MOTORS RUFC
Ground Address: Vauxhall Recreation Club,
Brache Estate, 20 Gypsy Lane, Luton, Beds
Tel: 01582 748224
website: www./vauxhallmotorsrufc/home.htm
Brief Directions: Off M1 at J10, follow signs to
Luton Airport. Ground on left as you approach 2nd
R/about.
Club Secretary: Mr. W. J. MacLaughlan, 242
Poynters Road, Luton, Beds., LU4 0LD.
Tel: 01582 653380
Fixtures Secretary: Mr. M. J. Neate, 32
Gardeners Close, Flitwick, Beds., MK45 5BU.
Tel: (H) 01525 716393
Club Colours: Royal blue and gold hoops with
black shorts.
League Contact: Mr. K. Green, 9 How End Road,
Haughton Conquest, MK45 3JT
Tel: 0410 702357 (M)
League: East Midlands 2

VESEYANS RFC
Ground Address: Memorial Ground,
Little Hardwick Road, Streetly, Sutton Coldfield,
West Midlands   Tel: 0121 353 5388
Brief Directions: A452 to Brownhills. Turn left at
the Hardwick pub and the ground is 1 mile further
on the left.
Club Secretary: Mr Karl Ward, Claret Wood,
Streetly Wood, Sutton Coldfield. B74 4HJ.
Tel: (B) 07000 527592 (H) 0121 353 8115
Email: info@sportingclubgroup./com

Fixtures Secretary: Ross Jeffries, 30 Brookes
Road, Sutton Coldfield. B72 1HP
Tel: 07980- 647943
Club Colours: Black and white hoops, black
shorts
League: North Midlands 1

VIPERS RFC
Ground Address: Blaby Bypass, Whetstone,
Leicester
Tel: 0116 2864777
Brief Directions: M1 J21, follow A46 to round-
about at Fosse Park, right onto B4114, straight
over next roundabout, next roundabout left, next
roundabout right, club on left at end of d/c
Club Secretary: Andrew Barraclough, 47 Kiplins
Drive, Enderby, Leicester LE99 5QR
Tel No: 0116 2865164
Fixtures Secretary: Ian Reid, 52 Stanhope Road,
Wigston, Leicester LE18 3SJ
Tel: (H) 0116 281 0472
Club Colours: Green with gold and black hoops
League: Midlands 3 East (South)

WARLEY RFC
Ground Address: St John's Recreation
Grounds,St John's Road, Smethwick, Warley,
West Midlands.
Brief Directions: From Jt2 on M5, follow A4123
to Birmingham.Turn left at Hen & Chicken Pub,
continue to traffic lights, turn right into Warley,
then first left is St Johns Rd.
Club Secretary: Keiron Ward, 72 Oak Road,
Oldbury, Warley. B68 0BD
Tel: (H) 0121 422 4639 (W) 0121 200 2120
Email: keironw@aol.com
Fixtures Secretary: Peter Davies, 23 Holly Road,
Oldbury, Warley, B68 0AU.
Tel: (H) 0121 422 0166
Club Colours: Red and white hoops, black shorts
League: North Midlands 1

WARWICK RFC
Ground Address: Hampton Road, Warwick.
CV34 6RD
Tel: 01926 410972
Brief Directions: Exit M40, follow signs for
Warwick, take left into Shakespeare Avenue, club
opposite junction, on Hampton Road
Club Secretary: Peter O Rourke, 96 Clinton
Lane, Kenilworth, Warks. CV8 1AX
Tel: (H) 01926 858239 (W) 0831 510696
Fixtures Secretary: John Eley
Tel: (H) 01926 403144
Club Colours: Black & purple hoops, black, black
& purple hoops
League: Warwickshire 2

MIDLAND

WEDNESBURY RUFC

Ground Address: Woden Road North, Old Park, Wednesbury. WS10 9NP
Tel: 0121 502 2477
www.wednesbury-rufc.co.uk
Brief Directions: Jct 9 off M6 on A461 to Wednesbury. R. at 1st lights to Myvod Rd. Over 2 R'abouts into Woden Road North. Clubhouse is .5 mile on right.
Club Secretary: Peter Hughes , 28 Alder Road, Wednesbury, West Midlands WS10 9PX.
Tel: (H) 0121 556 5005
Email: peter.hughes@focus.co.uk
Fixtures Secretary: Nigel Belmore, 37 Church Lane, West Bromwich, West Midlands, B71 1DB.
Tel: 0771 5084226
Club Colours: Black & green hoops, black shorts
League: Midlands 4 West (North)

WELLINGBOROUGH OLD GRAMMARIANS RFC

Ground Address: New Memorial Sports Field, Sywell Road, Wellingborough, Northants NN8 8BS
Tel: 01933 226188
Brief Directions: From Park Farm North go along Sywell Road, ground is on right.
Club Secretary: Ewan Cameron, 4 Tannery Cottages, Irthlingborough, Northants NN9 5QU
Tel No: 01933 652773
Email: ewan@tannerycottages.freeserve.co.uk
Fixtures Secretary: Terry Keating, 44 Naseby Close, Wellingborough, Northants. NA8 5XB
Tel: 01933 679424
Club Colours: Claret and white hoops, black shorts
League: East Midlands 1

WELLINGBOROUGH RFC

Ground Address: Cut Throat Lane, Great Doddington, Northants. NN29 7TZ
Tel: 01933 222260
Brief Directions: Leave A45 at Geat Doddington/Earls Barton, turn left at end of slip road, left at small crossroads in approx 500mtr, clubhouse is at top of hill on right, approx 500 metres
Club Secretary: Bob Stevenson, 12 South Street, Woolaston, Northants NN29 7RX
Tel: (H) 01933 664538 (W) 01933 226077
Email: rjstevensonwrfc@aol.com
Fixtures Secretary: Ian Brown, 71 Fullwell Road, Bozeat, Northants. NN29 7LX
Tel: (H & W) 01933 663622
Club Colours: White shirts with scarlet hoop
League: Midlands 2 East

WEST BRIDGFORD RFC

Ground Address: The Memorial Ground, Stamford Road, West Bridgford, Nottingham.
Tel: 0115 9232506
Brief Directions: Enter West Bridgford on A52, just over Gamston Bridge turn left, 1st left onto Brockley Rd, left at T junction, 2nd left onto Rufford Way, club on next bend

Club Secretary: K Howells, 113 Beaumont Close, Keyworth, Nottingham NG12 5JJ.
Tel: (H) 0115 9374468
Fixtures Secretary: N Davies, 17 Chantrey Road, West Bridford, Nottingham.
Tel: 0115 846 5172 (H) 0115 9473859(W)
Club Colours: Black shirts with red and gold hoops, black shorts and socks
League: NLD/Lerics 1 East

WESTWOOD DEACONIANS RUFC

Ground Address: Deacon's School, Queens Gardens, Peterborough.
Tel: 0410 205015 - Fix Sec mobile number
Brief Directions: Head for east side of the City on Dual Carriagway - at R/ablout Jct 5 (Nr. Perkins Engines) go for City centre. Next R/about 3rd exit, straight on at lights, right at mini R/about, 5th right
Club Secretary: Andy Sullivan, 15 Swallowfield, Werrington, Peterborough PE4 5BN
Tel: 01744 324370.
email: apsull@perkins.com
Fixtures Secretary: Mark Middleton, 89 Coniston Road, Gunthorpe, Peterborough PE4 7GU
Tel No: 01733 771426
Club Colours: Red, white and hoops
League: East Midlands 1

WHEATON ASTON RUFC

Ground Address: Monckton Recreation Centre, Pinfold Lane, Penkridge, Staffordshire.
Tel: 01785 712264
Brief Directions: M6 J12, A5 towards Telford, at 1st island take A449 to Stafford, when you enter Penkridge take 1st left past Ford dealership, club 800 yds on left
Club Secretary: Martin Donoghue, Clouds End, 3 Sandy Lane, Brewood, Staffs. ST19 9ET.
Tel: 01902 851700   01785 840 907
Fixtures Secretary: Nick Hammond, 1 Primrose Close, Wheaton Aston, Staffs. ST19 9PX
Tel: 01785 840 907
Club Colours: Black shirts with gold collar and cuffs, black shorts
League: Midlands 4 West (North)

WHITTINGTON

Ground Address: Whittington Barracks, Tarnworth Road, Whittington, Staffs.
Brief Directions: Off A51, between Lichfield and Tamworth
Club Secretary: Mrs L. Emery, 284 Whetstone Road, Aldridge, Walsall WS9 0RU.
Tel: (H) 01922 863213
Fixtures Secretary: S. Clark, 25 Wissage Lane, Lichfield WS13 6DQ.
Tel: 01543 252894
Club Colours: Blue and White Hoops
League: Staffordshire 1

WILLENHALL RFC
Ground Address: Bognor Road, Essington, Nr Wolverhampton, NV11 2BA
Tel: 01922 405694
Brief Directions: M6 M54 off at J.1, take road towards Wolverhampton, 1st left past T. lights into Bognor Rd, 1 mile towards Essington, club on right
Club Secretary: Elfyn Pugh, 9 Five-Fields Road, Willenhall, West Midlands WV12 4NZ.
Tel: (H) 01902 607747
Fixtures Secretary: Ray Mitford, 70 Barmouth Close, Willenhall, West Midlands WV12 5SH.
Tel: 01922 497316
Club Colours: Maroon with black shorts
League: Midlands 4 West (North)

WOLVERHAMPTON RUFC
Ground Address: Rear of Castlecroft Hotel, Castlecroft Road, Wolverhampton WV3 8NA.
Tel: 01902 763900
Website: wolverhamptonrugby.co.uk
Brief Directions: Wolverhampton ring road, take A454 Compton Rd/Bridgnorth Rd to traffic lights at Mermaid, turn left, 2nd right into Castlecroft Ave, ground straight ahead, behind hotel
Club Secretary: Dr D J Rutherford, Rose Cottage, 3 Woodland Cottages, Penn, Wolverhampton WV6 7QW
Tel: (H) 01902 335926 (W) 01902 24847
Fixtures Secretary: Mr.R.N.Astbury 1 Hamble Grove, Perton , South Staffs.WV6 7QW.
Tel: (H) 01902 741495
Club Colours: All Black
League: Midlands 2 West

WOODRUSH RFC
Ground Address: Icknield Street, Forhill, Birmingham. B38 0EL
Tel: 01564 822878
Brief Directions: M42 J3, take A435 to Birmingham, left to Weatheroak, over crossroads, past Kings Norton Golf Club, left at T junction, 1st right, ground on right
Club Secretary: Peter Leahy, 8 Burns Close, Redditch, Worcs, B97 5BS
Tel: (H) 01527 543722
Fixtures Secretary: Mr. C. Parsons, 51 Sycamore Drive, Hollywood, Birmingham B43 5QX
Tel: 01564 824605
Club Colours: Emerald green and white hoops
League: Midlands 4 West (South)

WORCESTER WANDERERS
Ground Address: Sixways, Pershore Lane, Hindlip, Worcester WR3 8ZE
Brief Directions: Take Jct 6 off M5 towards Droitwich. Turnleft after 400 yards as signposted Worcester Rugby Centre.
Club Secretary: John Stitch, Oak Hall Farm Barn, Sinton Green, Hallow, Worcester. WR2 6NT
Tel No: 07767 690670 (M) 01905 641887 (H)
Email: john.sitch@allieddunbar.co.uk

Fixtures Secretary: Mike Clarke, 17 Himbleton Road, Worcester. WR2 6BA
Tel No: 01905 428767
Club Colours: Blue and Gold
League: North Midlands 2

WORKSOP RUFC
Ground Address: The Meadows, Stubbing Lane, Worksop, Notts. S80 1NF   Tel: 01909 484247
Brief Directions: Get onto Worksop bypass at roundabout with Mill House pub, take road to town centre then take 1st left into Stubbing Lane, club and grounds at end of road
Club Secretary: Ken Thompson, 35 Common Road, Thorpe Salvin, Worksop, Notts. S80 3JJ.
Tel No: 01909 771761
Email: kgthompson@tinyworld.co.uk
Fixtures Secretary: John Gibson, 9 Clumber Place, Worksop, Notts. S80 1SB
Email: john.gibson@ citb.co.uk
Club Colours: Black and white hooped shirts
League Contact: Alan Hopkinson, 27 Slack Walk, Worksop, Notts, S80 1UT.
Tel: 01909 488146 (H) 01909 504134 (W)
League: NLD/Leics 1 West

YARBOROUGH BEES RUFC
Ground Address: Yarborough Sports Centre, Riseholme Road, Lincoln Tel: 01522 524228
Brief Directions: Follow A46 to junction with A15 turn - signed Ermine, turn into Yarborough School 400 yards approx
Club Secretary: H Sampson, 7 Shannon Avenue, Lincoln. LN6 7JG
Tel: (H) 01522 691631
Fixtures Secretary: Tony Goude, 44 Rooklands, Scotter, Gainsborough, Lincs DN21 3TT.
Tel: 01724 763825
Club Colours: Maroon, amber & black hoops.
League: NLD/Leics 2 East

YARDLEY & DISTRICT RFC
Ground Address: No 1 Cole Hall Lane, Stechford, Birmingham.
Tel: 0121 789 8450
Brief Directions: B'ham outer ringroad A4040 to Stechford, at T/light jcn of A4040/ A47 take A47 Coleshill Rd, over 1st island, immediate right into H'way, 1st island right, over next island, ground left after bridge
Club Secretary: Steve Griffiths, 11 Orkney Avenue, Hodge Hill, Birmingham. B34 6BY Tel No : 0121 748 2887
email: steve.griffiths@capgemini.co.uk
Fixtures Secretary: Andrew Smith, 34 Easthope Road, Stechford, Birmingham B33 9LJ
Tel No: 0121 624 6938
email: gusanders@aol.com
Club Colours: Royal blue and amber hoops with black shorts
League: North Midlands 1

MIDLAND

ABOVE
Northampton Mens Own and
Pueble Nou Engineers together
after their game in Barcelona in May
2001.

LEFT:
Shrewsbury centre, Chris Hyde,
making another crucial break in their
Championship (Midlands 3 West
(North)) winning match against
Newcastle.
Photo: Calum Baker

BELOW:
South Leicester RFC 1st XV
Champions of Midlands 3 East
(South) with an unbeaten record -
P:18 W:18; Pts F: 707 Pts A: 161.

LONDON & SOUTH EAST DIVISION

A complete club index appears at the back of the book.
This shows which Division and league each club is in for the 2001-02 season

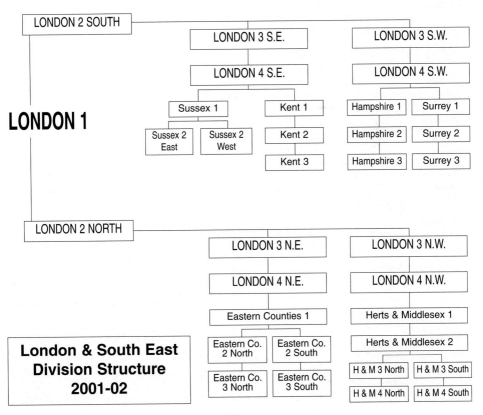

London & South East
Division Structure
2001-02

LONDON & SOUTH EAST LEAGUES OFFICIALS 2001-2002

	Division	Position
P Astbury 32, Kneller Gardens, Isleworth, Middlesex, TW7 7NW Tel: 020 8898 7977 (H & Fax) Email: paulnastbury@aol.com	**LSE**	**Chairman**
M A Ward English Clubs Championship, PO Box12 Beccles, Suffolk NR34 9HZ Tel: 01502 711343 (H) Fax: 01502 710233 Email: londonrfu.competitions@btinternet.com	**LSE**	**Secretary**
M Stott Brick Kiln Farm, North Walsham, Norfolk, NR28 9LH Tel/Fax: 01692 409043(H) Email: mikestott@tesco.net	**Eastern Counties**	**L.C.C.** Member
N Hagerty 1 Hodder Close, Chandlers Ford, Southampton, Hampshire, SO53 4QD Tel: 023 8026 3447(H) Email: neilhagerty@scanplan.co.uk	**Hants**	**L.C.C.** Member
D J Williams 7 Sadlers Way, Hertford, Herts SG14 2DZ Tel: 01992 586744 (H) Fax: 01992 410552	**Herts**	**L.C.C.** Member
D Attwood 6 Somerset Gardens, Lewisham, London SE13 7SY Tel: 020 8692 2820 (H) Fax: 020 8355 9410 Email: dattwood@dattwood.screaming.net	**Kent**	**L.C.C.** Member
R Willingale Fairmile Farm Cottage, Cobham, Surrey, KT11 1JY Tel: 01932 866927 (H) Fax: 01932 860239	**Middlesex**	**L.C.C.** Member
P.J.H. Ralston C/o Village Sports, 209 Worple Road, Raynes Park, London, SW20 8QY Tel: 020 8949 8912 (H) Email: paddy@kings.org.uk	**Surrey**	**L.C.C.** Member
B Vincent 29 St Botolphs Rd, Worthing, Sussex BN11 4JS Tel: 01903 206516 (H) Fax: 01903 603313	**Sussex**	**L.C.C.** Member
P.J.H. Ralston C/o Village Sports, 209 Worple Road, Raynes Park, London, SW20 8QY Tel: 020 8949 8912 (H) Email: paddy@kings.org.uk	**London 1**	**League Sec**
D J Williams 7 Sadlers Way, Hertford, Herts SG14 2DZ Tel: 01992 586744 (H) Fax: 01992 410552	**London 2 North**	**Leagues Sec**
B Vincent 29 St Botolphs Rd, Worthing, Sussex BN11 4JS Tel: 01903 206516 (H) Fax: 01903 603313	**London 2 South**	**League Sec**
M J Stott Brick Kiln Farm, North Walsham, Norfolk Tel/Fax: 01692 409043 (H)	**London 3 N East**	**League Sec**
D Gerschlick 20a The Avenue, Potters Bar, Hertfordshire EN6 1EB Tel/Fax: 01707 644433 (H)	**London 3 N West**	**League Sec**
G Farrow 84 Sedge Crescent, Weedswood, Chatham, Kent, ME5 0QD Tel: 01634 666255 (H)	**London 3 S East**	**League Sec**
R Smith 19 Longstock Close, Andover, Hampshire, SP10 3HN. Tel: 01264 359491 (H)	**London 3 S West**	**League Sec**
R Hatch 99 Ernest Rd, Wivenhoe, Essex CO7 9LJ Tel/Fax: 01206 823548 (H)	**London 4 N East**	**League Sec**
R Willingale Fairmile Farm Cottage, Cobham, Surrey, KT11 1JY Tel: 01932 866927 (H) Fax: 01932 860239	**London 4 N West**	**League Sec**

J Carley
11 Vlissingen Drive, Deal, Kent CT14 6TZ
Tel/Fax: 01304 381273 (H)

London 4 S East — League Sec

N Hagerty
1 Hodder Close, Chandlers Ford, Southampton SO53 4QD
Tel: 02380 263447 (H)

London 4 S West — League Sec

R Hatch
99 Ernest Rd, Wivenhoe, Essex CO7 9LJ
Tel/Fax: 01206 823548 (H)

Eastern Counties 1 — League Sec

B Rees
45a Eastwood Road, Goodmayes, Ilford, Essex, IG3 8UT
Tel: 020 8597 1158 (H)

Eastern Counties 2 North — League Sec

D Chapman
55 Bridge Street, Stowmarket, Suffolk, IP14 1BP
Tel: 01449 672787 (H) Fax: 01449 616309

Eastern Counties 2 South — League Sec

L Hymans
32 Devon Way, Canvey Island, Essex, SS8 9YD
Tel: 01268 693899 (H)

Eastern Counties 3 North — League Sec

I M Forton
183 Middletons Lane, Norwich, Nolfolk, NR6 5SB
Tel: 01603 400049 (H)

Eastern Counties 3 South — League Sec

J Sneezum
Bursledon Lodge, Salterns Lane, Old Bursledon, Southampton SO3 8DH
Tel/Fax: 023 8040 2286 (H)

Hants All Leagues — League Sec

P Woolgar
114 Elgin Avenue, Ashford, Middlesex, TW15 1QG
Tel: 01784 259734 (H)

Herts/Middx 1 — League Sec

A Rabjohn
62 Central Avenue, Hounslow, Middlesex TW3 2QL
Tel/Fax: 020 8894 1850 (H)

Herts/Middx 2 — League Sec

G Payne
16 Brackenbridge Drive, South Ruislip, Middlesex, HA4 0NG
Tel: 020 8845 0874 (H)

Herts/Middx 3 North — League Sec

N Always
20 Herndon Road, London, SW18 2DG
Tel/Fax: 020 8870 6818

Herts/Middx 3 South — League Sec

J Gregory
58 Luton Rd, Redbourne, Hertfordshire AL3 6PY
Tel: 01582 792798 (H) Fax: 01582 793483

Herts/Middx 4 North — League Sec

B East
64 Station Rd, Harpenden, Herts AL5 4TL
Tel/Fax: 01582 762209 (H)

Herts/Middx 4 South — League Sec

J Carley
11 Vlissingen Drive, Deal Kent CT14 6TZ
Tel/Fax: 01304 381273 (H)

Kent All Leagues — League Sec

I Johnson
209 Portsmouth Road, Cobham, Surrey, KT11 1JR
Tel: 01932 862694 (H) Fax: 01932 863528

Surrey 1 — League Sec

M P Tanner
1 Woodland Way, Morden, Surrey SM4 4DS
TelFax: 020 8540 5784 (H)

Surrey 2 — League Sec

P Ralston
C/o Village Sports, 209 Worple Road, Raynes Park, London, SW20 8QY
Tel: 020 8949 8912 (H)

Surrey 3 — League Sec

John Thompson
Chennies, London Road, Watersfield, Pulborough, West Sussex RH20 1ND
Tel: 01798 831338 (H)

Sussex 1 — League Sec

Andy Stephenson
79 Cedar Drive, Southwater, Horsham, West Sussex, RH13 7UF
Tel: 01403 731138 (H)

Sussex 2 (E & W) — League Sec

LONDON & SOUTH EAST

LONDON ONE

2000-01 LEAGUE TABLE

	P	W	D	L	PF	PA	PD	Pts
Old Colfeians	20	18	2	0	742	212	530	38
Havant	20	16	0	4	550	294	256	32
Staines	20	14	2	4	482	363	119	30
Norwich	20	13	0	7	538	285	253	26
Thanet Wanderers	20	10	1	9	483	508	-25	21
Harlow	20	10	0	10	393	433	-40	20
Sutton & Epsom	20	9	1	10	433	471	-38	19
Cambridge	20	6	2	12	329	437	-108	14
Winchester	20	5	0	15	314	517	-203	10
Thurrock	20	3	0	17	229	529	-300	6
Guildford & Godalming	20	2	0	18	248	692	-444	4

Met Police withdrew. All results and fixtures have been removed.

LONDON & SOUTH EAST

2001-02 FIXTURE GRID	Basingstoke	Cambridge	Cheshunt	Harlow	Havant	Haywards Heath	London Nigerians	Norwich	Staines	Sutton & Epsom	Thanet Wanderers	Winchester
Basingstoke		1.09	9.03	22.09	9.02	6.10	26.01	27.10	5.01	17.11	13.04	8.12
Cambridge	16.03		27.10	9.03	5.01	22.09	17.11	9.02	13.04	6.10	8.12	26.01
Cheshunt	8.09	12.01		10.11	23.02	22.12	29.09	1.12	2.02	6.04	20.10	1.09
Harlow	23.02	8.09	5.01		17.11	9.02	13.04	6.10	8.12	26.01	16.03	27.10
Havant	29.09	10.11	22.09	22.12		1.12	2.02	6.04	20.10	1.09	12.01	9.03
Haywards Heath	2.02	23.02	17.11	29.09	13.04		8.12	26.01	16.03	27.10	8.09	5.01
London Nigerians	20.10	22.12	9.02	1.12	6.10	6.04		1.09	12.01	9.03	10.11	22.09
Norwich	12.01	29.09	13.04	2.02	8.12	20.10	16.03		8.09	5.01	23.02	17.11
Staines	10.11	1.12	6.10	6.04	26.01	1.09	27.10	9.03		22.09	22.12	9.02
Sutton & Epsom	22.12	2.02	8.12	20.10	16.03	12.01	8.09	10.11	23.02		29.09	13.04
Thanet Wanderers	1.12	6.04	26.01	1.09	27.10	9.03	5.01	22.09	17.11	9.02		6.10
Winchester	6.04	20.10	16.03	12.01	8.09	10.11	23.02	22.12	29.09	1.12	2.02	

BASINGSTOKE R.F.C.

Founded: 1948

President	John Evans CBE, TD. Meadow View, Green Lane, Ellisfield RG25 2QP 01256 381470 (H)
Chairman	Dr Stephen Tristram 5 Paddock View, Old Basing, Basingstoke RG24 0DB
	01256 328327 (H) 0370 227312 (M)
Secretary	David Crabbe, 126 Pack Lane, Kempshott, Basingstoke, Hants. RG22 5HP 01256 465085
Match / Fixture Sec.	Kevin Barrett Burnt Oak, Silchester Road, Little London, Tadley, Hants. RG26 5EP
	0118 970 0906 0118 970 1755 (Fax/Ansaphone)

Ground Address: Down Grange, Pack Lane, Kempshott, Basingstoke RG22 5HH Tel: 01256 323308 Fax: 01256 814390
e-mail: brfc@bstoke-club.freeserve.co.uk   Web site: www.rugby.basingstoke.net/brfc.html
Capacity: 2,000 approx   150 Covered Seats

Directions:	M3 J7. Head towards town, turn left at 2nd r'about (1st - Sainsbury, 2nd Kempshott) into Heather Way,
	right at junction (Kempshott Lane) & right at lights into Pack Lane.
	250 yards on right turn into Coniston Rd - clubhouse on left
	Nearest Railway Station: Basingstoke - 3 miles
Car Parking:	Spaces at ground + 2 nearby car parks **Admission:** Matchday - £3 members £5 non-members
Clubhouse:	Open normal licensing hours. Meals availableSeats 150. Contact Ron/Sue Marchant 01256 323308
Club Shop:	Open during clubhouse hours.**Training Nights:**Monday and Thursday
Programme	Size: A5 Pages: 20 Price: with admission Editor: C Hibberd 01256 844340

Colours: Blue / amber (white) shirts, blue shorts **Change colours:** White with blue & yellow hoops

CAMBRIDGE R.U.F.C.

Founded: 1923

President	R Bishop	'El Mirador", 14 The Fairway, Bar Hill, Cambs. CB3 8SR 01954 789279 (H)
Chairman	J Fear	10 Parkway, Shudy Camps, Cambridge CB1 6RQ 01799 584432
Hon. Secretary	D J Martin	45 York Street, Cambridge CB1 2PZ 01223 314705
Fixture Secretary	A Dockerill	10 Church Leys, Fenstanton, Huntingdon, Cambs. PE26 9QD 01480 468317
League Contact	Secretary as above	

Ground	**Address:** Grantchester Road, Cambridge CB3 9ED Tel: 01223 312437 Web site: http://www.crufc.co.uk
	Capacity: 3,750 250 Covered standing
	Directions: Leave M11 at Exit 12 (A603) to Cambridge. Take 1st right into Granchester Road (opp. Wolfson
	College). Ground 300 yds on right, just past the last house.
	Nearest Railway Station: Cambridge Car Parking: Spaces for 350+ cars at ground.
	Admission: £3 league & cup matches only
Clubhouse	Open Tues & Thurs eve & Saturday & Sunday during season
Club Shop	Open Saturday & Sunday during season
Programme	Size: A5 Pages: 8 Price: £1 Editor: Sally Hunt, 48 High St., Over, Cambs. 01954 230764
	Advertising: Contact Sarah Powell, 103 High St., Cottenham. 01954 250733

Colours: Blood and sand   **Change colours:** Blue & white squares   **Training Nights:** Tuesday & Thursday 7.15pm

CHESHUNT RFC

Founded: 1952

President	John Healy
Chairman	Mark Ferris, 44a Harlech Rd., Southgate, London N14 7BX 0208 882 0036 (H) 0208 258 5863 (B)
Club Secretary	Stephen Waller, 35 Woodland Mount, Hertford, Herts., SG13 7JD.
	01992 302799 (H) 01992 466600 (B)
Fixtures Secretary	Mo Phillips, 28 Pekram Close, Turnford, Herts. EN10 6AT Tel: 01992 440415 (H)
Director of Coaching	Gavin Reynolds, 6 Alexandra Road, St. Albans, Herts. AL1 3AZ Tel: 01727 762219 (H)
League Contact:	As Secretary
GroundAddress:	Rosedale Sports Ground, Andrews Lane, Cheshunt, Herts. EN7 6TB
	Tel: 01992 623983 Fax: 01992 636636 Website: cheshuntrfc.co.uk Email: cheshuntrfc@tesco.net
Directions:	M25 J25, head north. At 1st roundabout take first exit along Ellis Way. Straight over next 2 r'abouts,
	1st left into Andrews Lane, and club entrance is 200 yds on left

Capacity: Ample - all uncovered standing   **Car Parking:** Ample at ground
Nearest Railway Stations: Cuffley (1.5 miles), Cheshunt (1.5 miles) & Theobalds Grove (1 mile)

Admission:	£2 incl. programme **Training Nights:** Tuesday & Thursday
Clubhouse:	Open every evening except Monday **Club Shop:** Open matchdays and Sunday am
Programme:	Size: A5 Price: with admission Pages: 24 Editor: Steve Waller 01992 302799
	Advertising: Contact Steve Waller (Editor)

Colours: Green and white hoops, white shorts, red socks   **Change colours:** All Blue

HARLOW R.U.F.C.

Founded: 195

Secretary	David Enyon	12 Highfield, Harlow, Essex CM18 6HE
		Tel: 01279 426389 (H)
Fixture Secretary	John Pendleton	56 Priory Court, Harlow, Essex
		Tel: 01729 439265 (H)
Treasurer	A Webb	33 Peacocks, Harlow, Essex
		Tel: 01279 830584 (H)

Ground Ram Gorse, Elizabeth way, Harlow, Essex CM20 2JQ   Tel: 01279 426389
Directions Phone Fixtures Secretary

Club Colours: Red shirts, green trimmings and green shorts

HAVANT R.F.C.

Founded: 195

President: Raymond Quinn   5 Holt Gardens, Rowlands Castle, Hants. Tel: 02392 - 413931 (H), 241122 (B), 257596 (F)
Chairman: Richard Pearcey,   Wisteria House, 34 Queens Rd., Waterlooville PO7 7SB
Tel: 0411 644525 (M), 01730 236236 (B), 01730 269596 (F)
Treasurer: Stephen Lawrence 323 Havant Rd, Farlington, Portsmouth PO6 1DD. Tel: 02392 369492 (H), 02392 834699 (B)
Secretary: Mick Chalk   16 Highclere Ave, Havant, Hants PO9 4RB. Tel: 02392 - 472239 (H) 723749 (B) 726455 (F)
Chair of Finance: Colin Sewell   02392 - 731705 (H) 421055 (F)   **Chair of Rugby:** Adam King   **Press Officer** Ray Quin
Fixture Secretary/League Contact: As Secretary

Ground: Clubhouse, Fraser Rd, Bedhampton, Havant, Hants. PO9 3EJ Tel: 02392 477843 Fax: 02392 492311
Web: www.havant-rfc.co.uk   **Capacity:** 2,700   **Seated:** 200   **Standing:** 2,500   **Car Parking:** 200 at ground, 200 nearby.
Directions: From the A3(M) take the B2177 to roundabout. Follow signs to Bedhampton - straight on over mini-roundabout.
Straight across traffic lights then bear left at level crossing. Take second left (James Road) then turn into Fraser Road at T-junction. Clubhouse is 200 yards on the right. Nearest Railway Station: Bedhampton - go east - James Rd then as above
Admission: Season tickets - Standing Adults £60 Matchdays - Adult £3. Extra for seat £2.
Clubhouse: Normal licensing hours, snacks available Functions: Up to 100, contact Julian Davies 01705 492311
Club Shop: Open matchdays & Sun am. Contact J Davies 02392 477843
Colours: Blue & white hoops/red band   **Change colours:** Red/navy   **Nickname:** Hav   **Training Nights:** Tues. & Thur
Programme Size: A5   Price: With entry Pages: 36   Advertising contact Julian Davies
Editor: Bill Sugden, 01243 372323 (H) 01243 371103 (F)

HAYWARDS HEATH RFC

Founded: 195

President	The Hon. Nicholas Soames, MP
Chairman	Tony Dalby, 109 Western Rd., Hurstepierpoint, W. Sussex BN6 9SY 01273 833736
Club Secretary	Neil Milton, 'Littlemead', Albourne Rd., Hurstepierpoint, W. Sussex BN6 9SL 01273 835439
Fixtures Secretary	B. Killick, 106 Royal George Rd, Burgess Hill, W. Sussex RH15 9SL Tel: 01444 233361
League Contact	Brian Wattam, 18 Priory Rd., Burgess Hill, W. Sussex RH15 9HB 01444 247367
Match Secretary	David Kemp, Hammingden Farm, Highbrook, Ardingly, W. Sussex 01444 892292
Coach	Steve Heaton, 29 Heath Way, Horsham, W. Sussex 01403 257661

Ground Address: The Clubhouse, Whitemans Green, Cuckfield, Haywards Heath, W. Sussex RH17 5HX.
Tel: 01444 413950   email: neilmilton@eur???.co.uk   Web site: www.hhrfc.co.uk
Capacity: Seated: Standing: Covered -   Uncovered -
Directions: Left turn off A23 towards Cuckfield on B215. Right at first junction onto B2114 towards Cuckfield. Ground on right
about   1/2 mile west of Cuckfield village.   Nearest Railway Station: Haywards Heath (3 miles)
Car Parking: Plenty on site   **Admission**:   No charge - spectators are requested to buy a programme.
Club Shop: Mon - Fri Normal hours @ 18 High St., Cuckfield 01444 416587   **Clubhouse**:   Open matchdays
Training Nights: Monday & Thursday
Programme: Size: A5 Price: £1 Pages: 20 Editor: Paul Graham Advertising: Contact Paul Graham 01444 453525
Colours: Red and black quarters, black shorts **Change colours:** Blue & white hoops

LONDON NIGERIANS RFC

Founded: 1991

Chairman	Onome Sideso		
Chief Executive	Tunde Aiyegbusi	131 Dartmouth Road, London NW2 4ES	07976 361607
Secretary	Bayo Ogunbufunmi	12 Defiant, Further Acre, Colindale, London NW9 5YT	07947 730976
Treasurer	Lakis Kakouris	07956 870911	
Fixture Secretary	Ola Afuwape	131. Fords Park Road, London E16 1PR	07930 484355

Ground Address: Linford Christie Stadium, Wormwood Scrubs, Off Du Cane Road, London W12
Tel: 020 8740 7379   Website: http://www.londonnigerian.com

Capacity   Total - 1000   Covered Seated - 200   Uncovered standing - 800

DIRECTIONS   By Tube: Central Line to East Acton Station. Out exit & turn left up Erconwald St. Take 2nd rt into Wulfstan St. Walk down to T-Juction & left into Du Cane Rd. Past the prison & left into Artillery Rd. Walk through to Linford Christie Stadium.

By Road: From Baker Street: A40(M) Westway towards Oxford. Turn off as if for Shepherds Bush. At r'about take A40 exit as if rejoining the A40. Stay in left lane and take exit for "Local Traffic". Stay in right hand lane. At the lights, turn right up Wood Lane. First left turn into Du Cane Rd. About 300 yards down and just past Hammersmith Hospital, turn right into Artillery Rd. Drive through to Linford Christie Stadium.   **From Hanger Lane:** A40(M) Western Avenue towards Central London. Take the turnoff for Shepherds Bush. At the r'about turn left up Wood Lane. First left into Du Cane Road. Then as above..

Nearest Railway Station: East Acton or White City on the Central Line (London Underground)

Car Parking: Available up to 80 cars   **Admission:**   Free

Clubhouse: Open Tues & Thur eves and match days. Training Nights: Tues & Thur 7-9.30 pm

Colours: Bottle green & white quarters/green/bottle green with white hoops **Change Colours:** Black/green/green

NORWICH R.F.C.

Founded: 1885

President	John Drinkell	mail c/o Rugby Office	Tel: 01502 731551 (H)
Chairman	Mike Srokowski	mail c/o Rugby Office	Tel: 01603 716961 (H)
Director of Rugby	James Sinclair		
Community Projects	Ed Stead	Norwich RFC, Beeston Hyrne, North Walsham Road, Norwich NR12 7BW	
League Contact	James Sinclair	Tel: 01603 426259 Fax: 01603 413670 website: lionrugby.com	

Ground Address: Beeston Hyrne, North Walsham Road, Norwich NR12 7BW   Tel: 01603 426259   Fax: 01603 413670
Capacity: 1,000 Seated: None   Standing: 1,000

Directions: Follow the outer ring road and turn onto the B1150 (signed Coltishall/North Walsham). Over two sets of traffic lights and the ground is 400 yards on the left.   **Nearest Railway Station:** Norwich
Car Parking: 500 at ground   **Admission:**   Matchday tickets £4

Clubhouse: Private Functions, contact rugby office on 01603 426259
Club Shop: Contact rugby office as above.

Programme: Advertising: Contact Roy Bishop 01508 499325
Colours: Maroon, gold & green,   **Change colours:** All navy   **Nickname:** Lions
Training Nights: Tuesday & Thursday nights (seniors).   Wednesday (youth)

STAINES R.F.C.

Founded: 1926

Web site: www.stainesrugby.co.uk

Club Secretary	Kevin McMahon, 23 Cherry Orchard, Staines, Middx, TW13 7NB	Tel: 01784 463220
Fixture Secretary	P Adams, 10 Sutherland Close, Weybridge, Surrey KT13 9EN	Tel: 01932 858087
League Contact:	R Lawless, 17 Florence Road, Walton on Thames, Surrey KT12 2AL	Tel: 01932 247347
Ground	The Reeves, Feltham Hill Road, Hanworth, Middlesex, TW13 7NB	
	Tel 020 8890 3051 e-mail: Dave@stainesrugby.c.uk	
	Capacity: All uncovered standing	
Directions	Take Lower Feltham exit from A316 turn left pass Unigate Dairy into Feltham Hill Road, Ground 400yds on left.	
	Nearest Railway Station: Feltham	
Car Parking	Yes	
Club Shop	Yes contact Pam	
Training Nights	Tuesday & Thursday	

Club Colours: Blue & Red Shirts/ White Shorts   **Nickname:** Swans

SUTTON & EPSOM R.F.C.

Founded: 1881

President	Ian Lovatt	43 Cedar Road, Sutton, Surrey SM2 5DJ 020 7251 6802 (B) 020 8643 5264 (H)
Secretary	Bob Poole	Well Cottage, Loxwood Rd, Wisborough Green, W. Sussex RH14 0DJ
& League Contact		020 8770 6441 (B) 01403 700594 (H)
Fixture Sec.	Ian Frazer	111 Benhill Road, Sutton, Surrey SM1 3RR 020 8643 4835 (H) 020 7542 8549 (B)
Rugby Director	Peter Hatch	24 Staines Ave., North Cheam, Surrey SM3 9BQ 020 8644 4438 (H) 01372 722999 (B)
1st XV Manager	Willie Moore	31 Riverholme Ave., Ewell, Surrey KT19 9TG 020 8224 3523 (H) 01372 722999 (B)
Press Officer	John Ashton	020 8644 9664 (H) 0403 189661 (M)

Ground: Cuddington Court, Rugby Lane, West Drive, Cheam Surrey SM2 7NF Tel: 0208 642 0280
Web site: www.serfc.freeserve.co.uk
Capacity: 2,000 approx 300 Covered Seats **Car Parking:** 500 spaces at ground
Directions: M25, J8>A217>A240 Reigate road>A24 Ewell by-pass>A232 Cheam road>West Drive, club entrance at junction with Hays Walk. or M25, J10>A3 (London bound)>A240 Kingston road>A232 Cheam road, then as above.
Nearest Railway Station: Cheam BR
Admission: Matchday - £2.50 incl. programme. Season tickets not available
Clubhouse: Yes **Club Shop:** Open league matchdays, training nights & Sunday am.
Colours: Narrow black & white hoops **Change colours:** Peacock blue **Training Nights:** Mon & Thur (1st XV) - others Wed.
Programme Size: A5 Price: with admission Pages: 40 Editor: John Ashton
Advertising Rates Page £250, 1/2 £150, 1/4 £80, i/s cover or back cover £350

THANET WANDERERS RUFC

Founded: 1886

Secretary / Fixture Secretary / League Contact

	Peter Hawkins	51 Park Road, Ramsgate, Kent CT11 9TL
		Tel: 01843 593142 (H, B & F) e-mail: peterhawkins2000@yahoo.co.uk
Director of Rugby	Geoff Redmond	4 Abbey Grove, Ramsgate, Kent CT11 0JG Tel: 01843 - 595810 (H&B) 852365 (F)
Head Coach	Andy Williamson	105 Minnis Road, Minnis Bay, Birchington, Kent CT7 9NY
		Tel: 01843 - 845981 (H) 591075 (B) 851907 (Fax)

Ground St Peters Recreation Ground, Callis Court Road, Broadstairs, Kent CT10 3AE Tel: 01843 866763
Capacity: 2000 uncovered standing **Admission** Nil
Directions A2 M2, A299, A256 A255 From Broadstairs Broadway turn left at traffic lights into St Peters Park Road. Take the first right under the railway bridge and the ground is on the left after about 400 metres.
Nearest Railway Station: Broadstairs Car Parking: 50 spaces at the ground, others in the nearby streets.
Clubhouse: Open normal licensing hours. Food available For functions contact Bill May 01843 604376 or 01304 611248 (B)
Club Shop: Open matchdays & Sun. am. Contact Mrs Penny Smith 01843 850904

Programme: Size: A5 Pages: 24 Price: £1.50 Advertising: Full page £450 Half: £300 Quarter: £175
Programme Editor & Director of Marketing: Peter Ruranski 01843 845942 (H) 01843 570044 (B) 01843 570055 (F)
Colours: Blue black & gold hoops **Change colours:** Black & white
Nickname: Wanderers **Training:** Tuesday & Thursday

WINCHESTER R.F.C.

Founded:

President	Dai Henley, The Old Post Office, Knapp Lane, Ampfield, Romsey SO51 9BT Tel: 01794 512243 (H)
Executive Director	Paul Beckett, 14 Waverley Drive, South Wonston, Winchester SO21 3EF Tel: 01962 889492 (H)
Operations Manager	Rob Memory, 7 Portal Rd., Highcliffe, Winchester SO23 0PX
Treasurer	Fiona Beckett, 14 Waverley Drive, South Wonston, Winchester SO21 3EF Tel: 01962 889492 (H)
Secretary	John H Prosser MBE, 10 Princess Court, St Peter St., Winchester SO23 8DN
	Tel: 01962 863550 (H) email: jhprosser10@aol.com
Fixture Secretary	Godfrey L Toogood, 31 Winslade Rd, Harestock, Winchester, Hants. SO22 6LN Tel: 01962 881991
League Contact:	Secretary

Ground: North Walls Park, off Nuns Road, Winchester SO23 7EF
Tel: 01962 867021 Fax: 01962 876045 Website: www.winchesterrugby.com
Directions: M3, Junction 9, A34/A33 signed to Basingstoke. After 1 mile fork right then first left onto B3047. Continue for 1.4 miles, left into Russell Rd, right at the end, left into Hillier Way and ground is at the end.

Colours: Black with amber band **Change colours:** All red
Training Nights: Tuesday & Thursday 7.15pm

LONDON DIVISION FINAL LEAGUE TABLES 2000-01

London 2 North

	P	W	D	L	PF	PA	PD	Pts	-
Cheshunt	22	18	0	4	580	338	242	36	
London Nigerians	22	17	1	4	681	300	381	35	
Bishop's Stortford	22	17	0	5	540	285	255	34	
Old Verulamians	22	12	1	9	448	331	117	25	
Woodford	22	11	1	10	416	432	-16	23	
Old Albanians	22	10	1	11	425	394	31	21	
Ipswich	22	10	0	12	400	332	68	20	
Diss	22	9	1	12	323	500	-177	19	
Sudbury	22	7	2	13	318	547	-229	16	
Ruislip	22	7	1	14	329	482	-153	15	
Romford & Gidea Park	22	4	3	15	297	544	-247	11	
Chelmsford	22	4	1	17	255	527	-272	9	

London 2 South

	P	W	D	L	PF	PA	PD	Pts	-
Haywards Heath	22	21	0	1	613	188	425	42	
Canterbury	22	18	0	4	778	162	616	36	
Wimbledon	22	16	0	6	455	310	145	32	
Maidstone	22	12	1	9	400	327	73	25	
*Effingham & Leatherhead	22	13	1	8	544	376	168	23	4
Old Mid-Whitgiftian	22	10	0	12	319	454	-135	20	
Beckenham	22	10	0	12	317	535	-218	20	
Gravesend	22	8	0	14	425	443	-18	16	
Sevenoaks	22	7	1	14	323	501	-178	15	
Alton	22	6	0	16	238	582	-344	12	
*Old Guildfordians	22	7	1	14	333	493	-160	3	12
*Tonbridge Juddian	22	2	0	20	225	599	-374	2	2

London 3 North East

	P	W	D	L	PF	PA	PD	Pts	-
Southend	18	16	0	2	484	190	294	32	
Rochford Hundred	18	13	0	5	553	221	332	26	
Basildon	18	13	0	5	448	269	179	26	
Brentwood	18	10	1	7	346	306	40	21	
*Chingford	18	11	0	7	298	338	-40	20	2
Wymondham	18	6	1	11	253	393	-140	13	
*Shelford	18	6	1	11	260	364	-104	11	2
Campion	18	5	0	13	319	377	-58	10	
*Braintree	18	5	0	13	221	509	-288	8	2
Lowestoft & Yarmouth	18	3	1	14	250	465	-215	7	

London 3 North West

	P	W	D	L	PF	PA	PD	Pts	-
Hertford	18	15	1	2	473	159	314	31	
Twickenham	18	15	1	2	440	211	229	31	
Barnet Saracens Elizabethans	18	11	1	6	261	304	-43	23	
Imperial Medicals	18	10	2	6	398	271	127	22	
Old Merchant Taylors	18	8	1	9	290	342	-52	17	
Harpenden	18	7	1	10	266	328	-62	15	
Ealing	18	7	0	11	291	278	13	14	
Finchley	18	6	1	11	195	332	-137	13	
West London	18	5	2	11	204	317	-113	12	
*Welwyn	18	1	0	17	151	427	-276	0	2

London 3 South East

	P	W	D	L	PF	PA	PD	Pts	-
Tunbridge Wells	18	17	1	0	507	162	345	35	
Sidcup	18	15	0	3	510	223	287	30	
Worthing	18	14	1	3	429	145	284	29	
East Grinstead	18	9	0	9	357	244	113	18	
Charlton Park	18	8	1	9	200	221	-21	17	
*Brighton	18	8	1	9	260	286	-26	13	4
Lewes	18	5	1	12	255	341	-86	11	
Crawley	18	4	0	14	262	366	-104	8	
*Cranbrook	18	6	0	12	198	342	-144	6	6
Askeans	18	1	1	16	62	710	-648	3	

London 3 South West

	P	W	D	L	PF	PA	PD	Pts	-
Portsmouth	16	15	0	1	541	140	401	30	
Gosport and Fareham	16	13	0	3	583	190	393	26	
Andover	16	12	0	4	362	262	100	24	
Jersey	16	8	1	7	396	341	55	17	
*Old Blues	16	7	0	9	425	368	57	12	2
Dorking	16	6	0	10	243	348	-105	12	
*Old Wimbledonians	16	5	1	10	229	420	-191	9	2
University Vandals	16	4	0	12	219	469	-250	8	
Old Emanuel	16	1	0	15	215	675	-460	2	

Warlingham, having conceded three games, have had their matches removed from the records for clarity of the other placings. Warlingham will be placed bottom of the league.

London 4 North East

	P	W	D	L	PF	PA	PD	Pts	-
Bury St. Edmunds	18	16	0	2	458	144	314	32	
Hadleigh	18	14	2	2	450	213	237	30	
Saffron Walden	18	12	2	4	511	185	326	26	
Woodbridge	18	10	1	7	332	328	4	21	
West Norfolk	18	9	2	7	415	242	173	20	
Thetford	18	8	2	8	267	346	-79	18	
*Canvey Island	18	8	0	10	284	342	-58	14	2
Ely	18	4	0	14	212	415	-203	8	
Newmarket	18	3	0	15	166	527	-361	6	
Holt	18	1	1	16	123	476	-353	3	

London 4 North West

	P	W	D	L	PF	PA	PD	Pts	-
Letchworth Garden City	20	19	0	1	739	165	574	38	
Bank Of England	20	17	0	3	800	218	582	34	
Hampstead	20	15	0	5	437	324	113	30	
Fullerians	20	14	0	6	406	271	135	28	
Grasshoppers	20	11	0	9	451	365	86	22	
St Albans	20	10	0	10	435	426	9	20	
Hemel Hempstead	20	7	0	13	313	414	-101	14	
*London New Zealand	20	11	0	9	345	260	85	12	10
*Chiswick	20	3	0	17	265	545	-280	4	2
*Tring	20	2	0	18	266	650	-384	2	2
Old Millhillians	20	1	0	19	105	924	-819	2	

London 4 South East

	P	W	D	L	PF	PA	PD	Pts	-
*Dartfordians	18	18	0	0	505	141	364	34	2
Old Dunstonians	18	14	0	4	443	234	209	28	
*Bognor	18	13	0	5	508	263	245	24	2
Eastbourne	18	10	0	8	390	240	150	20	
Beccehamian	18	8	0	10	212	350	-138	16	
Folkestone	18	7	1	10	251	368	-117	15	
Hove	18	6	1	11	273	427	-154	13	
Heathfield & Wald'n	18	5	1	12	235	315	-80	11	
*Chichester	18	4	1	13	178	369	-191	7	2
Park House	18	3	0	15	230	518	-288	6	

London 4 South West

	P	W	D	L	PF	PA	PD	Pts	-
Chobham	20	18	0	2	676	169	507	36	
Cobham	20	17	0	3	596	225	371	34	
Barnes	20	14	0	6	550	259	291	28	
Tottonians	20	12	0	8	497	323	174	24	
Cranleigh	20	12	0	8	312	337	-25	24	
Purley John Fisher	20	9	0	11	338	466	-128	18	
Utd Services, Portsmouth	20	8	0	12	322	422	-100	16	
Old Reedonians	20	8	0	12	353	475	-122	16	
Southampton	20	7	0	13	303	383	-80	14	
Old Alleynian	20	5	0	15	347	539	-192	10	
*Esso (Fawley)	20	0	0	20	126	822	-696	-10	

LONDON & SOUTH EAST

East Counties 1

	P	W	D	L	PF	PA	PD	Pts	
Eton Manor	18	15	1	2	403	207	196	31	
Upminster	18	14	1	3	433	222	211	29	
Billericay	18	12	1	5	297	177	120	25	
Mersea Island	18	10	1	7	280	226	54	21	
Maldon	18	9	0	9	284	277	7	18	
Old Edwardians	18	9	0	9	210	417	-207	18	
Colchester	18	7	0	11	350	297	53	14	
Cantabrigian	18	6	0	12	282	314	-32	12	
Wanstead	18	5	0	13	198	242	-44	10	
*Bancroft	18	1	0	17	128	486	-358	-8	10

East Counties 2 North

	P	W	D	L	PF	PA	PD	Pts	
Beccles	18	15	1	2	495	165	330	31	
Ipswich Y.M.	18	14	0	4	413	120	293	28	
Lakenham Hewett	18	11	2	5	316	213	103	24	
*Crusaders	18	11	1	6	371	241	130	21	2
*Thurston	18	9	2	7	264	314	-50	18	2
*Wisbech	18	12	1	5	439	160	279	15	10
Harwich & Dovercourt	18	5	1	12	246	533	-287	11	
*Southwold	18	5	0	13	193	413	-220	8	2
*Norwich Union	18	2	0	16	132	464	-332	0	4
*Brightlingsea	18	2	0	16	222	468	-246	-2	6

East Counties 2 South

	P	W	D	L	PF	PA	PD	Pts	
Stanford Le Hope	16	16	0	0	412	165	247	32	
Upper Clapton	16	13	0	3	339	166	173	26	
Westcliff	16	9	0	7	244	199	45	18	
Thames	16	9	0	7	337	326	11	18	
Ilford Wanderers	16	8	0	8	174	190	-16	16	
East London	16	6	0	10	221	276	-55	12	
South Woodham Ferrers	16	6	0	10	221	351	-130	12	
Old Brentwoods	16	4	0	12	248	325	-77	8	
Old Cooperians	16	1	0	15	116	314	-198	2	

Old Palmerians have withdrawn. All results and fixtures removed.

East Counties 3 North

	P	W	D	L	PF	PA	PD	Pts	
Stowmarket	16	15	0	1	622	68	554	30	
Haverhill & District	16	14	0	2	477	88	389	28	
Sawston	16	11	0	5	370	177	193	22	
Broadland	16	11	0	5	303	195	108	22	
Witham	16	8	0	8	145	148	-3	16	
Swaffham	16	5	0	11	273	462	-189	10	
American Exiles	14	2	0	12	81	405	-324	4	
Mistley	14	2	0	12	101	498	-397	4	
March BRAZA	14	1	0	13	98	429	-331	2	

Clacton have withdrawn. All results and fixtures removed.

East Counties 3 South

	P	W	D	L	PF	PA	PD	Pts	
May & Baker	20	19	1	0	524	109	415	39	
Millwall Albion	20	14	0	6	586	158	428	28	
Ongar	20	12	1	7	462	222	240	25	
Old Bealonians	20	10	2	8	336	295	41	22	
*Loughton	20	11	1	8	451	260	191	21	2
Burnham-On-Crouch	20	9	1	10	393	332	61	19	
Dagenham	20	9	0	11	433	316	117	18	
*Ravens	20	9	1	10	358	406	-48	17	2
*Pegasus	20	9	0	11	286	339	-53	16	2
*Rayleigh Wyverns	20	4	1	15	200	550	-350	5	4
Kings Cross Steelers	20	0	0	20	127	1169	-1042	0	

Hampshire 1

	P	W	D	L	PF	PA	PD	Pts	
Farnborough	18	18	0	0	640	134	506	36	
Trojans	18	15	1	2	499	183	316	31	
Petersfield	18	11	0	7	516	284	232	22	
Romsey	18	11	0	7	358	244	114	22	
Guernsey	18	10	1	7	395	286	109	21	
Sandown & Shanklin	18	9	1	8	289	280	9	19	
Hamble	18	5	0	13	243	465	-222	10	
Millbrook	18	4	1	13	222	420	-198	9	
*Ventnor	18	3	0	15	167	414	-247	4	2
*New Milton & District	18	2	0	16	162	781	-619	2	2

Hampshire 2

	P	W	D	L	PF	PA	PD	Pts	
Fareham Heathens	16	15	0	1	308	100	208	30	
Nomads	16	13	0	3	380	161	219	26	
Fordingbridge	16	11	1	4	270	151	119	23	
Lytchett Minster	16	8	1	7	342	188	154	17	
Isle Of Wight	16	6	1	9	182	191	-9	13	
Portcastrians	16	6	1	9	223	315	-92	13	
Overton	16	5	2	9	317	329	-12	12	
Eastleigh	16	5	0	11	201	399	-198	10	
*Southampton Institute	16	0	0	16	139	528	-389	-4	4

Hants Constabulary have withdrawn. All fixtures removed

Hampshire 3

	P	W	D	L	PF	PA	PD	Pts	
Fleet	14	14	0	0	385	87	298	28	
Kingsclere	14	12	0	2	395	122	273	24	
Alresford	14	8	0	6	370	138	232	16	
Ellingham & Ringwood	14	6	1	7	171	191	-20	13	
A.C. Delco	14	4	2	8	140	169	-29	10	
Chineham	14	5	0	9	169	238	-69	10	
Paxton Pumas	14	4	1	9	223	328	-105	9	
Brockenhurst	14	1	0	13	55	635	-580	2	

Herts/Middlesex 1

	P	W	D	L	PF	PA	PD	Pts	
Richmond	18	17	0	1	816	72	744	34	
London Scottish	18	17	0	1	554	118	436	34	
Harrow	18	13	0	5	312	190	122	26	
Feltham	18	12	0	6	340	265	75	24	
Old Hamptonians	18	8	0	10	277	277	0	16	
Enfield Ignatians	18	8	0	10	247	417	-170	16	
Stevenage Town	18	6	0	12	243	389	-146	12	
Lensbury	18	5	0	13	199	395	-196	10	
Mill Hill	18	2	0	16	136	474	-338	4	
Uxbridge	18	2	0	16	135	662	-527	4	

Herts/Middlesex 2

	P	W	D	L	PF	PA	PD	Pts	
Civil Service	16	13	0	3	381	136	245	26	
U.C.S. Old Boys	16	12	0	4	576	236	340	24	
Haringey	16	12	0	4	491	168	323	24	
Hitchin	16	10	0	6	412	247	165	20	
Datchworth	16	8	1	7	250	277	-27	17	
*H.A.C.	16	9	0	7	463	221	242	16	2
Northolt	16	4	1	11	168	474	-306	9	
Old Haberdashers	16	3	0	13	127	570	-443	6	
Hendon	16	0	0	16	97	636	-539	0	

Herts/Middlesex 3 North

	P	W	D	L	PF	PA	PD	Pts	
Kilburn Cosmos	16	13	0	3	607	122	485	26	
Old Grammarians	16	12	1	3	327	184	143	25	
Old Tottonians	16	11	0	5	479	182	297	22	
Chess Valley	16	11	0	5	393	261	132	22	
Cuffley	16	9	0	7	300	226	74	18	
Watford	16	5	0	11	291	411	-120	10	
Old Streetonians	16	4	1	11	206	630	-424	9	
Southgate	16	4	0	12	207	425	-218	8	
Old Ashmoleans	16	2	0	14	213	582	-369	4	

Millfield O.B. have withdrawn. All Results and Fixtures removed.

Herts/Middlesex 3 South

	P	W	D	L	PF	PA	PD	Pts	
Old Actonians	16	14	0	2	588	103	485	28	
Hammersmith & Fulham	16	12	1	3	486	142	344	25	
*Wasps	16	12	0	4	366	99	267	22	2
London French	16	10	0	6	371	181	190	20	
St Nicholas O.B.	16	8	1	7	278	271	7	17	
Old Abbotstonians	16	5	0	11	178	394	-216	10	
Old Isleworthians	16	5	0	11	151	407	-256	10	
Quintin	16	2	0	14	64	772	-708	4	
*London Tribes	16	3	0	13	206	319	-113	2	4

G.W.R. withdrawn. All results and fixtures removed.

Herts/Middlesex 4 N

	P	W	D	L	PF	PA	PD	Pts	-
Hatfield	12	11	0	1	264	81	183	22	
Q.E.II Hospital	12	10	0	2	293	84	209	20	
Royston	12	8	0	4	145	95	50	16	
Ware	12	5	0	7	68	196	-128	10	
Sudbury Court	12	4	1	7	136	104	32	9	
Hackney	12	2	0	10	55	271	-216	4	
Pinner & Grammarians	12	1	1	10	61	191	-130	3	

Herts/Middlesex 4 S

	P	W	D	L	PF	PA	PD	Pts	-
Osterley	10	8	1	1	316	157	159	17	
Belsize Park	10	8	0	2	227	91	136	16	
British Airways	10	4	1	5	230	138	92	9	
Orleans F.P.	10	3	2	5	211	171	40	8	
Hayes	10	4	0	6	174	298	-124	8	
Thamesians	10	1	0	9	72	375	-303	2	

Centaurs withdrawn. All fixtures and results removed.

Kent 1

	P	W	D	L	PF	PA	PD	Pts	-
Guy's Hospital	18	16	0	2	601	148	453	32	
Betteshanger	18	15	0	3	461	200	261	30	
Whitstable	18	13	0	5	237	175	62	26	
Gillingham Anch.	18	10	0	8	315	300	15	20	
*Lordswood	18	11	0	7	343	219	124	18 4
Bromley	18	8	0	10	280	353	-73	16	
Medway	18	5	1	12	224	335	-111	11	
New Ash Green	18	5	0	13	262	378	-116	10	
Brockleians	18	4	0	14	212	507	-295	8	
Old Elthamians	18	2	1	15	181	501	-320	5	

Kent 2

	P	W	D	L	PF	PA	PD	Pts	-
Ashford	16	15	1	0	416	119	297	31	
Erith	16	12	0	4	380	169	211	24	
Aylesford	16	10	0	6	303	204	99	20	
HSBC	16	8	2	6	262	265	-3	18	
Sittingbourne	16	6	1	9	259	281	-22	13	
*Sheppey	16	6	1	9	258	312	-54	11 2
Nat. West. Bank	16	5	0	11	239	329	-90	10	
*Dover	16	4	1	11	214	402	-188	7 2
Darenth Valley	16	2	2	12	179	429	-250	6	

Kent 3

	P	W	D	L	PF	PA	PD	Pts	-
Bexley	10	8	0	2	233	54	179	16	
Old Gravesendians	10	8	0	2	269	141	128	16	
Greenwich	10	7	0	3	198	88	110	14	
Foots Cray	10	4	0	6	167	231	-64	8	
*Deal Wanderers	10	2	0	8	123	295	-172	2 2
*Edenbridge	10	1	0	9	124	305	-181	-12 14

Met Police Hayes have withdrawn. Allfixtures and results remover.

Kent 4

	P	W	D	L	PF	PA	PD	Pts	-
Vigo	10	9	0	1	163	101	62	18	
Old Shootershillians	10	7	0	3	283	97	186	14	
Old Olavians	10	6	0	4	161	165	-4	12	
Old Williamsonians	10	4	0	6	143	197	-54	8	
Faversham	10	3	0	7	128	171	-43	6	
*Orpington	10	1	0	9	89	236	-147	0 2

Surrey 1

	P	W	D	L	PF	PA	PD	Pts	-
Farnham	16	13	1	2	455	178	277	27	
Kingston	16	13	1	2	394	252	142	27	
London Irish Amateur	16	13	0	3	424	209	215	26	
Old Reigatian	16	12	0	4	357	161	196	24	
Old Wellingtonians	16	10	2	4	452	231	221	22	
Old Tiffinians	16	10	0	6	436	213	223	20	
Old Rutlishians	16	10	0	6	299	242	57	20	
Old Paulines	16	9	1	6	438	303	135	19	
K.C.S. Old Boys	16	8	0	8	404	287	117	16	
Old Whitgiftians	16	7	1	8	350	330	20	14	
Merton	16	6	0	10	221	261	-40	12	
Old Cranleighans	16	5	1	10	185	393	-208	11	
Old Walcountians	16	4	2	10	210	497	-287	10	
Old Caterhamians	16	3	2	11	173	333	-160	8	
Raynes Park	16	3	2	11	213	362	-149	7	
Woking	16	3	0	13	168	504	-336	6	
Streatham-Croydon	16	0	1	15	94	517	-423	1	

Surrey 2

	P	W	D	L	PF	PA	PD	Pts	-
Law Society	14	13	0	1	535	160	375	26	
Battersea Ironsides	14	13	0	1	366	96	270	26	
London Exiles	14	13	0	1	446	188	258	26	
Old Freemens	14	10	1	3	375	152	223	21	
London Media	14	8	1	5	335	242	93	17	
Mitcham	14	8	1	5	220	176	44	17	
Shirley Wanderers	14	7	0	7	210	218	-8	14	
Haslemere	14	6	0	8	261	307	-46	12	
London Fire Brigade	14	5	1	8	163	321	-158	11	
Old Haileyburians	14	5	0	9	269	343	-74	10	
Teddington	14	5	0	9	135	267	-132	10	
Lightwater	14	3	0	11	160	245	-85	6	
Chipstead	14	3	0	11	127	311	-184	6	
Worth Old Boys	14	3	0	11	134	377	-243	6	
Wandsworthians	14	1	0	13	96	429	-333	2	

Surrey 3

	P	W	D	L	PF	PA	PD	Pts	-
Old Amplefordians	8	7	0	1	247	46	201	14	
Old Abingdonians	8	7	0	1	249	100	149	14	
Egham	8	6	0	2	172	104	68	12	
Reigate & Redhill	8	5	0	3	222	127	95	10	
London Cornish	8	4	0	4	145	86	59	8	
Bec Old Boys	8	3	0	5	167	255	-88	6	
Old Suttonians	8	2	0	6	51	255	-204	4	
Croydon	8	1	1	6	36	207	-171	3	
Economicals	8	0	1	7	85	194	-109	1	

St Georges Hospital,
Old Bevonians
and Surrey University
have had all fixtures and results removed due to lack of games played.

Sussex 1

	P	W	D	L	PF	PA	PD	Pts	-
Uckfield	18	16	0	2	636	143	493	32	
Hastings & Bexhill	18	16	0	2	412	142	270	32	
*Horsham	18	13	0	5	466	227	239	24 2
*Crowborough	18	11	0	7	413	293	120	20 2
Chichester IHE	18	9	0	9	233	318	-85	18	
Hellingly	18	8	1	9	271	270	1	17	
Pulborough	18	7	1	10	347	347	0	15	
*Seaford	18	4	1	13	307	348	-41	5 4
Newick	18	2	0	16	107	741	-634	4	
*Royal Sun Alliance	18	2	1	15	144	507	-363	3 2

Sussex 2 East

	P	W	D	L	PF	PA	PD	Pts	-
Rye	12	10	1	1	234	97	137	21	
Sussex Police	12	9	0	3	376	192	184	18	
*Old Brightonians	12	8	1	3	244	82	162	15 2
*Ditchling	12	6	1	5	278	195	83	11 2
Plumpton	12	3	1	8	179	229	-50	7	
*Burgess Hill	12	2	1	9	121	284	-163	3 2
Robertsbridge	12	1	1	10	46	399	-353	3	

Sussex 2 West

	P	W	D	L	PF	PA	PD	Pts	-
St Francis	12	11	0	1	411	135	276	22	
Shoreham	12	8	0	4	185	156	29	16	
Norfolk Arms	12	7	0	5	362	158	204	14	
*Arun	12	7	1	4	241	113	128	13 2
B.A. Wingspan	12	4	2	6	157	175	-18	10	
Barns Green	12	3	1	8	77	346	-269	7	
Midhurst	12	0	0	12	65	415	-350	0	

* denotes points deducted in right hand column

LONDON & SOUTH EAST

LONDON & S.E. DIVISION FIXTURE GRIDS 2001-2002

London 2 North

	Bishop's Stortford	Diss	Hertford	Ipswich	Metropolitan Police	Old Albanians	Old Verulamians	Southend	Sudbury	Thurrock	Twickenham	Woodford
Bishop's Stortford		1.09	9.03	22.09	9.02	6.10	26.01	27.10	5.01	17.11	13.04	8.12
Diss	16.03		27.10	9.03	5.01	22.09	17.11	9.02	13.04	6.10	8.12	26.01
Hertford	8.09	12.01		10.11	23.02	22.12	29.09	1.12	2.02	6.04	20.10	1.09
Ipswich	23.02	8.09	5.01		17.11	9.02	13.04	6.10	8.12	26.01	16.03	27.10
Metropolitan Police	29.09	10.11	22.09	22.12		1.12	2.02	6.04	20.10	1.09	12.01	9.03
Old Albanians	2.02	23.02	17.11	29.09	13.04		8.12	26.01	16.03	27.10	8.09	5.01
Old Verulamians	20.10	22.12	9.02	1.12	6.10	6.04		1.09	12.01	9.03	10.11	22.09
Southend	12.01	29.09	13.04	2.02	8.12	20.10	16.03		8.09	5.01	23.02	17.11
Sudbury	10.11	1.12	6.10	6.04	26.01	1.09	27.10	9.03		22.09	22.12	9.02
Thurrock	22.12	2.02	8.12	20.10	16.03	12.01	8.09	10.11	23.02		29.09	13.04
Twickenham	1.12	6.04	26.01	1.09	27.10	9.03	5.01	22.09	17.11	9.02		6.10
Woodford	6.04	20.10	16.03	12.01	8.09	10.11	23.02	22.12	29.09	1.12	2.02	

London 2 South

	Beckenham	Canterbury	Effingham & Leatherhead	Gosport and Fareham	Gravesend	Guildford & Godalming	Maidstone	Old Mid-Whitgiftian	Portsmouth	Sevenoaks	Tunbridge Wells	Wimbledon
Beckenham		1.09	9.03	22.09	9.02	6.10	26.01	27.10	5.01	17.11	13.04	8.12
Canterbury	16.03		27.10	9.03	5.01	22.09	17.11	9.02	13.04	6.10	8.12	26.01
Effingham & Leatherhead	8.09	12.01		10.11	23.02	22.12	29.09	1.12	2.02	6.04	20.10	1.09
Gosport and Fareham	23.02	8.09	5.01		17.11	9.02	13.04	6.10	8.12	26.01	16.03	27.10
Gravesend	29.09	10.11	22.09	22.12		1.12	2.02	6.04	20.10	1.09	12.01	9.03
Guildford & Godalming	2.02	23.02	17.11	29.09	13.04		8.12	26.01	16.03	27.10	8.09	5.01
Maidstone	20.10	22.12	9.02	1.12	6.10	6.04		1.09	12.01	9.03	10.11	22.09
Old Mid-Whitgiftian	12.01	29.09	13.04	2.02	8.12	20.10	16.03		8.09	5.01	23.02	17.11
Portsmouth	10.11	1.12	6.10	6.04	26.01	1.09	27.10	9.03		22.09	22.12	9.02
Sevenoaks	22.12	2.02	8.12	20.10	16.03	12.01	8.09	10.11	23.02		29.09	13.04
Tunbridge Wells	1.12	6.04	26.01	1.09	27.10	9.03	5.01	22.09	17.11	9.02		6.10
Wimbledon	6.04	20.10	16.03	12.01	8.09	10.11	23.02	22.12	29.09	1.12	2.02	

London 3 North East

	Basildon	Brentwood	Bury St. Edmunds	Chelmsford	Chingford	Hadleigh	Rochford Hundred	Romford & Gidea Park	Shelford	Wymondham
Basildon		22.09	9.03	6.10	2.02	27.10	12.01	17.11	13.04	8.12
Brentwood	16.03		12.01	9.03	17.11	6.10	13.04	2.02	8.12	27.10
Bury St. Edmunds	29.09	10.11		22.12	23.02	1.12	20.10	6.04	26.01	22.09
Chelmsford	23.02	29.09	17.11		13.04	2.02	8.12	27.10	16.03	12.01
Chingford	20.10	22.12	6.10	1.12		6.04	26.01	22.09	10.11	9.03
Hadleigh	26.01	23.02	13.04	20.10	8.12		16.03	12.01	29.09	17.11
Rochford Hundred	10.11	1.12	2.02	6.04	27.10	22.09		9.03	22.12	6.10
Romford & Gidea Park	22.12	20.10	8.12	26.01	16.03	10.11	29.09		23.02	13.04
Shelford	1.12	6.04	27.10	22.09	12.01	9.03	17.11	6.10		2.02
Wymondham	6.04	26.01	16.03	10.11	29.09	22.12	23.02	1.12	20.10	

LONDON & SOUTH EAST

London 3 North West

	Bank Of England	Barnet Saracens Elizabethans	Ealing	Finchley	Harpenden	Imperial Medicals	Letchworth Garden City	Old Merchant Taylors	Ruislip	West London
Bank Of England		22.09	9.03	6.10	2.02	27.10	12.01	17.11	13.04	8.12
Barnet Saracens Elizabethans	16.03		12.01	9.03	17.11	6.10	13.04	2.02	8.12	27.10
Ealing	29.09	10.11		22.12	23.02	1.12	20.10	6.04	26.01	22.09
Finchley	23.02	29.09	17.11		13.04	2.02	8.12	27.10	16.03	12.01
Harpenden	20.10	22.12	6.10	1.12		6.04	26.01	22.09	10.11	9.03
Imperial Medicals	26.01	23.02	13.04	20.10	8.12		16.03	12.01	29.09	17.11
Letchworth Garden City	10.11	1.12	2.02	6.04	27.10	22.09		9.03	22.12	6.10
Old Merchant Taylors	22.12	20.10	8.12	26.01	16.03	10.11	29.09		23.02	13.04
Ruislip	1.12	6.04	27.10	22.09	12.01	9.03	17.11	6.10		2.02
West London	6.04	26.01	16.03	10.11	29.09	22.12	23.02	1.12	20.10	

London 3 South East

	Brighton	Charlton Park	Crawley	Dartfordians	East Grinstead	Lewes	Old Dunstonians	Sidcup	Tonbridge Juddian	Worthing
Brighton		22.09	9.03	6.10	2.02	27.10	12.01	17.11	13.04	8.12
Charlton Park	16.03		12.01	9.03	17.11	6.10	13.04	2.02	8.12	27.10
Crawley	29.09	10.11		22.12	23.02	1.12	20.10	6.04	26.01	22.09
Dartfordians	23.02	29.09	17.11		13.04	2.02	8.12	27.10	16.03	12.01
East Grinstead	20.10	22.12	6.10	1.12		6.04	26.01	22.09	10.11	9.03
Lewes	26.01	23.02	13.04	20.10	8.12		16.03	12.01	29.09	17.11
Old Dunstonians	10.11	1.12	2.02	6.04	27.10	22.09		9.03	22.12	6.10
Sidcup	22.12	20.10	8.12	26.01	16.03	10.11	29.09		23.02	13.04
Tonbridge Juddian	1.12	6.04	27.10	22.09	12.01	9.03	17.11	6.10		2.02
Worthing	6.04	26.01	16.03	10.11	29.09	22.12	23.02	1.12	20.10	

London 3 South West

	Alton	Andover	Chobham	Cobham	Dorking	Jersey	Old Blues	Old Guildfordians	Old Wimbledonians	University Vandals
Alton		22.09	9.03	6.10	2.02	27.10	12.01	17.11	13.04	8.12
Andover	16.03		12.01	9.03	17.11	6.10	13.04	2.02	8.12	27.10
Chobham	29.09	10.11		22.12	23.02	1.12	20.10	6.04	26.01	22.09
Cobham	23.02	29.09	17.11		13.04	2.02	8.12	27.10	16.03	12.01
Dorking	20.10	22.12	6.10	1.12		6.04	26.01	22.09	10.11	9.03
Jersey	26.01	23.02	13.04	20.10	8.12		16.03	12.01	29.09	17.11
Old Blues	10.11	1.12	2.02	6.04	27.10	22.09		9.03	22.12	6.10
Old Guildfordians	22.12	20.10	8.12	26.01	16.03	10.11	29.09		23.02	13.04
Old Wimbledonians	1.12	6.04	27.10	22.09	12.01	9.03	17.11	6.10		2.02
University Vandals	6.04	26.01	16.03	10.11	29.09	22.12	23.02	1.12	20.10	

London 4
North East

	Braintree	Campion	Canvey Island	Eton Manor	Lowestoft & Yarmouth	Saffron Walden	Thetford	Upminster	West Norfolk	Woodbridge
Braintree		22.09	9.03	6.10	2.02	27.10	12.01	17.11	13.04	8.12
Campion	16.03		12.01	9.03	17.11	6.10	13.04	2.02	8.12	27.10
Canvey Island	29.09	10.11		22.12	23.02	1.12	20.10	6.04	26.01	22.09
Eton Manor	23.02	29.09	17.11		13.04	2.02	8.12	27.10	16.03	12.01
Lowestoft & Yarmouth	20.10	22.12	6.10	1.12		6.04	26.01	22.09	10.11	9.03
Saffron Walden	26.01	23.02	13.04	20.10	8.12		16.03	12.01	29.09	17.11
Thetford	10.11	1.12	2.02	6.04	27.10	22.09		9.03	22.12	6.10
Upminster	22.12	20.10	8.12	26.01	16.03	10.11	29.09		23.02	13.04
West Norfolk	1.12	6.04	27.10	22.09	12.01	9.03	17.11	6.10		2.02
Woodbridge	6.04	26.01	16.03	10.11	29.09	22.12	23.02	1.12	20.10	

London 4
North West

	Chiswick	Fullerians	Grasshoppers	Hampstead	Harrow	Hemel Hempstead	London New Zealand	London Scottish	St Albans	Welwyn
Chiswick		22.09	13.04	2.02	6.10	27.10	12.01	9.03	17.11	8.12
Fullerians	16.03		8.12	17.11	9.03	6.10	13.04	12.01	2.02	27.10
Grasshoppers	1.12	6.04		12.01	22.09	9.03	17.11	27.10	6.10	2.02
Hampstead	20.10	22.12	10.11		1.12	6.04	26.01	6.10	22.09	9.03
Harrow	23.02	29.09	16.03	13.04		2.02	8.12	17.11	27.10	12.01
Hemel Hempstead	26.01	23.02	29.09	8.12	20.10		16.03	13.04	12.01	17.11
London New Zealand	10.11	1.12	22.12	27.10	6.04	22.09		2.02	9.03	6.10
London Scottish	29.09	10.11	26.01	23.02	22.12	1.12	20.10		6.04	22.09
St Albans	22.12	20.10	23.02	16.03	26.01	10.11	29.09	8.12		13.04
Welwyn	6.04	26.01	20.10	29.09	10.11	22.12	23.02	16.03	1.12	

London 4
South East

	Askeans	Beccehamian	Betteshanger	Bognor	Cranbrook	Eastbourne	Folkestone	Guy's Hospital	Hove	Uckfield
Askeans		22.09	9.03	6.10	2.02	27.10	12.01	17.11	13.04	8.12
Beccehamian	16.03		12.01	9.03	17.11	6.10	13.04	2.02	8.12	27.10
Betteshanger	29.09	10.11		22.12	23.02	1.12	20.10	6.04	26.01	22.09
Bognor	23.02	29.09	17.11		13.04	2.02	8.12	27.10	16.03	12.01
Cranbrook	20.10	22.12	6.10	1.12		6.04	26.01	22.09	10.11	9.03
Eastbourne	26.01	23.02	13.04	20.10	8.12		16.03	12.01	29.09	17.11
Folkestone	10.11	1.12	2.02	6.04	27.10	22.09		9.03	22.12	6.10
Guy's Hospital	22.12	20.10	8.12	26.01	16.03	10.11	29.09		23.02	13.04
Hove	1.12	6.04	27.10	22.09	12.01	9.03	17.11	6.10		2.02
Uckfield	6.04	26.01	16.03	10.11	29.09	22.12	23.02	1.12	20.10	

London 4 South West

	Barnes	Cranleigh	Farnborough	Farnham	Old Emanuel	Purley John Fisher	Richmond	Tottonians	Trojans	Und Services, Portsmouth	Warlingham
Barnes		1.09	9.03	9.02	6.10	26.01	22.09	27.10	5.01	13.04	8.12
Cranleigh	16.03		27.10	5.01	22.09	17.11	9.03	9.02	13.04	8.12	26.01
Farnborough	8.09	12.01		23.02	22.12	29.09	10.11	1.12	2.02	20.10	1.09
Farnham	29.09	10.11	22.09		1.12	2.02	22.12	6.04	20.10	12.01	9.03
Old Emanuel	2.02	23.02	17.11	13.04		8.12	29.09	26.01	16.03	8.09	5.01
Purley John Fisher	20.10	22.12	9.02	6.10	6.04		1.12	1.09	12.01	10.11	22.09
Richmond	23.02	8.09	5.01	17.11	9.02	13.04		6.10	8.12	16.03	27.10
Tottonians	12.01	29.09	13.04	8.12	20.10	16.03	2.02		8.09	23.02	17.11
Trojans	10.11	1.12	6.10	26.01	1.09	27.10	6.04	9.03		22.12	9.02
United Services, Portsmouth	1.12	6.04	26.01	27.10	9.03	5.01	1.09	22.09	17.11		6.10
Warlingham	6.04	20.10	16.03	8.09	10.11	23.02	12.01	22.12	29.09	2.02	

Eastern Counties 1

	Beccles	Billericay	Ely	Holt	Maldon	Mersea Island	Newmarket	Old Edwardians	Stanford Le Hope	Upper Clapton
Beccles		22.09	9.03	6.10	2.02	27.10	12.01	17.11	13.04	8.12
Billericay	16.03		12.01	9.03	17.11	6.10	13.04	2.02	8.12	27.10
Ely	29.09	10.11		22.12	23.02	1.12	20.10	6.04	26.01	22.09
Holt	23.02	29.09	17.11		13.04	2.02	8.12	27.10	16.03	12.01
Maldon	20.10	22.12	6.10	1.12		6.04	26.01	22.09	10.11	9.03
Mersea Island	26.01	23.02	13.04	20.10	8.12		16.03	12.01	29.09	17.11
Newmarket	10.11	1.12	2.02	6.04	27.10	22.09		9.03	22.12	6.10
Old Edwardians	22.12	20.10	8.12	26.01	16.03	10.11	29.09		23.02	13.04
Stanford Le Hope	1.12	6.04	27.10	22.09	12.01	9.03	17.11	6.10		2.02
Upper Clapton	6.04	26.01	16.03	10.11	29.09	22.12	23.02	1.12	20.10	

Eastern Counties 2 North

	Cantabrigian	Colchester	Crusaders	Harwich & Dovercourt	Haverhill & District	Ipswich Y.M.	Lakenham Hewett	Stowmarket	Thurston	Wisbech
Cantabrigian		22.09	9.03	6.10	2.02	27.10	12.01	17.11	13.04	8.12
Colchester	16.03		12.01	9.03	17.11	6.10	13.04	2.02	8.12	27.10
Crusaders	29.09	10.11		22.12	23.02	1.12	20.10	6.04	26.01	22.09
Harwich & Dovercourt	23.02	29.09	17.11		13.04	2.02	8.12	27.10	16.03	12.01
Haverhill & District	20.10	22.12	6.10	1.12		6.04	26.01	22.09	10.11	9.03
Ipswich Y.M.	26.01	23.02	13.04	20.10	8.12		16.03	12.01	29.09	17.11
Lakenham Hewett	10.11	1.12	2.02	6.04	27.10	22.09		9.03	22.12	6.10
Stowmarket	22.12	20.10	8.12	26.01	16.03	10.11	29.09		23.02	13.04
Thurston	1.12	6.04	27.10	22.09	12.01	9.03	17.11	6.10		2.02
Wisbech	6.04	26.01	16.03	10.11	29.09	22.12	23.02	1.12	20.10	

Eastern Counties 2 South

	Bancroft	East London	Ilford Wanderers	May & Baker	Millwall Albion	Old Brentwoods	South Woodham Ferrers	Thames	Wanstead	Westcliff
Bancroft		22.09	9.03	6.10	2.02	27.10	12.01	17.11	13.04	8.12
East London	16.03		12.01	9.03	17.11	6.10	13.04	2.02	8.12	27.10
Ilford Wanderers	29.09	10.11		22.12	23.02	1.12	20.10	6.04	26.01	22.09
May & Baker	23.02	29.09	17.11		13.04	2.02	8.12	27.10	16.03	12.01
Millwall Albion	20.10	22.12	6.10	1.12		6.04	26.01	22.09	10.11	9.03
Old Brentwoods	26.01	23.02	13.04	20.10	8.12		16.03	12.01	29.09	17.11
South Woodham Ferrers	10.11	1.12	2.02	6.04	27.10	22.09		9.03	22.12	6.10
Thames	22.12	20.10	8.12	26.01	16.03	10.11	29.09		23.02	13.04
Wanstead	1.12	6.04	27.10	22.09	12.01	9.03	17.11	6.10		2.02
Westcliff	6.04	26.01	16.03	10.11	29.09	22.12	23.02	1.12	20.10	

Eastern Counties 3 North

	American Exiles	Brightlingsea	Broadland	March BRAZA	Mistley	Norwich Union	Sawston	Southwold	Swaffham	Witham
American Exiles		22.09	9.03	6.10	2.02	27.10	12.01	17.11	13.04	8.12
Brightlingsea	16.03		12.01	9.03	17.11	6.10	13.04	2.02	8.12	27.10
Broadland	29.09	10.11		22.12	23.02	1.12	20.10	6.04	26.01	22.09
March BRAZA	23.02	29.09	17.11		13.04	2.02	8.12	27.10	16.03	12.01
Mistley	20.10	22.12	6.10	1.12		6.04	26.01	22.09	10.11	9.03
Norwich Union	26.01	23.02	13.04	20.10	8.12		16.03	12.01	29.09	17.11
Sawston	10.11	1.12	2.02	6.04	27.10	22.09		9.03	22.12	6.10
Southwold	22.12	20.10	8.12	26.01	16.03	10.11	29.09		23.02	13.04
Swaffham	1.12	6.04	27.10	22.09	12.01	9.03	17.11	6.10		2.02
Witham	6.04	26.01	16.03	10.11	29.09	22.12	23.02	1.12	20.10	

Eastern Counties 3 South

	Burnham-On-Crouch	Dagenham	Kings Cross Steelers	Loughton	Old Bealonians	Old Cooperians	Ongar	Pegasus	Ravens	Rayleigh Wyverns
Burnham-On-Crouch		22.09	9.03	6.10	2.02	27.10	12.01	17.11	13.04	8.12
Dagenham	16.03		12.01	9.03	17.11	6.10	13.04	2.02	8.12	27.10
Kings Cross Steelers	29.09	10.11		22.12	23.02	1.12	20.10	6.04	26.01	22.09
Loughton	23.02	29.09	17.11		13.04	2.02	8.12	27.10	16.03	12.01
Old Bealonians	20.10	22.12	6.10	1.12		6.04	26.01	22.09	10.11	9.03
Old Cooperians	26.01	23.02	13.04	20.10	8.12		16.03	12.01	29.09	17.11
Ongar	10.11	1.12	2.02	6.04	27.10	22.09		9.03	22.12	6.10
Pegasus	22.12	20.10	8.12	26.01	16.03	10.11	29.09		23.02	13.04
Ravens	1.12	6.04	27.10	22.09	12.01	9.03	17.11	6.10		2.02
Rayleigh Wyverns	6.04	26.01	16.03	10.11	29.09	22.12	23.02	1.12	20.10	

Hampshire 1

	Esso (Fawley)	Fareham Heathens	Guernsey	Hamble	Millbrook	Nomads	Petersfield	Romsey	Sandown & Shanklin	Southampton
Esso (Fawley)		22.09	9.03	6.10	2.02	27.10	12.01	17.11	13.04	8.12
Fareham Heathens	16.03		12.01	9.03	17.11	6.10	13.04	2.02	8.12	27.10
Guernsey	29.09	10.11		22.12	23.02	1.12	20.10	6.04	26.01	22.09
Hamble	23.02	29.09	17.11		13.04	2.02	8.12	27.10	16.03	12.01
Millbrook	20.10	22.12	6.10	1.12		6.04	26.01	22.09	10.11	9.03
Nomads	26.01	23.02	13.04	20.10	8.12		16.03	12.01	29.09	17.11
Petersfield	10.11	1.12	2.02	6.04	27.10	22.09		9.03	22.12	6.10
Romsey	22.12	20.10	8.12	26.01	16.03	10.11	29.09		23.02	13.04
Sandown & Shanklin	1.12	6.04	27.10	22.09	12.01	9.03	17.11	6.10		2.02
Southampton	6.04	26.01	16.03	10.11	29.09	22.12	23.02	1.12	20.10	

Hampshire 2

	Eastleigh	Fleet	Fordingbridge	Isle Of Wight	Kingsclere	Lytchett Minster	New Milton & Dist.	Overton	Portcastrians	Ventnor
Eastleigh		22.09	9.03	6.10	2.02	27.10	12.01	17.11	13.04	8.12
Fleet	16.03		12.01	9.03	17.11	6.10	13.04	2.02	8.12	27.10
Fordingbridge	29.09	10.11		22.12	23.02	1.12	20.10	6.04	26.01	22.09
Isle Of Wight	23.02	29.09	17.11		13.04	2.02	8.12	27.10	16.03	12.01
Kingsclere	20.10	22.12	6.10	1.12		6.04	26.01	22.09	10.11	9.03
Lytchett Minster	26.01	23.02	13.04	20.10	8.12		16.03	12.01	29.09	17.11
New Milton & District	10.11	1.12	2.02	6.04	27.10	22.09		9.03	22.12	6.10
Overton	22.12	20.10	8.12	26.01	16.03	10.11	29.09		23.02	13.04
Portcastrians	1.12	6.04	27.10	22.09	12.01	9.03	17.11	6.10		2.02
Ventnor	6.04	26.01	16.03	10.11	29.09	22.12	23.02	1.12	20.10	

Hampshire 3

	A.C. Delco	Alresford	Brockenhurst	Chineham	Ellingham & Ringwood	Paxton Pumas	Southampton Inst.	Verwood
A.C. Delco		22.09	12.01	20.10	23.02	10.11	16.03	1.12
Alresford	8.12		20.10	23.02	10.11	16.03	1.12	12.01
Brockenhurst	29.09	26.01		10.11	16.03	1.12	8.12	27.10
Chineham	26.01	27.10	9.03		1.12	8.12	29.09	16.03
Ellingham & Ringwood	27.10	9.03	17.11	6.04		29.09	26.01	22.09
Paxton Pumas	9.03	17.11	6.04	22.09	12.01		27.10	26.01
Southampton Institute	17.11	6.04	22.09	12.01	20.10	23.02		10.11
Verwood	6.04	29.09	23.02	17.11	8.12	20.10	9.03	

Herts & Middlesex 1

	Civil Service	Enfield Ignatians	Feltham	Lensbury	Mill Hill	Old Hamptonians	Stevenage Town	Tring	U.C.S. Old Boys	Uxbridge
Civil Service		22.09	9.03	2.02	27.10	12.01	17.11	6.10	13.04	8.12
Enfield Ignatians	16.03		12.01	17.11	6.10	13.04	2.02	9.03	8.12	27.10
Feltham	29.09	10.11		23.02	1.12	20.10	6.04	22.12	26.01	22.09
Lensbury	20.10	22.12	6.10		6.04	26.01	22.09	1.12	10.11	9.03
Mill Hill	26.01	23.02	13.04	8.12		16.03	12.01	20.10	29.09	17.11
Old Hamptonians	10.11	1.12	2.02	27.10	22.09		9.03	6.04	22.12	6.10
Stevenage Town	22.12	20.10	8.12	16.03	10.11	29.09		26.01	23.02	13.04
Tring	23.02	29.09	17.11	13.04	2.02	8.12	27.10		16.03	12.01
U.C.S. Old Boys	1.12	6.04	27.10	12.01	9.03	17.11	6.10	22.09		2.02
Uxbridge	6.04	26.01	16.03	29.09	22.12	23.02	1.12	10.11	20.10	

Herts & Middlesex 2

	Datchworth	H.A.C.	Hammersmith & Fulham	Haringey	Hitchin	Kilburn Cosmos	Northolt	Old Actonians	Old Haberdashers	Old Millhillians
Datchworth		22.09	9.03	6.10	2.02	27.10	12.01	17.11	13.04	8.12
H.A.C.	16.03		12.01	9.03	17.11	6.10	13.04	2.02	8.12	27.10
Hammersmith & Fulham	29.09	10.11		22.12	23.02	1.12	20.10	6.04	26.01	22.09
Haringey	23.02	29.09	17.11		13.04	2.02	8.12	27.10	16.03	12.01
Hitchin	20.10	22.12	6.10	1.12		6.04	26.01	22.09	10.11	9.03
Kilburn Cosmos	26.01	23.02	13.04	20.10	8.12		16.03	12.01	29.09	17.11
Northolt	10.11	1.12	2.02	6.04	27.10	22.09		9.03	22.12	6.10
Old Actonians	22.12	20.10	8.12	26.01	16.03	10.11	29.09		23.02	13.04
Old Haberdashers	1.12	6.04	27.10	22.09	12.01	9.03	17.11	6.10		2.02
Old Millhillians	6.04	26.01	16.03	10.11	29.09	22.12	23.02	1.12	20.10	

Herts & Middlesex 3 North

	Chess Valley	Cuffley	Hatfield	Hendon	Old Grammarians	Old Tottonians	Q.E.II Hospital	Watford
Chess Valley		22.09	26.01	6.10	23.02	17.11	16.03	8.12
Cuffley	12.01		6.10	23.02	17.11	16.03	8.12	26.01
Hatfield	29.09	2.02		17.11	16.03	8.12	12.01	27.10
Hendon	2.02	27.10	9.03		8.12	12.01	29.09	16.03
Old Grammarians	27.10	9.03	1.12	13.04		29.09	2.02	22.09
Old Tottonians	9.03	1.12	13.04	22.09	26.01		27.10	2.02
Q.E.II Hospital	1.12	13.04	22.0937282.00	6.10	23.02		17.11
Watford	13.04	29.09	23.02	1.12	12.01	6.10	9.03	

Herts & Middlesex 3 South

	Belsize Park	London French	Old Abbotstonians	Old Isleworthians	Osterley	St Nicholas O.B.	Wasps	Wembley
Belsize Park		22.09	26.01	6.10	23.02	17.11	16.03	8.12
London French	12.01		6.10	23.02	17.11	16.03	8.12	26.01
Old Abbotstonians	29.09	2.02		17.11	16.03	8.12	12.01	27.10
Old Isleworthians	2.02	27.10	9.03		8.12	12.01	29.09	16.03
Osterley	27.10	9.03	1.12	13.04		29.09	2.02	22.09
St Nicholas O.B.	9.03	1.12	13.04	22.09	26.01		27.10	2.02
Wasps	1.12	13.04	22.09	26.01	6.10	23.02		17.11
Wembley	13.04	29.09	23.02	1.12	12.01	6.10	9.03	

Herts & Middlesex 4 North

	Hackney	Millfield O.B.	Old Ashmoleans	Old Streetonians	Pinner & Grammarians	Royston	Southgate	Ware
Hackney		16.03	22.09	26.01	23.02	17.11	6.10	8.12
Millfield O.B.	1.12		13.04	22.09	6.10	23.02	26.01	9.03
Old Ashmoleans	12.01	8.12		6.10	17.11	16.03	23.02	26.01
Old Streetonians	29.09	12.01	2.02		16.03	8.12	17.11	27.10
Pinner & Grammarians	27.10	2.02	9.03	1.12		29.09	13.04	22.09
Royston	9.03	27.10	1.12	13.04	26.01		22.09	2.02
Southgate	2.02	29.09	27.10	9.03	8.12	12.01		16.03
Ware	13.04	17.11	29.09	23.02	12.01	6.10	1.12	

Herts & Middlesex 4 South

	British Airways	G.W.R.	Hayes	London Tribes	Orleans F.P.	Quintin	Sudbury Court	Thamesians
British Airways		22.09	26.01	6.10	23.02	17.11	16.03	8.12
G.W.R.	12.01		6.10	23.02	17.11	16.03	8.12	26.01
Hayes	29.09	2.02		17.11	16.03	8.12	12.01	27.10
London Tribes	2.02	27.10	9.03		8.12	12.01	29.09	16.03
Orleans F.P.	27.10	9.03	1.12	13.04		29.09	2.02	22.09
Quintin	9.03	1.12	13.04	22.09	26.01		27.10	2.02
Sudbury Court	1.12	13.04	22.09	26.01	6.10	23.02		17.11
Thamesians	13.04	29.09	23.02	1.12	12.01	6.10	9.03	

LONDON & SOUTH EAST

Kent 1

	Ashford	Brockleians	Bromley	Erith	Gillingham Anch.	Lordswood	Medway	New Ash Green	Park House	Whitstable
Ashford		22.09	9.03	6.10	2.02	27.10	12.01	17.11	13.04	8.12
Brockleians	16.03		12.01	9.03	17.11	6.10	13.04	2.02	8.12	27.10
Bromley	29.09	10.11		22.12	23.02	1.12	20.10	6.04	26.01	22.09
Erith	23.02	29.09	17.11		13.04	2.02	8.12	27.10	16.03	12.01
Gillingham Anch.	20.10	22.12	6.10	1.12		6.04	26.01	22.09	10.11	9.03
Lordswood	26.01	23.02	13.04	20.10	8.12		16.03	12.01	29.09	17.11
Medway	10.11	1.12	2.02	6.04	27.10	22.09		9.03	22.12	6.10
New Ash Green	22.12	20.10	8.12	26.01	16.03	10.11	29.09		23.02	13.04
Park House	1.12	6.04	27.10	22.09	12.01	9.03	17.11	6.10		2.02
Whitstable	6.04	26.01	16.03	10.11	29.09	22.12	23.02	1.12	20.10	

Kent 2

	Aylesford	Bexley	Darenth Valley	Dover	H.S.B.C.	Nat. West. Bank	Old Elthamians	Old Gravesendians	Sheppey	Sittingbourne
Aylesford		22.09	9.03	6.10	2.02	27.10	12.01	17.11	13.04	8.12
Bexley	16.03		12.01	9.03	17.11	6.10	13.04	2.02	8.12	27.10
Darenth Valley	29.09	10.11		22.12	23.02	1.12	20.10	6.04	26.01	22.09
Dover	23.02	29.09	17.11		13.04	2.02	8.12	27.10	16.03	12.01
H.S.B.C.	20.10	22.12	6.10	1.12		6.04	26.01	22.09	10.11	9.03
Nat. West. Bank	26.01	23.02	13.04	20.10	8.12		16.03	12.01	29.09	17.11
Old Elthamians	10.11	1.12	2.02	6.04	27.10	22.09		9.03	22.12	6.10
Old Gravesendians	22.12	20.10	8.12	26.01	16.03	10.11	29.09		23.02	13.04
Sheppey	1.12	6.04	27.10	22.09	12.01	9.03	17.11	6.10		2.02
Sittingbourne	6.04	26.01	16.03	10.11	29.09	22.12	23.02	1.12	20.10	

Kent 3

	Deal Wanderers	Edenbridge	Faversham	Foots Cray	Greenwich	Met. Police, Hayes	Old Olavians	Old Shootershillians	Old Williamsonians	Orpington	Vigo
Deal Wanderers		1.09	9.03	22.09	9.02	6.10	26.01	27.10	5.01	17.11	13.04
Edenbridge	16.03		27.10	9.03	5.01	22.09	17.11	9.02	13.04	6.10	8.12
Faversham	8.09	12.01		10.11	23.02	22.12	29.09	1.12	2.02	6.04	20.10
Foots Cray	23.02	8.09	5.01		17.11	9.02	13.04	6.10	8.12	26.01	16.03
Greenwich	29.09	10.11	22.09	22.12		1.12	2.02	6.04	20.10	1.09	12.01
Met. Police, Hayes	2.02	23.02	17.11	29.09	13.04		8.12	26.01	16.03	27.10	8.09
Old Olavians	20.10	22.12	9.02	1.12	6.10	6.04		1.09	12.01	9.03	10.11
Old Shootershillians	12.01	29.09	13.04	2.02	8.12	20.10	16.03		8.09	5.01	23.02
Old Williamsonians	10.11	1.12	6.10	6.04	26.01	1.09	27.10	9.03		22.09	22.12
Orpington	22.12	2.02	8.12	20.10	16.03	12.01	8.09	10.11	23.02		29.09
Vigo	1.12	6.04	26.01	1.09	27.10	9.03	5.01	22.09	17.11	9.02	

LONDON & SOUTH EAST

Surrey 1

	Battersea Ironsides	K.C.S. Old Boys	Kingston	Law Society	London Irish Amateur	Merton	Old Alleynian	Old Caterhamians	Old Cranleighans	Old Paulines	Old Reedonians	Old Reigatian	Old Rutlishians	Old Tiffinians	Old Walcountians	Old Wellingtonians	Old Whitgiftians
Battersea Ironsides		27.10	06.10				22.09		17.11	08.12		09.03	02.02	12.01			
K.C.S. Old Boys			01.12		02.02	06.04	10.11				12.01				09.03	20.10	29.09
Kingston				17.11	12.01	09.03	20.10				08.12				02.02	29.09	06.04
Law Society	20.10	08.12						10.11	12.01	02.02		29.09	06.04	09.03			
London Irish Amateur	01.12			26.01				22.12			06.04	23.02	10.11	20.10	29.09		
Merton	26.01			16.03	06.10			23.02			22.09	22.12	01.12		27.10		
Old Alleynian				27.10	08.12	02.02		06.10			17.11				12.01	06.04	09.03
Old Caterhamians	29.09	17.11	27.10						08.12	12.01		06.04	09.03	02.02			
Old Cranleighans		26.01	22.12			09.03	29.09	01.12							06.04	10.11	20.10
Old Paulines		23.02	26.01				20.10	22.12			16.03				29.09	01.12	10.11
Old Reedonians	10.11			22.12					01.12	02.02		09.03	20.10	29.09	06.04		
Old Reigatian		06.10	22.09			16.03		27.10	17.11				12.01	08.12		23.02	
Old Rutlishians		22.09	16.03			23.02		06.10	27.10					17.11		26.01	22.12
Old Tiffinians		16.03	23.02			10.11	26.01		22.09	6.10						22.12	01.12
Old Walcountians	22.12			23.02	22.09			26.01				16.03	01.12	10.11			20.10
Old Wellingtonians	16.03			06.10	17.11	12.01		22.09			27.10				08.12		02.02
Old Whitgiftians	23.02			22.09	27.10	08.12		16.03			06.10	26.01			17.11		

Surrey 2

	Haslemere	Lightwater	London Exiles	London Fire Brigade	London Media	Mitcham	Old Abingdonians	Old Amplefordians	Old Freemens	Old Haileyburians	Raynes Park	Shirley Wanderers	Streatham-Croydon	Teddington	Woking
Haslemere			20.10	22.12	09.03	02.02	12.01			01.12				29.09	17.11
Lightwater	27.10		08.12		06.10	22.09	09.03						02.02		12.01
London Exiles				02.02			09.03		12.01	06.10	22.09		27.10	22.12	
London Fire Brigade		23.02			29.09	01.12		27.10	06.10		26.01	16.03	08.12		
London Media			29.09	01.12		12.01		22.12		23.02		17.11	16.03	20.10	
Mitcham		16.03		23.02	08.12		17.11	01.12	26.01			20.10	23.02	29.09	
Old Abingdonians			23.02		08.12			27.10				29.09	26.01	16.03	
Old Amplefordians	26.01	16.03		20.10					23.02	29.09		08.12			
Old Freemens	06.10	01.12	17.11		22.09	09.03	02.02			22.12		12.01			
Old Haileyburians		26.01			27.10	06.10	22.09						09.03	08.12	
Raynes Park	16.03	20.10						22.12	12.01	29.09		17.11	02.02	01.12	
Shirley Wanderers	23.02	29.09			17.11	26.01	22.12	1.12		16.03	20.10				
Streatham-Croydon	8.12		26.01	22.09			06.10					27.10		23.02	
Teddington		17.11			12.01		02.02	20.10		22.09	09.03	22.12			01.12
Woking					09.03					22.09	08.12	02.02	27.10	06.10	

Surrey 3

	Bec Old Boys	Chipstead	Croydon	Economicals	Egham	London Cornish	Old Bevonians	Old Suttonians	Reigate & Redhill	Wandsworthians	Worth Old Boys
Bec Old Boys					08.12	27.10			06.10	22.09	26.01
Chipstead	17.11		06.10	08.12			26.01			22.09	
Croydon	20.10			17.11	29.09	08.12				26.01	
Economicals	12.01				01.12			27.10	06.10	22.09	
Egham		01.12	27.10	26.01			22.09				06.10
London Cornish		20.10			17.11			22.09	26.01	08.12	
Old Bevonians	02.02			29.09		12.01			01.12	27.10	
Old Suttonians		29.09	02.02		20.10				08.12	17.11	
Reigate & Redhill		02.02	12.01		29.09					20.10	01.12
Wandsworthians		12.01	01.12		02.02		06.10				27.10
Worth Old Boys	29.09			20.10			02.02	17.11	12.01		

LONDON & SOUTH EAST

Sussex 1

	Chichester	Chichester IHE	Crowborough	Hastings & Bexhill	Heathfield & Wald'n	Hellingly	Horsham	Rye	St Francis	Sussex Police
Chichester		22.09	9.03	6.10	2.02	27.10	12.01	17.11	13.04	8.12
Chichester IHE	16.03		12.01	9.03	17.11	6.10	13.04	2.02	8.12	27.10
Crowborough	10.11	29.09		22.12	23.02	1.12	20.10	6.04	26.01	22.09
Hastings & Bexhill	29.09	23.02	17.11		13.04	2.02	8.12	26.01	22.09	10.11
Heathfield & Wald'n	22.12	20.10	6.10	1.12		6.04	26.01	22.09	10.11	9.03
Hellingly	23.02	26.01	13.04	20.10	8.12		16.03	12.01	29.09	17.11
Horsham	1.12	10.11	2.02	6.04	27.10	22.09		9.03	22.12	6.10
Rye	20.10	22.12	8.12	26.01	16.03	10.11	29.09		23.02	13.04
St Francis	6.04	1.12	27.10	22.09	12.01	9.03	17.11	6.10		2.02
Sussex Police	26.01	6.04	16.03	10.11	29.09	22.12	23.02	1.12	20.10	

Susex 2 East

	Burgess Hill	Ditchling	Newick	Old Brightonians	Plumpton	Robertsbridge	Seaford
Burgess Hill		22.09	12.01	20.10	23.02	10.11	16.03
Ditchling	8.12		20.10	23.02	10.11	16.03	1.12
Newick	29.09	26.01		10.11	16.03	1.12	8.12
Old Brightonians	26.01	27.10	9.03		1.12	8.12	29.09
Plumpton	27.10	9.03	17.11	6.04		29.09	26.01
Robertsbridge	9.03	17.11	6.04	22.09	12.01		27.10
Seaford	17.11	6.04	22.09	12.01	20.10	23.02	

Sussex 2 West

	Arun	B.A. Wingspan	Barns Green	Midhurst	Norfolk Arms	Pulborough	Royal Sun Alliance	Shoreham
Arun		22.09	12.01	20.10	23.02	10.11	16.03	1.12
B.A. Wingspan	8.12		20.10	23.02	10.11	16.03	1.12	12.01
Barns Green	29.09	26.01		10.11	16.03	1.12	8.12	27.10
Midhurst	26.01	27.10	9.03		1.12	8.12	29.09	16.03
Norfolk Arms	27.10	9.03	17.11	6.04		29.09	26.01	22.09
Pulborough	9.03	17.11	6.04	22.09	12.01		27.10	26.01
Royal Sun Alliance	17.11	6.04	22.09	12.01	20.10	23.02		10.11
Shoreham	6.04	29.09	23.02	17.11	8.12	20.10	9.03	

The successful London Nigerians team who won promotion to London 1 by defeating Canterbury in the play-off.

ALRESFORD RFC
Ground Address: Bighton Cricket Club, Bighton Lane, Bighton, Nr Alresford Tel: 01962 793106
Brief Directions: On entering Bighton from the A31,turn left after Three Horseshoes public house. Ground is on the right.
Club Secretary: C.J.W.Day, 3 The Spinney, Wood Lane, Alresford, Hants. Tel: 0421 564 882
Fixtures Secretary: Robin Howard.
Tel: 01962 733169
Club Colours: Gold, green and black
League: Hampshire 3

ALTON RFC
Ground Address: Anstey Park, Anstey Road, Alton, Hampshire. GU34 2RL
Tel: 01420 82076 Website: www.alton-rfc.com
Brief Directions: From A31 take A339 towards Alton Town. After approx half a mile ground on right.
Club Secretary: Mrs. Sian C. Mills, 12 Waterside Court, Alton, Hampshire, GU34 2PQ.
Tel : 01420 543241 Email: nicksiannmills@aol.com
Fixtures Secretary: Martin Simpson, 10 Gauvain Close, Alton, Hampshire. GU34 2SB
Tel: (H) 01420 86880
Club Colours: Red & black irregular hoops
League: London 3 South West

AMERICAN EXILES
League: Eastern Counties 3 North

ANDOVER RFC LTD
Ground Address: The Goodship Ground, Foxcotte Park, Charlton Down, Andover, Hants., SP11 0TA.
Tel: 01264 339518
Brief Directions: From town centre take ring road to Portway Ind Estate, turn into Goch Way, right onto Hatherden Rd, follow road for 0.75 mile to round-about, turn into Sports Centre

Club Secretary: Bob Sillence, 11 The Link, Andover, Hants., SP10 3BX. Tel: 01264 337862
Fixtures Secretary: The Fixtures Secretary, The Goodship Ground, Foxcotte Park, Andover, Hants., SP11 0TA. Tel 01264 339518
Club Colours: Black. Change: Green
League: London 3 South West

ARUN RUFC
Ground Address: The Littlehampton School, Hill Road, Littlehampton, West Sussex
Tel : 01903 713944
Brief Directions: Off Horsham Road, Littlehampton
Club Secretary: S White, 66 Holmes Lane, Rustington, West Sussex. BN16 3PU
Tel : (H) 01903 774434
Fixtures Secretary: P Best
Tel : (H) 01903 723969
Club Colours: Red, white and navy quarters
League: Sussex 2 West

ASHFORD (KENT) RFC LTD
Ground Address: Kinneys Field, Canterbury Road, Bybrook, Ashford, Kent, TN24 9QQ.
Tel: 01233 624693   www.ashford-rfc.co.uk
Brief Directions: M20 Junction 9 follow signs for Canterbury. Turn right just after the Post House. Southern Water sign at entrance.
Club Secretary: Jenny Lake, 6 Wellesley Villas, Wellesley Road, Ashford, Kent, TN24 8EL
Tel: (H) 01233 624795
Fixtures Secretary: Simon Hall, 1 Patterson Cottages, Aldington, Nr. Ashford, Kent, TN25 8BG
Tel: (H) 01233 720174
Club Colours: Red, amber and black hoops
League: Kent 1
League Contact: I B Nelson, 137 Lower Queens Rd, Ashford, Kent, TN24 8HB   Tel : 01233 610282
Email: iannelson@tinyworld.co.uk

ASKEAN RFC
Ground Address: Ground Share: Blackheath Rugby Club, Rectory Field, Charlton Road, London, SE3
Tel: 020 8858 1578   Website: www.askeans.co.uk
Brief Directions: Multi sited club - contact Ian Lunn - fixture secretary for full details.
Train to Blackheath Station - Bus 54 or 75 to Charlton Road, entrance to Rectory Field.
Club Secretary: Alison Gaze, 11A Old Road, Lewisham, London, SE13 5SH.
Tel: 020 8852 9943 Email: connon@supanet.com
Fixtures Secretary: Ian Lunn, 58 Longton Grove, Sydenham, London, SE26 6QE.
Tel: 020 8778 4823 Email: ianlunn@hotmail.com
Club Colours: Blue, black, white
League: London 4 South East
League Contact: As Fixtures Secretary

AYLESFORD RFC
Ground Address: Ferry Field Ground, Hall Road, Aylesford, Kent, ME20 7DS. Tel: 01622 790380
www.aylesfordrugby.co.uk
Brief Directions: Leave M20 at J5. Head westwards on A20. Turn R. at the second set of traffic lights (Hall Road). Turn R. into Ground after motorway bridge.
Club Secretary: Mike Parker, `Parkdale', Leeds Road, Langley Heath, Maidstone, Kent, ME17 3JG. - Email: michaelparker@btinternet.com
Tel: 01622 861405
Fixtures Secretary: David Bracewell, 1 Hillside Cottages, Malling Road, Teston, Maidstone, Kent, ME18 5AN. Tel: 01622 813772
Club Colours: Red and navy hoops, thin silver/grey line between
League: Kent 2

BANCROFT RFC
Ground Address: Buckhurst Way, Buckhurst Hill, Essex. IG9 6JD   Tel: 020 8504 0429
Brief Directions: Mid way between Woodford and Buckhurst Hill Stations.
Adjacent Roding Valley Central Line Station.
Club Secretary: S B Thirsk, 4 Bentley Way, Woodford Green, Essex. IG8 0SE. Tel: (H) 020 8504 1468   (W) 020 8559 7640
Email: stephen.thirsk@whiskers.co.uk
Fixtures Secretary: Graham Wiseman, 45 Sedley Rise, Loughton, Essex, IG10 1LS. Tel: (H) 020 8508 3480   (W) 020 7930 9711
Email: graham.wiseman@som.com
Club Colours: Blue, black, claret, light blue hoops
League: Eastern Counties 2 South
League Contact: As Club Secretary

BANK OF ENGLAND RFC
Ground Address: Bank of England Sports Club, Priory Lane, Roehampton, London, SW5 5JQ.
Tel : 020 8876 8417
Brief Directions: Turn off A205 South Circular Road into Priory Lane (along side Rosslyn Park). Turn right into Bank Lane after .25 mile entrance on right.
Club Secretary: Bryan Brown, 62 Gilpin Avenue. East Sheen, London SW14 8QY.
Tel : 020 8878 3396(H) 020 7601 4949 (W)
Email: bryan.brown@bankofengland.co.uk
Fixtures Secretary: Mike Anderson, Chailey,

Loudhams Wood Lane, Chalfont St. Giles, H8 4AP.
Tel : 020 7491 9600 (W) 01494 764336 (H)
Email: mike@mondiale-property.com
Club Colours: Old gold, blue & white
League: London 3 North West
League Contact: As Fixture Secretary

BARNES RFC
Ground Address: Barnes Harrodians Sports Club, Barn Elms, Queen Elizabeth Walk, Barnes, London SW13 8DG.
Tel : 0181 876 7685
Website: www.barnesfc.org
Brief Directions: From Hammersmith and Kensington cross Hammersmith Bridge, down Castlenau for 3/4 mile, left into Quenn Elizabeth Walk at Red Lion PH, Ground at end of road 1/2 mile long. (Plenty parking).Clubhouse on left after Red Lion in Queen Elizabeth Walk
Club Secretary: Paul Kirby, 53 Stanhope Gardens, London SW7 5RF.
Tel: (H) 0171 373 9120
Tel : (W) 0171 602 5678
Email: paul.kirby1@virgin.net
Fixtures Secretary: Christy Pickering. Tel No: 01372 749523
Club Colours: Green and gold shirts, green shorts.
League: London 4 South West

BARNET SARACENS ELIZABETHANS RFC
Ground Address: Byng Road, Barnet, Hertfordshire, EN5 4NP   Tel: 020 8449 0040
www .barnetsaresrfc.com
Brief Directions: From M25 (Jct 23) on A1081 to Barnet. At pedestrian crossing, right into Alston Rd., through restriction, third right (Wentworth Road, then left (Byng Road), ground at end.
Club Secretary: Peter Yates, Woodlands, 19 Homefield Road, Ware, Herts. SG12 7NG. Tel: (H)01920 484382 (W) 01992 503304
Fixtures Secretary: Peter Glenister, 47 Bury Lane, Codicote, Hitchin, Herts SG4 8XX
Tel: (H) 01438 820692
Club Colours: Dark blue with maroon hoops
League: London 3 North West
League Contact: Maurice Martin, 20 North Mount, 1147-1161 High Road, London, N20 0EP
Tel : 020 8446 4401
Email: pers.appearances@talk21.com

BARNS GREEN RFC
Ground Address: Christ's Hospital School, Horsham, West Sussex.
Club Secretary: Miss Sue Blanchard, 42 Finians Field,Barns Green, West Sussex. RH13 7PW.
Tel :H 01403 731652
Fixtures Secretary: Mr P A Bailey,
Tel: (H)01403 730058 (W)0120 8667 5504
Club Colours: Gold & green quarters.
League: Sussex 2 West

BASILDON RFC
Ground Address: Gardiners Close, Basildon, Essex. SS14 3AW
Tel : 01268 533136
Website: www.basildonrfc.com
Brief Directions: Frm wst: A127 London/S'thend

arterial rd, past 1st signs for B'don, rt A132, rt at 2nd r'bout A1235, rt at 1st lights (not Zebra) Gardiners Lane south is first left-ground at end.
Club Secretary: Errol Knott, 25 The Knares, Basildon, Essex, SS16 5SB
Tel: 01268 543911 Email: eknott@btinternet.com
Fixtures Secretary: Gary Clinton, 39 Luncies Road, Basildon, Essex, SS14 1SG
Tel: 01268 472257
Club Colours: Bottle green & white stripes, green shorts, green & white socks
League: London 3 North East
League Contact: Scott Liebenberg, 72 Beridge Road, Halstead, Essex, CO9 1LB.
Tel: 01787 477806 Email: basrugby@aol.com

BATTERSEA IRONSIDES RFC
Ground Address: Garret Green, Burntwood Lane, Earlsfield, London. SW17   Tel: 0208 879 9913
Brief Directions: From south: turn left at Tooting Broadway towards Wandsworth, after 2nd R'about Burntwood Ln is 1st main road on right, Garret Green is 500m on right, club a further 300m on left
Club Secretary: Martin Paul Tanner, 1 Woodland Way, Morden, Surrey. SM4 4DS
Tel: (H) 0208 540 5784 (W) 0585 778712
Fixtures Secretary: Andy Taggat, 10 Binden Road, London, W12 9RJ Tel: 0208 6717729
Club Colours: Green jerseys with white band, white shorts, red socks
League: Surrey 1

BEC OLD BOYS
Ground Address: Sutton Manor Sports & Social Club, Northey Avenue, Cheam, Surrey. SM2 7HJ.
Tel: 0181 642 3423
Brief Directions: Right off of A217 into Northey Avenue
Club Secretary: Mr Nick Ryan, 201 Lennard Road, Beckenham, Bromley. BR3 1QN. Tel: (H) 0181 778 9984 (W) 0171 247 7441
Fixtures Secretary: Mr Rick Mayhew
Tel: (H) 0181 286 2463
Club Colours: Blue, old gold and white hoop
League: Surrey 3

BECCEHAMIAN RFC
Ground Address: Sparrows Den, Corkscrew Hill, West Wickham, Kent   Tel: 0181 777 8105
Brief Directions: Corner of Corkscrew Hill and Addington Road (A2022)
Club Secretary: S. Corcoram, c/.o Goodwill & Corcoram, Shaftesbury House, 20 Tylmey Road, Bromley, Kent, BR1 2RL.
Fixtures Secretary: C Putmer
Tel: (H) 0181 777 6307
Club Colours: Maroon, black and silver hoops
League: London 4 South East

BECCLES RUFC
Ground Address: Beef Meadow, Common Lane, Beccles, Suffolk.   Tel: 01502 712016
Website: www.becclesrugbyclub.co.uk
Brief Directions: Into Beccles from Safeway round-about, over mini roundabout, follow road left over railway crossing 1st left is Common Lane
Club Secretary: Miss K. Shy, 38 School Road,

Ringsfield, Beccles, Suffolk, NR34 8NZ.
Tel : 07788 148779
Fixtures Secretary: Simon Clarke, 16 Grove road, Beccles, Suffolk
Tel: 01502 710121
Club Colours: Black and emerald quarters
League: Eastern Counties 1
League Contact: As Fixture Secretary

BECKENHAM RFC
Ground Address: Balmoral Avenue, Elmers End, Beckenham, Kent. BR3 3RD
Tel: 020 8650 7176
Brief Directions: Entrance in Balmoral Ave which runs between Eden Park Ave & Upper Elmers End Rd (A214). From bottom of Beckenham High St take Croydon Rd (A222), left into Eden Park Avenue
Club Secretary: Mr M L Parker, c/o H & V Controls Ltd, 2 Orchard Business Centre Kangley Bridge Road, Sydenham. SE26 5AQ
Tel: (W) 020 8776 7272 Email: martin.parker@con-nect-2.co.uk
Fixtures Secretary: Mr J M Arger, 15 Thatcher Road, Staplehurst, Kent, TN12 0ND
Tel: (H) 01580 891550
Club Colours: Royal blue and old gold hoops
League: London 2 South
League Contact: Rory Brown, 17 Siward Road, Bromley, Kent, BR2 9JY.
Tel: 0208 4641723 Email: rorybrown40@hotmail.com

BELSIZE PARK RFC
Ground Address: Regents Park, London, NW1
Brief Directions: Inner Circle, Regents Park, London, NWI (near Chester Gate)
Club Secretary: Brian East, 64 Station Road, Harpenden, Herts, AL5 4TL
Tel: 0158 276 2209 Email: the.easts@ntlworld.com
Fixtures Secretary: Hugh Reeve-Tucker, 21 Stonor Road, London, W14 8RZ
Tel: 0207 602 0715 Email: hreevetucker@heathlam-bert.com
Club Colours: Black and lavender
League: Hertfordshire & Middlesex 3 South
League Contact: As Fixture Secretary

BETTESHANGER CW RFC
Ground Address: The Welfare Ground, Cavell Square, Deal, Kent. CT14 9HR
Tel: 01304 372080
Brief Directions: Dover - Deal road A258. Left at Q8 Garage. Continue approx I mile. Right down Mill Hill, 1st left Redsull Avenue, 2nd left, Douglas Road, next left - Sports Gound
Club Secretary: Cliff Davies, 46 Mongehan Road, Deal, Kent, CT14 9PG.
Tel: 01304 379088 - Email: cliff-davies@hotmail.com
Fixtures Secretary: Bob Sykes, 232 Reculver Road, Beltinge, Herne Bay, Kent, CT6 6QB. Tel: 01227 374246
Club Colours: Red and white hoops, blue shorts, red socks
League: London 4 South East
League Contact: John Ace, 89 Cavell Square, Deal, Kent   Tel: 01304 361934

BEXLEY RFC
Ground Address: Hall Place Park, Bourne Road, Bexley, Kent
Club Secretary: Peter Butler, 194 Claremont Road, Hextable, Kent. BR8 7QU   Tel: (H) 01322 664389
Fixtures Secretary: Paul Herbert
Tel: (H) 01322 555556
Club Colours: Royal blue and white hooped shirts, blue shorts, blue socks with white tops
League: Kent 2

BILLERICAY RFC
Ground Address: Willowbrook Sports & Social Club, Stock Road, Billericay, Essex
Club Secretary: Neil Jarvis, Brenenden, North Road, Crays Hill, Billericay, Essex. CM11 2XD
Tel: (H) 01268 289481 (W) 0171 797 8000
Fixtures Secretary: Sean Norris
Tel: (H) 01277 654952
Club Colours: Black with gold band, black shorts, black and gold socks
League: Eastern Counties 1

BISHOPS STORTFORD RFC
Ground Address: Silver Leys, Hadham Road, Bishops Stortford, Herts. CM23 2QE
Tel: 01279 652092 Website: www.bsrfc.co.uk
Brief Directions: From north/south, M11 J8, A120 signed Puckeridge. From east/west, A120 to Tesco roundabout, Tesco on right, ground 400m left. Alternatively see map on website.
Club Secretary: Jim Smith, 16 Millcroft, Bishops Stortford, Herts. CM23 2BP.
Tel: 01279 831667. Email: jim.smith5@ntlworld.com
Fixtures Secretary: Terry Ellis, Flat 2, 72 South Street, Bishops Stortford, Herts. CM23 3AZ
Tel No: 01279 461186.
Email: the@stort7.fsnet.co.uk
Club Colours: Royal blue and white hoops
League: London 2 North

BOGNOR RFC
Ground Address: The Clubhouse, Hampshire Avenue, Bognor Regis, West Sussex. PO21 5JY.
Tel: 01243 824000
Brief Directions: Head west on A259 from the centre of Bognor. Turn left into Hampshire Avenue (marker for club on lamp post). Take 1st turn on left.
Club Secretary: John Donoghue, 62 Victoria Drive, Bognor Regis PO21 2TG.
Tel: 01243 823287 (H) 07971 052857 (M)
Fixtures Secretary: Ian Misselbrook.
Tel: 01243 866354.
Club Colours: Purple, emerald and silver hoops
League: London 4 South East

BRAINTREE RUFC
Ground Address: The Clubhouse, Beckers Green Road, Braintree, Essex CM7 6PR.
Tel : 01376 311181 Website: www.brufc. com
Brief Directions: From Braintree bypass A120 exit at Galleys Corner roundabout to Braintree East (B1018 Cressing Road), 300 metres turn right into Beckers Green Road, Ground at end of road.
Club Secretary: Adrian Hanson, 28 Bridport Way, Kings Park, Braintree, CM7 9FJ
Tel: 01376 328545

Fixtures Secretary: Chris Copsey,1 Chelsea Mews, Braintree, Essex CM7 9UR   Tel: 01376 384219
e-mail: chris.bri@ukgateway.net
Club Colours: Black & amber quarters
League: London 4 North East
League Contact: As Secretary

BRENTWOOD RFC
Ground Address: King Georges Playing Fields, Ingrave Road, Brentwood, Essex. CM13 2AQ.
Tel : 01277 210267
Brief Directions: M25 Jct28.Follow A1023 towards Brentwood town centre along High street to double mini roundabout. Rt. into Ingrave Road ground .75 mile on right opposite `Masons Restaurtant'.
Club Secretary: Petert McMullan, `Turnstile House', 25 Hutton Village, Hutton, Brentwood CM13 1RT
Tel: 01277 200420
Email: petermcmullan@ukgateway.net
Fixtures Secretary: Nick Priddle, Foxhurst, Coxes Farm Rd, Billericay. CM11 2UA
Tel: (H) 01277 656685
Club Colours: Claret, grey & white hoops, black shorts
League: London 3 North East
League Contact: James Metcalfe, 1 Abbenberg Way, Brentwood, CM13 2UG
Tel: 01277 234637

BRIGHTLINGSEA RFC
Ground Address: Colne Community School, Church Road, Brightlingsea, Essex
Brief Directions: Colne School is on the main road as you enter the town
Club Secretary: Roger Kemble, 8 Duke Street, Brightlingsea, Essex. CO7 0EA
Tel: (H) 01206 302432
Email: rogerkemble@fetchmail.co.uk
Fixtures Secretary: Ian Polley, 9 Bellfield Avenue, Brightlingsea, Essex, CO7 0NT/
Tel: 01206 303549
Club Colours: Red, black shorts
League: Eastern Counties 3 North
League Contact: As Secretary

BRIGHTON FOOTBALL CLUB (RFC)
Ground Address: Waterhall Playing Fields, Waterhall Road, Off Mill Road, Brighton, East Sussex. BN1 8YR.
Tel : 01273 562729
Brief Directions: From London A23 to Patcham roundabout, round roundabout, turn into Mill Rd, underneath Railway arch, 1st right, 1st left, straight up to clubhouse
Club Secretary: Mrs Cheryl Vivian, 32 Prinsep Road, Hove, E. Sussex, BN3 7AB.
Tel: 01273 720458 Email: cheryl.vivian.@csfb.com
Fixtures Secretary: R Greenwood, 11 Lyminster Avenue, Brighton, E. Sussex, BN1 8JL
Tel : (H) 01273 502898
Club Colours: Blue shirts, shorts, red socks
League: London 3 South East
League Contact: E. D'Arcy,
2 Stanbridge Road, Staplefield Lane, Staplefield, Haywards Heath, RG17 6AS
Tel : 01444 401403
Email: ed.calypso@btinternet.com

BRITISH AIRWAYS RFC
Ground Address: Concorde Centre, Crane Lodge Road, High Street, Cranford Middlesex, TW5 9PQ.
Tel : 020 8562 0291
Brief Directions: Take M4, Jct 3 follow A312 to Feltham. At 1st lights turn left, then left at lst mini R'about. Clubhouse is right at 2nd mini R'about
Club Secretary: Andy Lord,143 High Street, Teddington, Middlesex. TW11 8HH
Tel: 020 8977 4815
E-mail: andylord@ukgateway.net
Fixtures Secretary: Pete Attard, 460 Redford Close, Feltham, Middlesex, TW13 4TP. Tel: 020 8384 8489
E-mail: p-attard@hotmail.com
Club Colours: Red, white and blue quarters
League: Hertfordshire & Middlesex 4 South
League Contact: Paul Knight, 89 Bury Avenue, Hayes, Middlesex, UB4 8LF
Tel: 07931 546352

BRITISH AIRWAYS WINGSPAN RUFC
Ground Address: Bewbush Leisure Centre, Coachmans Drive, Bewbush, Crawley.
Tel: 01293 546477
Brief Directions: Turn west off A23 at Cheals r'about, signed Horsham, on A264, 3rd exit at 2nd r'about (Breezehurst Drive), sports centre is 0.5 mile on left
Club Secretary: Mike Duff, 10 Brooklands Road, Tollgate Hill, Crawley, Sussex. RH11 9QQ.
Tel: (H) 01293 409908 (W) 01293 662258
Fixtures Secretary: Harry Townsend
Tel: (H & W) 01342 322508
Club Colours: Red, white and blue
League: Sussex 2 West

BROADLAND RFC
Ground Address: Cobham Playing Field, Cobham, Great Yarmouth, Norfolk Tel: 01493 445692
Brief Directions: From Norwich A47. 1st R/about take 3rd exit over bridge. 400 yards on right.
Club Secretary: Ms S Watson, 44A Southtown Road, Great Yarmouth, Norfolk. NR31 0DT.
Tel : 01493 657052
Fixtures Secretary: D Todd, 3 Wayne Close, Lowestoft, Suffolk. Tel: (H) 01502 512671
Club Colours: Red, white and blue hoops
League: Eastern Counties 3 North

BROCKENHURST COLLEGE RFC
Ground Address: Brockenhurst College, Lyndhurst Road, Brockenhurst, Hants.   Tel: 01590 625555
Brief Directions: M27 J.1 signs to Brockenhurst turn L. just prior to Rose & Crown Pub. Ground on Left.
Club Secretary: Mark Bloodworth, Brockenhurst College, Lyndhurst Road, Hants SO41 0FG.
Tel : 01590 625555 Ext. 314
Club Colours: Black & white
League: Hampshire 3

BROCKLEIANS RFC
Ground Address: Eltham Palace Road, Eltham, London. SE9 5LX   Tel: 0208 8508650
Website: brockleians.co.uk
Brief Directions: A20 to junction with South Circular, turn into Eltham Palace Road at World of Leather.
Club Secretary: Paul Parish, 38 Cobden Road,
South Norwood, London SE25 5NX
Tel : (H) 208 656 0790
Email: paul.parish@skillbase.net
Fixtures Secretary: George Wright
Tel: (H) 01622 738396
Club Colours: Chocolate, emerald and old gold
League: Kent 1
League Contact: S. Loader, 15 Westland Drive, Hayes, Bromley, Kent, BR2 7HE
Tel: 0208 4621884

BROMLEY RFC
Ground Address: Warman Trust Ground, Barnet Wood Road, Hayes, Bromley, Kent
Tel: 0208 462 3430 Website: bromleyrfc.org
Brief Directions: M25 J.4 & A21 towards Bromley. At Locksbottom filter left at lights on A232. .5 mile to next lights then right & 1st left to Barnet Wood road.
Club Secretary: Steve Wardingley
Fourways,108 West Common Road, Hayes, Bromley, Kent, BR2 7BY   Tel : 0208 325 6276
Email: stephen.wardingley@hall.burton.com
Fixtures Secretary: Roger Simpson, 24 Lakeside, Wickham Road, Bromley, Kent, BR3 6LX.
Tel : 0208 402 5123
Email: rogerco@18shortlands.fsnet.co.uk
Club Colours: Black/amber, black
League: Kent 1
League Contact: As Secretary

BURGESS HILL RFC
Ground Address: Poveys Close, Burgess Hill, West Sussex, RH15 0BW Tel: 01444 232221
All mail to be addressed to the Secretary's address - not the ground address
Website: www.bhrfc@freeserve.co.uk
Brief Directions: Royal George Road turn into Southway at Weald public house right into Poveys Close - ground at end.
Club Secretary: Mike Bushell, 4 Kirdford Close, Burgess Hill, West Sussex. RH15 0BW
Tel: (H) 01444 246795
Email: mj@bushell75.freeserve.co.uk
Fixtures Secretary: Tony Balsdon, 102 Marlborough Drive, Burgess Hill, West Sussex. RH15 0EU
Tel: (H) 01444 246170 (W) 01273 273234
Email: gillandtony@tesco.net
Club Colours: All black
League: Sussex 2 East

BURNHAM-ON-CROUCH RUFC
Ground Address: Dengie Hundred Sports Centre, Millfields, Station Road, Burnham-on-Crouch, Essex. CM0 8HS Tel : 01621 784633 (O)
01621 784656 (Bar) Website: brufc.org. uk
Brief Directions: From all main routes continue east (north of River Crouch), pick up B1010 into B-o-Crouch, right at T jctn, over rail bridge into town centre, library on right entrance to ground immediate right
Club Secretary: Simon Bouch, 13 Willow Close, Burnham on Crouch, Essex CM0 8DJ.
Tel: 01621 786683. Email: dinny@bluecarrots.com
Fixtures Secretary: Warwick Bridge, 12 Glendale Road, Burnham on Crouch, Essex, CM0 8LY. Tel: (H) 01621 783807 Email: whbridge@hotmail.com
Club Colours: Navy blue
League: Eastern Counties 3 South
League Contact: As Fixture Secretary

BURY ST EDMONDS RFC
Ground Address: The Harbeden, Southgate Green, Bury St Edmonds, IP33 2BL   Tel: 01284 753920
Brief Directions: Leave A14 on A134 (B.S.E. East & Sudbury), ground is 400 yards on right, next to BP Petrol Station
Club Secretary: H. Whitfield, The Harbeden, Southgate Green, Bury St. Edmonds, IP33 2BL Tel: 01284 753920 Email: harry.whitfield@btinternet.com
Fixtures Secretary: Simon Lord, Ash Trees, 32 Bury Road, Barrow, Bury St. Edmunds, IP29 5AB.
Tel : (H) 01284 811189
Club Colours: Green and gold bands
League: London 3 North East
League Contact: As Secretary

CAMPION RFC
Ground Address: Cottons Park, Cottons Approach, Romford, Essex. RM7 7AA   Tel: 01708 753209
Brief Directions: Frm W. exit A12 at lights after Moby Dick pub, rt -Mawney Rd, before T jnct rt - Marks Rd, ground 1st left. Frm E., A12 thro' 3 lights after Gallows Crnr, lt-Hawney Rd before T Jct. Rt. Marks Road
Club Secretary: P O'Brien, 68 Lancaster Drive, Elm Park, Hornchurch, Essex. RM12 5ST
Tel: (H) 01708 446980 (W) 01708 342453
Fixtures Secretary: M. Chapman, 37 Monkwood Close, Romford, Essex, RM1 2NQ.
Tel: 01708 727685
Email: matthew.chapman@ubs.com
Club Colours: Red and black hoops
League: London 4 North East
League Contact: As Secretary

CANTABRIGIAN RFC
Ground Address: Sedley Taylor Road, Cambridge. CB2 2PW   Tel: 01223 516061
Brief Directions: Leave M11 exit 11(A1309) to Cambridge. Right at 2nd traffic lioghts into Long Rd.,. Left after railway bridge into Sedley Taylor Rd.Ground down narrow entrance immediately on left.
Club Secretary: R L Ladds, 4 Flamstead Road, Cambridge. CB1 3QU
Tel: (H) 01223 249008 (W) 01223 553398
Fixtures Secretary: J Edmonds, 25 Granta Terrace, Great Shelford, Cambs. CA2 5DJ
Tel: (H) 01223 563256 (W) 01223506606
Club Colours: Navy blue and white hoops
League: Eastern Counties 2 North

CANTERBURY RFC
Ground Address: Merton Lane (North), Nackington Rd, Canterbury, Kent CT4 7BA   Tel : 01227 761301
Website: www.canterbury.co.uk
Brief Directions: Exit A2 for Canterbury, at 4th roundabout take 3rd exit, (old Dover Rd). Turn R. into Nackington Raod (B2068) 9/10ths mile turn right at sign, do not cross bypass.
Club Secretary: Robin Gipson, 1 Maple Close, Rough common, Canterbury, Kent, CT2 9BX. Tel: 01227 761997 Email: robingipson@hotmail.com
Fixtures Secretary: Kevin Lavelle, 5, South Canterbury Road, Canterbury, Kent. CT1 3LH
Tel: 01227 464656
Club Colours: Black and amber hoops
League: London 2 South

CANVEY ISLAND RUFC
Ground Address: Trewkes Creek, Dovervelt Road, Canvey Island, Essex
Tel: 01268 681881
Brief Directions: A130 to Sports Centre (Waterside Farm) Keep complex on right and Castle View School on left. Take 1st left after school. Ground 300yds on left
Club Secretary: Mr Stephen Clarke, 26 Thelma Avenue, Canvey Island, Essex. SS8 9DT
Tel : (H) 01268 699858
Fixtures Secretary: Mick Smith, 6 Elsinor Avenue, Canvey Island, Essex.   Tel: 01268 690756
Club Colours: Red and blue
League: London 4 North East
League Contact: As Fixture Secretary

CHARLTON PARK RFC
Ground Address: 60A broad Walk, Blackheath, London SE3 8NB
Brief Directions: A2 to Kidbrooke then followRochesrter Way eastbound for 250 yds. Broad Walk is on left. Entrance to club on right after 200 yds.
Club Secretary: Andy Potts, 37 Beechhill Road, Eltham, London SE9 1HJ 0181 859 8775
Email: porlid@globalnet.co.uk
Fixtures Secretary: Murray Rowland, 23 Thaxtedf Road, London SE9 3PU
Tel No: 020 8859 6776
Club Colours: Red and White Hooped shirts, blue shorts and red socks.
League: London 3 South East

CHELMSFORD RFC
Ground Address: Coronation Park, Timsons Lane, Springfield, Chelmsford, Essex. CM2 6AF
Tel: 01245 261159
Brief Directions: A12 - take Boreham/North Springfield turning, head for Chelmsford, over 1st roundabout, 2nd roundabout 3rd exit, over round-about, 1st turning after Plough pub Timsons Lane
Club Secretary: Lawrence Crispin, 33 Jenner Mead, Chelmer Village, Chelmsford , Essex CM2 6SJ
Tel: 01245 465021
Fixtures Secretary: Clare St. John -Coleman, 139 Pollards Gren, Chelmsford, Essex CM2 6UX Tel : 01245 602239 (H) 0585 344367(M)
Club Colours: Navy Blue shirts and shorrts, navy blue & white hooped socks
League: London 3 North East

CHESS VALLEY
Ground Address: Rickmansworth Sports Club, Park road, Rickmnsworth, Herts WD3 1HU
Tel: 01923 445440
Brief Directions: M25 Jct 18 follow A404 to Rickmansworth. Club between town and Croxley Green and is signposted at bottom of Scots Bride Hill.
Club Secretary: Graeme Coles, 3 Gordon wayt, Chalfont St Giles, Bucks. HP8 4QU
Tel : 01494 876312 (W) 01494 874655(H)
Fixtures Secretary: Guy Sworey.
Tel: 0208 572 5301 (W) 07780604732 (M)
Club Colours: Bottle green shirts with pink collars, black , green & black
League: Hertfordshire & Middlesex 3 North

CHICHESTER RFC
Ground Address: Oaklands Park, Wellington Road, Chichester, West Sussex   Tel: 01243 779820
Brief Directions: Oaklands Park is near The Festival Theatre in Broyle Road to the north of Chichester centre. (Chichester to Midhurst road)
Club Secretary: M.E.J.Duke, 92 Whyke Lane, Chichester, West Sussex. PO19 2ATt
Tel No: 01243 775476
Email: duke.matthew@ukonline.co.uk
Fixtures Secretary: F. Corby, Caretakers Cottage, School Lane, Selsey, West Sussex, PO20 9EH.
Tel No: 01243 602354
Club Colours: Dark blue and light blue hoops
League: Sussex 1

CHINEHAM RFC
Club Secretary: Mr. G. Turner, 1 Little Copse Chase, Chineham, Basingstoke, Hants, RG24 8GL
Fixtures Secretary: Mrs. Jem Cooper, 26 Birchwood, Chineham, Basingstoke.
League: Hampshire 3

CHINGFORD RFC
Ground Address: Lea Valley Playing Fields, Waltham Way, Chingford, London. E4 8AQ
Tel: 020 8529 4879
Brief Directions: M11 to A406 westbound, approx 3 miles to Cook's ferry junction.Then A1009 over mini roundabout. Ground 1 mile on left.
Club Secretary: Peter Wilton, 39 College Gardens, Chingford. E4 8AQ   Tel No: 020 8529 2052
Fixtures Secretary: David Butler, c/o Chingford RFC
Tel No: 020 8529 4879 (H)
Club Colours: Black with royal blue & white hoops
League: London 3 North East

CHIPSTEAD RFC
Ground Address: The Meads, High Road, Chipstead, Surrey   Tel: 01737 553035
Brief Directions: Opposite The white Hart pub. Entrance to the ground is between the White Hart and the pond.
Club Secretary: I. Browne, 10 Sandown Court, Grange Road, Sutton, Surrey, SM2 6SQ. Tel 020 8643 1691 - Email: browne-ian@hotmail.com
Fixtures Secretary: R. W. Adair, 56 Woodcrest Road, Purley, Surrey CR8 4JB
Tel: (H) 0181 668 3428 (W) 0181 686 8911
Club Colours: Blue and Gold jerseys
League: Surrey 3

CHISWICK RFC
(Formerly known as Old Meadonians)
Ground Address: The Boat House, Riverside Lands, Chiswick, London, W4.   Tel: 020 8994 6956
Brief Directions: From London A316 to Richmond. Turn left immediately before Chiswick Bridge, follow river to The Boat House.
Club Secretary: David K. Samuel, 39 Weavers close, Isleworth, Middlesex, TW7 6ET. Tel: 020 8569 8691 - Email: david@samueld.freeserve.co.uk
Fixtures Secretary: Steve Moore, Flat 2, 32 Park Parade, Harlsden, London, NW10 4JE
Tel: 0926 290360
Club Colours: Maroon and blue
League: London 4 North West

CHOBHAM RFC
Ground Address: Fowlers Wells, Windsor Road, Chobham, Woking, Surrey. GU24 8NA
Tel : 01276 858616
Website: chobham-rugby.co.uk
Brief Directions: Take road to Sunningdale out of village centre (B383), ground is 500 yards on right behind Cobham Working Mens Club
Club Secretary: Nigel Heslop, 98 Broad Street, Guildford, GU3 3BE
Tel: 01483 535840 Email: nigel@hesllop6.demon.co.uk
Fixtures Secretary: Andy Haris, 6 Bloomfield, Knaphill, Woking, GU21 2BL   Tel: 01483 480893
Colours: Blue with red & gold hoops, green shoulders
League: London 3 South West
League Contact: Peter Hague, 28 Oaktree Road, Knaphill,Woking, GU21 2RZ   Tel: 01483 473827

CIVIL SERVICE FC (RU)
Ground Address: Dukes Meadows, Riverside Drive, Chiswick. W4   Tel: 0181 994 1204
Brief Directions: By road: From Hogarth Roundabout (A4) take A316 towards Richmond.After 1/2 mile turn left at traffic lights into Riverside Drive.By Train: Waterloo to Barnes Bridge, over bridge on right
Club Secretary: N G Alway, 20 Herndon Road, London. SW18 2DG
Tel: (H)0208 870 6818 (W) 0207 583 5333
e-mail: nickalwaysrugby@hotmail.com
Fixtures Secretary: R Hulme
Tel: (H) 01438 832 054
Club Colours: White shirts, blue shorts
League: Hertfordshire & Middlesex 1

COBHAM RFC
Ground Address: The Memorial Ground, Fairmile Lane, Cobham, Surrey   Tel: 01932 863245
Brief Directions: Ground situated on junction of Fairmile Lane and the Portsmouth road (A307) approx 3 miles from Esher, 1 mile from Cobham opposite Fairmile Hotel
Club Secretary: Andrew Harburn, 21 The Avenue, Surbiton, Surrey, KT5 8JW. Tel: 0181 8482738
Fixtures Secretary: Ian Johnson, 209 Portsmouth Road, Cobham, Surrey, KT11 1JR. Tel: (H) 01932 862694 (W) 0181 942 1033
Club Colours: Blue, maroon and gold quarters
League: London 3 South West

COLCHESTER RFC
Ground Address: Mill Road Playing Fields, Mill Road, Colchester. CO4 5JF Tel: 01206 851610
Brief Directions: Turn off A12 onto A1232, right at roundabout into business park, right at next round-about, straight over next roundabout into Mill Road, ground is 400yds on right
Club Secretary: Bill Anslow, 31 Chapel Road, West Bergholt, Colchester, CO6 3JB. Tel: 01206 240983 - Email: bill@greyowlgolf.com
Fixtures Secretary: Jon Roberts, 5 Spencer Close, Maldon, Essex, CM9 6BX. Tel: (H) 01621 854043
Club Colours: All B lack
League: Eastern Counties 2 North

LONDON & SOUTH EAST

CRANBROOK RFC
Ground Address: Tomlin Ground, Angley Road, Cranbrook, Kent. TN17 3LB Tel: 01580 712777
Brief Directions: Off A229 Hastings road, 14 miles south of Maidstone, 4 miles north of Hawkhurst at junction of Cranbrook bypass with Whitewell Lane
Club Secretary: Nick Reed, 6 Northridge, Northian,East Sussex. TN31 6PG
Tel No: 01797 252374
Fixtures Secretary: Simon Haydon, 1 Church Cottages,Beckley, East Sussex.
Tel No: 01797 260 345
Club Colours: Magenta and white
League: London 4 South East

CRANLEIGH RFC
Ground Address: Wildwood Lane, Alfold, Cranleigh, Surrey.
Tel: 01483 275843
Brief Directions: From Guildford take A281 towards Horsham, after 9.5 miles, before Alford crossroads, turn left at Wildwood Lane (signed Cranleigh RFC) 400 yards.
Club Secretary: Kevin Maxted,16 Taylors Crescent, Cranleigh, Surrey. GU6 7EL Tel No: 01483 276220
Email: kevin.maxted@royalmail.co.uk
Fixtures Secretary: Nigel Spong, `Millook', New Park Road, Cranleigh, Surrey, GU6 7EZ. Tel No: 01483 272700
Club Colours: Red and blue quarters, red socks, blue shorts
League: London 4 South West

CRAWLEY RFC
Ground Address: Willoughby Fields, 1 Ifield Avenue, Crawley, West Sussex, RGH11 7X.
Tel : 01293 533995
Website: www.crawleyrugbyclub.co.uk
Brief Directions: Off A23 Crawley bypass from north take M23 J10 onto A23 bypass, 1.5 miles pass Sainsburys, right at next roundabout into Ifield Ave towards Charlwood, ground approx 0.75 mile on right
Club Secretary: Paul Chapman, 19 Longwood View, Furnace Green, Crawley, West Sussex, RH10 6PB.
Tel No: 01293 446961
Email: pschap@tesco.net
Fixtures Secretary: Dave Haime, 93 Maiden Lane, Langley Green, Crawley, West Sussex, RH11 7RJ.
Tel: 01293 410648
Club Colours: Maroon and blue hoops
League: London 3 South East

CROWBOROUGH RFC
Ground Address: Steel Cross, Crowborough, East Sussex Tel: 01892 654832
Brief Directions: South on A26 from Tunbridge Wells, Club signposted at roundabout after village of Boarshead
Club Secretary: Gavin Tyler, 3 Wallis Close, Crowborough, East Sussex. TN6 2YA e-mail: gavin.tyler@ dual.pipex.com
Tel: (H) 01892 665153 (W) 01892 506155
Fixtures Secretary: Paul Astill, 2 Bryants Field, Crowborough TN61 BH Tel: 01892 653136
Club Colours: Red with graduated white hoops, blue shorts
League: Sussex 1

CROYDON RFC
Ground Address: Layhams Road (junction with King Henry's Drive), Keston, Bromley, Kent.
Tel: 01959 573409
Website: www.croydonrfc.org
Brief Directions: A2022 to Addington Village, at r'bout 200yds beyond Gravel Hill, fork south to New Addington as signed up Lodge Ln, left at next r'bout into King Henry's Drive, left at end into Layhams Rd
Club Secretary: Trevor Davies,Woodside, 51A Chaldon Common Rd.,Chaldon,Caterham, Surrey. CR3 5DH. Tel: 01883 345 288
Email: ttrevdavies@aol.com
Fixtures Secretary: Alan Doe, 16 Cherry Hill Gardens, Waddan, Croydon, CR0 4QL
Tel: (H) 0208 681 0793
Club Colours: Black, magenta & white hoops
League: Surrey 3

CRUSADERS RUFC
Ground Address: Beck Hythe, Little Melton, Nr Norwich, Norfolk Tel: 01603 811157
Brief Directions: Situated in Little Melton, S.E. of Norwich. From southern bypass take Watton Rd (B1108), turn left past the garden centre, thro' village, pass village inn, next left, 1st right, club 400yds right
Club Secretary: John Alton Jones, Norwich Food Co, 19 Alston Road, Hellesden Park, Norwich
Tel: (W) 01603 486666
Fixtures Secretary: Michael Bridgman
Tel: (H) 01603 250926
Club Colours: Gold and emerald green hoops
League: Eastern Counties 2 North

CUFFLEY RFC
Ground Address: King George V Playing Fields, Cuffley, Herts.
Brief Directions: Travel from Currley to Potters Bar (B156) Ground is approx 700 yards on the left.
Club Secretary: C A Palmer, 10 Connaught Road, Harpenden, Herts. AL5 4HF Tel: (H) 01582 768152
Fixtures Secretary: P Cushing, 10 Lilac Drive, Lutterworth, Leicestershire, LE17 4FP.
Tel: (H) 01455 557568
Club Colours: Red and black
League: Hertfordshire & Middlesex 3 North

DAGENHAM RUFC
Ground Address: The Pavilion, Central Park, Dagenham, Essex. RM10 7DA Tel: 0208 593 8202
Website: www.geocities.com/mjrogers74/DRUFC.html
Brief Directions: From A13 turn into Ballards Rd, jctn of Princess Bowl/ McDonalds. On to Bull r'about take1st L. Pass Dagenham East R'stn. Over Eastbrook P.H. jctn. Ground 300yds jright thro' park gates
Club Secretary: Ben Fowler, 4 The Limes, Hornchurch, Essex, RM11 2GT
Tel: 01708 479249 Email: ben.fowler@ubsw.com
Fixtures Secretary: Dickie Moreton, 21 Central Park Avenue, Dagenham, Essex. RM10 7DA
Tel : (H) 0208 984 8444
Club Colours: Red and white quarters
League: Eastern Counties 3 South
League Contact: Marc Randall, 3 Cambeys Road, Dagenham, Essex, RM10 8YA Tel: 0208 592 6642

DARENTH VALLEY RFC
Ground Address: The Leigh Clubhouse, Leigh City Technical College, Green Street, Dartford, Kent
Tel: 01322 290801 or 07980 683415
Brief Directions: M25 J1, take road towards Dartford (across M25), 1st left at roundabout (past petrol garage) and 1st right onto College campus
Club Secretary: Ken Parr,98 High Road, Wilmington, Dartford, Kent. DA2 7OW
Tel No: 07980 683415
Email: darenthvalley.rfc@btinternet.com
Fixtures Secretary: Peter Murray, 21 Sundridge Hill, Cuxton, Rochester, Kent. ME2 1LH
Club Colours: Black shirts with white V and black shorts
League: Kent 2

DARTFORDIANS RUFC
Ground Address: Bourne Road, Bexley, Kent
Tel: 01322 524176
Club Secretary: Jack Morris, 7 Irving Way, Swanley, Kent. BR8 7EP
Tel: (H) 01322 669817
Fixtures Secretary: D Rapley
Tel: (H) 0181 857 6198
Club Colours: Maroon and old gold.
League: London 3 South East

DATCHWORTH RFC
Ground Address: Datchworth Green, Datchworth, Herts. SG3 6TL
Tel: 01438 812490
Brief Directions: Leave A1(M) at J6 (Welwyn) on B197 north towards Stevenage, at Woolmer Green turn right towards Datchworth, pitches and clubhouse behind tennis courts
Club Secretary: Mrs L D Wyatt, 7 Hazeldell, Watton-at-Stone, Hertford. SG14 3SL
Tel: (H) 01920 830407
Fixtures Secretary: N.Bennett,6 Brockwell Shot, Walkern, Herts. SG2 7PJ
tel No: 01438 861153
Club Colours: Navy blue, green and white.
League: Hertfordshire & Middlesex 2

DEAL WANDERERS RUFC
Ground Address: Clubhouse, Western Road, Deal, Kent.
Tel :01304 365892
Brief Directions: The ground is located at the junction of West Street and Western Avenue to the North West of the town centre
Club Secretary: Ian Parker, 18 Middle Deal Road, Deal, Kent CT14 9RF
Tel No: 01304 373130
Fixtures Secretary: Andy Bodman. 49 Telegraph Rd., Deal, Kent Ct14 9DE
 Tel No: 01304 375750
Club Colours: Blue & Amber Hoops
League: Kent 3

DISS RFC
Ground Address: Mackenders, Bellrope Lane, Roydon, Diss, Norfolk
Tel: 01379 642891
Website: dissrfc,com
Brief Directions: 1 mile west of Diss on A1066

through Roydon village, at end of 40mph limit turn into Bellrope Lane opposite White Hart pub, club 150 yards on left
Club Secretary: N.Kingsley, c/o Newman & Co. ,104 Victoria Rd, Diss, Norfolk. IP 22 4SG
Tel No 01379 640640
Fixtures Secretary: Paul Mitchell, 19 Denmark Street, Diss, Norfolk. IP22 3LE
01379 650638 (H) 01953 887736(W)
Club Colours: Royal blue and white
League: London 2 North

DITCHLING RFC
Ground Address: The Playing Fields, Lewes Road, Ditchling, East Sussex
Tel: 01273 843423
Brief Directions: From the village crossroads, head east on the Lewes Road and the ground is approx 0.25 mile down on the left
Club Secretary: Craig Rixon, 2C Plaistow Lane, Bromley, Kent. BR1 4DS
Tel No: 0208 466 6159
Fixtures Secretary: Chris Atkinson, 61 St Andrews Road, Burges Hill RH15 0PJ
Tel No: 01444 248199
Club Colours: Myrtle green shirts and white shorts with green & yellow socks.
League: Sussex 2 East

DORKING RFC
Ground Address: The Pavilion, The Big Field, Kiln Lane, Brockham, Betchworth, Surrey. RH3 7LZ
Tel : 01737 843928
Website: www.dorkingrugbyclub.co.uk
Brief Directions: From Dorking take A25 to Reigate after 2 miles turn right towards Brockham, then first left into Kiln Lane
Club Secretary: James Toon, 4 Vincent Lane, Dorking, Surrey RH4 3HE
Tel: (H) 01306 741455
e-mail: james-toon@crown.uk.com
Fixtures Secretary: Mark Bell, 117 Gatton Park ROad, Redhill, Surrey RH1 2EB
Tel: 01737 766 987
E-mail: mark.bell@tgb.toyota.co.uk
Club Colours: Red and white hoops and blue shorts with red & white socks
League: London 3 South West

DOVER RFC
Ground Address: Crabble Athletic Ground, Crabble Road, River, Dover, Kent
Tel: 01304 210296
Website: www.doverrfc.co.uk
Brief Directions: From M2/A2, at Esso garage take River exit, left at mini r'bout, sharp right at lights, 300m on left. From M20/A20 leave Dover on Canterbury Rd, fork left at lights on Crabble Hill, 300m on left
Club Secretary: Ian Dean, 102 Templeside, Temple Ewell, Dover, Kent. CT16 3BA
Fixtures Secretary: P.Batty-Smith, 46 Lower Road, River, Dover CT17 0QY
Tel No: 01304 823163
Club Colours: Light and dark blue hoops
League: Kent 2

EALING
Ground Address: Trailfinders Sports Club, Vallis Way, Ealing, London. W13. Tel: 0208 998 7928
Website: www.ealingrugby.co.uk
Brief Directions: Take B452 (Argyle Road) towards Ealing at junction with A40 and after two sets of lights turn right at mini roundabout into Vallis Way
Club Secretary: Lawson Mayor, 32 Wyresdale Crescent, Greenford Middlesex. UB6 8TH
Tel No: 020 8997 7330
Email: lawson@lawsonmayor.co.uk
Fixtures Secretary: Paul Monteith, 5 Bullfinch Close, Oakham, Rutland. LE15 6BS
Tel No: 01572 757021
Club Colours: Green and white hoops, white shorts.
League: London 3 North West

EAST GRINSTEAD RFC
Ground Address: Saint Hill Green, East Grinstead, West Sussex. RH19 4JU   Tel: 01342 322338
Website: www.egrfc.co.uk
Brief Directions: On Minor Road to Horsted Keynes off B2110 Turners Hill Road
Club Secretary: Bob Russell, 1 ose Cottages, Plaistow,Street, Lingfield, Surrey.RH7 6AU
Tel No: 01342 834648
Fixtures Secretary: Mrs Nikki Ward,46 Hackenden Close, East Grinstead, West Sussex. RH19 3DS
Tel No: 01342 322701
Club Colours: White with varied blue hoops.
League: London 3 South East

EAST LONDON RUFC
Ground Address: Holland Road, West Ham, London. E15 3BP   Tel: 0171 476 5526
Brief Directions: From Canning Town roundabout proceed down Manor Road, turn right before West Ham tube station follow road round and turn right at Holland Road
Club Secretary: Ian Bessant, 111Croydon Road, Plaistow, London E13 8EP
Tel: (H) 0171 474 3770 (W) 0171 9767213
Fixtures Secretary: Rob Williams
Tel: (H) 0181 558 8651 (W) 0181 5563322
Club Colours: Maroon and navy hoops
League: Eastern Counties 2 South

EASTBOURNE RFC
Ground Address: Park Avenue, Hampden Park, Eastbourne, East Sussex. BN22 9QN
Tel: 01323 503076
Website: www.eastbournerugby.co.uk
Brief Directions: 500yds north of Eastbourne District General Hospital, clearly signposted.
Club Secretary: Peter B Lloyd, 51 Burton Road, Eastbourne, East Sussex. BN21 2RF
Tel No: 01323 723905
Email: pblloyd@tinyworld.co.uk
Fixtures Secretary: Charlie Wise, 128 Wannock Road, Lower Willington, East Sussex BN20 0DB
Tel No: 01323 482435
Club Colours: Navy blue with gold hoops.
League: London 4 South East

EASTLEIGH RFC
Ground Address: Bishopstoke Pavilion, Bishopstoke Road, Eastleigh

Tel: 023 80641312
Brief Directions: From Eastleigh Railway Station take turning over railway bridge to Fair Oak and ground is approx 600 yards up on the left
Club Secretary: Mark Jones, 71 St Ronans Road, Southsea, Portsmouth PO4 0PP
Tel No: 02392 715069
Fixtures Secretary: Dr J .S. Sneezum, Bursledon Lodge, Salterns Lane, Old Bursledon, Southampton, SO31 8DH.   Tel: (H) 023 80402286
Club Colours: Black with Red and amber hoops
League: Hampshire 2

ECONOMICALS RUFC
Ground Address: LSE Sports Ground, Windsor Avenue, New Malden, Surrey
Tel: 020 8942 1229
Brief Directions: A3 southbound, right at New Malden roundabout, 3rd left into Presbury Rd leads into Windsor Ave. A3 north, left into South Lane, 2nd left Thetford Rd leads into Windsor Ave
Club Secretary: Steve Bowen, 60 South Eden Park Road, Beckenham, Kent, BR3 3BG
Tel: 020 87762953
Fixtures Secretary: Steve Bowen
Tel: (H) 020 87762953
Club Colours: Black with a Green and Gold Band
League: Surrey 3

EDENBRIDGE RFC
Ground Address: The Pavilion, Lingfield Road Recreation Ground, Lingfield Road, Edenbridge, Kent. TN8   Tel: 01732 862435
Brief Directions: From Edenbridge High Street travelling south, turn right into Stangrove Road, left into Crouch House Road, right into Lingfield Road.
Club Secretary: Nick Martin, Little Acre, Swan Lane, Edenbridge TN8 6AJ
Tel No: 01732 86271
Fixtures Secretary: John Martin, Little Acre, Swan Lane, Edenbridge, Kent, TN8 6AJ.
Tel: (H) 01732 862761
Club Colours: Black and yellow hoops
League: Kent 3

EFFINGHAM & LEATHERHEAD RFC
Ground Address: King George V Playing Fields, Browns Lane, Effingham, Surrey, KT24 5ND
Tel: 07070 704136.
E-mail: www.eaglesrugby.co.uk.
Brief Directions: M25 J.10. Effingham signpost left on slip road south bound from M25 to A3, follow road until Lord Howard pub on R. go R. then L. forward until lights, then L. and 1st L.
Club Secretary: Robin Page, 20 Southfields Road, london SW18 1QN
Tel Nos: 0208 877 1428 (H) 0207 665 0942 (W)
Email: robin.page@vizold.co.uk
Fixtures Secretary: Ed Newton, 42 Milner Road, Kingston upon Thames, Surrey, KT1 2AU.
Tel: 0181 549 8213 (H) - 0171 6283700 (W)
Club Colours: Emerald green and amber hoops
League: London 2 South

EGHAM RFC
Ground Address: Sports Field, Kings Lane, Englefield Green, Surrey TW20

Tel: 01784 43298
Website: www.72-dpi.co.ukeghamrfc
Brief Directions: From A30 into Englefield Green.
St. Judes Road, left at R/about to Bond Street to
Kings Lane, club on left.
Club Secretary: Roger B. W. Hayes. 7 Albert Road,
Englefield Green, Surrey, TW20 0RQ.
Tel: 01784 431299
Fixtures Secretary: Tim Richards.
Tel Nos: 01784 439880 (H) 07710 126629 (M)
Club Colours: Mid blue with gold hoop
League: Surrey 3

ELLINGHAM & RINGWOOD RFC
Ground Address: Picket Post, Ringwood, Hants
Tel: 01425 476668
Brief Directions: On A31 eastbound after leaving
Ringwood behindShell garage next to Burley turning.
Club Secretary: Steve Benson, 50 Linbrook Drive,
Ringwood, Hampshire BH24 3LT Tel: 01425 474991
Email: bensonx4@talk21.com
Fixtures Secretary: P{eter Carlett, 18 Parsonage
Barn Lane, Ringwood, Hampshire. BH24 1PX
Tel No: 01425 476691
Club Colours: Navy blue with amber hoop
League: Hampshire 3

ELY RUFC
Ground Address: Downham Road Playing Fields,
Ely, Cambs   Tel: 01353 662363
Website: elyrufc.co.uk/index.html
Brief Directions: Just North of Ely. L.H.S. of A10
bypass signed Downham Market, King's Lynn.
Club Secretary: Christopher Ormerod, 14, Ponts
Hill, Littleport, Cambs.
Tel/FAX: 01353 863425 Mobile: 07767 248056
Fixtures Secretary: Martin Hammond, Hillcrest
House, 110 Bexwell Road, Downham Market,
Norfolk, PE38 9LH
Tel: (H) 01366 384990 Fax: 01366 385739
Club Colours: Gold and black hoops, black shorts
League: Eastern Counties 1

ENFIELD IGNATIANS RFC
Ground Address: Enfield Playing Fields, Queen
Elisabeth Stadium, Donkey Lane, Off Carterhatch
Lane, Enfield, Middlesex
Tel: 020 8363 2877
Brief Directions: M25 J25 south on A10 to
Carterhatch Lane, turn right, immediately left into
Donkey Lane. From A406 north on A10 to
Carterhatch Lane, turn left.
Club Secretary: Glyn Jones, 45 Halifax Road,
Enfield, Middlesex, EN2 0PR.
Tel: (H) 020 8366 3207 (W) 020 8379 3563
Fixtures Secretary: Phil Beschizza, 61 Munster
Gardens, London, N13 5DO.
Tel: 020 8807 3887H - 01483 882497W
Club Colours: Blue and gold
League: Hertfordshire & Middlesex 1

ERITH RFC
Ground Address: Northumberland Heath Playing
Fields, Sussex Road, Erith, Kent
Tel: 01322 432295
Website: www.erithrfc.co.uk
Brief Directions: A2 towards London, Black Prince

turn off towards Erith, turn left into Brook St and left
into Sussex Road
Club Secretary: David Hi;ll,31 Halt Robin Road,
Belvedere, Kent DA17 6DN
Tel No: 01322 432342
Email:buzz@dave-hill.fsnet.co.uk
Fixtures Secretary: Chris McGurk, 13 Winifred
Road, Erith, Kent, DA8 2AJ.
Tel: 01322 447673 - E-mail;
chris@chrismcgurk.idps.co.uk
Club Colours: Light and dark blue hoops, blue
shorts
League: Kent 1

ESSO (FAWLEY) RFC
Ground Address: Esso Recreation Ground, 179-
181 Long Lane, Holbury, Southampton, SO45 1PA.
Tel: 023 0889 3750
Website: www.fawleyrfc.co.uk
Brief Directions: From M27 J2 (271)) follow A326 to
Fawley for approx 8 miles. Ground on right after
Hardley Roundabout.
Club Secretary: David Blackmore, 4 Valley Close,
Blackfield, Southampton SO45 1WU
Tel: 023 8024 3550
Email: secretary@ fawleyrfc.co.uk
Fixtures Secretary: Ray Lewis, 2 Sherwood Way,
Blackfield, Southampton. SO45 1ZQ
Tel: 023 8089 8391
Club Colours: Scarlet shirts and socks, blue shorts,
League: Hampshire 1

ETON MANOR RFC
Ground Address: The New Wilderness, Wanstead
Sports Gnd, Nutter Lane, Wanstead, London E11 2BA
Tel: 0208 532 2946
Website: www.eton manor.net
Brief Directions: From north A12-eastern Ave.right
into Wanstead High St.. Rt into Grove Park, rt in to
Avenue and rt again into Leicester Rd. Left to end of
Ritter Lane
Club Secretary: Roy Morris, waterside, 242 Broad
Rd., Bocking, Essex. CM7 5NJ
Tel: 01376 344599
Fixtures Secretary: Streve Kemp, 1 Wordsworth
Close, Romford, Essex.RM3 7PD
Tel: 01708 375652
Club Colours: Dark blue with light blue hoops
League: London 4 North East

FAREHAM HEATHENS RFC
Ground Address: Cams Alders Sports Centre,
Highfield Avenue, Fareham   Tel: 01329 221793
Brief Directions: From Fareham centre A27 west
signed S'hampton, at Fire station r'about, stay on
A27 for 100m, right at lights Redlands Lane, right at
next junction by pub/church, Sports Centre next left
Club Secretary: C.R .Townsend, 41 North Lane,
Burton Petersfield GU31 5RS
Tel: (H) 0147300 269390
E-mail: dirobdaisy@yahoo.co.uk
Fixtures Secretary: Pete Mitchell, 2 Chilworth
Gardens, Clanfield, Portsmouth, PO8 0LD.
Tel: 01705 348744 E-mail:
peter.mitchell2@virgin.net
Club Colours: Red and black quarters
League: Hampshire 1

FARNBOROUGH RUFC
Ground Address: Tile Barn Close, Farnborough, Hampshire. GU14 8LS   Tel: 01252 542750
Brief Directions: M25 J4, follow road signs to A325 Farnborough, follow signs to Rugby Club
Club Secretary: Paul L. Davies, 33 Wentworth Crescent, Ash Vale, Aldershot, Hants., GU12 5LE
Tel No: 07831 196927
Email: paul.davies47 @ntlworld.com
Fixtures Secretary: Barry Mackay, 43 The Grove, Farnborough, GU14 6QS   Tel: 01252 512363H
Club Colours: Dark and light blue hoops
League: London 4 South West

FARNHAM RUFC
Ground Address: Westfield Lane, Wrecclesham, Farnham, Surrey. GU10 4QP Tel: 01252 721138
Brief Directions: Take A325 to Petersfield from A31 Farnham bypass, after 0.75 mile pass Bear & Ragged Staff pub on right turn next right into Riverdale, 1st left onto recreation ground
Club Secretary: Derek R Wall, 22 Hope Lane, Farnham, Surrey. GU9 0HZ Tel: (H) 01252 710476
Fixtures Secretary: Bob Smith, 21 Riverside Close, Farnborough, Hants GU14 8Q5.
Tel: 01252 650719 (H) 01256 484185(W)
Club Colours: Black & yellow with one white hoop
League: London 4 South West

FAVERSHAM RUFC
Ground Address: The Lodge, Recreation Ground, Whitstable Road, Faversham, Kent. ME13 8HA
Tel: 01795 590593
Brief Directions: From M2 J.6 take A251 north to Faversham at T/Jct turn right onto A2. Take 4th turn left into Love Lane, just after shell petrol station. follow Love Lane into Whitstable Road, take 2nd turn left Park Road (approx .75 mile from A2). Car park and changing rooms at end on left.
Club Secretary: Julie Padfield,80 St Mary's Road, Faversham, Kent ME13 8EH   Tel: 01795 532678
Fixtures Secretary: Dave Suter, 7 Forbes Road, Faversham, Kent, ME13 8QF.   Tel: 01795 536504
Club Colours: Sky blue and white quarters
League: Kent 3

FELTHAM RFC
Ground Address: Park Road, Hanworth, Middlesex
Tel: 0181 894 3609
Brief Directions: Off Hounslow Road, Hanworth adjacent to A316 (Chertsey Road)
Club Secretary: Keith Tullett, 9 Hall Road, Isleworth, Middlesex. TYW7 7PJ   Tel No: 0208 568 0543
Fixtures Secretary: Phil Walker, 27 Shaftsbury Avenue, Norwood Green, Middlesex. UB2 4HH
Tel No: 0208 574 1347
Club Colours: Dark blue, light blue and gold
League: Hertfordshire & Middlesex 1

FINCHLEY RFC
Ground Address: Summers Lane, Finchley, London. N12 0PD   Tel: 020 8445 3746
Website: finchleyrfc.co.uk
Brief Directions: From North Circular Rd (A406) take A1000 (High Road Finchley), to Summers Lane.

Club Secretary: J.Ottley, 1 Orchard Court, Clifford Road, New Barnet EN5 5PQ
Tel: 0208 441 6636 (H) 0207 218 1863 (W)
Fixtures Secretary: Pat O'Donohue, 33 Ladbroke Road, Bush Hill Park, Enfield, Middlesex. EN1 1HU
Tel Nos: 020 8292 7801 (H) 01708 716133 (W)
Club Colours: Scarlet and white 55mm hoops
League: London 3 North West

FLEET RUFC
Ground Address: Southwood Sports Ground,Southwood, Farnborough, Hants.
Website: www.fleet.rugbyclub.org.uk
Brief Directions: Leave M3 at junction4A follow signs for Farnborough Sports Ground opposite Nokia entrance via Kennels Lane.
Club Secretary: Merrik Knight, 31 Osborne Road, Farnborough, Hants. GU14 6AE
Tel No: 01252 654818   Email: merrikpih2aol.com
Fixtures Secretary: Lauren Btcheldor, Twisell Thorne, Church Crookham, Fleet GU13 0YT
Tel: 01252 623701
Club Colours: Red ,white and blue.
League: Hampshire 2

FOLKESTONE RFC
Ground Address: New Burlington Field, Bargrove, Newington, Folkestone, Kent. CT18 8BH
Tel : (H) 01303 266887
Website: folkestonerugby.co.uk
Brief Directions: Take the Hythe Road (B2065) from the A20 (Ashford to Folkestone Road), 1 m on left. From London M20 Exit J12 (Cheriton).Follow A20 for 1m then B2065 to Hythe.1/4m on Rt.
Club Secretary: Barry Keating, Thornhill Farm,Stowting Common, Nr Asjhford,Kent
Tel: (H) 01233 750170 - (W) 01303 850206
Email: bgk@weh.co.uk
Fixtures Secretary: A D Ruddock,40 Langdon Road, Cheriton, Folkestone. CT19 4HY
Tel: (H) 01303 276530
Club Colours: Green and white hooped shirts
League: London 4 South East

FOOTSCRAY RUFC
Ground Address: 239A Foots Cray Road, New Eltham, London. SE9 2EL
Brief Directions: Please contact Fixture Secretary
Club Secretary: Sue Ward, 56 Blendon Road,Bexley, Kent. DA5 1BS
Tel: (H) 020 8303 8204
e-mail: rward@innbusiness.co.uk
Fixtures Secretary: Tony Codd, 74 Felthampton Road, New Eltham, London SE9 3NX
Tel: (H) 0181 857 6040
Club Colours: Royal Blue and gold hoops
League: Kent 3

FORDINGBRIDGE RFC
Ground Address: The Recreation Ground, Fordingbridge, Hants   Tel: 01425 652047
Brief Directions: Off A338 (12 miles south of Salisbury and 8 miles north of Ringwood) alongside by- pass, western side adjacent to River Avon.

Club Secretary: Mr K.A.Young, 1 Elmwood Avenue, Fordingbridge, Hants. SP6 1DL
Tel No: 01425 652681
Email: kenalf.rosewood@virgin.net
Fixtures Secretary: John Trim, Trees, Fryern Court Road, Fordingbridge, Hants SP6 1NG
Tel: (H) 01425 655156 (W) 01202 664781
Club Colours: Sky blue with black shorts
League: Hampshire 2

FULLERIANS RFC
Ground Address: Watford Grammar School, New Field, Coningesby Drive (end of Parkside Dr), Watford, Herts Tel : 01923 237974
Website: fullerians.com
Brief Directions: From Hunton Bridge Roundabout on A41 (J19 M25) follow Hempstead Rd towards Watford town centre. Turn rt.at lights into Langley Way then turn right at end into Coningesby Drive
Club Secretary: Chris Windsor, 11 Nascot Road, Watford, Herts WD1 3RD
Tel: (H) 01923 442355 (W) 020 7943 6169
e-mail; cwindsor@fosterandpartners.com
Fixtures Secretary: NickThomas, 11 Ashridge Close, Bovingdon, Herts. Hp3 0QG
Tel: 01442 831 386(H) 07970 499452 (M) 02074308300 W)
e-mail: nickthomas99@hotmail.com
Club Colours: Red, green and black hooped shirts
League: London 4 North West

GILLINGHAM ANCHORIANS RFC
Ground Address: Watling Street Playing Fields, off Darland Avenue, Gillingham, Kent
Tel: 01634 851495
Brief Directions: Leave M2 by A278, turn left at terminal roundabout (signed A2 Gillingham), across new roundabout, left at 2nd traffic lights at Darland Ave, ground 200 yards on left
Club Secretary: Michael Niven, 62 Trevale Road, Rochester, Kent ME1 3PE
Tel No: 01634 310549
Email: niven-michael/Pyahoo,co.uk
Fixtures Secretary: Doug Chidley, 67 Parkfield Road, Rainham, Gillingham, Kent ME8 7TA
Tel: (H) 01634 376891
Club Colours: Purple, black and white hoops
League: Kent 1

GOSPORT AND FAREHAM RFC
Ground Address: Gosport Park, Dolphin Crescent, Gosport, Hants. PO12 2HE
Tel: 023 9258 9852
Brief Directions: M27 J11, A32 Gosport at dble r'bout, left at 2nd r'bout, past HMS Sultan left at r'bout, r.h. lane after Kellys Hotel & immediate left, 5th right (Molesworth Rd), turn right & left over bridge
Club Secretary: Iain R. Rackham, 265 Hawthorn Crescent, Cosham ,Portsmouth PO6 2TL Tel: 023 9279 6625 - Email: iainrack@cwcom.net
Fixtures Secretary: Peter Tomlinson, 18 Freemantle Road, Gosport, Hants., PO12 4RD.
Tel: (H) 023 9261 7673
Club Colours: Royal blue and old gold. Change Red
League: London 2 South

GRASSHOPPERS RFC
Ground Address: Macfarlane Sports Field, Macfarlane Lane, off Syon Lane, Middlesex.
Tel: 0181 568 0010
Brief Directions: Train: to Syon stn, lft out of stn to major Xroads, straight on across Gt Wst Rd (A4), ground 0.5 mile on right after Tescos. Road: Frm L'don on A4, rt into Syon Ln at Gillette Cnr
Club Secretary: Mr. A Dean, 29 Albert Road, Twickenham, Middlesex TW1 4HU
Fixtures Secretary: Andy Brown
Tel: (H) 0181 560 4844 (W) 0181 560 2583
Club Colours: Green, gold and black hoops, black shorts and socks
League: London 4 North West

GRAVESEND RFC
Ground Address: The Rectory Field, Milton Road, Gravesend, Kent. DA12 2PP
Tel: 01474 534840
Brief Directions: M25 A2 intersection, head towards Dover, leave A2 at Gravesend East (Valley Drive), follow 1.75 mile to end, right at roundabout, 1st left, ground 0.75 miles on left
Club Secretary: John Moore, 375A Singlewell Road, Gravesend, Kent. DA11 7RL
Tel: (H) 01474 362998
Fixtures Secretary: Bobby Wright
Tel: (H) 01474 327303
Club Colours: Four inch black and white hoops
League: London 2 South

GREAT WESTERN RAILWAY RFC
Ground Address: G. W. Railway (London) RFC, Castle Bar Park, Vallis Way, West Ealing W13.
Tel : 0181 998 7928
Brief Directions: By train to Ealing Broadway, then to Castle Bar Park Halt via E1, E2 or E9 buses.
Club Secretary: Peter Allsop, 41 Lyncroft Avenue, Pinner, Middlesex HA5 1JU.
Tel : (H) 0181 866 0532
Fixtures Secretary: Roy Sullivan, Tel: (H) 0181 575 6074
Club Colours: Cardinal and black jerseys.
League: Hertfordshire & Middlesex 4 South

GREENWICH RFC
Ground Address: The Pavilion, Old Mill Road, Plumstead, London SE18.
Tel : 020 8854 8637
Brief Directions: Off Plumstead Common opposite Old Mill public house.
Club Secretary: Nick Wallden,277 Wickham Lane, Abbey Wood, London SE2 0NX
Tel: 020 8854 0092
Fixtures Secretary: George Dorton, 119 Rangefield Road, Bromley, Kent, BR1 4RG.
Tel: 020 8854 0092
Club Colours: Red and black quarters, black shorts.
League: Kent 3

GUERNSEY RUFC
Ground Address: Footes Lane, St Peter Port, Guernsey
Tel: 01481 254590
Brief Directions: Centre of the Island , 1/2 mile from airport.
Club Secretary: B J Mildon, P O Box 181, St Peter Port, Guernsey
Tel: (H) 01481 265493 (W) 01481 715055
Fixtures Secretary: Greg Ahme, La Chanson, Route de L'Ancresse, Vale, Guernsey.
Tel: 01481 45090
Club Colours: Green and white
League: Hampshire 1

GUILDFORD & GODALMING RFC
Ground Address: Broadwater, Guildford Road (A3100), Godalming, Surrey. GU7 3BU.
Tel : 01483 416199/424900
Web Site: http://www.ggrugby.co.uk
Brief Directions: A3100 from Guildford centre to Godalming - beside Broadwater lake, 1 mile before Godalming for A3 by-passing Guildford: B3000 thro' Compton - 3 miles - T junction - right to Godalming - 300 yards on right.
Club Secretary: David Gambold, 10 Treebys Avenue, Jacobs Well, Guildford, Surrey. GU4 7NT e-mail: jacobswell.fsnet.co.uk
Tel: 01483 566304 (H) 01483 565771 (B) 01483 300168 (Fax)
Fixtures Secretary: Len Bodill, 4 Orchard Road, Burpham, Guildford, Surrey. Tel: 01483 570580 (H)
Club Colours: Green and white bands
League: London 2 South
League Contact: Tony Parker, Hatch Cottage, Rock Hill, Hambledon, Surrey GU8 4DT.
Tel: 01428 683577

GUY'S & ST. THOMAS' HOSPITALS RFC
Ground Address: Honor Oak Park, London. SE23 1NW
Tel: 020 8690 1612
Brief Directions: South Circular A205 onto B218 (Brockley Rise), crossroads B238 turn right 200 yards club on right
Club Secretary: Mr. J.G. Combes, Dept. of Oral Medicine & Pathology, Floor 28, Guy's Hospital, London, SE1 9RT. - Tel: 0973 22239
Email: jgcombes@aol.com
Fixtures Secretary: Mr. T. Nedas, 35 Sutherland Walk, London, SE17 3EF.
Tel: 020 7701 0426 - Tmail: timothy.nedas@kcl.ac.uk
Club Colours: Navy Blue and gold 4" hoops
League: London 4 South East

HAC (HONOURABLE ARTILLERY COMPANY) RFC
Ground Address: Artillery Ground, Armoury House, City Road, London. EC1Y 2BQ. Tel: 0171 606 4644
Brief Directions: Metropolitan/Northern & Circle lines to Moorgate station, proceed north, towards Finsbury Square on City Road, entrance to Artillery ground 200m on left
Club Secretary: John Bennett, Coram Street Farm, Hadleigh, Suffolk, IP7 5NR. Tel: 01473 823761
Email: john.bennett@whi.sbjs.co.uk
Fixtures Secretary: Colin Pritchard, 31 Bedford Avenue, Little Chalfont, Buckinghamshire. HP6 6PS

Tel: (H) 01494 76 2982 (W) 0171 439 1791
Club Colours: Maroon/Dark Blue Hoops
League: Hertfordshire & Middlesex 2

HACKNEY RFC
Ground Address: Spring Hill, Stamford Hill, London. E5   Tel: 0181 806 5289
Club Secretary: David Clarke, 31 Cowley Road, Wanstead, London. E11 2HA
Tel: (H) 020 8926 2310 - Email: david@richard-johnclarke.com
Fixtures Secretary: George Noga , 11 Hookstone Way, Woodford Green, Essex IG8 7LF
Tel: (H) 020 8304 2577 (W) 020 8985 2349
Club Colours: Green, blue, yellow and light blue quarters
League: Hertfordshire & Middlesex 4 North

HADLEIGH RUFC
Ground Address: Layham Road Sports Ground, Hadleigh, Ipswich, Suffolk. IP7 5NE
Tel: 01473 823231
Brief Directions: From Hadleigh High St turn into Layham Rd (flanked by library and chemist), over bridge and go on round bends, ground is on the left
Club Secretary: Jane Stannard, 21 Kersey Close, Stowmarket, Suffolk IP14 2BG Tel: 01449 774960
Fixtures Secretary: Nick Bray, 28 Wheatfields, Whatfield, Ipswich, Suffolk. IP7 6RB
Tel No: 01473 823661
Club Colours: Maroon and gold
League: London 3 North East

HAMBLE
Ground Address: Hamble School, Satchell Lane, Hamble, Southampton
E-mail: www.hamb le.rugby@btinternet.co.uk
Brief Directions: Take Jct 8 off M27, Satchell Lane is a left off Hamble lane Approx. 2 miles from jct 8
Club Secretary: Helen Adams, 48 Woolwich Close, Bursledon, Southampton. SO331 8GE Tel No: 023 8040 6465
Email: helen@antlerhomes.ukf.net
Fixtures Secretary: Gary Camfield
Tel : 0238 0437664
Club Colours: Navy & skyblue,with navy,sky and white hoops
League: Hampshire 1

HAMMERSMITH & FULHAM RFC
Ground Address: Hurlingham Park, Hurlingham Road, London. SW6
Tel: 0171 736 5186
Website:www.hfrfc.co.uk
Brief Directions: From Putney Bridge (southside) turn right into New Kings Rd (A308) and right again under rail bridge into Hurlingham Rd, Hurlingham Park is 300m on right
Club Secretary: Chris Cuthbertson, 17 Wheatsheaf Lane, London. SW6 6LS
Tel: (H) 0171 381 5064
Email: chriscuthbertson@hotmail.com
Fixtures Secretary: Lyndon Walters
Tel: (H) 0171 790 1233
Club Colours: Red with navy and white bands
League: Hertfordshire & Middlesex 2

HAMPSTEAD RFC
Ground Address: Hampstead Heath Extension, Hampstead Way, London. NW11
Tel: 020 8458 4548
Brief Directions: North Circular to Finchley Road left into willifield Way. Cross Meadway, enter Hampstead Way. Ground on left
Club Secretary: Mark Spilsbury, 39 Langbourne Avenue, Holly Lodge, Highgate, London N6 6PS
Tel No: 020 8347 7178 - Email: spilsresearch@aol.com
Fixtures Secretary: Ian Everett, 44 Lodge Lane, Prestwood, Bucks, HP16 0QG.
Tel: 07970 884025 - Email: everett@barclays.net
Club Colours: Maroon and gold halves separated by a white band
League: London 4 North West

HARINGEY RFC
Ground Address: New River Sports Centre, White Hart Lane, Wood Green. N22 5QW
Brief Directions: By tube to Wood Green, then W3 bus to White Hart Lane. By road: New River Sports Centre is positioned towards the Wood Green end of White Hart Lane
Club Secretary: Peter A. Wilson, 13 Chambers Gardens, East Finchley, London N2 9AL
Tel: (H) 0181 883 7974
Fixtures Secretary: Jimmy Smith,Flat 1, 69 Cadogan Terrace, Hackney, London E95HP
Tel: 0208 9854114 (H) 0207 202 4185(W)
Club Colours: Green, scarlet and white
League: Hertfordshire & Middlesex 2

HARPENDEN RFC
Ground Address: Redbourn Lane, Harpenden, Herts. AL5 2BA
Tel: 01582 460711
Brief Directions: Take B487 off A1081 (was A6) on south side of Harpenden Ground is 400 metres past entrance to Golf Club
Club Secretary: Andy Bianchi, 9 Regent St., Dunstable, Beds. LV6 1LP   Tel: 01582 615708
Email: gandy.bianchi@ntlworld.com
Fixtures Secretary: Paul Thompson, 7 Kirkdale Road, Harpenden, Herts AL5 2PT
Tel: (H) -01582 622103 (W) 07771 530756
Club Colours: All black with white trim
League: London 3 North West

HARROW RFC
Ground Address: Grove Field, Wood Lane, Stanmore, Middlesex. HA7 4LF.
Tel: 020 8954 2615
Brief Directions: From A41, take A5 signed Edgware (Brockley Hill). Turn Right into wood Lane (Past Orthopaedic Hospital). Ground 400m on Right - Junction with Warren Lane.
Club Secretary: Hannah Wyatt, 25 Tylersfield, Abbots Langfield,Herts. WD5 OPS
Tel: 01923 494068- Email: harrowrfc@hotmail.com
Fixtures Secretary: Chris Green, 26 Anmersh Grove, Stanmore, Middlesex, HA7 1PA
Tel: 020 8537 9544
Club Colours: Navy blue with white hoops
League: London 4 North West

HARWICH AND DOVERCOURT RUFC
Ground Address: Swimming Pool Road, Wick Lane, Dovercourt, Harwich, Essex. CO12 3TS
Tel: 01255 240225
Brief Directions: A120 to Ramsey roundabout, 3rd exit, right at War Memorial into Fronks Rd, 2nd right into Hall Lane, left into Wick Lane, right towards swimming pool, clubhouse past pool
Club Secretary: Keiran Coyles, 4 Acorn Close, Dovercourt, Harwich, Essex. CO12 4XF
Tel: (H) 01255 504432 (W) 01255 224822
Fixtures Secretary: Barry Male, 28 Maves Lane, Dovercourt, Harwich, Essex
Tel: (H) 01255 886165 (W) 01255 244813
Club Colours: Black shirts with one white hoop, black shorts, black socks with white top
League: Eastern Counties 2 North

HASLEMERE RUFC
Ground Address: The Pavilion, Woolmer Hill Sports Ground, Haslemere, Surrey GU27 1QA
Tel: 01428 643072
Brief Directions: Off A3 turn down Sandy Lane at Bramshott Chase towards Hammer Vale, turn left to Woolmer Hill and then left to Woolmer Hill Sports Ground and school
Club Secretary: Martin Coakley, 3 St Mary's Terrace, Mill Lane, Guildford, Surry GU7 3T2
Tel: 01483 562434 Fax: 01483 562433
Fixtures Secretary: R,Davies ,6 Heath Rd., Hammor, Haslemere,Surrey GV27 3
Tel: 01428 641390. e-mail: big.billy@tesco.net
Club Colours: Light blue and white hoops
League: Surrey 2

HASTINGS AND BEXHILL RFC
Ground Address: William Parker School Site, Park Avenue, hastings, East Sussex.
Tel : 01424 444255
Brief Directions: Take London road out of Hastings town centre and then into St Helens Road adjacent to Alexander Park and follow signs to Rugby Club.
Club Secretary: Len.Bolton.180 Harrow Road, St Leonards on-Sea, East Sussex TN 34 2JW. Tel No: 01424 755612
e-mail: elbow@totalise.co.uk
Fixtures Secretary: Ken Nichols, 189 St. Helens Road, Hastings, East Sussex TN34 2EA. Tel: 01424 423614
Club Colours: Blue and white hoops.
League: Sussex 1

HATFIELD RFC
Ground Address: Roe Hill Sports Ground, Briars Lane, Hatfield, Hertfordshire
Tel: 01707 269814
Brief Directions: Take exit for Briars Lane from roundabout by swimming pool and Asda in town centre. Up hill 1st left and ground is on the right.
Club Secretary: Robin Nicholson, 18 Brocket Road, Welwyn Garden City, Herts. AL8 7TY
Tel No: 01707 258372
Fixtures Secretary: Graham Waddingham, 9 Stable Mews, Brookmans Park, Herts, AL9 6NX
Tel: (H) 01707 663659 (W) 01707 666013
Club Colours: Green, white, brown and gold
League: Hertfordshire & Middlesex 3 North

HAVERHILL & DISTRICT RFC
Ground Address: Castle Pavillion, School Lane, Haverhill, Suffolk. CB9 9DE
Tel: 01440 702871
Website: www.haverhillrugbyclub.com
Brief Directions: From Haverhill bypass. take the R/about exit signed Clements Estate. Take 2nd left up School Lane. Map & details on website.
Club Secretary: Ian Stewart, 7 Minster Road, Haverhill, Suffolk, CB9 0DR.
Tel: (H) 01440 706076. Email: stewarts@cwcom.net
Fixtures Secretary: Gordon Anderson, 2 Arundel Walk, Haverhill, Suffolk, CB9 9BE.
Tel: 01440 763555
Club Colours: Maroon with Blue Banding
League: Eastern Counties 2 North

HAYES RFC
Ground Address: Grosvenor Playing Fields, Kingshill Avenue, Hayes, Middlesex
Tel: 020 8845 4963
Brief Directions: From A40, off at "Target" R/about head south, at next R/about (White Hart) take Yeading Lane, at 1st major set of lights turn right into Kingshill Ave, ground is 1 mile on right
Club Secretary: Neil Fretwell, 15 Sandgate House, QueensWalk,Ealing, London, W5 1TN. Tel: 07956 304909 Email: fretwellneil@aol.com
Fixtures Secretary: Neil Fretwell - as above
Tel: 0956 304909
Club Colours: Navy blue and yellow quarters
League: Hertfordshire & Middlesex 4 South

HEATHFIELD & WALDRON RFC
Ground Address: Hardy Roberts Recreation Ground, Cross in Hand, Heathfield, East Sussex
Tel: 01435 868747
Website: www.hwrfc.co.fc
Brief Directions: Adjacent to Cross in Hand public house in centre of village opposite Esso garage
Club Secretary: Peter R Mercer, `Mapsedge', Cross in Hand, Heathfield, East Sussex. TN21 0TA. Tel: 01435 863396 (Tel/Fax)
Email: mercer@mapsedge.fsnet.co.uk
Fixtures Secretary: John Murphy, C/o Club Tel No: 01435 868747
Club Colours: Green and white quarters, green shorts and socks
League: Sussex 1

HELLINGLY RUFC
Ground Address: Hellingly Sports Club, Horsebridge, Hailsham, East Sussex
Brief Directions: Turn east off A22 onto A271, ground half mile on right opposite White Hart pub and before Kings Head.
Club Secretary: Peter Stotesbury, Sunnyside, Marshfoot Lane, Hailsham, East Sussex. BN27 2RB. Tel: (H) 01323 843835
Email: peter.stotesbury@lineone.net
Fixtures Secretary: Jim Bedford, 3 Goodwin Close, Hailsham, East Sussex, BN27 3DE
Tel: 01323 845660
Club Colours: Black and Amber
League: Sussex 1

HEMEL HEMPSTEAD (CAMELOT) RUFC
Ground Address: Club House, Chaulden Lane, Hemel Hempstead, Herts. HP1 2BS.
Tel : 01442 230353
Website: wew.camelot-rfc.co.uk
Brief Directions: Kodak R/about take Station Road exit (left off Kodak Tower) 2nd right into St. Johns Road through Boxmoor Village into Northridge Way, Club 250 yds on left at Chaulden Lane.
Club Secretary: John Clapham, 49 Brook Court, Watling Street, Radlett. WD7 7JA. Tel: 01923 852104
Email: jonathan.clapham@which.net
Fixtures Secretary: Bob Skinner, 137 Fern Drive, Hemel Hempstead, Herts. Tel: 01442 246586
Club Colours: Royal Blue and white quarters
League: London 4 North West
League Contact: Andrew Jackson, 21 Long Chaulden, Hemel Hempstead, HP1 2HT
Tel: 01442 248640

HENDON RFC
Ground Address: Copthall Playing Fields, Great North Way, Hendon. NW4 1PS Tel: 020 8203 1737
Brief Directions: From north - M1 J2, ground 200 yards on left.From A41 take A1 south - ground 800 yards on left.
Club Secretary: T Brownsell, 9 Winscombe Way, Stanmore, Middlesex. HA7 3AX
Tel: (H) 020 8954 7060 FAX: 020 8954 2845
Email: tomann@tbrownsell.freeserve.co.uk
Fixtures Secretary: C Silver, 1 Gyles Park, Stanmore, Middlesex, HA7 3AX
Tel: (H) 020 8952 0806
Club Colours: Green, black and white hoops
League: Hertfordshire & Middlesex 3 North

HERTFORD RFC
Ground Address: Highfields, Hoe Lane, Ware, Herts. SG12 9NZ   Tel: 01920 462975
Brief Directions: Exit A10 at turning for Hertford. Take B1502 from R/about. Take first left into Hoe Lane. Club is first turning on left.
Club Secretary: Nigel Dawes, The Old Rectory, Redgrave Rd., South Lopham, Norfolk IP22 2HL
Tel: 01379 688106 (H) 01379 687789 (F)
Fixtures Secretary: John Atkinson, 86 Winterscroft Road, Hoddesdon, Herts. EN11 8RJ
Tel: (H) 01992 462206
Club Colours: Black, royal blue and gold
League: London 2 North

HITCHIN RFC
Ground Address: King George V Recreation Ground, Old Hale Way, Hitchin, Herts
Tel: 01462 43267   Website: www. hitchinrfc.com
Brief Directions: At Angel Reply pub turn into Bearton Road, take 2nd left into Old Hale Way, turn into ground by phone box
Club Secretary: G Morgan, 209 Cambridge Road, Hitchin, Herts. SG4 0JP
Tel: (H) 01462 635197 (W)01462 444633
Fixtures Secretary: Roger Hood., 1 Tithe Close, Codicote , Hitchin,Herts. SG4 8UX
Tel No: 01438 820534
Club Colours: Maroon and white shirts, white shorts, maroon socks.
League: Hertfordshire & Middlesex 2

HOLT RFC
Ground Address: Bridge Road, High Kelling, Holt, Norfolk. NR25 6QT   Tel: 01263 712191
Brief Directions: Take Cromer Road (A148) from Holt, after approx 1.5 miles turn left into Bridge Road (signposted Holt RFC)
Club Secretary: Ken Bessent, 29 Alma Terrace, Norwich, Norfolk, NR3 3EE.   Tel: 01603 662403
Email: sec@holtrfc.freeserve.co.uk
Fixtures Secretary: Ross Haddow, Breck farm, Stody, Melton Constable, Norfolk, NR24 2ER. Tel: 01263 860572 - Email: rossh@farmline.com
Club Colours: All black
League: Eastern Counties 1

HORSHAM RUFC
Ground Address: Coolhurst Ground, Hammer Pond Road, Coolhurst, Horsham, W. Sussex. RH13 6PJ
Tel: 01403 265027
Brief Directions: From centre of Horsham take A251 to Brighton. At St. Leonards Arms pub turn left. Take 2nd right signed Bucks Head and Ground is 600m on left.
Club Secretary: Barry Johnson, 5 Riverside, Storrington, Pulborough, W. Sussex, RM20 4NN
Tel: 01903 744357
Email: johnson.barry@talk21.com
Fixtures Secretary: John Goode, 24 Oakhill Road, Horsham, West Sussex, RH13 5SF. - Tel: 01403 243496
Email: john.goode@abspumps.com
Club Colours: Emerald green and white
League: Sussex 1

HOVE RFC
Ground Address: Hove Park, Goldstone Crescent, Hove, East Sussex.
Tel :01273 505103 Website: www.hoverrfc.com/
Brief Directions: Adjacent to Brighton and Hove FC on A27 Coast Road.
Club Secretary: James Angus, 28 Lyndhurst Road, Hove, Sussex, BN3 6FA. Tel: (H) 01273 726309
Fixtures Secretary: Mike Richardson. T6, Wayside, Westdene, Brighton, BN1 5HL   Tel: 01273 500512
Club Colours: Maroon and sky blue hoops.
League: London 4 South East

HSBC RFC
Ground Address: NSBC Group Sports & Social Club, Lennard Road, Beckenham, Kent, BR3 1QW.
Tel: 020 8778 7784
Brief Directions: Adjoining new Beckenham British Rail Station
Club Secretary: Nick Cosgrave, 29 Magdalen Grove, Orpington, Kent, BR6 9NE.
Tel: 01689 830247
Fixtures Secretary: Derek Smith, 2 Hurst Gardens, Hurstpierpoint, West Sussex, BN6 9ST
Tel: 0850 505722
Club Colours: Red, white & black hoops
League: Kent 2

ILFORD WANDERERS RFC
Ground Address: The Club House, Forest Road, Barkingside, Ilford, Essex. IG6 3HJ. website: www.ilfordrfu.co.uk
Tel: 0208 500 4622

Brief Directions: By road: A12 to Gants Hill r'bout take Cranbrook Rd to Barkingside High St, into Forest Rd at Fulwell Cross R/A Fairlop Oak pub, ground 1 mile left, signposted
Club Secretary: Stev Wavel, 37 Sedley Rise, Loughton, Essex. IG10 1LS
Tel No: 020 8508 0891
Fixtures Secretary: Beiron Rees, 161a Aldborough Road, Seven Kings, Ilford, Essex IG3 8HU
Tel: (H) 0181 5971158
Club Colours: Red, green and white hoops
League: Eastern Counties 2 South

IMPERIAL MEDICALS RFC
Ground Address: Imperial College Athletic Ground, Udney Park Road, Teddington, Middlesex, TW11 1BB.   Tel : 0208 9773100
Brief Directions: Exit Teddington Station into Station Road, Turn right into Cromwell Road. Udney Park Road is third on left.
Club Secretary: Ral Young FRCS, West Middlesex Hospital, Twickenham Road, Isleworth, Middlesex, TW7 6AF Tel:0208 565 5768 (W)
Email: youngral@breathemail.net
Fixtures Secretary: Prof P Sever FRCP, St Mary's Hospital, Praed St. , Paddington, London. W2 1NY.Tel: (W) 020 7886 1117 020 7886 6145 (FAX)
Email: p.sever@ic.ac .uk
Club Colours: Navy blue with a red & yellow astide light blue hoop. Badge Phoenix
League: London 3 North West
League Contact: Justin Vale FRCS, Dept of Urology, St. Mary's Hospital, Praed Street, London, W2 1NY   Tel : 0208 991 2389   Email: jvale@ic.ac.uk

IPSWICH RFC Ltd.
Ground Address: Humber Doucy Lane, Ipswich. IP4 3PZ   Tel: 01473 724072 Fax: 710439
club website: http//member.aol.com
Brief Directions: A12 ToysRus r'bout straight over towards Ipswich at 3rd traffic light garage on L&R Turn L. go over 2 sets lights. 2 r'bouts. Over bridge turn L. at end T.Junction
Club Secretary: Roy T. Bouch, Sunnyside, School Road, Coddenham, IP6   Tel: 01449 760252
Email: roy-boy 45 @ hotmail.com
Fixtures Secretary: Mrs Lisa Greetham
Tel: (H) 01473 724072
e-mail: irufc@aol.com
Club Colours: Black and Amber
League: London 2 North

IPSWICH YM RUFC
Ground Address: The Street, Rushmere, Ipswich, Suffolk   Tel: 01473 713807
Brief Directions: From Colchester Road turn Right/Left into Rushmere Road. Straight across cross road past church on left. Club 50 metres on right.
Club Secretary: Mr R Daniels, 85 Western Avenue, Felixstowe, Suffolk. IP11 9NT
Tel: (H) 01394 283907 (W) 01473 553149
Fixtures Secretary: Mr R Hullis, 2 Godbold Close, Kesgrave, Ipswich IP5 7SE
Tel: (H) 01473 625027 (W) 01473 622701
Club Colours: Amber and Maroon hoops
League: Eastern Counties 2 North

ISLE OF WIGHT RFC
Ground Address: The Clubhouse,
Wootton Recreation Ground, Wootton,
Isle of Wight. PO33 4NQ   Tel: 01983 883240
Brief Directions: Right at the Cedars, Wootton, into
Church Road, left into Footways, left onto Recreation
Ground
Club Secretary: T.B.A.
Fixtures Secretary: Dave Metcalfe,Afton View,
Blackbridge Road, Freshwater, I.o.W. PO409Q
Tel: (H) 01983 755339
Club Colours: Navy, gold hoops
League: Hampshire 2

JERSEY RFC
Ground Address: Ruedes Landes, St Peter,
Jersey, C I. JE3 7BG   Tel: 01534 499929
Brief Directions: Opposite airport
Club Secretary: C.Lynch,3 Ville de L'Eglise, St
Peters, Jersey, Channel Islands, JE3 7AR
Tel: 01534 482304
Fixtures Secretary: Kate Adams, Perry Farm, St
Mary, Jersey, Channel Islands JE3 3EL
Tel: 01534 613072 (W) 01534 484509 (H)
Club Colours: Red shirts, white shorts
League: London 3 South West

K.C.S. OLD BOYS RFC
Ground Address: Arthur Road, Motspur Park, New
Malden, Surrey. KT3 6LX
Tel: 020 8336 2512 Website: kings.org.uk
Brief Directions: 10 mins walk from Motspur Park
station. From A3 at New Malden underpass, south
along A2043, approx 400m left into Motspur Park
(Rd), cto Arthur Rd, 2nd right after level crossing
Club Secretary: Mrs. Trish Tamplin, 69 St. Mary's
Road, Long Ditton, Surrey KT6 5HC
Tel: 020 8398 5228
Fixtures Secretary: Andy Todd
Tel: (H) 020 8942 0048 (W) 0120 8395 3808
Club Colours: Red, blue and old gold hoops
League: Surrey 1
League Contact: As Secretary

KILBURN COSMOS RFC
Ground Address: Brondesbury (Fields) Park, on
Aylestone Avenue, NW6
(Changing facilities at South Ham pstead Cricket
Club, entrance Milverton Road, NW6.
Brief Directions: A40 to Wood Lane. Go towards
Harrow Road.1st Left is Wrothashey Road. Go over
R/about onto All Souls Avenue. Turn Left Sidmouth
Road then Right into Milverton Road.
Club Secretary: Julien Laugenie, 29 Holland Road,
London.NW10 5AH   Tel No: 020 8960 1940
Email: jlll@bloomberg.net
Fixtures Secretary: Owen Sanders, 146 Fleetwood
Road, Willesden, London, NW10.
Tel No: 07958 648917
Club Colours: Black,Gold, Blue & Green Quarters.
League: Hertfordshire & Middlesex 2

KINGS CROSS STEELERS RFC
Ground Address: Holland Road, West Ham,
London, E15 3BP.   Tel: 020 7474 6761
Website:kxrfc.com
Brief Directions: Turn off A13 just before

CanningTown Hyover, turn north on A1011, (Manor
Road), turn right just before West Ham tube station
into Memorial Avenue.
Club Secretary: Chris Galley, 25 Richart House
Drive, Royal Albert Dock, London, E16 3RF. Tel:
0161 499 4994. Email: london@compuserve.com
Fixtures Secretary: Julian Kiely.Tel No: 07960
764789(M) 020 8679 9286 (
Email: julian.kiely@hmce.gov.ukH)
Colours: Irish green & royal blue inverse quarters
League: Eastern Counties 3 South

KINGSCLERE RFC
Ground Address: The Field Gate Centre, Field Gate
Drive, Kingsclere, Newbury, Berkshire.
Tel :01635 298497
Brief Directions: From A339 follow signs to village
centre then follow signs to the Field Gate Centre.
Club Secretary: Chris Smith, 30 Oakfield Close,
Ecchinswell, Newbury, Berkshire.
Tel :(H) 01635 298006
Fixtures Secretary: D.Barton, `The Gables',
Hannington, Basingstoke, Hants.
Tel: 01256 782383
Club Colours: Red and white hoops or All Black
League: Hampshire 2

KINGSTON RFC
Ground Address: King Edward Recreation Ground,
Hook Road, Chessington, Surrey. KT9 1PL
Tel : 0181 397 8385
Brief Directions: Leave A3 at Hook roundabout, fol-
low sign for A243 Chessington, entrance approx 200
yards on the right
Club Secretary: J. Scrimshaw, 66 Drake Road,
Chessington, Surrey, KT9 1LW.
Fixtures Secretary: C. Holden, 14 Bramshott Court,
Southbank, Surbiton. Surrey, KT6 6DD.
Club Colours: Maroon and white hoops, blue shorts
League: Surrey 1

LAKENHAM - HEWETT RFC
Ground Address: Hilltops, Norwich Road,
Swardeston, Norwich, Norfolk
Tel: 01508 578826
Brief Directions: Approach Norwich on the
Southern bypass, leave on the Norwich/Ipswich exit
(A140), head towards Norwich, turn 1st left (B1113),
ground is on right about 1.25 miles
Club Secretary: Gavin Willoughby,2o Blackwell
Avenu,Sprowston, Norwich NR7 8XN
Tel No: 01603 414445
Email: gav.willoughby@hotmail.com
Fixtures Secretary: Bruce Ridgeway
Tel: (H) 01603 897771 (W) 01603 628333 Ext 271
Club Colours: Red shirts & socks, black shorts.
League: Eastern Counties 2 North

LAW SOCIETY RFC
Ground Address: C /O Bevonians RFC, Ballard
Coombe, Robin Hood way , London SW15 3QF Hill,
Wimbledon, London, SW20   Tel: 020 8946 3156
Brief Directions: A3 London bound between Robin
Hood roundabout & New malden
Club Secretary: Peter Watts, 16 Bedford St., Covent
Garden, London WC2E 9HF   Tel: 020 7395 3000
Email: pwatts@wedlakebell.co.uk

Fixtures Secretary: Simon Lee, 57 Upper Culver Road, St. Albans, Herts. AZ1 4EE
Tel: 020 7832 9625W - Email: salee@bridge.com
Club Colours: Purple and Black
League: Surrey 1

LENSBURY RFC
Ground Address: St Mary's Sports Ground, opposite Teddington Studios, Broom Road, Teddington, Middlesex. TW11 9NU
Brief Directions: By rail: Teddington Station, through High St towards River, over traffic lights into Broom Road
Club Secretary: Andy Brampton, 29 Admiralty Way, Teddington, Middlesex. TW11 0NL
Tel: 07768 598896   Email: abrampton@hotmail.com
Fixtures Secretary: Secretary as above.
Club Colours: Black
League: Hertfordshire & Middlesex 1

LETCHWORTH GARDEN CITY RFC
Ground Address: Baldock Road, Letchworth, Herts
Tel: 01462 682554
Brief Directions: Turn off A1 to Letchworth (jct 9), at 2nd R/about turn right on to the A505 towards Baldock. Ground situated behind North Herts Laisure Centre.
Club Secretary: Kevin McMahon,
Whitecroft, 3 Purcell Close, Tewin Wood, Welwyn, Herts., AL6 0NN.   Tel: 01438 798500H
Email: kmcmahon@bma.org.uk
Fixtures Secretary: Dick Cairns, 21 Hitchin Rd., Stevenage, Herts SG1 3BJ   Tel; 01438 355233
Club Colours: Gold and Black
League: London 3 North West

LEWES RFC
Ground Address: Stanley Turner Ground, Kingston Road, Lewes, East Sussex   Tel: 01273 473732
Brief Directions: From railway station take old road to Newhaven, passing Swan Inn on right, cross bypass bridge and entrance is on the left
Club Secretary: Alan Page, 13 Greater Paddock, Ringmer, Lewes, East Sussex. BN8 5LH
Tel : (H) 01273 813419
e.mail: alan@greaterpaddock.demon.co.uk
Fixtures Secretary: Steve Rhodes, 12 Harrow Close, Seaford BN25 3PE
Tel: (H) 01323 492462
Club Colours: Blue and white hoops
League: London 3 South East

LIGHTWATER RFC
Ground Address: The Sports Centre, The Avenue, Lightwater, Surrey. GU18 5RQ
Tel: 01276 472664
Brief Directions: Take Junction 3 off M3 towards Guildford. turn right 100yds down A322 into Lightwater and follow signs to Country Park.
Club Secretary: Tony Sharp, 65 Cedar Close, Bagshot, Surrey. GU19 5AB
Tel: (H) 01276 472994
Fixtures Secretary: Dave Forsaith, 87 Wordsworth Avenue, Yateley, Hants GU46 6YP
Tel: (H) 01252 665387
Club Colours: Green and white hoops, black shorts
League: Surrey 2

LONDON CORNISH RFC
Ground Address: Richardson Evans Memorial Ground, Roehampton Lane, Kingston, Surrey.
Tel: 0181 788 3628
Brief Directions: On main A3, 200 yards north of Robin Hood roundabout
Club Secretary: Dave Fletcher, 27 Riverbank, Laceham Road, Staines, Middlesex. TW18 2QE
Tel: (H) 01784 461927 (W) 0181 813 9494
e-mail: david.fletcher@concordelogistics.com
Fixtures Secretary: Angus Milne, 13 Durand Gardens, London SW9 0PS
Tel: (H) 020 7735 5100 (W) 0171 716 6645
Club Colours: Black with narrow gold hoops
League: Surrey 3

LONDON EXILES RUFC
Ground Address: Barn Elms Playing Field, Queen Elizabeth Walk, Barnes, London. SW15.
Tel: 020 8876 7685
Brief Directions: A205 (S. Circular) to Junction with A306 turn towards Barnes Bridge. Q. Elizabeth Walk is a small turning on R. at second set of Traffic Lights by the Red Lion Public House.
Club Secretary: Tim Edghill, 65 Ravenswood Road, Balham, London, SW12 9PN. Tel: 020 8673 2628
Fixtures Secretary: Chris Pearse, 11 Martindale Road, Balham, London, SW12 9PW.
Tel: 020 8673 2115
Club Colours: Claret, navy blue and white hoops
League: Surrey 2

LONDON FIRE BRIGADE RFC
Ground Address: Priest Hill Sports Ground, Banstead Road, Ewell, Surrey. KT17 3HG.
Tel: 0181 394 1946
Brief Directions: Junction of Cheam Road and Banstead Road, Ewell, next to Ewell East railway station
Club Secretary: Charlie Gilbert, 15 Park Road, Banstead, Surrey. SM7 3BY
Tel: (H) 01737 362191
Fixtures Secretary: Steve Russell,8 Kings Road, Belmont, Surrey SM2 6DG
8287 0638 (H) 8661 3356 (W)
Club Colours: Flame, ember, charcoal
League: Surrey 2

LONDON FRENCH RFC
Ground Address: Barn Elms Sports Ground, Castelmau/ Rocks Lane, Barnes, London. SW20
Website: www.londonfrenchrfc.co.uk
Brief Directions: From North over Hammersmith Bridge, down Castelnau to junction with Red Lion pub. Ground is on the corner.
Club Secretary: Peter Dow, 34 Crescent Lane, London, SW4 9PU.
Tel: 020 7622 3488 - Email:
peterdow@btinternet.com
Fixtures Secretary: Glenn Whiting, 11 Eglantine Road, London, SW18 2DE
Tel: 020 8870 2743 - Email: glenn.whiting@gb.swiss-bank.com
Club Colours: French (Royal) blue shirt, white shorts, red socks
League: Hertfordshire & Middlesex 3 South

LONDON & SOUTH EAST

LONDON IRISH AMATEUR
Ground Address: The Avenue,
Sunbury-on-Thames, Middlesex
Tel: 01932 783034
Brief Directions: M3 to J.1, follow signs to Kingston.
After .25 mile turn right into The Avenue. Ground is
.25 miles on right. Website:
london.irish.amateur.co.uk
Club Secretary: Bart O'Conner, 8 Furzewood,
Sunbury-on-Thames, Middlesex TW16 6SJ.
Tel : 01932 786306
Email: bart@rocit.freeserve.co.uk
Club Colours: Green, white, green with white tops
League: Surrey 1
League Contact: Bosco McAuliffe, Brentmead, 49
Pembrooke Road, Ruislip, HA4 8NQ
Tel : 01895 624160

LONDON MEDIA RUFC
Ground Address: Battersea Park, London
Brief Directions: Albert Bridge Road entrance to
Battersea Park (near Albert Bridge)
Club Secretary: Nick Field, 315a Cavendish Road,
Balham, London. SW12 0PQ.
Tel: (H) 0181 673 3809 (W) 0171 734 5358
Club Colours: Black and white quarters
League: Surrey 2

LONDON NEW ZEALAND RFC
Ground Address: c/o Birkbeck Sports Ground,
Birkbeck Avebue, Greenford, Middlesex.
Tel No: 0208 578 1930
Brief Directions: Central Line tube to Greenford. By
oad A40 to Greenford exit, turnnorth towards Harrow
on Greenford road. Then take first left ,Ingram way
and first right, Oldfield Lane then first left Birkbeck
Ave.
Club Secretary: Miss Wendy Whitechurch, 25
Canbury Avenue, Kingston, Surrey, KT2 6JP
Tel: 020 8546 3647 (H)
Email: wendyw@charterhouse.sa.com
Fixtures Secretary: Richard Peacock, Oakfell,
Downley Common, Hifgh Wycombe, Bucks.
Tel: 01494 448157
Club Colours: All black
League: London 4 North West

LONDON SCOTTISH FC
Ground Address: Richmond Athletic Ground, Kew
Foot Road, Richmond, Surrey,
TW9 2SS. Telephone to be arranged
Brief Directions: From Richmond station (BR and
underground) turn right to large R'about, turn left
down A316 to Twickenham. Ground 150 yards on
right.
Club Secretary: Iain Young, 51 Cross Deep
Gardens, Twickenham, TW1 4QZ
Email: iain.young@tileandleivis.com
Fixtures Secretary: R. M. Gillespie, 3 Hurstwood,
22 Cambalt Road, Putney, London, SW15 6EW
Tel : 020 8785 9060
Club Colours: Navy blue, white, red
League: London 4 North West
League Contact: As Fixture Secretary

LONDON TRIBES
League: Hertfordshire & Middlesex 4 South

LORDSWOOD RUFC
Ground Address: Lordswood Sports & Social Club,
Martin Grove, North Dane Way, Lordswood,
Chatham, Kent
Tel : 01634 669 138
Brief Directions: M2 J3, A229 t'wd Chatham, 3rd
exit at 3rd r'bout (Walderslade), over 1st r'bout, 3rd
exit at 2nd r'bout (Lordswood Lane), 3rd exit at
r'bout (Albermarle Rd), left at end, clubhouse 500yds
on right
Club Secretary: Sam Wellings, 167 Ballens Rd,.
Lordswood, Kent ME5 8PG
Tel No: 01634 861924
Fixtures Secretary: B ryn Jones, 212 Luton Road,
Chatham, Kent. ME95BS
Tel No: 01634 306829
Club Colours: Black with gold collar
League: Kent 1

LOUGHTON RFC
Ground Address: Squirrels Lane, Hornbeam Road,
Buckhurst Hill, Essex.   Tel : 0171 504 0065
Brief Directions: A11 out of NE London to
Woodford Green, turn right following police station
into Monkhams Lane, follow to end and straight over
crossroads into Chesnut Avenue, continue onto
Squirrels Lane.
Club Secretary: Craig Clark, 15 Herenard Green,
Coughton, Essex. Tel : (H) 0181 502 4854
Fixtures Secretary: Brian Westley,
Tel : (H) 01689 819365   Tel : (W) 0171 777 2883
Club Colours: White with 1 green & 2 black hoops.
League: Eastern Counties 3 South

LOWESTOFT & YARMOUTH RUFC
Ground Address: Gunton Park, off Corton Long
Lane, Old Lane, Corton, Nr Lowestoft, Suffolk.
Tel: 01502 730350
Brief Directions: From south A12 through
Lowestoft. Just before dual carriageway turn right
into Corton Long Lane. 300yds turn right into Old
Lane. Ground at end on right.
Club Secretary: June Nelson, 70 Upper Cliff Road,
Gorleston, Gt. Yarmouth, Norfolk, NR31 6AJ. Tel:
01493 653095 - Email: thenel@aol.com
Fixtures Secretary: Tex Colby, 59 Worthing Road,
Lowestoft, Suffolk, NR32 4HE. Tel: 01502 585924
Club Colours: Blue and white hoops
League: London 4 North East

LYTCHETT MINSTER RFC
Ground Address: South Manor Drive, Lytchett
Minster, Poole
Brief Directions: Follow A35 Poole to Dorchester, at
end of dual carriageway follow signs to village,
changing accommodation next to church
Club Secretary: Mrs Hazel Warren, 4 Dacombe
Drive, Upton, Poole, Dorset. BH16 5JL
Tel No: 01202 623694
Email: hazel@warren4 -fsnet.co.uk
Fixtures Secretary: Mark Hobson , Broomheyes,
Beacon Hill, Poole, Dorset. Tel No: 01202 623287
Club Colours: Red and blue hoops, white shorts
League: Hampshire 2

MAIDSTONE FC
Ground Address: The William Day Memorial Ground, The Mote, Willow Way, Maidstone, Kent. ME16 0RN   Tel: 01622 754159
Brief Directions: From M20 J.7 Proceed 1-2 miles on A249 towards Maidstone at R/about keep L. onto A20. 100 yds to traffic lights turn R to Square Hill turn L at mini R/about into Mote Avenue
Club Secretary: Tom Challis, 72 Roseacre Lane, Bearsted,Maidstone ME14 4JG
Tel : 01622 631083
Email: tomchallis@aewyeth.law,co.uk
Fixtures Secretary: Tony Kelleher, 5 Conway Road, Maidstone, ME16 0HD
Tel: (H & W) 01622 754872
Club Colours: Red, white and black hoops
League: London 2 South

MALDON RUFC
Ground Address: Drapers Farm Sports Club, Drapers Chase, Heybridge, Maldon, Essex.
Tel : 01621 852152
Brief Directions: A414 to Maldon. Then northern by-pass to Heybridge.Follow signs to Goldhanger. Half a mile up Goldhanger road on left.
Club Secretary: S.Harris, 40 Colchester Road, Heybridge, Maldon, CM9 4AN
Tel: 01621 851755
Fixtures Secretary: Nick Foss, 23 Ramsey Close, Heybridge, Maldon CM9 4YZ Tel: 01621 843124
Club Colours: Royal blue and white hoops
League: Eastern Counties 1

MARCH BRAZA RUFC
Ground Address: March Braza Sports Pavilion, Elm Road, March, Cambridgeshire.
Tel : 01354 59741
Brief Directions: Follow signs for HMP Whitemoor Sportsfield, on junction off side road to prison.
Club Secretary: Miss Andria Mills, 2 Broad Alder Farm, Mount Pleasant, Chatteris. PE16 6XL
Tel No: 01354 661398
Fixtures Secretary: Colin Buck.
Tel No: 01354 650074
Club Colours: Maroon and white hoops.Change: Green with single gold band.
League: Eastern Counties 3 North

MAY AND BAKER
Ground Address: Dagenham Road, Dagenham, Essex.   Tel : 0181 919 3156
Brief Directions: A13 to oprds, from London ,left at McDonalds to roundabout. First exit past Dagenham East Station to traffic lights. Right and right again at mini roundabout into Sports ground.
Club Secretary: Terry Simmons, 14 Causton Square, Broad St.,Dagenham, Essex. RM10 9HP
Tel NO: 020 8593 1788
Fixtures Secretary: Mike Parnell,
Tel : (H & W) 01245 231302
Club Colours: Black with single red band., black shorts and red socks.
League: Eastern Counties 2 South

MEDWAY RFC
Ground Address: Priestfield, Rochester, Kent ME1 3AD   Website: www.mrfc.net
Brief Directions: M2 J3, follow A249 to Chatham, at Bridgewood roundabout left (Maidstone/Rochester Road), past Comet on right, take left turn signed B, ground 200m on left
Club Secretary: Michael Burford, 20 Wouldham Road, Borstal , Rochester, Kent ME1 3LB
Tel : 01634 319013
Email: mikburford@cablenet.co.uk
Fixtures Secretary: Tony Bourne, 65 Hawthorn Avenue, Gillingham, Kent ME8 6TS
Tel: 01634 375947
Club Colours: Scarlet and Old Gold.
League: Kent 1

MERSEA ISLAND RFC
Ground Address: East Mersea Activity Centre, East Road, East Mersea, Colchester, Essex. Website: www.mersearugby.co.uk
Brief Directions: Turn left over Causeway coming onto Island (check tide is not over road). Centre is the 3rd road on the right, follow road to the centre
Club Secretary: Graham Marfleet, The Gables, 10 Yorick Avenue, West Mersea, Colchester, Essex, CO5 8HZ.   Tel : 01206 385218
Fixtures Secretary: Graham Woods, 24 Churchfields, West Mersea, Colchester, Essex CO5 8QJ.   Tel : (H) 01206 383525
Club Colours: Light Blue
League: Eastern Counties 1
League Contact: As Secretary

MERTON RFC
Ground Address: Morden Recreation Ground, Faversham Road, Morden, Surrey
Tel: 020 8646 5192
Website: www.angelfire.com/sports/mertonrfc
Brief Directions: From Rose Hill roundabout take St Helier Ave (A297), 1st left into Middleton Rd, then 4th exit from roundabout into Faversham Rd, entrance to ground is 100 yards on left
Club Secretary: Terry Clouter, 14 Park Crescent, Twickenham, TW2 6NT.   Tel: 020 8898 5286 - Email:terry@1extreme.freeserve.co.uk
Fixtures Secretary: Paul Webster, 39 Elthiron Road, London, SW6 4BW Tel: (H) 020 7736 0149
Email: margewebster39@hotmail.com
Club Colours: Black
League: Surrey 1

METROPOLITAN POLICE HAYES
Ground Address: The Annexe Sports Ground,St Dunstans,West Whickham. Kent.
Webste:mphayesfc.co.uk
Brief Directions: From Bromley Station tr@ATS Westmorland Rd. TR atnext ATS Hayes Lane.2nd left Bradbourne Rd at bottom of St beside Old Dunstonians RFC DunstansLane
Club Secretary: Gary Morant, 57 Orchard Way, Shirley, Croydon, Surrey, CR0 7NQ. Tel: 020 8777 3700 - Email: gary.morant@task21.com
Fixtures Secretary: K.Carvalho, Willow, 3 The Mead, West Wickham, Kent
Tel: 020 8289 1761 - Email: kendo6@ukonline.co.uk
Club Colours: Maroon shirts and black shorts
League: Kent 3

LONDON & SOUTH EAST

METROPOLITAN POLICE RFC
Ground Address: Met Police (Imber Court) Sports Club, Ember Lane, East Molesey, Surrey KT8 0BT
Tel: 020 8398 1267 Fax 020 8398 9755
Brief Directions: M25 Jnc 12, M3 towards London Jnc 1, take A308 to Hampton Court, turn right over bridge A309 to next roundabout, turn right into Ember Court Rd, club at end.
Club Secretary: Neil Sinclair, Room 912 Tintagel House, Albert Embankment, London SE1 7TT. Tel: 07971 048966 (M)
Fixtures Secretary: Simon Gill, Room 1707, New Scotland Yard, London SW1H 0BG
Tel : 07989 400239 (M)
Club Colours: Blue & white hoops
League: London 2 North
League Contact: Secretary, as above

MIDHURST RFC
Ground Address: Cowdray Ruins, Cowdray Park, Midhurst, West Sussex
Tel: 01730 816658
Brief Directions: At mini roundabout junction of A286 and A272 take entrance to Cowdray Park, turn left 200 yards along drive
Club Secretary: Simon Flint, Broadoak, Chichester Road, Midhurst, West Sussex. GU29 9PF
Tel: (H) 01730 816465 (W) 0181 390 1144
Fixtures Secretary: Simon Jenkins, 40 Osborne Road, Petersfield, Hampshire 2AE
Tel: (H) 01730 260540
Club Colours: Gold with royal blue hoop.
League: Sussex 2 West

MILL HILL RFC
Ground Address: Copthall Playing Fields, Page Street, Mill Hill, London. NW7 2EJ
Tel: 020 8203 0685
Brief Directions: Next to J2 of M1, follow signs for Barnet Copthall and club is top of Page Street at entrace road to Stadium
Club Secretary: Mr. Ian Webster, 76 Grants Close, Mill Hill, London NW7 1DE
Tel: (H) 020 8346 8136
Email: ian-webster@ic24.net
Fixtures Secretary: G.G. Williams, 10 Malden Road, Watford, Herts., WD1 3EW.
Tel: 01923 228071
Club Colours: Chocolate and old gold hoops
League: Hertfordshire & Middlesex 1

MILLBROOK RUFC
Ground Address: Lordshill Pavilion, Redbridge Lane, Lordshill, Southampton
Tel: 02380 739759
Brief Directions: M27 J3 to M271 to J1, A3051, 1st left into Redbridge Lane, 1 mile on right
Club Secretary: Mrs Jackie Ings, 27 Gemini Close, Lordshill, Southampton, SO16 8BG.
Tel :02380 345559 (H)
Emailk: chrisjackie@ings.fsnet.co.uk
Fixtures Secretary: Wayne Renwick
Tel: (H) 01489 892231
Club Colours: Emerald and scarlet hoops
League: Hampshire 1

MILLFIELD OLD BOYS RFC
Ground Address: Harrow RFC, Wood Lane, Stanmore, Middlesex
Tel: 0181 954 2615
Club Secretary: Angela Lesly, Westmill Fisheries, PO Box 24, Ware, Herts. SG12 0YN
Tel: (H) 01920 486534
Fixtures Secretary: Alan Burns
Tel: (H) 01920 486534
Club Colours: Red, green and blue hoops, white shorts
League: Hertfordshire & Middlesex 4 North

MILLWALL ALBION RFC
Ground Address: Victoria Park, Parnell Road, London, E3.
Brief Directions: A13 off at Old Ford slip. Right at top of slip into Wick Lane. Follow to R/about, last exit. Straight to Cadagon Terrace. Car Park opposite Top of the Morning Public House.
Club Secretary: N.P. Webb, 2 Macquarie Way, London, E14 3AU.
Tel: 020 7987 0575
Email nwebb@lineone.net
Fixtures Secretary: N. May, 4 The Mission, Commercial Road, London, E14.
Tel: 020 7515 4741 - Email njm@onionbooks.co.uk
Club Colours: Black & white hoops with red trim.
League: Eastern Counties 2 South

MISTLEY RFC
Ground Address: Mistley Parish Playing Fields, Shrubland Rd., Furzehill, Mistley, Manningtree, Essex. CO11 2QL
Brief Directions: %Take B1352 from Manningtree towards Harwich through Mistley. Over railway bridge, past Anchor Inn, turn right into Shrubland Road at corner of next left hand bend.
Club Secretary: Miss Charlotte Carter, Rutherglen Villa, Shrubland Road, Nistley, Manmningtree, Essex CO11 1HS
Tel No: 01206 395176
Fixtures Secretary: David Wood, 40 California Road, Mistley, Manningtree, Essex CQ11 1JG
Tel: 01206 391949
Club Colours: Red and purple quarters, black shorts
League: Eastern Counties 3 North

MITCHAM RUFC
Ground Address: Poulter Park, Bishopsford Cottage, Morden, Surrey
Tel: 01208 648 3567
Website: www.mitchamrufc.co.uk
Brief Directions: The ground can only be entered from Bishopsford Road(The main Sutton to Mitcham Road).
Club Secretary: Damian Brady,7 LaburnamCourt, 48 James Road, Sutton, Surrey. SM1 2TR
Tel No: 0208 643 8170
Email: damian .bradley@ombudsman.gsi.gov.uk
Fixtures Secretary: Richard Tapley, 101 Peaches Close, Sutton, Surrey SM2 7BL
Tel No: 0208 643 0650
Club Colours: Lavender and green hoops
League: Surrey 2

NATIONAL WESTMINSTER BANK RFC
Ground Address: Copers Cope Road, Beckenham, Kent. BR3 1NZ   Tel: 0181 650 4559/650 9217
Brief Directions: Freq trains to Charing X and London Bridge to Lower Sydenham. Out of Station on down side. Turn right at bottom into Worsley Bridge Rd. 1st Right (100yds) into Coopers Cope Rd, on right.
Club Secretary: Nigel Adam, 40 Montana Gardens, London SE26 5BF
Tel No: 0181 461 4056 (H) 0171 462 2003 (W)
Fixtures Secretary: L. A. Giblin, 656 Davidson Road, Croydon, Surrey CR0 6DJ
Tel: (H) 0181 654 1884
Club Colours: Light and dark blue hoops
League: Kent 2

NEW ASH GREEN RFC
Ground Address: Punch Croft, New Ash Green, Kent.   Tel : 01474 874660
Brief Directions: Contact Secretary
Email: tracy-tonka@hotmail.com
Club Secretary: Tracy Shopland, 57 Wellington Street, Gravesend, Kent DA12 1JQ.
Tel: (H) 01474 567263
Fixtures Secretary: Rod Banks, 14 Over Minnis, New Ash Green, Longfield, Kent DA3 8JA
Tel No: 01474 873699
Club Colours: Dark green and black quarters, black shorts.
League: Kent 1

NEW MILTON & DISTRICT RFC
Ground Address: Ashley Sports Field, Ashley Road, Ashley, New Milton, Hants
Tel: 01425 610401
Brief Directions: From town centre, head towards Ashley. About 1 mile from centre there is a Right turn marked Sports Club. It is immediately after a junior school.
Club Secretary: N E Hanmer, Walsingham, Andrew Lane, Ashley, New Milton, Hants
Tel: (H) 01425 612613 - 023 8066 3437W - 023 8086 8799F
Fixtures Secretary: A Williams, 57 Oakwood Avenue, New Milton, Hants.
Tel No: 01425 628428
Club Colours: Green with band of blue, gold, blue.
League: Hampshire 2

NEWICK RFC
Ground Address: King George V Playing Fields, Allington Road, Newick, East Sussex.
Brief Directions: A272 from Haywards Heath, right at village green, 2nd right, playing field Allington Road, on first bend, left into field
Club Secretary: Mrs. Diane Thomas, Pinecroft, Allington Rd., Newick, East Sussex BN8 4NA. Tel: (H) 01825 723824
Email: diane.pinecroft@ic24.net
Fixtures Secretary: Martin Barling, Cairn Cottage,41 Western Road, Newick.
Tel: 01825 724054
Club Colours: Dark blue and maroon hooped jerseys and socks.White shorts
League: Sussex 2 East

NEWMARKET RUFC
Ground Address: Sports Pavilion, Scaltback Middle School, Elizabeth Avenue, Newmarket, Suffolk. CB8 0DJ
Tel: 01638 663082
Brief Directions: A14 (Newmkt bypass), A142 towards Newmkt, right at Tesco r'bout, left at T junction, past 3 factories on right, turn right into Elizabeth Ave, clubhouse at rear of school
Club Secretary: Robert Voss, 58 King Edward VII Road, Newmarket, Suffolk. CB8 0EU
Tel: (H) 01638 669596
Fixtures Secretary: John Taylor, 32 High Street, Stetchworth, Newmarket, CB8 9TJ
Tel: (H) 01638 507483
Club Colours: Black w/ emerald green cuffs & collar
League: Eastern Counties 1

NOMADS RFC
Ground Address: Farlington's Recreation Ground, Eastern Road, Portsmouth, Hampshire.
Tel : 01705 691574
Brief Directions: North side of A27, behind Hilton International Hotel.
Club Secretary: Ken Walker, 5 Panton Close, Emsworth, Hampshire. PO10 7XW.
Tel : 01243 379141
 e-mail: ken@ walkerk 84.fsnet.co.uk
Fixtures Secretary: Adrian Bold. Tel No: 01489 880694
e-mail: adrian bold@nomads rfc.org.uk
Club Colours: Red and black irregular hoops.
League: Hampshire 1

NORFOLK ARMS
Ground Address: Steyning Grammar School, Shooting Field, Steyning.
Tel No: Norfolk Arms - 01903 812215
Website: www.norfoilk armsfc.co.uk
Brief Directions: Locate Steyning Grammar School coach park on Horsham Road, Steyning. The pitches are on school playing fields.
Club Secretary: Graham Wilkins, 4 Roman Road, Steyning. BN44 3FN   Tel No: 01903 814950
Fixtures Secretary: Mark Kentell, Flat 3, Glenview, Station Road, Steyning. Bn44 3YL
Tel No: 01903 814303
Club Colours: Red shirts with black shorts
League: Sussex 2 West

NORTHOLT RFC
Ground Address: Cayton Green Park, Cayton Road, Greenford, Middlesex. UB6 8BJ.
Tel: 0181 813 1701
Brief Directions: A40 Western Av to Greenford (Bridge Htl jcn/A4127 G'ford Rd), go as if to join A40 to London but stay lft & join slip parallel with A40 (R'mede Gdns), to end, left into Cayton Rd, ground at end
Club Secretary: Mr. Geoff Payne, 16 Brackenbridge Drive, South Ruislip, Middlesex, HA4 0NG.
Fixtures Secretary: Geoff Payne, 16 Brackenbridge Drive, South Ruislip, Middlesex. HA4 0
Tel: 020 8845 0874 (H) 07775 714357 (M)
Email: nrfc geoff@aol.com
Club Colours: Sky and navy blue hoops
League: Hertfordshire & Middlesex 2

LONDON & SOUTH EAST

NORWICH UNION RFC
Ground Address: Pinebanks Sports and Leisure Club, White Farm Lane, off Harvey Lane, Norwich, Norfolk, NR2 3HL.Tel: 01603 433752
Website: www.nurfc.com
Brief Directions: Approach city from S.E. A47 bypass, at end enter city towards Thorpe St Andrew, right into Pound Ln, immediate left before lights onto B1150, 1st left at r'bout Harvey, 4th left, club at end
Club Secretary: Steve Knights, 14 Avenue Road, Norwich, NR2 3HL.   Tel: 01603 477467
Email : steve@s knights.fsnet.co.uk
Fixtures Secretary: Garry Sayer, 82 Northumberland Street, Norwich. NR2 4EY
Tel No: 01603 614515
Club Colours: Green and white quarters
League: Eastern Counties 3 North

OLD ABBOTSTONIANS RFC
Ground Address: Gainsborough Playing Fields, Raeburn Road, off Pole Hill Road, Hayes, Middlesex
Tel: 020 8845 1452
Brief Directions: A40 exit for Hillingdon Long Lane towards Uxbridge Rd, left at BP station, left into Pole Hill Rd (Midland Bank at corner), round bend, 1st left after bus stop, club at end
Club Secretary: Denis Halloran, 8 Swallow Drive, Northolt, Middlesex. UB5 6UH
Tel: (H) 020 8842 2154
Fixtures Secretary: Vic Deevers, 102 Clarkes Drive, Hillingdon, Middlesex, UB8 3UN. Tel: 01895 437396
Club Colours: Blue and red
League: Hertfordshire & Middlesex 3 South

OLD ABINGDONIANS RFC
Ground Address: Share with Old Cranleighans, Old Portsmouth Rd.,Thames Ditton, Surrey KT7 0HB
Tel No: 0020 8389 3092
Brief Directions: Same as Old Cranleighans.
Club Secretary: Richard Wright, 8 Riverbanks Close, Harpenden ,Herts. AL5 5EJ
Tel No: 01582 460844
Email: wright-r@hotmail.com
Fixtures Secretary: Andrew Harding, Flat 4, 4 St Stephens Gardens, London. W2 5QX
Tel: 07961 431221 (M) 020 7792 0298 (H)
Email: landoharski@hotmail.com
Club Colours: Black, cerise & white hoops
League: Surrey 2

OLD ACTONIANS RFC
Ground Address: Gunnersbury Drive (off Paper Lane), London. W5   Tel: 0181 567 4556
Brief Directions: Coming west from Acton Town tube station, cross North Circular Rd, take 1st right (opposite Gunnersbury Park main entrance), ground 50yds on left of G'sbury Drive
Club Secretary: Mr. Wostek Swistak, 4 Cavendish Avenue, London W13 0JG
Tel No 07710 395 106
e-mail: wojtek.swistak@db.com@siebel.com
Fixtures Secretary: Brian Mulholland, 65 Brookville Road, London SW6 7BH
Tel No: 07831 229 244
Club Colours: Royal blue with three white hoops and red collar
League: Hertfordshire & Middlesex 2

OLD ALBANIAN RFC
Ground Address: Woollams, Harpenden Road, St Albans, Herts
Tel: 01727 864476
Website: www.oarugby.com
Brief Directions: Take turning to Harpenden off ring road to north of City. Turn immediately right down Old Harpenden Road. Ground on right.
Club Secretary: John Kilvington, 7 Garden City, Edgware, Middlesex, HA8 7NQ.
Tel: 0208 4511396
Fixtures Secretary: Elliott Newmarch. 67 Pondfield Crescent. St Albans, Herts.
Tel NOs: 0956 237457 (M) 01727 765605 (H)
Email:jear@supanet.com
Club Colours: Red, blue and yellow hoops, blue shorts
League: London 2 North

OLD ALLEYNIAN FC
Ground Address: Old Alleynian Club, Dulwich Common, Dulwich, London. SE21 7HA
Tel: 020 8693 2402
Brief Directions: Situated on the South Circular Road between College Road and Lorsdhip Lane. 10 minutes walk from West Dulwich Train Station.
Club Secretary: Jason Daniels, Flat 3, 1 Park Hill Road, Bromley, Kent. BR2 0JX
Tel:020 8466 0115
Fixtures Secretary: Alastair N Capon, 182 Hayes Lane, Bromley, Kent. BR2 9EL.
Tel: 020 8462 0886
Club Colours: Dark blue, light blue and black hoops
League: Surrey 1

OLD AMPLEFORDIANS
Ground Address: KCS Old Boys RFC, Arthur Rd.,Motspur Park, New Malden, Syrrey. KT3 6LX.
Tel No: 0208 336 2512
Website: www.oarfc.org.co.uk
Brief Directions: Short walk from Motspur Park station.From A3 at New Malden underpass go south along A2043 . Left into Motspur Park Rd after aprox 400 yds.. into Arthur Road ,2nd rtigh after railway crossing
Club Secretary: Nick Hughes, 20C Ongar Rd.,London. SW6 1SJ
tel No: 0207 386 5334
Email: nick.hughes@schroders.com
Fixtures Secretary: Nick Dumbell, 25 Greencroft Gardens, London. NW6 3LN
Tel No: 0207 372 6784
Club Colours: Red and Black
League: Surrey 3

OLD ASHMOLEANS RFC
Ground Address: Ashmole School, Burleigh Gardens, Southgate, London. N14
Tel: 020 8886 3344
Website: www.oarfc.co.uk
Brief Directions: At Southgate underground station roundabout, turn into Ashfield Parade, bear right into Burleigh Gardens, school entrance 250 metres on left

Club Secretary: Geoff Bull,60 Ladysmith Road,Enfield, Middlesex EN1 3AA
tel No: 0208363 5991 (H)
Email: geoff bull01@btinternet.com
Fixtures Secretary: Simon Stamp, 5 Leaf House, 22 King Edward Road, New Barnet, Herts EN5 5AP
Tel No: 020 8449 3036,
Club Colours: Black with red & green hoops, black shorts
League: Hertfordshire & Middlesex 4 North

OLD BEALONIANS RFC
Ground Address: ICC, Valentines Park, Cranbrook Road, Ilford, Essex.
Tel No: 0208 554 8381
Brief Directions: Cranbrook Road is off Gants Hill Roundabout with the ground entrance opposite Redcliffe Gardems.
Club Secretary: John Williams,2 Ravenoak way, Chigwell, Essex. IG7 4EL
Tel No: 0208 500 9544
Email: williamsjd1 @talk21.com
Fixtures Secretary: Kevin Gregory
Tel No: 0208 597 4104
Club Colours: Red , Black and Gold
League: Eastern Counties 3 South

OLD BLUES RFC
Ground Address: Dornan Fields, Arthur Road, Motspur Park, Nr New Malden, Surrey
Tel: 0181 336 2566
Website: oldblues.com/rugby-club/index.htm
Brief Directions: From London A3, along Kingston bypass, take sliproad signed Worcester Pk & Cheam, 1st left after pillarbox into Motspur Pk, over levelcrossing into W. Barnes Ln, 2nd right
Club Secretary: Giles Simons, 105 Gaskarth Road, London SW12 9NP
Tel No: 0203 378 1604 (H) 0207 786 6954
Email: giles simons@firthrossmartin.com
Fixtures Secretary: Vinod Fernandez, 3 Boyd Close, Crescent Road, Kingston. KT2 7RL
Tel Nos: 0208 54607(H) 0207 475 7630 (W)
Club Colours: Navy blue, cardinal red & old gold
League: London 3 South West

OLD BRENTWOODS RFC
Ground Address: Old Brentwoods Clubhouse, Ashwells Rd, Bentley, Brentwood, Essex CM15 9SE
Tel: 01277 374070
Website: www.obrfc.org
Brief Directions: Take the Onger road from Brentwood and after 2 1/²2 miles turn right at the end of the "straight mile" into Ashwells Road. Ground 1/4 mile on left.
Club Secretary: T.J.Faiers, I Woodway, Shenfield, Essex CM15 8ILP
Tel: 01277 214503 (H) 020 8270 4567/8 (W)
Fixtures Secretary: Roger Seaman, 5 The Knoll , Rayleigh, Essex SS6 7HD
Tel: 01268 774113 (H) 01268 560040 (W)
Club Colours: Dark Blue and Light Blue Hoops.
League: Eastern Counties 2 South

OLD BRIGHTONIAN RFC
Ground Address:
Share with Brighton FC (RFU)
Waterhall Playing Fields, Mill Road, Patcham, Brighton.
Tel: 01273 562729
Brief Directions: From London & north- A23 turn right at 1st roundabout entering Brighton, past garage under railway bridge, 100 metres sign post, turn right
Club Secretary: C D Loadsman, 20 Meadow Close, Hove, Sussex
Tel: (H) 01273 552988 (W) 01273 736000
Fixtures Secretary: P Rumney
Tel: (H) 01273 504981
Club Colours: Light blue and magenta hoops on navy
League: Sussex 2 East

OLD CATERHAMIANS RFC
Ground Address: Park Avenue, Caterham, Surrey. CR3 6AH
Tel: 01883 343488
Website: www//come.to/old-cats
Brief Directions: From Caterham Station up Church Hill, 1st left into Stanstead Road, Park Avenue 1st on right
Club Secretary: Mrs L Myland, Ash Trees, 15 Portley Lane, Caterham, Surrey. CR3 5JR
Tel: (H&B) 01883 343319 -
Email: lesley.myland@btinternet.com
Fixtures Secretary: Mark Rowland
Tel: 01737 771605
Email: rowland@furnesswithy.demon.co.uk
Club Colours: Black, amber, silver, mauve with black shorts
League: Surrey 1

OLD COOPERIANS RUFC
Ground Address: Wanstead Sports Ground, Nutter Lane, Wanstead, London E11
Brief Directions: Please phone fixture secretary.
Club Secretary: John C Green, Greenlow House, Melbourn, Herts. SG8 6OG
Tel: (H) 01763 260624
Fixtures Secretary: Chris Nicholls
Tel: (H & Fax) 0181 592 9450
Club Colours: Dark blue with thin gold and light blue hoops
League: Eastern Counties 3 South

OLD CRANLEIGHAN RFC
Ground Address: Old Portsmouth Road, Thames Ditton, Surrey. KT7 0HB
Tel: 0020 8398 3092
Brief Directions: Please phone Fixture Secretary
Club Secretary: Mark Lubbock,51 Balham Park Road, London, SW12 8DX.
Tel: 020 8673 4458
Email: mark.lubbock@ashursts.com
Fixtures Secretary: Tony Price
Tel: (H) 020 8949 1194 (W) 020 8533 7588
Club Colours: Blue white and gold hoops
League: Surrey 1

OLD DUNSTONIAN RFC
Ground Address: St Dunstan's Lane, Langley Park, Beckenham, Kent. BR3 3SS
Tel: 020 8650 1779
Brief Directions: Frm Bromley Sth station, rt at lights Westmoreland Rd, rt at next lights Hayes Ln, 2nd lft Brabourne Rs, at the bottom entrance to St D'stans Ln is almost opp. between no's 114/6 Wickham Way
Club Secretary: Mike Rogers, `Aboyne', Pickhurst Lane, West Wickham, Kent. BR4 0HN
Tel: (H) 020 8462 3064 (W) 020 7447 2238
Fixtures Secretary: Tony Greenwood, 5 Silverstone Court, Wanstead Road, Bromley, Kent. BR1 3DZ Tel No: 020 8464 7459 (H) 07980 082002 (M)
Email: rogers@pearsoned-ema.com
Club Colours: Navy and white hoop
League: London 3 South East

OLD EDWARDIANS RFC
Ground Address: Westlands Playing Fields, London Road, Romford, Essex
Website:: old edwardians@freeservers.com
Brief Directions: On A118 towards London from Romford (known locally as London Road)
Club Secretary: Graham Roberts:,7 Lampern Close,Billericay, Essex.CM!@ 0FF
Tel No: 01277 631240
Email: graham\roberts@ cwcom.net
Fixtures Secretary: Barry Robinson. , 31 Claridge Road, Dagenham, Essex.Tel No: 0181 491 9262 (H)
Club Colours: Navy blue shirts, white shorts or red and white
League: Eastern Counties 1

OLD ELTHAMIANS RFC
Ground Address: Old Elthamians Sports Club, Foxbury Avenue,Chislehurst, Kent, BR7 6HA.
Tel: 020 84671296
Brief Directions: From M25 (S.E.) take A20 towards London,take second exit (A222) towards Bromley and Chislehurst. Then second right is Foxbury Avenue.
Club Secretary: Ian McKinnon, 25 The Gardens, Beckenham, Kent. BR3 2PH
Tel: (H) 020 8650 1936
Email: mckinnon-ian@hotmail.com
Fixtures Secretary: David Organ, 33 St. Mary's Avenue, Shortlands, Bromley, Kent, BR2 0PU.
Tel: (H) 020 8464 2542
Club Colours: Royal blue and amber hoops
League: Kent 2

OLD EMANUEL RFC
Ground Address: Blagdons, Blagdon Lane, New Malden, Surrey   Tel: 0181 942 3857
Brief Directions: Using London A-Z locate where Burlington Rd crosses A3 at New Malden. Using north bound slip road to London ground is situated 200 yards on left
Club Secretary: IanBlair,12 Moor Lane, Chessington, Surrey.FT9 1BS
Tel: (H) 020 8397 1272 (W) 0171 872 3349
Fixtures Secretary: Peter Lippiatt, 27 Overdale, Ashtead, Surrey KT21 1PW   Tel: 01372 279593
Club Colours: All white.
League: London 4 South West

OLD FREEMANS RFC
Ground Address: City of London Freemen's School, Ashtead Park, Ashtead, Surrey. KT21 1ET. Tel: 01372 274158
Brief Directions: From Epsom Leatherhead A24 road turn into Park Lane Epsom end of Ashstead take 1st left through gates into park. Entrance to school ground 400 yards on right.
Club Secretary: Peter Ling, 74 Woodlands Road, Bookham, Surrey. KT24 4HH. Tel: 01372 459172.
Fixtures Secretary: M J Bailey, 123 Overdale, Ashstead, Surrey. KT21 1PZ.
Tel: (H) 01372 278505 (W) 0181 642 3419
Club Colours: Dark blue, maroon & gold shirts, dark blue shorts
League: Surrey 2

OLD GRAMMARIANS RFC
Ground Address: The Sports Field, Corner of Worlds End Lane/Green Dragon Lane, Winchmore Hill, Enfield, Middlesex. - Tel: 020 8364 2459.
Brief Directions: M25 J24 (Potters Bar), A1005 towards Enfield, after about 3 miles right down Slades Hill, 4th left into Bincote Rd to Worlds End Ln, L turn to Green Dragon Ln entrance 80yds on left.
Club Secretary: Barry White, 239 Chase Side, Enfield, Middlesex, EN2 0RA.
Tel: 020 8350 4179 - Email: barrywhite@barrywhite.co.uk
Fixtures Secretary: Dennis Morden, 415 Baker Street, Enfield, Middlesex, EN1 3QZ. Tel: 020 8342 0689 - Email: dennis.morden@bt.com
Club Colours: Navy Blue with red and light blue hoops, Navy Blue
League: Hertfordshire & Middlesex 3 North

OLD GRAVESENDIANS RFC
Ground Address: Fleetway Sports Ground, Bronte View, Parrock Road, Gravesend, Kent DA12 1PX.
Tel : 01474 365503
Brief Directions: A2 to Gravesend (not Gravesend East), take A227 (Tolgate) towards town.Turn right at lights at 2nd Road Jct. First turning at roundabout into Parrock Rd.. Ground third of mile on right
Club Secretary: Jeremy Strike, 33 Portland Road, Gravesend, Kent.
Tel No: 01474 534438
Email: jstrike@blueyonder.co.uk
Fixtures Secretary: Stuart Hodge , 61 Parrock Aveneue.Gravesend. Kent. DA12 1ZG. Tel: 01474 569214
Club Colours: Sky and navy blue hoops - Emerald & Scarlet Hoops
League: Kent 2

OLD GUILDFORDIANS RFC
Ground Address: Stoke Park, London Road, Guildford, Surrey
Tel: 01483 300752
club website: ogrfc.co.uk
Brief Directions: A3 turn off to Burpham, follow signs for Guildford town centre, Stoke Park on right after large roundabout, club house at northern end of Stoke Park
Club Secretary: Dr Peter Lamont, The Farmhouse, Brockenhurst Close, Woking Surrey GU2 4DS

Tel: 01483767336 (H) 01483 835733(F)
 e-mail: jandplamont@ ntlworld,com
Fixtures Secretary: Alex Maguire, 48 Woking Road,
Guildford, Surrey GU1 1QD
Tel: (H) 01483 536514
Club Colours: Green with red and white hoops,
green shorts
League: London 3 South West

OLD HABERDASHERS
Ground Address: Old Haberdashers' Sports
Ground, Croxdale Road, Boreham Wood,
Hertfordshire WD6 4PY.
Tel : 020 8953 1987
Brief Directions: Borehamwood & Elstree Station at
R/about take Theobald Street towards Radlett.
Croxdale Road on Right after .5 mile. Ground on
Left.
Club Secretary: Martin Baker, Rookwood, Hedsor
Road, Bourne End, Bucks, SL8 5EE. Tel: 07710
070749
Email martin.s.baker@bt.com
Fixtures Secretary: Andy Gray, 10 Tronvere Park,
Hemel Hempstead, Herts, HP1 3HY.
Tel : 01442 400319. Email: graya@ms.com
Club Colours: Blue, white and magenta hooped
shirts with blue shorts.s.
League: Hertfordshire & Middlesex 2

OLD HAILEYBURIANS
Ground Address: 27 Ruxley Lane, Kingston Road,
Ewell, Surrey. KT19 0JB
Tel: 0181 393 3901
Brief Directions: Reached from London by
Portsmouth Rd (A3), take left filter to Epsom about
200 yds from Tolworth underpass along Kingston Rd,
after 1 mile right into Ruxley Lane, 100 yards on left
Club Secretary: Roderick Sheen, 29 Kenilworth
Avenue, London. SW19 7LN
Tel: (H) 0181 879 7851 (W) 0171 782 0990
Fixtures Secretary: Tony Russell.
Tel: 020 7376 8836
e-mail: tony prop@ aol.com
Club Colours: Magenta and white hoops
League: Surrey 2

OLD HAMPTONIANS RFC
Ground Address: The Pavilion, Dean Road,
Hampton, Middlesex. TW12 1AQ
Tel: 0181 979 2784
Brief Directions: Leave A316 (London to M3) at
signs for A316 Hampton proceed on Uxbridge Road
for half mile. R. into Hanworth Road pass 3 schools
on R. before turning R into Dean Road
Club Secretary: B.Robinson,208 Elm Road,
Kingston, Surrey K12 6HP
Fixtures Secretary: Subhash Kamath, 267
Uxbridge, Middlesex TW12 1AR
Tel No: 0181 979 4339
Club Colours: Gold, silver and black hoops
League: Hertfordshire & Middlesex 1

OLD ISLEWORTHIANS RFC
Ground Address: Memorial Ground, Wood Lane,
Isleworth, Middlesex   Tel: 0181 560 7949
Brief Directions: A4 (Great West Road) or London
Road to Isleworth

Club Secretary: Huw Davies, 230 Whitton Dene,
Isleworth, Middlesex. TW7 7LU
Tel: (H) 0181 8985929 (W) 01344 662958
Fixtures Secretary: Robert Davis, 4 York Road,
Camberley, Surrey, GU15 4HR.
Tel: (H)01276 676242 (W) 01483 798712
Club Colours: Blue jersey with a horizontal red
band and grey stripe
League: Hertfordshire & Middlesex 3 South

OLD MERCHANT TAYLORS' FC
Ground Address: Durrants, Lincoln Way, Croxley
Green, Herts. WD3 3ND
Tel: 01923 773014
Website: omtrugby.com
Brief Directions: M25 Jct 18.to Rick'worth. A412 to
Croxley Grn.1st exit to C.G. at SportsmanPH.T.Jct rt
to BaldwinsLn, left Manor Way at mini round't. Rt.
Kenilw'th Drive, left Roch'ter Way. Durrants ahead.
Club Secretary: M G Foster, 199 Uxbridge Road,
Rickmansworth, Herts. WD3 8DP.
Tel : (H) 01923 771552 (W) 07973 657412
e-mail: mrkfost@aol.com
Fixtures Secretary: G W Shilling, The Lodge,
Wellingrove, Woodcock Hill, Rickmansworth,
Herts. WD3 1TP
Tel: (H) 01923 774506 (W) 01923 774506
Club Colours: Black shirts, black shorts
League: London 3 North West

OLD MID-WHITGIFTIAN RFC
Ground Address: Lime Meadow Avenue,
Sanderstead, Surrey. CR2 9AS
Tel: 0181 657 2014
Brief Directions: From Stanstead Hill rndabout, 0.75
mile along Limpsfield Rd towards Warlingham,past
old fire station & garage, left into Sanderstead Crt
Ave, 100yds right, club at end
Club Secretary: John Crate, 16 Mallard Way,
Wallington, Surrey. SM6 9LZ
Tel: 0181 647 9081
Fixtures Secretary: Andy Hillburn
Tel: (H) 0181 657 1825 (W) 0181 917 8888 Ext
4571
Club Colours: Black with irregular silver and blue
hoops.
League: London 2 South
League Contact: Secretary, as above

OLD MILLHILLIANS RFC
Ground Address: Millhillians Sports Ground,
Headstone Lane, Middlesex. HA2 6BR
Tel: 020 8428 2281
Brief Directions: Entrance to ground 20 yds to left
of Headstone Lane station, exit on opposite side, 5
minutes walk from station
Club Secretary: The Secretary, c/o Millhillians
Sports Ground as above.
Tel: 020 8349 3637
Fixtures Secretary: D.G.A. Penson, 43 Wesley
Square, London W11 1TS
Tel: 020 7243 3544 (H)
Club Colours: Chocolate and white hoops, black
shorts
League: Hertfordshire & Middlesex 2

LONDON & SOUTH EAST

OLD OLAVIANS RUFC
Ground Address: St Olave's School, Goddington Lane, Orpington, Kent Tel: 01689 830744
Directions: Join A224, either from A20 at Crittals Corner or M25 at J.4. Follow signs to Orpington and Goddington Lane is near Volvo BP Garage.
Club Secretary: Chris Stanbridge, 52 Elgar Way, Horsham, West Sussex, RH13 6RH.
Tel: 01403 248177
Fixtures Secretary: Les Fairhurst, 9 Ruskin Walk, Bromley, Kent, BR2 8EP   Tel: 020 8462 8992
Club Colours: Purple, black and white hoops
League: Kent 3

OLD PAULINE FC
Ground Address: St Nicholas Road, off Speer Road, Thames Ditton, Surrey. KT7 0PW
Tel: 020 8398 1858
Brief Directions: From r'bout in Hampton Court Way (A309) turn east, 400m to Thames Ditton Station, after railway arch 1st left into Speer Rd, 2nd right into St Nicholas Rd
Club Secretary: Derek Etherton, 25 Kenton Avenue, Sunbury-on-Thames, Middlesex, TW16 5AS
Tel: 01932 779030 - 0831 491 174M
Email: delga@tesco.net
Fixtures Secretary: Tim Cunis, 62 Derby Road, East Sheen, London, SW14 7DP.
Tel: 020 8878 3099
Email: rugby@tjdcunis.demon.co.uk
Club Colours: Red, white and black hoops
League: Surrey 1

OLD REEDONIANS
Ground Address: North Avenue, Whiteley Village, Walton-on-Thames, Surrey. KT12 4DX.
Tel: 01932 849616
Brief Directions: From A3/A245 junction towards Woking. After 1/4 mile turn right on B365 (Seven Hills Road). At 1st r'about turn right into Burwood Rd. Enter village & ground is 1/4 mile on right.
Club Secretary: John B Rogers, 8 Model Cottages, East Sheen, London. SW14 7PH.
Tel: (H & W) 0181 876 1512
Fixtures Secretary: David Nash, 41 Kennel Road, Fetcham, Surrey. KT12 2JR.
Tel: (H) 01372 452601 (W) 0181 560 4111.
Club Colours: Dark blue, light blue, red & white hoops.
League: Surrey 1

OLD REIGATIAN RFC
Ground Address: Park Lane, Reigate, Surrey RH2 9DL. Tel : 01737 245634
Directions: Park Lane on A25 Reigate 3/4 mile on RHS
Club Secretary: D Forsyth, 76 Station Street, Redhill, Surrey RH1 1PL   Tel: (H) 01737 773533
Fixtures Secretary: D Payton, The Croft, Babylon Lane, Lower Kingswood, Surrey KT20 6UU
Club Colours: Green and blue hoops.
League: Surrey 1

OLD RUTLISHIANS RFC
Ground Address: Old Rutlishians Association, Poplar Rd, Merton Park. SW19 Tel: 020 8542 3678
Brief Directions: Kingston Rd Merton to Dorset Rd

by Merton Park level crossing, proceed along Dorset Rd to Melrose Ave, take left fork for Poplar Road.
Club Secretary: Philip Rumbelow, 5A Moreton Road, Worcester Park, Surrey. KT4 8EY
Tel No: 020 8330 5586
Email: rumbelows@tinyworld.co.uk
Fixtures Secretary: John Petrides, 1The Ridgeway, Sanderstead CR4 0LG Tel: 020 8657 7750
Club Colours: Gold, silver, azure and black
League: Surrey 1

OLD STREETONIANS
Ground Address: Hackney Marshes, Homerton Road, London E9.   Tel : 0208 985 8206
Brief Directions: From North approach from A106 (Eastway).From South approach from A102 (M)
Club Secretary: Lynn Hay, 73 Swallowfield Rd., London SE7 7NT Tel: 0208 858 1213
e-mail:lynn@richardhay.demon.co.uk
Fixtures Secretary: As Secretary
Club Colours: Red and royal blue quarters.
League: Hertfordshire & Middlesex 4 North

OLD SUTTONIANS RFC
Ground Address: Sutton Grammar School Playing Fields, Northey Avenue,, Cheam, Sutton, Surrey.
Website: oldsutts-rfc.co.uk
Brief Directions: On A232 between Cheam & Ewell take exit on St Pauls church roundabout into Northey Avenue. Ground is 1/4 mile on the right.
Club Secretary: S J Udall, 91 Beresford Rd.,Cheam, Sutton.Surrey SM2 6ES
Tel No: 020 8642 9892
Email: stuart.udall@ aspect.com
Fixtures Secretary: I M Connell,3 Blackstole Road, Wrotham, Nr Sevenoaks, Kent. TN15 7DB
Tel: (H)01732882032
Club Colours: Red, white and black hoops
League: Surrey 3

OLD TIFFINIAN RFC
Ground Address: Grist Memorial Ground, Summer Road, off Hampton Court Way, East Molesey, Surrey.
Tel: 0181 398 1391
Brief Directions: Hampton Court roundabout along Hampton Court way (A309).To turn into Summer Road you have to go to roundabout and come back, it is then first left.
Club Secretary: Andy Green, 28 Amberwood Rise, New Malden, Surrey KT3 5JF. Tel: (H) 020 8942 7194 (M) 07713 9519 47
Email s:- andy.r.green@talk21.com (H)
andy.green-fmd@defra.gsi.gov.uk(W)
Fixtures Secretary: Greer Kirkwood, 63 Shaftesbury Way, Strawberry Hill, Twickenham, Middlesex, TW2 5RW. Tel: (H) 0181 898 1767
Club Colours: Violet, white & navy blue hoops
League: Surrey 1

OLD TOTTONIANS RFC
Ground Address: Churchfields Playing Fields, Great Cambridge Rd/Harrow Drive, Edmonton, London. N9
Tel: 020 8364 3099
Club website: www.oldtottonians.co.uk
Brief Directions: "Churuhfields" is located on the main A10 (Southbound) at Enfield between the Bury Street and Church Street junctions.

LONDON & SOUTH EAST

Club Secretary: Trevor De La Salle, 55 Welsummer Way, Le Motte Chase, Cheshunt, Herts. EN8 0UG
Tel: (H) 01992 638492 (W) 020 26231819
Fixtures Secretary: John Cockrill, 7 Sutherland Way, Cuffley, Herts, EN6 4EG
Tel: (H) 01707 872507 (W) 020 78709239
e-mail; john@ cockrillf.freeserve.co.uk
Club Colours: Blue and amber hooped shirts
League: Hertfordshire & Middlesex 3 North

OLD VERULAMIAN RFC

Ground Address: Cotlandswick, London Colney, Nr. St Albans, Hertfordshire AL2 1DW
Tel : 01727 822929 www.ovrugbyfc.co.uk
Brief Directions: Just off North Orbital Road (A414) ground opposite nursery
Club Secretary: Tony Charlwood, 14 Westwater, Penfleet, Essex, SS7 5TE
Tel: 01268 565964 Email: tony.charlwood@morley
Fixtures Secretary: Ian Stewart, 44 Abbotts Park, St. Albans, Herts., AL1 1TW   Tel: 01727 750252
Email:pamela.stewart1@ntlworld.com
Club Colours: Royal blue with gold 'V'
League: London 2 North
League Contact: As secretary

OLD WALCOUNTIANS RFC

Ground Address: Clockhouse, Carshalton Road, Woodmansterne, Banstead, Surrey. SM7 3HU.
Tel: 01737 354348
Brief Directions: Carshalton Rd is approx 2 miles from A217, off Croydon Lane, the clubhouse is approx 0.5 mile along Carshalton Rd on the left
Club Secretary: Mrs Sharon Fry, 37 St James Avenue, Sutton, Surrey SM12TQ. Tel: 0208 643 7893. E-mail: sharon. fry@1c24.net
Fixtures Secretary: Mr R McDowell
Tel: (H) 0181 669 6801
Club Colours: Black with blue and gold hoops.
League: Surrey 1

OLD WELLINGTONIAN RFC

Ground Address: 27 Ruxley Lane, Kingston Road, Ewell, Surrey (Shared with Old Haileyburians RFC).
Tel: 020 8393 3901
Brief Directions: East off the A3 from Tolworth Roundabout.
Club Secretary: Nick Dennis, 24 Coleford Road, London SW18 1AD   Tel: (H) 020 8874 8486
Fixtures Secretary: Nick Prichard, 46 Atbara Road, Teddington, Middlesex, TW11 9PD
Tel: 020 8943 3626
Colours: Black with orange, light blue & yellow stripes
League: Surrey 1

OLD WHITGIFTIAN RFC

Ground Address: Croham Manor Road, South Croydon, Surrey. CR2 7BG
Tel: 0208 686 2127 (office) 0208 688 3248 (bar)
Brief Directions: 1 mile south of Central Croydon on A235, fork left at The Swan & Sugarloaf pub into Selsdon Rd, 300 yds mini r'bout 2nd exit into Croham Rd, ground 0.5 mile on right
Club Secretary: Huntley Norman, ' St. Dorothys', 52 Croham Manor Rd., South Croydon, Surrey CR2 7BE . Tel: (H&W) 020 8688 7199
Email: Huntley norman@aol.com

Fixtures Secretary: As Secretary above.
Club Colours: Red, black and blue hooped shirts
League: Surrey 1

OLD WILLIAMSONIANS RFC

Ground Address: Maidstone Road, Rochester, Kent. Tel:01634 842883
Club Secretary: Mark Ian Smith, 43 Holland Road, Chatham, Kent, ME5 9TW.
Tel: 01634 669458
Fixtures Secretary: Linton Stickings, 2 Cornwallis Cottages, Heath Road, Linton, Maidstone, Kent. Tel: 01622 743994
Club Colours: Navy blue, single gold hoop
League: Kent 3

OLD WIMBLEDONIANS RFC

Ground Address: 143 Coombe Lane, London, SW20 0NQ   Tel: 020 8879 0700
Brief Directions: From Raynes Park station follow Coombe Lane towards Kingston. Cross traffic lights at West Barnes Lane junction, ground approx 800 yds on lefthand side.
Club Secretary: Mrs Margaret Parsons, Hawth, Glaziers Lane, Normandy, Guildford. GU3 2EA
Tel: (H) 01483 811103
Email: m.parsons@talk21.com
Fixtures Secretary: Richard Brayne-Nicholls, 76 Camberley Ave., Raynes Park, London, SW20 0BQ.
Tel: 020 8542 5714
Club Colours: Bottle green, maroon & gold hoops
League: London 3 South West

ONGAR RFC

Ground Address: Love Lane, Ongar, Essex
Tel: 01277 383636
Brief Directions: To Ongar from Brentwood A128, turn right into town, proceed along High St, before tube station on left turn right into Love Lane, ground 300 metres
Club Secretary: Nigel Doubleday, 31 Rochford Avenue, Waltham Abbey, Essex. EN9 1SL
Tel: (H) 01997 768950
Email: ndoubleday@lineone.net
Fixtures Secretary: Peter Hodgson, 74 The Paddocks, Ingatestone, Essex.
Tel: (H) 01277 354404 (W) 0468 277258
           (M)07768 277258
Club Colours: Blue with amber band
League: Eastern Counties 3 South

ORLEANS F.P. RFC

Ground Address: Orleans Park, off Richmond Road, Twickenham
Tel: 0958 489391
Brief Directions: Off Richmond Road adjacent to Orleans Park School
Club Secretary: Paul Tanner, 81 Twining Avenue, Twickenham, TW2 5LL.
Tel: 020 8898 3976 -
Email: paul.tanner@morrisonplc.com
Fixtures Secretary: Graham Todd
Tel: (H) 020 8898 4982
Club Colours: Gold , maroon and white hoops.
League: Hertfordshire & Middlesex 4 South

ORPINGTON RFC
Ground Address: Hoblingwell Wood Recreation Ground, Leesons Way, St Pauls Cray, Orpington, Kent. BR5 2QB
Tel: 01689 823913
Brief Directions: From M25 Jct 3, take A20 towards London. Take first exit, A224 Orpington, then first right, third left and third right into Leesons Way.
Club Secretary: Chris Evens c/o PO Box 145, Orpington, Kent BR5 2ZY
Tel: (H) 01689 896709 (W) 01959 514152
Fixtures Secretary: Dave Corry c/o PO Box 145, Orpington, Kent BR5 2ZY
Tel: (H) 01689 811396
Club Colours: Black and yellow hoops. Change: All Black
League: Kent 3

OSTERLEY RFC
Ground Address: TThe Jersey Road Sports Ground,Jersey Road, Osterley, Middlesex TW5 0TP.
Tel No: 0208 574 3774
Website: www.osterley-rugby.co.uk
Brief Directions: On A4 take Stucley Road , west of Osterley Tube Station ,into Jersey Road and look for Brunel University Sports Ground.
Club Secretary: Richard Evans, 111 Rowlands Avenue, Pinner, Middlesex. HA5 4AW
Tel : (H) 020 8428 5797
Email: r.evans@nabarro.com
Fixtures Secretary: John Green, 92 Roxborough Avenue, Isleworth Middlesex TW7 5HJ
Tel No: 0208 568 5557
Club Colours: Black and white hoops
League: Hertfordshire & Middlesex 3 South

OVERTON RFC
Ground Address: The Old Cricket Ground, Laverstoke Park, Watch Lane, Laverstoke, Nr. Overton, Hampshire
Website:www.overtonrugbyclub.com
Brief Directions: B3400 to Laverstock by Phonebox turn into Watch Lane - Follow signs - If you think you are lost you are there.
Club Secretary: Roger Filbey, 101 Old Winton Road, Andover, Hants., SP10 2DR - Tel: 01264 365529 - Email: roger.annemieke@tesco.net
Fixtures Secretary: Alex Coles, 15 Rochford Road, Basingstoke, Hants RG21 7TQ
Tel: (H) 01256 410836
Club Colours: Royal blue - Change Dark Green
League: Hampshire 2

PARK HOUSE FC
Ground Address: Barnet Wood Road, Hayes, Kent. BR2 7AA Tel: 0181 462 7318
Brief Directions: A21 to Bromley (or from M25 J4), turn off on A233 (Oakleigh Rd) towards Biggin Hill, Barnet Wood Road is a turning on the right
Club Secretary: Robert D Elves, 47 Ramillies Road, Sidcup, Kent. DA15 9JA
Tel: (H) 020 8 304 9170 (W) 02084 671447
Fixtures Secretary: G Bunnage, 48 Southborough Road, Bickley, Kent BR1 2EL
Tel: (H) 0181 467 1447 (W) 0181 401 0111
Club Colours: Black shirts with red circlet
League: Kent 1

PAXTON PUMAS
Ground Address: Brookfield School, Brook Lane, Warsash
Brief Directions: Barns Lane leads to Brook Lane and enter through Park Gate.
Club Secretary: Sue Moorhouse, Formax Farm, Titchfield, Hants. Po14 4AX
Tel No: 01329 842303
Fixtures Secretary: Tim Moorhouse as above
League: Hampshire 3

PEGASUS RFC
Club Secretary: Mr. R. Tomlinson, 7 Golf Ride, South Benfleet, Essex, SS7 1EQ
Fixtures Secretary: As above
League: Eastern Counties 3 South

PETERSFIELD RFC
Ground Address: Penns Place, Petersfield, Hants. GU31 4EP   Tel: 01730 264588
Brief Directions: East edge of town, co-located with East Hants District Council Offices and Taro Leisure Centre
Club Secretary: Geoff Litchfield, 13 Copse Close, Petersfield. GU31 4DL   Tel: (H) 01730 265072.
Email: glitch@tinyworld.co.uk
Fixtures Secretary: Albert Winterbottom, 8 Woodbury Avenue, Petersfield, Hants, GU32 2EE.
Tel No: 01730 261860
Club Colours: Red with white hoop
League: Hampshire 1

PINNER & GRAMMARIANS RFC
Ground Address: Shaftesbury Playing Fields, Grimsdyke Road, Hatchend Pinner, Middlesex
Tel: 0181 428 3136 Clubhouse repairs so may not bre available
Brief Directions: By rail: Hatch End (NSG & B'loo), west A410 Uxbrge Rd to Hatch End B'way Shps, rt G'sdyke Rd, 2nd rt H'view, 1st lt C'burn Ave, club lt. Road: frm E. same, frm W. A410 Uxbrg Rd, lt G'dyke Rd
Club Secretary: David Hiles, 31 Lulworth Close, South Harrow, Middlesex. HA2 9NR
Tel : (H & Fax) 020 8864 0787
Email: david@thehiles.co.uk
Fixtures Secretary: Phil Kojcinovic. 39 Puddingstone Drive,St Albans, Herts.
Tel No: 01727 845 205(H) 01923 231 936 (W) 0956 679824 (M)
Club Colours: Navy and 1" scarlet hoops
League: Hertfordshire & Middlesex 4 North

PLUMPTON RFC
Ground Address: The Racecourse, Plumpton Green, East Sussex
Brief Directions: Plumpton Racecourse opposite railway station in village of Plumpton Green
Club Secretary: Chris Woodward, 2 Monks Way, Lewes, East Sussex. BN7 2EX
Tel: (H) 01273 476219
Fixtures Secretary: Mark Slade, 2 Park Close,Burgess Hill, West Sussex.RH15 *HC
Tel No: 01444 343792
Club Colours: Maroon and amber hoops
League: Sussex 2 East

PORTCASTRIAN RFC
Ground Address: Iford Lane Playing Fields, Iford Lane, Southbourne, Bournemouth, Dorset. BH6 5NF
Tel: 01202 434565
Brief Directions: Turn towards Southbourne off A228 (Wessex Way) into Iford Lane, past Bournemouth Hospital to Iford Lane, playing fields on left
Club Secretary: Martin Davis, 64 Withermoor Road, Bournemouth, Dorfset. BH9 2PB Tel Nos : (H) 01202 519406 (W) 01202 291483
Email: davis martin1@talk21 ,com
Fixtures Secretary: Glyn Howells, Flat 3, Avon Court, 43 Warren Avenue, Christchurch BH23 3JY
Tel: 01202 484799
Club Colours: Royal blue, yellow and red hoops
League: Hampshire 2

PORTSMOUTH RFC
Ground Address: Norway Road, Hilsea, Portsmouth
Tel: 01705 660610
Brief Directions: From A27 take A2030 towards Southsea. at first lights take right turn and continue over bridge. Ground is on left.
Club Secretary: Ian Wilson, 116 Rowner Road, Gosport, Hants. PO13 9RG   Tel No: 01329 230752
Fixtures Secretary: Mr W. Arnold, 61 Chetwynd Road, Southsea, Hampshire.
Tel: (H) 01705 821109 (W) 01705 819125
Club Colours: Black with 3 white & gold hoops
League: London 2 South

PULBOROUGH RFC
Ground Address: Sports & Social Club, Rectory Lane, Pulborough, West Sussex. Tel: 01798 873020
Brief Directions: Approach by Rectory Lane branching north off east end of Lower Street opposite Arundale School
Club Secretary: Chris Brazier, 2 Heather Farm Cottages, Chobham Rd., Horsell Common, Woking, Surrey GU21 4XY   Tel: (W) 01798 812345
Fixtures Secretary: Michael Ford, 14 Ravenscroft, Sturrington, West Essex   Tel: (H) 01903 745697
Club Colours: Black and white hoops
League: Sussex 2 West

PURLEY JOHN FISHER RFC
Ground Address: Parsons Pightle, Coulsdon Road, Old Coulsdon, Surrey. CR5 1EE. Tel: 01737 553042
Brief Directions: M25 J7 - M23-A23, turn right in Coulsdon to Marl Pit Lane, to end turn right, Coulsdon Road, ground 0.5 mile on right
Club Secretary: Simon Witham, 2 Kingswood Avenue, Sanderstead, Surrey. CR2 9DQ
Tel: (H) 0181 657 2089 (W) 0171 247 4466
Fixtures Secretary: Martin Bazley
Tel: (H) 0181 660 2157 (W) 0171 377 5423
Club Colours: Black and white
League: London 4 South West

QUEEN ELIZABETH II HOSPITAL RFC
Ground Address: Hatfield Hyde Sports Club, King George V Playing Fields, Beehive Lane, Welwyn Garden City, Hertfordshire. Al7 4BP
Tel: 01707 326700

Brief Directions: From A1 take WGC exit, follow signs to QE II Hospital, when in the road "Howlands" turn into Beehive Lane, turn left past Beehive public house
Club Secretary: Adan Bowe,
1 Drycroft, Welwyn Garden City, Herts. AL7 4PH
Tel : 01707 332303 (H)
E-mail: abowe@ikon,com
Fixtures Secretary: Rod Ibbinson,
29 The Moors, Welwyn Garden City, Herts .
Tel: 01707 331341 (H) 0374 980145 (M)
e-mail; ribinson@ ruberoid.com.uk
Club Colours: Myrtle green and amber shirts, black shorts and green socks
League: Hertfordshire & Middlesex 3 North

QUINTIN RFC
Ground Address: Quintin Hogg Memorial Ground, Cavendish Road, Grove Park, London W4 .
Tel: 0181 994 0467
club website:www.btinternetcom/-quintinrfc
Brief Directions: Go north from Chiswick Bridge 1st left Hartington Rd (Pitches on left.) continue turn 1st right Cavendish Rd for entry to Pavilion on right side of road.
Club Secretary: Nigel Smith,
4 Australia Avenue, Maidenhead, Berks. SL6 7DJ.
Tel: (H) 01628 675899
Email: nigel.smith4 @ which.net
Fixtures Secretary: Jon Adcock,
2 Meadowbank Road, Lightwater, Surrey GU18 5SX
Trl: (H) 01276 475305
Club Colours: Scarlet and green hoops, blue shorts
League: Hertfordshire & Middlesex 4 South

RAVENS RFC
Ground Address: Ford Sports Club, Aldborough Road South, Newbury Park, Ilford, Essex.
Tel: 020 8590 3797.
Brief Directions: Off Eastern Avenue (A12) Newbury Park
Club Secretary: A.F. Rowley,
169 Kiln Road, Thundersley, Essex, SS7 1SJ.
01702 558389
Fixtures Secretary: P. Maguire,
52 Rutland Road, Ilford, Essex, IG1 1ER.
Tel: 020 8478 6010
Club Colours: Dark blue and yellow hoops
League: Eastern Counties 3 South

RAYLEIGH WYVERNS RFC
Ground Address: John Fisher Playing Fields, Little Wheatleys Chase, Rayleigh, Essex
Brief Directions: From A127 take A130 towards Chelmsford, next roundabout turn right, towards Rayleigh (A129), take 1st right Little Wheatleys Chase, ground 500 yds on right after school
Club Secretary: S J Earl, 22 The Fairway, Leigh-on-Sea, Essex. SS9 4QL
Tel: (H) 01702 524111
Fixtures Secretary: N. McQuire, 6 Copper Beeches, Thundersley, Essex SS7 3UA
Tel: 01268 772835
Club Colours: Scarlet and emerald quarters
League: Eastern Counties 3 South

RAYNES PARK RFC
Ground Address: Raynes Park Sports Ground, Taunton Avenue, Raynes Park, London. SW20
Brief Directions: Shannon Corner exit A3 to Raynes Park, last turning left (Camberley Ave) before Coombe Lane/West Barnes Lane traffic lights
Club Secretary: Russell Price, 101 Belmont Avenue, New Malden, Surrey. KT3 6QE. Tel: (H) 0181 949 2448 (W) 0171 299 5082
Fixtures Secretary: Roger Dunckley,441 Merton Road,Southfields,London SW18 5LB
Tel No: 07901556004
Club Colours: Blue and gold quarters, blue shorts and socks
League: Surrey 2

REIGATE & REDHILL RFC
Ground Address: Eric Hodgkins Memorial Ground, Colley Lane, Reigate, Surrey. Tel: 01737 221110
Brief Directions: M25 J8 south on Reigate Hill, turn right before level crossing, to end of road turn right then keep left into Colley Lane, club 200m on right
Club Secretary: Norman Phillips, 28 Hurstleigh Drive, Redhill, Surrey. RH1 2AA. Tel: (H) 01737 212912
Fixtures Secretary: Bob Collingbourne, 18 Weatview Close, Redhill, Surrey. RH16ST
Email: robert.collingbourne@ pfiser.com
Club Colours: Royal blue with white hoops
League: Surrey 3

RICHMOND FC
Ground Address: The Athletic Ground, Kew Foot Road, Richmond, Surrey TW9 2SS
Tel: 020 8332 7112 Website: www.richmondfc. co.uk
Brief Directions: The Athletic Ground lies on the north side ofthe A316 just west of Richmond Circus R'about and adj. to Royal Mid Surrey Golf Course and the Swimming Pool, Pools on the Park
Club Secretary: Andrew Gordon address and telephone number as ground
Email: andrewg@richmondfc.co.uk
Fixtures Secretary: Vic Balchin, 11 Troutbeck Close, Twyford, Berkshire, RG10 9DA.
Tel/Fax: 0118 9345765
Club Colours: Old Gold, red & black hoops
League: London 4 South West
League Contact: Andy Quigley, 46 Coval Road, East Sheen, London, SW14 7RL
Tel: 020 8878 2838 Email: quigas@aol.com

ROBERTSBRIDGE RFC
Ground Address: Robertsbridge Community College, Knelle Road, Robertsbridge, East Sussex. TN32 5EA
Brief Directions: From the village follow signs to the railway station, go over the level crossing, take the 2nd right then go straight up to the college
Club Secretary: Bernard Davies , 12 Ridgeway, Hurst Green, East Sussex TN19 7PJ.
Tel : 01580 860325
Fixtures Secretary: Paul Strovell, 12 Ridgeway, Hurst Green, East Sussex TN19 7PJ
Tel No: 07944 653204(M) 01959515915
Club Colours: Blue and Black Quarters
League: Sussex 2 East

ROCHFORD HUNDRED RFC
Ground Address: The Clubhouse, Magnolia Road, Hankwell, Essex. SS4 3AD
Tel: 01702 544021
Brief Directions: Please phone Fixture Secretary
Club Secretary: R Simon Wakefield, 54 Parklands Drive, Springfield, Chelmsford, Essex. CM1 7SP
Tel : (H) 01245 266158 (W) 01702 541581
Email: swakefield@contechs.co.uk
Fixtures Secretary: Mr Colin Chandler
Tel: (H) 01277 766748
Club Colours: Black shirt and shorts, black socks with white tops
League: London 3 North East

ROMFORD & GIDEA PARK RFC
Ground Address: Crowlands, Crow Lane, Romford, Essex. RM7 0EP
Tel: 01708 760068
Brief Directions: A12 to Moby Dick pub, from London right, into Whalebone Lane Nth,at lights left London Rd, 0.5 mile into Jutsums Ln,underbridge,(unsuitable for coaches) left into Crow Ln, ground 100yds on right
Club Secretary: D G E Davies, 25 Stanley Avenue, Gidea Park, Romford, Essex. RM2 5DL. Tel: 01708 724870 (Tel/Fax)
Fixtures Secretary: Tony Healey ,27 Lansbury Avenue, CHadwell Heath, Romford.
Tel No: 020 8599 6451
Club Colours: Black, purple and white hoops with black shorts.
League: London 3 North East

ROMSEY RUFC
Ground Address: Romsey Sports Centre, Lower Southampton Road, Romsey, Hampshire. SO51 8AF
Tel : 01794 519400
Brief Directions: On A27 into Romsey, Sports centre is next to Romsey Rapids Swimming centre on Southampton Road.
Club Secretary: V. Messenger, 12a The Harrage, Romsey, Hants., SO57 8AE.
Tel: 10794 514638
Email: mesiai@ lineone.net
Fixtures Secretary: Malcolm Pain, 2 Nursery Road, Bitterne Park, Southampton. SO18 1NS Tel: 02380 557572
Club Colours: Royal blue with gold hoops, blue shorts, gold topped blue socks
League: Hampshire 1

ROYAL & SUN ALLIANCE
Ground Address: Royal & Sun Alliance Club, North Heath Lane, Horsham, West Sussex RH12 4PJ.
Tel : 01403 352404
Website: www.rsarugby-fsnet.co.uk
Brief Directions: Leave A264 at roundabout for Roffey, 3rd exit at next roundabout, go half mile and turn left into North Heath Lane at mini roundabout, ground is half mile on LHS.
Club Secretary: K. J. Reed, 12 Dale Close, Horsham, West Sussex RH12 4JD Email: keith.reed@uk.royalsun.com
Tel: 01403 242929 (H) 01903 233765 (W)
Fixtures Secretary: C. Nicholas, 44 Cissbury Close, Horsham, West Sussex RH12 5JT.

Tel : 01903 275393 Email: carl.nicholas@esure.com
Colours: Navy with yellow, green & white chevron
League: Sussex 2 West
League Contact: Email: brian@lewsec.clara.net

ROYSTON RUFC
Ground Address: Heath Sports Club, Baldock
Road, Royston. SG8
Tel: 01763 243613
Brief Directions: A10 north or south to roundabout
by cinema, turn west through town centre, past golf
club on left, A505 from Baldock turn right at Little
Chef, club on right
Club Secretary: Colin Dacey, 4 Valley Rise,
Royston, Herts., SG8 9EY.
Fixtures Secretary: Godfrey Everett, 24 Clarkes
Way,Bassingbourne, Royston, Herts. SG8 5LT
Tel: (H) 01763 243846
Club Colours: Black and white hoops, black shorts,
black socks
League: Hertfordshire & Middlesex 4 North

RUISLIP RFC
Ground Address: West End Road, Ruislip,
Middlesex. HA4 6DR
Tel: 01895 633102
Website: ruisliprfc.co.uk
Brief Directions: M25, J16 oto M40 towards London
and onto A40. After Northolt Airport turn left into
West End Road A4180. Ground 3 miles on left.
Nearest station is Ruislip Underground.
Club Secretary: Stephen Aldcroft, 30 Elmbridge
Drive, Ruislip, Middlesex.
Tel: 07973 313380 -
Email: stev@richmondplastics.co.uk
Fixtures Secretary: Steve Hazell, 23 Hopfield
Avenue, Byfleet, Surrey
Tel: (H) 01932 400361 (W) 020 8641 8510
Club Colours: Maroon and white hooped shirts,
white shorts, maroon socks
League: London 3 North West

RYE RFC
Ground Address: New Road, Rye, East Sussex
Tel: 01797 227844
Brief Directions: Situated east of main town on the
A259 coast road
Club Secretary: Jason Bowen, 15 South Undercliff,
Rye, East Sussex. TN31 7HN.
Tel: (H) 01797 227838
Email: bowen@freenetrame.co
Fixtures Secretary: D.Ramus, Moat farm, Moat
Lane, Iden, East Sussex TN31 7UU.
Tel: 01797 280 049
e-mail; daveram@cwcom.net
Club Colours: Red and white quarters, black shorts,
black socks
League: Sussex 1

SAFFRON WALDEN RFC
Ground Address: Springate, Henham, Nr Bishops
Stortford
Tel: 01279 850791
Club Secretary: B Peachey, 2 Gloucester Place,
Clare, Suffolk. CO10 8QR
Tel: (H) 01787 278464 (W) 01277 260600
Fixtures Secretary: D. Cassells, 25 Cambridge

Crescent, Bassingbourn, Royston SG8 5LP
Tel: (H) 01763 243978 (W) 01223 203704
Club Colours: Myrtle green
League: London 4 North East
League Contact: As Secretary

SANDOWN & SHANKLIN RFC
Ground Address: The Clubhouse, Station
Approach, The Fairway, Lake, Sandown, Isle of
Wight. PO36 9ES
Tel : 01983 404707
Website: www.ssrfc.co.uk
Brief Directions: By rail: Pitch is adjacent to
Sandown Station. Use underpass to reach club. By
road: Follow main Sandown Shanklin road to Lake,
take `The Fairway' - Pitch on right opposite high
school.
Club Secretary: Nigel Stotesbury, 25 Albony View,
Camphill, Newport, Isle of Wight, PO30 5PF.
Tel : 01983 521981
Fixtures Secretary: Colin Bond, 8 St. Johns
Crescent, Sandown, Isle of Wight, PO36
Tel : (H) 01983 402374
Club Colours: Dark blue with red, white and blue
hoops
League: Hampshire 1
League Contact: Graham Thomas, 53 Collingwood
Road, Shanklin, Isle of Wight.
Tel: 01983 863572

SAWSTON RFC
Ground Address: Sawston Village College, New
Road, Sawston, Cambs. CB2 4BP
Tel: 01223 836615
Brief Directions: M11 J10, take A505 to Sawston,
next roundabout take A1301 marked
Sawston/Cambridge, after 1 mile turn right to
Sawston then 1st left New Road, College on left
Club Secretary: Paul Clerke, 1 Crossways, Linton,
Cambridge. CB1 6NQ
Tel: (H) 01223 843985 (W) 01223 834555 Ext 3575
Fixtures Secretary: Philip Mason
Tel: (H) 01279 812545 (W) 0171 377 6161 Ext 289
Club Colours: Black, navy and white quarters
League: Eastern Counties 3 North

SEAFORD RFC
Ground Address: The Salts Recreation Ground,
The Esplanade, Seaford
Tel: 01323 892355
Brief Directions: Situated on the sea front just off
the A259
Club Secretary: Andy Smith, 11 Chichester Road,
Seaford, Sussex BN25 4DJ.
Tel No: 01323 490993 e-mail:
 andy.smith 20@ virgin.net
Fixtures Secretary: Paul Joy, 4 Kingston Close,
Deaford.
tel No: 01323 894042
Club Colours: Scarlet shirts with navy blue shorts
League: Sussex 2 East
League Contact: As Secretary

LONDON & SOUTH EAST

SEVENOAKS RUFC
Ground Address: Knole Paddock, Plymouth Drive, Sevenoaks, Kent. TN13 3RP
Tel: 01732 452027
Brief Directions: J.5 M25. Follow signs to Sevenoaks. At Riverhead R/about turn R. up Amhersa Hill. L. after BR station R. at top then L. around Cricket Ground - Plymouth Drive on right.
Club Secretary: Howard G Pearl, Nearly Corner, Hemerham, Kent TN15 6NQ
Tel: 01732 763431
Fixtures Secretary: Nick Wagstaff
Tel: 01732 461742
Club Colours: Navy & Gold
League: London 2 South
League Contact: As Secretary

SHELFORD RUFC
Ground Address: Davey Field, Cambridge Road, Gt Shelford, Cambridge
Tel: 01223 843357
Website: shelfordrugby.co.uk
Brief Directions: M11 J11 heading into Cambridge, right at traffic lights into Shelford Rd, continue for 1 mile, club is on the right opposite Scotsdale Garden Centre
Club Secretary: Lydia Seymour, 22 London Road, Gt. Shelford, Cambridge. CB2 5DD
Tel: (H) 01223 503644
Fixtures Secretary: Ian Coupe, 95 Tamarin Gardens, Cherry Hinton, Cambridge. CB1 9GQ
Club Colours: Maroon and white hoops, blue shorts
League: London 3 North East

SHEPPEY FOOTBALL CLUB LTD
Ground Address: The Clubhouse, Scocles Field, Lower Road, Minster, Sheerness, Kent ME12
Tel: 01795 872082
Brief Directions: A249 to Sheppey, from M2 or M20 on Sheppey, at 1st roundabout take
Club Secretary: Mrs Linda Neal, 16 New Road, Minster, Sherness, Kent.
Tel No: 01795 873983 (H) 01795 439409 (W)
Fixtures Secretary: As Secretary.
Club Colours: White with single red hoop, black shorts
League: Kent 2
League Contact: As Secretary

SHIRLEY WANDERERS RUFC
Ground Address: Kent Gate, 135 Addington Road, West Wickham, Kent
Tel: 0181 777 5298
Brief Directions: From West Wickham, go down Corkscrew Hill and turn right at bottom. Club about 1/4 mile on left.
Club Secretary: J.A.Pound, 4 Tanglewood Close, Shirley, Surrey CR0 5HX. Tel: 0209 8656 4336
Fixtures Secretary: Geoff Jeffcoat,96 Woodland Way, West Wickham,Kent BR4 9LT
Tel: (H) 0208 777 5174
           (W) 0181 761 3000
Club Colours: All white
League: Surrey 2

SHOOTERS HILL RFC
Ground Address: 123/125 Mayday Gardens, Kidbrooke, London. SE3   Tel: 0181 856 1511
Brief Directions: From Well Hall r'bout take signs for Woolwich & Ferry, over lights at top of hill, next left Broadwalk, over 4 humps, left into Mayday Gdns, follow road to green on left, entrance to ground in corner
Club Secretary: B.A.C. Kennett, 18 Elmwood Drive, Bexley, Kent DA5 3PT
Tel: 0208 304 4982
Fixtures Secretary: I.Trevett, 76 Southwood Road, London. SE9 3QT   Tel No: 020 8850 6693
Club Colours: Red, blue, green and yellow
League: Kent 3

SHOREHAM RFC
Ground Address: Kings Manor School, Kingston Lane, Shoreham-by-Sea, West Sussex
Tel: 01273 597625
Brief Directions: Take A27 to Shoreham (Old Shoreham Road) westward Kingston Lane is on left at traffic lights before Holmbush shopping centre r'bout, Kings Manor School 0.5 mile on right
Club Secretary: Simon Edgar, 17 Newtimber Gardens, Shoreham-by-Sea, West Sussex BN43 5GQ.
Tel: (H) 01273 701618 (W) 0831 236918
Fixtures Secretary: Mrs Sandy Beal
Tel: (H) 01273 884827
Club Colours: Amber and bottle green quarters
League: Sussex 2 West

SIDCUP RFC
Ground Address: Crescent Farm, Sydney Road, Sidcup, Kent. DA14 6RA
Tel: 0208 3002336
Website: sidcuprfc.co.uk
Brief Directions: A20-A222 towards Sidcup (Chislehurst Rd), proceed to 1st traffic lights (Police Station), left into Main Road, left just past fire station into Sydney Rd, ground 200mtrs on left
Club Secretary: Allan Jones, 53 Goodwin Drive, Sidcup, Kent. DA14 4NX
Tel: 0208 302 2382
Fixtures Secretary: Malcolm Leamon, 43 Glen House Road , Eltham, London SE9 1JH. Tel: 0208 859 5598
Club Colours: White shirts with navy blue collar and cufs. Maroon Shorts
League: London 3 South East

SITTINGBOURNE RUFC
Ground Address: Gore Court Sports Club, The Grove, Key Street, Sittingbourne, Kent. ME10 1YT
Tel: 01795 423813
Brief Directions: From M2 eastbound, A249 to Sittingbourne & Sheerness, after 2 miles take A2 towards Sittingbourne, after 0.5 mile turn left just after Sports ground, left again into club car park
Club Secretary: Steve Smith, 34 Crouch Hill Court, Lower Halstow, Sittingbourne, Kent. ME9 7EJ
Tel: (H) 01795 843356
Fixtures Secretary: Denise Smith as above.
Tel: (H) 01795 843356
Club Colours: Blue and gold hoops
League: Kent 2

LONDON & SOUTH EAST

SOUTH WOODHAM FERRERS RFC
Ground Address: Saltcoats Park, Ferrers roRd, South Woodham Ferrers.
Tel: 01245 320041
Brief Directions: From A127 take A130 to Chelms Road at Rettenden Turnpike take A132 to South Woodham Ferrers. On entering town follow signs to Saltcoats Ind. Est.. Ground on left after 3rd R/about. From A12 Chelms Road take A130 Southend at Rettenden Turnpike A132 as above.
Club Secretary: David Parkinson, 43 Clements Green Lane, South Woodham Ferrers, Essex, CM3 5JS. Tel: 01245 321376
Email: nosnikrap 4 @bt internet.com
Fixtures Secretary: Paul Gregory, 1 Maydene, South Woodham Ferrers, Essex, CM3 5ND.
Tel No: 01245 328930
Club Colours: All black
League: Eastern Counties 2 South

SOUTHAMPTON INSTITUTE
Ground Address: Hardmoor Playing Fields, Stoneham Lane, Eastleigh. SO5 3HT
Tel: 01703 617574
Brief Directions: Exit junction 5 on M27 (Airport turn off)
Club Secretary: Matt Bishop, Flat 1, Lecksley Court, Archers Rd, Southampton SO15 2LE
Tel NO: 023 8023 3410
Email: matthew bishop@solent.ac.ulc
Fixtures Secretary: Secretary as above.
Club Colours: Maroon and white
League: Hampshire 3

SOUTHAMPTON RFC
Ground Address: Test Park Playing Fields, Lower Brownhill Road, Millbrook, Southampton, Hants.
Tel: 023 8073 7777
Brief Directions: M27 onto M271, take 1st slip road, 1st exit towards Lordshill, after 150 yds turn right into Lower Brownhill Road
Club Secretary: Paul Raine, Tanglewood, Winchester Rd., Boorley Green , Southampton SO32 2DH. Tel: (H) 01489 788460
Fixtures Secretary: Rob Swain .Tel No: 023 8036 7140
Club Colours: Red and white hoops
League: Hampshire 1

SOUTHEND RFC
Ground Address: Warners Bridge Park, Sumpters Way, Southend on Sea SS2 5RR
Tel : 01702 546682
Brief Directions: A127 to Southend turn left Sutton Road, turn right at R/about into Temple Farm Ind. Estate. Follow road to the end turn left club is 50 yards at end of road.
Club Secretary: Neil Harding, 77 Hillside Crescent, Leigh-on-Sea, Essex, SS5 1HH.
Tel: 01702 477799
Fixtures Secretary: Frank Dyton, 1 The Coastways, Westcliffe-on-Sea, Essex, SS0 0AU.
Tel : 01702 475075
Club Colours: Brown brown and white
League: London 2 North
League Contact: As Secretary

SOUTHGATE RFC
Ground Address: Nortel Ltd, Oakleigh Road South, New Southgate, London. N11 1HBT
Tel : 0181 945 2655/2181
Website: www.southgate-rfc.clara.co.uk
Brief Directions: A406 frm E., exit for Arnos Grove, pass Arnos Grve stn to r'bout, 2nd exit for Oakl'gh Rd Sth. A406 frm W., left for New Southgate stn, right at Turrets pub, 1st exit r'bout for Oakl'gh Rd Sth
Club Secretary: David Hockey, 5 The Vineries, Enfield, Middlesex. EN1 3DQ
Tel: (H) 0181 342 0202 (W) 020 7270 1551
e-mail: david.hockey@nilo.gov.uk
Fixtures Secretary: Simon Shuttler, 60 Exeter Road,Southgate, London N14
Tel: (H) 0181 368 5025 (W) 0181 446 8324
Club Colours: Dark blue, light blue and gold irregular hoops
League: Hertfordshire & Middlesex 4 North

SOUTHWOLD RFC
Ground Address: The Pavilion, The Common, Southwold, Suffolk
Brief Directions: First right at Kings Head Hotel and proceed towards water tower
Club Secretary: Mrs CLare Webb, 34-35 Elm FM Cottages, Elms Lane, Wangford, Suffolk
Tel: 01502 578578
Fixtures Secretary: Jeremy Taylor , 27 The Firs, Reydon, Suffolk. IP18 6Y5
Tel No: 01502 724476
Club Colours: Black with Gold hoop.
League: Eastern Counties 3 North

ST ALBANS RFC
Ground Address: Boggey Mead Spring, Oaklands Lane, Smallford, St Albans, Herts. AL4 0HR
Tel: 01727 869945
Club Secretary: N J Millar, 39 Watford Road, St Albans, Herts. AL1 2AE
Tel: (H) 01727 830169 (W) 01582 794007
Fixtures Secretary: Mr. Tim Andrews, 77 Batchwood Drive, St. Albans, Herts. Tel: (H) 01727 857440
Club Colours: Royal blue and gold hoops, navy shorts
League: London 4 North West

ST FRANCIS RFC
Ground Address: Southgate Playing Fields, Southgate Avenue, Crawley, West Sussex. Tel No: 01293 616941
Website: ww st-francis -rugby.com
Brief Directions: M23 J11, take A23 to Crawley, right at roundabout into Southgate Ave, ground approx 1 mile on right hand side
Club Secretary: Mark Eastman, 182 Buckswood Dr, Gossops Green, Crawley, West Sussex RW11 8PS
Tel No: 07968 803171
Email: mark.eastman @st.albans-church.co.uk
Fixtures Secretary: Vince McGahan, 83 Winchester Road, Tilgate, Crawley, West Sussex.
(H) 01293 547194 (W) 01293 503389
Club Colours: Black with blue and two white hoops
League: Sussex 1

ST NICHOLAS OLD BOYS RFC
Ground Address: c/o Ickenham Cricket Club, Oak Avenue, Ickenham, Middlesex
Tel: 01895 639366
Brief Directions: A40 exit Hillingdon Circus, follow signs toIckenham, turn left to Oak Avenue past Total Garage.
Club Secretary: Alison Summerfield, 13 Paignton Road, Ruislip, MIddlesex HA4 0BU
Tel No: 01895 632161
Fixtures Secretary: Bob Maynard, 117 Swakeleys Road, Ickenham, Middlesex UB10 8DF
Tel: (M) 0973 503 530 - (H) 01895 632161
Club Colours: Red shirts with black & white hoops, black shorts
League: Hertfordshire & Middlesex 3 South

STANFORD-LE-HOPE RFC
Ground Address: Stanford-Le-Hope Recreation Ground, Stanford-Le-Hope, Essex.
Tel : 01375 640957
Brief Directions: A13 to Stanford-Le-Hope then turn off at A1014. Right at roundabout into Corringham Rd. First left Rainbow Lane, First Right Billet Lane. Clubhouse at far end on right.
Club Secretary: Darren Watkins, 169 London Road, Grays, Essex, RM17 5YP.
Tel : (H) 01375 374776
Fixtures Secretary: Kyran M cDonald, 3 St. James Avenue East, Stanford-Le-Hope, Essex , SS17 7BQ
Tel: (H) 01375 403520
Club Colours: Red, White and Black stripes.
League: Eastern Counties 1

STEVENAGE TOWN RFC
Ground Address: North Road, Stevenage, Herts. SG1 4BB
Tel: 01438 359788
Website: www.resultsclub.com
Brief Directions: Take A1M Stevenage North Jcn 7, take road towards Graveley, 1st right (past garden centre) towards St'age, ground 400yds on right, parking on access road by pitches
Club Secretary: Ben Tranter. 30 Ivel Road,Stevenage, Herts.
Tel No: 01438 317734
Fixtures Secretary: Fred McCarthy,48 Fenner Drive, Biggleswade, Beds. SG18 8ND
Telk No: 01767 221243 SG2 2LN
Tel: (H) 01438 811590 (W) 01438 767231
Club Colours: Black shirts with green hoop, black shorts, green socks
League: Hertfordshire & Middlesex 1

STONEHAM PARK RUFC
(Formerly AC Delco)
Ground Address: Stoneham Park Sports and Social Club, Sports Ground, Stoneham Lane, Eastleigh, Southampton, Hants
Tel: 023 80613334
Brief Directions: M27 Jct 5. Stoneham Lane Northbound. Ground on left just after Concorde club on right.
Club Secretary: Steve Lines, 18 Mead Road Chandlers Ford, SO53 2EZ
Tel: 023 80273166
Email: stevielines@aol.com

Fixtures Secretary: John Hunter, 100 Newton Road, Weston, Southampton
Tel No: 023 80396688
Club Colours: Navy blue and red quarters or navy blue and light blue hoops
League: Hampshire 3

STOWMARKET RUFC
Ground Address: Chilton Fields Sports Club, Chilton Way, Off Onehouse Road, Stowmarket, Suffolk, IP14 1SZ
Tel: 01449 613181
Brief Directions: From Bury St Edmonds direction along A14, take exit marked Stowmarket, 2nd exit at roundabout, left onto housing estate, follow road, last road on the right
Club Secretary: Mrs Tracy Harrison, 5 Sycamore Close, Wattisham Airfield,Suffolk IP7 7SG
Tel: 01449 740196
Fixtures Secretary: Darryl Chapman, 55 Bridge Street, Stowmarket, Suffolk, IP14 1BP.
Tel: 01449 672787
Club Colours: Navy blue, white and red
League: Eastern Counties 2 North

STREATHAM-CROYDON RUFC
Ground Address: Rosevale, 159 Brigstock Road, Thornton Heath, Surrey. CR7 7JP.
Tel: 0181 684 1502
Brief Directions: A23 turn off at Thornton Heath Pond, 1st left is Brigstock Road, club 400 yards on right
Club Secretary: Mr. M. Bond, 61 Monarch Parade, London road, Mitcham, Surrey, CR4 3HA.
Fixtures Secretary: R V Towers
Tel: (H) 0181 658 2333 (W) 0181 698 8911
Club Colours: Maroon shirts, white shorts
League: Surrey 2

SUDBURY and LONDON SPRINGBOKS
(Previously Sudbury Court)
Ground Address: East Lane Pavilion, East Lane, North Wembley, Middlesex
Tel: 0181 904 8485
Brief Directions: By road: at junction of Watford Road and East Lane turn into East Lane, ground 400 yards on right. By train: To North Wembley station turn left ground 600yds on left.
Club Secretary: John Conway, 38 Courthope Road, Hampstead, London. NW3 2LD
Email: jcconway@msn.com
Fixtures Secretary: David Keeling, 17 Nunnery Lane, Luton, Beds. LU3 1XA
Tel: 01582 652417
Club Colours: Green,Gold,Red,White,and Blue shirt with black shorts and socks.
League: Hertfordshire & Middlesex 4 South

SUDBURY RUFC
Ground Address: Moorsfield, Rugby Road, Great Cornard, Sudbury, Suffolk
Tel : 01787 377547
Brief Directions: Ground on B 1508 Colchester, Bures, Sudbury road, 1.5 miles from Sudbury town centre in Great Cornard. From town centre left after Kings Head, 1st right into Rugby Rd

LONDON & SOUTH EAST

Club Secretary: P M E Maddocks, 8 Nether Court, Halstead, Essex. CO9 2HE
Tel : (H) 01787 473027
Fixtures Secretary: G Underwood, 11 Bures Road, Sreat Cornard, Sudbury, Suffolk CO10 0EJ
Tel: (H) 01787 373045
Club Colours: Blue jersey and wide white hoop
League: London 2 North

SUSSEX POLICE RFC
Ground Address: Brighton Rugby Club, Patcham, Waterhall, Brighton, Sussex
Tel: 01273 562729
Brief Directions: A23 London to Brighton road, turn right at Patcham along Mill Road, then left into Waterhall ground
Club Secretary: P Johnson, Police Station, Kingsham Road, Chichester, Sussex. Tel: (H) 01243 825408 (W) 01243 520230
Fixtures Secretary: C Gale
Tel: (H) 01444 458482 (W) 01444 451555
Club Colours: Blue and gold quarters, blue shorts, blue socks
League: Sussex 1

SWAFFHAM RUFC
Ground Address: North Pickenham Road, Swaffham, Norfolk
Tel: 01760 724829
Brief Directions: Into town centre, at traffic lights take A47 towards E. Dereham, turn right at Gradys Hotel along North Pickenham Road, ground 400 metres on right
Club Secretary: Hugh Green, Gemini Cottage, Weasenham St Peter, Kings Lynn, Norfolk. PE32 2TD
Tel: (H) 01328 838269
Fixtures Secretary: Eric Nye, 7 Warstade Way, Swaffham, Norfolk PE37 7NX
Tel: 01760 723377
Club Colours: Amber and black hoops with black shirts.
League: Eastern Counties 3 North

TEDDINGTON R.F.C.(
Ground Address: Bushy Park, Teddington, Middlesex   Tel: 020 8977 4989
Website: www.teddingtonrfc.co.uk
Brief Directions: Ground adjacent to Teddington Cricket Club in Bushy Park, at the rear of N.P.L.
Club Secretary: Peter Woolgar, 114 Elgin Avenue, Ashford, Middlesex. TW15 1QG
Tel: (H) 01784 259734
Email: pjwoolgar@hotmail.com
Fixtures Secretary: Rod Bromfield, 104 Station Road, Hampton, Middlesex
Tel: (H) 020 8979 5635
Club Colours: Dark blue
League: Surrey 2

THAMES RUFC
Ground Address: St Cedds Playing Field, Garron Lane, Aveley, South Ockendon, Essex
Tel No: 01708 852907
Brief Directions: Turn off Tunnel Junction, down Ship Lane, right at T junction, second off roundabout. First left, second left.
Club Secretary: Tony Smith,67 St.Michaels Close, Aveley, Essex   Tel: 01708 868331
Fixtures Secretary: Paul Brett, 10 Oakdene Road, Orpington, Kent. BR5 2AJ   Tel: 01689 836463
Club Colours: Emerald Green and black hoops
League: Eastern Counties 2 South

THAMESIANS RFC
Ground Address: Marble Hill Park, off Richmond Road, Twickenham, Middlesex. TW1 2NL
Tel No: 020 8892 1900
Brief Directions: Entrance to ground is on Richmond Road (A305) with dressing rooms adjacent to car park.
Club Secretary: Mark DeBrett, 89 Lime Grove, New Malden, Surrey, KT3 3TR
Tel: 020 8942 1314   Email: mdebrett@aol.com
Fixtures Secretary: Shane Kelly,
Flat 2, No. 1 The Barons, St. Margarets, Twickenham, Middlesex, TW1 2AN.
Tel: 07711 823093 or 020 8744 1707
Email: skelly@colt.net
Club Colours: Maroon/green, white or green shorts
League Contact: As Fixture Secretary
League: Herts/Middlesex 4 South

THE OLD BEVONIANS RFC
Ground Address: Ballard Coombe, Robin Hood Way, London. SW15 3QF
Tel: 0181 942 2907
Brief Directions: Along A3, London bound side between New Malden & Robin Hood R'about.
Club Secretary: Mrs A. Lefeure, 100 Longfellow Road, Worcester Park, Surrey. KT4 8BR Tel: 0208330 2278 (H) 0181 286 9674 (W)
Email: bevonians@hotmail.com
Fixtures Secretary: Ben Line, 6 Highdown, Worcester Park, Surrey KT4 8BE
Tel No: 020 8330 1712
Club Colours: Black, amber and green hoops
League: Surrey 3

THETFORD RFC
Ground Address: Two Mile Bottom, Mundford Road, Thetford, Norfolk, IP24 1LZ
Tel: 01842 755176
Brief Directions: From Thetford by-pass at top R/about take A134 King's Lynn Road. 1.5 miles down at bottom of hill on right hand side - concealed entrance.
Club Secretary: Iain Harper, 15 Anna Sewell Close, Thetford, Norfolk, IP24 1TN.   Tel: 01842 765369
Email: iainharper@aol.com
Fixtures Secretary: Gordon Hodgkinson, 48 Nunnery Drive, Thetford, Norfolk, IP24 3EN.
Tel: 01842 784667
Club Colours: Red and white hooped shirts, white shorts, red & white socks.
League: London 4 North East

LONDON & SOUTH EAST

THURROCK RFC
Ground Address: Oakfield, Long Lane, Grays, Essex RM16 2QH
Tel: 01375 374877 FAX: 01375 380641
Brief Directions: M25 from north J31/A13 direction Southend, 2nd exit (Grays), 4th exit from 2nd round-about, off 1st left (Long Lane), 3 miles east to above address, left at flats.
Club Secretary: Mrs D Howells, 6 Branksom Ave., Stanford-le-Hope, Essex. SS17 8AZ. Tel: 01375 404280 e-mail: diane@howellsd.freeserve.co.uk
Fixtures Secretary: Kevin Hymas "Clearwater", Argent Street, Grays, Essex, RM17 6PGTel: 01375 383666 (H) 01375 850100 (W)
Club Colours: Black with white hoops
League: London 2 North
League Contact: Fixture Secretary, as above.

THURSTON RUFC
Ground Address: Robinson Field, Ixworth Road, Thurston, Suffolk Tel: 01359 232450
Brief Directions: Exit A14 Thurston and follow Thurston signs, along Thurston Rd past Cracknells garage on right, under railway bridge, head out of village (school on left), ground 200 yards on right
Club Secretary: Paul Wreathall, 14 Gardiner Close, Bury St Edmunds ,Suffolk
Tel No: 01284 769545
Fixtures Secretary: Jeremy Kendall, 1 Harrington Close, Bury St Edmunds, Suffolk.IP33 2AE
Tel No: 01284 703043
Club Colours: Navy blue shirts with red collar & cuffs, blue shorts, stockings
League: Eastern Counties 2 North

TONBRIDGE JUDDIANS RFC
Ground Address: Deaconsfield, The Slade, Tonbridge, Kent TN9 1HR Tel: 01732 350548
Website: www.tonbridge-juddians.co.uk
Brief Directions: In Tonbridge High Street, turn opposite Rose & Crown Hotel into Castle Street. Follow signs to swimming pool but turn right at bottom of Slade into club car park
Club Secretary: G.D. Pettitt, 31 Thorpe Avenue, Tonbridge, Kent. TN10 4PW
Tel No: 01732 356818
Fixtures Secretary: David Carver, 50 Pennington Place, Southborough, Tunbridge Wells, Kent, TN4 0AQ.   Tel: (H) 01892 543736
Club Colours: Red, white & blue hooped shirts
League: London 3 South East

TOTTONIANS RFC
Ground Address: Water Lane, Totton, Hampshire. Tel: 01703 663810
Brief Directions: From centre of Totton follow directions to Totton College/Recreation Centre. The club is located next door.
Club Secretary: Mr G Searle, Meadow End, Romsey Road, Kings Sombourne, Stockbridge, Hampshire. SO20 6PR
Tel: (H) 01794 388779 (W) 01256 482572
Fixtures Secretary: Steve Anderson, 2 Redwood Gardens, Larchwood, Totton, Southampton SO40 8SY Tel: 02380 873565
Club Colours: Green, black and white hoops
League: London 4 South West

TRING RUFC
Ground Address: Pendley Sports Ground, Cow Lane, Tring, Herts., HP23
Tel: 01442 825710
Brief Directions: A41 to Tring at R/about follow signs to Northchurch. First left to Cow Lane. Club 600 metres on the right
Club Secretary: Paul Lamberth, 10 Long Field Gardens, Tring, Herts., HP23 4DN. Tel: 07767 247264
 Email: paul-lambert@hotmail.com
Fixtures Secretary: Malcolm Rose, 25 Grenadine Way, Tring, Herts., HP23 5EA.
Tel: 01442 381110
Club Colours: Black with goldhooped sleeves
League: Hertfordshire & Middlesex 1

TROJANS RFC
Ground Address: Stoneham Park, Stoneham Lane, Eastleigh, Hants. SO50 9HT
Tel: 023 80612400/80613068
Website: www.trojansrugby.co.uk
Brief Directions: M27 J5, proceed south signed Southampton on A335 to 1st lights, right into Bassett Green Rd, right at next lights into Stoneham Ln, under motorway and immediate left
Club Secretary: J W J Mist, Westbury House, 14 Bellevue Road, Southampton. SO15 2AY
Tel: (H) 023 8058 3450 (W) 023 8033 2844
Fixtures Secretary: C G Holt, The Chase, 338 Hill Lane, Southampton, SO15 7PH.
Tel: (W) 023 8077 1195
Club Colours: Blue with narrow red hoops
League: London 4 South West

TUNBRIDGE WELLS RFC
Ground Address: St Marks Recreation Ground, Frant Road, Tunbridge Wells
Tel: 01892 527448 Website: www.twrfc.com
Brief Directions: Southern outskirts of town, 0.5 miles along the a267 (Frant Road) left hand side at brow of hill
Club Secretary: Steve Bassi, Myringa, Broom Park, Langton Green, Tunbridge Wells, Kent. TN3 0RF
Tel No: 01892 863619
Email: stev@bassij.fsnd.co.uk
Fixtures Secretary: Colin Sharples, White Craigs, Stonewall Park Road, Langrton Green, Tunbridge Wells.Kent. TA3 0HG
Tel No: 01892 862580
Club Colours: Navy blue and white quarters
League: London 2 South

TWICKENHAM RFC
Ground Address: Park Fields, South Road, Hampton, Middlesex, TW12 3PE.
Tel: 020 8979 2427
Website: www.twickenhamrugby.com
Brief Directions: A316 to Unigate Dairy, take road to Hampton, turn right into Oak Ave, South Rd on right by Royal Oak public house
Club Secretary: J. N. Francis, 50 Hatherop Road, Hampton, Middlesex, TW12 2RF
Tel : (H) 0020 8941 0877
Email: jon @crowfield,ltd.uk

Fixtures Secretary: S. Weathers, 41 Silver Crescent, Chiswick, London, W4 5SF.
Tel: 020 87471127
Club Colours: Red and black irregular hoops
League: London 2 North

UCKFIELD RFC
Ground Address: Hempsted Playing Fields, Nevill Road, Manor Park, Uckfield
Tel: 01825 768956
Brief Directions: The Manor Park Estate is on northern outskirts of the town, turn into Browns Ln entrance & take 2nd road on left, the ground is at the end of the 3rd road on the right
Club Secretary: Mr. Pete Dunn, 9 North Row, Uckfield, TN22 1ES
Tel No: 01825 760780
Fixtures Secretary: Mrs Maureen Poole, Pentlands, 9 Keld Avenue, Uckfield TN22 5BN. Tel: (H) 01825 761151
Club Colours: Amber with purple and white hoops
League: London 4 South East

UCS OLD BOYS RFC
Ground Address: Farm Avenue, London. NW2
Tel: 020 8830 6376
Brief Directions: Please phone fixture secretary
Club Secretary: Paul Gee, 63 Blackhorse Lane, South Mimms, Herts. EN6 3PS
Tel: (H) 01707 662 748 (M) 0402 803961 (W) 01707 871702
Email: paul.gee5@btinternet.com
Fixtures Secretary: Simon Dickinson, 48 Riffel Road, London, NW2 4PH.
Tel: 020 8208 4617
Club Colours: Maroon, black and white
League: Hertfordshire & Middlesex 1

UNITED SERVICES PORTSMOUTH RFC
Ground Address: United Services Sports Club, Burnaby Road, Portsmouth, Hampshire. Tel: 01705 830125
Brief Directions: Enter Portsmouth via M275, follow signs to Isle of Wight Car Ferries, ground on right under railway bridge
Club Secretary: Tex.Houston, 36 Leifgh Road, Fareham, Portsmouth, Hants.
Tel: 01329 280589
Fixtures Secretary: High Wrightson, USRFC Portsmouth, Burnaby Road, Portsmouth
Tel No: 02392 547195 (W) 07778 935010 (M)
Club Colours: Navy blue & red hoops, navy blue shorts
League: London 4 South West

UNIVERSITY COLLEGE CHICHESTER
Ground Address: U.C.C., Bishop Otter Campus,College Lane,Chichester
Brief Directions: Signposted to University College from Chichester
Club Secretary: Ian Davies, U.C.C., College Lane, Chichester. PO19 4PE
Tel: 01243 816043
Fixtures Secretary: As Above
Club Colours: Navy & Gold . Change colours: Green- emerald
League: Sussex 1

UNIVERSITY VANDALS RFC
Ground Address: Brownacres, The Towing Path, Walton-on-Thames, Surrey
Tel: 01932 227659
Club Secretary: Mr. R. Webb, 52 Carlton Road, Walton on Thames, Surrey, KT12 2GD.
Fixtures Secretary: C J Cockrean
Tel: (H) 01932 226837
Club Colours: Black, purple and emerald green
League: London 3 South West

UPMINSTER RFC
Ground Address: Hall Lane Playing Fields, Hall Lane, Upminster, Essex
Tel: 01708 220320
Website: meve@ford.com
Brief Directions: From M25 take A127 towards Romford, take Upminster turn off, ground 0.5 mile on left over mini roundabout
Club Secretary: M Eve, 142 Cranson Park Avenue, Upminster, Essex. RM14 3XJ
Tel: (H) 01708 225383 (W) 01708 858935
Fixtures Secretary: A, Collen, 31 Lime Avenue, Upminster,Essex.
Club Colours: Yellow and blue hoops
League: London 4 North East

UPPER CLAPTON FC
Ground Address: Upland Road, Thornwood Common, Epping, Essex. CM16 6NL
Tel: 01992 572588
Brief Directions: M11 north, jct 7.Follow signs to B1393 to Epping. Upland Rd. on right after 500yds after Rooky Garage.
Club Secretary: David Miller, 13 Rushfield, Sawbridgeworth, Herts. CM21 9NE
Tel: 01279 724131 or 01279724849
Email: dwofclapton@aol.com
Fixtures Secretary: Damien Bateman, 14 Connaught Court, 14c Orford Road, Walthamstow, London. E18
Tel No: 0207242 9777
Club Colours: Red and white 7inch hoops, white shorts, red & white socks
League: Eastern Counties 1

UXBRIDGE RFC
Ground Address: Uxbridge Cricket Club, Gatting Way, Park Road, Uxbridge, Middlesex. UB8 1RN
Tel : 01895 237571
Website: www.uxbridgerfc.co.uk
Brief Directions: Car: Turn off A60 Uxbridge B483 into Park road - entrance to club .5 mile onleft - Gatting Way. Train: Metropolitan & Piccadilly Line - Uxbridge
Club Secretary: Tony Mahood, 20 Highfield Road, Flackwell Heath, Bucks. HP10 9AN
Tel : 01628 528233 Email: tony.j.mahood@britishair-ways.com
Fixtures Secretary: Bob McPherson, 44 Campden Road, Ickenham, Middlesex UB10 8EU
Tel: (H) 01895 852065 Email: bob.mcpherson@bar-clays.net
Club Colours: Black, white & red, horizontal hoops, black, red
League: Hertfordshire & Middlesex 1

LONDON & SOUTH EAST

VENTNOR RFC
Ground Address: The New Pavilion, Watcombe Bottom, Whitwell Road, Upper Ventnor, Isle of Wight
Tel: 01983 834155
Brief Directions: Approach Ventnor via Wroxall and take the Whitwell Road, ground next to end of speed limit
Club Secretary: Tony Flower, 2 Stonebowe Gardens, Niton. PO38 2AH
Tel No: 01983 730567
Fixtures Secretary: John Adams, B1-1K Avenue Rd., Wroxall, Isle of Wight
Tel No: 01983 854201
Club Colours: Navy and white hoop.
League: Hampshire 2

VERWOOD
Ground Address: Potterne Park, Potterne Way, Verwood, Dorset
Website: www.verwoodrfc.org.uk
Brief Directions: From centre of town,travel west along Manoe Road (B3072) PotterneWay 1.5 miles on left.
Club Secretary: Andy Hoggins, 17 Shelley Close, Ashley Heath, Ringwood BH24 2JA
Tel No: 01425 475963
Email: ahoggins@btinternet.com
Fixtures Secretary: Neil Scarisbrick,32 Acacia Avenue, Verwood, Dorset. BH31 6LQ
Tel No: 01202 823351.
Club Colours: Red and white quarters
League: Hampshire 3

VIGO RFC
Ground Address: Swanswood Field, Vigo Village, Havvel Road, Vigo, Kent   Tel: 01732 823830
Brief Directions: Please phone Fixture Secretary
Club Secretary: Mr. D. Oliver, 5 Streamside, Ditton, Aylesford, Kent, ME20 6SY.
Fixtures Secretary: John Taylor
Tel: (H) 01322 227363 (W) 0171 488 0733
Club Colours: Black shirts with red V , black shorts
League: Kent 3

WANDSWORTHIANS RFC
Ground Address: Kings College Sports Ground, Windsor Avenue, New Malden, Surrey. KT3 5HA. Tel: 0181942 0495
Brief Directions: Please phone Fixture Secretary
Club Secretary: Graham Sparkes, 21 Nursery Close, Ravenna Road, London, SW15 6AS
Tel No: 020 8789 3097
Email: graham.sparkes@ streetmanagement.org.uk
Fixtures Secretary: Gary Kirkwood
Tel: (H) 0181 640 0263 (W) 0181 665 3756
Club Colours: Maroon, white and gold hoops
League: Surrey 3

WANSTEAD RFC
Ground Address: Roding Lane North, Woodford Bridge, Essex   Tel: 020 85501561
Club website: www.wansteadrfc.org.uk
Brief Directions: From Charlie Brown's roundabout immediately under M11 and North Circular Road, take the eastern carriage way of the Southend Road,left at Harvesters Pub-ground 400 yds on left.

Club Secretary: Julian Greatrex,15 Grange Avenue, Woodford Green,Essex.IG8 9JT. Tel: 0208 504 0191
e-mail: julian.greatrex@ btinternet.com
Fixtures Secretary: J.Denton,19 Hornbeam Close,Buckhurst Hill, Essex 1G9 6JS
Tel No: 0208 559 2457
Club Colours: Blue and white hoops.
League: Eastern Counties 2 South

WARE RFC
Ground Address: Wodson Park, Ware, Herts.
Tel: 01920 487091
Brief Directions: From A10 take Ware (North) turn off. Continue along Watton Road to R/about in Ware. Turn Left - Wodson Park is .5 mile on right.
Club Secretary: Ian Williams, Pond House, Back Lane, Nazeing, Essex, EN9 2DD
Tel: 01992 892925   Email: i-a-n@lineone.net
Fixtures Secretary: Martin Warner, 37 Clarks Close,Ware, Her Sg12 0HQ
Tel: 01920 464617ts
Club Colours: Red, white & blue hoops. Blue shorts.
League: Hertfordshire & Middlesex 4 North

WARLINGHAM RFC
Ground Address: Limpsfield Road, Hamsey Green, Warlingham, Surrey. CR6 9RB.Tel: 01883 62 2825
Website: www.warlingham-rfc.com
Brief Directions: Frm A235 Sth Croydon, B269 - Hamsey Green, on leaving H. Green ground on rt after H.G. Gardens. Frm M25 J6, A22 4 miles, rt on B270, 1st left, right at T jcn, ground on right
Club Secretary: Peter Upton, 87 Church Way, Sanderstead, Surrey CR2 0JN
Tel No: 0208 657 8844
Email: peter.upton@prudential.co.uk
Fixtures Secretary: Paul Fettes, 63 Mitchley Hill, Sanderstead, Surrey.
Tel: (H) 0181 657 7628
Club Colours: Light blue and white hoops
League: London 4 South West

WASPS
Ground Address: Former North Thames Gas Sports Ground. Twyford Avenue, Acton, London W39QA
Tel No 020 8992 1400
Website: www.waspsfc.co.uk
Brief Directions: Twyford Avenue is a turn off the north side of Uxbridge Road, approx 1/2 mile east of the junction with the North Circular Road.
Club Secretary: Graham Wynde, 94 Stapleton Hall Road, Stroud Green, London. N4 4QA
Tel No: 020 8347 9240
Email: graham@wynde.demon.co.uk
Fixtures Secretary: Denis Shayler, 79 Waverley Road, Harrow, Middlesex. HA29RG
Tel No: 020 8866 2764.
Club Colours: Blackshirts and shorts with black and gold socks.
League: Hertfordshire & Middlesex 3 South

WATFORD RFC
Ground Address: Knutsford Playing Fields, Radlett Road, Watford, Herts   Tel: 01923 243292
Brief Directions: From A41 (M1 J5) take Watford/ town centre link road, right at 1st roundabout, over

bridge, car park on left, ground on right.
Club Secretary: Debby Wood, 60 Harris Road,
Watford, Herts   Tel: : 01923 678162
Email: bed-wood@btinternet.com
Fixtures Secretary: B.Cox,10 Sherbourne Way,
Croxley Green, Rickmansworth WD3 3PF
Tel: 01923 497834
Club Colours: Red, white and blue hoops/ black/red
League: Herts/Midlesex 3 North

WELWYN RUGBY CLUB
Ground Address: Hobbs Way, Colgrove, Welwyn
Garden City, Herts   Tel: 01707 329116
Brief Directions: A1(M) J4, follow signs to Gosline
sports park, bear left into Parkway, left at next r'bout
into Turmore Dale, 1st left into Colgrove, 30 yds right
into Hobbs Way
Club Secretary: J M Sargeant, 67 Woodhall Lane,
Welwyn Garden City, Herts. AL7 3TG.
Tel: (H) 01707 331186
Fixtures Secretary: K Smith, 20 Rookwood Drive,
Stevenage, Herts.
Tel: (H & W) 01438 351807 (Fax) 01438 249129
Club Colours: Maroon, blue and white hoops, blue
shorts, maroon socks
League: London 4 North West

WEMBLEY & KODAK RFC
Ground Address: Roger Bannisters Playing Fields,
Uxbridge Road, Harrow Weald, Middlesex
Tel: 0181 420 1789
Brief Directions: From Harrow on Hill take Harrow
View to roundabout, ground on right. From Watford
take Oxley Lane, ground on left
Club Secretary: Mrs. Nicola McKeon, 16 Brinsley
Road, Harrow Weald, Middlesex, HA3 5NY
Tel: (H) 020 8427 0900 email: tish@08002go.com
Fixtures Secretary: John Conlon, 17 Cleverley
Cres., Ealing W5 1DZ Tel. 020 8992 2169
email: johnconlon@moose.co.uk
Club Colours: Black & white quarters
League: Herts/Midlesex 3 South

WEST LONDON RFC
(Formerly Old Gaytonians RFC)
Ground Address:
South Vale, Sudbury Hill, Middlesex HA1 3PN.
Tel : 020 8423 4133
Brief Directions: A4127 Greenford Road to Sudbury
Hill. South Vale opposite Rising Sun pub. Ground
200 yards on right.
Club Secretary: Mr. S. G. Taffs, 17 South Hill Grove,
Harrow, Middlesex, HA1 3PR. Tel: 020 8423 3120
Fixtures Secretary: Mr. P. Cowan, 119 Canonbury
Avenue, Pinner, Harrow, Middlesex, HA5 1TR. Tel:
020 8248 3372
Club Colours: Black with single white hoop. Black
shorts, red socks.
League: London 3 North West

WEST NORFOLK RUFC
Ground Address: Gatehouse Lane,
North Wootton, Kings Lynn
Tel: 01553 631307
Website: www.westnorfolkrugby.com

Brief Directions: A149 to K. Lynn to Hunstanton
bypass A148 to K. Lynn r'bout at top of hill, right at
lights in Castle Rising Rd, left at T junction to North
Wootton, through village to green, left at Gatehouse
Lane
Club Secretary: Dr R.T. Hewson, Grange Meadows,
Manor Road, North Wootton, King's Lynn PE30 3PZ.
Tel No: 01553 631660
Email: royhewson@aol.com
Fixtures Secretary: M.H.Ballman. 1 Thornhill
Cottages, Great Heath Road, North Elham,Dereham
NR20 5EY
Tel No 01362 668935Tel No: 01362 668935
Club Colours: French grey with cerise band, navy
shorts
League: London 4 North East

WESTCLIFF RFC
Ground Address: The Gables, Aviation Way,
Southend-on-Sea, Essex. SS2 6UN.
Tel: 01702 541499
Brief Directions: A127 turn left at Perrys Ford
Garage at Kent Elms corner about .5 mile from
Southend. After 200yds turn R. in to Snakes Lane go
to end turn R and L at 4th r'about to Aviation Way .
Ground 600yds.
Club Secretary: John Duncombe, 6 The Approach,
Rayleigh, Essex, SS6 9AA.
Tel: 01268 785852 0 Email:
john@jduncombe.psner.co.uk
Fixtures Secretary: Don Faulkner, 128 West Road,
Westcliff on Sea , Essex SS0 9DD
Tel No: 01702 311737872
Club Colours: Maroon and old gold hoops
League: Eastern Counties 2 South

WHITSTABLE RFC
Ground Address: Reeves Way, Chestfield,
Whitstable, Kent. CT5 3QS Tel: 01227 794343
Brief Directions: A299 Thanet Way to Whitstable,
by Chestfield roundabout. The ground is opposite
Chestfield & Swalecliffe Railway Station
Club Secretary: Mr. A. Russell, Meadow Lea, Herne
Common, Herne Bay, Kent, CT6 7LB.
Fixtures Secretary: Roger Dengate, 70 Regent St.
Whitstable, Kent. CT5 1JQ.
Tel: (H) 01227 264604
Club Colours: Blue and white.
League: Kent 1

WIMBLEDON RFC
Ground Address: Beverley Meads, Barham Road,
Wimbledon, London. SW20 0ET
Brief Directions: Barham Rd off Copse Hill, off
Coombe Lane which is off A3. Nearest train station
Raynes Park (BR, Network SE), take No 57 bus to
Copse Hill, club at end of Barham Rd
Club Secretary: Terry Bagworth, 38 Chase Side
Avenue, Wimbledon, London SW20 8LV.
Tel : 0208 543 5386
Email: terence.bagworth@btinternet.com
Fixtures Secretary: Richard Baker, 19 Chartwell
Place, Epsom , Surrey. KT18 5SH
Tel No: 01372 729331
Club Colours: Maroon and Cambridge blue
League: London 2 South

WISBECH RUFC

Ground Address: Chapel Road, Harecroft Road, Wisbech, Cambridgeshire. PE1 1RG
Tel: 01945 481500
Brief Directions: Along South Brink, (from A47) proceed to Old Market Place, turn left, ground approx 200 yards on right next to garage
Club Secretary: J R C Pallant,139 Lynn Road, Wisbech, Cambs. PE13 3DH
Tel: 01945 588147
Fixtures Secretary: David Dobson, 5 Buckingham Walk, Wisbech, Cambridgeshire, PE13.
Tel: (H) 01945 461223
Club Colours: Red shirts, blue shorts
League: Eastern Counties 2 North

WITHAM RUFC

Ground Address: Club House, Spa Road, Witham, Essex. CM8 1UN
Tel: 01376 511066
Brief Directions: Leave A12, through Witham to lights at Spinks Lane (signed), turn right under railway bridge, left into private road to club house.
Club Secretary: Mrs Pam Whelan, 34 Highfields Road, Witham, Essex, CH8 2HJ
Tel : 01376 515871 - Email:
tomandpam@supanet.com
Fixtures Secretary: Graham Ball,9 Juniper Crescent, Witham,Essex. CH8 2NX
Tel No: 01376 516505
Club Colours: Brown and white hoops, navy shorts and socks
League: Eastern Counties 3 North

WOKING RFC

Ground Address: Byfleet Recreation Ground, Stream Close, off Rectory Lane, Byfleet, Surrey. Tel: 01932 343693
Brief Directions: Leave A3 at Painshill (Cobham & Byfleet) junction A245 to Byfleet, over 3 main roundabouts, turn left at 4th into High Rd and then right into Rectory Lane
Club Secretary: Andrew Jones, 66 Kings Rd, New Haw, Surrey KT15 3BQ
Tel : (H) 01932 880936 (W) 0181 214 2525
Fixtures Secretary: Mr Ian Vousden
Tel : (H) 01483 836817
Club Colours: Blue and gold hoops, black shorts
League: Surrey 2

WOODBRIDGE RUFC

Ground Address: Hatchley Barn, Oxford Road, Bromeswell, Woodbridge, Suffolk. IP12 2PP
Tel: 01394 460630
Brief Directions: From N.or S. A12 take B1084 to Orford R/about, L. straight on past turning to Eyke, entrance half mile on right.
Club Secretary: B.J. Owens, 5 Orwell Court, Woodbridge, Suffolk, IP12 4DF.
Tel: 01394 385314H/08700521960F/
EMail - orcor@demon.co.uk
Fixtures Secretary: M. Fisher, Two Gates, The Street, Eyke, Woodbridge, Suffolk, IP12 2QG. Tel: 01394 460494H/01394 460553F
Club Colours: Sky Blue/Black Shorts
League: London 4 North East

WOODFORD RFC

Ground Address: Highams, High Road, Woodford Green, Essex. IG8 9LB Tel: 0181 504 6769
Brief Directions: Woodford tube station, north via Snakes Ln to Woodford High Rd, turn left for 500yds, club entrance on right 25 yds off main road next to Woodford High School
Club Secretary: P.James,46 Suffield Road, London E4 9TA   Tel: 020 8524 9658
Fixtures Secretary: G.Kane, 134 Wallwood Road, Leytonstone, London E11 1AN Tel: 020 8539 0390
Club Colours: White, Lavender, Black and Purple .
Change strip: Red
League: London 2 North

WORTH OLD BOYS SOCIETY RFC

Ground Address: North Avenue, Whiteley Village, Walton On Thames.
Brief Directions: From A3 take A245 to Byfleet.B365, rt into Seven Hills Rd. At roundabout take rt into Burnwood Rd to Whiteley Village on rt.
Club Secretary: Jon Nickel, 65A Burlington Road, London SW6 4NBH   Tel No : 07970 544825
Emai;l jonathon.nichell@yestelevision.com
Fixtures Secretary: Paul Kozary 21 Hampton Road, Teddington, Middlesex TW11 0JN
Tel Nos: 0208977 1925 (H) 0207475 3976 (W)
Club Colours: Blue and gold quarters
League: Surrey 3

WORTHING RFC

Ground Address: The Rugby Park, Roundstone Lane, Angmering, West Sussex BN16 4AX.
Tel/Fax: 01903 784706
Brief Directions: A27 Worthing to Arundel Road, leave at Clapham follow signs to Angmering and A259 Worthing to Littlehampton Road, Turn north at Roundstone Pub R/about, quarter mile on right.
Club Secretary: Robin White, 12 Ferring Street, Ferring, West Sussex.   Tel No: 01903 242574
Fixtures Secretary: Nigel Lyons,
48 Brook Barn Way, Goring-by-Sea, Worthing, West Sussex, BN12 4DW. Tel: 01903 506880
Club Colours: Blue, chocolate and gold hoops
League: London 3 South East

WYMONDHAM RUFC

Ground Address: Foster Harrison Memorial Ground, Tuttles Lane East, Wymondham, Norfolk
Tel: 01953 607332
Brief Directions: Northern exit A11 by-pass follow signs B1135 to Dereham - Tuttles Lane starts at second R/about adjacent Summerfields, 200yds on right behind trees.
Club Secretary: Martin Warren, 14 Newark Close, Thorpe St Andrew, Norwich. NR7 0YJ
Tel: (H) 01603 437805
Email: mwarren@lawrence-wood.com
Fixtures Secretary: Rob Lockhart, 14 The Green, North Burlingham, Norwich NR11 1SH
Tel No: 01603 270060 / 712392
Club Colours: Red and black hooped shirts, black shorts and socks
League: London 3 North East

LONDON & SOUTH EAST

SOUTH WEST DIVISION

A complete club index appears at the back of the book.
This shows which Division and league each club is in for the 2001-02 season

South West Division Structure 2001-02

SOUTH WEST 1

SOUTH WEST 2 EAST		SOUTH WEST 2 WEST	
SOUTHERN COUNTIES NORTH	SOUTHERN COUNTIES SOUTH	WESTERN COUNTIES WEST	WESTERN COUNTIES NORTH
Berks., Bucks. & Oxfordshire 1	Dorset & Wiltshire 1	Devon & Cornwall	Gloucestershire Premier / Somerset Premier

Berks, Bucks & Oxon 2 | D & W 2 North | D & W 2 South | Devon 1 | Cornwall 1 | Gloucesters.1 | Somerset 1

Devon 2 | Cornwall 2 | Gloucesters.2 | Somerset 2

Devon 3 | Glos. 3 North | Glos. 3 South

SOUTH WEST LEAGUE OFFICIALS 2001-2002

Chairman of Competition Sub-Committee

A Boyer 11 Christopher Court, Boundary Road, NEWBURY, Berks, RG14 7PQ
Tel: 01635 40574 (H)

Deputy Chairman

N.J. Barber 2, The Crescent, Alexandra Road, ST IVES, Cornwall, TR26 1BY
Tel/Fax: 01736 796861 (H) 01752 665951 (B). Email: nbarb@cwcom.net

League Co-ordinating Secretary

M. Gee Foxglove Cottage, 70 Halsetown, ST IVES, Cornwall, TR26 3LZ
Tel/Fax: 01736 797777 (H) Email: swrfu@lineone.net

Deputy League Co-ordinating Secretary

B. Flanders The Cottage, Bishops Green, NEWBURY, Berks, RG20 4HS
Tel/Fax: 01635 269646 (H)

South West 1 A. Townsend League Co-ordinating Secretary
2 Kencourt Close, Kenilworth Avenue, GLOUCESTER, GL2 0QL
Tel/Fax: 01452 522721 (H) Email: allan@townsend30.fsnet.co.uk
(Deputy) J. Lipscomb, 16 Main Road, Western Zoyland, BRIDGWATER, Somerset, TA7 0EB
Tel/Fax: 01278 691345 (H)

South West 2 West J. Lipscomb League Co-ordinating Secretary
16 Main Road, Western Zoyland, BRIDGWATER, Somerset, TA7 0EB
Tel/Fax: 01278 691345 (H)
(Deputy) A. Townsend, 2 Kencourt Close, Kenilworth Avenue, GLOUCESTER, GL2 0QL
Tel/Fax: 01452 522721 (H) Email: allan@townsend30.fsnet.co.uk

South West 2 East B. Flanders Leagues Co-ordinating Secretary
& Berks/Bucks The Cottage, Bishops Green, NEWBURY, Berks, RG20 4HS
& Oxon 1 & 2 Tel/Fax: 01635 269646 (H)Secretary
SW2E (Deputy) D. McAteer, 1 Rowlands Close, Mortimer West End, READING, RG7 3US
Tel: 0118 970 1245 (H) 0118 9303066 (B) Fax: 0118 9303 411 (B) 079 7667 0365 (M)
Email: reading@fentonplant.co.uk
BB01&2 (Deputy) H. Pocock, 10 Laceys Drive, Hazlemere, HIGH WYCOMBE, Bucks, HP15 7JY
Tel/Fax: 01494 713879 (H) Email: Humphandgwen@aol.com

Cornwall/Devon League Mrs B. Davis League Co-ordinating Secretary
3 Kernow House, New Road, ST COLUMB, Cornwall, TR9 6AZ
Tel/Fax: 01637 881879 (H) 01209 215620 (B)
(Deputy) G. Simpson, 108 Pattinson Drive, Mainstone, PLYMOUTH, PL6 8RU
Tel/Fax: 01752 206662 (H) Email: gks49@hotmail.com

Cornwall 1 & 2 N.J. Barber Leagues Co-ordinating Secretary
2, The Crescent, Alexandra Road, ST IVES, Cornwall, TR26 1BY
Tel/Fax: 01736 796861 (H) 01752 665951 (B) Email: nbarb@cwcom.net
(Deputy) D. Jenkins, Albaston Post Office, Albaston, GUNNISLAKE, Cornwall, PL18 9HQ
Tel/Fax: 01822 832785 (H) Email: davejenkins@talk21.com

Devon 1 J. D Irvine League Co-ordinating Secretary
1 Great Rea Road, BRIXHAM, Devon, TQ5 9SW
Tel: 01803 882219 (H) Email: jamesdirvine@netscapeonline.co.uk
(Deputy) G. Simpson, 108 Pattinson Drive, Mainstone, PLYMOUTH, PL6 8RU
Tel/Fax: 01752 206662 (H) Email: gks49@hotmail.com

Devon 2 P. Harris League Co-ordinating Secretary
15 Blagdon Close, CREDITON, Devon, EX17 1EL
Tel: 01363 772847 (H) Fax: 01363 775499 (H) 079 6810 4524 (M)
Email: prharris@tinyonline.co.uk
(Deputy) J. D Irvine, 1 Great Rea Road, BRIXHAM, Devon, TQ5 9SW
Tel: 01803 882219 (H) Email: jamesdirvine@netscapeonline.co.uk

Devon 3 G. Simpson League Co-ordinating Secretary
108 Pattinson Drive, Mainstone, PLYMOUTH, PL6 8RU
Tel/Fax: 01752 206662 (H) Email: gks49@hotmail.com
(Deputy) P. Harris, 15 Blagdon Close, CREDITON, Devon, EX17 1EL
Tel: 01363 772847 (H) Fax: 01363 775499 (H) 079 6810 4524 (M)
Email: prharris@tinyonline.co.uk

Dorset & Wilts 1	N. Stafford	League Co-ordinating Secretary
	Veryan, 46 Bulkington, DEVIZES, Wilts, SN10 1SL	
	Tel: 01380 828264 (H) Email: crotchet@quaver0.freeserve.co.uk	
(Deputy)	K. Jones, 13 Stratfield Road, BASINGSTOKE, Hants, RG21 5RS	
	Tel: 01256 410461 (H) 0118 982 6750 (B)	
Dorset & Wilts 2 North	K. Jones	League Co-ordinating Secretary
	13 Stratfield Road, BASINGSTOKE, Hants, RG21 5RS	
	Tel: 01256 410461 (H) 0118 982 6750 (B)	
(Deputy)	D. McAteer, 1 Rowlands Close, Mortimer West End, READING, RG7 3US	
	Tel: 0118 970 1245 (H) 0118 9303066 (B) Fax :0118 9303 411 (B) 079 7667 0365 (M)	
	Email: reading@fentonplant.co.uk	
Dorset & Wilts 2 South	P. Richell	League Co-ordinating Secretary
	26 Durweston, BLANDFORD FORUM, Dorset, DT11 0QE	
	Tel/Fax: 01258 452918 (H) 01305 251414 (B) Email: peter.richell@btinternet.com	
(Deputy)	C. Drake, Folly's End, Wyke, GILLINGHAM, Dorset, SP8 4NA	
	Tel: 01747 825856 (H) 01747 826505 (B) Email: tcldrake@follys.freeserve.co.uk	
Gloucester Premier	A. Barnes	League Co-ordinating Secretary
	18 Podsmead Place, Tuffley, GLOUCESTER, GL1 5PD	
	Tel: 01452 525530 (H)	
(Deputy)	C. Ravenhill, 18 Merevale Rd, Longlevens, GLOUCESTER, GL2 0QY Tel: 01452 304317 (H)	
Gloucester 1, 2, 3N & 3S	C Ravenhill	Leagues Co-ordinating Secretary
	18 Merevale Road, Longlevens, GLOUCESTER, GL2 0QY	
	Tel: 01452 304317 (H)	
(Deputy)	Mrs W. Bunce, County Office, Foxhole Farm, Kinsham, TEWKESBURY, Glos. GL20 8HU.	
	Tel: 01684-773900 (B) on Mon., Wed. & Fri. from 9am to 1pm	
Southern Counties North	M. Wild	League Co-ordinating Secretary
	4 Stanton Way, Langley, SLOUGH, SL3 7LB	
	Tel/Fax: 01753 770870 (H) 01628 604311 (B) Email: mikewild_srfc@yahoo.co.uk	
(Deputy)	H. Pocock, 10 Laceys Drive, Hazlemere, HIGH WYCOMBE, Bucks, HP15 7JY	
	Tel/Fax 01494 713879 (H) Email: Humphandgwen@aol.com	
Southern Counties South	D McAteer	League Co-ordinating Secretary
	1 Rowlands Close, Mortimer West End, READING, RG7 3US	
	Tel:0118 970 1245 (H) 0118 9303066 (B) Fax:0118 9303 411 (B) 079 7667 0365 (M)	
	Email: reading@fentonplant.co.uk	
(Deputy)	N. Stafford, Veryan, 46 Bulkington, DEVIZES, Wilts, SN10 1SL	
	Tel: 01380 828264 (H) Email: crotchet@quaver0.freeserve.co.uk	
Somerset Premier 1 & 2	C MacDonald	Leagues Co-ordinating Secretary
	8 Sycamore Drive, CREWKERNE, Somerset, TA18 7BT	
	Tel: 01460 78959 (H/B) Fax: 01460 78293 Email: cb-honsec-somerset@therfu.com	
(Deputy)	R. Fisher, 20 Rookery Road, Knowle, BRISTOL, BS4 2DS Tel: 0117 983 6325 (H)	
Western Counties North	W. Bishop	League Co-ordinating Secretary
	Helvellyn, 1 Wiltshire Place, Kingswood, BRISTOL, BS15 4XA	
	Tel: 0117 957 5729 (H) 0117 935 2017 (B) Fax: 0117 940 1290 (B)	
	Email: bill.bishop@mitreprinting.co.uk	
(Deputy)	R. Fisher, 20 Rookery Road, Knowle, BRISTOL, BS4 2DS Tel: 0117 983 6325 (H)	
Western Counties West	D. Jenkins	League Co-ordinating Secretary
	Albaston Post Office, Albaston, GUNNISLAKE, Cornwall, PL18 9HQ	
	Tel/Fax: 01822 832785 (H) Email: davejenkins@talk21.com	
(Deputy)	D. Preece, 35 Higher Boskerris, Carbis Bay, ST IVES, Cornwall, TR26 2TL.	
	Tel: 01736 796694 (H)	

Other Committee Members

J. Dance	Birch Cottage, Padworth Common, READING, RG7 4QG
	Tel: 0118 970 0288 / 0118 970 1246 (H) Fax: 0118 970 1237. Email: cb-honsec-berks@therfu.com
B. Morrison	First Eleven Sports Agency, P O BOX 11, READING, RG6 3DT
	Tel: 0870 741 5117 (B) Fax: 0870 741 5119 (B) Email: rugby@firsteleven.co.uk
K. Plain	Foxhole Farm, Kinsham, TEWKESBURY, Gloucestershire, GL20 8HU
	Tel/Fax: 01684 772096 (H/B) Email: cb-honsec-glos@therfu.com
R. G. Wildash	25 Marina Gardens, WEYMOUTH, Dorset, DT4 9QZ
	Tel/Fax: 01305 773286 (H) Email: wwildash@aol.com

SOUTH WEST ONE

2000-01 LEAGUE TABLE

	P	W	D	L	PF	PA	PD	Pts	
Old Patesians	22	21	0	1	593	209	384	42	
Cinderford	22	21	0	1	576	225	351	42	
Maidenhead	22	12	1	9	444	376	68	25	
*Barnstaple	22	13	0	9	568	379	189	24	2
Bridgwater & Albion	22	11	1	10	478	434	44	23	
Dorchester	22	10	0	12	351	510	-159	20	
*Swanage & Wareham	22	10	0	12	402	411	-9	18	2
Keynsham	22	9	0	13	422	453	-31	18	
Berry Hill	22	9	0	13	375	530	-155	18	
Truro	22	8	1	13	430	433	-3	17	
*Torquay Athletic	22	4	1	17	252	560	-308	7	2
*Gloucester Old Boys	22	2	0	20	180	551	-371	-2	6

2001-02 FIXTURE GRID

	Barnstaple	Bridgwater & Albion	Cheltenham	Chinnor	Dings Crusaders	Dorchester	Keynsham	Maidenhead	Reading	Stroud	Swanage & Wareham	Weston-Super-Mare
Barnstaple		16.03	22.09	02.03	06.10	09.02	27.10	26.01	17.11	05.01	08.12	06.04
Bridgwater & Albion	08.09		26.01	22.09	17.11	02.03	05.01	06.10	08.12	09.02	06.04	27.10
Cheltenham	09.03	10.11		12.01	29.09	01.12	23.02	13.04	20.10	22.12	02.02	16.03
Chinnor	29.09	09.03	17.11		05.01	06.10	08.12	09.02	06.04	27.10	08.09	26.01
Dings Crusaders	23.02	12.01	02.03	01.12		13.04	20.10	22.12	02.02	16.03	10.11	22.09
Dorchester	20.10	29.09	05.01	23.02	08.12		06.04	27.10	08.09	26.01	09.03	17.11
Keynsham	02.02	01.12	06.10	13.04	09.02	22.12		16.03	10.11	22.09	12.01	02.03
Maidenhead	10.11	23.02	08.12	20.10	06.04	02.02	08.09		09.03	17.11	29.09	05.01
Reading	12.01	13.04	09.02	22.12	27.10	16.03	26.01	22.09		02.03	01.12	06.10
Stroud	01.12	20.10	06.04	02.02	08.09	10.11	09.03	12.01	29.09		23.02	08.12
Swanage & Wareham	13.04	22.12	27.10	16.03	26.01	22.09	17.11	02.03	05.01	06.10		09.02
Weston-Super-Mare	22.12	02.02	08.09	10.11	09.03	12.01	29.09	01.12	23.02	13.04	20.10	

BARNSTAPLE R.F.C.

Founded: 1877

President	K Abrahams	c/o Barnstaple R.F.C., Pottington Road, Barnstaple EX31 1JH Tel: 01271 345627
Chairman	E Gubb	c/o Barnstaple R.F.C as above
Secretary	C Jones	Lilac Cottage, Velator, Braunton, Devon EX33 2BG
Fixture Secretary	S Swanson	5 Church Cottages, Swimbridge, Barnstaple, Devon EX32 0PP Tel. 01271 830514
League Contact	Secretary	

Ground   **Address:** Pottington Road, Barnstaple, EX31 1JH   Tel/Fax: 01271 345627
Capacity: 3,000   Covered Seats: 500   Uncovered Standing: 2,500
Website: www.beehive.thisisnorthdevon.co.uk/barnstaplerfc
Directions   Take the A361 from Banstaple to Ilfracombe, then go left at the second set of traffic lights after Rolle Quay Bridge in Barnstaple.
Nearest Railway Station: Barnstaple   **Car Parking:** Plenty at the ground

Admission: Matchday: £4.00 OAPs £2.00 Children Free   Season tickets: Not available.
Clubhouse: Yes   **Club Shop:** Yes   **Colours:** Red/white/red **Change colours:** Black/white/red
Nickname: Barum   **Training Nights:** Tuesday & Thursday 7pm
Programme   Size: A5   **Pages:** 32   **Price:** Free   **Editor:** C Jones   **Advertising:** Contact Secretary

BRIDGWATER & ALBION R.F.C.

Founded: 1875

President	Mike Berry	c/o Maxwells, King Square, Bridgwater Tel: 01278 423008
Chairman	Bob Hudson	10 Cypress Drive, Puriton, Bridgwater Tel: 01278 683525
Club Secretary	Tony Pomeroy	Hafod-Y-Gan, Newton Road, North Petherton, Somerset TA6 6SN
		Tel: 01278 662181 Fax: 01278 662178 email: apomeroy@ukgateway.net
General Manager	Tim Fanning	c/o the club office Tel: 01278 423900 (Club) Fax: 01278 446608
Fixtures Secretary	Ralph Sealey	Cape House, Stawell, Bridgwater, Som. Tel: 01278 722934

Ground Address: Bath Road, College Way, Bridgwater, Somerset. TA6 4TZ.   Website: barfc.co.uk
Tel: 01278 423900   Fax: 01278 446608   email: timfanning@barfc.co.uk
Capacity: 5,000 Seated: 630   Standing - Covered: 500   Uncovered: 3,870
Directions: The ground is sign-posted from the A38 and A39   **Car Parking:** 400 spaces available at ground
Nearest Railway Station: Bridgwater (BR) (Bristol to Exeter line). 10 minute walk to the ground.
Club Shop: Matchdays only 12-5. Contact Ben Carp c/o the club
Clubhouse: Open normal licensing hours, snacks available. Function capacity 300, contact Tim Fanning 01278 423900

Training Nights: Tuesday & Thursday   **Nickname:** 'Bridgey'
Programme: Size: A5 Price: £1 Pages: 8/12 Editor: Tony Pomeroy Advertising: Contact Tim Fanning c/o the club
Colours: Black with red & amber hoops   **Change colours:** Scarlet with black & amber inserts

CHELTENHAM RFC

Founded: 1889

President	Keith Plain, Foxhole Farm, Kinsham, Tewkesbury. GL20 6JG 01684 772096 (H & Fax)
Chairman	Stephen Ratcliffe, 10 Waterside Close, Andoversford, Cheltenham, Glos. 01242 820824 (H), 01242 233430 (B)
Fixtures Secretary	Mike Edwards, 2 Greenbank, Guiting Power, Cheltenham. GL54 5UU 01451 850232 (H), 01452 412444 (B)
Press Officer	Tom Parker, 39 Long Mynd Avenue, Cheltenham GL51 5QT 01242 694299 (H & Fax)
Club Secretary	David Evans, Cliff Cottage, Leckhampton Hill, Cheltenham GL53 9QG 01242 514519 (H), 01452 509555 (B)
Ground Address:	Prince of Wales Stadium, Tommy Taylors Lane, Cheltenham, Glos GL50 4NJ Tel: 01242 525393/522085
Capacity:	2500 Seated: 500 Standing: Uncovered 2000

Directions: From North: M5 J10, 1.5 miles A4019, over lights to r'about, left into Kingsditch Lane. 1st right over bridge then 1st left into Windyridge Rd.. At end turn right and after 400 yds right again into Tommy Taylors Lane. Ground .5 mile on right. **From South:** M5 J11, towards Cheltenham. Pass Golden Valley Hotel and GCHQ to next r'about. Turn left along Princess Elizabeth Way for 1.5 miles to r'about, straight over into Kingsditch Lane - then as above. **From East:** Enter Cheltenham on A40 and proceed thro' Charlton Kings, to lights at junction with Hewllt Rd. Turn right (signed Evesham) and along All Saints Rd, Pittville Circus and Wellington Rd. and turn right onto A435. Continue to r'about at racecourse. Turn left into Swindon Lane and 3rd left into Tommy Taylors Lane.
Nearest Railway Station: Cheltenham (Taxi or bus)   **Car Parking:** 300 on ground no charge
Admission: Season - Adults Member £45, V-P £60, Matchday - Adults £4 Children/OAPs £2
Clubhouse: Normal Licensing hours, snacks available.   **Club Shop:** Open match-days, Manager J G Pitman 01242 525393
Programme: Size: A5   Price: 50p   Pages: 24 + cover   Editor: T Parker 01242 694299
Colours: Red & black shirts.   **Change colours:** Blue   **Training Nights:** Tuesday & Thursday

CHINNOR RFC

Founded: 1963

President	Ken Vaughan	The Old Barn, Brook Street, Watlington, Oxon. 01491 612788
Chairman	Richard John	March House, Mill Lane, Chalgrove, Oxon. 01865 400623
Club Secretary	Gary Porter	16 Haddenham Rd., Kingsey, Bucks. HP17 8LS 01844 291807
Treasurer	Mike Thompson	5 Yeates Close, Thame, Oxon. 01844 261454
Fixtures Secretary		01844 213735
League Contact	Secretary as above	

Ground Address: The Pavilion, Kingsey Road, Thame, Oxon. OX9 3PB   Website: chinnor-rfc.com
Tel: 01844 213735 Fax: 01844 213907
Capacity: Ample - all uncovered seating
Directions: Situated on the Thame Western bypass at the junction with the A4129 Thame-Princes Risborough road
Car Parking: 100 plus Nearest Railway Station: Thame / Haddenham Parkway
Admission: Matchday £3 No season tickets available
Club Shop: Yes
Clubhouse: Open 7-11.30pm Mon - Fri, all day Sat & Sun.
Training Nights: Tuesday & Thursday
Programme: Size: A5 Price: with entry Pages: 40 Editor: Sue O'Donnell
Colours: Wide black and narrow white hooped jersey, black shorts   Change colours: Gold/black

DINGS CRUSADERS RFC

Founded: 1897

Club Secretary	Rob Stevens , 4 Fonthill Way, Bitton, Bristol BS30 6JY 0117 9329 128 (H) 0117 9881 564 (B)
	email: rob.stevens@tinyworld.co.uk
League Contact	Gary James, 17 Quantock Close, North Common, Bristol BS15 5UR 0117 961 2397 (H)

GroundAddress: Landseer Avenue, Lockleaze, Bristol. BS7 Tel: 0117 969 1367
Capacity: 1000 Standing: Covered - 5 Uncovered - 995
Directions: M4, J19 > M32 J2 (B4469) towards Horfield.
Turn right at second set of traffic lights before railway bridge towards Lockleaze.
After about a mile turn left into Hogarth Walk and right at the end into Landseer Avenue.
Car Parking: Spaces for 50 cars   Nearest Railway Station: Bristol Parkway

Admission: Matchday £2 including programme
Club Shop: None
Clubhouse: Large clubhouse and bar with gym attached
Training Nights: Tuesday & Thursday 7pm

Programme: Size: A5 Price: with admission Pages: 10 Advertising: Contact Club Secretary
Colours: Royal blue and black hoops   **Change colours:** Blue and grey hoops

DORCHESTER R.F.C.

Founded: 1934

President	Harry Brewer	Stallen Cottage, Nether Compton, Sherborne, Dorset DT9 4PZ 01935 812815
Chairman	Don Brierley	3 Sutton Close, Sutton Poyntz, Weymouth DT3 6LJ 01305 833244
Secretary	Graham Aspley	5 Nappers Court, Charles St., Dorchester DT1 1EE 01305 269944
Treasurer	John Palmer	45 Ackerman Rd., Dorchester DT1 1NZ 01305 262929
Fixtures Sec.	Tony Foot	1 Cutsome Close, Dorchester DT1 2SN 01305 250137
League Contact	Martin Bartlett	Tel: 01305 871209 0797 418 5734 (M)

Ground Coburg Road, Dorchester, Dorset DT1 2HX   Tel: 01305 265692
Capacity: Ample - all uncovered standing   **Car Parking**: 100 spaces beside clubhouse
Directions: From the by-pass follow signs to "West Dorset Leisure Centre"
Nearest Railway station: Dorchester South & Dorchester West

Admission Matchday: £3   Season tickets are available
Clubhouse Open Tues & Thur evenings, & all day Saturday
Club Shop No, but club ties & blazers are available
Training Nights: Tuesday & Thursday
Programme Size: A5   Pages: 40 Price: With admission Editor: Andrew Foot (Clubhouse Manager)
Advertising: Contact editor at clubhouse
Colours: Green & white hoops/navy blue   **Change colours:** All red

KEYNSHAM R.F.C.

Founded: 1923

President	Dennis Cockbaine	'Somercourt', Homefield Rd., Saltford, Bristol 01225 873118
Chairman	Jon Bishop	89 Albert Rd., Keynsham, Bristol BS31 1AE 0117 986 0867 (H) 0117 921 8713 (B)
Hon. Secretary	Ian Tweedie	1 Oakfield Road, Keynsham, Bristol BS31 1JQ 0117 986 2645
		e-mail: Ian@Tweedie32.freeserve.co.uk
Hon. Treasurer	Colin Murrin	50 Dunster Rd., Keynsham, Bristol BS31 1WZ 0117 986 5331 (H)
Hon. Coach	Jerry Barnes	60 Frome Rd., Radstock, Bath BA3 3LF 07885 925181 (M)
Fixture Secretary	David Veal	118 Harrington Rd., Stockwood, Bristol BS14 8JR 01275 543416
League Contact	Eric Slater	4 Castle Rd., Kingswood, Bristol BS15 1PF 0117 961 5718 (H)

Ground **Address:** Crown Fields, Bristol Rd., Keynsham BS31 2BE **Tel:** 0117 987 2520
 Capacity: All uncovered standing **Car Parking:** Unlimited
 Nearest Railway Station: Keynsham, 10 mins walk

Directions Follow A4 from Bristol city centre, follow signs for Keynsham & Keynsham town centre. As you enter Keynsham the rugby club is on the left hand side.

Admission: Matchday: £3.00, incl programme. Season tickets: Not available.
Clubhouse: Open lunch & evening every day. Available for hire, contact Liz Way at the club.
Club Shop: open matchdays & sun. am
Colours: Amber & black **Change colours:** Black **Training Nights:** Tuesday & Thursday
Programme Size: A5 **Pages**: 10 **Price**: With admission **Advertising**: Contact Jim Brooks 01761 470229

MAIDENHEAD R.U.F.C.

Founded: 1921

President	K J Lawton	3 Manor Lane, Maidenhead, Berks. 01628 629688
Chief Executive	G R Fisher	`Bramleigh', Shopenhangars Road, Maidenhead SL6 2PZ 01628 625555
Hon. Secretary	R M (Dick) Brown	49 Bannard Rd, Maidenhead, Berks. SL6 4NP 01628 670586(H) 01628 670816(B)
Finace Director	R Keeping	'The Pines', 5 Longworth Drive, Maidenhead, Berks. SL6 8XA 01628 635987
Club Coach	S Edwards	`Highfield House', High Road, Cookham, Berks. 01628 521125
Fixture Secretary	C G Reeves	21 Belmont Road, Maidenhead, Berks. 01628 620601
League Contact	Fixture Secretary, as above	

Ground Address Braywick Park, Braywick Road, Maidenhead, Berks. Tel: 01628 629663 Tel/Fax: 01628 635452
 Capacity: 1,750 Covered Seats: 250 Uncovered Standing: 1,500

Directions From M4 junct 8/9 follow signs A308(M) Maidenhead Town Centre. A308(M) to r'about, left on A308 towards Maidenhead. After 1/2 mile filter right across dual carriageway & club is directly opposite.

Nearest Rail Station: Maidenhead - 800 yds from clubhouse. **Car Parking:** 100 spaces plus 150 overflow park, 100 yds away
Admission: Matchday: £2 + £1 transfer to stand Season tickets: Not available.
Clubhouse: Open Tue, Thur, Sat & Sun. Food available matchdays. For functions - contact Peter Powell 01628 629663
Club Shop: Currently open Sat & Suns. **Colours**: Magenta, violet & black **Change colours:** Green, violet & white
Training Nights: Tuesday & Thursday 7.15 for 7.30 sharp **Nickname**: `Maids`
Programme: **Size**: A5 **Pages**: 32 **Price**: with admission **Editor**: Contact club
 Advertising: Contact Club Steward - Peter Powell 01628 629663

READING R.F.C.

Founded: 1898

President	Ted Goodhew	10 Lamplighters Walk, Fords Farm, Reading RG31 7YU	01189 451015
Chairman	Hugh Crabtree	Ashleigh House, 236 Wokingham Rd., Reading RG6 1JS	01189 261236
Club Secretary	Tim Gilbert	130 St Peters Rd., Reading RG6 1PH	01189 668077
Commercial Manager	Mark Richards	c/o Reading RFC	01189 696592
Publicity	Dave Parish	19 Doddington Close, Lower Earley RG6 4BJ	01189 313321
Operations	Andrew Green	23 Tennyson Rd., Woodley, Berks. RG5 3RH	01189 697733
Rugby Administrator	Phil Betts	7 Sherwood Rd., Winnersh, RG41 5NH	01189 78706

Ground: Holme Park, Sonning Lane, Reading RG4 6ST Tel: 01189 696592 Fax: 01189 696593
 Capacity: 2,500 Seated: 200 Standing: 2,300 e-mail: enquiries@readingrfc.co.uk
Directions: A4 Reading to Maidenhead Road, turn left 2.5 miles out of Reading, sign posted Sonning.
Nearest Railway Station: Reading Mainline, by short taxi journey (10 mins). **Car Parking:** 250 at ground, 200 nearby
Admission: Matchday: Standing Adults £5, including programme
Club Shop: Open Sat 1-5 plus training times Contact Andrew Green, c/o Club
Clubhouse: Open daily depending upon club activities Snacks & bar meals available.
Functions: Capacity 150 - contact Andy Weller 01189 696592
Training Nights: Tuesdays & Thursdays (Seniors) **Nickname:** Green Machine
PROGRAMME Size: A5 Pages: 72 Price: with admission Editor: Mark Richards Advertising: Contact Mark Richards
Colours: Myrtle & white 'V'/myrtle. **Change colours:** Yellow with myrtle 'V', collar & cuffs

STROUD RFC

Founded: 1873

President	Russ Hillier, "Marijon", Pagan Hill Lane, Stroud, Glos, GL5 4AW	Tel: 01453 764381 (H)
Chairman	Jenkyn Kennedy, 26 Pauls Rise, N. Wood Chester, Stroud GL6 9EQ	
Club Secretary	Mike Jenkins, 31 Rowley, Cam, Dursley, Glos, GL11 5NT	Tel: 01453 547085 (H)
Hon. Treasurer	Mrs Lesley Gomer, 40 Oxmoor, Abbeydale, Gloucester GL4 5XW	Tel: 01452 415867
Fixtures Secretary	Russ Hillier, "Marijon", Pagan Hill Lane, Stroud, Glos, GL5 4AW	Tel: 01453 764381 (H)
League Contact	Fixture Secretary, as above	

Ground   **Address**: Fromehall Park, Dudbridge, Stroud, Glos. GL5 3HS   Website: stroudrfc.co.uk
Tel: 01453 763019 Fax: 01453 758799 (M-F 9-5) emailsrfc@spring.co.uk
Directions: 1 mile south of Stroud on A46 at Golden Cross cross roads - opposite 'Great Mills' store
Car Parking: 100 spaces   Nearest Railway Station: Stroud Capacity: 600 all uncovered standing
Admission: £3 incl. programme
Club Shop: None, club items available on matchdays.
Clubhouse: Open every evening mon - Sat and Sun lunchtime.
Training Nights: Tuesday & Thursday
Programme: Size: A5 Price: with admission Pages: 40 Editor: Sarah Cook & Roger Whitfield
Advertising: Contact Sarah Cook 07973 257499 (M) 01453 750918 (H)
Colours: Blue and white hoops   **Change colours:** Red and white hoops

SWANAGE & WAREHAM R.F.C.

Founded: 1953

President	Michael White, Woodside, Carey, Wareham	Tel: 01929 553161
Chairman	Martin Hill, 9 Sherford Close, Wareham	Tel: 01929 551652
Secretary	Keith Jeffrey, 20 Greenway Rd., Weymouth, Dorset DT3 5BE Tel: 01305 815344	
Fixture Secretary	John Constable, Grand View, Puddletown Rd, Worgret, Wareham, Dorset BH20 Tel: 01929 551468	
League Contact	Brian Marshall, 1 Keysworth Drive, Sandford, Wareham, Dorset BH20 7BD Tel: 01929 556614	

Ground   **Address:** Bestwall, Wareham, Dorset.Tel: 01929 552224
Capacity: All uncovered standing   Website: www.swanage-wareham-rfc.freeserve.co.uk
Directions: Approach the traffic lights at the crossroads in Wareham town centre. Turn into Bestwall
Road and the ground is at the bottom of the road on the left.
Car Parking: 200 spaces available at ground **Nearest Railway Station:** Wareham
Admission: Matchday £2   Season tickets: Not available
Clubhouse: Yes   **Club Shop:** No

Programme: **Size**: A5   **Pages**: 12   **Price**: with admission   **Advertising:** Contact chairman
Editor: Ron Butler, 20 Miles Ave., Sandford, Wareham 01929 553826
Colours: Maroon shirts, white shorts, maroon socks.   **Change colours:** Green & gold
Training Night: Tuesday   **Nickname:** 'Swans'

WESTON SUPER MARE RFC

Founded: 1875

President	John Brentnall c/o Messers Ward & Co., 37 The Boulevard, Weston-s-Mare 0117 922 0208 (H), 01934 413545 (B)
Chairman	Bill Poole 19 Worlebury Park Road, Worlebury, W-s-M. 01934 626870 (H)
Club Secretary	Steve Sharp 10 Southview, Yatton, Bristol BS49 4AH 01934 876285 (H), 07808 094082 (M)
Hon. Treasurer	Graham Buller 15 Chalfont Rd., Weston-s-Mare BS22 3PZ 01934 429396 (H)
Fixture Secretary	Mark Philp 9 Ashleigh Rd., Weston-s-Mare BS23 2XG 01934 636942 (B)
Chairman of Rugby	Colin Reeves 48 Meade Vale, Weston-s-Mare 01934 511293
Club Manager	Mark Philp 9 Ashleigh Rd., Weston-s-Mare BS23 2XG 01934 636942 (B) & at club

Ground Address: Recreation Ground, Drove Road, Weston Super Mare, North Somerset BS23 3PA
Tel: 01934 625643/623118   Fax: 01934 625643   email: westonrfc@lineone.com   Web site: weston-warriors.co.uk
Capacity: 6,499   Seated: 499   Standing - Covered: 300 Uncovered: 5,700
Directions: M5 Jnc 21, follow dual carriageway into Weston, (following signs for town centre). At the 5th roundabout the ground is just over on the left. Nearest Railway Station: Weston Super Mare, 100 yards from ground
Car Parking: 200 at ground, 50+ nearby   **Club Shop:** Open Sat & Sun matchdays.   **Training Nights:** Tuesday & Thursday
Admission: Season ticket from £72 - £96, OAPs £20, Junior £15. Matchday (incl. prog) £5, OAPs £2.50
Clubhouse: Every evening (except Sun.) 7.00-11.00, matchdays 12.00-11.00, Sundays 12.00-3.00.   Snacks & bar meals available.
Programme: **Size:** A5 **Price:** with entry **Pages:** 16+cover **Editor:** Jon Cornish (Waterside Printers) 01275 340090, 343916 (Fax)
Advertising Rates Colour Full page £300 Mono - Full page £200, half £100
Colours: Royal blue with red and white flashings, blue shorts   **Change colours:** Red shirts, blue shorts **Nickname**: Seasiders

SOUTH WEST

SOUTH WEST DIVISION FINAL LEAGUE TABLES 2000-01

South West 2 East

	P	W	D	L	PF	PA	PD	Pts	-
Chinnor	22	18	0	4	640	226	414	36	
Slough	22	18	0	4	423	347	76	36	
Chippenham	22	17	0	5	686	233	453	34	
Abbey	22	14	0	8	568	264	304	28	
*Amersham & Chiltern	22	13	0	9	470	349	121	24	2
Aylesbury	22	12	0	10	369	419	-50	24	
Marlow	22	11	1	10	451	406	45	23	
Tadley	22	10	0	12	374	457	-83	20	
Olney	22	7	1	14	259	534	-275	15	
Stow-on-the-Wold	22	6	2	14	228	420	-192	14	
Witney	22	2	0	20	223	526	-303	4	
High Wycombe	22	1	2	19	188	698	-510	4	

South West 2 West

	P	W	D	L	PF	PA	PD	Pts	-
Dings Crusaders	22	19	0	3	604	237	367	38	
Stroud	22	18	0	4	633	246	387	36	
Matson	22	13	1	8	429	301	128	27	
*Hornets	22	14	0	8	516	331	185	26	2
Brixham	22	12	0	10	468	411	57	24	
Cheltenham North	22	12	0	10	378	482	-104	24	
Camborne	22	10	0	12	352	547	-195	20	
*St Mary's O.B. (SW)	22	10	0	12	415	362	53	18	2
Ivybridge	22	8	0	14	308	487	-179	16	
St Austell	22	7	0	15	327	483	-156	14	
Clevedon	22	3	1	18	291	617	-326	7	
*Penryn	22	5	0	17	277	494	-217	6	4

Southern Counties North

	P	W	D	L	PF	PA	PD	Pts	-
Windsor	20	18	0	2	583	113	470	36	
Grove	20	14	2	4	459	183	276	30	
Beaconsfield	20	14	1	5	439	202	237	29	
Swindon	20	14	1	5	405	242	163	29	
Oxford Harlequins	20	10	1	9	434	341	93	21	
Chipping Norton	20	10	1	9	298	368	-70	21	
Buckingham	20	9	0	11	254	265	-11	18	
Bicester	20	6	0	14	364	413	-49	12	
Phoenix	20	6	0	14	199	508	-309	12	
Bletchley	20	3	1	16	132	486	-354	7	
Drifters	20	2	1	17	204	650	-446	5	

Southern Counties South

	P	W	D	L	PF	PA	PD	Pts	-
Redingensians	16	14	1	1	389	162	227	29	
Salisbury	16	14	0	2	465	155	310	28	
Wootton Bassett	16	9	1	6	246	170	76	19	
Wimborne	15	9	0	6	192	147	45	18	
Devizes	16	7	1	8	222	239	-17	15	
Ivel Barbarians	16	4	1	11	218	314	-96	9	
*Bournemouth	16	5	0	11	232	248	-16	8	2
Swindon College	15	4	0	11	140	391	-251	8	
Corsham	16	3	0	13	123	401	-278	6	

Sherborne have withdrawn and their results have been removed

Western Counties North

	P	W	D	L	PF	PA	PD	Pts	-
Cleve	22	20	0	2	575	197	378	40	
Taunton	22	17	1	4	706	364	342	35	
Old Redcliffians	22	14	0	8	511	296	215	28	
*Old Richians	22	14	1	7	436	296	140	27	2
Chew Valley	22	12	1	9	351	357	-6	25	
Whitehall	22	10	0	12	341	350	-9	20	
*Coney Hill	22	11	0	11	285	298	-13	20	2
Gordon League	22	9	1	12	377	452	-75	19	
North Bristol	22	7	0	15	333	495	-162	14	
Spartans	22	6	1	15	284	487	-203	13	
Cirencester	22	5	0	17	296	624	-328	10	
Barton Hill	22	4	1	17	214	493	-279	9	

Western Counties West

	P	W	D	L	PF	PA	PD	Pts	-
Crediton	20	17	1	2	531	235	296	35	
Withycombe	22	16	2	4	523	273	250	34	
Exmouth	22	16	0	6	618	273	345	32	
Tiverton	22	12	1	9	490	380	110	25	
Newton Abbot	21	10	0	11	381	370	11	20	
Okehampton	18	8	1	9	328	381	-53	17	
Hayle	20	7	1	12	353	427	-74	15	
Devonport Services	20	7	1	12	293	435	-142	15	
Paignton	21	7	1	13	334	498	-164	15	
South Molton	18	7	0	11	294	349	-55	14	
St Ives (SW)	21	6	0	15	299	515	-216	12	
Wellington	17	4	0	13	215	523	-308	8	

Cornwall/Devon

	P	W	D	L	PF	PA	PD	Pts	-
St Just	18	12	1	5	405	238	167	25	
Bideford	14	12	0	2	411	111	300	24	
Old Plymothian & Mann.	17	12	0	5	394	270	124	24	
Wessex	18	11	0	7	295	189	106	22	
Newquay Hornets	18	10	0	8	220	199	21	20	
*Kingsbridge	17	8	0	9	227	260	-33	14	2
Teignmouth	17	7	0	10	195	366	-171	14	
Bude	18	6	0	12	214	375	-161	12	
*Sidmouth	18	5	1	12	234	320	-86	9	2
*Perranporth	17	2	0	15	161	428	-267	0	4

Cornwall 1

	P	W	D	L	PF	PA	PD	Pts	-
Saltash	16	15	0	1	358	117	241	30	
Wadebridge Camels	16	14	0	2	615	103	512	28	
*Bodmin	16	10	0	6	290	188	102	18	2
Falmouth	16	8	0	8	197	240	-43	16	
*Liskeard-Looe	16	9	0	7	286	199	87	14	4
St Agnes	16	7	0	9	305	333	-28	14	
*Helston	16	4	1	11	190	333	-143	7	2
Redruth Albany	16	3	1	12	112	443	-331	7	
*St Day	16	1	0	15	111	508	-397	0	2

Cornwall 2

	P	W	D	L	PF	PA	PD	Pts	-
Mounts Bay	14	13	0	1	432	97	335	26	
Callington	13	11	0	2	335	156	179	22	
Illogan Park	13	10	0	3	345	125	220	20	
Veor	14	5	0	9	108	328	-220	10	
*Stithians	13	5	0	8	141	273	-132	8	2
*Roseland	14	5	0	9	236	260	-24	4	6
*Camborne S o M	14	5	0	9	161	228	-67	2	8
*Lankelly Fowey	13	0	0	13	13	304	-291	-10	10

Devon 1

	P	W	D	L	PF	PA	PD	Pts	-
Torrington	18	18	0	0	559	141	418	36	
*Old Technicians	18	14	1	3	331	181	150	27	2
Honiton	18	10	0	8	423	266	157	20	
*Tavistock	18	9	0	9	374	366	8	16	2
Cullompton	18	7	1	10	324	400	-76	15	
Tamar Saracens	18	7	0	11	275	347	-72	14	
Ilfracombe	18	7	0	11	288	444	-156	14	
Exeter Saracens	18	6	1	11	261	307	-46	13	
Topsham	18	4	3	11	234	435	-201	11	
Plymouth Civil Service	18	5	0	13	216	398	-182	10	

Devon 2

	P	W	D	L	PF	PA	PD	Pts	-
Devonport HSOB	14	13	0	1	292	109	183	26	
Old Public Oaks	13	9	0	4	255	125	130	18	
*Totnes	13	9	0	4	350	208	142	16	2
*Marjons	13	8	1	4	300	186	114	15	2
Prince R/Woodland F	14	4	0	10	182	253	-71	8	
Buckfastleigh	14	3	1	10	144	410	-266	7	
North Tawton	11	3	0	8	83	215	-132	6	
*Plymouth Argaum	14	3	0	11	218	318	-100	4	2

SOUTH WEST

Devon 3	P	W	D	L	PF	PA	PD	Pts	-
Dartmouth	10	7	1	2	239	79	160	15	
Plympton Victoria	10	6	0	4	108	122	-14	12	
*University of Plymouth	8	6	1	1	203	81	122	11	2
Salcombe	10	5	0	5	165	159	6	10	
St Columba & Torpoint	8	2	0	6	38	167	-129	4	
*Bovey Tracey	10	1	0	9	69	214	-145	-6	8

Rolle Rats have withdrawn and their results removed.

Gloucester Premier	P	W	D	L	PF	PA	PD	Pts	-
Thornbury	18	16	0	2	528	165	363	32	
Old Centralians	18	13	0	5	506	324	182	26	
Drybrook	18	12	0	6	500	272	228	24	
Longlevens	17	11	0	6	400	321	79	22	
Bristol Saracens	18	9	1	8	403	290	113	19	
Avonmouth OB	18	7	1	10	310	335	-25	15	
Chipping Sodbury	18	7	1	10	289	347	-58	15	
Aretians	18	6	0	12	328	310	18	12	
Bream	17	5	1	11	201	474	-273	11	
*Brockworth	18	1	0	17	157	784	-627	0	2

Gloucester 1	P	W	D	L	PF	PA	PD	Pts	-
Chosen Hill F. P.	18	17	0	1	502	162	340	34	
Hucclecote	18	13	0	5	378	253	125	26	
Old Bristolians	18	13	0	5	391	270	121	26	
*Ashley Down Old Boys	17	10	0	7	348	225	123	18	2
Cheltenham Civil Service	18	7	1	10	406	411	-5	15	
Old Cryptians	17	7	1	9	311	328	-17	15	
Frampton Cotterell	17	7	0	10	396	407	-11	14	
Westbury on Severn	14	6	1	7	196	249	-53	13	
Cheltenham Saracens	17	4	1	12	242	430	-188	9	
*Tetbury	18	0	0	18	109	544	-435	-4	4

Gloucester 2	P	W	D	L	PF	PA	PD	Pts	-
Painswick	17	16	0	1	503	152	351	32	
Tewkesbury	18	15	0	3	450	192	258	30	
*Southmead	18	15	0	3	504	207	297	28	2
Dursley	17	9	0	8	317	217	100	18	
*Kingswood	18	9	1	8	299	291	8	17	2
Bishopston	18	8	0	10	407	302	105	16	
Old Elizabethans	18	6	1	11	288	364	-76	13	
*Smiths (Industries)	18	5	0	13	219	474	-255	8	2
*Bristol Telephones	18	4	0	14	257	558	-301	6	2
Cainscross	18	1	0	17	116	603	-487	2	

Gloucester 3 North	P	W	D	L	PF	PA	PD	Pts	-
Widden Old Boys	12	10	1	1	344	104	240	21	
Ross On Wye	12	8	1	3	213	131	82	17	
*Gloucester Civil Service	12	6	1	5	152	112	40	11	2
Newent	12	5	0	7	180	271	-91	10	
*Gloucester All Blues	12	4	1	7	66	143	-77	9	2
*Tredworth	12	6	0	6	156	151	5	6	6
*Fairford	12	1	0	11	95	294	-199	0	2

Gloucester 3 South	P	W	D	L	PF	PA	PD	Pts	-
St Brendans Old Boys	10	8	0	2	292	89	203	16	
Old Colstonians	10	8	0	2	237	99	138	16	
Minchinhampton	10	6	0	4	233	136	97	12	
Cotham Park	10	6	0	4	144	127	17	12	
Wotton-under-Edge	10	2	0	8	79	295	-216	4	
Bristol Aeroplane Co	10	0	0	10	93	332	-239	0	

Somerset Premier	P	W	D	L	PF	PA	PD	Pts	-
Walcot Old Boys	22	22	0	0	648	211	437	44	
Gordano	22	16	1	5	472	253	219	33	
Midsomer Norton	22	16	0	6	416	256	160	32	
*Bristol Harlequins	22	13	0	9	378	296	82	24	2
Yatton	22	11	0	11	467	314	153	22	
Old Culverhaysians	22	11	0	11	322	339	-17	22	
Wiveliscombe	22	10	0	12	344	380	-36	20	
Oldfield Old Boys	22	9	0	13	307	382	-75	18	
*Avon	22	8	0	14	315	436	-121	14	2
Tor	22	7	0	15	267	404	-137	14	
St Bernadettes O.B.	22	6	1	15	234	358	-124	13	
Combe Down	22	2	0	20	189	730	-541	4	

Somerset 1	P	W	D	L	PF	PA	PD	Pts	-
Minehead Barbarians	22	19	1	2	668	164	504	39	
Wells	22	19	1	2	615	174	441	39	
North Petherton	22	19	0	3	826	254	572	38	
Imperial	22	12	1	9	373	343	30	25	
Stothert & Pitt	22	11	0	11	382	353	29	22	
*Broad Plain	22	12	0	10	367	341	26	22	2
Avonvale	22	10	0	12	391	413	-22	20	
*Nailsea & Backwell	22	7	1	14	324	390	-66	13	2
Chard	22	5	2	15	198	582	-384	12	
Old Sulians	22	5	0	17	176	481	-305	10	
*Old Ashtonians	22	5	1	16	201	493	-292	9	2
*Bristol Barbarians	22	4	1	17	200	733	-533	7	2

Somerset 2	P	W	D	L	PF	PA	PD	Pts	-
Crewkerne	16	16	0	0	720	112	608	32	
Burnham on Sea	16	11	0	5	442	203	239	22	
Bath Saracens	16	11	0	5	343	239	104	22	
Blagdon	16	9	0	7	356	281	75	18	
Castle Cary	16	5	1	10	152	382	-230	11	
Morganians	16	4	1	11	157	357	-200	9	
*Bath Old Edwardians	16	8	0	8	310	463	-153	4	12
Cheddar Valley	16	1	0	15	151	593	-442	2	
*Winscombe	16	6	0	10	293	294	-1	0	12

Berks/Bucks & Oxon 1									
	P	W	D	L	PF	PA	PD	Pts	-
Oxford	14	11	0	3	281	108	173	22	
Milton Keynes	14	10	1	3	213	112	101	21	
*Wallingford	14	9	0	5	275	194	81	16	2
Thatcham	14	8	0	6	206	176	30	16	
*Chesham	14	6	1	7	196	203	-7	11	2
*Pennanians	14	6	1	7	232	252	-20	9	4
Littlemore	14	4	1	9	190	273	-83	9	
*Berkshire Shire Hall	14	0	0	14	69	344	-275	-10	10

Berks/Bucks & Oxon 2									
	P	W	D	L	PF	PA	PD	Pts	-
Wheatley	14	12	0	2	270	155	115	24	
*Henley Wanderers	14	12	0	2	613	134	479	22	2
Aldermaston	14	10	0	4	344	103	241	20	
Abingdon	14	8	0	6	192	173	19	16	
Harwell	14	6	0	8	138	381	-243	12	
Gosford All Blacks	14	5	1	8	215	204	11	11	
Winslow	14	1	1	12	64	342	-278	3	
*Didcot	14	1	0	13	38	382	-344	-4	6

Dorset & Wilts 1	P	W	D	L	PF	PA	PD	Pts	-
Frome	14	12	0	2	492	120	372	24	
Oakmeadians	14	11	0	3	365	170	195	22	
Cooper Avon Tyres	14	10	1	3	234	188	46	21	
Westbury	14	7	2	5	289	201	88	16	
Minety	14	5	1	8	138	223	-85	11	
Trowbridge	14	4	0	10	154	241	-87	8	
*Bridport	14	5	0	9	155	446	-291	4	6
*North Dorset	14	0	0	14	122	360	-238	-6	6

Dorset & Wilts 2 North									
	P	W	D	L	PF	PA	PD	Pts	-
Calne	12	10	0	2	387	45	342	20	
Supermarine	12	9	1	2	271	115	156	19	
Bradford on Avon	12	8	0	4	252	90	162	16	
Hungerford	12	8	0	4	227	175	52	16	
Marlborough	12	3	0	9	68	368	-300	6	
*Colerne	12	2	0	10	98	278	-180	2	2
*Pewsey Vale	12	1	1	10	75	307	-232	1	2

Dorset & Wilts 2 South									
	P	W	D	L	PF	PA	PD	Pts	-
Blandford	14	12	0	2	515	117	398	24	
Martock	14	12	0	2	407	171	236	24	
Weymouth	14	10	0	4	435	133	302	20	
Poole	14	8	0	6	408	241	167	16	
Wincanton	14	6	0	8	278	237	41	12	
Puddletown	14	6	0	8	187	383	-196	12	
Warminster	14	2	0	12	112	408	-296	4	
*Verwood	14	0	0	14	67	719	-652	-4	4

* denotes points deducted in right hand column

SOUTH WEST

SOUTH WEST DIVISION FIXTURE GRIDS 2001-2002

South West 2 West

	Berry Hill	Brixham	Camborne	Cheltenham North	Cleve	Crediton	Gloucester O. B.	Hornets	Matson	Taunton	Torquay Athletic	Truro
Berry Hill		16.03	22.09	02.03	06.10	09.02	27.10	26.01	17.11	05.01	08.12	06.04
Brixham	08.09		26.01	22.09	17.11	02.03	05.01	06.10	08.12	09.02	06.04	27.10
Camborne	09.03	10.11		12.01	29.09	01.12	23.02	13.04	20.10	22.12	02.02	16.03
Cheltenham North	29.09	09.03	17.11		05.01	06.10	08.12	09.02	06.04	27.10	08.09	26.01
Cleve	23.02	12.01	02.03	01.12		13.04	20.10	22.12	02.02	16.03	10.11	22.09
Crediton	20.10	29.09	05.01	23.02	08.12		06.04	27.10	08.09	26.01	09.03	17.11
Gloucester Old Boys	02.02	01.12	06.10	13.04	09.02	22.12		16.03	10.11	22.09	12.01	02.03
Hornets	10.11	23.02	09.02	06.04	02.02	08.09			09.03	17.11	29.09	05.01
Matson	12.01	13.04	09.02	22.12	27.10	16.03	26.01	22.09		02.03	01.12	06.10
Taunton	01.12	20.10	06.04	02.02	08.09	10.11	09.03	12.01	29.09		23.02	08.12
Torquay Athletic	13.04	22.12	27.10	16.03	26.01	22.09	17.11	02.03	05.01	06.10		09.02
Truro	22.12	02.02	08.09	10.11	09.03	12.01	29.09	01.12	23.02	13.04	20.10	

South West 2 East

	Abbey	Amersham & Chiltern	Aylesbury	Chippenham	Marlow	Olney	Redingensians	Salisbury	Slough	Stow-on-the-Wold	Tadley	Windsor
Abbey		16.03	22.09	02.03	06.10	09.02	27.10	26.01	17.11	05.01	08.12	06.04
Amersham & Chiltern	08.09		26.01	22.09	17.11	02.03	05.01	06.10	08.12	09.02	06.04	27.10
Aylesbury	09.03	10.11		12.01	29.09	01.12	23.02	13.04	20.10	22.12	02.02	16.03
Chippenham	29.09	09.03	17.11		05.01	06.10	08.12	09.02	06.04	27.10	08.09	26.01
Marlow	23.02	12.01	02.03	01.12		13.04	20.10	22.12	02.02	16.03	10.11	22.09
Olney	20.10	29.09	05.01	23.02	08.12		06.04	27.10	08.09	26.01	09.03	17.11
Redingensians	02.02	01.12	06.10	13.04	09.02	22.12		16.03	10.11	22.09	12.01	02.03
Salisbury	10.11	23.02	08.12	20.10	06.04	02.02	08.09		09.03	17.11	29.09	05.01
Slough	12.01	13.04	09.02	22.12	27.10	16.03	26.01	22.09		02.03	01.12	06.10
Stow-on-the-Wold	01.12	20.10	06.04	02.02	08.09	10.11	09.03	12.01	29.09		23.02	08.12
Tadley	13.04	22.12	27.10	16.03	26.01	22.09	17.11	02.03	05.01	06.10		09.02
Windsor	22.12	02.02	08.09	10.11	09.03	12.01	29.09	01.12	23.02	13.04	20.10	

Western Counties West

	Bideford	Exmouth	Hayle	Ivybridge	Newton Abbot	Okehampton	Penryn	South Molton	St Austell	St Just	Tiverton	Withycombe
Bideford		16.03	22.09	02.03	06.10	09.02	27.10	05.01	26.01	17.11	08.12	06.04
Exmouth	08.09		26.01	22.09	17.11	02.03	05.01	09.02	06.10	08.12	06.04	27.10
Hayle	09.03	10.11		12.01	29.09	01.12	23.02	22.12	13.04	20.10	02.02	16.03
Ivybridge	29.09	09.03	17.11		05.01	06.10	08.12	27.10	09.02	06.04	08.09	26.01
Newton Abbot	23.02	12.01	02.03	01.12		13.04	20.10	16.03	22.12	02.02	010.11	22.09
Okehampton	20.10	29.09	05.01	23.02	08.12		06.04	26.01	27.10	08.09	09.03	17.11
Penryn	02.02	01.12	06.10	13.04	09.02	22.12		22.09	16.03	10.11	12.01	02.03
South Molton	01.12	20.10	06.04	02.02	08.09	10.11	09.03		12.01	29.09	23.02	08.12
St Austell	10.11	23.02	08.12	20.10	06.04	02.02	08.09	17.11		09.03	29.09	05.01
St Just	12.01	13.04	09.02	22.12	27.10	16.03	26.01	02.03	22.09		01.12	06.10
Tiverton	13.04	22.12	27.10	16.03	26.01	22.09	17.11	06.10	02.03	05.01		09.02
Withycombe	22.12	2.02	08.09	10.11	9.03	12.01	29.09	13.04	01.12	23.02	20.10	

Cornwall/Devon

	Devonport Services	Newquay Hornets	Old Plymothian & Mann.	Paignton	Saltash	St Ives (SW)	Torrington	Wadebridge Camels	Wellington	Wessex
Devonport Services		16.03	29.09	23.02	26.01	20.10	10.11	22.12	01.12	06.04
Newquay Hornets	22.09		10.11	29.09	23.02	22.12	01.12	20.10	06.04	26.01
Old Plymothian & Mann.	09.03	12.01		17.11	13.04	06.10	02.02	08.12	27.10	16.03
Paignton	06.10	09.03	22.12		20.10	01.12	06.04	26.01	22.09	10.11
Saltash	27.10	06.10	01.12	02.02		06.04	22.09	10.11	09.03	22.12
St Ives (SW)	02.02	17.11	23.02	13.04	08.12		27.10	16.03	12.01	29.09
Torrington	12.01	13.04	20.10	08.12	16.03	26.01		29.09	17.11	23.02
Wadebridge Camels	17.11	02.02	06.04	27.10	12.01	22.09	09.03		06.10	01.12
Wellington	13.04	08.12	26.01	16.03	29.09	10.11	22.12	23.02		20.10
Wessex	08.12	27.10	22.09	12.01	17.11	09.03	06.10	13.04	02.02	

Cornwall 1

	Bodmin	Bude	Callington	Falmouth	Helston	Liskeard-Looe	Mounts Bay	Perranporth	St Agnes
Bodmin		16.03	29.09	23.02	20.10	26.01	10.11	22.12	01.12
Bude	22.09		10.11	29.09	22.12	23.02	01.12	20.10	06.04
Callington	09.03	12.01		17.11	06.10	13.04	02.02	08.12	27.10
Falmouth	06.10	09.03	22.12		01.12	20.10	06.04	26.01	22.09
Helston	02.02	17.11	23.02	13.04		08.12	27.10	16.03	12.01
Liskeard-Looe	27.10	06.10	01.12	02.02	06.04		22.09	10.11	09.03
Mounts Bay	12.01	13.04	20.10	08.12	26.01	16.03		29.09	17.11
Perranporth	17.11	02.02	06.04	27.10	22.09	12.01	09.03		06.10
St Agnes	13.04	08.12	26.01	16.03	10.11	29.09	22.12	23.02	

Cornwall 2

	Camborne S o M	Illogan Park	Lankelly Fowey	Redruth Albany	Roseland	St Day	Stithians	Veor
Camborne S o M		22.12	06.10	26.01	10.11	17.11	16.03	08.12
Illogan Park	22.09		17.11	12.01	16.03	27.10	08.12	23.02
Lankelly Fowey	12.01	09.03		01.12	26.01	13.04	10.11	22.09
Redruth Albany	27.10	06.10	16.03		08.12	23.02	22.12	17.11
Roseland	23.02	01.12	27.10	13.04		22.09	09.03	12.01
St Day	09.03	26.01	08.12	10.11	22.12		06.10	16.03
Stithians	01.12	13.04	23.02	22.09	17.11	12.01		27.10
Veor	13.04	10.11	22.12	09.03	06.10	01.12	26.01	

SOUTH WEST

Devon 1

	Cullompton	Devonport HSOB	Honiton	Kingsbridge	Old Public Oaks	Old Technicians	Sidmouth	Tamar Saracens	Tavistock	Teignmouth
Cullompton		16.03	29.09	23.02	20.10	26.01	10.11	22.12	01.12	06.04
Devonport HSOB	22.09		10.11	29.09	22.12	23.02	01.12	20.10	06.04	26.01
Honiton	09.03	12.01		17.11	06.10	13.04	02.02	08.12	27.10	16.03
Kingsbridge	06.10	09.03	22.12		01.12	20.10	06.04	26.01	22.09	10.11
Old Public Oaks	02.02	17.11	23.02	13.04		08.12	27.10	16.03	12.01	29.09
Old Technicians	27.10	06.10	01.12	02.02	06.04		22.09	10.11	09.03	22.12
Sidmouth	12.01	13.04	20.10	08.12	26.01	16.03		29.09	17.11	23.02
Tamar Saracens	17.11	02.02	06.04	27.10	22.09	12.01	09.03		06.10	01.12
Tavistock	13.04	08.12	26.01	16.03	10.11	29.09	22.12	23.02		20.10
Teignmouth	08.12	27.10	22.09	12.01	09.03	17.11	06.10	13.04	02.02	

Devon 2

	Dartmouth	Exeter Saracens	Ilfracombe	Marjons	Plymouth Civil Service	Plympton Victoria	Topsham	Totnes
Dartmouth		22.12	06.10	26.01	10.11	17.11	16.03	08.12
Exeter Saracens	22.09		17.11	12.01	16.03	27.10	08.12	23.02
Ilfracombe	12.01	09.03		01.12	26.01	13.04	10.11	22.09
Marjons	27.10	06.10	16.03		08.12	23.02	22.12	17.11
Plymouth Civil Service	23.02	01.12	27.10	13.04		22.09	09.03	12.01
Plympton Victoria	09.03	26.01	08.12	10.11	22.12		06.10	16.03
Topsham	01.12	13.04	23.02	22.09	17.11	12.01		27.10
Totnes	13.04	10.11	22.12	09.03	06.10	01.12	26.01	

Devon 3

	Buckfastleigh	North Tawton	Plymouth Argaum	Prince R/Woodland F	Salcombe	St Columba & Torpoint	University of Plymouth
Buckfastleigh		17.11	12.01	16.03	08.12	27.10	23.02
North Tawton	09.03		01.12	26.01	10.11	13.04	22.09
Plymouth Argaum	06.10	16.03		08.12	22.12	23.02	17.11
Prince R/Woodland F	01.12	27.10	13.04		09.03	22.09	12.01
Salcombe	13.04	23.02	22.09	17.11		12.01	27.10
St Columba & Torpoint	26.01	08.12	10.11	22.12	06.10		16.03
University of Plymouth	10.11	22.12	09.03	06.10	26.01	01.12	

SOUTH WEST

Western Counties North

	Chew Valley	Clevedon	Coney Hill	Gordon League	North Bristol	Old Centralians	Old Redcliffians	Old Richians	St Mary's O.B. (SW)	Thornbury	Walcot Old Boys	Whitehall
Chew Valley		16.03	22.09	02.03	06.10	09.02	27.10	26.01	17.11	05.01	08.12	06.04
Clevedon	08.09		26.01	22.09	17.11	02.03	05.01	06.10	08.12	09.02	06.04	27.10
Coney Hill	09.03	10.11		12.01	29.09	01.12	23.02	13.04	20.10	22.12	02.02	16.03
Gordon League	29.09	09.03	17.11		05.01	06.10	08.12	09.02	06.04	27.10	08.09	26.01
North Bristol	23.02	12.01	02.03	01.12		13.04	20.10	22.12	02.02	16.03	10.11	22.09
Old Centralians	20.10	29.09	05.01	23.02	08.12		06.04	27.10	08.09	26.01	09.03	17.11
Old Redcliffians	02.02	01.12	06.10	13.04	09.02	22.12		16.03	10.11	22.09	12.01	02.03
Old Richians	10.11	23.02	08.12	20.10	06.04	02.02	08.09		09.03	17.11	29.09	05.01
St Mary's O.B. (SW)	12.01	13.04	09.02	22.12	27.10	16.03	26.01	22.09		02.03	01.12	06.10
Thornbury	01.12	20.10	06.04	02.02	08.09	10.11	09.03	12.01	29.09		23.02	08.12
Walcot Old Boys	13.04	22.12	27.10	16.03	26.01	22.09	17.11	02.03	05.01	06.10		09.02
Whitehall	22.12	02.02	08.09	10.11	09.03	12.01	29.09	01.12	23.02	13.04	20.10	

Somerset Premier

	Avon	Bristol Harlequins	Gordano	Midsomer Norton	Minehead Barbarians	Old Culverhaysians	Oldfield Old Boys	St Bernadettes O. B.	Tor	Wells	Wiveliscombe	Yatton
Avon		16.03	22.09	02.03	06.10	09.02	27.10	26.01	17.11	05.01	08.12	06.04
Bristol Harlequins	08.09		26.01	22.09	17.11	02.03	05.01	06.10	08.12	09.02	06.04	27.10
Gordano	09.03	10.11		12.01	29.09	01.12	23.02	13.04	20.10	22.12	02.02	16.03
Midsomer Norton	29.09	09.03	17.11		05.01	06.10	08.12	09.02	06.04	27.10	08.09	26.01
Minehead Barbarians	23.02	12.01	02.03	01.12		13.04	20.10	22.12	02.02	16.03	10.11	22.09
Old Culverhaysians	20.10	29.09	05.01	23.02	08.12		06.04	27.10	08.09	26.01	09.03	17.11
Oldfield Old Boys	02.02	01.12	06.10	13.04	09.02	22.12		16.03	10.11	22.09	12.01	02.03
St Bernadettes O.B.	10.11	23.02	08.12	20.10	06.04	02.02	08.09		09.03	17.11	29.09	05.01
Tor	12.01	13.04	09.02	22.12	27.10	16.03	26.01	22.09		02.03	01.12	06.10
Wells	01.12	20.10	06.04	02.02	08.09	10.11	09.03	12.01	29.09		23.02	08.12
Wiveliscombe	13.04	22.12	27.10	16.03	26.01	22.09	17.11	02.03	05.01	06.10		09.02
Yatton	22.12	02.02	08.09	10.11	09.03	12.01	29.09	01.12	23.02	13.04	20.10	

Somerset 1

	Avonvale	Broad Plain	Burnham on Sea	Chard	Combe Down	Crewkerne	Imperial	Nailsea & Backwell	North Petherton	Old Ashtonians	Old Sulians	Stothert & Pitt
Avonvale		16.03	22.09	02.03	06.10	09.02	27.10	26.01	17.11	05.01	08.12	06.04
Broad Plain	08.09		26.01	22.09	17.11	02.03	05.01	06.10	08.12	09.02	06.04	27.10
Burnham on Sea	09.03	10.11		12.01	29.09	01.12	23.02	13.04	20.10	22.12	02.02	16.03
Chard	29.09	09.03	17.11		05.01	06.10	08.12	09.02	06.04	27.10	08.09	26.01
Combe Down	23.02	12.01	02.03	01.12		13.04	20.10	22.12	02.02	16.03	10.11	22.09
Crewkerne	20.10	29.09	05.01	23.02	08.12		06.04	27.10	08.09	26.01	09.03	17.11
Imperial	02.02	01.12	06.10	13.04	09.02	22.12		16.03	10.11	22.09	12.01	02.03
Nailsea & Backwell	10.11	23.02	08.12	20.10	06.04	02.02	08.09		09.03	17.11	29.09	05.01
North Petherton	12.01	13.04	09.02	22.12	27.10	16.03	26.01	22.09		02.03	01.12	06.10
Old Ashtonians	01.12	20.10	06.04	02.02	08.09	10.11	09.03	12.01	29.09		23.02	08.12
Old Sulians	13.04	22.12	27.10	16.03	26.01	22.09	17.11	02.03	05.01	06.10		09.02
Stothert & Pitt	22.12	02.02	08.09	10.11	09.03	12.01	29.09	01.12	23.02	13.04	20.10	

SOUTH WEST

Somerset 2

	Bath Old Edwardians	Bath Saracens	Blagdon	Bristol Barbarians	Castle Cary	Cheddar Valley	Morganians	Winscombe
Bath Old Edwardians		22.12	06.10	26.01	10.11	17.11	16.03	08.12
Bath Saracens	22.09		17.11	12.01	16.03	27.10	08.12	23.02
Blagdon	12.01	09.03		01.12	26.01	13.04	10.11	22.09
Bristol Barbarians	27.10	06.10	16.03		08.12	23.02	22.12	17.11
Castle Cary	23.02	01.12	27.10	13.04		22.09	09.03	12.01
Cheddar Valley	09.03	26.01	08.12	10.11	22.12		06.10	16.03
Morganians	01.12	13.04	23.02	22.09	17.11	12.01		27.10
Winscombe	13.04	10.11	22.12	09.03	06.10	01.12	26.01	

Gloucestershire Premier

	Avonmouth OB	Barton Hill	Bristol Saracens	Chipping Sodbury	Chosen Hill F. P.	Cirencester	Drybrook	Hucclecote	Longlevens	Spartans
Avonmouth OB		16.03	29.09	23.02	20.10	26.01	10.11	22.12	01.12	06.04
Barton Hill	22.09		10.11	29.09	22.12	23.02	01.12	20.10	06.04	26.01
Bristol Saracens	09.03	12.01		17.11	06.10	13.04	02.02	08.12	27.10	16.03
Chipping Sodbury	06.10	09.03	22.12		01.12	20.10	06.04	26.01	22.09	10.11
Chosen Hill F. P.	02.02	17.11	23.02	13.04		08.12	27.10	16.03	12.01	29.09
Cirencester	27.10	06.10	01.12	02.02	06.04		22.09	10.11	09.03	22.12
Drybrook	12.01	13.04	20.10	08.12	26.01	16.03		29.09	17.11	23.02
Hucclecote	17.11	02.02	06.04	27.10	22.09	12.01	09.03		06.10	01.12
Longlevens	13.04	08.12	26.01	16.03	10.11	29.09	22.12	23.02		20.10
Spartans	08.12	27.10	22.09	12.01	09.03	17.11	06.10	13.04	02.02	

Gloucestershire 1

	Aretians	Ashley Down O. B.	Bream	Brockworth	Frampton Cotterell	Old Bristolians	Old Cryptians	Painswick	Tewkesbury	Westbury on Severn
Aretians		16.03	29.09	23.02	20.10	26.01	10.11	22.12	01.12	06.04
Ashley Down Old Boys	22.09		10.11	29.09	22.12	23.02	01.12	20.10	06.04	26.01
Bream	09.03	12.01		17.11	06.10	13.04	02.02	08.12	27.10	16.03
Brockworth	06.10	09.03	22.12		01.12	20.10	06.04	26.01	22.09	10.11
Frampton Cotterell	02.02	17.11	23.02	13.04		08.12	27.10	16.03	12.01	29.09
Old Bristolians	27.10	06.10	01.12	02.02	06.04		22.09	10.11	09.03	22.12
Old Cryptians	12.01	13.04	20.10	08.12	26.01	16.03		29.09	17.11	23.02
Painswick	17.11	02.02	06.04	27.10	22.09	12.01	09.03		06.10	01.12
Tewkesbury	13.04	08.12	26.01	16.03	10.11	29.09	22.12	23.02		20.10
Westbury on Severn	08.12	27.10	22.09	12.01	09.03	17.11	06.10	13.04	02.02	

Gloucestershire 2

	Bishopston	Cheltenham Civil Service	Cheltenham Saracens	Dursley	Kingswood	Old Colstonians	Old Elizabethans	Southmead	St Brendans O.B.	Widden Old Boys
Bishopston		16.03	29.09	23.02	20.10	26.01	10.11	01.12	22.12	06.04
Cheltenham Civil Service	22.09		10.11	29.09	22.12	23.02	01.12	06.04	20.10	26.01
Cheltenham Saracens	09.03	12.01		17.11	06.10	13.04	02.02	27.10	08.12	16.03
Dursley	06.10	09.03	22.12		01.12	20.10	06.04	22.09	26.01	10.11
Kingswood	02.02	17.11	23.02	13.04		08.12	27.10	12.01	16.03	29.09
Old Colstonians	27.10	06.10	01.12	02.02	06.04		22.09	09.03	10.11	22.12
Old Elizabethans	12.01	13.04	20.10	08.12	26.01	16.03		17.11	29.09	23.02
Southmead	13.04	08.12	26.01	16.03	10.11	29.09	22.12		23.02	20.10
St Brendans Old Boys	17.11	02.02	06.04	27.10	22.09	12.01	09.03	06.10		01.12
Widden Old Boys	08.12	27.10	22.09	12.01	09.03	17.11	06.10	02.02	13.04	

Gloucestershire 3 North

	Fairford	Gloucester All Blues	Gloucester Civil Service	Newent	Ross On Wye	Smiths (Industries)	Tredworth
Fairford		22.12	06.10	26.01	10.11	17.11	16.03
Gloucester All Blues	22.09		17.11	12.01	16.03	27.10	08.12
Gloucester Civil Service	12.01	09.03		01.12	26.01	13.04	10.11
Newent	27.10	06.10	16.03		08.12	23.02	22.12
Ross On Wye	23.02	01.12	27.10	13.04		22.09	09.03
Smiths (Industries)	09.03	26.01	08.12	10.11	22.12		06.10
Tredworth	01.12	13.04	23.02	22.09	17.11	12.01	

Gloucestershire 3 South

	Bristol Aeroplane Co	Bristol Telephones	Cainscross	Cotham Park	Minchinhampton	Tetbury	Wotton-under-Edge
Bristol Aeroplane Co		22.12	06.10	26.01	10.11	17.11	16.03
Bristol Telephones	22.09		17.11	12.01	16.03	27.10	08.12
Cainscross	12.01	09.03		01.12	26.01	13.04	10.11
Cotham Park	27.10	06.10	16.03		08.12	23.02	22.12
Minchinhampton	23.02	01.12	27.10	13.04		22.09	09.03
Tetbury	09.03	26.01	08.12	10.11	22.12		06.10
Wotton-under-Edge	01.12	13.04	23.02	22.09	17.11	12.01	

Southern Counties South

	Bournemouth	Cooper Avon Tyres	Corsham	Devizes	Frome	Ivel Barbarians	Oakmeadians	Swindon College	Wimborne	Wootton Bassett
Bournemouth		16.03	29.09	23.02	20.10	26.01	10.11	22.12	01.12	06.04
Cooper Avon Tyres	22.09		10.11	29.09	22.12	23.02	01.12	20.10	06.04	26.01
Corsham	09.03	12.01		17.11	06.10	13.04	02.02	08.12	27.10	16.03
Devizes	06.10	09.03	22.12		01.12	20.10	06.04	26.01	22.09	10.11
Frome	02.02	17.11	23.02	13.04		08.12	27.10	16.03	12.01	29.09
Ivel Barbarians	27.10	06.10	01.12	02.02	06.04		22.09	10.11	09.03	22.12
Oakmeadians	12.01	13.04	20.10	08.12	26.01	16.03		29.09	17.11	23.02
Swindon College	17.11	02.02	06.04	27.10	22.09	12.01	09.03		06.10	01.12
Wimborne	13.04	08.12	26.01	16.03	10.11	29.09	22.12	23.02		20.10
Wootton Bassett	08.12	27.10	22.09	12.01	09.03	17.11	06.10	13.04	02.02	

Dorset & Wiltshire 1

	Blandford	Bridport	Calne	Martock	Minety	North Dorset	Trowbridge	Westbury
Blandford		22.12	06.10	26.01	10.11	17.11	16.03	08.12
Bridport	22.09		17.11	12.01	16.03	27.10	08.12	23.02
Calne	12.01	09.03		01.12	26.01	13.04	10.11	22.09
Martock	27.10	06.10	16.03		08.12	23.02	22.12	17.11
Minety	23.02	01.12	27.10	13.04		22.09	09.03	12.01
North Dorset	09.03	26.01	08.12	10.11	22.12		06.10	16.03
Trowbridge	01.12	13.04	23.02	22.09	17.11	12.01		27.10
Westbury	13.04	10.11	22.12	09.03	06.10	01.12	26.01	

Dorset & Wiltshire 2 North

	Bradford on Avon	Colerne	Cricklade	Hungerford	Marlborough	Pewsey Vale	Supermarine
Bradford on Avon		22.12	06.10	26.01	10.11	17.11	16.03
Colerne	22.09		17.11	12.01	16.03	27.10	08.12
Cricklade	12.01	09.03		01.12	26.01	13.04	10.11
Hungerford	27.10	06.10	16.03		08.12	23.02	22.12
Marlborough	23.02	01.12	27.10	13.04		22.09	09.03
Pewsey Vale	09.03	26.01	08.12	10.11	22.12		06.10
Supermarine	01.12	13.04	23.02	22.09	17.11	12.01	

Dorset & Wiltshire 2 South

	Poole	Puddletown	Sherborne	Warminster	Weymouth	Wincanton
Poole		22.12	06.10	26.01	10.11	17.11
Puddletown	22.09		17.11	12.01	16.03	27.10
Sherborne	12.01	09.03		01.12	26.01	13.04
Warminster	27.10	06.10	16.03		08.12	23.02
Weymouth	23.02	01.12	27.10	13.04		22.09
Wincanton	09.03	26.01	08.12	10.11	22.12	

SOUTH WEST

Southern Counties North

	Beaconsfield	Buckingham	Chipping Norton	Grove	High Wycombe	Milton Keynes	Oxford	Oxford Harlequins	Swindon	Witney
Beaconsfield		16.03	29.09	23.02	20.10	26.01	10.11	22.12	01.12	06.04
Buckingham	22.09		10.11	29.09	22.12	23.02	01.12	20.10	06.04	26.01
Chipping Norton	09.03	12.01		17.11	06.10	13.04	02.02	08.12	27.10	16.03
Grove	06.10	09.03	22.12		01.12	20.10	06.04	26.01	22.09	10.11
High Wycombe	02.02	17.11	23.02	13.04		08.12	27.10	16.03	12.01	29.09
Milton Keynes	27.10	06.10	01.12	02.02	06.04		22.09	10.11	09.03	22.12
Oxford	12.01	13.04	20.10	08.12	26.01	16.03		29.09	17.11	23.02
Oxford Harlequins	17.11	02.02	06.04	27.10	22.09	12.01	09.03		06.10	01.12
Swindon	13.04	08.12	26.01	16.03	10.11	29.09	22.12	23.02		20.10
Witney	08.12	27.10	22.09	12.01	09.03	17.11	06.10	13.04	02.02	

Berkshire Buckinghamshire & Oxfordshire 1

	Bicester	Bletchley	Chesham	Drifters	Henley Wanderers	Pennanians	Phoenix	Thatcham	Wallingford	Wheatley
Bicester		16.03	29.09	23.02	20.10	26.01	10.11	22.12	01.12	06.04
Bletchley	22.09		10.11	29.09	22.12	23.02	01.12	20.10	06.04	26.01
Chesham	09.03	12.01		17.11	06.10	13.04	02.02	08.12	27.10	16.03
Drifters	06.10	09.03	22.12		01.12	20.10	06.04	26.01	22.09	10.11
Henley Wanderers	02.02	17.11	23.02	13.04		08.12	27.10	16.03	12.01	29.09
Pennanians	27.10	06.10	01.12	02.02	06.04		22.09	10.11	09.03	22.12
Phoenix	12.01	13.04	20.10	08.12	26.01	16.03		29.09	17.11	23.02
Thatcham	17.11	02.02	06.04	27.10	22.09	12.01	09.03		06.10	01.12
Wallingford	13.04	08.12	26.01	16.03	10.11	29.09	22.12	23.02		20.10
Wheatley	08.12	27.10	22.09	12.01	09.03	17.11	06.10	13.04	02.02	

Berkshire Buckinghamshire & Oxfordshire 2

	Abingdon	Aldermaston	Berkshire Shire Hall	Didcot	Gosford All Blacks	Harwell	Littlemore	Winslow
Abingdon		22.12	06.10	26.01	10.11	17.11	16.03	08.12
Aldermaston	22.09		17.11	12.01	16.03	27.10	08.12	23.02
Berkshire Shire Hall	12.01	09.03		01.12	26.01	13.04	10.11	22.09
Didcot	27.10	06.10	16.03		08.12	23.02	22.12	17.11
Gosford All Blacks	23.02	01.12	27.10	13.04		22.09	09.03	12.01
Harwell	09.03	26.01	08.12	10.11	22.12		06.10	16.03
Littlemore	01.12	13.04	23.02	22.09	17.11	12.01		27.10
Winslow	13.04	10.11	22.12	09.03	06.10	01.12	26.01	

SOUTH WEST

CLUBS

ABBEY RFC
Ground Address: Rosehill, Peppard Road, Emmer Green, Reading, Berkshire. RG4 8XA
Tel: 0118 972 2881 E-Mail: www.abbeyrfc.org
Brief Directions: From Reading take the B481 Peppard road. Grund is half a mile north of the Reading boundary.
Club Secretary: Eric Moyse, 9 Lancaster Close, Reading, Berks. RG1 5HB Tel: 0118 9751216
E-mail: moyse@abbey-rugbyfsnet.co.uk
Fixtures Secretary: Mrs Lynne Lee, 'Cotswold', Behoes Lane, Woodcote, Oxon. RG8 0PP
Tel: (H) 01491 680102
Club Colours: Navy blue with green and white hoops
League: South West 2 East
Contact: Alan Kilford, 21 Laurel Drive, Tilehurst, Reading, Berks. RG31 5DY
Tel: 0118 961 4672 E-mail:
alan@lightsave.demon.co.uk

ABINGDON RUFC
Ground Address: Southern Sports Park, Lambrick Way, Abingdon. OX14 5TJ
Tel: 01235 553810 Website: www.abingdonrufc.com
Brief Directions: Exit Abingdon on the B4017, Drayton Road, Just prior to leaving the town limits, take left into Preston Road. Lambrick Way is 3rd turning on the right.
Club Secretary: T. J. Davies, Stonehill Cottage, Oday Hill, Abingdon OX14 4AA
Tel: (H) 01235 527973
E-mail: tdavies.graphictech@virgin.net
Fixtures Secretary: Simon Beackon, 26 West Quay, Abingdon, Oxon. OX14 5TL
Tel: 01235 529328 (H) 07951 068098 (M)
Club Colours: Green and gold hooped shirts
League: Berks/Bucks & Oxon 2
Contact: Steven Stratton, 8 Hobbs Close, Abingdon, Oxon. OX14 3UX
Tel: 01235 204174 (H) 07950 311527 (M)

ALDERMASTON RFC
Ground Address: Aldermaston Recreational Society Sports Ground, Tadley, Hants Tel: 01189 817233
Brief Directions: From Basingstoke follow directions for Tadley on A340, then for Awe Aldermaston, then for Recreational Society.
Club Secretary: David Jenkins, 53 Long Grove, Baughurst, Tadley, Hants. RG26 5NU
Tel: 01189 813078 email: dai@larfin.freeserve.co.uk
Fixtures Secretary: Kevin Banbury, 22 Almswood Rd., Tadley, Hants. RG26 4QG
Tel: 01189 811 894
email: basher@banbury77.freeserve.co.uk
Club Colours: Scarlet shirts, black shorts
League: Berks/Bucks & Oxon 2
League Contact: David Jenkins, as above

AMERSHAM & CHILTERN RFC
Ground Address: Ash Grove, Weedon Lane, Amersham, Bucks. HP6 5QU
Tel: 01494 725161 Website: chilternrugby.com
Brief Directions: From Amersham/Chesham road, take Copperkings Lane (signed Hyde Heath), Weedon Lane is 2nd left
Club Secretary: I McKenzie Esq, 17 Highover Park, Amersham, Bucks. HP7 0BN
Tel: (H) 01494 431966
E-Mail: mail@chilternrugby.com
Fixtures Secretary: R Cook, 12 Bois Lane , Chesham Bois, Amersham, Bucks, HP6 6BP
Tel: (H) 01494 433144
E-Mail: mail@chilternrugby.com
Club Colours: Maroon & White
League: South West 2 East
Contact: as Secretary

ARETIANS RFC
Ground Address: Station Road, Little Stoke, Bristol. BS12 6HW
Tel: 01454 888069
Brief Directions: M5 J16, A38 into Bristol, at flyover turn left signed Yate (Gypsy Patch Ln), along road to railway bridge, directly left past bridge, ground approx 600yds on right on Station Rd
Club Secretary: Andy Vaughan, 42 Elm Close, Little Stoke, Bristol
Tel: (H) 0117 9756513 (W) 0117 9557767
Fixtures Secretary: Glyn Griffiths,44 Mead Road, Stoke Gifford, Bristol. Tel : 01453 812118
Club Colours: Black
League: Gloucester 1
Contact: as Secretary

ASHLEY DOWN OLD BOYS RFC
Ground Address: Lockleaze Combination Ground, Bonnington Walk, Lockleaze, Bristol
Tel: 0117 9312642
Brief Directions: From Filton Avenue, into Bonnington Walk, left at railway bridge, 0.25 mile along lane
Club Secretary: Chris Tyack, 106 Parrys Lane, Stoke Bishop, Bristol BS9 1BJ
Tel: 0117 9684343
Fixtures Secretary: Patrick Donovan, 38 Memorial Road, Hanham, Bristol BS15 3JG .
Tel: 0117 9679649
Club Colours: Purple and white
League: Gloucester 1

AVON RFC

Ground Address: Hicks Field, London Road East, Bath, Somerset

Tel: 01225 852446 Website: avonrfc.co.uk

Brief Directions: On A4 towards Batheaston approx 0.5 mile from A46/A4 junction, entrance on right hand side

Club Secretary: David Loader, 114 Southdown Road, Southdown, Bath, Somerset. BA2 1JJ Tel: 01225 316864(H) 01249 713218 (B) 01249 714211 (F) E-mail: daveloader@aventeng.co.uk

Fixtures Secretary: Wayne Griffiths, 4 Lower Stoke, Limpley Stoke, Bath BA2 7FU

Tel: 01225 722433 (H) 07780 997506 (M)

E-mail: wayne.griffiths@capgemini.co.uk

Club Colours: Black and amber hoops

League: Somerset Premier

Contact: as Secretary

AVONMOUTH OLD BOYS RFC

Ground Address: Barracks Lane, Avonmouth, Bristol

Tel: 0117 982 9093

Brief Directions: Exit M5 J.18 to Bristol. Left at roundabout to Shirehampton, then 2nd left (opp. shops) and continue for 400 yards.

Club Secretary: R.K. Kennett, 41 Woodland Grove, Westbury-on-Trym, Bristol, BS9 2BD.

Tel: 0117 968 3598

E-mail: chris.rodkennett@btinternet.com

Fixtures Secretary: A Woodruff, 69 Priory Road, Shirehampton, Bristol, BS11 9PA.

Tel: 0117 983 3066 (H)

Club Colours: Red / Black

League: Gloucester Premier

Contact: as Secretary

AVONVALE RFC

Ground Address: Bathford Playing Fields, Bathford Playing Fields, Bathford, Bath,

Tel: 01225 858295 Website: www.avonvalerfc.co.uk

Brief Directions: A4 out of Bath, through Batheaston, right at next roundabout, under railway bridge and next left, clubhouse is along a track next to phone box 200yds up Bathford Hill. See website for maps

Club Secretary: Paul Beazer, 1 Tropenell Close, Corsham, Wilts, SN13 9UG.

Tel No: 01249 716135 (H)

Email: beez@totalise.co.uk

Fixtures Secretary: Steve Vowles, 77 Lockswood Road, Lower Weston, Bath BA1 3ES

Tel: (H) 01225 333852 (W) 01225 766451

Club Colours: Navy blue & white

League: Somerset 1

Contact: as Secretary

AYLESBURY RFC

Ground Address: Ostlers Field, Brook End, Weston Turville, Aylesbury, Bucks. HP22 5RN

Tel: 01296 612556 / 614786

Website: www.arfc.org.uk

Brief Directions: A413 from Wendover to Aylesbury. 2 miles rt to B4544 - thro. - ground is on left Weston Turville. Or A41 from Aylesbury, turn rt after 3 miles before Aston Clinton, club is then on right.

Club Secretary: Derek Spence, 2 Dennis Close, Aston Clinton, Bucks. HP22 5US

Tel: 01296 631882

E-mail: Secretary-ARFC@cwcom.net

Fixtures Secretary: James P Williams, Tumbleweed, Winslow Rd., Granborough, Bucks MK18 3NJ

Tel: (H) 01296 670798

Club Colours: Black and magenta hooped shirts, black shorts and socks

League: South West 2 East

Contact: Mark Rose, Skippings Farm NSE, Chesham Lane, Chalfont St. Peter Tel: 01494 876114

BARTON HILL OLD BOYS RFC

Ground Address: Argyle Road Playing Fields, Duncombe Lane, Speedwell, Bristol.

Tel: 0117 987 2895

Brief Directions: Follow roads to Lodge Causeway, Fishponds. At lights half way up Causeway turn right opposite St. Josephs and take second left into Duncombe Lane.

Club Secretary: G. Baker, 7 Pendennis Road, Staplehill, Bristol, BS16 5JB.

Fixtures Secretary: Rob Porter, 72A Regent Street, Kingswood, Bristol. Tel: 07775 690291

Club Colours: White with a cherry band

League: Gloucester Premier

BATH OLD EDWARDIANS

Ground Address: King Edward School Sports Ground, Bathampton, Bath

Tel: 01225 780019

Directions: M4 J18, A46 to Bath, London Rd towards Batheaston then follow signs to Bathampton village.Ground is opp. church. From Bath take A36.

Club Secretary: Dan Miller, 7 Herbert Road, Oldfield Park, Bath, BA2 3PP.

Tel No: 01225 319424 (H) 01225 462871 (W)

Email: miller@ bath.blandb.co.uk

Fixtures Secretary: Steve Ryland
8 Nelson Place, West Bath BA1 2BA

Tel No: 01225 477312

Club Colours: Gold, maroon and blue hoops

League: Somerset 2

BATH SARACENS RFC

Ground Address: Civil Service Sports Ground, Claverton Down, Bath, Avon.

Tel: 01225 832403

Brief Directions: From Bath take A367 to Frys Garage mini roundabout.Take first left, then straight on for 2 miles and turn right immediately after Ralph Allen School.

Club Secretary: Mike York, 2 Linden Gardens, Bath, BA1 2YB Tel: (H) 01225 424613

e-mail mike@ yorkcom .freeserve.co.uk

SOUTH WEST

Fixtures Secretary: R.Lawrence, 91 English Combe Lane, Bath BA2 2EH.
Tel: 01225 427356
Club Colours: Blue with red and gold hoops.
League: Somerset 2

BEACONSFIELD RFC
Ground Address: Oak Lodge Meadow, Windsor End, Beaconsfield, Bucks.
Tel: 01494 673783
Brief Directions: Take J2 from A40 follow directions to old town, at the R/about take 1st left and proceed for .5 mile along Windsor End.
Club Secretary: Mike Eagle, 12 South Park View, Gerrads Cross, Bucks., SL9 8HN
Tel: 01753 887809 - Email: eaglegx@hotmail.com
Fixtures Secretary: Peter Miles, 17 Kings Road, Chalfont St. Giles, Bucks., HP8 4HS.
Tel No: 01494 875461
Club Colours: Green and gold hoops, green shorts
League: Southern Counties North

BERKSHIRE SHIRE HALL RUFC
Ground Address: Royal County of Berkshire Sports & Social Club, Sonning Lane, Sonning, Reading
Tel: 01734 691340
Brief Directions: From Reading head towards A4 up Sheppards House Hill, pass Mobil garage on right, take left Sonning Lane, 2nd turning on the right
Club Secretary: Mark Porter
105 Severn Way,Reading RG30 4HW
Tel No: 07785 265412 E mail: mark.porter@inter-servefm.com
Fixtures Secretary: Steve Bentey
Tel: (H) 118 954 2030
Club Colours: Royal Blue & gold.
League: Berks/Bucks & Oxon 2

BERRY HILL
Ground Address: Lakers Road, Berry Hill, Coleford, Gloucestershire GL16 7LY
Tel: 01594 833295
email: hjcole@btinternet.com
Brief Directions: From M4 Severn Bridge, M48 to Chepstow, B422B to Coleford, follow signs to Berry Hill. From M50 to Ross, A40 to Monmouth then A4136 to Berry Hill.
Club Secretary: David Pitaway, Ty Mai, Crow Ash Road, Berry Hill, Coleford, Glos. GL16 7RB
Tel: (H) 01594 836372
Fixtures Secretary: G R Goddard, 71a Cheltenham Road, Glousestershire GL2 0JG
Tel: (W) 01452 306749
Club Colours: Black and amber quarters
League: South West 2 West
Contact: John Cole, 2 The Close, Broadwell, Coleford, Glos. GL16 7DJ. Tel: 01594 835351

BICESTER RUFC
Ground Address: Oxford Road, Bicester, Oxon. OX6 8AB   Tel: 01869 241000
Brief Directions: As you approach Bicester from south on A34, the ground is on the right on the edge of town just past Tescos
Club Secretary: G.Davies, 166 Barry Avenue, Bicester ,Oxon. OX26 2HB
Tel No; 01869 241993
Fixtures Secretary: G Davies
Tel: (H & W) 01869 241993
Club Colours: Amber, red and brown hooped shirts, navy shorts
League: Berks/Bucks & Oxon 1

BIDEFORD RFC
Ground Address: King Georges Field, Riverside, Bank End, Bideford, Devon
Tel: 01237 474049
Brief Directions: N.D. link road, left end of Bideford New Bridge, into town until reach river, immediate left at Charles Kingsley statue, proceed River Bank Road to Bideford RFC car park
Club Secretary: Bob Booth, 41 Goodwood Park road,, Northam, Bideford EX 39 2RR
Tel: 01237 421259
Fixtures Secretary: C.Balsdon, 15 Middleton Road, Bideford, Devon EX39 3LU
Tel: 01237 472166
Club Colours: Red and white hooped shirts, white shorts, red socks
League: Western Counties West

BISHOPSTON RFC
Ground Address: Bonnington Walk, Lockleaze, Bristol
Tel: 0117 969 1916
Brief Directions: From Almondsbury M'way inter-change, A38 to Bristol, left at lights at end of Toronto Rd, cross lights at Filton Ave into B'nington Wk, ground on left straight after rail bridge
Club Secretary: Jim Hockley, 21 Pinewood Close, Westbury-on-Trym, Bristol. BS9 4AJ. Email: jim@jhockley.fsnet.co.uk
Tel: (H) 0117 962 3509
Fixtures Secretary: Stuart Brain
Tel: (H) 0117 958 5560
Club Colours: Red with black hoop edged in cente-nary gold
League: Gloucester 2

BLAGDON RFC
Ground Address: The Mead, Blagdon Village
Tel: 01761 463196
Brief Directions: Turn left off the A38 at Churchill traffic lights and follow road for approx 3 miles into Blagdon
Club Secretary: John Thompson, Nadams PPaddock, High Street, Chew Magna, North Somerset.
Tel No: 07808 578807
Fixtures Secretary: Steve Clarke, Tudor Barn, South W iacombe, East Harptree,Bristol BS40 6BL
Tel: 01761 221619
Club Colours: Green , Black and white hoops
League: Somerset 2

SOUTH WEST

BLANDFORD RFC

Ground Address: Blandford School Ground at the Milldown Leisure Centre, Milldown Road, Blandford.
Brief Directions: From town centre, follow signs to Sturminster Newton, Pitches situated at Melldown Leisure Centre opposite hospital.
Club Secretary: o.d.Griffiths,1 Old Oak way, Winterbourne,Whitchurch, Blandford Dorset. Dt11 0TN.
Tel No: 01258 881380
Email: owen.griffiths@southernprint.co.uk
Fixtures Secretary: Dave Stringer,21 Damory Street, Blandford, Dorset DT11 7EU
Tel: (H) 01258 456954
Club Colours: Red, Yellow & Brown
League: Dorset & Wilts 1

BLETCHLEY RUFC

Ground Address: Manor Fields, Bletchley, Milton Keynes, Bucks
Tel: 01908 372298
Brief Directions: On B488 from Leighton Buzzard, fork right at 'The Plough', from this fork take 3rd right - Manor Road, proceed down road over bridge to ground
Club Secretary: C W Spence, 17 Milesmere, Two Mile Ash, Milton Keynes. MK8 8QP
Tel: (H) 01908 561876 (W) 0171 374 3051
Fixtures Secretary: I Punter
Tel: (H) 01908 642994
Club Colours: Burgundy and white hoops
League: Berks/Bucks & Oxon 1

BODMIN RFC

Ground Address: Clifden Park, Carminnow Cross, Bodmin, Cornwall PL31 1BC
Tel: 01208 74629
Brief Directions: Off A38 before Flyover at A30 take B Road signed Lanhydrock 400yds turn right down private drive.
Club Secretary: Andy Richards, Chy Kensa, Robartes Road, Bodmin Pl31 1JG
Tel No: 07979 718355
Email: andy.richards@connexians-cd.org.uk
Fixtures Secretary: Keith Richards,Youmes-Den, Westheath Road, Bodmin PL31 1QG.
Tel No: 01208 77643
Email: keithlr77643@netscapeonline.co.uk
Club Colours: Light Blue with Dark Blue hoops edged with white.
League: Cornwall 1

BOURNEMOUTH RFC

Ground Address: Bournemouth Sports Club, Chapel Gate, Parley Lane, Bast Parley, Christchurch, Dorset. BH23 6BD
Tel: 01202 581933
Brief Directions: Take Bournemouth spur road (A338 Ringwood-Bournemouth). Follow signs to Hurn Airport. Ground is just to west of the airport.
Club Secretary: Alistair Raworth, Flat 2, 2 St. Anthony's Road, Meyrick Road, Bournemouth, Dorset BH26 PD . Tel: 01202 252188

Email: alistairrainworth@btinteract.com
Fixtures Secretary: ndy Cumming,106 Avon Road,Charminster, Bournemouth, Dorset BH8 8SF.
Tel NO: 01202 393012
Club Colours: Sable and gold
League: Southern Counties South

BRADFORD on AVON

Ground Address: St Lawrence School, Ashly Road, Bradford on Avon, Wiltshire BA15 1DZ
Brief Directions: Take Winsley Road out of Boa. Then 2nd right into churches. St Lawrence School car park on right through gates.
Club Secretary: J. S. Pendrey, 6 Fitzmaurice Close, Bradford on Avon, Wiltshire BA15 1UE
Tel: (H/W) 01225 864186
e-mail: john.pendrey @crrs.co.uk
Fixtures Secretary: Andy Gerrish, 14 Huntingdon Street, Bradford on Avon, Wiltshire BA15 1RF
Tel: (H) 01225 864165
Club Colours: Red & Black
League: Dorset & Wilts 2 North

BREAM RFC

Ground Address: High Street, Bream, Nr Lydney, Glos. GL15 6JG
Tel: 01594 562320
Brief Directions: Approx 3 miles off main A48 Gloucester to Chepstow road, turn right after Westbury Homes Site on right hand side
Club Secretary: Colin Henderson, 12 Maypole Road, Bream, Lydney, Glos, GL15 6XN
Tel: (H) 01594 562430
Fixtures Secretary: As Secretary
Club Colours: Red and black
League: Gloucester 1

BRIDPORT RFC

Ground Address: Bridport Leisure Centre, Skilling Hill Road, Bridport, Dorset. DT6 3LN
Tel: 01308 420555
Brief Directions: Take A35 Bridport By-Pass, at R'bout south of Town turn R. (North). After 300yds turn L. at Traffic Lights opp. Safeway store.
Club Secretary: Richard Salt, 21 South Street, Bridport, Dorset. DT6 3NR
Tel: (H) 01308 458347 (W) 01308 422236
e-mail: awg-law.com
Fixtures Secretary: Michael Wotton, 42 Culverhayes, Beaminster, Dorset DT8 3DG.
Tel: 01308 863498
Club Colours: Blue and white quarters
League: Dorset & Wilts 1

BRISTOL AEROPLANE COMPANY RFC

Ground Address: Bristol Aerospace Welfare Association Sports Ground, 589 Southmead Road, Filton, Bristol. BS12 7DG
Tel: 0117 9768066
Brief Directions: Travel south along A38, right at the roundabout at top of Filton Hill into Southmead Road, ground on the right
Club Secretary: Julian Mason-Flucke, 42

SOUTH WEST

Quarrington Road, Horfield, Bristol
Tel Nos: 0117 9514573 (H) 0117 9795920 (W)
Fixtures Secretary: Mark Dewhurst,10 Kendon
Drive, Westbury-on-Trym , Bristol BS10 5BP.
Tel: 0117 9624240 (H) 0117 9364899(W)
Club Colours: Red, white and blue hoops
League: Gloucester 3 South

BRISTOL BARBARIANS
Ground Address: Norton Lane,
Witchurch, Bristol BS14   Tel: 01275 833514
Brief Directions: On A37 from Bristol, past Black
Lion pub, over bridge, right by playground. 1st gate
on right.
Club Secretary: Colin Rowland, 57 Fitzgerald Road,
Knowle, Bristol BS3 5DH
Tel: (H) 0117 9775200
Fixtures Secretary: Les Brunyee, 43 Millmead
House, Silcox Road, Hartcliffe, Bristol, BS13
Tel: (H) 01179 644685
Club Colours: Black & White hoops
League: Somerset 2

BRISTOL HARLEQUINS RFC
Ground Address: Valhalla, Broomhill Road,
Brislington, Bristol. BS4
Tel: 0117 972 1650
Brief Directions: The ground is situated behind
St.Brendan College on the A4 between Bath and
Bristol.
Club Secretary: Ian Nunnerly, 17 Warmington
Road,Knowle, Bristol BS14 9HG
Tel: 0117 9711597
Fixtures Secretary: Ed Morrison, 4
Lowbourne,Whitchurch, Bristol BS14 0AN
Tel: (H) 01275 832580
Club Colours: Blue, black and white hoops
League: Somerset Premier

BRISTOL SARACENS RFC
Ground Address: Bakewell Memorial Ground,
Station Road, Cribbs Causeway, Henbury, Bristol.
Tel: 01179 500037
Brief Directions: M5 J17 towards Bristol city centre,
approx 1000 metres at 2nd roundabout on right
Club Secretary: A E Swash, 6 Downs Road,
Westbury-on-Trym, Bristol. BS9 3TX.
Tel: (H) 01179 629047
Email: aeswash@bak2 mu.co.uk
Fixtures Secretary: M.T.Healy, 64 Lower High St.,
Shirehampton, Bristol BS11 0AB
Tel No: 01179 827018
Club Colours: Myrtle green and white hooped
shirts, black shorts
League: Gloucester Premier

BRISTOL TELEPHONE AREA RFC
Ground Address: B.T.R.A. Sports Ground,
Stockwood Lane, Stockwood, Bristol. BS14
Tel: 01275 891776
Brief Directions: Take A37 (Wells Road) for approx
4 miles from city centre, left at Black Lion pub at
Whitchurch, ground approx 1 mile on right

Club Secretary: Mark Morgan, 21 Durville Road,
Headley Park, Bristol BS13 7PS
Tel: 01179 642331 e-mail: organm99@hotmail.com
Fixtures Secretary: Chris Watts, 22 Ladman Road,
Stockwood, Bristol BS148QQ
Tel: (H) 01275 543208
Club Colours: Blue with red & white V neck.
League: Gloucester 3 South

BRIXHAM RFC
Ground Address: Astley Park, Rea Barn Road,
Brixham, TQ6 9ED
Tel: 01803 882162 and 01803 855511 (Fax)
Website: www.brixhamrugby.org
Brief Directions: Follow signs for Torbay thern
Brixham. Follow signs for Berry Head
Club opposite Police Station.
Club Secretary: Bob Houston, Astley Park, Rea
Barn Road, Brixham, TQ6 9ED. Tel: (H) 01803
550427 (W) 01548 855000
Email: brixrugby@netscapeonline.co.uk
Fixtures Secretary: J D Irvine B.E.M., 1Great Rea
Rd., Brixham, TQ5 9SW
Tel: (H) 01803 882219 - Email:
jamesdirvine@netscape.co.uk
Club Colours: Black with 6" white band
League: South West 2 West

BROAD PLAIN RFC
Ground Address: Hengrove School, Patherton
Rd., Hengrove, Bristol
Tel No: 0117 9552782
Brief Directions: Take A37 ,the Wells Road out of
Bristol, two miles from city centre turn right at 'Happy
Landings' pub then left at 'The Glass Cutter'.Follow
signs for Hengrove school in Petherton Road.
Club Secretary: Don Collins, 77 Lake Road,
Henleaze, Bristol. BS10 5JE
Tel: (H) 0117 9622094 (W) 0117 9248051
Fixtures Secretary: Bob Slocombe, 113 Hayward
Road, Redfield, Briistol.B55
Club Colours: Blue, maroon and gold hoops
League: Somerset 1

BROCKWORTH RFC
Ground Address: Badgers Mount, Mill Lane,
Brockworth.
Tel: 01452 862556
(All mail to Secretary please)
Directions: From south: M5 turn off at junct. 11A,
follow signs to Gloucester, 1st left to Brockworth at
roundabout, straight over next, past Du-Pont, left at
lights into Vicarage Lane, straight over small round-
about, 1st right into Mill Lane, 400 metres on LHS.
Club Secretary: Dave Alden, 37 Boverton Avenue,
Brockworth, Glos. GL3 4ER
Tel No: 01452 551353
Email: dabr23668@cablenet.co.uk
Fixtures Secretary: Nick Joiner,17 Tanners Close,
Brockworth, Glos.(01452 863702)
Club Colours: Black shirts with white 'V'
League: Gloucester 1

BUCKFASTLEIGH

Ground Address: The Cricket Club, Buckfastleigh, Devon   Tel: 01364 643895
Club Secretary: Sue Farley, 6 Holne Road,Buckfastleigh, Devon. TQ11 0BE
Tel : 01364 643696
e-mail: sue@ millwood.uk.com
Fixtures Secretary: Cid Tozer, 11 Oaklands Park, Buckfastleigh, Devon.   Tel: 01364 642488
Club Colours: Black and gold
League: Devon 3

BUCKINGHAM RUFC

Ground Address: Floyd Field, Moreton Road, Maids Moreton, Buckingham   Tel: 01280 815474
E-mail: www.buckinghamrugby.co.uk
Brief Directions: From Buckingham town centre, take A413 to Towcester, after approx 0.5 mile ground is on the left
Club Secretary: Finlay Gemmell, 22 Elmfields Gate, Winslow, Bucks. MK18 3JG
Tel: (H) 01296 714640 (W)01753 704131
email: finlay-gemmell@hitmail.com
Fixtures Secretary: Anthony Smith, 10 Mare leys, Buckingham Mk18 7AX   Tel: (H) 01280 815634
Club Colours: Green and white hoops, black shorts
League: Southern Counties North

BUDE RFC

Ground Address: Bencoolen Meadow (off Kings Hill), Bude, Cornwall. EX23 8DG
Tel: 01288 354795
Brief Directions: Into Stratton Road and turn left at th bottom of hill then first right turn and right again into club.
Club Secretary: Mrs A Troke, Kiama, Church Path, Bude, Cornwall. EX23 8LH   Tel: 01288 354826
Fixtures Secretary: Mr J A Boundy, Linhays,Butterbeare Cross,Bridgerule
Tel: (H) 01288 381296 (W) 01288 353766
Club Colours: Maroon and sky blue hoops
League: Cornwall 1

BURNHAM ON SEA RFC

Ground Address: B.A.S.C. Ground, Stoddens Road, Burnham on Sea, Somerset. TA8 2DE
Tel: 01278 788355
Brief Directions: Signposted from M5, J22.
Club Secretary: Roy Page, Old Holt Farm, Edingworth Road, Edingworth, Nr. Weston Super Mare, BS24 0JA.
Fixtures Secretary: Andy Marsh, 217 Berrow Road, Burnham on Sea, Somerset TA8 2JG
Club Colours: Blue and white hoops
League: Somerset 1

CAINSCROSS RFC

Ground Address: Victory Park, Caincross, Ebley, Stroud, Glos   Tel: 01453 766707
Brief Directions: Take second exit from Horse Trough Roundabout. Westward round Ebley into Church Road (on left just before Imo carwash). When travelling from M5

Club Secretary: Dave Roberts, Renfrew, 24 Upper Church Road, Cainscross, Stroud.
Fixtures Secretary: Richard Stonebridge
tel: 01453 758659
Club Colours: Amber and blue
League: Gloucester 3 South

CALLINGTON RFC

Ground Address: Duchy College Ground, Stoke Climsland, Callington, Cornwall.
Directions: Callington to Launceston Road, turn off at Kelly Brayy to Stoke Climsland. At Stoke Climsland follow signs to Ventodon then Duchy Coll.
Club Secretary: Michelle Campbell, Heartland Ho., 11 Church St, Callington, Cornwall, PL17 7BL.
Tel: 01579 382875
Fixtures Secretary: John Pritchard, Chilsworhy, Gunnislake, Cornwall PL18   Tel: 01822 833371
Club Colours: Red & Black Quarters, Black Shorts
League: Cornwall 1

CALNE RFC

Ground Address: The Recreation Ground, Anchor Road, Calne, Wiltshire. SN11 8DX
Tel: 01249 812206
Brief Directions: Turn into Bank Row opposite Lansdowne Strand Hotel, past Somerfields into Mill St, follow road uphill into Anchor Rd, car park on left after 500 yards
Club Secretary: Leigh Martin, 12 Brewer Mead, Chippenham, Wilts. SN 15 3FB
Tel: 01249 443284
Fixtures Secretary: Ian West, 23 Tern Close, Calne, Wilts.   Tel: (H) 01249 813737
Club Colours: Blue with red and white hoop
League: Dorset & Wilts 1

CAMBORNE RFC

Ground Address: Recreation Ground, Camborne.
Tel: O1209 713227 (Gd)   01209 712684 (Club)
Brief Directions: Leave the A30 at Camborne West junction(A3047). Then left at roundabout and right after 200 yds.Then first right after cul de sac.Pass school on right and take left where road divides.
Club Secretary: I .Matthewws, 68 Hughville Street Camborne, Cornwall. TR148TS
Tel: 01209 713901 (H) 01326 372424 (W)
Fixtures Secretary: David Smith, 65 Hughville Street, Camborne, Cornwall TR14 8TS
Tel: (H)01209 716992
Club Colours: Cherry and white
League: South West 2 West

CAMBORNE SCHOOL OF MINES RFC

Ground Address: The Memorial Ground, Boundervean Lane, Penponds, Camborne (not a postal delivery address)
Tel: 01209 612959 - Clubhouse Tel: 01209 711935
Brief Directions: Off Pendraves Road, Camborne, B3303 to Helson, turn right into Boundervean Lane. Before railway bridge, ground is 250m on right.
Club Secretary: P.J.Foster 22 Gwarth an Drae, Helston, Cornwall. TR13 0BS

Tel No: 01326 560310
Email: p.j.foster@csm.ex.ac.uk
Fixtures Secretary: N. R. Clarke, 2 Tremayne
Close, Devoran, Truro, TR3 6QE.
Tel: (H) 01872 865139 (W) 01209 717724
Club Colours: Navy, gold and silver hoops
League: Cornwall 2

CASTLE CARY RUFC
Ground Address: Brookhouse Field, Sutton,
Ditcheat, Shepton Mallet, Somerset.
Tel: 01963 351178
Brief Directions: A371 to Castle Cary from Shepton
Mallet, turn right at Brookhouse Inn, 2nd on right
Club Secretary: Mr A J Bailey, 2 Enfield Terrace,
Weymouth Road, Evercreech, Somerset. Tel: (H)
01749 830268
Fixtures Secretary: J. Franklin, 17 Cothier
Meadows, Castle Cary, Somerset..
Tel No: 01963 351193
Club Colours: Red and black hoops. Change: All
Blue.
League: Somerset 2

CHARD RFC
Ground Address: The Park, Essex Close,
Chard, Somerset   Tel: 01460 62495
Brief Directions: Bottom of Chard High Street (by
Cerdic DIY shop), 100 yards up Essex Close.
Club Secretary: Mr N J Urch, 2 South View, Listers
Hill, Ilminster, Somerset
Tel: (H) 01460 57864 (W) 01935 702913
nurch@supanet.com
Fixtures Secretary: Mr R Stuckey, 9 Cerdic Close,
Chard, Somerset
Tel: (H) 01460 63579 (W) 01460 63781
Email: robert@jercstuckey.screaming.net
Club Colours: Black, red and gold
League: Somerset 1

CHEDDAR VALLEY RFC
Ground Address: Sharpham Road Playing Fields,
Cheddar, Somerset   Tel: 01934 743623
Club Secretary: Ceri Davies, 16 Round Oak Grove,
Cheddar, Somerset. BS27 3BW
Tel: (H) 01934 744167
Fixtures Secretary: Callum Mackenzie
Tel: (H) 01934 744277
Club Colours: Sky blue and scarlet hoops
League: Somerset 2

CHELTENHAM CIVIL SERVICE RFC
Ground Address: Civil Service Sports Ground,
Tewkesbury Road, Uckington, Cheltenham.
Tel: 01242 680424/680847
Brief Directions: 2 miles from Cheltenham on the
main road to Tewkesbury (A4019)
Club Secretary: Brian Didlick, 15 Stoneville Street,
Cheltenham. GL51 8PH   Tel: (H) 01242 519285
Fixtures Secretary: As Secretary
Club Colours: Navy Blue
League: Gloucester 2
Contact: Club Secretary

CHELTENHAM NORTH RFC
Ground Address: Stoke Orchard Road, Bishops
Cleeve, Nr Cheltenham   Tel: 01292 675968
Brief Directions: Junction 10 or 11 Cheltenham,
head out of Cheltenham past racecourse on A435
towards Bishops Cleeve, turn toward Stoke Orchard
village, 500 yards on left
Club Secretary: Andrew David Page, Baytrees,
Chargrove Lane, Up Hatherley, Cheltenham
Tel: (H) 01242 510932
Fixtures Secretary: J.Cresswell,177 New Barn
Lane, Prestbury, Cheltenham, Glos.GL52 3LH
Tel No: 01242 261414
Club Colours: Black with red band, black shorts,
and black socks with red tops.
League: South West 2 West

CHELTENHAM SARACENS RFC
Ground Address: King George V Playing Fields,
Brooklyn Road, St Marks, Cheltenham, Glos
Brief Directions: From Gloucester & M5 follow dual
carriageway to main GCHQ roundabout take 1st exit
then right at square junction.
Club Secretary: David Millar, 11 Scott House,
Princess Elizabeth Way, Cheltenham,
Glos. GL51 0HF Tel: 01242 700726
Email: ozziedmillar@hotmail.com
Fixtures Secretary: J.Knight   Tel: 01242 522408
Club Colours: Royal Blue with black and gold hoops
League: Gloucester 2

CHESHAM RUFC
Ground Address: Chesham Park Community
College, Chartridge Lane, Chesham, Bucks. HP5
2RG Tel: 01494 793827
Brief Directions: Chartridge Lane of St. Marys Way
in central Chesham. Club is 400 metres on left.
Furthest College gate is entrance
Club Secretary: M M Hogg, 37 Lye Green Road,
Chesham, Bucks. HP5 3LS
Tel: (H) 01494 771576 (W) 01494 791656 FAX:
01494 791649
e-mail: morris.hogg@btinternet.com
Fixtures Secretary: Dick King, 75 Darvell Drive,
Chesham, Bucks HP5 2QN
Tel: (H) 01494 786056
Club Colours: Blue and claret hoops
League: Berks/Bucks & Oxon 1

CHEW VALLEY RFC
Ground Address: Lobbingtons, Chew Lane, Chew
Stoke, Bristol   Tel No: 01275 333660
Brief Directions: Through Chew Magna, on to
Chew Stoke, next to the school
Club Secretary: Jim Gethin, April Cottage, Top
Sutton, Bishop sutton, Bristol BS39 5UW
Tel: 01275 332080
e-mail: jim-gethin@compuserve.com
Fixtures Secretary: Ian Hall, 2 Chalk Farm Close,
Norton Malreward, Pensford, Bristol BS39 4HQ. Tel
No: 01275 837987
Club Colours: Green and white hoops
League: Western Counties North

SOUTH WEST

CHIPPENHAM RFC
Ground Address: Allington Field, Frogwell, Chippenham. SN14 0YZ
Tel: 01249 446997
Brief Directions: A420 twoards Bristol. Turn left by Allington Farm shop for Corsham & Sheldon Manor. After 600 yards turn sharp left, entrance on left. NB Now no entrance from Frogwell.
Club Secretary: Stuart Murrow, 34, Park Lane, Chippenham, Wiltshire.SN!5 1LN
Tel No: 01249 6657720 (H) 01249 442125
Fixtures Secretary: Adie Lloyd, 27 Lords Mead, Chippenham.
Tel: (H) 01249 656793
Club Colours: Black & white irregular hoops
Change Colours: Red
League: South West 2 East

CHIPPING NORTON RUFC
Ground Address: Greystones, Burford Road, Chipping Norton, Oxon. OX7 5UZ
Tel: 01608 643968 Tel. & Fax.
Brief Directions: Follow A361 to Burford out of Chipping Norton
Club Secretary: Nigel Hall,
c/o V.M.Murphy & Co, Finsbury House, New Street,Chipping Norton OX7 ELL
Tel No: 01608 641041 (W)
e-mail: murphy-vincent@hotmail.com
Fixtures Secretary: T Cripps, 4 Portland Place, Chipping Norton, Oxon OX7 5AG
Tel: (H) 01608 641182
e-mail: ttc@connectfree,co.uk.
Club Colours: Black and red hoops
League: Southern Counties North

CHIPPING SODBURY RFC
Ground Address: The Ridings, Wickwar Road, Chipping Sodbury, South Gloucestershire
Tel: 01454 312852
Brief Directions: Take Wickwar Road out of Chipping Sodbury, ground .5 mile on left hand side.
Club Secretary: Alan Richards, 12 Tyning Close, Yate, Bristol, BS37 5PN.
Tel: 01454 882284
Email: a.richards@blueyonder.co.uk
Fixtures Secretary: Mr. G. Beer, 2 Merlin Way, Chipping Sodbury, BS37
Tel: 01454 882052
Club Colours: Black
League: Gloucester Premier
Contact: As Fixture Secretary

CHOSEN HILL FP RFC
Ground Address: Brookfield Lane, Churchdown, Gloucester   Tel: 01452 712384
Club Website: www.chosenhillrfc.co.uk
Brief Directions: Equi-distant between Cheltenham/Gloucester on edge of village of Churchdown towards Cheltenham
Club Secretary: Dave Morris, 20 Moselle Drtive, Churchdown, Gloucester GL3 2R
Tel No: 01452 37856955

Email: davemorris@micron2,freeserve.co.uk
Fixtures Secretary: Bob Newton.
Tel Nos: 01452 857046 (H) 01452 335367 (W)
Club Colours: Myrtle green and white
League: Gloucester Premier

CIRENCESTER RFC
Ground Address: The Whiteway, Cirencester, Glos
Tel: 01285 654434
Brief Directions: Positioned at traffic lights on main Gloucester to Swindon A419 road, approx 1 mile from town centre
Club Secretary: Henry Church, 38 Purley Road, Cirencester, Glos. GL7 1GP
Tel: 01285 643373
e-mail: henry.church@crfc.co.uk
Fixtures Secretary: Mrs Sharon Scrivens, 230 Stratton Heights, Stratton, Cirencester.
Tel: 01285 642140
Club Colours: Red and black hoops, black shorts,red and black hooped socks
League: Gloucester Premier

CLEVE RFC
Ground Address: The Hayfields, Cosham Street, Mangotsfield, Bristol
Brief Directions: M4 onto M32, M32 J1, carry straight through traffic lights to next roundabout, follow directions to Downend, then to Mangotsfield, turn into Cosasham St. Ground 300yds on Rt.
Club Secretary: Mrs Carole King, 1 Kingston Close, Mangotsfield, Bristol BS16 9BH.
Tel No: 0117 9561804
Fixtures Secretary: S.Williams, 15 Lincombe Road, Downend, Bristol
Tel: 0117 9402159
Club Colours: Maroon
League: South West 2 West

CLEVEDON RFC
Ground Address: Coleridge Vale Playing Fields, Southey Road, Clevedon, N. Somerset. BS21 6PF
Tel: 01275 877772
Brief Directions: M5 J20, straight across two R/abouts, turn lest at T/lights, turn left at Arrifa garage. Follow signs there after.
Club Secretary: Paul Squires, 20 Sumerlin Drive, Clevedon, North Somerset.
BS21 6YW Tel: 01275 874497 -
Email: paul-squires1 @ bt internet.com
Fixtures Secretary: John Evans, 79 Kenn Road, clevedon, North Somerset, BS21 6HE
Tel: (H) 01275 871443
Club Colours: Old Gold & Royal blue hoops
League: Western Counties North

COLERNE RFC
Ground Address: Higgins Field, Bath Road, Colerne, Wiltshire
Brief Directions: Under water tower on main road past village
Club Secretary: Mrs Karen Sayers, 8 Cleaves Avenue, Colerne, Wiltshire. SN14 8BX

Tel: (H) 01225 744355
Fixtures Secretary: Mark Gratton, 6 Westminster Gardens, Chippenham, SN14 0DFTel: 01249 658586
Club Colours: Black
League: Dorset & Wilts 2 North

COLLEGE OF ST MARK AND ST JOHN
(Previously Marjons)
Ground Address: The College of St Mark and St John, Driviford Road, Plymouth.Pl6 8BH
tel: 01752 636700 x 3071
Brief Directions: A 386 north from Plymouth follow signs for Airport . Ground is opposite airport.
Club Secretary: Gareth Jones, Senior Lecturer at College of St Mark+ St John,Derriford Road, Plymouth, Devon. Pl6 8BH.
Tel: 01752 636700 x 8618
Fixtures Secretary: Adam Last c/o college Extension 3071
Club Colours: Red and black quarters.
League: Devon 2

COMBE DOWN RFC
Ground Address: Holly's Corner, North Road, Combe Down, Bath. BA2 5DE
Tel: 01225 832075
Brief Directions: Follow A3062 out of Bath to Combe Down
Club Secretary: Ms P. Bird, 83 Corston View, Bath, BA2 2PQ Tel: 01225 835153
Fixtures Secretary: Paul Ashman, 215 Wellsway, Bath.   Tel No: 01225 427958
Club Colours: Black and amber
League: Somerset 1

CONEY HILL RFC
Ground Address: Metz Way, Coney Hill, Gloucester
Tel: 01452 306239/381533
Brief Directions: Gloucester ring road (Eastern Ave) to Texas DIY store, turn into Metz Way, club 0.25 mile on left
Club Secretary: D C Veale, 13 Stanway Road, Coney Hill, Gloucester. GL4 4RE
Tel: (H) 01452 306510
Fixtures Secretary: Len Hayward, 14 Latymer Croft, Churchdown Glos. GL3 2QW
Tel: (H) 01452 855769
Club Colours: Amber & Black
League: Western Counties North

COOPER AVON TYRES (Melksham) RFC
Ground Address: Cooper Avon Sports & Social Club,Melksham House, Market Place Melksham, Wiltshire SN12
Tel: 01225 704982
Brief Directions: Follow signs to football club at Melksham market place,
Club Secretary: Pat Holtom, 63 Foresters Park Rd, Mellksham, Wilts. Sn12 7RW
Tel No: 10225 703396
Email: Pat@63stone,freeserve.co.uk
Fixtures Secretary: Marc Bound,5 Kenilworth Gardens, Melksham, Wilts.

Tel No: 01225 709892
Club Colours: Navy blue and sky blue hoops
League: Southern Counties South

CORSHAM RFC
Ground Address: Lacock Road, Corsham, Wilts/., SN13 9QG
Brief Directions: .5 mile outside Corsham on road to Lacock
Club Secretary: J G Wiltshire, 84 Springfield Close, Rudloe, Corsham, Wilts. SN13 0JR
Tel: (H) 01225 810800
Fixtures Secretary: R Slade, 49 Paul Street, Corsham, Wilts
Tel: (H) 01249 712683
Club Colours: Red and white hoops
League: Southern Counties South

COTHAM PARK RFC
Ground Address: Beggar Bush Lane, Failand, Bristol BS8 3TJ   Tel: 01275 392501
Brief Directions: M5 J19, A369 towards Bristol, left on A3129 (Beegar Bush Lane)
Club Secretary: Mark Chappell,Garden Flat, 289 Hotwell Road, Bristol. BS8 4NQ. Tel : 0117 9086710
e-mail: mchappellu@cableinet.co.uk
Fixtures Secretary: Mike Gill
Tel: (H) 0117 9076387 (W) 0117 9306200
Club Colours: Black and white hoops
League: Gloucester 3 South

CREDITON RFC
Ground Address: Blagdon,Ground, Cheriton Road, Crediton. EX17 1BY
Tel: 01363 772784
Brief Directions: M5 to Exeter, A377 to Crediton then A3072 towards Tiverton, club on left hand side of road
Club Secretary: Mrs Marilyn Daw, Clotworth, Coldridge, Crediton, Devon EX17 6AR
Tel & FAX: (H) 01363 83446
Fixtures Secretary: Mr Mick Leyman,Peppers Lake, New Buildings, Sandford, Crediton EX17 4BW
Tel: 01363 85092
Club Colours: Black and amber
League: South West 2 West

CREWKERNE RFC
Ground Address: Henhayes, Main Car Park, South Street, Crewkerne, Somerset. TA18 7JJ.
Tel: 01460 76422
Brief Directions: Head towards town centre, look for signs to Crewkerne Aqua Centre and follow to main car park.
Club Secretary: Mrs.Jeanette Gollings, 59 Seycamore Close, Holway, Taunton, Somerset TA1 2QJ. Tel: (H) 01823 279837
e-mail:crfc@jennandnigel.p9.co.uk
Fixtures Secretary: Trevor Boyer, 8 St James, Beaminster, Dorset DT8 3PW
Tel: 01308 863169
Club Colours: Scarlet and black hoops.
League: Somerset 1

SOUTH WEST

SOUTH WEST

CRICKLADE
League: Dorset & Wilts 2 North
For further information contact:
League Co-ordinating Secretary.
K. Jones,
13 Stratfield Road, Basingstoke, Hants, RG21 5RS
Tel: 01256 410461 (H) 0118 982 6750 (B)
Deputy
D. McAteer,
1 Rowlands Close, Mortimer West End,
Reading, RG7 3US
Tel: 0118 970 1245 (H) 0118 9303066 (B)
Fax :0118 9303 411 (B) 079 7667 0365 (M)
Email: reading@fentonplant.co.uk

CULLOMPTON RFC
Ground Address: Stafford Park, Knowle Lane,
Cullompton, Devon. EX15 1PZ
Tel: 01884 32480
Brief Directions: M5 J28 town centre, turn right by
Manor Hotel, past fire station turn left to Langlands
Rd, turn right at end of road, club at top of lane
Club Secretary: C,V,Smith, Warren Farm,
Kentisbeare EX15 2BR
Tel No: 01884 266704
e-mail: clive5@6tinternet.com
Fixtures Secretary: D J Keeling
Tel: (H) 01823 660199
Club Colours: Scarlet and black hoops
League: Devon 1

DARTMOUTH RFC
Ground Address: Clubhouse: Roseville Pavilion,
Roseville Street, Dartmouth, TQ6 9QH
Brief Directions: Milton Lane: Enter Dartmouth from
Totnes. First right,past Park& Ride , Dartmouth
School and Community College
Club Secretary: Dr. P.S. Jackson, High & Over, 140
Above Town, Dartmouth TQ6 9RH
Tel: 01803 833101
Fixtures Secretary: Mr S Atkins, 125 Victoria Road,
Dartmouth, TQ6 9DY
Tel: (H) 01803 832381
Club Colours: Green and red hoops
League: Devon 2

DEVIZES RFC
Ground Address: Chivers Ground, Devizes Sports
Club, London Road, Devizes, Wiltshire. Tel: 01380
723763
Brief Directions: Beside the Wiltshire Constabulary
H.Q. on the A361 in Devizes town centre.
Club Secretary: Nick Dark, Ashleigh, Salisbury
Street, Devizes Wilts. SN10 1QA
Tel No: 0777 979 3057
Email: nick.dark@ lineone.netj
Fixtures Secretary: Clive Meaney, 10 Park Road,
Market Lavington, Devizes, Wilts. Tel: 0797 661
0547
Club Colours: Broad Black and white hoops
League: Southern Counties South

DEVONPORT HIGH SCHOOL OLD BOYS RFC
Ground Address: Devonport High School for Boys,
Paradise Road, Millbridge, Plymouth, Devon. PL1 5
Tel: 01752 564682
Website: msn.co.uk
Brief Directions: A38 to Home P"k,along Outland
Rd,to Mllehouse traffic lights. Into Mllehouse Rd ,left
at top of hill ights into Molesworth Rd. Right at bot-
tom of hill lights then top of hill left to DHS
Club Secretary: Geoff Simpson, 108 Pattinson
Drive, Mainstone, Plymouth, Devon. PL6 8
Tel: (H) 01752 206662
Email: gks49@hotmail.com
Fixtures Secretary: Chris Hill,7 Hats Hill Close,
Mainstone, Plymouth, Devomn. PL6 8RU
Tel: (H) 01752 776792
Club Colours: Green & white hoops, black shorts
League: Devon 1

DEVONPORT SERVICES RFC
Ground Address: The Rectory, 2nd Avenue,
Devonport, Plymouth. PL1 5QE.
Tel: 01752 50559
Brief Directions: Maps are issued to visiting clubs
Club Secretary: Allan Berry, 36 Beechwood Avenue,
Plymouth , Devon   PL4 6PW
Tel: 01752 662443
Fixtures Secretary: G Kelly, 24 Youldon Way,
Morrabridge, Yelverton, Devon. PL20 7SN
Tel: 01822 854251
Club Colours: Navy shirts, blue shorts
League: Cornwall/Devon

DIDCOT RUFC
Ground Address: Edmonds Park, Park Road,
Didcot
Brief Directions: From roundabout at Georgetown
filling station/Wallingford Arms, take road to West
Hagbourne, ground is about 0.5 mile on left
Club Secretary: Beverley Arnold, 42 Merritt
Road,Didcot,Oxon. OX11 tDX
Tel: 01235 210337 e-mail: BA@sbs.oxon.sch.uk
Fixtures Secretary: Steve Bryan, 17 Itchen
Court,Ladygrove,Didicot,Oxoxn.OX11 7SA. Tel:
01235 811122. e-mail: sbryan@lineone.net
Club Colours: Red and white hoops or quarters
League: Berks/Bucks & Oxon 2

DRIFTERS RFC
Ground Address: Farnham Common Sports Club,
One Pin Lane, Farnham Common, Buck
Tel: 01753 644190   Website: tcsc.org.uk
Brief Directions: From M40 J2, or M4 J6 take A355
`One Pin Lane' half mile north of Farnham Common.
Club Secretary: Dave Hancock, 19 Thurston Road,
Slough, Berks, SL1 3JW.   Tel: 01753 576512
Fixtures Secretary: Terry Davies, 5 Evenlode Road,
Bourne End, Bucks. SL8 5ND
Tel: 01628 529663 (H) 07932 724659 (M)
Club Colours: Black with magenta and gold chest
band
League: Berks/Bucks & Oxon 1

DRYBROOK RFC
Ground Address: Mannings Ground, High Street, Drybrook, Glos
Tel: 01594 542595
Brief Directions: Gloucester to Mitcheldean via Huntley, ground is on outskirts of village on Mitcheldean Road
Club Secretary: Glyn Tingle, 16 Woodland Road, Drybrook, Glos. GL17 9HE
Tel: (H) 01594 544334 01594 542769 (W)
Fixtures Secretary: Derek Trigg
Tel: (H) 01594 542258
Club Colours: Green with black on white band
League: Gloucester Premier

DURSLEY RFC
Ground Address: Stinchcombe Stragglers, Hounds Green, The Avenue, Stinchcombe, Dursley, Glos. GL11 6AJ   Tel: 01453 543693
Brief Directions: On the Dursley to Wotton-under-Edge road (B4060), on right just before entering Stinchcombe village
Club Secretary: Simon Bilous, 8 Ferney, Dursley, Glos. GL11 5AB   Tel: (H) 01453 545493
Email: simon@domekbilous.demon.co.uk
Fixtures Secretary: Tony Powell, 55 Oakfield Way, Sharpness, Glos. GL13 9UT Tel No: 01453 811484
Club Colours: Maroon and amber
League: Gloucester 2

EXETER SARACENS RFC
Ground Address: Exhibition Fields, Summer Lane, Whipton, Exeter, Devon
Tel: 01392 462651
Brief Directions: From M5 follow signs for Exeter Arena or from other direction follow Whipton signs then Exeter Arena signs
Club Secretary: David Mortimore, 39 Lonsdale Road, Heavitree, Exeter, EX1 3DP
Tel: 01392 433305
Fixtures Secretary: David McIlroy, Downderry, 7 Westclyst, Exeter, Devon.
Tel: 01392 469146
Colours: Red shirts with white collar, black shorts
League: Devon 2

EXMOUTH RFC
Ground Address: Imperial Recreation Ground, Royal Avenue, Exmouth. EX8 1DG
Tel: 01395 263665
Brief Directions: M5 to Sandy Gate-Exeter, exit here, follow Exmouth signs 8 miles, enter Exmouth on town bypass from which ground can be seen adjacent to River Exe
Club Secretary: Peter Appleby, 18 Hulham Road, Exmouth, Devon EX8 3HS
Tel No: 01395 222665
Email: pete.appleby@virgin.net
Fixtures Secretary: Gerry. Williams, 40 Bapton Close, Exmouth, EX8 3LQ.
Tel & Fax: 01395 271373
Club Colours: Heliotrope&white hoops, white shorts
League: Western Counties West

FAIRFORD CB0
Ground Address: Farmors Shool, Fairford.
Clubhouse Tell No: 01285 713540
Brief Directions: From A417, Cirencester-Lechlade Road turn into High Styreet. Then at T junction right along Park Street. Turn left at T junction and school is half a mile on left
Club Secretary: DavidBowman, 17 Crabtree Park, Fairford, Glos., GL7 4LT.
Tel No: 01285 713685
Email: annebowman@tingworld.co.uk
Fixtures Secretary: Mick Marks, 12 The Plies, Fairford, Glos. GL7 4LY
Tel No: 01285 713834
Club Colours: Emerald and Black Hoops.
League: Gloucester 3 North

FALMOUTH RFC
Ground Address: The Recreation Ground, Dracaena Avenue, Falmouth, Cornwall
Tel: 01326 311304
Brief Directions: Right at traffic lights on A39 (by SAAB Garage) and left into and along Dracaena Avenue, visible from main road. Ground at junction of Tregenver and Killigrew roads.
Club Secretary: F.H. Murton, 3 Wellington Place, Carnon Downs, Truro, TR3 6LF.
Tel: 01872 863679
Fixtures Secretary: Glenn Wilkes, 33 Carrine Road, Truro, TR1 3 XB.   Tel: (H) 01872 277249
Club Colours: Black with white hoops
League: Cornwall 1

FRAMPTON COTTERELL RFC
Ground Address: Crossbow House,School Road, Frampton Cotterell, Bristol
Tel: 01454 772947
Brief Directions: Off B3058 Winterbourne to Chipping Sodbury road
Club Secretary: Steve Buckley, 25 Ratcliffe Drive, Stoke Gifford, Bristol BS34 8TZ
Tel No: 0117 9070344
Email: stevebucks@supanet.com
Fixtures Secretary: Ali Poole, 173 Longcroft, Yate, Bristol BS37 7YU
Tel: 01454 324874
Club Colours: Green, black and gold shirts
League: Gloucester 1

FROME RFC
Ground Address: Gypsy Lane, Frome, Somerset. BA11 2NA   Tel: 01373 462506
Brief Directions: Follow signs for Leisure Centre, Frome RFC is signposted from the Bath Road/Princess Anne Road traffic lights
Club Secretary: Ray Harding, 93 Dakfield Road, Frome, Somerset BA11 4JH
Tel NO: 01373 461638 (H) 01373 456410 (W)
ray.harding@which.net
Fixtures Secretary: Symon Crouch 7Alder Walk, Frome, Somerset   Tel: 01373 465600
Club Colours: Red, black & white hoops.
League: Southern Counties South

SOUTH WEST

GLOUCESTER ALL BLUES RFC
Ground Address: The Oxleaze, Westgate Bridge, Westgate Street, Gloucester
Tel: 01452 306984
Website: gabrec.co.uk
Brief Directions: South Wales road out of Gloucester (signposted to Ross-on-Wye, Chepstow and Ledbury) then first left after crossing River Severn (Westgate Bridge)
Club Secretary: Robert Hart, The Uplands, Minsterworth, Glos. GL2 8JH
Tel. Nos: 01452 750223 (H) 01452 425656 (W)
Fixtures Secretary: I.Taylor, 58 Sandyleaze, Elmbridge, Gloucester GL2 0PX
Tel No: 01452 526223
Club Colours: Navy blue shirts, shorts and socks,Change: Navy & Sky Blue
League: Gloucester 3 North

GLOUCESTER CIVIL SERVICE TIGERS RFC
Ground Address: CSSA, Estcourt Road, Gloucester. GL1 3LG
Tel: 01452 528317
Brief Directions: M5 J11, A40 to Gloucester, continue on A40 to Longford roundabout, left at Longford Inn (Beefeater), left at next roundabout, ground is on immediate right
Club Secretary: R.W. Shepherd, 95 Lavington Drive, Longlevens, Gloucester GL2 0HR.
Tel No: 01452 532802
Fixtures Secretary: G.Bolmer, 17 Edwy Parade, Kingsholm, Gloucester GL1 2QH
Tel: 01452 410269
Club Colours: Blue, red, white hoops, white shorts, red socks
League: Gloucester 3 North

GLOUCESTER OLD BOYS RFC
Ground Address: Horton Road, Gloucester
Tel: 01452 302390
Brief Directions: M5 J11A, follow signs to city centre, 3rd exit at roundabout adjacent to Wall's ice cream factory, 2nd left is Horton Road
Club Secretary: Ray Ellis, 15 Armscroft Way, Gloucester. GL2 0ST
Tel: (H) 01452 525375 (W) 01452 416033
Fixtures Secretary: S Turner, 19 St Mark's Street, Gloucester. Tel: 01452 422973
Club Colours: Claret, gold and navy
League: South West 2 West
Contact: Secretary, as above

GORDANO RFC
Ground Address: The National Stadium, Caswell Lane, Portbury, Nr Bristol BS20 9TH.
Tel: 01275 373486
Brief Directions: Jct 19 at M5, take A369, head into village of Portbury and bear left at the village green.
Club Secretary: Caroline Goddard, 6 Clayton close, Portishead,North Somerset. BS20 6YU
Tel: 01275 642928

Fixtures Secretary: A Stanton,
Tel: (H) 01275 791775
Club Colours: Red and black shirts, black shorts.
League: Somerset Premier

GORDON LEAGUE RFC
Ground Address: Hempsted Lane, Gloucester. GL2 6JN
Tel: 01452 303434 Office   Fax 01452 507475
Brief Directions: Into Hempsted Lane past Colin Campbell pub, 500 yards on left
Club Secretary: Karl Gwilliam, 7 Patseamur Mews, Longlevens, Gloucester, GL2 0XL
Fixtures Secretary: Mark Hayward, 17 Leonard Road, Tredworth, Gloucester, GL1 4PQ
Tel: (H) 01452 536012
Club Colours: White, red sash, black socks
League: Western Counties North

GOSFORD ALL BLACKS RFC
Ground Address: Stratford Brake Sports Ground, Langford Lane, Kidlington, Oxon
Tel: 01865 373994
Brief Directions: Take A44 Evesham road from Oxford, follow signs to Oxford Airport, club is opposite airport.Or take A4260 to Kidlington roundabout and follow signs to Stratford Brake Sports ground.
Club Secretary: Martin Lambert,57 Brunstock Beck,Didcot, Oxon. OX11 7YG
Tel: 01235 810405
e-mail:martin@manor-didcot.oxon.sch.uk
Fixtures Secretary: Dave Duthie, 10 Lovell Close, Duckington, Witney, Oxon, OX8 7YQ
Tel: (H) 01993 702261
Club Colours: All Black
League: Berks/Bucks & Oxon 2

GROVE RFC
Ground Address: Recreation Ground, Cane Lane, Grove, Wantage, Oxfordshire
Tel: 01235 762750
Brief Directions: Frm Oxford (A338), turn right into village, rt at r'bout, lft at r'bout (Brereton Dv), lft at end to Cane Ln. Frm sth enter vlge at lights, lft at r'bout into D'worth Rd, follow as above
Club Secretary: Mrs Sylvia Morrison, 19 Hardwell Close, Grove, Oxon.
Tel No: 01235 223903
Fixtures Secretary: Wayne Latimer, 30 Mallard Way, Grove, Wantage, Oxon.
Tel: 01235 771004
Club Colours: Red, white and blue hoops, navy shorts and red socks
League: Southern Counties North

HARWELL RUFC (50th Anniversary Season)
Ground Address: Central Sports Field, A.E.A. Harwell Laboratory, Nr Didcot, Oxon
Brief Directions: To the left of main gate at Harwell Laboratory on old Newbury-Abingdon road (A4185)
Club Secretary: Douglas Bosley,55 West Lockinge, nr Wantage,Oxon. OX12 8QE. Tel: 01235 833688
Email: dougbosley@btinternet.com

Fixtures Secretary: Jenny Bosley
Tel: (H) 01235 833688
Club Colours: Royal blue, light blue and white hooped shirts
League: Berks/Bucks & Oxon 2

HAYLE RUGBY CLUB
Ground Address: Memorial Park, Marsh Lane, Hayle, Cornwall, TR27 4PS.
Brief Directions: Take A30 to first roundabout, ground immediately in front
Club Secretary: Rod Porter, c/o Haytle RFC
Tel No: (H) 01736 757203
Fixtures Secretary: Mike Gee, Sunhail, 7 Hellesvean Close, St. Ives, Cornwall.
Tel: (H) 01736 797168
Club Colours: Green, black and white
League: Western Counties West

HELSTON RFC
Ground Address: King George V Memorial Playing Fields, Clodgey Lane, Helston
Tel: 01326 573742
Brief Directions: A394 into north of town past Tesco superstore, 0.25 mile on right, before Flambards Theme Park
Club Secretary: Mrs A.M.Dodd, 78 Bulwark Road, Helston, Cornnwall TR13 8JG
Tel No: 01326 564785
Fixtures Secretary: Mrs Bev Davis
Tel: (H) 01326 563744
Club Colours: Navy and white hoops
League: Cornwall 1

HENLEY WANDERERS
Ground Address: Dry Leas, Marlow Road, Henley on Thames, RG9 2JA
Tel No: 01491413156
Brief Directions: Leave Henley on the Oxford Road and fork right into Marlow Road. Dry leas is on the left ater 100 yardy
Club Secretary: David Shove, 201 Greys Road, Henley on Thames, Oxon RG9 1QU Tel No: 01491 576541
Email: dave@shove.fsnet.co.uk
Fixtures Secretary: Alan Richardson. Tel Nos: 01491 574664 (H) 01628 487755(W)
Club Colours: Bottle Green with gold collar, blue shorts and green socks.
League: Berks/Bucks & Oxon 1

HIGH WYCOMBE RUFC
Ground Address: Kingsmead Road, High Wycombe, Bucks. HP11 1JB.
Tel: 01494 532024
Brief Directions: M40, J4 to A404 (Amersham) into town centre. A40 ((Beaconsfield). After 3rd mini r'about right into Abbey Barn Rd. After 800 yds sharp left into Kingsmead Rd.
Club Secretary: Don Dickerson, 3 Talbot Ave., High Wycombe, Bucks. HP13 5HZ.
Tel: (H) 01494 532024 (B) 01494 479722

Fixtures Secretary: George Brown, Deerleap, Primrose Hill, Widmerend, High Wycombe, Bucks. HP15 6NU.
Tel: (H) 01494 716700
Club Colours: Broad green with narrow black & white hoops
League: Southern Counties North

HONITON RFC
Ground Address: Allhallows Playing Fields, Northcote Lane, Honiton
Tel: 01404 41239
Brief Directions: From traffic lights in High St, turn into Dowell St, continue for 0.5 mile, turn right at the Fire station into Northcote Lane, follow road around to the Sports Centre
Club Secretary: Jeremy Rice, 184 High St., Honiton, Devon. EX141LA
Tel: 01404 46820
jeremyrice@btinternet.com
Fixtures Secretary: Roy Freemantle,321 Joslin Road, Honiton, Devon.Ex14 1RH
Tel: (H) 01404 41888
Club Colours: Red, amber and black hoops Change Colours: BLack
League: Devon 1

HORNETS RFC
Ground Address: Hutton Moor Park, Hutton Moor Road, Weston-Super-Mare, North Somerset. BS22 8L
Tel: 01934 621433
Website: hornetrugbu.net
Brief Directions: J.21 M5 dual carriage way to Weston-Super-Mare. Straight across two R/abouts - turn right at filter light - Ground on right.
Club Secretary: Keith Powell, 103 Sunnyside road North, Weston-Super-Mare, North Somerset, BS213 3PZ. Tel: 01934 625750
Fixtures Secretary: John Wilson, Correspondance to the Club
Tel: 01934 513543H - 01179 293211W
Club Colours: Black and Amber
League: South West 2 West

HUCCLECOTE RFC
Ground Address: The Old School Field, Churchdown Lane, Hucclecote, Glos .GL3 3QH Tel No: 01452 621281Website: hucclecotefc.co.ukE
Brief Directions: Exit M5 (north) Jct 11A, To Glos take left at Zoons Ct round't to Glos Trading Estate roundabout. Rt. to Hucclecote.Rt. at lights to Churchdown Lane. Club on right past school.
Club Secretary: John Ring, 9 Conway Road, Hucclecote, Glos. GL3 3PD
Tel: (H) 01452 618920
Fixtures Secretary: Len Taylor, 41 Larkhay Road, Hucclecote, Gloucester Gl3 3NR.
Tel: 01452 619718
Club Colours: Black and amber
League: Gloucester Premier

SOUTH WEST

HUNGERFORD RFC

Ground Address: The Triangle Field, Priory Road, Hungerford, Berks.
Tel No: 01488 684662
Brief Directions: A4 to Hungerford. Turn into High Street at Bear Hotel junction. Travel through town and up high street , until left into Priory Road after 3/4 mile. Signposted to Football Club and Coombe. After mile pitch is on left after John O'Gaunt School.
Club Secretary: Adrian Chapman.
Tel No: 0780 2281837
Fixtures Secretary: Simon Ford, 28 Shalbourne Close, Hungerford,Berks. RG17 0QH
Club Colours: Claret and porter hoops, black shorts.
League: Dorset & Wilts 2 North

ILFRACOMBE RFC

Ground Address: Brimlands, Hillsborough Road, Ilfracombe, North Devon
Tel: 01271 864249
Brief Directions: From town centre take road to east signed Combe Martin, look out for swimming pool, club on left close by
Club Secretary: Ian Roberts,
Lower Court Barn,Shortacombe, East Down, Barnstable, North Devon. EX31 4NT
Tel: (H) 01271 850542
Fixtures Secretary: Stuart Swanson, 5 Church Cottages, Swimbridge, Barnstaple
Tel: (H) 01271 850514
Club Colours: Blue and white hoops
League: Devon 2

ILLOGAN PARK RFC

Ground Address: Illogan Park, Paynters Lane End,Illogan, Redruth, Cornwall
Brief Directions: Turn off A30 at Portrath and head for Pool.Turn right down Cheriot Road for one mile . Ground is on left.
Club Secretary: G R Tonkins, 20 Lower Pengegon, Camborne, Cornwall. TR14 8RX
Tel: (H) 712395 (W) 218785
Fixtures Secretary: R J McLellan
Tel: (H) 01872 572696
Club Colours: Yellow and black
League: Cornwall 2

IMPERIAL RFC

Ground Address: Bristol Imperial Sports Ground, West Town Lane, Knowle, Bristol
Tel: 01275 546000
Brief Directions: From Wells road (A37) and Bath road (A4), turn into West Town Lane
Club Secretary: Andy Buckle, 227 Headley Lane, Headley Park, Bristol. BS13 7QB.
Tel: 07967 467333
e-mail: andy.buckle@ itlmail.co.uk
Fixtures Secretary: Jack Gommo
Tel: (H) 01275544811
Club Colours: Myrtle and amber shirts, blue shorts, myrtle and amber socks
League: Somerset 1

IVEL BARBARIANS RFC LTD

Ground Address: Midford Recreation Groupnd, Yeovil, Somerset   Tel: 01935 427127
Website: ivelbarbarians.fsnet.co.uk
Brief Directions: A37 to Yeovil, adjacent to Yeovil College
Club Secretary: Mrs. Sharon Bellingham, c/o the club Tel 01935 427955 (H)
Email: skppy456@icqmail.com
Fixtures Secretary: K. Smith, 39 Welbeck Road, Yeovil, Somerset, BA21 5PH.
Tel: (H) 01935 420206
Club Colours: Black and white quarters with black shorts
League: Southern Counties South

IVYBRIDGE RFC

Ground Address: Cross-in Hand, Exeter Road, Ivybridge   Tel: 01752 894392
Brief Directions: From A38 Exeter/Plymouth main road, follow the `Park & Ride' signs. The ground is almost opposite the station entrance.
Club Secretary: Dennis Kiely, 7 Rivers Close,Ivybridge, Devon. PL21 0JN
Tel No: 01752 893720
Fixtures Secretary: J.M.Eddington, Cramond Lodge, Filham, Ivybridge, Devon. PL21 0DJ
Tel: 01752 893901
Club Colours: Green shirts and black shorts .
Change: Blue shirts, black shorts
League: Western Counties West

KINGSBRIDGE RFC

Ground Address: High House, Kingsbridge, Devon. TQ7 1JL   Tel: 01548 852051
Brief Directions: From centre of Kingsbridge take Dartmouth road alongside estuary, take first left and first right to the top of the hill
Club Secretary: Martin Newman, Fourwinds, 46 Saffron Park, Kingsbridge, Devon. TQ7 1RL
Tel: (H) 01548 853976
Fixtures Secretary: Derrick Marshall, 5 Welle House Gardens, Kingsbridge, Devon.
Tel: 01548 852618
Club Colours: Blue and white hoops, with change colours of blue and black
League: Devon 1

KINGSWOOD RFC

Ground Address: The Pavilion, Deanery Road Playing Field, Grimsbury Road, Kingswood, Bristol. BS15
Tel: 0117 9675001
Brief Directions: Bristol on A420, turn right into Grimsbury Rd immediately before Tennis Court pub, ground is 1st left
Club Secretary: Miss Hannah Carey, 119 Orchard Road, Kingswood, bristol BS15 9TZ
Tel No: 0117 9601432
Fixtures Secretary: Mark McGarrigle
Tel No:0117 9478145
Club Colours: Sky blue and chocolate brown
League: Gloucester 2

LANKELLY FOWEY RFC
Ground Address: Lankelly Farm, Lankelly Lane, Lankelly, Fowey, Cornwall
Brief Directions: On entering Fowey, turn right into Lankelly Lane, follow road until T junction, turn left, ground is 100yds on right
Club Secretary: G.Rew, 123 Creakavose Park, St Stephen, St Austell. PL26 7NB
Tel: 01726 821471
Fixtures Secretary: R Sainsbury, 13 Greenbank, Polruan, Fowey PL23 1QP
Tel: (H) 01726 870830 (W) 01726 862228
Club Colours: Navy blue and white hoops
League: Cornwall 2

LISKEARD - LOOE RFC
Ground Address: Lux Park, Coldstyle Road, Liskeard, Cornwall   Tel: 01579 342665
Brief Directions: Ask for the Leisure Centre, near town centre
Club Secretary: D,Williams, 9 Clifton Terrace, New Road, Liskeard Cornwall. PL14 4HN.
Tel No: 01579 344082
Fixtures Secretary: J.Polson, 3 Barrass Close, Liskeard, Cornwall. Pl14 6EX
Tel No: 01579 340018
Club Colours: Red and black hoops
League: Cornwall 1

LITTLEMORE RUFC
Ground Address: Peers School, Sandy Lane West, Littlemoor, Oxon. OX4 5JY   Tel: 01865 436271
Brief Directions: Oxon ring road to Cowley (eastern bypass A4142), past the Rover plant on left, left turn and signpost to Peers School
Club Secretary: Geoff Wakeham, 124 Church Way,Court Place Gardens, Iffley, Oxford, OX4 4EW.
Tel: 01865 749374
Fixtures Secretary: Carl Wright, 37 Ock Drive, Berinsfield, Oxon.   Tel: 01865 341720
Club Colours: Royal blue & white quarters
League: Berks/Bucks & Oxon 2

LONGLEVENS RFC
Ground Address: Longford Lane, Longlevens, Gloucester   Tel: 01452 306880
Brief Directions: M5 J11 - Golden Valley bypass towards Gloucester, right at 2nd lights into Old Cheltenham Rd, Church Rd then Longford Ln. Or A38 T'kesbury rd turn right into Longford Ln past Queens Head
Club Secretary: Colin Dunford, 66 Estcourt Road, Gloucester. GL1 3LG
Tel: (H) 01452 522795 (W) 01452 529751
Fixtures Secretary: Greg Thomas, 21 Rodney Close, Longlevens, Gloucester GL2 9DG
Tel: (H) 01452 526352
Club Colours: Red   **League:** Gloucester Premier

MARLBOROUGH
Ground Address: Rugby Club House, Frees Avenue, The Common, Marlborough, Wiltshire.
Tel: 01672 514717
Brief Directions: Take Swindon road out of

Marlborough then left at Common and right into Frees Avenue.
Club Secretary: Mrs Joyce Adams, 10 Ailesbury Way, Burbage, Marlborough, Wilts. SN8 3TD
Tel: (H) 01672 810718
Fixtures Secretary: Mr Alec Thomas, 2 Dando Drive, Marlborough, Wilts.   Tel: (H) 01672 512296
Club Colours: Black and amber hoops, black shorts
League: Dorset & Wilts 2 North

MARLOW RUFC
Ground Address: Riverwoods Drive, Marlow, Bucks
Tel: 016284 77054/83911
Club Secretary: Graham Cutts, 6 Eastern Dene, Hazlemere, Bucks. HP15 7BT
Tel: (H) 01494 711391 (W) 01494 431717
Fixtures Secretary: Graham Cutts
Tel: (H) 01494 711391 (W) 01494 431717
Club Colours: Black and white hoops, black shorts
League: South West 2 East

MARTOCK RFC
Ground Address: Martock Recreation Ground, Stoke Road, Martock   (no telephone at ground)
Website: martockrugby.co.uk
Brief Directions: Take Martock exit from A303 at Percombe Hill, left at T junction to join Stoke Road, ground on left after 1 mile
Club Secretary: Philip Jackson, Church Lodge Cottage, Church Street, Martock, Somerset. TA12 6JL   Tel: (H) 01935 823514
Fixtures Secretary: Peter Cockle, 19 Birch Road, Martock, Somerset. TA12 6DR
Tel Nos: 01935 823198 (H) 01454 272050 (W)
Club Colours: Green and black quarters
League: Dorset & Wilts 1

MATSON RFC
Ground Address: Redwell Road, Matson, Gloucester   Tel: 01452 528963
Brief Directions: Three miles south of city centre on B4073, adjacent to dry ski slope
Club Secretary: Don Danter c/o Matson RFC
Tel; 01452 528 963
Fixtures Secretary: Alvin Woodhouse, 90 Alfred Street, Gloucester.
Tel: 01452 535582 (H) 0777 5754208 (M)
Club Colours: Black shirts and white shorts
League: South West 2 West

MIDSOMER NORTON RFC
Ground Address: Norton Down Playing Fields, Stratton-on-the-Fosse, Somerset. BA3 4RD
Tel: 01761 412827
Brief Directions: From town centre follow Shepton Mallet road (B3355) for approx 800 yards
Club Secretary: Corinne Edwards, Hillview, Mendip Road, Stoke St Michael, Somerset. BA3 5JU
Tel : 01749 841425
Fixtures Secretary: Rob Porter,Upper Lentney Farm,Kilmersdon, Radstock, Bath. BA3 5SL
Tel: 01761 432325
Club Colours: Red and white hoops, black shorts
League: Somerset Premier

MILTON KEYNES RUFC
Ground Address: Sam Coster Pavilion, Field Lane, Greenleys, Wolverton, Milton Keynes, Bucks. MK12 6AZ
Tel: 01908 313858
Brief Directions: Travel from Stony Stratford town centre towards Wolverton, rt at double r'bout into Gt Monics St (V5), proceed across r'bout, rt into Field Ln, rt at T j'tion, next left to clubhouse
Club Secretary: Gary Spinks, Harley House, Bow Brickhill, Bucks. MK17 9LH
Tel No: 01908 277138
Fixtures Secretary: David Eales.
Tel No: 01296 714422
Club Colours: Black and white hoops, black shorts
League: Southern Counties North

MINCHINHAMPTON RFC
Ground Address: Minchinhampton Sports & Social Club, Tobacconist Road, Minchinhampton, Glos
Tel: 01453 88
Brief Directions: From centre of village take Tetbury road (Tetbury Street), 1st left, clubhouse straight ahead
Club Secretary: Rob Edmonds, Woodlands Cottage, 205 Slad Road, Stroud, Glos., GL5 1RJ.
Tel: (H) 01453 766662 (W) 01452 308989
Fixtures Secretary: Pete Weaving
Tel: (H) 01453 755561
Club Colours: Green, white and black hoops
League: Gloucester 3 South

MINEHEAD BARBARIANS RFC
Ground Address: Tom Stewart Field, Ellicombe, Minehead, Somerset. TA24 6TR
Tel: 01643 707155
Brief Directions: A39 to Minehead from Taunton/Bridgwater, left at roundabout signed Ellicombe, ground 100 metres
Club Secretary: Jonathon Sweetland, Bramley, Higher Orchard, Woodcombe, Minehead, Somerset. TA24 8SD
Tel: 01643 705283
Fixtures Secretary: Mr Cameron Ford, 13 Sampford Brett, Taunton, TA4 4LA
Tel: (H) 01984 633237 or Clubhouse
Club Colours: Black and white hoops
League: Somerset Premier

MINETY RUGBY FOOTBALL CLUB
Ground Address: The Playing Fields, Silver Street, Minety, Nr Malmesbury, Wiltshire
Tel: 01666 860 802
Website:minetyrugbyclub.index.html
Brief Directions: From Swindon take A419 to Cirencester, turn off at Cricklade, through Cricklade to Minety, right at Q8 garage (Minety Motors) to the playing fields
Club Secretary: Kevin Vancil, 12 Essex Walk, Walcot, Swindon, Wilts., SN3 3EY
Tel: (H) 01793 525898 (W) 01793 504945
Email: kevinvancil@aol.com

Fixtures Secretary: Mark Turner, 11 Cantors Way, Minety, Malmesbury, Wilts., SN16 9QZ. Tel: (H) 01666 860680 or 01666 860923
Email: mturner@interra.com
Club Colours: Green and purple hoops
League: Dorset & Wilts 1

MORGANIANS RFC
Ground Address: Chedzoy Lane, Bridgwater, Somerset
Tel: 01278 423434
Brief Directions: On A39 Bridgwater to Glastonbury road, over M5 motorway, 1st right into Chedzoy Lane opposite Mole Valley Farms
Club Secretary: Peter Donnachie, 23 Almond Tree Close, Bridgwater, Somerset. TA6 4EB Tel: 07974 235071
Fixtures Secretary: Roy Grimstead., 40 Leyton Drive, Bridgwater, Somerset TA6 4XY
Tel: 01278 445232
Club Colours: Navy shirts with gold and red hoops
League: Somerset 2

MOUNTS BAY
League: Cornwall 1
For further information contact:
Cornwall 1 & 2 Leagues Co-ordinating Secretary
N.J. Barber, 2, The Crescent, Alexandra Road, St Ives, Cornwall, TR26 1BY
Tel/Fax: 01736 796861 (H) 01752 665951 (B)
Email: nbarb@cwcom.net
(Deputy) D. Jenkins, Albaston Post Office, Albaston, Gunnislake, Cornwall, PL18 9HQ
Tel/Fax: 01822 832785 (H)
Email: davejenkins@talk21.com

NAILSEA & BACKWELL RFC
Ground Address: West End Park, West End Lane, Nailsea.   Tel: 01278 810818
Brief Directions: Directions signed from Town Centre
Club Secretary: Anita Heappey, Wareham Lodge, Whitesfield Road, Nailsea BS48 4JE.
Tel: 01275 851478 - 0973 499779M
Email: anita@familyheappey.fsnet.co.uk
Fixtures Secretary: Nigel Crawley, 25 Cleave Place, Nailsea, North Somerset BS48 2WF.
Tel No: 01275 543875
Club Colours: Black/White
League: Somerset 1

NEWENT RFC
Ground Address: Recreation Ground, Watery Lane, Newent, Glos
(Correspondence to: George Hotel, Newent)
Tel: 01531 820203
Brief Directions: Drive into centre of town, turn right into Watery Lane by the library/health centre, ground is on the right about 400 metres along Watery Lane
Club Secretary: G. Hall, The Red Lion, 2 Broad Street, Newent. GL18 1Q
Tel No: 01531 820215

SOUTH WEST

Fixtures Secretary: N. Hine, 21 Coopers Way,
Newent, Glos, GL18 1TJ
Tel: (H) 01531 820 519
Club Colours: Green and gold
League: Gloucester 3 North

NEWQUAY HORNETS RFC
Ground Address: Newquay Sports Centre,
Tretvenson Road, Newquay, Cornwall
Tel: 01637 875533
Website: newquayhornetsrfc.co.uk
Directions: Newquay via A3058, lft Chester Rd, 2nd
lft Whitegate Rd, lft at T jcn, club 50 yds lft. Frm
Redruth, N'quay via A392, across mini r'bouts into
Edgcumbe Ave, rt Hilgrove Rd, 1st rt, club at end
Club Secretary: John Grindle, 1 Polwhele Road,
Newquay, Cornwall
Tel No: 01637 874540(H) 01637 898787 (W)
Email: grindle@jeal64.freeserve.co.uk
Fixtures Secretary: As Secretary
Club Colours: Green and white hoops
League: Cornwall/Devon

NEWTON ABBOT RFC
Ground Address: Rackerhayes, Newton Road,
Kingsteignton, Newton Abbot, Devon. TQ12 3AD
Tel: 01626 354150
Brief Directions: Follow signs for Racecourse,
ground is opposite the course behind Fairway
Furniture
Club Secretary: Maurice Young, 51 Lime Tree Walk,
Milber, Newton Abbot, Devon, TQ12 4LF
Tel: (H) 01626 206776
Fixtures Secretary: Mr Gordon Hooper,
39 Wilton Way, Abbotskerswell, Newton Abbot,
Devon, TQ12 5PG   Tel: (H) 01626 369791
Club Colours: White shirts & shorts, black socks
with gold, red & white trim
League: Western Counties West

NORTH BRISTOL RFC
Ground Address: Oaklands, Gloucester Road,
Almondsbury, Bristol. BS32 4AG
Tel: 01454 612740
Brief Directions: M5 J16 onto A38, then to
Gloucester, entrance 150 yards from Motorway
behind motorway police station.
Club Secretary: L.Hayward, 51 Brdeman Grove,
Filton, Bristol BS34 7HP
Tel No: 01179 698905
Fixtures Secretary: M Cottle, 33 Clavell Road,
Henbury, Bristol. BS10 7EJ
Tel: (H) 0117 9506182
Club Colours: Red and royal blue hoops.
League: Western Counties North

NORTH DORSET RFC
Ground Address: Slaughtergate, Longbury Hill
Lane, Gillingham, Dorset
Tel: 01747 822748
Brief Directions: Take Wincanton Road (B3081)
from town centre, Longbury Hill Lane is on right

about 1 mile from the town, 300 yds after the end of
30mph zone
Club Secretary: W.J.White, Lime Tree House,
Queen Street, Gillingham, Dorset. SP8 4DX
Tel No: 01202 312911
Email: jimwhite@jwmortgagesolutions.com
Fixtures Secretary: Clive Drake, Folly's End, Wyke,
Gillingham, Dorset SP8 4NA
Tel: 01747 825586
Club Colours: Emerald Green and navy
League: Dorset & Wilts 1

NORTH PETHERTON RFC
Ground Address: Beggars Brook, North Petherton,
Nr Bridgwater, Somerset
Tel: 01278 663028
Brief Directions: M5 J24, A38 Taunton, through
North Petherton, layby on left at exit of North
Petherton
Club Secretary: Chris Facey, 9 Hawridge Road,
Bridgwater, Somerset TA6 7NE
Tel: 01278 459767 (H) 01278 435334(W)
Fixtures Secretary: J.Upfield, 12 Pilots Helm, North
Petherton, Somerset Ta6 6TB
Tel: 01278 663892
Club Colours: Black and white hoops / Black / Red,
white and blue hoops
League: Somerset 1

NORTH TAWTON RFC
Ground Address: Taw Meadows, Fore Street,
North Tawton, Devon
Tel No: 01837 82907
Brief Directions: On entering the town from De
Bathe Cross, take the 1st turning right before reach-
ing the square
Club Secretary: Mrs Gillian Hoggins, The Old
Forge, North St., North Tawton, Devon. EX20 2D
Tel & Fax: 01837 82516
Email: p.hoggins@talk21.com
Fixtures Secretary: Mrs Sarah Quick, 7 Victoria
Cottages, North Tawton, Devon Ex20 2DF. Tel:
01837 82704
Club Colours: Black and amber shirts, black shorts
League: Devon 3

OAKMEADIANS RUFC
Ground Address: Meyrick Park Pavilion,
Bournemouth. BH2 6LJ
Tel: 01202 789497
Brief Directions: Bournemouth town centre then
head for Meyrick Park Golf Club, approx 0.5 mile
from town centre
Club Secretary: Sonja Dimmer,
The Flat, Cricket Pavilion, Meyriock Park,
Central Drive, Bournemouth BH2 6LJ.
Tel No 01202 789497
Fixtures Secretary: Ginny Phillips, 47 Headswell
Avenue, Bournmouth, Dorset BH10 6JX
Tel: (H) 01202 525311
Club Colours: Blue, green and white hoops
League: Southern Counties South

SOUTH WEST

OKEHAMPTON RFC
Ground Address: Oaklands Park Showfield, Oaklands, Okehampton Tel: 01837 52508
Brief Directions: Off the Hatherleigh Road, 250m from town centre
Club Secretary: Max Sansom, Moorcroft, Stoney Park Lane, Okehampton, Devon, EX20 1SW
Tel: 01837 53387
Fixtures Secretary: Robert Barkwell,Ebenezer Hall, North Street, Okehampton, Devon
Tel No: 07768 614950
Club Colours: Maroon and amber unequal hoops
League: Western Counties West
Contact: Mark Curtis,34 Fern Meadow, Okehampton, Devon. Tel No: 01837 54787

OLD ASHTONIANS RFC
Ground Address: Ashton Park School, Blackmoors Lane, Bower Ashton, Bristol Tel: c/o 0117 9877796
Brief Directions: From city follow signs for Portishead, school is indicated at 1st roundabout (turn left)
Club Secretary: Ian Reed, 42 Stockwood Crescent, Knowle, Bristol. BS4 1AW
Tel: (H) 0117 9833942 (W) 0777 3863431
Fixtures Secretary: Tony Excell, 18 Perrycroft Rd., Bishopsworth, Bristol. BS13 7RY.
Tel: (H) 0117 9642352
Club Colours: Blue shirt, yellow band, black shorts
League: Somerset 1

OLD BRISTOLIANS
Ground Address: Memorial Playing Field, Longwood Lane, Failand, Nr Bristol.
Tel: 01275 392137
Brief Directions: M5 junction 19 head for Bristol, turn right at main lights onto B3129 for Failand, turn left after country club into Longwood Lane.
Club Secretary: Samantha Barden, 168 Cranbrook Road, Redland, Bristol BS6 7DQ.
Tel: 0117 9423017 Email: sbarden@vwl.co.uk
Fixtures Secretary: Don Furze.
Tel: (H) 0117 986 5222
Club Colours: Maroon, gold and green hoops.
League: Gloucester 1

OLD CENTRALIANS RFC
Ground Address: Saintbridge Sports Centre, Painswick Road, Gloucester. GL4 9QX
Tel: 01452 303768
Brief Directions: Follow B4073 from Gloucester Ring Road. Approx 400mts on right just before traffic lights Cross Roads.
Club Secretary: Matt Vye, 36 Middlecroft, Abbey Mead, Gloucester. GL4 4RL
Tel No: 01452 611085 (H) 07787133631 (M)
Fixtures Secretary: Fred Crowther, 9 Richmond Gardens, Longlevens, Gloucester, GL2 0DS
Tel: 01452 415810
Club Colours: Navy blue&royal blue quarters with gold trimmimgs.
League: Western Counties North

OLD COLSTONIANS RFC
Ground Address: New Road, Filton, Bristol, changing during season to Colston School, Bell Hill, Stapleton, Bristol.
Brief Directions: Near Parkway Railway Station, next to Filton High School
New ground: M32 Eastville roundaboutuphill towards Stapleton.Enter school gates at top of hill
Club Secretary: John Hall, 94 Nightingale Gardens, Nailsea, Bristol. BS48 2BN
Tel: 01275 854195
e-mail:john.c.hall@ udv.com
Fixtures Secretary: Steve Back, 9 Welsford Avenue, Stapleton, Bristol BS16 1BW
Tel: 0117 9390456
Club Colours: Black, blue and gold hoops
League: Gloucester 2

OLD CRYPTIANS RFC
Ground Address: Memorial Ground, Tuffley Avenue, Gloucester. GL1 5NS Tel: 01452 532002
Brief Directions: Off Bristol Road to Tuffley Avenue, ground 1 mile on right before Stroud Road
Club Secretary: Alan Roberts, 1 Ardea Close, Quedgeley, Gloucester.Gl2 4LP
Tel No: 01452 728573 Email: alan-r@lineone.net
Fixtures Secretary: Derek Howell, 255C Stroud Road, Gloucester, GL1 5JZ
Tel: (H) 01452 414010 (W) 01452 425611
Club Colours: Gold, maroon and navy blue
League: Gloucester 1

OLD CULVERHAYSIANS RFC
Ground Address: The Glasshouse, Bradford Road, Combe Down, Bath. (Clubhouse: Old Fosse Road, Bath)
Brief Directions: Take Wells road out of Bath.Approx 1 mile, turn left at roundabout opposite Red Lion pub, across next junction, 200 yards on right
Club Secretary: Dick Stevens, 43 Inverness Road, East Twerton, Bath BA2 3RX
Tel: 01225 422433
Fixtures Secretary: Martin Lynch, 2 Lyme Road, Newbbidge, Bath. BA1 3LN
Tel: 01225 448511
Club Colours: Black
League: Somerset Premier

OLD ELIZABETHANS RFC
Ground Address: Severn Road, Hallen, Bristol. BS10 7RZ Tel: 0117 9591072
Brief Directions: M5 J17, turn towards Pelning at roundabout then 1st left, continue for 2-3 miles until junction with King William IV pub on right, turn right, club 200 yards on left
Club Secretary: David Perkins, 855 Filton Avenue,Filton, Bristol
Tel: 0117 9692545
Fixtures Secretary: P.Abel, 2 Dubin Crescent, Henleaze, Bristol BS8 4A6 Tel: 07973 194508
Club Colours: Blue, white and old gold hoops
League: Gloucester 2

SOUTH WEST

OLD PLYMOTHIAN & MANNAMEADIAN RFC
Ground Address: King George V Playing Fields, Elburton, Plymouth, Devon
Brief Directions: A38 take 1st Plymouth junction to Marsh Mills roundabout, follow signs for Kingsb'dge for 3-4 miles, at r'bout (Plympton signed to left) 1st left, ground 0.25 mile on right
Club Secretary: Mr Ernie Bolster, 22 Carlton Close, Lower Compton, Plymouth, Devon
Tel: (H) 01752 223908 (W) 01752 673626
Fixtures Secretary: Mr Simon Matthews
Tel: (H) 01752 730114 (W) 01392 382222
Club Colours: Claret and blue quarters
League: Cornwall/Devon

OLD PUBLIC OAKS RFC
Ground Address: King George V Playing Fields, ElburtoWebsite: oporfc.org.uk
Brief Directions: On leaving A38 at Marsh Mills roundabout, take A374 towards city, turn left onto A379 Billacombe Rd, left at 3rd roundabout into Haye Rd, ground on right
Club Secretary: Dave Barrett,,17 Warwick Orchard Close, Plymouth, Devon.PL5 3NZ
Tel No. 01752 782449
Email(via website) oporfc .org.uk
Fixtures Secretary: Keith Potter, 29 Green Park Road, Plymstock,Plymouth PL9 9HU
Tel No: 01752 219471
Club Colours: Green and gold hoops
League: Devon 1

OLD REDCLIFFIANS RFC
Ground Address: Stockwood Lane, Brislington, Bristol   Tel: 0117 9778501
Brief Directions: A34 from Bristol, turn right at McDonalds/Park & Ride, travel for 0.25 mile, ground on right hand side
Club Secretary: Richard Yandell, 11 Imperial Walk, Knowle, Bristol. BS14 9AD
Tel: (H) 0117 9777657 (W) 0117 9873636
Fixtures Secretary: Russell Yandell
Tel: (H) 01275 373444 (W) 01275 836077
Club Colours: Red and black hoops. Change Colours: Blue
League: Western Counties North

OLD RICHIANS RFC
Ground Address: Sandleaze, Longlevens, Gloucester. GL2 0PU
Tel: 01452 524649
Brief Directions: Turn into Nine Elms Road from Cheltenham Road and follow to Sir Thomas Rich's School
Club Secretary: Josie Collier, 5 Foxleigh Crescent, Gloucester. GL2 0XW
Tel Nos 01452 386808(H) 077142 60905 (M)
Email: westway@blueyonder.com
Fixtures Secretary: Steve Collier, 5 Foxleigh Crescent, Longlevens, Gloucester, GL2 0XW
Tel: (H) 01452 386808 (M) 07941 365473
Club Colours: Royal blue and gold
League: Western Counties North

OLD SULIANS RFC
Ground Address: Lansdown Road, Bath
Tel: 01225 310201
Brief Directions: Follow Lansdown Road from city centre, ground is on left 400 m past MOD site
Club Secretary: Terry Haines, 24 Rockcliffe Avenue, Bath. BA2 6QP
Tel: (H) 01225 465107
Fixtures Secretary: Tony Slee, 8 Heathfield Close, Weston, Bath BA1 4NW
Tel: 01225 317256
Club Colours: Blue with red band Change colours: Green
League: Somerset 1

OLD TECHNICIANS RFC
Ground Address: Weston Mill Oak Villa, Ferndale Road, Weston Mill, Plymouth, Devon
Tel: 01752 363352
Brief Directions: A38 turn off onto B3396 to Devonport, left at 1st traffic lights, club approx 100 yards on left
Club Secretary: Mr. J. Pengilley, 338 Beaumont Road, Mount Gould, Plymouth, Devon, PL4 9FN.
Fixtures Secretary: Terry Chinner, 37 Underlane, Plymouth, PL7 1QX
Tel: (H) 01752 341979
Club Colours: Black with white circlet
League: Devon 1

OLDFIELD OLD BOYS
Ground Address: Shaft Road, Combe Down, Bath.
Tel: 01225 834135
Brief Directions: Into Bath, follow signs for University, follow on towards Combe Down, turn down Shaft Road.
Club Secretary: Steve Godwin, 12 Lime Grove Gardens, Bath, Somerset BA2 4HE
Tel: (H) 01225 318012
Tel (W) 01258 451441
Fixtures Secretary: Gary Paul, 1 Down Way, Coombe Down, Bath BA2 4SE
Tel: 01225 836121
Club Colours: Maroon and gold.
League: Somerset Premier

OLNEY RFC
Ground Address: Recreation Ground, East Street, Olney, Bucks
Tel: 01234 712880
Brief Directions: From Newport Pagnell & Milton Keynes take A509, on entering Olney past church & right at market place, left into East St, ground 300 yards on right
Club Secretary: Laurence O'Connor, 6 Crabtree Close, Olney, Bucks. MK46 5DO
Tel: 01234 713390
e-mail: laurence@jo'connor3.fsnet.co.uk
Fixtures Secretary: Alec Tebby
Tel: (H) 01933 663385 (W) 0850 560660
Club Colours: Cerise and french grey
League: South West 2 East

SOUTH WEST

OXFORD HARLEQUINS RFC
Ground Address: * Horspath Rd Rec.,
Cowley, Oxford.   Tel: 01865 775765 or
Marston Ferry Road, Oxford. Tel: 01865 552813
Brief Directions: * Off the Eastern ring road sign-
posted to Horspath or
follow signs to Summertown, north Oxford, go
towards city centre and left at Marston Ferry Road.
Club Secretary: Keith Latham, 29 Churchill Way,
Long Hansborough,Witney, Oxon. OX29 8JJ.
Tel No 01993 881985
Email: keith.latham@tinyworld.co.uk
Fixtures Secretary: Keith Latham, 39 Churchill Way,
Long Harborough, Oxon.   Tel: 01993 881985
E-mail: keith.latham@tinyworld.co.uk
Colours: Amber, dark blue, white & maroon quarters
League: Southern Counties North

OXFORD RFC
Ground Address: Southern by pass,
North Hinksey Village, Oxford   Tel: 01865 243984
Brief Directions: Ground can only be approached
from A34 going south, turn left off A34, sign posted
Club Secretary: Mrs Kay Honner,
361 Woodstock Road, Oxford. OX2 8AA
Tel No: 01865 438655
Email: kevin.honner@ntlworld.com
Fixtures Secretary: Roger Mountford,
28 Crecy Walk, Woodstock, Oxford OX20 1US
Tel: (H) 01993 812389
Club Colours: Green, black and silver hoops
League: Southern Counties North

PAIGNTON RFC
Ground Address: Queens Park,
Queens Road, Paignton, Devon
Tel: 01803 557715
Brief Directions: Into Paignton town centre, over
railway track towards beach, next right turn into
Queens Road.
Club Secretary: G Nelson-Smith, 1 St. Andrews Rd.,
Paignton, Devon TQ4 6HA Tel: 01803 524212
Fixtures Secretary: Gary Castleton, 18 New Street,
Paignton, Devon TQ3 3HN.
Tel: 01803 525254 (H)   01803 556618 (W)
Club Colours: Red and white hoops
League: Cornwall/Devon

PAINSWICK RFC
Ground Address: Broadham Fields, Stroud Road,
Painswick, Nr Stroud, Glos
Tel: 01452 813735
Brief Directions: Situated adjoining the A46 on the
southern edge of the village on the Stroud side of
Painswick
Club Secretary: Mr. P. Haines, Savannah, Church
Road, Cainscross, Stroud, GL5 4JE.
Fixtures Secretary: I. Hogg, 146 Fieldcourt
Gardens, Quedgeley, Gloucester
Tel: (H & W) 01452 725457
Club Colours: Cherry and white hoops, navy shorts
League: Gloucester 1

PENNANIANS RUFC
Ground Address: Farnham Park, Beaconsfield
Road, Farnham Royal, Buckinghamshire. SL2 3BU
Tel: 01753 646252
Club Secretary: Mrs E. James, 47 Pearl Gardens,
Slough, Berks, SL1 2YX
Tel: (H) 01753 734910 (W) 01344 28821
Fixtures Secretary: Richard Kearney
Tel: (H) 01753 581963
Club Colours: Black shirt with 2 white hoops
League: Berks/Bucks & Oxon 1

PENRYN RFC
Ground Address: The Memorial Ground,
Kernick Road, Penryn
Tel: 01326 372239
Brief Directions: From Exeter A38 to Plym'th Head
twds L'keard, follow signs for Truro. From Truro A39
to Falm'th, continue to the Distributor Rd, at r'bout
turn to Ind. Est. (Asda), ground 2nd left
Club Secretary: Peter Webber,
Avallon, West End, Penryn, Cornwall TR10 8HE
Tel: 01326 376613 (H/F)   07775 615774 (M)
Fixtures Secretary: Mike Gregory,
20 Penvale Close, Penryn
Tel No: 01326 373820
Club Colours: Red and black hoops
League: Western Counties West

PERRANPORTH RC
Ground Address: Ponsmere Valley,
Perranporth, Cornwall, TR6 0DB
Tel No: 01872 572968
Brief Directions: From Newquay turn right at
Goonhavern roundabouts, continue for approx 2
miles, past Golf Club on right, down steep hill, 1st
turning left
Club Secretary: Glyn Barnicoat, Tresavean Farm
House, Lanner, Cornwall TR16 6AL
Tel No: 01209214680
Email; glyn.b@ic24.net
Fixtures Secretary: Steve Arthur, Oakridge farm,
Goonhaven, Truro, Cornwall TR49GG
Tel: 01872 540590
Club Colours: Green and yellow
League: Cornwall 1

PEWSEY VALE RFC
Ground Address: Pensey Vale Comprehensive
School, Wilcot Road, Pewsey, Wiltshire
Brief Directions: A345 to Pewsey, into Wilcot Road,
2nd left into Pewsey Vale School car park, change at
the adjacent Sports Centre, pitches are to the back
of the school
Club Secretary: Mr David Steven Aroskin, 47 Swan
Meadow, Pewsey, Wiltshire. SN9 5HP
Tel: (H & W) 01672 562218
Fixtures Secretary: Mr Kevin Robinson, 4 Stratton
Road, Pewsey. Wiltshire SN9
Tel: (H) 01672 562989
Club Colours: Red, white, royal blue and black
quarters
League: Dorset & Wilts 2 North

SOUTH WEST

PHOENIX RFC
Ground Address: The Sports Ground, Institute Road, Taplow, Bucks. SL6 0NS
Tel: 01628 664319
Brief Directions: M4 J7, take A4 towards Maidenhead, after Sainsburys superstore take next right (0.5 mile) then 1st left after the bridge is Institute Road
Club Secretary: Neil Bennett, 29 Belgrave Road, Slough, Berks SL1 3RG
Tel: 01753 570341 01753 615612 (W)
Fixtures Secretary: S.K.Turner, 20 Balmoral Close, Cippenham, Slough SL1 6JP
Tel: 01628 661660 (H) 01344 746052 (W)
Club Colours: Red & Black Quarters, black shorts, black socks with red trim
League: Berks/Bucks & Oxon 1

PLYMOUTH ARGAUM RFC
Ground Address: The Clubhouse,Bickleigh Down Road, Roborough, Plymouth. PL6 7AD
Tel: 01752 772156
Website: argaum.org.uk
Brief Directions: At Roborough village turn down Bickleigh Down Rd, pass Medlands and carry on down lane, clubhouse on the right
Club Secretary: Richard Belli, 7 Lincoln Avenue, Lipson, Plymouth Pl4 7NT
Tel No: 01752316926
Email: secretary@argaum.org.uk
Fixtures Secretary: Andy Rees, 38 Huxham Close, Plymouth PL6 5LH
Tel No: 01752 516675
Club Colours: Black, bottle green, white
League: Devon 3

PLYMOUTH CIVIL SERVICE RFC
Ground Address: Civil Service Sports Ground, Recreation Road, Beacon Down, Plymouth PL2 3HA.
Tel: 01752 702303
Brief Directions: Ground directly behind Plymouth Albion's ground at Beacon Park. Top of Ham Drive.
Club Secretary: Chris Travers,C.S.S.A. Recreation Rd., Beacon Down, Plymouth PL23NA
Tel: 01752 702303
Fixtures Secretary: Paul Routley, 1 Chaddlewood Close, Plympton. PL7 2HR.
Tel: 01752 338575
Club Colours: Red & white hooped shirts, black shorts., red socks
League: Devon 2

PLYMPTON VICTORIA RFC
Ground Address: King George V Playing Fields, Elburton, Plymstock, Plymouth, Devon.
Club Secretary: A.R.Dibble, 8 Wolrige Way, Plympton,Plymouth PL7 2RU
Tel: 01752 519512
Fixtures Secretary: C.G.Mayne, 12 Canhaye Close, Plympton,Plymouth PL7
01752 311147
Club Colours: Red, gold and black.
League: Devon 2

POOLE RFC
Ground Address: Hamworthy Rec., Turlin Moor , Blandford Road, Hamworthy, Poole, Dorset
Tel: 01202 687170
Brief Directions: From Poole quay, follow directions for Hamworthy, over the lifting bridge and continue for 2 miles.
Club Secretary: Mrs Tessa Ingle-Finch, 6 Mansfield Avenue, Parkstone, Poole, Dorset. BH14 0DQ
Tel: (H) 01202 241993
E-mail: tessa.inglefinch@btinternet.com
Fixtures Secretary: Mrs Karen Lambert, 12 Goldfinch Rd, Creekmoor, Poole, Dorset BH17 7TD
Tel : 01202 658714 (H)
E-mail: peter.lambert@pofm.com
Club Colours: Blue and amber
League: Dorset & Wilts 2 South

PRINCE ROCK (WOODLAND FORT) RFC
Ground Address: Bull Point, St. Budeaux, Devon
Brief Directions: Leave A38 at St. Budeaux/Ernesettle exit. Take 2nd exit off R/about to St. Budeaux. Follow Victoria Road to end. At oneway system go straight on. Take 1st R. follow sing to Bull Point. Talke 2nd L. (Bourne Rd). Turn L. at end. Changing Rms are about 200m on right.
Club Secretary: Mrs Chris Barrett, 3 Budshead Road, Plymouth PL5 2QY   Tel: 01752 367853
Email: chris@ dbarrett3.fsnet.co.uk
Fixtures Secretary: Les Fowden 1 Hayes Rd., Oreston, Plymouth, Devon. PL9 7QA.
Tel: 01752 405018
Club Colours: Green and Amber quarters
League: Devon 3

PUDDLETOWN
Ground Address: Greenfields, Puddletown, Dorchester, Dorset.   Tel: 01305 848808
Brief Directions: Leave Dorchester on A35 east, after 1/4 mile turn left on B3143, 3 miles on RHS, old army camp club.
Club Secretary: Dick Corbett, Winder, St Margarets lodge, Martinstown, Nr. Dorchester, Dorset. DT2 9JP
tel No: 01305 889410
Fixtures Secretary: PhilSmeeth, 21 London Close, Piddlehinton, Dorset. DT0 7TQ
Tel: (H) 01300 348310
Club Colours: Red shirts, black shorts, red socks
League: Dorset & Wilts 2 South

REDINGENSIANS RFC
Ground Address: Old Bath Road, Sonning, Nr., Reading   Tel: 0118 9695259
Brief Directions: On the A4 east of Reading, next to Sonning Golf Club
Club Secretary: J H Cook, 95 Century Court, Grove End Rd, London. NW8 9LD
Tel: (H) 0171 289 1887 (W) 020 7953 2280
Fixtures Secretary: G F Nattriss, 64 Broadwater Rd, Twyford, Berks. RG10 0EU
Tel: (H) 0118 9340685 (W) 01753 444281
Club Colours: Dark blue, light blue and white hoops
League: South West 2 East

SOUTH WEST

REDRUTH ALBANY RFC
Ground Address: Trewirgie Hill, Redruth, Cornwall.(Post to Clubhouse , 2 Station Hill , Redruth , Cornwall,. TR15 2PP)
Tel: 01209 216945
Brief Directions: Adjacent to Redruth Cricket Club behind Trewirgie School, Falmouth Rd, Redruth, 0.5 mile from train station. Or ring club house for directions.
Club Secretary: M.Stevens, 32 Bellevue, Redruth, Cornwall. TR15 1LF.
Tel No: 01209 215904
Fixtures Secretary: W. J. Rogers, Pencoys, Roskear, Camborne, TR14 8DN.
Tel: (H) 01209 714102
Club Colours: Royal blue shirts, black shorts
League: Cornwall 2

ROSELAND RFC
Ground Address: Philleigh, Truro, Cornwall. TR2 5ET
Brief Directions: 15 miles from Truro on the Roseland Peninsula, signposted via Tregony and Towary, St Mawes.
Club Secretary: I Lemoine, 10 The Square, Gerrans, Portscatho ,Truro Tr25 EB
Tel: 01872 580059
Fixtures Secretary: C J Trerise
Tel: (H) 01872 560248
Club Colours: Navy and scarlet
League: Cornwall 2

ROSS ON WYE RFC
Ground Address: Ross-on-Wye Sports Centre, Wilton Rd, Ross-on-Wye.
Tel: 01989 563256
Brief Directions: End of M50 stay on Bypass A40 to Monmouth. 3rd R/about left for town centre by Esso garage. Turn right by car park.
Club Secretary: Miss Sarah Bourne, 1 Prospect Terrace, Homs Road, Ross on Wye HR9 7DE
Tel: 01989 562081
Fixtures Secretary: David Cooke, 22 Brampton Avenue, Ross on Wye, Herefordshire, HR9 7EW.
Tel: 01989 564626
Club Colours: Royal blue and white hoops
League: Gloucester 3 North

SALCOMBE RFC
Ground Address: Two Meads, Camperdown Road, Salcombe, Devon
Tel: 01548 842639
Brief Directions: On entering Salcombe take 1st left, 1st right, 2nd left
Club Secretary: Graham Jacobs, Highleigh, Grenville Road, Salcombe, Devon, TQ8 8BJ.
Tel: (H) 01548 842521
Fixtures Secretary: P,Maycock, 7 Bens Close, Galmpton, Kingsbridge, Devon. TQ8 8BJ
Tel No: 01548 842521
Club Colours: Red shirts, white shorts, white shorts, red and white socks
League: Devon 3

SALISBURY RFC
Ground Address: Castle Road, Salisbury
Tel: 01722 325317
Website; salisburyrfc.org.uk
Brief Directions: On A345 Salisbury to Amesbury Road, just to the south of Old Sarum
Club Secretary: Dr G W Jack, 14 Windlesham Road, Salisbury, Wiltshire. SP1 3PY
Tel: (H) 01722 335542
Fixtures Secretary: Mr. M. Plimsoll , Longways, Southampton Road, Whaddon, Sailsbury, Wilts.
Tel: (H) 01722 710718
Club Colours: Green and white
League: South West 2 East

SALTASH RFC
Ground Address: Moorlands Lane, Saltash, Cornwall   Tel: 01752 847227
Brief Directions: From A38 westward over Tamar Bridge, through tunnel, left at 1st roundabout, right at lights, then 2nd right into Moorlands Lane, clubhouse at end of lane
Club Secretary: The Secretary c/o Salt Ash RFC, Moorelands Lane, Salt Ash Cornwall PL12 4JH
Tel No: 01752 847227
Fixtures Secretary: Bill Ryan, 7 Clear View, Saltash,Cornwall. (01752 843565)
Club Colours: Black, gold and red hoops
League: Cornwall/Devon

SHERBORNE RFC
Ground Address: The Terrace Playing Fields, Sherborne, Dorset.
Tel: 01935 812478
Brief Directions: The ground is on the A352, half a mile south of the town centre going towards Dorchester.
Ebsite: sherbornerugby.freeserve,co,uk
Club Secretary: Paul Jacobs, 1 The Furlong, Sherborne, Dorset DT9 4DQ
Tel: 01935 813673
e-mail: paul.jacobs@lineone.net
Fixtures Secretary: Kev Hunt, 5 Mill Lane, Yetminster, Sherborne, Dorset. DT9 6ND
Tel No: 01935 873641
Email: nicki.hunt@tesco.ney
Club Colours: Black with graduated white hoops.
League: Dorset & Wilts 2 South

SIDMOUTH RFC
Ground Address: Blackmore Ground, Heydons Lane, Sidmouth   Tel: 01395 516816
Brief Directions: (Via footpath), behind Sidmouth/ Victoria Cottage Hospital.(Follow signs to Hospital)
Club Secretary: P.R.H. Rossiter, "Gulls", Kings Lane, Sidmouth, Devon, EX10 8DU
Tel: (H) 01395 516414
Email: paul@greenbooks.co.uk
Fixtures Secretary: T. J. O'Brien, 2 Rivulet Cottages, Sidford, Sidmouth, Devon, EX10 0RT
Tel: (H) 01395 577403
Club Colours: Green, white shorts
League: Devon 1

SOUTH WEST

SLOUGH RFC

Ground Address: Tamblyn Fields,
Upton Court Park, Upton Court Road, Langley,
Slough, Berkshire. SL3 7LT
Tel: 01753 522107/692115
Brief Directions: M4 J5 towards Slough on A4
(London Rd), left at 2nd traffic lights into Upton Court
Rd, club entrance approx 500 metres on left, 200
metres down Dedicated Drive
Club Secretary: Mike Wild,
4 Stanton Way, Slough SL3 7LB
Fax: 01753 770870
e-mail: mikewild-srfc@yahoo.co.uk
Fixtures Secretary: Clive Blackman
Tel: (H) 01753 684403 (W) 01895 836579
Colours: Sage green jersey with single white hoop
League: South West 2 East

SMITHS (INDUSTRIES) RFC

Ground Address: The Newlands, Evesham Road,
Bishops Cleeve, Cheltenham, Glos
Tel: 01242 672752
Brief Directions: 2 miles due north of Cheltenham
on A435
Club Secretary: Gerald Owen, 79 Station Road,
Bishops Cleeve, Cheltenham, Glos., GL52 4HJ.
Tel: (H) 01242 676345
Fixtures Secretary: Carl. Slatter,
54 Golden Millar Road, Wymans Brook,
Cheltenham, Glos., GL50 4RD.
Tel: 01242 232269
Club Colours: Royal Blue and White
League: Gloucester 3 North

SOUTH MOLTON RFC

Ground Address: Pathfields, Station Road,
South Molton, Devon   Tel: 01769 572024
Brief Directions: Taking Pathfields exit on the North
Devon link road when reading signs for South
Molton, take first right then first left
Club Secretary: Mrs Annie White, 8 Duke Street,
South Molton, Devon. EX36 3AL
Tel: (H) 01769 573741 (W) 01769 573204
Fixtures Secretary: Denis Cronk
Tel: (H) 01769 550402
Club Colours: All Black
League: Western Counties West

SOUTHMEAD RFC

Ground Address: Greenway Sports Centre,
Greystoke Avenue, Southmead, Bristol
Tel: 0117 9593060
Brief Directions: A38 to Filton, Southmead Road
into Doncaster Road, Southmead
Club Secretary: Mr Mike Davies, 90 Twenty Acres,
Brentry, Bristol. BS10 6PR
Tel: (H) 0117 9497017
Fixtures Secretary: Mr Mike Haddow
Tel: (H) 01454 614019
Club Colours: Blue shirt with emerald green hoop
League: Gloucester 2

SPARTANS RFC

Ground Address: Archdeacon Meadow, Cattle
Market Complex, St Oswald Road, Gloucester
Tel: 01452 410552
Brief Directions: M5 J12 for Gloucester, into Glos,
take signs for docks, past docks, veer right just
before Esso g'ge, take l/h lane, under railbridge, 1st
left at Bell & Gavel, down as far as can go
Club Secretary: Stephen Martin, 130 Oxford Road,
Gloucester GL1 3ED
Tel: 01452 538400
Fixtures Secretary: Paul Smith
Tel: (H) 01452 305612
Club Colours: Red and black
League: Gloucester Premier

ST AGNES RFC

Ground Address: Enys Park,
Trevaunance Road, St Agnes
Tel: 01872 553673
Brief Directions: Turn left opposite church, turn right
after 800 yards, Enys Park is 200 yards on right
Club Secretary: Mrs A.J.Thompson, 4 Tregease
Road, St Agnes, Cornwall. TR5 0SL
Tel No: 01872 553719
Email: actionken@aggie4.freeserve.co.uk
Fixtures Secretary: T.B.A.
Club Colours: Black and red hoops
League: Cornwall 1

ST AUSTELL RFC

Ground Address: Tregorrick Park, Tregorrick Lane,
St Austell, Cornwall. PL26 7AG
Tel: 01726 76430
Brief Directions: Located on the road behind Asda
superstore and next to Mount Edgecumbe Hospice.
From St Austell By-Pass take turning to Penrice
Hopital.First right before Hospital.
Club Secretary: Amanda Kellow, 27 Polmarth
Close, St Austell, Cornwall Pl25 3TW
Tel No: 01726 76294
Email: amanda.Kellow@internet.com
Fixtures Secretary: Bernie Shepherd,128 Landreath
Place, St Blazey, Par, Cornwall. Pl24 2LA
Tel No: 01726 816995(H) 07979 321324 (M)
Club Colours: Red and white hoops
League: Western Counties West

ST BERNADETTE OLD BOYS RFC

Ground Address: Hengrove Park, Bamfield,
Whitchurch, Bristol
Tel: 01275 891500
Brief Directions: A37 out of town, turn right at
Airport Rd traffic lights, turn left 0.5 mile by The
Happy Cock pub, club is 0.25 mile on right
Club Secretary: Brian Murphy, 4 Rookery
Way,Whitchurch, Bristol BS14 0DT
Tel: 01275 837702
Fixtures Secretary: Tony Aldridge
Tel: (H) 0117 9770075
Club Colours: Green and blue hoops
League: Somerset Premier

SOUTH WEST

ST BRENDAN'S OLD BOYS RFC
Ground Address: Combination Ground, Northway, Gloucester Road North, Filton, Bristol. BS12 7QG
Tel: 0117 9692 793
Brief Directions: J. 15 M5 connect to A38 towards Bristol - opposite BAC runway on the left.
Club Secretary: Richard A Kolanko, 91 Church Road, Horfield, Bristol. BS7 8SD
Tel: (H) 0117 9241390
Email: richard.kolanko@btinternet.com
Fixtures Secretary: Larry Brien
Tel: 07788 744112M
Club Colours: Maroon and old gold hoops
League: Gloucester 2

ST COLUMBA TORPOINT RFC
Ground Address: Defiance Field, Torpoint, Cornwall
Brief Directions: Torpoint Ferry, keep on main Liskeard road, in 2 miles ground on left
Club Secretary: P C Summers, 112 Rochford Crescent, Ernesettle, Plymouth. PL5 2QD
Tel: (H) 01752 362785
Fixtures Secretary: as Secretary
Club Colours: Scarlet with thin royal blue hoops with change colours of blue.
League: Devon 3

ST DAY RFC
Ground Address: The Playing Field, St Day, Redruth, Cornwall
Brief Directions: Leave A30 at Scorrier exit, left past Cross Roads Hotel, at crossroads go straight across, ground just less than 1 mile on left
Club Secretary: P C Newcombe, 21 Martinvale Parc, Mount Ambrose, Redruth TR15 1SD
Tel: (H) 01209 212834
Fixtures Secretary: As Secretary
Club Colours: White with cherry hoop.
League: Cornwall 2

ST IVES RFC
Ground Address: Alexandra Road, St. Ives, Cornwall, TR26 1ER   Tel: 01736 795346
Brief Directions: M5/A30 to Hayle A3074 then B3311 coach route to St. Ives, Alexandra Road is second left after Fire Station
Club Secretary: N. J. Barber, 2 The Crescent, Alexandra Road, St. Ives, TR26 1BY.
Tel: (H&F) 01736 796861 (W) 01752 665951
Fixtures Secretary: Mike Gee, Lowenna, 70 Halsetown, St Ives, Cornwall, TR26 3LZ.
Tel: (H&F) 01736 797777
Club Colours: Blue & white hoops
League: Cornwall/Devon
League Contact: D Preece, King William IV, Church Rd., Madron, Penzance TR20 8SS Tel: 01736 363022 email: denis-preece@lineone.net

ST JUST RFC
Ground Address: St Just RFC, Tregeseal, St Just-in-Penwith, Cornwall. TR19 7PF
Tel: 01736 788593
Club Secretary: N. Jelbart, Flat 4, The Queens Hotel, The Promenade, Penzance, TR18 4HG.

Fixtures Secretary: P Whitman
Tel: (H) 01736 788150
Club Colours: All black
League: Western Counties West

ST MARY'S OLD BOYS RUFC?
Ground Address: Northwood Park, Trench Lane, Winterbourne, Bristol   Tel: 01454 250489
Brief Directions: M5 J16 towards Bristol, turn left at 1st roundabout then left again onto Woodlands Lane, Bradley Stoke ground 1 mile on left
Club Secretary: Mrs L Collins,18 Belmont,Road,St Andrews, Bristol BS6 5AS Tel No: 0117 9249879
Fixtures Secretary: Mr W Hopkins
Tel: (H) 0145 419571
Club Colours: Emerald green and black
League: Western Counties North

STITHIANS RFC
Ground Address: Playing Field, Stithians, Truro, Cornwall   Tel: 01209 860148
Brief Directions: Opposite the church in the centre of the village. The village lies in the centre of the triangle formed by Redruth, Falmouth and Helston.
Club Secretary: T J Knight, 27A Droskyn Way Close, Perranporth, Cornwall, TR6 0DS.
Tel: 01872 573926
Fixtures Secretary: C Burley, 54 Collins Park, Stithians, Truro, Cornwall. Tel: (H) 01209 860148
Club Colours: Maroon
League: Cornwall 2

STOTHERT & PITT RFC
Ground Address: Adamsfield, Corston, Bath. BA1 9AY   Tel: 01225 874802
Brief Directions: On A4 road, Bristol side of Bath
Club Secretary: R V Garraway, 2 Westfield Park South, Lower Weston, Bath. BA1 3HT
Tel: (H) 01225 316863
Fixtures Secretary: Carlos Orzabal, 74 Clarance Street, Walcot, Bath Somerset BA1 5NS
Tel: 01225 314845
Club Colours: Blue, black and amber
League: Somerset 1

STOW-ON-THE-WOLD & DISTRICT RFC
Ground Address: Oddington Road, Stow-on-the-Wold, Cheltenham, Glos (No post box)
Tel: 01451 830887
Brief Directions: From 'Unicorn' traffic lights in Stow take Oddington/Chipping Norton Road, ground is 1.5 miles on right
Club Secretary: N Drury, 2 Chestnut Corner, White Hart Lane, Stow-on-the-Wold, Cheltenham, Glos
Tel: (H) 01451 831686 (W) 01608 650428
Fixtures Secretary: A Jones Tel: (H) 01993 842757
Club Colours: Black and white hoops
League: South West 2 East

SUPERMARINE RFC
Ground Address: Supermarine Sports and Social Club, Highworth Road, South Marston, Nr Swindon, Wiltshire   Tel: 01793 824828

SOUTH WEST

Brief Directions: Take A419 M4 to Cirencester Rd, turn off at north or south 'Honda' junction, follow A361 signed Highworth, club entrance off round-about for industrial estate
Club Secretary: Geoff Bath, 2 Folly Drive, Highworth, Wiltshire Tel: (H) 01793 861619
e-mail: gee3ee58@ukonline.com
Fixtures Secretary: Ian Frizzle, 277 Windrush, Highworth ,Wilts. Tel: (H) 01793 763135
Club Colours: Sky Blue and dark blue quarters
League: Dorset & Wilts 2 North

SWINDON COLLEGE OLD BOYS RFC
Ground Address: Nationwide Sports Social Club, Pipers Way, Swindon, Wilts.
Tel No: 01793 513513
Brief Directions: M4 J15.Take A419 and turn left at first roundabout into Marlborough Road. After one mile turn left into Pipers Way and ground is on left after 800 yards
Club Secretary: Mark Lea, 152 Albion Street, Swindon SN1 5LP Tel No: 01793 522834
Fixtures Secretary: Adrian Briggs, 54 Bowood Road, Swindon, Wilts. SN1 4LP
Tel Nos: 01793 617950 (H) 0780 3278288(M)
Club Colours: Black shirt with two red stripes on left sleeve, black shorts.
League: Southern Counties South

SWINDON RFC
Ground Address: Greenbridge Road, Swindon, Wilts. SN3 3LA   Tel: 01793 521148
Brief Directions: M4 Jct 15. Follow A419 towards Cirencester for 3 miles. Take Oxford Road follow signs to town centre for 1 mile. At Greenbridge R/about turn left, mini R/about turn right into Greenbridge Road.
Club Secretary: Cliff Spainswick, c/o S.R.F.C., Greenbridge Road, Swindon, Wilts., S3 3LA. Tel: 0976 700770 - Email: chalk1@atlasco.uk
Fixtures Secretary: Dave McAteer, 47 Colebrook Road, Coleview, Swindon, S3 4EB.
Tel 01793 828990
Club Colours: Blue and amber hoops, white shorts
Change: Green & Black
League: Southern Counties North

TADLEY RUGBY CLUB RFC
Ground Address: Red Lane, Aldermaston, Reading, Berks.   Tel: 0118 970 0072
Brief Directions: M4 J.12 - Follow A4 towards Newbury/Thatcham A340 towards Basingstoke/Tadley at Aldermaston Village turn left - Ground 1 mile on left.
Club Secretary: R W Mears, 22 Winchfield Gardens, Tadley, Hants. RG26 3TX
Tel: (H) 0118 9811648
Fixtures Secretary: A,Boyer, 11 Christopher Court, Boundary Road, Newbury RG14 7PQ
Tel No: 01635 40574
Club Colours: Black with amber alt. hoop
League: South West 2 East

TAMAR SARACENS RFC
Ground Address: Parkway Sports Club, Ernesettle Lane, Ernesettle, Plymouth, Devon
Tel: 01752 363080
Brief Directions: A38 to St Budeaux, turn off then towards Ernesettle
Club Secretary: Ken Giannasi, 74 Kathleavan Street, St. Budeaux, Plymouth, Devon, PL5 1PY.
Tel: 01752 367466
Fixtures Secretary: John Bentley,29 Dunster Close,Chaddlewood, Plympton, Plymouth Pl7 3FN
Tel: (H) 01752 207356
Club Colours: Green & black. Change: Red &white
League: Devon 1

TAUNTON RFC
Ground Address: Priory Park, Priory Bridge Road, Taunton, Somerset   Tel: 01823 275670
MOVING TO NEW GROUND IN NOVEMBER
Brief Directions: From M5 exit 25 follow signs to town centre,then county cricket ground and ground on right after roundabout by Great Mills store.
PLEASE PHONE SECRETARY for new directions
Club Secretary: George Wilson, 10 Obridge Road, Taunton. TA2 7PX   Tel: (H) 01823 282495
Email: wilsontrfc@supanet.com
Fixtures Secretary: Rodney Reed
Tel: (H) 01823 276354
Club Colours: Crimson, black and white hoops
League: South West 2 West

TAVISTOCK RFC
Ground Address: Sandy Park, Trelawney Road, Tavistock, Devon, PL19 8ET
Tel: 01822 618275
Brief Directions: From town centre take Brentor Road, under railway viaduct, 2nd right
Club Secretary: Peter Garland, Rowes, Horndon, Pter Tavy,Tavistock, Devon. Pl19 9NQ
Tel No: 01822 810619
Fixtures Secretary: Martin Griffiths, 23 St.Maryhaye, Tavistock, Devon PL19 8LR
Tel: (H) 01822 613030
Club Colours: Black and red hoops
League: Devon 1

TEIGNMOUTH RFC
Ground Address: Bitton Sports Ground, Bitton Park Road, Teignmouth
Tel: 01626 774714
Brief Directions: Adjacent to Shaldon Bridge, off main Teignmouth to Newton Abbot road
Club Secretary: Robert Lovendge, 59 Second Avenue, Teignmouth, Devon. TQ14 9DN
Tel: (H) 01626 775891
Fixtures Secretary: Brian Abraham, 10 Gloucester Road, Teignmouth, Devon.
Tel No: 01626 776346
Club Colours: Red, white and black hoops
League: Devon 1

SOUTH WEST

TETBURY RFC
Ground Address: Recreation Ground, Hampton Street, Tetbury, Glos Tel: 01666 505052
Brief Directions: On the B4014 (Hampton St.) out of Tetbury towards Avening, the ground is situated on the right behind the betting shop.
Club Secretary: Mrs Tracey Wright,67 Charlton Road, Tetbury, GLos. GL8 8DX
Tel No: 01666 503098
Email: jeffwrightbuild@yahoo.co.uk
Fixtures Secretary: Ian Hancock, Summer Cottage,39 Charlton Road, Tetbury, Glos. GL8 8DX
Tel No: 01666 504505
Club Colours: Black and gold
League: Gloucester 3 South

TEWKESBURY RFC
Ground Address: The Moats, Lankett Lane, Tewkesbury, Glos., GL20 5PG.
Tel: 01684 294364
Brief Directions: From Cross in centre of town, take A38 to Gloucester. Take 1st left (after approx 200yds) into Gander Lane, past cricket club & car park enter lane alongside caravan clubsite. Follow lane to end.
Club Secretary: John Williams, Kimberley, Lincoln Green Lane, Tewkesbury, GL20 7DW.
Tel: 01684 298829.
Email: tewkesbury-rfc@yahoo.co.uk
Fixtures Secretary: Heather Lampitt, Tewkesbury RFC at the ground address
Tel: 07775 871454
Club Colours: Black and amber
League: Gloucestershire 1

THATCHAM RFC
Ground Address: Henwick Worth Playing Fields,Henwick Lane, Thatcham, Berkshire.
Brief Directions: Henwick Playing Fields are on the north side of the A4 which runs from Newbury through Thatcham to Reading. The entrance in Henwick Lane is on the eastern side of Thatcham.
Club Secretary: Mr Les Hayes, 7 Turners Drives Thatcham, Berks., RG19 4QB.
Fixtures Secretary: Mrs Kathi Surtees
Tel: (H) 01635 868285 (W) 0171 2101387
Club Colours: Red and blue quarters
League: Berks/Bucks & Oxon 1

THE TOR RFC
Ground Address: Lowerside Park, Lowerside Lane, Glastonbury, Somerset Tel: 01458 832236
Brief Directions: Adjacent to and signposted off A39 Glastonbury bypass
Club Secretary: Mrs Caro; Mountain, 16 Badgers Green Road, street, Somerset. BA16 0PT
Tel No: 01458 446582
Email: hmountain@ tinyworld.co.uk
Fixtures Secretary: Mr Keith Elver,18 Hurmans Close, Ashcott, Bridgwater,somerset TA7 9PT
Tel: (H) 01458 211044 (W) 01749 673199
Club Colours: Maroon shirts with blue shorts
League: Somerset Premier

THORNBURY RFC
Ground Address: Rockhampton Road, Newton,Thornbury, Bristol. BS12 1LG
Tel: 01454 412096
Brief Directions: From Thornbury: at Royal George pub take Gloucester rd out of town, after Anchor pub take 2nd left (ignore turn directly next to pub), club is down this lane approx 0.5 mile on the right
Club Secretary: Howard Roy Bowker, 2 Broncksea Road, Filton Park, Bristol. BS7 0SE
Tel: (H) 0117 969 8744
Fixtures Secretary: Maurice Carling
Tel: (H) 01454 885353
Club Colours: Black and amber hoops
League: Western Counties North

TIVERTON RFC
Ground Address: The Coronation Field, Bolham Road, Tiverton, Devon. EX16 6SG
Tel: 01884 252271
Brief Directions: M5 J27 north towards Tiverton, 7 miles roundabout at end of d/carriageway left to Tiverton, ground 250mtrs on right just before foot-bridge over road
Club Secretary: Margarte Sampson, 5 Shillands, Tiverton, devon. Ex16 5AA
Tel Nos: 01884 255287 (H) 07811 1066059 (M)
Fixtures Secretary: Mark Green, 5 Marguerite Road, Tiverton, Devon, EX16 5BA
Tel: (H) 01884 256573
Club Colours: Light and dark blue
League: Western Counties West

TOPSHAM RFC
Ground Address: The Bonfire Field, Exeter Road, Topsham. EX3 0LY   Tel: 01392 873651
Directions: Approaching Topsham from Exeter it is the last field on the left before the built up area.
Club Secretary: Matt Shane, 33 Rayburn Close, Taunton, Somerset, TA1 2RH. Tel: 01823 289420
Fixtures Secretary: Sam Pascoe, Flat 3, 7 Richmond Road, Exeter.   Tel: 01392 491115
Club Colours: Light & dark blue hoops
League: Devon 1
Contact: As Fixture Secretary

TORQUAY ATHLETIC RFC
Ground Address: Torquay Recreation Ground, Sea Front, Torquay, Devon Tel: 01803 293842
Brief Directions: Head for sea front, ground on main sea front road adjacent to railway station
Club Secretary: Stuart Bradshaw, 6 All Hallows Road, Preston, Paignton, Devon, TQ3 1EB
Tel: (H) 01803 390762 (W) 01392 204134
Fax 01392 204159
Fixtures Secretary: Dave Thompson, 44 Bidwell Brook Drive, Paignton, Devon. TQ4 7NF Tel: (H) 01803 845115
email:daveliz44@dthompson49.freeserve.co.uk
Club Colours: Black and white. Change: Red
Contact: Secretary, as above
League: South West 2 West

SOUTH WEST

TORRINGTON RUFC
Ground Address: Donnacroft, Torrington.
Tel: 01805 622055
Directions: Situated on B3227 South Molton Road.
Club Secretary: Daren Nudds, 4 South Street,
Torrington, Devon.   Tel: 01805 624899
Fixtures Secretary: David Hickman
Tel: (H) 01769 560131
Club Colours: Green black and white hoops
League: Cornwall/Devon

TOTNES RFC
Ground Address: The Clubhouse, Borough Park,
Totnes, Devon. TQ9 5XW   Tel: 01803 867796
Brief Directions: Pitch on public park adjacent to
British Rail station
Club Secretary: Mrs Christine Rive, 3 St. Johns
Terrace, Totnes, Devon, TQ9 5JH.
Tel: 01803 865261
Fixtures Secretary: Aubrey Bourne, 18 Hunters
Moon, Dartingto, Totnes, Devon, TQ9 6JC
Tel: (H) 01803 864462 - Email:acb@shines.swis.net
Club Colours: Royal blue, white shorts
League: Devon 2

TREDWORTH RUFC
Ground Address: The Llannett Playing Fields, King
Edwards Avenue, Lindon, Gloucester
Tel: 01452 525465
Brief Directions: Along A38 towards Glos turn right
into Tuffley Ave, then 5th into the OVAL which then
leads to ground on right hand side
Club Secretary: Daniel Smith, 138 Melbourne St.
East,Tredworth, Gloucester GL1 4NP
Tel: 01452 536723
Fixtures Secretary: As Secretary
Club Colours: Green shirts with black shorts
League: Gloucester 3 North

TROWBRIDGE RFC
Ground Address: Green Lane, Trowbridge,
Wiltshire. BA14 7DH   Tel: 01225 761389
Directions: Head for West Ashton from County Way
Club Secretary: Bryn Parfitt, 60 Paxcroft Way,
Trowbridge, Wiltshire. BA14 7DJ
Tel: (H) 01225 351044
Fixtures Secretary: Mickey Milton, 13 Blair Road,
Trowbridge, Wilts.   Tel: 01225 767204
Club Colours: Dark blue, light blue and gold hoops
League: Dorset & Wilts 1

TRURO RFC
Ground Address: St Clements Hill, Truro, Cornwall,
TR1 1NY.
Tel: 01872 274750
Brief Directions: A30, leave signpost for Trispen, to
Truro at large roundabout, enter St Clements Hill
next to Police station, ground on right at top of hill
Club Secretary: John Collier, 1 Bishop Temple
Road, Truro. TR1 1YP   Tel No: 01872 225632
Fixtures Secretary: Mike Woolcock, 9 Green Close,
Truro TR1 2DD. Tel: 01872 262020

Club Colours: Royal blue and amber
League Contact: Steve Enoch, 16 Woodlands Ct.,
Tremorvah Wood Lane, Truro TR1 1SA.
Tel: 01872 242289
League: South West 2 West

UNIVERSITY OF PLYMOUTH
Ground Address: Polytechnic Sports Ground,
Ernesettle Lane, Plymouth
Tel: 01752 365071
Club Secretary: Richard Mogford, Students Union,
University of Plymouth, Drakes Circus, Plymouth PL4
8AA
Tel: 01752 663337
Club Colours: Black and amber hoops, black shorts
League: Devon 3

VEOR RFC
Ground Address: Wheal Gerry, Cliff View Road,
Canborne, Cornwall
Brief Directions: Turn off A30 signed Canborne &
Pool, right at traffic lights down hill, right again before
pedestrian crossing, 0.5 mile right again after TA
centre, ground 100 yds on right
Club Secretary: Coloin Pasce, 40 Barripper Road,
Camborne, Cornwall TR14 7QW
Tel: (H) 01209 716172
Fixtures Secretary: Colin Pascoe
Tel: (H) 01209 716172
Club Colours: Black and Gold
League: Cornwall 2

WADEBRIDGE CAMELS RFC
Ground Address: Molesworth Field, Egloshayle,
Wadebridge
Tel: 01208 815311
Brief Directions: Opposite Egloshayle Church
Club Secretary: M Richards, Pendraze, St. Minner,
Wadebridge, Cornwall, PL27 6RD. Terl No 012088
69092 (H) 01726860308 (W)
Email: mark-richards@wmail.msn.com
Fixtures Secretary: Chris Taylor
Tel: (H) 01208 813919
Club Colours: Chocolate and gold
League: Cornwall/Devon

WALCOT RFC
Ground Address: Albert Field, Lansdown, Bath
Tel: 01225 330199
Brief Directions: Follow signs from city centre to
Lansdown, proceed along top to racecourse/golf
club, halfway on right is ground opposite Bath car
park & ride sign
Club Secretary: D.Williams, 7 Pioneer Avenue,
Combe Down, Bath. BA2 5QX
Tel No: 01225 833352
Fixtures Secretary: T.Mallon, 99 Ringsiwell
Gardens, Bath.
Tel No: 01225 331902
Club Colours: Black and white hoops
League: Western Counties North

SOUTH WEST

WALLINGFORD RFC
Ground Address: Wallingford Sports & Social Club,Hithercroft Road, Wallingford, Oxon
Tel: 01491 835044
Brief Directions: Situated on Wallingford bypass on west side of town, bypass signposted on all approaches to Wallingford
Club Secretary: Mrs Norma Henderson,12 Lapwing Lane,Cholsey, OX10 9DR
Tel: 01491 652075
Fixtures Secretary: Steve Loxley, 4 Egerton Road, Wallngford, Oxon. OX10 0HL
Tel No: 01491 833576
Club Colours: Amber and black
League: Berks/Bucks & Oxon 1

WARMINSTER RFC
Ground Address: Folly Lane Sports Ground, Folly Lane, Warminster, Wilts.   Tel: 01985 301788
Brief Directions: From A350 r'about on by-pass head into Warminster. Past 'Bell & Crown' on left, next left into Fore St.. At next r;'about 2nd left into Thornhill Rd, then left into Folly Lane. Ground 200 yds on right
Club Secretary: Mrs E Jenkins, 15 Were Close, Warminster, Wilts. BA12 8TB. Tel No: 01985 212261
Fixtures Secretary: Steve Evans
Tel: (H) 01985 212750
Club Colours: Royal blue and gold hoops.
League: Dorset & Wilts 2 South
Contact: G Marden, 2 Woodland Rd., Warminster, Wilts. BA12 8HJ   Tel: 01985 301788

WELLINGTON RFC
Ground Address: The Athletic Ground, Corams Lane, Wellington, Somerset. TA21 8LL
Tel: 01823 663758
Brief Directions: Leave M5 J25 or from a A38 from Taunton, right at central traffic lights into North St, left at Sportsman Inn, enter via sports centre car park
Club Secretary: N. Robins, 37 Bircham Road, Taunton, Somerset. TA2 8EX.
Fixtures Secretary: G R Vickery, 7 Seymour Street, Wellington, Somerset TA21 8JT
Tel: (H) 01823 664695 (W) 01823 335166
Club Colours: Red and black hoops.
League: Cornwall/Devon

WELLS RFC
Ground Address: Charter Way, off Portway, Wells, Somerset, BA5 2ES   Tel: 01749 672823
Brief Directions: Off the Portway A371 or follow signs to the Leisure Centre (which is next door)
Club Secretary: Alan Goymer, Green Gables, Glencot Rd., Wookey Hole, Wells, Som. BA5 1BQ
Tel No: 01749 675252
Fixtures Secretary: Mike Clements, Sunrise, Easton, Wells, Somerset, BA5 1EE
Tel: 01749 870561 (H) 01275 873047 (W)
Club Colours: Black and white hoops
League: Somerset Premier

WESSEX RFC
Ground Address: Flowerpot Field, Exwick, Exeter
Brief Directions: From J31 M5 to A30 follow signs to Exeter then Exwick, along Buddle Lane turn right into Oakhampton Road, turn left onto Western Road
Club Secretary: Phil Langford, 7 Kinnerton Way, Exwick, Exeter EX4 2BL
Tel: (H) 01392 211959 (W) 01395 873781 Ext 4304
Fixtures Secretary: Stewart Gringer, 8 Linda Close, Exeter EX1 3EU
Tel Nos: 01392 660544 (H) 01392 252566 (W)
Club Colours: Bottle green shirts with amber collars and white shorts
League: Cornwall/Devon

WESTBURY RFC
Ground Address: Leighton Sports Ground, Wellhead Lane, Westbury, Wilts. Tel: 01373 826438
Brief Directions: Warminster Road (A350), opposite Cedar Hotel turn into Wellhead Lane, ground 300 metres on left
Club Secretary: R. D. Jones, 36 Westbury Road, Yarnbrook, Nr. Trowbridge, Wiltshire, BA14 6AG.
Tel: 01225 766647 or 764824
Email: Jrugbymaster@aol.com
Fixtures Secretary: As club secretary above
Club Colours: Irregular Green and black hoops
League: Dorset & Wilts 1

WESTBURY-ON-SEVERN RFC
Ground Address: Parish Grounds, Westbury-on-Severn, Glos.   Tel: 01452 760359
Website: xtravision.com@wosrfc
Brief Directions: A48 from Gloucester to Chepstow. Ground on left hand side before entering Westbury-on-Severn.
Club Secretary: Phil Bleathman, The Hollies, Elton, Westbury-on-Severn, Glos. GL14 1JJ
Tel (H & W) 01452 760751 also Fax.
Email: hollies@pbleathman.freeserve.co.uk
Fixtures Secretary: Alan Hyett, 1 Moyshill Villas, Strand Lane, Westbury-on-Severn, Glos.GL14 1PG.   Tel: 01452 760495
Club Colours: Royal blue and white hoops
League: Gloucester 1

WEYMOUTH RFC
Ground Address: Monmouth Avenue, Weymouth, Dorset   Tel: 01305 778889
Brief Directions: 3rd turn left after passing Safeways supermarket
Club Secretary: Mrs G Llewellyn, 2 Goulds Hill Close, Upwey, Weymouth   Tel: (H) 01305 812415
Fixtures Secretary: Dick Foyle Tel: (H) 01305 266144
Colours: Light blue, dark blue circle, black shorts
League: Dorset & Wilts 2 South

WHEATLEY RUFC
Ground Address: Playing Fields, Holton, Wheatley, Oxford   Tel: 01865 873476
Brief Directions: Leave A40 at Wheatley signs in Oxford towards London, turn left at T junction and ground is on left about 500 yards from the turn

Club Secretary: Bryan Davies, 31 Anxey Way, Haddenham, Bucks, HP17 8DJ.
Tel: (H) 01844 292846
Fixtures Secretary: Stuart West, 39 Kelham Hall Drive, Wheatley, Oxford, OX33 1SL
Tel: (H) 01865 872850
Colours: Purple, white & black bands, black shorts
League: Berks/Bucks & Oxon 1

WHITEHALL RFC
Ground Address: Foundry Lane, Speedwell, Bristol
Tel: 0117 9659636
Brief Directions: Off B4465 Whitehall Road at Crofts End, turn right into Deep Pit Rd, take 2nd left. From M32 J2 follow sign post up Muller Rd, left at roundabout
Club Secretary: Richard Haycock, 61 Headford Avenue, St George, Bristol BS5 8PE
Tel: 0117 9672276
Fixtures Secretary: Alex Ferguson, 8 Stoneleigh Road, Knowle, Bristol BS24 2RJ
Tel: 0117 9772898
Club Colours: Myrtle green and gold
League: Western Counties North

WIDDEN OLD BOYS RFC
Ground Address: Memorial Ground, Tuffley Avenue, Gloucester   Tel: 01452 304080
Brief Directions: M5 north J12, right at 1st roundabout at end of bypass, left at next roundabout into Stroud Rd, approx 150m left into Tuffley Avenue
Club Secretary: Stuart McWalter, 52 The Causeway, Quedgeley, Gloucester GL2 4LD
Tel: 01452 724739
Email: stuart.mcwalter@tesco.net
Fixtures Secretary: Andy Alder, 42 Darrell Close, Quedgeley, Gloucester GL24YR
Tel: (H) 01452540071
Colours: Green shirts with red band & white hoops
League: Gloucester 2

WIMBORNE RFC
Ground Address: Leigh Park, Wimborne, Dorset
Tel: 01202 882602
Brief Directions: A31, take B3073, approx 2 miles East of Wimborne follow road towards town centre. After 1.5 miles turn left into Gordan Rd, Leigh Park 250 yards ahead.
Club Secretary: Michael Moysey, 42 Lacy Drive, Wimborne, Dorset. BH21 1DG
Tel: (H) 01202 841478
Email: Nichael@ m moysey.freesave.co.uk
Fixtures Secretary: Debbie Noyce, 24 Walters Drive, PImperne, Blandford, Dorset DT71 8UX.
Tel: 01258 451608
Colours: All black. Change: Green/white quarters
League: Southern Counties South

WINCANTON RUFC
Ground Address: Wincanton Sports Ground, Balsam Fields, Wincanton, Somerset
Brief Directions: Into Wincanton from A303, after Fire station turn right down Moor Lane 0.5 mile

Club Secretary: Mr. J. Bastable, Church Farm, Charlton Musgrove, Wincanton, Somerset. BA9 8ES.
Fixtures Secretary: Mr Glen Ware, c/o Dolphin Hotel, High Street, Wincanton, Somerset. BA9 9JF.
Colours: Black and amber Change C olours: Yellow
League: Dorset & Wilts 2 South

WINDSOR RFC
Ground Address: Home Park, Datchet Road, Windsor, Berkshire   Tel: 01753 860807
Brief Directions: Off M4, signed Windsor, follow d/carriageway to 1st slip road off left, left at roundabout, left at next roundabout, keep left past railway station, next left into Home Park
Club Secretary: Ms Carole Quelch, 67 Fairfax Road, Farnborough, Hants., GU1 8JR.
Fixtures Secretary: Peter Davison
Tel: (H) 01753 840559
Colours: Black, green, gold and maroon quarters
League: South West 2 East

WINSCOMBE RFC
Ground Address: Longfield Recreation Ground, Winscombe, North Somerset   Tel: 01934 842720
Brief Directions: Turn off A38 into Winscombe, turn left at right hand bend to ground.
Club Secretary: Alun George, 3 Landseer Close, Worle, Weston-Super-Mare. BS22 9NL
Tel: (H) 01934 518270
Fixtures Secretary: Ted Sands, 7 Belmont Road, Winscombe, North Somerset.
Tel: 01934 843463 (H) 0870 9044424 (M)
Club Colours: Black with white hoops
League: Somerset 2

WINSLOW RUFC
Ground Address: The Winslow Centre, Park Road, Winslow, Buckingham. MK18
Brief Directions: A413 through Winslow, 0.5 mile towards Buckingham from town centre, turn left into Avenue Road, 1st right into Park Road
Club Secretary: Simon Drakeford, 31 Green Way, Newton Longville, Bucks. MK17 OAP
Tel: (H) 01908 644239
Fixtures Secretary: Colin Brown, Gardeners Cottage, 27 Horn Street, Winslow. MK18 3AP
Tel: (H) 01296 714312
Club Colours: Blue and gold hoops
League: Berks, Bucks & Oxon 2

WITHYCOMBE RUGBY & RECREATION CLUB RFC
Ground Address: Raleigh Park, 36 Hulham Road, Exmouth, Devon. EX8 3HS   Tel: 01395 266762
Brief Directions: M5 south J30, take A376 to Exmouth, at Box Junction before traffic lights turn left into Hulham Rd, ground 200 yards on right
Club Secretary: David M Josey, 2 Larch Close, Marley Gardens, Exmouth, Devon. EX8 5NQ
Tel: (H) 01395 275038
Fixtures Secretary: D.J.Field, 4 Mossop Close, Ottery St Mary , Devon.EX11 1AP
Tel No: 01404 811102
Club Colours: Emerald green and black hoops
League: Western Counties West

SOUTH WEST

WITNEY RFC

Ground Address: The Clubhouse, Hailey Road, Witney, Oxon. OX8 5UH
Tel: 01993 771043 Fax: 01993 779985
Brief Directions: Leave Witney centre by Bridge St, towards Oxford & Bicester, left at mini roundabout, keep along main road passing garage on right, ground on left after about 1 mile
Club Secretary: Chris Tucker, 19 Stanton Harcourt Road, Witney, Oxon. OX8 6L
Tel: 01993 700323 (W) 0589 444655
E-mail: wtfc.co@virgin.net
Fixtures Secretary: Pete Holliday
Tel: (H) 01993 705327 (W) 01527 498259
Club Colours: Black hoops on sky blue
League: Southern Counties North

WIVELISCOMBE RFCC

Ground Address: Recreation Ground, West Road, Wiveliscombe, Nr Taunton, Somerset. TA4 2TB
Tel: 01984 623897
Brief Directions: Take B3227 from Taunton to Barnstaple, ground is on left towards end of town
Club Secretary: Guy Mabley, 3 Manor Park, Norton Fitzwarren, Taunton, Somerset
Tel: 01823 270002
Fixtures Secretary: Arthur.Moore, 23 Newlands Road, Ruishton, Taunton, Somerset. TA3 5JZ
Tel No: 01823 442642
Club Colours: Navy blue with red sash
League: Somerset Premier

WOOTTON BASSETT RFC

Ground Address: Rylands Field, Stoneover Lane, Wootton Bassett, Wiltshire   Tel: 01793 851425
Website: bassettrfc.co.uk
Brief Directions: M4 J16, follow signs for Wootton Bassett over R/about, up hill, Stoneover Lane on left, club 300 metres on left.

Club Secretary: Chris Elias, Ty Canol, Wanshot close, Wroughton, Wilts., SN4 0RF. Tel: 01793 845396 - Email: chris.elias@cbs.natwest.com
Fixtures Secretary: Jim Brierley, 25 Broad Town Road, Wooton Bassett, Wilts. SN4 7RB
Tel: (H) 01793 731780
Club Colours: Black shirts & shorts
League: Southern Counties South

WOTTON-UNDER-EDGE RFC

Ground Address: K L B School Ground, Kingswood Road, Wotton-under-Edge
Tel: 01453 842138 (Falcon Hotel)
Brief Directions: Take b4058 towards M5 out of Wotton, Ground on Left at foot of hill.
Club Secretary: Adam Henshaw, 21 Wortley Terrace, Wotton-under-Edge Glos. GL12 7JY
Tel: (H) 01453 844530
Fixtures Secretary: Chris Hull, 56 Bradley Road, Wotton-under-Edge Glos. GL12 7DT
Tel: (H) 01453 844958
Club Colours: Black and amber hoops
League: Gloucestershire 3 South

YATTON RFC

Ground Address: The Park, North End, Yatton, Avon   Tel: 01934 832085
Brief Directions: From centre of village, travel towards Clevedon, club is on right 300 yards after Railway bridge
Club Secretary: Paul Edwards, Greenacre, Sandmead Road, Sandford, N. Somerset. BS49 5DX
Tel No: 01934 822425
Fixtures Secretary: Nick Williams, Karibu, Station Road, Congresbury, N . Somerset
Tel: (H) 01934 877250
Club Colours: Amber and black
League: Somerset Premier

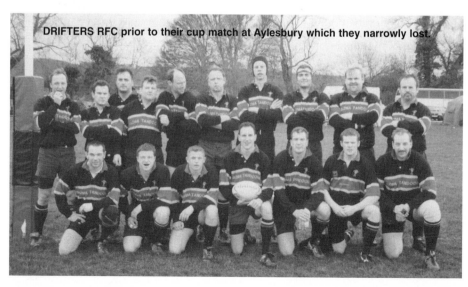

DRIFTERS RFC prior to their cup match at Aylesbury which they narrowly lost.

AFFILIATED CLUBS

AEI (RUGBY) — 1917
Hillmorton Road
Rugby
Warwickshire
CV22 4AR
01788 576921

Mr R I Stephens
Hon. Secretary
AEI (Rugby)
10 Northampton Lane
Dunchurch, Rugby
Warwickshire
CV22 6QA

Mr A G Chronnell
Hon. Fixture Secretary
AEI (Rugby)
24 Kirkby Close
Brownsover, Rugby
Warwickshire
CV21 1TT

AESCULAPIANS — 1986
The Rugby Club
49 Hallam Street
London
W1
020 7580 7917

Mr S D W Payne FRCS LLM
Hon. Secretary
Aesculapians
28 Emanuel Avenue
Acton
London
W3 6JJ

Mr J E T Payne
Hon. Fixture Secretary
Aesculapians
28 Emanuel Avenue
Acton
London
W3 6JJ

ALDBOURNE DABCHICKS — 1992
Ewins Hill
Aldbourne
Wiltshire

Mr A Woodrow
Hon. Secretary
Aldbourne Dabchicks
61 Whitley Road
Aldbourne
Marlborough,
Wilts. SN8 2BU

Mr C Flett
Hon. Fixture Secretary
Aldbourne Dabchicks
71 Cottage Road
Aldbourne
Marlborough
SN8 2EB

ANDERSEN — 1990

Mr D J Evans
Hon. Secretary
Andersen
c/o Arthur Andersen
1 Surrey Street
London
WC2R 2PS
020 7438 3000

Mr Richard Llewellyn
Hon. Fixture Secretary
Andersen
c/o Arthur Andersen
1 Surrey Street
London
WC2R 2PS

ANGLIA (CAMBRIDGE)
1990
c/o The Gymnasium
Anglia Polytechnic University
East Road, Cambridge
CB1 1PT

Hon. Secretary
Doug Cosnett
Anglia (Cambridge)
c/o The Gymnasium
Anglia Polytechnic University
East Road, Cambridge
CB1 1PT

Mr C Upham
Hon. Fixture Secretary
Anglia (Cambridge)
APU
Cambridge

ANSTEY — 1980
Bennion Road
Beaumont Leys
Leicester
0116 235 5585

Mr Alan Chapman
Hon. Secretary
Anstey
1 Groby Road
Anstey
Leics
LE7 7FN

Mr Ian Pollock
Hon. Fixture Secretary
Anstey
14 Pinewood Close
Leicester
LE4 1ER

ASH — 1995
Recreation Ground
Queens Road, Ash,
Canterbury, Kent,

Mr Julian Gugenheim
Hon. Secretary
Ash
Bourne Park Cottage
Bourne Park Bridge
Canterbury, Kent
CT4 5BJ

Mr Alan Warner
Hon. Fixture Secretary
Guilton Lodge
Guilton
Ash
Kent
CT3 2H2

AXMINSTER — 1989
Gammons Hill
Kilmington
Axminster
EX13
01297 35989

Mrs Karen Hussey
Hon. Secretary
Axminster
Cranmere
Musbury Road
Axminster Devon
EX13 5JS

Mr M Carlisle
Hon. Fixture Secretary
Axminster
Apple Tree Corner
Colyford
Axminster, Devon
EX13 6QQ

AYLESTONE ATHLETIC — 1919
Victoria Park
Victoria Park Road
Leicester

Mr R H Dann
Hon. Secretary
Aylestone Athletic
32 Monsell Drive
Aylestone
Leicester
LE2 8PN

Mr Mark Walters
Hon. Fixture Secretary
Aylestone Athletic
113 Holmfield Road
Leicester
LE2 1SF

AYLESBURY ATHLETIC

HM Prison
Bierton Road
Aylesbury HP20 1EH
01296 424435 x318

PEO D Beer
Hon. Secretary
Aylesbury Athletic
HMYOI Aylesbury
Bierton Road
Aylesbury HP20 1EH

PEO R Hemming
Hon. Fixture Secretary
Aylesbury Athletic
HM Young Offender Inst
Bierton Road
Aylesbury, Bucks
HP20 1EH

BAE WARTON 1992
Bank Lane Playing Fields
Bank Lane
Warton, Preston
PR4 1AX
01772 856354/852788

Mr M.D Hubble
Hon. Secretary
BAe Warton
2 Ribble View Close
Warton
Nr Prescot, Lancashire
PR4 1LD

Mr M Jagger
Hon. Fixture Secretary
BAe Warton
6 Hazel Coppice
Lea
Preston, Lancashire
PR2 1XG

BALLIOL COLLEGE 1906
c/o Balliol college
Oxford
OX1 3BJ
01865 277777

Mr E Rees
Hon. Secretary
Balliol College
c/o Balliol College
Oxford OX1 3BJ

BARCLAYS BANK 1921
Barclays Bank Sports Club
Park View Road
Ealing, London
W5 2JF
020 8998 4904

Mr S C Payne
Hon. Secretary
Barclays Bank
Barclays Acquisition Finance
1st Floor, 54 Lombard Street
London EC3P 3AH

Mr D M Bevan-Jones
Hon. Fixture Secretary
Barclays Bank
23 Cypress Avenue
Whitton, Twickenham
Middlesex TW2 7JY

BARCLAYS BANK BIRMINGHAM DISTRICT
1955
Sunnybank Avenue
Perry Common
Birmingham B44 0HP

Mr K R Patterson
Hon. Secretary & **Fixture Secretary**
Barclays Bank Birmingham District
42 Pennymore Close
Trentham, Stoke on Trent
Staffordshire ST4 8YQ

BASILDON (BERKSHIRE) 1978
The Recreation Ground
Bethesda Street
Upper Basildon, Berkshire

Mr D Butcher
Hon. Secretary
8 Gratwicke Road
Tilehurst
Reading
Berkshire RG30 4TT

Mr J Hayes
Hon. Fixture Secretary
Basildon (Berkshire)
53 Willowtree Glade
Calcot
Reading

BEDFORD SCHOOL 1870
Burnaby Road
Bedford
01234 362200

Hon. Secretary
Bedford School
Burnaby Road, Bedford

BELGRAVIA
Imber Court
Ember Court Road
East Molesey, Surrey
020 8398 1267

Mr Shaun O'Neill
Hon. Secretary
Belgravia
6 Priory Close
Sunbury on Thames
Middlesex
TW16 5AB

Mr R Thorne
Hon. Fixture Secretary
Belgravia
Crime Prevention Office
Belgravia Police Station
Buckingham Palace Road
London

BENTON 1964
Civil Service Sports Ground
(Darsley Pk), Old Whitley Road
Newcastle-upon-Tyne
0191 2662726

Mr G Parker
Hon. Secretary
Benton
9 Wilson Terrace
Forest Hall
Newcastle upon Tyne
NE12 7JP

Mr R Jones
Hon. Fixture Secretary
Benton
9 Wilson Terrace
Forest Hall
Newcastle upon Tyne
NE12 7JP

BERWICK 1968
Scremerston
Berwick-upon-Tweed
TD15 2QY
01289 306416

Mr J H Greenwood
Hon. Secretary
Berwick
Ava Lodge
Castle Terrace
Berwick upon Tweed
TD15 1NP

Mr C Budzynski
Hon. Fixture Secretary
Berwick
17 Springfield Park
East Ord
Berwick Upon Tweed
TD15 2FD

BICTON COLLEGE OF AGRICULTURE 1947
Bicton College of Agriculture
East Budleigh
Budleigh Salterton
EX9 7BY
01395 562335

Mr I Wallace
Hon. Secretary
Agriculture
Bicton College of Agriculture
Bicton College of Agriculture
East Budleigh
Budleigh Salterton, Devon
EX9 7BY

Hon. Fixture Secretary
Bicton College of
Agriculture
Bicton College of
East Budleigh
Budleigh Salterton, Devon
EX9 7BY

BIRKENHEAD SCHOOL
11 Kingsmead Road South
Birkenhead
Merseyside
L43 6TA
0151 652 4014

Master I/C Rugby
Hon. Secretary
Birkenhead School
Birkenhead School
11 Kingsmead Road South
Birkenhead, Merseyside
L43 6TA

For Attention Of:
Hon. Fixture Secretary
Birkenhead School
11 Kingsmead Road South
Birkenhead
Merseyside
L43 6TA

BIRSTALL 1975
Longslade Community College
Wanlip Lane
Birstall, Leicestershire
LE4 4GH
0116 267 7107

Mr G Cree | Mr S Cox
Hon. Secretary | **Hon. Fixture Secretary**
64 Branting Hill Avenue | Birstall
Glenfield | 7 Roman Road
Leicester | Birstall
LE3 8GB | Leicestershire
 | LE4 4BB

BISHOP'S STORTFORD COLLEGE 1920
Maze Green Road
Bishop's Stortford
Hertfordshire
CM23 2QZ
01279 657911

Master I/C Rugby | For Attention Of:
Hon. Secretary | **Hon. Fixture Secretary**
Bishop's Stortford College | Bishop's Stortford College
Bishops Stortford College | Maze Green Road
Bishops Stortford | Bishop's Stortford
Hertfordshire | Hertfordshire
 | CM23 2QZ

BLACK BAA BAAS 1994
23a Varna Road
London
SW6 7LB

Mr Julian Samuel | Mr Julian Samuel
Hon. Secretary | **Hon. Fixture Secretary**
Black Baa Baas | Black Baa Baas
23A Varna Road | 23A Varna Road
Fulham | Fulham
London | London
SW6 | SW6

BLACK HORSE 1977
Balls Park
Mangrove Road
Hertford, Hertfordshire
SG13 8AJ

Mr C R Daniels | Mr S Martin
Hon. Secretary | **Hon. Fixture Secretary**
Black Horse | Black Horse
9 Currie Street | 25 Gladstone Road
Hertford | Ware
Hertfordshire | Hertfordshire
SG13 7DA | SG12 0AG

BLACKPOOL POLICE 1968
c/o Blackpool RUFC
Fleetwood Road
Blackpool, Lancashire
FY5 1RN
01253 853308

Mr D Crocombe | Mr C Farrow
Hon. Secretary | **Hon. Fixture Secretary**
Blackpool Police | Blackpool Police
53 Kendal Avenue | 10 Newton Road
High Furlong, Blackpool | St Annes on Sea
Lancashire | Lancashire
FY3 7LG | FY8 3JW

BLUE BOAR 1977
c/o Oxford RFC
North Hinksey Village
Southern Bypass, Oxford
01865 243984

Mr B Kentish | Mr B Kentish
Hon. Secretary | **Hon. Fixture Secretary**
Blue Boar | Blue Boar
Old Farmhouse | Old Farmhouse
Longworth | Longworth
Abingdon, Oxfordshire | Abingdon, Oxfordshire
OX13 5ET | OX13 5ET

BLUNDELL'S SCHOOL 1868
Tiverton
Devon
EX16 4DN
01884 252543

Mr N Ridgway | For Attention Of:
Hon. Secretary | **Hon. Fixture Secretary**
Blundell's School | Blundell's School
Blundell's School | Tiverton
Tiverton | Devon
Devon | EX16 4DN
EX16 4DN |

BORDER PARK 1961
Symons Park
Butteryhaugh
Kielder, Hexham
NE48 1HG

Mr C Earsman | Mr W.J Turnbull
Hon. Secretary | **Hon. Fixture Secretary**
Border Park | Border Park
Gladstone House, | The Old Manse
Stannersburn | Otterburn Rd,
Falstone, Hexham | Bellingham
Northumberland | Hexham, Northumberland
NE48 1DD | NE48 2DT

BOLSOVER RUFC
Oxcroft Miners Welfare
Clowne Road
Stranfree
Nr Chesterfield
Derbyshire

Hon. Secretary & **Fixture Secretary**
MR F Skinner
17 Oxcroft Lane
Bolsover
Chesterfield
Derbyshire
S44 6DJ

BP CHEMICALS 1972
BP Sports & Social Club
Salt End
Hedon Road, Hull
HU12 8DS
01482 896251

Mr S M Ladd | For Attention Of:
Hon. Secretary | **Hon. Fixture Secretary**
BP Chemicals | BP Chemicals
56 Lindengate Avenue | BP Sports & Social Club
Rockford Green | Salt End
Hull, east Yorkshire | Hedon Road, Hull
HU7 0ED | HU12 8DS

BRASENOSE COLLEGE
Abingdon Road
Oxford
01865 243478

Mr M Forbes	Mr M Forbes
Hon. Secretary	**Hon. Fixture Secretary**
Brasenose College RFC	Brasenose College RFC
Brasenose College	Brasenose College
Oxford	Oxford
OX1 4AJ	OX1 4AJ

BRAUNSTONE TOWN 1983
Mossdale Meadows
Kingsway
Braunstone
0116 263 0018

Mr R Bailey	Mr P Tyers
Hon. Secretary	**Hon. Fixture Secretary**
32 Ambleside Drive	9 Ivanhoe Street
Eyres Monsell	Newfoundpool
Leics. LE29 9LB	Leicester LE3 9GX

BRITISH STEEL 1953
The Bungalow
6th Form Centre, Needham Drive
Workington, Cumbria
01900 603570

Ms L Storey	For Attention of:
Hon. Secretary	**Hon. Fixture Secretary**
British Steel	British Steel
31 Pilgrim Street	The Bungalow
Workington	6th Form Centre,
Needham Drive	
Cumbria CA14 2RA	Workington, Cumbria

BRITISH UNIVERSITIES SPORTS ASSOCIATION 1919
8 Union Street
London SE1 1SZ
020 7357 8555

Mr G Gregory-Jones	C Dean
Hon. Secretary	**Hon. Fixture Secretary**
BUSA	BUSA
8 Union Street	8 Union Street
London SE1 1SZ	London SE1 1SZ

BROADMOOR STAFF - 2000
36 Pinewood Ave
Crowethorne
Berkshire RG45 6RP
01344 762038

Mr C G Pole	Mr Ian Hodsdon
Hon. Secretary	**Fixture Secretary**
19 South Meadow	36 Pinewood Avenuef
Crowthorne	Crowthorne
Berkshire RG45 7HJ	Berkshire RG45 6RP

BROMSGROVE SCHOOL
Bromsgrove
Worcestershire B16 7DU
01527 32863

Master I/C Rugby	For Attention Of:
Hon. Secretary	**Hon. Fixture Secretary**
Bromsgrove School	Bromsgrove School
Bromsgrove	Bromsgrove
Worcestershire B16 7DU	Worcestershire B16 7DU

BURBAGE 1983
Britannia Road Playing Fields
Britannia Road
Burbage
01455 636108

Mr C M Startin	Mr R Sansome
Hon. Secretary	**Hon. Fixture Secretary**
Burbage	Burbage
102 Strathmore Road	39 Duport Road
Hinckley	Burbage, Hinckley
Leicestershire LE10 0LR	Leicestershire LE10

BURTON JOYCE
The Poplars Burton Joyce Sport Ground
Station Road
Burton Joyce
Notts, NG14 5AN

Mr T Hallam	Mr C Maltby
Hon. Secretary	33 The Spinney
9 Copse Close	Bylcote
Burton Joyce	Nottingham
Nottingham NG14 5DD	NG14 5GX

BURTONWOOD 1964
Burtonwood Community Centre
Fir Tree Lane
Burtonwood, Warrington
01925 224480/225584

Mrs E Southern	Mr J Harper
Hon. Secretary	**Hon. Fixture Secretary**
25 Knight Road	8 Camborne Road
Burtonwood	Burtonwood
Warrington WA5 4QQ	Warrington WA5

CAMBRIDGE UNIVERSITY 1872
Univ. Football Ground
Grange Road
Cambridge
CB3 9BN
01223 354131 (355301 Fax)

Mr A W Jessop	Dr F J Clough
Hon. Secretary	**Hon. Fixture Secretary**
32 Highfield Avenue	33 Bridgewater Drive,
Cambridge	Great Glen,
CB2 2AD	Leicester LE8 9DX

CASTLETOWN 1991
Castletown RFU
Poulsom Park

Mr P D Martin	Mr J Quayle
Hon. Secretary	**Hon. Fixture Secretary**
16 Queen's Terrace	41 Campion Way RFC
Douglas	Abbeyfieldsk
Isle of Man	Douglas, Isle of Man
IM1 4BZ	IM2 7DT

CENTAURS RFC
Gower Road
Syon Lane
Isleworth
Middlesex
TW7 5QB

Mr M W Root	Mr J Goldie
Hon. Secretary	**Hon. Fixture Secretary**
116 Uxbridge Road	23 Northumberland Avenue
Hatch End	Isleworth
Pinner	Middlesex
Middlesex HA5 4DS	TW5 5HZ

CENTURIONS STH KENT POLICE SC 1984
New Burlington Field
Bargrove, Newington
Folkestone, Kent CT18 8BH
01303 266887

Mr R Thomas
Hon. Secretary
Centurions S. Kent Police SC
196 Canterbury Road
Folkestone
Kent
CT19 5PF

Mr K Howland
Hon. Fixture Secretary
Centurions S. Kent Police SC
Morton Cottage
Mill Lane
Monks Morton
Ashford, Kent

CHELTENHAM COLLEGE 1944
Cheltenham
Gloucestershire GL53 7LD
01242 513540

Master I/C Rugby
Hon. Secretary
Cheltenham College
Cheltenham
Glos. GL53 7LD

For Attention Of:
Hon. Fixture Secretary
Cheltenham College
Cheltenham
Glos. GL53 7LD

CHISWICK POLICE 1989
c/o Grasshoppers RFC
McFarlane Lane
Syon Lane, Osterley

Sgt N Baillie
Hon. Secretary
Chiswick Police Station
209 High Rd, Chiswick
London
W4 2DU

Sgt N Baillie
Hon. Fixture Secretary
Chiswick Police Station
209 High Rd, Chiswick
London
W4 2DU

CHRIST'S COLLEGE
College Sports Ground
162a Huntingdon Road
Cambridge
01223 276218

Mr D Till
Hon. Secretary
Christ's College
College Rugby Club
Christ's College
Cambridge
CB2 3BU

Mr D Till
Hon. Fixture Secretary
Christ's College
College Rugby Club
Christ's College
Cambridge
CB2 3BU

CHRIST'S HOSPITAL SCHOOL 1553
Christ's Hospital School
Horsham
Sussex RH13 7LS
01403 255283

Hon. Secretary
Christ's Hospital School
Horsham
Sussex RH13 7LS
01403 255283

CHRIST CHURCH
Iffley Road
Oxford
01865 243992

Mr B Gripaioss
Hon. Secretary
Christ Church
The Steward's Office,
Christ Church College
Oxford 0X1 1DP

CHURCHILL COLLEGE 1961
Churchill College
Cambridge CB3 0DS
01223 336000

Mr G de Rose
Hon. Secretary
Churchill College
Storey's Way
Cambridge CB3 0DS

For Attention Of:
Hon. Fixture Secretary
Churchill College
Cambridge
CB3 0DS

CITIZENS 1929
Old Dunstonians Sports Ground
St Dunstans Lane
Langley Park, Beckenham, Kent BR3 3SS
020 8650 1779

Mr C R Southgate
Hon. Secretary
Citizens
Sunny Bank, Kingsland
Nr Leominster
Herefordshire HR6 9SE

Mr P Upton
Hon. Fixture Secretary
Citizens
68 Addington Road
West Wickham
Kent BR4 9BJ

CLACTON RFC
The Recreation Ground
Valley Road
Clacton on Sea
Essex
CO15 4NA

Mr D Jaffray
Hon. Secretary
30 Craigfield Avenue
Clacton on Sea
Essex CO15 4HS

Mr G Wiggins
Hon. Fixture Secretary
39 Victoria Road
Clacton-On-Sea
Essex

CLAPHAM 1982
Twinwoods Road
Clapham
Bedfordshire
01234 353633

Mr D R Tough
Hon. Secretary
Millbrook House
109 High Street
Riseley, Bedfordshire
MK44 1DF

Mr M Baker
Hon. Fixture Secretary
82 High Street
Oakley
Bedfordshire
MK43 7RH

CLARE COLLEGE 1908
Clare College Sports Ground
Bentley Rd
Cambridge

Mr H M Vann
Hon. Secretary
Clare College
Cambridge
CB2 1TL

For Attention Of:
Hon. Fixture Secretary
Clare College Sports Ground
Bentley Rd
Cambridge

CLEVELAND CONSTABULARY 1968
Police HQ,
Ladgate Lane
Middlesborough TS8 9EH
01642 301461

PC 848 Barfield
Hon. Secretary & Hon. Fixture Secretary
Cleveland Constabulary
c/o ARV Unit
Police HQ, PO Box 70
Ladgate Lane, Middlesborough TS8 9EH

PC 848 Barfield

COLWORTH HOUSE RFC
Sharbrook
Bedfordshire
MK44 1LQ

Mr A Reynolds
Hon. Secretary
21 Alburgh Close
Bedford
MK41 0HG

Mr J Ainley
Bourn Cottage
Wilstead Road
Elstow
Bedfordshire

CLIFTON COLLEGE
32 College Road
Clifton
Bristol BS8 3JH
0117 315 7000

Mr I Williams
Hon. Secretary & Hon. Fixture Secretary
Clifton College
School House, College Road
Clifton, Bristol BS8 3HY

Mr I Williams

CORPUS CHRISTI
Leckhampton
Cranmere Road
Cambridge
CB3 9BL
01223 353231

Hon. Secretary

Hon. Fixture Secretary
Corpus Christi College Rugby Club
Cranmere Road
Cambridge
CB3 9BL

CORPUS CHRISTI & SOMERVILLE COLLEGES 1990
Corpus Christi College
Merton Street
Oxford
OX1 4JF
01865 276737

Mr J Barry
Hon. Secretary & **Hon. Fixture Secretary**
Corpus Christi & Somerville Colleges
Corpus Christi College
Merton Street, Oxford OX1 4JF

COSBY 1990
Victory Park
Park Road
Cosby, Leicester
0116 284 9244

Mr C W Elliott
Hon. Secretary & Hon. Fixture Secretary
Cosby
9 Wavertree Close
Cosby
Leicester LE9 1TNN

CRICKLADE 1992
VOWH Club
Cricklade High St.
Cricklade, Wilts
01793 750325

Mr P Gardiner
Hon. Secretary
Cricklade
4 Collett Place
Latton
Wiltshire SN6 6EH

Mr P Clements
Hon. Fixture Secretary
Cricklade
2 North Wall,
Cricklade
Wilts SN6 6DU

CUACO 1926
Cuaco Club
Copers Cope Road
Beckenham, Kent BR3 1RJ
020 8650 9902

Mr A P Wells
Hon. Secretary
CUACO
3rd Floor, CU House
69 Park Lane
Croydon, Surrey
CR9 1BG

For Attention Of:
Hon. Fixture Secretary
CUACO
Cuaco Club
Copers Cope Road
Beckenham, Kent
BR3 1RJ

CUMBRIA CONSTABULARY 1953
Winters Park
Penrith
Cumbria
CA11 8RG
01768 863151

Mr P D Hutton
Hon. Secretary
Cumbria Constabulary
24 Landsdown Close
Kendal
Cumbria LA9 7SB

Mr K Greenhow
Hon. Fixture Secretary
Cumbria Constabulary
County Police HQ
Carleton Hall
Penrith CA10 2AH

DARLINGTON RAILWAY ATHLETIC 1925
Brinkburn Road
Darlington
01325 468125

Mr T P Sanderson
Hon. Secretary
Darlington Railway Athletic
School House, Chapel Street
Middleton-St-George
Darlington DL2 1DA

Mr T P Sanderson
Hon. Fixture Secretary
Darlington Railway Athletic
School House, Chapel
Street
Middleton-St-George
Darlington DL2 1DA

DARWIN COLLEGE

The Hon Secretary
Hon. Secretary
Darwin College College Rugby Club
Darwin College
Cambridge CB3 9EU

DE LA SALLE (SHEFFIELD) 1956
De La Salle Association Club
(Behind Beauchief Hall)
Off Abbey Lane Sheffield
0114 236 7756

Mr J Halliday
Hon. Secretary
De La Salle (Sheffield)
Mayfield House
443 Greystones Rd
Sheffield S11 7BY

For Attention Of:
Hon. Fixture Secretary
De La Salle (Sheffield)
De La Salle Assoc. Club
(Behind Beauchief Hall)
Off Abbey Lane Sheffield

DERBYSHIRE CONSTABULARY 1926
Force Headquarters
Butterley Hall
Ripley, Derbyshire DE5 3RS
01773 570100

Mr I T Roe
Hon. Secretary
Derbyshire Constabulary
10 Otterburn Drive
Kedlaston Grange
Allestree, Derby DE22 2TJ

Mr I T Roe
Hon. Fixture Secretary
Derbyshire Constabulary
10 Otterburn Drive
Kedlaston Grange
Allestree, Derby DE22 2TJ

DEREHAM 1974
Moorgate Road
Dereham
Norfolk

Ms B Endresen
Hon. Secretary
Dereham
1 Bayfield Ave
Dereham
Norfolk NR19 1PH

DOVER COLLEGE 1870
Effingham Crescent
Dover
Kent CT17 9RX
01304 205969

Hon. Secretary
Dover College
Dover College
Effingham Crescent
Dover, Kent
CT17 9RX

For Attention Of:
Hon. Fixture Secretary
Dover College
Effingham Crescent
Dover
Kent
CT17 9RX

DOWNING COLLEGE
Long Road
Cambridge

Hon Secretary
Hon. Secretary
Downing College
College Rugby Club
Downing College
Cambridge CB3 9EU

For Attention Of:
Hon. Fixture Secretary
Downing College
Long Road
Cambridge

DOWTY 1961
Dowty Sports & Social Society
Staverton Division
Down Hatherley Lne, Gloucester GL2 9QD
01452 714567

Mrs G Blackwell
Hon. Secretary
Dowty
6 Kaybourne Crescent
Churchdown
Gloucestershire
GL3 2HL

Mr D Rose
Hon. Fixture Secretary
Dowty
7 Wren Terrace
Innsworth
Gloucester

DULWICH COLLEGE 1859
Dulwich Common
London SE21 7LD
020 8299 9237

Mr I Martin
Hon. Secretary
Dulwich College
Dulwich College
Dulwich
London

For Attention Of:
Hon. Fixture Secretary
Dulwich College
Dulwich Common
London
SE21 7LD

DURHAM SCHOOL 1850
Quarryheads Lane
Durham City DH1 4SZ
0191 386 4783

Mr P Gerrard
Hon. Secretary
Durham School
Quarryheads Lane
Durham City
DH1 4SZ

Mr P Gerrard
Hon. Fixture Secretary
Durham School
Quarryheads Lane
Durham City
DH1 4SZ

EASTBOURNE COLLEGE 1990
Old Wish Road
East Sussex
01323 21528

Master I/C Rugby
Hon. Secretary
Eastbourne College
Eastbourne College
Eastbourne
Sussex

For Attention Of:
Hon. Fixture Secretary
Eastbourne College
Old Wish Road
East Sussex

EAST PECKHAM & CAPEL (THE VILLAGERS) RFC 1977
Putlands Sport & Leisure Ctr
Mascalls Court Road
Paddock Wood, Kent TN12
01892 838290

Mr P Hale
Hon. Secretary & Fixture Secretary
East Peckham & Capel (The Villagers) RFC
52 Midsummer Road
Snodland, Kent ME6 5RP

ECCLES & ATTLEBOROUGH 1978
Gaymer's Ground
Attleborough
Norfolk NR17

Ms L Norman
Hon. Secretary
Eccles & Attleborough
Grove Lodge
Howard Street
Norwich, Norfolk
NR1 3RN

Mr N Young
Hon. Fixture Secretary
Eccles & Attleborough
48 Tedder Close,
Watton
Norfolk
IP25 6HX

EGOR 1978
Old Salians RFC
Clarendon Road
Sale, Manchester
0161 973 7250

Mr B Minor
Hon. Secretary
EGOR
45 Gorton Street
Peel Green
Eccles, Lancashire
M30 7LZ

Mr John Rogers
Hon. Fixture Secretary
EGOR
21 Dee Road
Astley
Manchester
M29 7HW

EMMANUEL COLLEGE
Wilberforce Road
Cambridge CB3 0EQ
01223 353961

Hon. Secretary
For Attention Of:
Hon. Secretary
Emmanuel College
Wilberforce Road
Cambridge CB3 0EQ

For Attention Of:
Hon. Fixture Secretary
Emmanuel College
Wilberforce Road
Cambridge
CB3 0EQ

EMANUEL SCHOOL 1910
Battersea Rise
London SW11 1HS
020 8874 4601

Hon. Secretary
Emanuel School
Emmanuel School
Wandsworth Common
London
SW11

For Attention Of:
Hon. Fixture Secretary
Emanuel School
Battersea Rise
London
SW11 1HS

ENGLAND FIRE SERVICE 1970

Mr Stuart Irwin
Hon. Secretary
England Fire Service
4 Linwood Grove
Leighton Buzzard
Bedfordshire LU7 8RP

ENTERTAINERS 1963
c/o Wimbledon RFC
Barham Road
London SW20 0ET
020 8946 3156

Mr C R Nicholas
Hon. Secretary & **Fixture Secretary**
Entertainers
68 Sutherland Grove
London
SW18 5QW

EPSOM COLLEGE 1870
Epsom
Surrey
KT17 4JQ
013727 24810

Mr A Wolstenholme
Hon. Secretary
Epsom College
Epsom
Surrey
KT17 4JQ

ESSEX POLICE
Coronation Park
Timson's Lane
Chelmsford, Essex
01245 452922

Hon. Secretary	Mr P Daly
Essex Police	**Hon. Fixture Secretary**
c/o Sports Secretary,	Essex Police
Police HQ,	c/o Sports Secretary,
Springfield	Police HQ, Springfield,
Chelmsford	Chelmsford
Essex CM2 1DA	Essex CM2 1DA

EXETER COLLEGE
Exeter College Sports Ground
Edgeway Road
New Marston, Oxford
01865 243710

Mr C Watts	For Attention Of:
Hon. Secretary	**Hon. Fixture Secretary**
Exeter College,	Exeter College Sports Ground
Oxford	Edgeway Road
OX1 3DP	New Marston, Oxford

FAIRBAIRN/CHIGWELL 1995
Salamander Sports Ground
Leigh Road
East Ham E6 2AS

Mr P Evans
Hon. Secretary & **Fixture Secretary**
Fairbairn/Chigwell
350 Ripple Road
Barking
Essex
IG11 7PQ

FAKENHAM 1982
Old Wells Road
Fakenham, Norfolk NR21 0BJ
01328 851007

Mr D J Swift	Mr C Evans
Hon. Secretary	**Hon. Fixture Secretary**
Fakenham	Fakenham
19 North Park	64 Boyd Avenue
Fakenham	Toftwood
Norfolk	East Dereham, Norfolk
NR21 9RG	NR19 1ND

FELIXSTOWE 1930
The Clubhouse,
Coronation Park
Felixstowe, Suffolk IP11 8LN
01394 270150

Mr D Cain	Mr Ian Bignell
Hon. Secretary	**Hon. Fixture Secretary**
Felixstowe	Felixstowe
16 Berners Road	7 Cloncurry Gardens
Felixstowe	Felixstowe
Suffolk	IP11 2QY
IP11 7LF	

FERMAIN TAVERN 1981
Footes Lane
St Peter Port, Guernsey
01481 54590

Mr A Coulson	Mr M T P Cahill
Hon. Secretary	**Hon. Fixture Secretary**
Fermain Tavern	Fermain Tavern
Jabulami	Le Marecage
Les Petites Capelles	Le Marais
St Sampson, Guernsey	L'eree
GY2 4GX	G77 9LD

FITZWILLIAM COLLEGE 1966
93 Oxford Road
Cambridge CB4 3PH
01223 353382

Mr Richard Rowstron	For Attention Of:
Hon. Secretary	**Hon. Fixture Secretary**
Fitzwilliam College	Fitzwilliam College
Fitzwilliam College	93 Oxford Road
Cambridge CB3 0DG	Cambridge CB4 3PH

FIVE HORSESHOES 1982
Dry Leas
Marlow Road, Henley on Thames
Oxfordshire
01491 574499/641282

Mr G Cromack	Mr P Cawthra
Hon. Secretary	**Hon. Fixture Secretary**
Five Horseshoes	Five Horseshoes
4 Milton Close	Beavers Lodge
Henley on Thames	Mill Road
Oxon RG9 1UJ	Shiplake Oxon RG9 3LH

FORD LEAMINGTON RFC
Newbold Comyn
Leamington Spa

Mr J Cronin	Mr E Newton
Hon. Secretary	**Hon. Fixture Secretary**
26 Alibone Close	86 Bury Road
Whitnash	Leamington Spa
Leamington	Warwickshire
CV31 2SR	CV31 3HW

FOREST OLD BOYS 1990
Redingensians
Old Bath Road, Sonning
Reading, Berkshire
01189 695259

Mr T Walters
Hon. Secretary
Forest Old Boys
Azalea Cottage
Merryhill Green Lane
Winnersh, Wokingham, Berks
Berks

Mr T Walters
Hon. Fixture Secretary
Forest Old Boys
Azalea Cottage
Merryhill Green Lane
Winnersh, Wokingham,

GIRTON COLLEGE
Huntingdon Road
Cambridge CB3 0JG
01223 338999

Mr Andrew Holland
Hon. Secretary & Fixture Secretary
Girton College
Cambridge
CB3 0JG

GLOUCESTERSHIRE CONSTABULARY 1948
Dowty Rotol RFC
Down Hatherley Lane
Gloucester GL2 9QD
01452 714567

Mr A M Drummond
Hon. Secretary
Gloucestershire Constabulary
Constabulary
The Orchard
Green Lane
Churchdown, Gloucester
GL3 2LB

Mr P Haines
Hon. Fixture Secretary
Gloucestershire
Savannah
Church Road, Caincross
Stroud
GL5 4JE

GONVILLE & CAIUS COLLEGE
Gonville & Caius College
Cambridge
CB2 1TA
01223 332400

Hon Secretary
Hon. Secretary
Gonville & Caius College
College Rugby Club
Gonville & Caius College
Cambridge
CB2 1TA

For Attention Of:
Hon. Fixture Secretary
Gonville & Caius College
Gonville & Caius College
Cambridge
CB2 1TA

GREENWICH ACADEMICALS 1937
Kidbroke Lane
Eltham, London SE9
020 8850 1221

Mr H Davies
Hon. Secretary
Greenwich Academicals
29 Cumberland Avenue
Welling
Kent
DA16 2PT

Mr D Hoggan
Hon. Fixture Secretary
Greenwich Academicals
270 Bedonwell Road
Upper Belvedere
Kent
DA17 5NZ

GREATER MANCHESTER FIRE SERVICE 1965

Mr M E Higgins
Hon. Secretary & Fixture Secretary
Greater Manchester Fire Service
1 Langside Drive
Ladybridge, Bolton BL3 4US

GREATER MANCHESTER POLICE 1974
Police Club
Hough End Centre
Mauldeth Road West, Manchester M21 1SX
0161 856 1798

Sgt M Sutton
Hon. Secretary
Greater Manchester Police
GMP Rugby Section
Mottram Police Station
Atherton Grove, Mottram,
Hyde SK14 6JE

Hon. Fixture Secretary
Greater Manchester Police RFC
Police Club
Hough End Centre
Mauldesh Road West
Manchester
M21 1SX

HAILEYBURY 1863
Hertford Heath
Hertford SG13 7NU
01992 462352

Master I/C Rugby
Hon. Secretary
Haileybury
Haileybury College
Hertford

For Attention Of:
Hon. Fixture Secretary
Haileybury
Hertford Heath
Hertford SG13 7NU

HARTPURY COLLEGE 1970
Hartpury House
Nr Gloucester GL19 3BE
01452 700283(T) 700629 (F)

Mr S Holley
Hon. Secretary & Fixture Secretary
Hartpury College
Hartpury House
Hartpury College, Gloucester GL19 3BE

HARRODIANS 1912
Barn Elms, Queen Elizabeth Wlk
Barnes
London SW13 9SA
020 8876 7685

Mr P Kirby
Hon. Secretary & Fixture Secretary
Harrodians
53 Stanhope Gardens, London SW7 5RF

HERTFORDSHIRE FIRE & RESCUE SERVICE 1974
Hertford RFC
Hoe Lane
Ware, Hertfordshire SG12 9NZ

Mr J Horastead
Hon. Secretary
Herts Fire & Rescue Service
61 Acme Road
Watford
Herts WD2 5HQ

Mr C Strickland
Hon. Fixture Secretary
Herts Fire & Rescue Service
HFRS HQ
Old London Road
Hertford SG13 7LD

HERTFORDSHIRE POLICE 1949
Police HQ
Stanborough Road
Welwyn Garden City AL8 6XF
01992 533327

Mr R Larter
Hon. Secretary
Hertfordshire Police
Police Station
Baldock Road
Buntingford
Hertfordshire, SG9 9DB

Mr S Gibbs
Hon. Fixture Secretary
Hertfordshire Police
Youth Offending Team
c/o County Police Stn,
Ware Road, Hertford

HERTFORD COLLEGE
Catte Street
Oxford OX13BW
01865 279400

Mr P Clememts	Mr J Wilson
Hon. Secretary	**Hon. Fixture Secretary**
Hertford College	Hertford College
Catte street	Catte Street
Oxford OX1 3BW	Oxford OX1 3BW

HMP ACKLINGTON
HM Prison Acklington
Morpeth
Northumberland NE65 9XF
01670 760411 Ext 333

Mr P Sanderson	Mr B Taylor
Hon. Secretary	**Hon. Fixture Secretary**
HMP Acklington	HMP Acklington
10 Foxhill Close	HMP Acklington
Fallowfield Estate	Morpeth
Ashington, Northumberland	Northumberland

HMP GARTH   1989
H.M.Prison Garth
Ulnes Walton Lane
Leyland, Preston PR5 3NE
01772 622722

Mr T Probert
Hon. Secretary & **Fixture Secretary**
H M Prison Garth
Ulnes Walton Lane
Leyland, Preston PR5 3NE

HMP LINCOLN   1989
HMP Lincoln
Greetwell Road
Lincoln LN2 4BD
01522 533633 Ext 401

Mr C K Lewis
Hon. Secretary & **Fixture Secretary**
HMP Lincoln
PE Dept, HMP Lincoln
Greetwell Road
Lincoln LN2 4BD

HM PRISON SERVICE   1976
HM Prison Service College
Newbold Revel, Nr Rugby
Warwickshire
01788 832666

Mr S N Sporcic	Mr R Sawbridge
Hon. Secretary	**Hon. Fixture Secretary**
HM Prison Service	HM Prison Service
HMP Birmingham	c/o H M Prison Leicester
Winson Green Rd	Welford Rd,
Birmingham B18 4AS	Leicester

HODDESDON WHITE SWANARIANS   1991
King George v Playing Fields
Wormley
Hertfordshire EN11 8TN

Mr S Stagg	Mr P Reast
Hon. Secretary	**Hon. Fixture Secretary**
Hoddesdon White Swanarians	Hoddesdon White
Swanarians	
10 Briscoe Rd	15 Stafford Drive
Hoddesdon	Broxbourne
Herts EN11 9DQ	Herts EN10 7JT

HOMERTON COLLEGE
Hills Road
Cambridge CB2 2PH
01223 507235/6

Mr A S Dinatar
Hon. Secretary & **Fixture Secretary**
Homerton College
College Rugby Club
Homerton College
Cambridge
CB2 2PH

HONDA   1990
Supermarine Sport/Social Club
Highworth Rd, South Marston
Swindon, Wiltshire SN3 4TZ
01793 824828

Mr T Lee	Mr N Harper
Hon. Secretary	**Hon. Fixture Secretary**
Honda	Honda
c/o Honda Engineering Europe	385 Cricklade Road
Highworth Road, South Marston	Goarse Hill
Swindon, Wiltshire	Swindon
SN3 4TZ	SN2 2AQ

HUGHES HALL

Hon Secretary
Hughes Hall
College Rugby Club
Hughes Hall
Cambridge CB1 2EW

HUMBERSIDE POLICE   1961
Inglemire Lane Police Club
Inglemire Lane
Hull, East Yorks
01482 856954

Mr J Harris	Mr P Snowden
Hon. Secretary	**Hon. Fixture Secretary**
Humberside Police	Humberside Police
3 Stewart Garth	c/o Humberside Police
Cottingham	F.I.B, Queens G'dens
Police St	
East Yorkshire HU16 5YQ	Hull

IMBER COURT   1947
Imber Court Sports Club
Ember Lane
East Molesey, Surrey KT8 0BT
020 8398 1267/6609

Mr J Bailey	Mr J Bowens
Hon. Secretary	**Hon. Fixture Secretary**
Imber Court	Imber Court
39 Hurstdene Avenue	10 Anette Way
Staines	Rickmansworth
Middlesex TW18 1JG	WD3 2DA

JERSEY UNITED BANKS   1969
Grainville Playing Fields
St Saviour's Hill
St Saviour, Jersey JE2 7LG
01534 34350

Mr S Young	Mr A Cotton
Hon. Secretary	**Hon. Fixture Secretary**
Jersey United Banks	Jersey United Banks
La rue de la Vallee	c/o Geest Limited
St Mary	31 The Parade
Jersey JE3 3DL	St Helier, Jersey JE2 3QQ

JERSEY POLICE   1998
Granville
St Saviour
Jersey JE2 7LG
01534 34350

Mr D A Joshua   Mr S Cross
Hon. Secretary   **Hon. Fixture Secretary**
Jersey Police   Jersey Police
Rouge Bouillon Police   Rouge Bouillon Police
Station   Station
St Helier, Jersey   St Helier, Jersey
Channel Islands   Channel Islands
JE4 8ZZ   JE4 8ZZ

JESUS COLLEGE
Jesus College
Cambridge CB5 8BL
01223 339339

Mr Chris Trimble
Hon. Secretary & **Fixture Secretary**
Jesus College
Cambridge CB5 8BL

JESUS COLLEGE   1890
Jesus College
Oxford OX1 3DW
01865 279700

Mr M Benjamin
Hon. Secretary
Jesus College,
Oxford OX1 3DW

KEBLE COLLEGE
University Parks
Oxford OX1 3PG
01865 272727

Mr S Craig   For Attention Of:
Hon. Secretary   **Hon. Fixture Secretary**
Keble College   Keble College
Keble College   University Parks
University Parks   Oxford
Oxford   OX1 3PG

KEW OCCASIONALS   1988
Richmond Athletic Ground
Kew Foot Road
Richmond TW9 2SS
020 8940 0397

Mr R Clark
Hon. Secretary & **Fixture Secretary**
Kew Occasionals
5 Maze Road
Kew, Richmond
Surrey
TW9 3DA

KING EDWARD'S SCHOOL, BIRMINGHAM   1875
Edgbaston Park Road
Birmingham B15 2UA
0121 472 1672

Hon. Secretary   For Attention Of:
King Edward's School, Birmingham **Hon. Fixture Secretary**
King Edward's School   K E School, Birmingham
Edgbaston Park Road   Edgbaston Park Road
Birmingham 15   Birmingham
                               B15 2UA

KING'S COLLEGE

Mr J Wasey
Hon. Secretary & **Fixture Secretary**
King's College
Cambridge
CB2 1ST

LADY MARGARET HALL & TRINITY COLLEGE
Marston Road
Oxford

Mr G Samual-Gibbon   For Attention Of:
Hon. Secretary   **Hon. Fixture Secretary**
L M Hall & Trinity College   L M Hl & Trinity College
Lady Margaret Trinity   Marston Road
Marston Rd   Oxford
Oxford

LEICESTERSHIRE CONSTABULARY   1951
c/o Syston RFC
Barkby Road
Queniborough, Leicester
LE7 3FE
0116 260 1223

Mr T Perridge   Mr C Cary
Hon. Secretary   **Hon. Fixture Secretary**
Leicestershire Constabulary   Leicestershire
Constabulary
Leics. Constabulary HQ.   Syston Police Station
St. John's   Melton Road
Narborough, Leics   Syston, Leics
LE3 5BX

LEYHILL   1988
HMP Leyhill
Wotton-under-Edge
Gloucester GL12 8BT
01454 260681 Ext 332

Mr P.E.O.T Probert
Hon. Secretary & **Fixture Secretary**
Leyhill
H.M.Prison Leyhill
Wooton-under-Edge
Glouscestershire

LEYS HIGH SCHOOL   1875
Woodrow Drive
Redditch
Worcestershire
01527 23088

Master I/C Rugby   For Attention Of:
Hon. Secretary   **Hon. Fixture Secretary**
Leys High School   Leys High School
Leys School   Woodrow Drive
Cambridge   Redditch
                               Worcestershire

LFB SOUTHERN COMMAND (MOOSEHEAD)   1986
Fire Station
Sunbury Street
London
SE18 5LU

Mr C Knight   Mr A Buss
Hon. Secretary   **Hon. Fixture Secretary**
LFB Southern Command (Moosehead)   LFB Southern
Command (Moosehead)
29 Cyclamen Road   52 Bransdale Crescent
Swanley   Orpington
Kent BR8 8HH   Kent

LINCOLNSHIRE POLICE 1958
Police HQ, Deep Dale Lane
Nettleham
Lincoln LN5 7PH
01522 532222

Mr C Moon
Hon. Secretary & **Fixture Secretary**
Lincolnshire Police
5 Manor Lane
Welton
Lincoln LN2 3JQ

LINCOLN COLLEGE
Bartlemas Close
Oxford OX4 2AA
01865 242357

Mr C Houston   Mr J Wynne
Hon. Secretary   **Hon. Fixture Secretary**
Lincoln College   Lincoln College
Lincoln College   Lincoln College
Bartlemas Close   Turl Street
Oxford OX4 2AA   Oxford OX1 3DR

LITTLEHEY 1988
HMP Littlehey
Perry
Huntingdon, Cambridgeshire PE18 0SR
01480 812202 Ext 248/249

Mr A P Curtis
Hon. Secretary & **Fixture Secretary**
Littlehey
6 Riverside Way
Islip, Kettering
Northamptonshire NN14 3LF

LLOYDS TSB 1913
Lloyds T.S.B.Sports Club
59 Lorne Gardens
Shirley, Croydon CR0 7RZ
020 8656 3901

Mr B Brazier   Mr P Wedderspoon
Hon. Secretary   **Hon. Fixture Secretary**
Lloyds TSB   Lloyds TSB
2 Crushes Close   4 Lucerne Court
Hutton   Abbey Park
Brentwood, Essex   Brackley Road
CM13 1PB   Beckenham BR3 1RB

LOGGERHEADS 1976
Sundorne Castle Ground
Shrewsbury
01743 53380

Mr R Macken
Hon. Secretary & **Fixture Secretary**
7 Raby Crescent,Longden
Road, Shrewsbury
Shropshire SY3 7JN

LONDON MANX 1987
Westminster Lodge
St Albans
Hertfordshire

Mr C J P Haslam   Mr R White
Hon. Secretary   **Hon. Fixture Secretary**
Pennine Lodge   Trees
24 Gerard Avenue, Thorley   Wycke Lane, Tollesbury
Bishops Stortford, Herts   Maldon, Essex
CM23 4DU

LONDON FIRE BRIGADE NW AREA 1989
Northolt RFC
Cayton Green Park, Cayton Road
Greenford, Middlesex UB6 8BJ
020 8813 1701

Mr K A Heymer   Mr Padraig McKeon
Hon. Secretary   **Hon. Fixture Secretary**
London Fire Brigade NW Area   London Fire Brigade
57 Manor Way   NW Area
North Harrow   16 Brinsley Road
Middlesex HA2 6BZ   Harrow Weald HA3 5HY

MAGDALENE COLLEGE
St John's Sports Field
Queens Road
Cambridge CB3 0AG
01223 508880

Hon. Secretary   **Hon. Fixture Secretary**
Magdalene College   Magdalene College
College Rugby Club   St John's Sports Field
Magdalene College   Queens Road
Cambridge CB3 0AG   Cambridge CB3 0AG

MAGDALEN COLLEGE
Marston Road
Oxford OX1 4AU
01865 247358

Mr M Blayford-Baker   Mr V Kashyap
Hon. Secretary   **Hon. Fixture Secretary**
Magdalen College   Magdalen College
Marston Road   Oxford
Oxford OX1 4AU   OX1 4AU

MALTON AND NORTON RUFC
The Club House
The Gannock
Old Malton Road
Malton
YO17 0EY

Mr W Laider
Hon. Secretary & **Fixture Secretary**
Ashdale
8 Second Avenue
Beacon Park Second Avenue
Pickering
North Yorkshire YO18 8AH

MANCHESTER YMCA 1903
The Hollies, Mersey Meadows
Mersey Road, Didsbury
Manchester
M20 2GB

Mr Kennedy
Hon. Secretary & **Fixture Secretary**
Manchester YMCA
14 Beeston Close
Sharples
Bolton BL1 7RT

MARLBOROUGH COLLEGE 1861
Marlborough
Wiltshire SN8 1PA
01672 515511

Mr J E Patching
Hon. Secretary & **Fixture Secretary**
Marlborough College
Elmhurst Boarding House
Bath Road, Marlborough SN8 1PA

MENWITH HILL 1982
Menwith Hill Station
Harrogate
North Yorkshire HG3 2RF
01423 777788

Mr Steven Wilhelm	Mr Jan Swenson
Hon. Secretary	**Hon. Fixture Secretary**
Menwith Hill	Menwith Hill
RAF Menwith Hill	Sports and Fittness Centre
Box 494	RAF Menwith Hill
North Yorkshire	North Yorkshire
HG3 2RF	HG3 2RF

MERCHANT TAYLORS' SCHOOL (CROSBY) 1871
Crosby
Liverpool, Merseyside L23 0QP
0151 928 3618

For Attention Of: **Hon. Secretary**
Hon. Fixture Secretary
Merchant Taylors' School (Crosby)
Crosby
Liverpool, Merseyside L23 0QP

MERCHANT TAYLORS' SCHOOL (LONDON) 1859
Sandy Lodge Lane
Northwood
Middlesex HA6 2HT

For Attention Of: **Hon. Secretary**
Hon. Fixture Secretary
Merchant Taylors' School (Lon)
Sandy Lodge Lane
Northwood, Middlesex HA6 2HT

MERSEYSIDE FIRE BRIGADE
Newbrigton RUFC
Reeds Lane
New Brighton Wirral L46 3RH
0151 677 1873

Mr S Smith	For Attention Of:
Hon. Secretary	**Hon. Fixture Secretary**
Merseyside Fire Brigade	Merseyside Fire Brigade
4a The Parade, Wood Rd	Newbrigton RUFC
Halewood	Reeds Lane
Liverpool	New Brighton Wirral
L26 1UZ	L46 3RH

MERSEYSIDE POLICE 1960
Police Sports Ground
Riversdale Road
Aiburth, Liverpool
0151 427 2208

Sgt E Sheppard	Mr A Doyle
Hon. Secretary	**Hon. Fixture Secretary**
Merseyside Police	Merseyside Police
38 Lynmouth Road	c/o Walton Lane Police Stn
Aigburth	Liverpool
Merseyside L17 6AW	L5 6RB

MERTON AND MANSFIELD COLLEGES
Manor Road
Oxford
01865 276289

Mr R Amlot	Mr Damian King
Hon. Secretary	**Hon. Fixture Secretary**
Mansfield College	Mansfield College
Oxford OX1 3TF	Oxford OX1 3TF

METROPOLITAN POLICE (CHIGWELL) 1943
Met Police Sports Club
Chigwell Hall, High Road
Chigwell, Essex IG7 6BD
020 8500 2735

Mr D Fleming	Mr J Harding
Hon. Secretary	**Hon. Fixture Secretary**
108 Swanshope	19 Amanda Close
Loughton	Chigwell
Essex IG10 2NB	Essex IG7

MILL HILL SCHOOL
The Ridgeway
Mill Hill, London NW7 1QS
020 8959 1176

For Attention Of: **Hon. Secretary**
Hon. Fixture Secretary
Mill Hill School
The Ridgeway
Mill Hill, London NW7 1QS

MONTELL CARRINGTON RUFC
Carrington Works
Urmston
Manchester M31 4AJ

Mr A Kelly
Hon. Secretary & **Hon. Fixture Secretary**
The Farmers Arms
Longley Lane
Northerndon
Manchester M22 4JR

NESTLE ROWNTREE RFC
Mille Crux Sports Ground
Nestle UK
Haxby Road
York YO1 1XY

Hon. Secretary	Mr G Lavender
Nestle Rowntree RFC	**Hon. Fixture Secretary**
Mille Crux Sports Ground	Nestle Rowntree RFC
Nestle UK	52 Wilton Rise
Haxby Road	Holgate
York YO1 1XY	York

NEW COLLEGE & TEMPLETON
St Cross Road
Holywell
Oxford OX1 3BN

Mr C Houghton	For Attention Of:
Hon. Secretary	**Hon. Fixture Secretary**
New College & Templeton	New College & Templeton
New College	St Cross Road
St Cross Rd, Holywell	Holywell
Oxford	Oxford
OX1 3BN	OX1 3BN

NEWLAND PARK/BUCKS COLLEGE 1955
Gorelands Lane
Chalfont St Giles
Buckinghamshire HP8 4AD
01494 603084

Miss M Tremlin	Mr R Brooks
Hon. Secretary	**Hon. Fixture Secretary**
Newland Park/Bucks College	New Parks
Newlands Park,Gorelands Lane	44 Bateman Road
Chalfont St Giles	New Parks Estate
Bucks	Leicester
HP8 4AD	LE3 9HD

NEW PARKS   1968
New Parks Community College
St Oswalds Road
New Parks, Leicester
0116 287 2115

Mr T Smith
Hon. Secretary
New Parks
10 The Birds Nest Avenue
New Parks Estate
Leicester LE3 9NB

NORTH MIDLANDS FOOTBALL UNION

Mr C S Potts	Mr D I Robins
Hon. Secretary	**Hon. Fixture Secretary**
North Midlands F. U.	North Midlands F. U.
17 Ellesmere Court,	Flat 4 Halas House
Newport	Holywell Road
Shropshire	Malvern Worcs
TF10 7SD	WR14 4LE

NORTHAMPTONSHIRE POLICE 1966
NCC Sports & Social Club
Wootton Hall Park
Mereway, Northampton
01604 700934

Sgt A M Collins
Hon. Secretary
Northamptonshire Police
Traffics Ops, Mere Way
Northampton NN4 8BH

NORTHUMBRIA POLICE
North Road
Ponteland
Northumberland
01661 72555 Ext 4306

Sgt J Chappell	PC A Park
Hon. Secretary	**Hon. Fixture Secretary**
Northumbria Police	Northumbria Police
Cedar House	7 Axwell Park Road,
61A Dunsgreen	Blaydon
Ponteland, Newcastle-Upon-Tyne	Tyne & Wear
NE20 9EJ	NE21 5NR

NORTH YORKSHIRE POLICE   1974
c/o York Railway Inst RUFC
New Lane, Acomb
York
01904 798930

Mr S Smith
Hon. Secretary & **Fixture Secretary**
North Yorkshire Police
7 Whitehouse Dale
Pulleyn Drive
York YO2 2EB

OAKLANDS COLLEGE   1921
Oaklands Campus
Hatfield Road, St Albans
Hertfordshire AL4 0JA
01727 737000

Mr L Brown
Hon. Secretary & **Fixture Secretary**
Oaklands College
Oaklands Campus, Hatfield Rd
St Albans, Herts AL4 0JA

OLD AMPLEFORDIANS   1985
KCS Old Boys Rugby Club
Arthur Rd,Off West Barnes Lane
Motspur Park, London SW20
020 8336 2512

Mr Nick Dumbell	For Attention Of:
Hon. Secretary	**Hon. Fixture Secretary**
Old Amplefordians	Old Amplefordians
25 Greencroft Gardens	KCS Old Boys Rugby Club
Hampstead	Arthur Rd,Off West Barnes
Lane	
NW6 3LN	Motspur Park, London
	SW20

OLD DOWEGIANS   1956
Douai School
Upper Woolhampton
Reading, Berkshire RG7 5TH
01635 862735

Mr A Foster	J D Dukney
Hon. Secretary	**Hon. Fixture Secretary**
Old Dowegians	Old Dowegians
Chardith, Station Road	6 Chisbury
Gomshall, Guildford	Marlborough
Surrey	Wiltshire
GU5 9LQ	SN8 3JA

OLD EPSOMIAN   1963

Mr I R Edmond	Mr S T Schlaefli
Hon. Secretary	**Hon. Fixture Secretary**
Old Epsomian	Old Epsomian
Little Orchards	40 Broadhurst Gardens
Prince of Wales Road	Reigate
Outwood, Surrey	Surrey
RH1 5QU	RG2 8AW

OLDHAM COLLEGE (VETS)   1964
Tudor Lodge
Victoria Avenue East
Moston, Manchester M10 9SH
0161 682 9234

Mr J K McGuire	Mr M Garner
Hon. Secretary	**Hon. Fixture Secretary**
Oldham College (Vets)	Oldham College (Vets)
5 Gleneagles Avenue	21 Stansfield Street
Hopwood	Failsworth
Heywood, Lancashire	Manchester
OL10 2BZ	M35 9FA

OLD JOHNIANS   1960
Oaken Lane
Claygate
Surrey

Mr C D J Pearce	Mr D Devine
Hon. Secretary	**Hon. Fixture Secretary**
C/o Pinecroft	Old Johnians
The Barton	135e New Kings Road
Cobham	Fulham
Surrey KT11 2NJ	London SW6 4SL

OLD MALVERNIAN   1989
c/o Staines RUFC
Felthamhill Road
Feltham, Middlesex
020 8890 3051

For Attention Of:	**Hon. Secretary**
	Hon. Fixture Secretary

Old Malvernian, c/o Staines RUFC
Felthamhill Road, Feltham, Middlesex

OLD NEWBURIANS 1991
St Bartholomews School
Andover Road
Newbury, Berkshire RG14 6JP
01635 521255

Mr C O Hobbs
Hon. Secretary & **Fixture Secretary**
Old Newburians
19 York Road
Newbury
Berkshire RG14 7NJ

OLD PALMERIANS RUFC
Palmers College
Chadwell Road
Grays, Essex

Mr A Platt	Mr A Cresswell
Hon. Secretary	**Hon. Fixture Secretary**
17 McLoud Close	16 Parkstone Road
Grays	Cricket Hill
Essex	Felixtowe
RM17 5RD	Suffolk IP11 8NF

OLD PERSEAN 1949
The Perse School for Boys
Hills Road
Cambridge CB2 2QF

Mr P Harvey
Hon. Secretary & **Fixture Secretary**
Old Persean
Rosemary Cottage
49 Woodditton Road
Newmarket, Suffolk CB8 9BQ

SALIANS RFC
Rockwood
Clarendon Crescent
Sale, Cheshire

Mr J Tracey	Mr N Foster
Hon. Secretary	**Hon. Fixture Secretary**
12a Poolcroft	Flat 8, 21 Clyde Road
Sale	West Didsbury
Cheshire	Manchester
M33 2LF	M20 2NJ

OLD STONEHAMIANS 1961
Berkshire Sports/Social Club
Sonning Lane
Reading, Berkshire
01189 691340

Mr R J Eccleston
Hon. Secretary & **Fixture Secretary**
Old Stonehamians
99 Blenheim Road
Caversham Heights
Reading, Berkshire
RG4 7RP

OLD STANDFORDIANS 1984
Luynes Riseane
Buntingford, Hertfordshire
01763 273062

Mr E T Moody	Mr A Watson
Hon. Secretary	**Hon. Fixture Secretary**
Old Standfordians	Old Standfordians
522 Hatfield Road	37 Downhall Ley
St Albans	Buntingford
Hertfordshire AL4 0SX	Herts SG99 9JT

OLD WELLINGBURIAN 1981
Sports Ground
The Embankment
Wellingborough, Northants NN8 1LD
01933 225922

Mr N J Fry	Mr M Thompson
Hon. Secretary	**Hon. Fixture Secretary**
Old Wellingburian	Old Wellingburian
25 St. Mary's Road	25 Neath Avenue
Kettering	Bedford
Northants	MK41 0RJ
NN15 7BP	

ONLEY PARK 1972
HMY01
Onley
Rugby CV23 8AP
01788 522022 Ext 333/332

Mr N T Mapletoft	**Hon. Fixture Secretary**
Hon. Secretary	Onley Park
Onley Park	c/o HMY01 Onley
10 Avon Street,	Rugby
Clifton, Rugby	CV23 8AP
Warwickshire CV23 0DQ	

ORIEL COLLEGE
Oriel Avenue
Gorleston, Gt Yarmouth
Norfolk NR31 7JJ
01865 726440

Mr J Schad	Mr C Nelson
Hon. Secretary	**Hon. Fixture Secretary**
Oriel College	Oriel College
Bartlemas Farm	Oriel College
Cowley Rd	Oxford
Oxford	OX1 4EW

ORWELL 1969

Mr S R J Bevan	Mr D Botwright
Hon. Secretary	**Hon. Fixture Secretary**
Orwell	Orwell
34 Princethorpe Rd	12 Vermont Road
Ipswich	Ipswich
Suffolk	Suffolk
IP3 8NX	IP4 2SR
01473 726134	

OUNDLE SCHOOL
Oundle
Peterborough PE8 4EN
01832 73536

Master in Charge	Mr J Olver
Hon. Secretary	**Hon. Fixture Secretary**
Oundle School	The Mill
Oundle	Mill Land
Peterborough	Tallington
PE8 4EN	Lincolnshire

OXFORD UNIVERSITY 1869
Jackdaw Lane
Off Iffley Road
Oxford OX4 1EQ
01865 432000

Mr D J R Cole
Hon. Secretary & **Hon. Fixture Secretary**
Oxford University
Lavender Hill
6 Braybrook Close, Oxford OX7 4NT

OXTED 1983
Holland Rd
Hurst Green
Oxted
01883 717468

Mr N Madgett
Hon. Secretary & **Fixture Secretary**
Oxted
69 Hurst Green Road
Oxted, Surrey RH8 9AJ

PELHAMIANS
Taunton Avenue
Raynes Park
London SW20
020 894683855

Mr J Nichols
Hon. Secretary & **Fixture Secretary**
Pelhamians
28 Presburg Road
New Malden, Surrey KT3 5AH

PEMBROKE COLLEGE
Pembroke College
Cambridge CB2 1RF
01223 359543

Mr R Macfarlane
Hon. Secretary & **Fixture Secretary**
Pembroke College
College Rugby Club
Pembroke College, Cambridge CB2 1RF

PEMBROKE COLLEGE
Oxford OX1 1DW
01865 276444

Mr M J Clayton-Stead
Hon. Secretary & **Fixture Secretary**
Pembroke College, Oxford OX1 1DW

PETERHOUSE
Bentley Road
Cambridge CB2 1RD
01223 338200

Mr A Smith
Hon. Secretary
Peterhouse
Cambridge CB2 1RD

Mr A Smith
Hon. Fixture Secretary
Peterhouse
Cambridge CB2 1RD

PHOENIX GAS 1985
British Gas Eastern SSC
Whitewebbs Lane
Enfield, Middlesex
01992 760716

Mr W K Shorter
Hon. Secretary
8 Thatchers Drive
Elmstead Market
Colchester, Essex
CO7 7YE

Mr P Clarke
Hon. Fixture Secretary
British Gas
Hertford Reporting Centre
Marshgate Drive, Hertford

PHYLLOSANS 1969

Mr A E Walsham
Hon. Secretary
Phyllosans
The New House
Queens St
Hook Norton, Oxon OX15 5PJ

Mr S Samra
Hon. Fixture Secretary
Phyllosans
7 Granton Avenue
Upminster
Essex RM14 2RX

PILNING 1972
Beach Road
Severn Beach
Bristol
014545 633549

Mr J R Cox
Hon. Secretary
Pilning
Oregon, Ableton Lane,
Severn Beach
Nr Bristol BS35 4PP

Mr S Hinksman
Hon. Fixture Secretary
Pilning
16 Station Road,
Pilning
Nr Bristol BS35 4JP

PLYMSTOCK 1988
Staddiscombe Playing Fields
Staddiscombe Road
Plymstock, Plymouth

Ms L Stewart
Hon. Secretary
Laburnham House
Fields
4 Woodland Avenue
Elburton, Plymouth
PL9 8JE

For Attention Of:
Hon. Fixture Secretary
Staddiscombe Playing

Staddiscombe Road
Plymstock, Plymouth

POTTON 1978
2nd Meadow
Henry Smith Playing Fields
Brook End, Potton
01767 261433

Mr P Carroll
Hon. Secretary
1 Catherine Close
Potton
Nr Sandy, Beds SG19 2PR

Mr G Corrin
Hon. Fixture Secretary
22 Mill Lane
Potton
Beds, SG19 2PG

PREP SCHOOL WANDERERS 1987
Wellington College
Crowthorne
Berkshire RG45 7PU
01344 772262

Mr M Farrow
Hon. Secretary
Orchard Cottage
Station Road
Cookham, Berkshire
SL6 9BU

Mr G Ruck
Hon. Fixture Secretary
Dorton House School
Seal Drive
Seal, Nr Sevenoaks, Kent

PRESCOT-RAINHILL 1949
Haresfinch Social Club
Haresfinch Road
St Helens, Merseyside

Mr K O'Keefe
Hon. Secretary
Prescot-Rainhill
39 French St
Toll Bar, St Helens
Merseyside

For Attention Of:
Hon. Fixture Secretary
Prescot-Rainhill
Haresfinch Social Club
Haresfinch Road
St Helens, Merseyside

PRUDHOE & STOCKSFIELD RFC
Stocksfield Cricket & Football
Stocksfield
Northumberland NE43 7NN

Mr P Jones
Hon. Secretary
152 New Ridley Road
Stocksfield
Northumberland
NE43 7EH

Mr J Reed
Hon. Fixture Secretary
Warden Flat
1 Gill Street
Newcastle upon Tyne
NE4 8BH

PRUDENTIAL IBIS   1993
Prudential Ibis Club
Scours Lane
Reading, Berkshire RG3 6AY
01189 424130

Mr P J Bishop
Hon. Secretary
Prudential Ibis
16 The Fells
Tilehurst
Reading, Berkshire
RG31 5XY

Mr G McCoy
Hon. Fixture Secretary
Prudential Ibis
27 Shaftesbury Road
Reading
Berkshire

QUEENS' COLLEGE
Queens College Playing Grounds
Barton Road
Cambridge
01223 335511

Mr Freddie New
Hon. Secretary
Queens' College
Queens College
Grounds
Cambridge
CB3 9ET

For Attention Of:
Hon. Fixture Secretary
Queens' College
Queens College Playing

Barton Road
Cambridge

QUEEN'S COLLEGE
Abingdon Road
Oxford
01865 242129

Mr A Parsons
Hon. Secretary
Queen's College RFC
Queen's College
OX1 4AW

Mr E Slim
Hon. Fixture Secretary
Queens College RFC
Queen's College
OX1 4AW

RACAL DECCA RFC
Raccal Decca S & S Club
Kingston Road
Tolworth
Surrey KT5 9NT

Mr D Donald
Hon. Secretary
4 Donalds Wood Gardens
Tolworth
Surrey
KT5 9NP

Hon. Fixture Secretary
Raccal Decca RFC
Raccal Decca S & S Club
Kingston Road
Tolworth
Surrey KT5 9NT

RAMSEY IOM   1981
New Ground,
Mooragh Promenade
Ramsey, Isle of Man

Mr D M Christian
Hon. Secretary
Ramsey IOM
Beaconsfield Cottage
Bowring Road
Ramsey, Isle Of Man
IM8 3EV

Mr Tommy Callister
Hon. Fixture Secretary
Ramsey IOM
3 Chapel Close
Ballaugh
Isle of Man

READING SCHOOL
Reading
Berkshire
01189 61406

Hon. Secretary
Reading School
Reading School
Reading, Berkshire

For Attention Of:
Hon. Fixture Secretary
Reading School
Reading, Berkshire

READING WEST INDIANS   1975
Redingensians Sports Ground
Old Bath Road, Sonning
Nr Reading, Berkshire
RG4 0TQ
0118 969 5259

Mr K H Hinds
Hon. Secretary
Reading West Indians
243 Waverley Road
Reading
Berkshire RG30 2QH

Mr J R Bell
Hon. Fixture Secretary
Reading Welsh Indians
36 Lismore Close
Woodley, Nr Reading
BerkshireRG5 3RT

ROBINSON COLLEGE
Cambridge CB3 9AN
01223 741270

For the attn. of

Robinson College
College Rugby Club
Robinson College
Cambridge CB3 9AN

Hon. Secretary
Hon. Fixture Secretary

RUGBY SCHOOL   1823
The Senior Common Room
20-22 Horton Crescent
Rugby, Warwickshire CV22 5DJ
01788 578006

Mr R D R Ray
Hon. Secretary & **Fixture**
Rugby School
Flat 2, 12 Hillmorton Road
Rugby, Warwickshire CV25 4DR

RUGBY WELSH   1936
Bakehouse Lane
Rugby
Warwickshire CV21 2DB
01788 565605

Mr K E Mills
Hon. Secretary
Rugby Welsh
18 Beatty Drive
Bilton, Rugby
Warwickshire CV22 7ET

Mr M James
Hon. Fixture Secretary
Rugby Welsh
17 Watson Road
Chapelfields
Coventry CV5 8EW

SEDGEFIELD   1985
Sedgefield Community College
Sedgefield, Stockton-on-Tees
Cleveland
01740 621097

Mr N Hetherington
Hon. Secretary
Sedgefield
8 West End
Sedgefield, Stockton-on-Tees
Cleveland TS21 2BS

Mr S Bintoff
Hon. Fixture Secretary
Sedgefield
3 Pineridge Avenue
Sedgefield
Cleveland TS21 3EF

SELWYN COLLEGE   1882
Fulbrooke Road
Cambridge CB3 14G
01223 741201

Mr C Dale
Hon. Secretary
Selwyn College
Selwyn College
Cambridge
CB39 DLE

For Attention Of:
Hon. Fixture Secretary
Selwyn College
Fulbrooke Road
Cambridge
CB3 14G

SHADWELL 1993
Aveley Sports And Social Club
Purfleet Road
Aveley, South Ockendon, Essex RM15 4DT
01708 863611

Mr S Fryatt
Hon. Secretary & **Fixture Secretary**
Shadwell
104 Hornchurch Road
Hornchurch, Essex RM11 1DL

SHEPSHED 1987
Hind Leys College
Forest Street, Shepshed
Loughborough, Leicestershire
01509 503592

Mr J Ryan   Mr R Short
Hon. Secretary   **Hon. Fixture Secretary**
Shepshed   Shepshed
23a Chapel Street   Hind Leys Cottage
Shepshed   Forest Street, Shepshed
Leicestershire LE12 9AF   Leicestershire

SHERBORNE SCHOOL 1846
Sherborne
Dorset
01935 81891

For Attention Of:
Hon. Secretary   **Hon. Fixture Secretary**
Sherborne School,   Sherborne School,
Sherborne,   Sherborne,
Dorset DT9 3AP   Dorset DT9 3AP

SHOTTERY 1985
Shottery Field
Shottery Road
Stratford Upon Avon

Mr D Evans   Mr S Burford
Hon. Secretary   **Hon. Fixture Secretary**
Shottery   Shottery
21 Oak Lane, Tiddington   20 Valetta Way
Stratford upon Avon   Wellesbourne
Warwickshire CV37 7BU   Warwicks

SIDNEY SUSSEX COLLEGE
Cambridge
CB2 3HU

Mr M Petevinos   For Attention Of:
Hon. Secretary   **Hon. Fixture Secretary**
Sidney Sussex College   Sidney Sussex College
College Rugby Club   CB2 3HU
Sidney Sussex College
Cambridge CB2 3HU

SNOWDOWN COLLIERY WELFARE 1937
Snowdown Colliery Welfare Recreation
Aylesham
Canterbury, Kent
01304 840278

Mr D Price   Mr I Prosser
Hon. Secretary   **Hon. Fixture Secretary**
Snowdown C.W.   Snowdown C.W.
157 Cornwallis Avenue   7 Dorman Avenue South,
Aylesham   Aylesham
Canterbury   Canterbury,
Kent CT3 3HJ   Kent CT3 3AB

SOUTHAMPTON POST OFFICE 1985
Test Park Playing Fields
Lower Brownhill Road
Southampton SO16 9HE
02380 737777

Mr P F Evans
Hon. Secretary & **Fixture Secretary**
Southampton Post Office
68 Northlands Road, Romsey, Hants SO51 5SE

SOUTHERN NOMADS 1982
King Williams College
Castletown, Isle of Man

Mr D Stewart   Mr R Hirst
Hon. Secretary   **Hon. Fixture Secretary**
Southern Nomads   Southern Nomads
Bay View House   Beulah
Victoria St., Porterin,   Fistard Road, Port St Mary
Isle of Man IM9 6LD   Isle of Man IM9 5HE

SOUTH LIVERPOOL 1963
Dunlop Sports and Social Club
Speke Hall Avenue
Speke, Liverpool L24
0151 486 1588

Mr L Sherrington   Mr D Edge
Hon. Secretary   **Hon. Fixture Secretary**
South Liverpool   South Liverpool
14 Brook Way   93 Millwood Road
Great Sankey   Speke
Warrington, Cheshire   Liverpool
WA5 1RZ   L24 2UR

SOUTH YORKSHIRE FIRE SERVICE 1975
Thornensians RUFC
Coulman Rd
Thorne, Doncaster DN8 5BU
01405 812746

Mr P R Shillito   Mr M Wordsworth
Hon. Secretary   **Hon. Fixture Secretary**
S. Yorkshire Fire Service   S. Yorkshire Fire Service
26 Westminster Close   2 Scott Walk
Bramley, Rotherham   Maltby, Rotherham
S. Yorks. S66 1WJ   S. Yorks. S66 8RA

SOUTH YORKSHIRE POLICE 1972
Niagra Sports Ground
Niagra Road, Sheffield S6 1LU
0114 2764946

PC S W Stokes   Mr John Turner
Hon. Secretary   **Hon. Fixture Secretary**
South Yorkshire Police   South Yorkshire Police
c/o West Bar Police Station c/o Crime Prevention Dept.
West Bar   Woodseats Police Station
Sheffield S1 2DA   Sheffield S8 0SL

ST ANNE'S AND ST JOHN'S COLLEGES
St Johns College Sports Ground
Woodstock Road
Oxford X1 3JP
01865 515561

Mr Peter Singfield   For Attention Of:
Hon. Secretary   **Hon. Fixture Secretary**
St Anne's & St John's Colleges St A. & St J. Colleges
St John's College   St Johns Coll. Sports Gnd
Oxford   Woodstock Road
OX1 3JP   Oxford

STANDARD TELEPHONES (GREENWICH) 1936

Mr R Williams
Hon. Secretary
Standard Telephones (Greenwich)
59 High St
Bexley
Kent
DA5 1AB

Mr G Dorton
Hon. Fixture Secretary
Standard Telephones
(Greenwich)
698 Downham Way
Downham
Kent

ST BEES SCHOOL 1870
The Foundation
St Bees
Cumbria
CA27 0DS
01946 822286 / 822254

Mr H Lewis
Hon. Secretary & **Fixture Secretary**
St Bees School
School House
St Bees School
Cumbria
CA27 0DS

ST CATHARINE'S COLLEGE
Grantchester Meadows
South Green Road
Cambridge
01223 352474

Hon. Secretary
St Catharine's College
College Rugby Club
St Catharine's College
Cambridge
CB2 1RL

For Attention Of:
Hon. Fixture Secretary
St Catharine's College
Grantchester Meadows
South Green Road
Cambridge

ST CATHERINE'S COLLEGE 1963
The Parks
Oxford OX1 3UJ
01865 271700

Mr Mohamed Hassam
Hon. Secretary & **Fixture Secretary**
St Catherine's College
St Catherine's College
Manor Road
Oxford
OX1 3UJ

ST EDMUND HALL 1930
Oxford
OX1 4AR
01865 557106 (Groundsman)

Mr S Gough
Hon. Secretary
St Edmund Hall
St Edmund Hall
Oxford
OX1 4AR

For Attention Of:
Hon. Fixture Secretary
St Edmund Hall
St Edmund Hall
Oxford
OX1 4AR

ST EDMUND'S COLLEGE

Hon Secretary
Hon. Secretary
St Edmund's College
College Rugby Clube
St Edmund's College
Cambridge CB2 0BN

ST HELIER 1892
1 Anley Street
St Helier
Jersey, Channel Islands JE2 3QE
01534 888179

Mr A Blaby
Hon. Secretary
St Helier
8 Valley Court
Les Grands Vaux, St Helier
Jersey
JE2 4NA

Mr M Preston
Hon. Fixture Secretary
St Helier
4 Maitland Barn
Trinity Hill
St Helier, Jersey
JE2 4JP

ST HUGH'S COLLEGE 1987
St Hughes College
St Margrets Rd
Oxford OX2 6LE

Mr N Fox
Hon. Secretary & **Fixture Secretary**
St Hugh's College
Oxford OX2 6LE

ST JACQUES 1978
KGV Playing Fields
Rue Cohu, Castel
Guernsey, Channel Isles
GY5 7SZ
01481 56617

Miss C Moxon
Hon. Secretary
St Jacques
The Willows
Blanche Carrier Lane, Vale
Guernsey, Channel Isles
GY3 5DL

Mr A R Ingroville
Hon. Fixture Secretary
St Jacques
Bordeaux Cottage
Brock Road, St Sampsons
Guernsey
GY2 4PN

ST JOHN'S COLLEGE 1867
Cambridge CB2 1TP
01223 338600

Mr D P Langford
Hon. Secretary
St John's College
College Rugby Club
St John's College
Cambridge
CB2 1TP

Mr I A De Weymarn
Hon. Fixture Secretary
St John's College
College Rugby Club
St John's College
Cambridge
CB2 1TP

ST PAUL'S SCHOOL
Lonsdale Road
Barnes SW13 9JT
020 8748 9162

Hon. Secretary
St Paul's School
St Paul's School
Barnes
London
SW13 9JT

For Attention Of:
Hon. Fixture Secretary
St Paul's School
Lonsdale Road
Barnes
SW13 9JT

ST PETER'S COLLEGE
Southern Bypass
Oxford OX1 5AA
01865 727468

Mr A Salvoni
Hon. Secretary
St Peter's College
St Peter's College
Southern Bypass
Oxford OX1 5AA

For Attention Of:
Hon. Fixture Secretary
St Peter's College
Southern Bypass
Oxford
OX1 5AA

ST PETER'S SCHOOL, YORK 1874
Clifton
Yorkshire YO3 6AB
01904 623213

Hon. Secretary
St Peter's School, York
St Peter's School
York

For Attention Of:
Hon. Fixture Secretary
St Peter's School, York
Clifton
Yorkshire YO3 6AB

SURREY CONSTABULARY 1967
Police HQ
Mount Browne
Sandy Lane, Guildford GU3 1HG
01483 571212

Mr D Harriott
Hon. Secretary
Surrey Constabulary
Police Helicopter Unit
Fairoaks Airport
Chobham, Surrey
GU24 8HU

Mr J Bennett
Hon. Fixture Secretary
Surrey Constabulary
Guildford Police Station,
Margaret Road,
Guildford, Surrey
GU1 4QS

SUTTON VALENCE SCHOOL 1874
Maidstone
Kent

Hon. Secretary
Sutton Valence School
Sutton Valence School
Sutton, Surrey

For Attention Of:
Hon. Fixture Secretary
Sutton Valence School
Maidstone

SUTTON BONINGTON
School of Agriculture
Sutton Bonington
Nr Loughborough LE12 5RD
0115 951 5151 Ext 8648

Mr John Hughes
Hon. Secretary
Sutton Bonington
SBRFC, Ameneities Building
University of Nottingham
Sutton Bonington Campus
Campus
LE12 5RD

Mr S Jones
Hon. Fixture Secretary
Sutton Bonington
SBRFC Ameneities Building
University of Nottingham
Sutton Bonnington

LE12 5RD

TESCO 1977
Tesco Country Club
Theobalds Lane
Cheshunt, Hertfordshire EN8 8YA
01992 625278

Mr S W Wyatt
Hon. Secretary
Tesco
7 Hazeldell
Watton at Stone
Herts SG14 3SL

Mr I Bundock
Hon. Fixture Secretary
Tesco
41 Telfords Yarde
6-8 The Highway
Wapping, London E1 9BQ

THE MOUNT 1989
HMP The Mount
Molyneaux Avenue HP3 0QL
01442 834363 Ext 252

Mr I Harris
Hon. Secretary
The Mount
PE Instructor, HMP The Mount
Molyneaux Avenue
Bovingdon, Hertfordshire
HP3 0NZ

For Attention Of:
Hon. Fixture Secretary
The Mount
HMP The Mount
Molyneaux Avenue
HP3 0QL

TONBRIDGE SCHOOL 1870
The '50'
Tonbridge School
High Street, Tonbridge, Kent TN9 1JP
01732 365555

Mr G P Gales
Hon. Secretary & Fixture Secretary
Tonbridge School
Clare House
57 London Road
Tonbridge, Kent

TRINITY COLLEGE 1872
Trinity Old Field
Grange Rd
Cambridge CB2 1TQ
01223 359566

For Attention Of:
Hon. Secretary
Trinity College, Trinity Old Field,
Grange Rd, Cambridge CB2 1TQ

For Attention Of:
Hon. Fixture Secretary

TRINITY HALL
Cambridge CB2 1TJ
01223 332500

For Attention of:
Hon. Secretary
Trinity Hall, College Rugby Club
Cambridge CB2 1TJ

For Attention Of:
Hon. Fixture Secretary
Cambridge

UNITED HOSPITALS 1875
St Mary's Hospital Athletic
Ground, Udney Park Road
Teddington, Middlesex
020 89773100

Mr David Badenock FRCS
Hon. Secretary
United Hospitals
123 Harley Street
London
W1N 1HE

Dr Andy Platts
Hon. Fixture Secretary
United Hospitals
Dept. Radiology
The Royal Free Hospital
Pond St. Hampstead
NW3 2QG

UNIVERSITY COLLEGE
Abingdon Road
Oxford
01865 243490

Mr T Rutherford
Hon. Secretary
University College
Abington Road,
Oxford OX1 4BH

For Attention Of:
Hon. Fixture Secretary
University College
Abingdon Road
Oxford OX1 4BH

UNIVERSITY COLLEGE SCHOOL 1882
Frognal
London
NW3
020 7435 2215

Hon. Secretary
University College School
University College School
Frogal, Hampstead
London
NW3 6XH

For Attention Of:
Hon. Fixture Secretary
University College School
Frognal
London
NW3

UPPINGHAM SCHOOL 1889
Uppingham
Leicestershire LE15 9QE
01572 822533

Mr Master I/C Rugby | For Attention Of:
Hon. Secretary | **Hon. Fixture Secretary**
Uppingham School | Uppingham School
Common Room, Uppingham School | Uppingham
Uppingham | Leicestershire
Rutland | LE15 9QE

WADHAM COLLEGE
Marston Ferry Road
Oxford OX1 3PN
01865 53819

Mr B O'Grady
Hon. Secretary & **Fixture Secretary**
Wadham College
Parks Rd, Oxford OX1 3PN

WARWICK 1976
Hampton Fields
Hampton Road
Warwick
01926 410972

Mr P O'Rourke
Hon. Secretary & **Fixture Secretary**
Warwick
35 Moreall Meadows
Gibbett Hill
Coventry CV4 7HL

WARWICKSHIRE CONSTABULARY 1947
Police HQ-P O Box 4
Leek Wootton
Warwickshire CV35 7QB
01926 415000

Mr G T Moreton | Mr S Foster
Hon. Secretary | **Hon. Fixture Secretary**
Warwickshire Constabulary | Warwickshire Constabulary
118 Higham Lane | Police Station
Nuneaton | Vicarage St, Nuneaton
Warwickshire | Warwickshire
CV11 6AX | CV11 4DW

WASHINGTON 1976
Northern Area Playing Fields
Stephenson Industrial Estate
Washington, Tyne & Wear

Mr P Guy | Mr J Watlen
Hon. Secretary | **Hon. Fixture Secretary**
Washington | Washington
13 Beech Terrace | 7 Bridekirk
South Moor, Stanley | Albany
County Durham | Washington
DH9 7EL | NE37 1ND

WATERLOOVILLE 1981
Rowlands Avenue
Waterlooville, Hampshire
01705 264080

Mr R Mowatt | Mr I Day
Hon. Secretary | **Hon. Fixture Secretary**
Waterlooville | Waterlooville
9 Holst Way | Bodywork Gym
Purbrook | 270a London Road
Waterlooville, Hants | Waterlooville, Hants
PO7 5SJ | PO7 7HG

WATTON
Dereham Road Sports Centre
Watton
Norfolk
01953 881281

Mr R Watson | Mr S Blackwood
Hon. Secretary | **Hon. Fixture Secretary**
Watton | Watton
4 Guarnock Terrace | 36 Queensway
King's Lynn | Watton
Norfolk PE30 5QT | Norfolk IP25 6BL

WELLINGTON COLLEGE 1859
Crowthorne
Berkshire
01344 772262

Hon. Secretary | For Attention Of:
Wellington College | **Hon. Fixture Secretary**
Wellington College | Wellington College
Crowthorne | Crowthorne
Berkshire | Berkshire

WEST CORNWALL POLICE 1947
Truro Rugby Grounds
Truro TR4 8NG
01209 714881

Mr M Boyling
Hon. Secretary & **Fixture Secretary**
West Cornwall Police
44 Messack Close
Falmouth
Cornwall TR11 4SH

WEST MIDLANDS POLICE 1935
W Mids Police Training Centre
Tally Ho!, Pershore Road
Edgbaston, Birmingham B5 7RN
0121 472 2944

Mr D Ashford | Mr J Grante
Hon. Secretary | **Hon. Fixture Secretary**
West Midlands Police | West Midlands Police
c/o Crime Manager | c/o CID Office
Sutton Coldfield Police Station, Lichfield Road,
Sutton Coldfield, W Midlands B74 2NR

WHEATSHEAF CABIN CREW 1992
Holders Rd
Amesbury
Wiltshire

Mrs L Gollop | For Attention Of:
Hon. Secretary | **Hon. Fixture Secretary**
Wheatsheaf Cabin Crew | Wheatsheaf Cabin Crew
39a Upperwoodford | Holders Rd
Salisbury | Amesbury
Wiltshire | Wiltshire

WHITGIFT SCHOOL 1871
Haling Park
Nottingham Road
South Croydon CR2 6YT
020 8688 9222

Hon. Secretary | For Attention Of:
Whitgift School | **Hon. Fixture Secretary**
Whitgift School | Whitgift School
Croydon | Haling Park
Surrey | Nottingham Road
CR2 6YT | South Croydon
| CR2 6YT

WHITWELL   1985
Markland Campus,
N Derbyshire Tertiary College
Sheffield Rd, Creswell, Notts F80 4HW
01909 724908

Mrs J Marshall
Hon. Secretary
Whitwell
3 Duke Street
Whitwell, Worksop
Nottingham S80 4TH

Mr M Passey
Hon. Fixture Secretary
Whitwell
40 Chesterfield Road
Barlborough
Derbyshire S43 4TT

WILTSHIRE POLICE
Police Headquarters
London Road
Devizes, Wiltshire SN10 2DN
01380 722341

Sgt. A Peach
Hon. Secretary
Wiltshire Police
Div. HQ. Wiltshire Police
Wood Lane, Chippenham SN15 3DH

WOLFSON COLLEGE
Cambridge CB3 9BB

Dr F Walclron - Lynch
Hon. Secretary
Wolfson College
Cambridge
CB3 9BB

Mr M Daniels
Hon. Fixture Secretary
Wolfson College
Cambridge
CB3 9BB

WOODRUSH RFC
Icknield Street
Forhill
Birmingham B38 0EL

Mr P Leahy
Hon. Secretary
8 Burns Close
Headless Cross
Redditch, Worcs
B97 5BS

Mr L Frogatt
Hon. Fixture Secretary
70 Meadow Road
Wythall
Birmingham
B47 6EQ

WORCESTER COLLEGE
Worcester Street
Oxford OX1 2HB
0836 251002

Dr J D Bradshaw
Hon. Secretary & **Fixture Secretary**
Worcester College
Oxford OX1 2HB

STUDENT R.F.U.

Anglia (Chelmsford) University
1969
Hon. Secretary & Fixture Secretary
Mr S Dupree
Anglia (Chelmsford) University
132 Baddow Hall Cresent
Great Baddow
Nr Chelmsford, Essex
CM2 7BU

Bath Spa University College
Hon. Secretary
F.A.O. Hon. Secretary
Bath Spa University College

Berkshire College of Agriculture
Hall Place
Burchetts Green
Nr Maidenhead, Berkshire
SL6 6QR
01628 824444

Hon. Secretary
Mr J Hansen
Berkshire College of Agriculture
Hall Place
Burchetts Green
Maidenhead SL6 6QR

Hon. Fixture Sec.
F.A.O. Hon. Fixture Sec.
Berkshire College of Agriculture
Hall Place
Burchetts Green
Nr Maidenhead, Berkshire
SL6 6QR

Bishop Burton College
1968
Bishop Burton College
Beverley
East Yorkshire
HU17 8QG
01964 553064

Hon. Secretary
Mr R A Rank
Bishop Burton College
Field View
Bishop Burton College
Beverley
East Yorkshire
HU17 8QF

Hon. Fixture Sec.
Mr C Coates
Bishop Burton College
Bexerby
East Yorkshire HU11 8QY

Bournemouth University
1976
Bournemouth Sports Club
East Parley, Chapel Gate
Bournemouth BH23 6DB
01202 581933

Hon. Secretary & Fixture Secretary
Ms Yvonne O'Connor
Bournemouth University
Dept of Sport and Recreation
Poole House,
Fern Barrow
BH12 5BB

Brunel University
1966
University Playing Fields
Kingston Lane
Uxbridge,
Middlesex UB8 3PH
01895 462200

Mr Sean McClean
Hon. Secretary
Brunel University
30 Packend Road
Gloucester GL1 3AL

Hon. Fixture Sec.
F.A.O. Hon. Fixture Sec.
Brunel University
University Playing Fields
Kingston Lane
Uxbridge,
Middlesex UB8 3PH

Brunel University College
1891
Jersey Road
Osterley
Middlesex TW7 4QR
020 8891 0721

Hon. Secretary
Mr J S Hunter
Brunel University College
Dept. of Sports Sciences
Brunel University (Osterley)
Borough Road, Isleworth, Middx
TW7 5DU

Hon. Fixture Sec.
Mr H Morgan
Brunel University College
52 Hitherbrook Road
Hayes, Middlesex UB3 3AD

Bucks College of Higher Education
Kingsmead Road
Loudwater
High Wycombe

Hon. Secretary & Fixture Secretary
Ms Louise Stormont
Bucks College of Higher Education
Bucks. College Students Union
Queen Alexandra Road
High Wycombe,
Bucks HP11 2JZ

Cheltenham & Glos College of Higher Education
1889
The Folley
Swindon Road
Cheltenham,
Gloucestershire
GL51 9AZ
01242 543439

Hon. Secretary
Ms N Browm
Cheltenham & Glos CHE
Student Union Office
Francis Close Hall
Swindon Rd,Cheltenham
GL51 9AZ

Hon. Fixture Sec.
Mr P Hunt
Cheltenham & Glos CHE
c/o Francis Close Hall
Swindon Rd
Cheltenham, Glos GL51 9AZ

City and Guilds College
Imperial College Athletic Gnd
Sipson Lane
Harlington, Middx
020 8759 9649

Hon. Secretary
City and Guilds College
Imperial College of Science
Technology & Medicine Level 3
Mech Eng, Exhibition Rd
London SW7 2BX

Hon. Fixture Sec.
City and Guilds College
City & Guilds Students Union
Exhibition Rd
London SW7 2BX

City University
1912
Kings College Sports Ground
Window Avenue
New Malden, Surrey KT3 5HA
020 8942 0495

Hon. Secretary
City University, Students Union
Northampton Square, London
EC1 0HB

Hon. Fixture Sec.
City University, Students Union
Northampton Square, London
EC1 0HB

Coventry University
1969
Westwood Heath Playing Fields
Kirby Corner Road
Coventry
024 76465642

Hon. Secretary
Mr Paul Carfield
Coventry University
Students Union
Priory Street, Coventry CV2 5FJ

Hon. Fixture Sec.
Mr Bryan Loftus
Coventry University RFC
Coventry University
Students Union
Priory Street, Coventry CV1 5FJ

Cranfield University
Bedford
Bedfordshire MK43 0AL
01234 750111 Ext 2606

Hon. Secretary
The Secretary
Cranfield University
Cranfield Univ. Rugby Club
Building 114, Cranfield Univ.
Wharley End, Beds MK43 0AL

Hon. Fixture Sec.
Mr M J Lewis
Cranfield University
4a The Crescent
Bedford MK40 2RT

Crewe & Alsager College
1946
Alsager College
Hassall Road, Alsager
Stoke-on-Trent ST7 2HL
01270 882580

Ms Barbara Clark
Hon. Secretary & Fixture Secretary
Crewe & Alsager College
Hassall Road, Alsager,
Stoke-on-Trent ST7 2HL

De Montfort Bedford University

Hon. Secretary
F.A.O. Hon. Secretary
De Montfort Bedford University

Durham University
1875
The Racecourse Ground
Green Lane, Durham DH1
0191 374 7021

Hon. Secretary & Fixture Secretary
Mr E R Wood
Durham University
1 Hillcrest Mews, Durham DH1 1RD

Edge Hill University College
1960
St Helens Road
Ormskirk, Lancashire L39 4QP
01695 575457

Hon. Secretary
Mr T D McMath
Edge Hill University College
81 Childwall Valley Road
Liverpool L16 4PD

Hon. Fixture Sec.
F.A.O. Hon. Fixture Sec.
Edge Hill University College
St Helens Road
Ormskirk
Lancashire L39 4QP

Farnborough College of Technology
1990
Farnborough Rugby Club
Tile Barn Close
Farnborough, Hampshire
01252 542750

Hon. Secretary
Mr B Burrowes
Farnborough College of Technology
Farnborough College Of Tech.
Students Union
Boundary Road, Farnborough
GU14 6SB

Hon. Fixture Sec.
Mr Niall Dooley
Farnborough College of Technology
FCOT S.U.
Boundary Road, Farnborough
Hants
GU14 6SB

Goldsmiths College
Loring Hall
Water Lane
Sidcup, Kent
020 8300 8712

Hon. Secretary
Mr J Courtney
Goldsmiths College
General Manager, GSCU
Dixon Road
New Cross, LONDON SE14 6NW

Hon. Fixture Sec.
Mr S Henwood
Goldsmiths College
Students Union Offices
Lewisham Way
New Cross, London SE14

Hadlow College
1968
Hadlow College
Hadlow
Tonbridge, Kent TN11 0AL
01732 850551

Hon. Secretary & Fixture Secretary
Mr S G Hewitt
Hadlow College
11 Appletons
Hadlow
Tonbridge, Kent TN11 0DT

Harper Adams Agricultural College
Harper Adams Univ College
Newport
Shropshire TF10 8NB
01952 815313

Hon. Secretary
Mr Harp
Harper Adams Agricultural College
Head of Student Services
Harper Adams College
Newport, Shropshire TF10 8NB

Hon. Fixture Sec.
Harper Adams Agricultural College
Harper Adams College
Newport
Shropshire TF10 8NB

Imperial College
Imperial College Athletic Grd
Sipson Lane
Harlington, Middx UB3 5AQ
020 8759 9649

Hon. Secretary
Mr T Collins
Imperial College
c/o Roger Pownall
Southside Bar, Imperial Coll.
Princes Gdn, South Kensington
SW7 1LU

Hon. Fixture Sec.
Mr M Chahal
Imperial College
c/o Imperial College RFC
Imperial College Union,
Beit Quad, London SW7 2BB

Kingston University Guild of Students
1948
Tolworth Court
Old Kingston Road
Tolworth, Surrey KT4 7QH
020 8330 2865

Hon. Secretary & Fixture Secretary
Mrs I Holmes
K.U. Guild of Students
Clubs/Societies Administrator
Kingston Univ Guild of Stds
Penrhyn Road, Kingston, Surrey
KT1 2EE

King's College Hospital
1869
The Griffin Sportsground
12 Dulwich Village
Dulwich, London SE21 7AL
020 8693 6900/2330

Hon. Secretary
Mr J Woods
Life Sciences
King's College London
150 Stamford Street
London SE1 9NN

Hon. Fixture Sec.
Mr K Gutridge
King's College Hospital
203 Camberwell New Road
London SE5 0TJ

King's College School
1864
Southside, Wimbledon Common
London SW19 4TT
020 8947 9311

Hon. Secretary & Fixture Secretary
Mr Master I/C Rugby
King's College School

Kings College
1862
KCLSU Sports Ground
Windsor Avenue
Berrylands, Surrey KT3 5HA
020 8942 0495

Hon. Secretary
Ms C Down
Kings College
KCLSU Strand
Macadam Building
Surrey Street, London WC2R 2NS

Hon. Fixture Sec.
Mr Tim Wright
Kings College

Leeds Medics and Dentists
1931
University Playing Fields
Weetwood, Leeds
0113 2751993

Hon. Secretary
Mr R Finch
12 Norwood Terrace, Leeds LS6 1EA

Hon. Fixture Sec.
Mr M Dodd
145 Hyde Park Rd, Leeds LS6 1AJ

Liverpool John Moores University
1971
Birkenhead Park RFC
Upper Park, Park Road North
Birkenhead, Wirral L41 8AD
0151 6524646

Hon. Secretary
Ms R Brown
Liverpool John Moores University
James Moore University

St Nicholas Centre
Great Orford Street
Liverpool L3 5YD

Liverpool Medical School
1960
Geoffrey Hughes Memorial Groun
Mather Avenue
Liverpool L18
0151 706 2000 Ext 4271

Hon. Secretary
Mr M Bishton
Liverpool Medical School
54 Wellington Avenue
Wavertree, Liverpool L15 0EH

Hon. Fixture Sec.
Mr J Oates
Liverpool Medical School
Duncan Building RLUH
Daulby Street
Liverpool L69 3BX

London School of Economics
1992
LSE Sports Ground
Windsor Avenue
New Malden, Surrey KT3
020 8942 1229

Hon. Secretary
Ms S Breaks
LSE Athletic Union
RM E178
East Building, Houghton Street
WC2 2AE

Hon. Fixture Sec.
Mr R Sellers
LSE A V
RM E178 East BDLG
Houghton Street, London
WC2A 2AE

London Guildhall University
1971
c/o Eton Manor RFC
Eaton Park, Ruckholt Road
Leyton E10
020 8539 7218

Hon. Secretary
Mr D Agyemang
London Guildhall University
Students Union
2 Goulston Street
London E1 7TP

Hon. Fixture Sec.
Mr S Murphy
London Guildhall University
Students Union
2 Goulston Street
London E1 7TP

Manchester Medicals
1876
University Sports Ground
Willenhall Road
Wythenshawe, Manchester
0161 998 4157

Hon. Secretary

Mr P Wheatley-Price
MSRC Office, Medical School
Stopford Building
Oxford Road, Manchester

Hon. Fixture Sec.
Mr C Repanos
MSRC Office, Medical School
Stopford Building, Oxford Road
Manchester

Manchester Metropolitan University
1957
c/o Heaton Moor RFC
Green Lane, Stockport

Hon. Secretary
Mr G J Davison
Manchester Metropolitan University
Students Union
Manchester Polytechnic
99 Oxford Road, Manchester
M1 7EL

F.A.O. Hon. Fixture Sec.
Manchester Metropolitan University
c/o Heaton Moor RFC
Green Lane, Stockport

Middlesex & University College
1985
Athletic Ground
Perry Street
Chislehurst, Kent BR7 6HA
020 8467 3859

Hon. Secretary
Mr D Squires
Middlesex & University College
UCL Union
25 Gordon Street
London WC1H 0AH

Hon. Fixture Sec.
Mr A Farmer
Middlesex & University College
UCMSSU
43-49 Huntley Street
London WC1E 6DG

Middlesex University
1972
Worlds End Lane
Green Dragon Lane
Enfield, Middlesex
020 8326 5601

Hon. Secretary
Mr T Hannan
Middlesex University
Athletic Union, Middlesex Univ
Chase Side, Cat Hill
Barnet EN4 8HT

F.A.O. Hon. Fixture Sec.
Middlesex University
Worlds End Lane
Green Dragon Lane
Enfield, Middlesex

Nene College
1981
Boughton Green Road
Northampton NN2 7AL
01604 735500

Hon. Secretary & Fixture Secretary
Mr P Robinson
Nene College
Student's Union, Park Campus
Boughton Green Road
Moulton Park, Northampton
NN2 7AL

Nottingham Medics
1977
Grove Farm
University Sports Fields
Lenton, Nottingham NG7
0115 951 3668

Hon. Secretary
Mr T Bryant
Nottingham Medics
93 Lenton Boulevard
Lenton, Nottingham NG7 2FQ

Hon. Fixture Sec.
Mr R Singleton
Nottingham Medics
c/o 79 Lenton Boulevard
Lenton
Nottingham NG7 2FQ

Nottingham Trent University
1992
Clifton Campus
Clifton Lane, Nottingham
0115 921 3316

Hon. Secretary
Mr H George
Nottingham Trent University
48 Musham Sreet
The Meadows
Nottingham NG2

F.A.O. Hon. Fixture Sec.
Nottingham Trent University
Clifton Campus
Clifton Lane, Nottingham

Oxford Brookes University
1994
Oxford Harlequins Club
Horspath Road Recreation Ground
Cowley, Oxford
01865 775765

Hon. Secretary
Mr M Dodwell
Oxford Brookes University
c/o Oxford Brookes Centre
Chesney Lane
Headington, Oxford OX3 0BD

Hon. Fixture Sec.
Mr S Rollerson
Oxford Brookes University
c/o Sports Department,Oxford
Brookes University, Cheney
Lane, Headington, Oxford
OX3 0BD

Queen Mary & Westfield College
QMW Sports Ground
Perry Lane
Chislehurst, Kent BR7 8HA
07887958216

Hon. Secretary
Mr Benedict Griffin
Queen Mary & Westfield College
The Oratory School
Woodecoat
nr Reading, Berks RG8 0PJ

Hon. Fixture Sec.
Mr W Thompson
Queen Mary & Westfield College

Royal Veterinary College
Royal Vetinary College
Haweshead Lane, North Mymms
Hatfield, Hertfordshire AL9 7TA
01707 647091/655486/666310

Hon. Secretary
Mr J C Dare
Royal Vetinary College
Hawksheadlane, N. Mymms
Hatfield, Herts AL9 7TA

Hon. Fixture Sec.
Mr S Cooke
Royal Vetinary College
Royal College Street
London NW1 0TU

Royal Agricultural College
1868
Royal Agricultural College
Stroud Road, Cirencester
Gloucestershire GL7 6JS
01285 652187

Hon. Secretary
Mr Jim Howard
Royal Agricultural College
Lane Farm, Holme
Huddersfield, West Yorks

Hon. Fixture Sec.
Mr Will Young
Royal Agricultural College
North Riding
1 Chapel Street
Yaxley, Peterborough

Royal Free Hospital
1954
Myddleton House
Bulls Cross, Enfield
01992 761553

Hon. Secretary
Mr G Shyamalan
Royal Free Hospital, Students Union
Royal Free School of Medicine
Rowlands Hill Street, London
NW3 2PF

Hon. Fixture Sec.
Mr R Mead
Royal Free Hospital Students Union
Royal Free School of Medicine
Rowland Hill Street, London
NW3 2PF

Royal School of Mines
1929
RSMFRC
RMSU Office,
RSM, Prince Consort Road
SW7 2BP
020 7594 8074
Middlesex County RFU

Hon. Secretary
F.A.O. Hon. Secretary
Royal School of Mines
RSMFRC
RMSU Office,
RSM, Prince Consort Road
SW7 2BP

Hon. Fixture Sec.
F.A.O. Hon. Fixture Sec.
Royal School of Mines
RSMFRC
RMSU Office,
RSM, Prince Consort Road
SW7 2BP

Royal Military College of Science
Shrivenham
Swindon
Wiltshire SN6 8LA
01793 785558

Hon. Secretary & Fixture Secretary
Lt Col P J Davies
Royal Military College of Science
Shrivenham
Windon, Wiltshire SN6 8LA

Royal Holloway, University of London
1985
Nobles Sportsground
Prune Hill
Egham TW20 0EX
01784 438702

Hon. Secretary
Mr A Purdon
Royal Holloway, University of London
Students Union, Royal Holloway
University of London, Egham
Hill, Egham, Surrey TW20 OEX

Hon. Fixture Sec.
Mr M Dunster
Royal Holloway, University of London
Students Union, Royal Holloway
University of London, Egham
Hill, Egham, Surrey TW20 OEX

School of Oriental and African Studies
1990
SOAS, Thornaugh Street
Russell Square, London WC1H 0XG
020 7580 0916

Hon. Secretary
The Sport Officer
c/o Students Union
SOAS, Thornaugh Street
Russell Square, London WC1H 0XG

F.A.O. Hon. Fixture Sec.
SOAS, Thornaugh Street
Russell Square
London WC1H 0XG

Seale-Hayne Agricultural College
1929
Seale-Hayne
Newton Abbot
South Devon TQ12 6NQ
01626 60557/332160

Hon. Secretary
Ms P Verrall
Seale-Hayne Agricultural College
c/o Seale Hayne Student Union
Ashburton Road
Newton Abott, Devon

Hon. Fixture Sec.
Mr Paul Heaton
Seale-Hayne Agricultural College
as above

Sheffield Hallam University
1965
Derbyshire Lane, Sheffield
0114 255 6435

Hon. Secretary
Ms D Hallatt
Sheffield Hallam Univ A.U.
Nelson Mandela Building
Pond St, Sheffield S1 2BW

F.A.O. Hon. Fixture Sec.
Sheffield Hallam University
Derbyshire Lane, Sheffield

Southampton University Hospitals
1975
Wellington Sports Grounds
Stoneham Lane
Eastleigh, Southampton
01703 612309

Hon. Secretary
Mr A Fityan
Southampton University Hospitals
Wellington Sports Grounds
Stoneham Lane
Eastleigh, Southampton

Mr Nick Harvey
Hon. Fixture Sec.
Southampton University Hospitals

South Bank University
1980
South Bank Univ Sportsground
Turney Road
London SE21 7JH
020 7737 0677

Hon. Secretary & Fixture Secretary
Vice President Clubs & Societies
South Bank University
South Bank Student Union
Keyworth Street
London SE1 6NG

Sparsholt College
1927
Sparsholt College
Sparsholt, Nr Winchester
Hampshire SO21 2NF
01962 776441

Hon. Secretary
Mr S Barlow
Sparsholt College
Sparsholt, Winchester
Hampshire SO21 2NF
Fixture Secretary
Mr N Wright
Sparsholt College
Sparsholt, Winchester
Hampshire SO21 2NF

Staffordshire University
1992
Leek Road Sports Centre
Leek Road
Stoke on Trent ST4 2DE

Hon. Secretary
Mr I Brittain
Staffordshire University
Athletic Union, Leed Road
Stoke-on-Trent, ST4 2DE

Hon. Fixture Sec.
Mr B Colleson
Staffordshire University
41 Boughey Road
Shelton Stoke-on-Trent

St George's Hospital London
1872
St Georges Hosp Sports Ground
Stoke Road
Cobham, Surrey
01932 864341

Hon. Secretary
F.A.O. Hon. Secretary
St Georges Hosp Sports Ground
Stoke Road
Cobham, Surrey

Hon. Fixture Sec.
Mr Toby Spolton
53 Arbourne Road
Mitcham, Surrey CR4 2BE

St John's College
1885
St John's Playing Fields
Hull Road, York
01904 410180

Hon. Secretary
The Rugby Hon Sec
St John's College
c/o Students Union
Univ College of Ripon and York
Lord Mayors Walk, York YO3 7EX

Hon. Fixture Sec.
Mr P Sheppard
St John's College
c/o Students Union
Univ College of Ripon and York
Lord Mayors Walk, York YO3 7EX

St Mary's College
1913
Strawberry Hill
Twickenham
Middlesex TW1 4SX

Hon. Secretary & Fixture Secretary
Mr T Booth
St Mary's College
Sports Science Dept.
St.Mary's U.C
Waldergrave Rd, Twickenham
TW1 4SX

Stoke on Trent College
1976
Stoke Road
Shelton
Stoke on Trent, ST4 2DG
01782 626206

Hon. Secretary
Mr C Linsell
Stoke on Trent College
Stoke Road, Shelton
Stoke-on-Trent, Staffs ST4 2DG

Hon. Fixture Sec.
F.A.O. Hon. Fixture Sec.
Stoke on Trent College
Stoke Road
Shelton
Stoke on Trent ST4 2DG

The Royal Hospitals
1865
Wadham Road
Walthamstow E17 4LT
020 8527 5724

Hon. Secretary
Mr A Goodwin
The Royal Hospitals
6 Sharon Gardens
London EP 7RX

Hon. Fixture Sec.
Dr P Colvin
The Royal Hospitals
4 Hardy Road
Blackheath, London SE3 7NR

UMIST
1978
Burnage RFC
Varley Park, Battersea Road
Heaton Mersey, Stockport SK4 3EA
0161 200 3292

Hon. Secretary
Mr Nick Tatlow
UMIST
40 Waterside Point
2 Anhalt Rd, London SW11 4PD

Hon. Fixture Sec.
Mr Duncan Weaver
UMIST
5 Birch Coppice
Wombourne
Wolverhampton WV5 8JY

University College London
University College London
Sports Ground, Bell Lane
Shenley, Hertfordshire
AL2 1BZ
01727 822215

Hon. Secretary
Mr D Squires
University College London
UCL Union
25 Gordon Street
London WC1H 0AH

Hon. Fixture Sec.
Mr M Burdett
University College London
UCL Union
25 Gordon Street
London WC1H 0AH

University of Bath
1967
Claverton Down
Bath
Avon BA2 7AY
01225 826607

Hon. Secretary
Ms Caroline Lambert
University of Bath
Claverton Down
Bath BA2 7AY

Hon. Fixture Sec.
Mr L Giles
University of Bath
Claverton Down
Bath BA2 7AY

University of Birmingham
1916
The Bournbrook
University of Birmingham
Birmingham B15 2TU

Hon. Secretary
Mr K Johnston
University of Birmingham
Athletic Union
Munrow Sports Centre
Edgbaston, Birmingham B15 2TU

Hon. Fixture Sec.
Mr Z Sennett
University of Birmingham
Rowdell Cottage, The Street
Washington, W. Sussex RH20 4AT

University of Birmingham Medics
1958
Wast Hills, Wast Hills Road
off Redditch Road
West Heath, Birmingham
0121 458 1060

Hon. Secretary
Mr J Geoghan
University of Birmingham Medics
89 Reservoir Rd
Selly Oak, Birmingham B29 6SU

Hon. Fixture Sec.
Mr N Bosanko
University of Birmingham Medics
18 Poole Crescent
Harborne
Birmingham B17 0PB

University of Bradford
1965
Woodhall Pavilion Sports Ground
Calverly Road
Bradford BD7 1DP
01274 662406

Hon. Secretary
Mr T Stevenson
Bradford University Athletic Assoc.
Students Union, Richmond Road,
Bradford, Yorks BD4 1DP

Hon. Fixture Sec.
Mr Alec Webster
Bradford University Athletic Assoc.
Students Union, Richmond Road,
Bradford, Yorks BD7 1DP

University of Bristol
1876
Coombe Dingle Playing Fields
Coombe Dingle, Coombe Lane
(off Parry's Lane), Bristol BS9 2BJ
0117 954 5874

Hon. Secretary
Mr R A Reeves
University of Bristol
Dept Sport, Exercise & Health
Woodland House
34 West Park, Bristol BS8 2LU

Hon. Fixture Sec.
Mr P Atkinson
University of Bristol
c/o University of Bristol
Woodland House, 34 West Park
Clifton, Bristol BS8 2LU

University of Buckingham
1982
Gawcott Sports Field
c/o University of Buckingham
Hunters Street, Buckingham
MK18 1EG
01280 814080 Ext 2342

Hon. Secretary
Mr S J Ridley
University of Buckingham
Sports Development Officer
Students Union Hunter Street
Buckingham MK18 1EG

F.A.O. Hon. Fixture Sec.
Gawcott Sports Field
c/o University of Buckingham
Hunters St, Buckingham MK18 1EG

University of Essex
1965
Wivenhoe Park
Colchester, Essex CO4 3SQ
01206 863211

Hon. Secretary
Mr G Masoud
University of Essex RFC,
Sports Federation, Wivenhoe
Park, Colchester CO4 3SQ

Hon. Fixture Sec.
Mr D Whiteman
University of Essex RFC,
Sports Federation, Wivenhoe
Park, Colchester CO4 3SQ

University of Exeter
1908
Ducks Meadow
Salmon Pool Lane
Exeter
01392 270397

Hon. Secretary
Mr N E Beasant
University of Exeter
Athletic Union Office,
Cornwall House,
St German's Rd, Exeter EX4 6TG

Hon. Fixture Sec.
Mr Craig Townsend
U. of E. Athletic Union Office
as above

University of Hull
1929
Inglemere Lane
Hull HU6 7RX
01482 466234

Hon. Secretary
Mr P Baker
University of Hull
c/o Athletic Union
University House
Cottingham Road, Hull HU6 7RX

Mr A Mawson
Hon. Fixture Sec.
University of Hull
c/o Athletic Union
University House
Cottingham Road, Hull HU6 7RX

University of Keele
1951
Keele Sports Centre
Univ of Keele
Staffs ST5 5BG
01782 583638

Hon. Secretary
Ms S Alderton
University of Keele
Athletic Union
Leisure Centre, Keele
Staffordshire ST5 5BG

Hon. Fixture Sec.
Mr R Gould
University of Keele
Athletic Union
Leisure Centre, keele Uni.
Newcastle Under Lyme, Staff.
ST5 5BG

University of Kent
1965
Canterbury, Kent CT2 7NL
01227 768027

Hon. Secretary
Ms T Else
Sport Sabbatical
University of Kent
University Sports Federation
Canterbury, Kent CT2 7NL

Hon. Fixture Sec.
Mr G Taylor
University of Kent
University Sports Federation
Canterbury, Kent CT2 7NL

University of Lancaster
1965
Student Activities
Lancaster University
Lancaster LA1 4YA
01524 593250

Hon. Secretary
Mr N Leach
L.U.R.F.C., Student Activities,
Lancaster University LA1 4YA

Hon. Fixture Sec.
Mr A Brown
L.U.R.F.C., Student Activities
Lancaster University LA1 4YA

University of Leeds
1905
Sports Offices,
Leeds University Union
PO Box 157, Leeds
LS1 1UH
0113 275 1993

Hon. Secretary
Mr S Reid
University of Leeds
72 Hartley Avenue
Leeds LS6 2LP

Hon. Fixture Sec.
Mr H Davies
University of Leeds

University of Leicester
1921
Stoughton Road
Oadby, Leicester LE2 2LL
0116 2719144

Hon. Secretary & Fixture Secretary
Mrs A Morgan
University of Leicester
Sports Association
Students' Union
University Road, Leicester LE1 7RH

University of Liverpool
1884
Geoffrey Hughes Sports Ground
Wyncote Fields, Mather Avenue
Allerton, Liverpool L18 6HF
0151 724 4948

Hon. Secretary & Fixture Secretary
Mr S A Wade
University of Liverpool
Sports Administrator
Athletic Union, PO Box 187
160 Mount Pleasant, Liverpool
L69 7BR

University of Manchester
1881
The Firs Athletic Ground
Moseley Road
Fallowfield, Manchester M14 6HE
0161 224 2143

Hon. Secretary & Fixture Secretary
Sports Administrator
University of Manchester
Univ Manchester Athletic Union
William Kay House
333 Oxford Road
Manchester M13 9PG

University of Newcastle
1963
Cochrane Park
Etherstone Avenue
Heaton, Newcastle upon Tyne 6
0191 286 0088

Hon. Secretary & Fixture Secretary
Mr M A Cox
Athletic Union Office,, Sports Centre,
Uni. of Northumbria, Newcastle
NE1 8ST

University of Nottingham
University Playing Fields
University Boulevard
Nottingham NG7 2RD
0115 925 6612

Hon. Secretary
Mr V P Williams
Director Physical Recreation
Sports Centre, University Park
University of Nottingham NG7 2RD

Hon. Fixture Sec.
Mr D Ryan
4 Albert Square,Nottingham NG7
2FH

University of Reading
1926
Whiteknights Park
off Queens Drive
Reading, Berkshire RG6 2AZ
01189 875123 (Students Union)

Hon. Secretary
Mr M Pask
University of Reading
Reading University SU
PO Box 230, Whiteknights
Reading, Berks RG6 6AZ

Hon. Fixture Sec.
Mr Constantine Lerounis
University of Reading
Reading Uni, Students Union
Whiteknights Campus,
Reading,Berks AG6 6AZ

University of Salford
1966
Castle Irwell Playing Fields
Cromwell Road, Salford M5 4WT
0161 736 7811

Hon. Secretary
Mr C Kirk
University of Salford
Students' Union
University of Salford
Salford, Lancashire M5 4WT

Hon. Fixture Sec.
Mr D Kavanagh
University of Salford
Students' Union
University of Salford
Salford, Lancashire M5 4WT

University of Sheffield
Norton Playing Fields
Warminster Road
Sheffield
01142 554536

Hon. Secretary
Mr K Jewitt
U.S.R.F.C.
Student Union AU office
Western Bank, Sheffield S10 1TG

Hon. Fixture Sec.
Mr C Peel
U.S.R.F.C.
Student Union AU Office
Western Bank, Sheffield S10 1TG

University of Southampton
1919
Wellington Sports Ground
North Stoneham Lane
Swaythling, Southampton
01703 612309

Hon. Secretary & Fixture Secretary
Andrew Bishop, Men's Rugby
University of Southampton
Athletic Union, University of
Southampton, Highfield
Southampton, Hants
SO17 1BJ

University of Sussex
1963
Sports Pavilion
University of Sussex, Falmer
Brighton
01273 678155/678228/678230

Hon. Secretary
Mr C Pittaway
University of Sussex
The Sports Complex
Pavilion Playing Fields
Falmer E.Sussex BN1 9QF

Hon. Fixture Sec.
Mr L Martin
University of Sussex
The Sports Complex
Pavilion Playing Fields
Falmer E.Sussex BN1 9QF

University of Warwick
1979
Athletic Union Pitches
University of Warwick
Coventry CV4 7AL
01203 523523 Ext 2287

Hon. Secretary
Mr C Oxby
University of Warwick
Warwick University Rugby Club
Students Union, Warwick Univ
Coventry CV4 7AL

Hon. Fixture Sec.
F.A.O. Hon. Fixture Sec.
University of Warwick
Athletic Union Pitches
University of Warwick
Coventry CV4 7AL

University of York
1965
York University
Heslington, York YO1 5DD
01904 412642

Hon. Secretary
Mr N MacKee
University of York
SU Office, Goodricke College
University of York
Heslington, York YO1 5DD

Hon. Fixture Sec.
Mr L Bostock
University of York Athletic Union
Goodricke College
University of York, York YO1 5DD

University of Teesside
1992
Saltersgill Sports Pavillion
Saltersgill Ave, Tollesby
Saltersgill
TS1 3BA
01642 326224

Hon. Secretary & Fixture Secretary
Mr C Henry
University of Teesside RFC
Societies & Recreation Officer
University of Teesside
Borough Road, Middlesbrough
TS1 3BA

University of Brighton
1992
Falmer Site
Brighton, Sussex BN1 9HP
01273 643547

Hon. Secretary
Mr Kelly
University of Brighton
c/o UBSU Sport
Steam House
Lewes Rd,Brighton BN2 4AF

Hon. Fixture Sec.
F.A.O. Hon. Fixture Sec.
University of Brighton
Falmer Site
Brighton Sussex BN1 9HP

University of Westminster
1992
Cavendish Road
off Hartington Road
Chiswick, London W4 3UH
020 7911 5892/0208 9956863

Hon. Secretary & Fixture Secretary
Mr Billy Jawandha
University of Westminster
Dept of Sport & Recreation
309 Regent St, London W1R 8AL

University of West of England
1992

Ms K Tomlinson
Hon. Secretary & Fixture Secretary
University of West of England
Activities Centre, University
of the West of England,
Frenchay Campus, Bristol.
BS16 1QY

University of Central England
1967
Union of Students at UCE
Franchise Street
Perry Barr, Birmingham B24 2SU
0121 331 6801

Hon. Secretary
The Sports Officer
Union of Students at UCF
Franchise Street
Perry Barr, Birmingham B42 2SU

Hon. Fixture Sec.
Mr Lynda Jones
University of Central England
Union of Students at UCE
Franchise Street
Perry Barr, Birmingham B42 2SU

University of Sunderland
1959
South Bents Avenue
Seaburn

Hon Secretary
University of Sunderland
Men's RUFC, USSU,
Wearmouth Hall, Chester Rd
Sunderland, Tyne & Wear
SR1 3SD

Hon. Fixture Sec.
Mr M R K Clayton
University of Sunderland
2 South Hill Crescent
Durham Road, Sunderland

University of Hertfordshire
1956
Angerland Common
Bishops Rise, Hatfield
Hertfordshire AL10 9AB
01707 284461

Hon. Secretary & Fixture Secretary
Mr G Niven
University of Hertfordshire
University of Hertfordshire SU
College Lane
Hatfield, Hertfordshire AL10 9AB

University of Huddersfield
1969
Salendine Nook Playing Fields
New Hey Road
Huddersfield
01484 657880

Hon. Secretary & Fixture Secretary
Mr P Wood
University of Huddersfield
Sport Officer Univ Huddersfiel
Student Union, Queensgate
Huddersfield HD1 3DH

University of North London
1939
Hackney Rugby Club
Spring Hill, London E5
020 8519 0017

Hon. Secretary
Mr I Jennings
University of North London
Sports & Recreation Officer
166-220 Holloway Road
London N7 8DB

Hon. Fixture Sec.
Mr J Morris
University of North London
166,220 Holloway Rd
University of North London

University of East London
1972
Ilford Wanderers Rugby Club
Off Forest Rd, Hainault
Ilford Essex IG6 3HJ
020 8500 4622

Hon. Secretary
Ms Linda Ray
University of East London
Students Union, Longbridge Rd
Dagenham, Essex RM8 2AS

F.A.O. Hon. Fixture Sec.
University of East London
Ilford Wanderers Rugby Club
Off Forest Rd, Hainault
Ilford Essex IG6 3HJ

University of Greenwich
1992
Sparrows Farm Centre
Sparrows Lane, New Eltham
London SE9 2BU
020 8859 2921

Hon. Secretary & Fixture Secretary
Miss R Hanshaw
University of Greenwich
Student Union, Univ Greenwich
Avery Hill Campus,
Southwood Site, Eltham, London
SE9 1UG

University of Wolverhampton
1935
Walsall RFC
Delves Road, Walsall W51 3JY
01922 26818

Hon. Rugby Secretary
University of Wolverhampton
Athletic Union
Wulfruna Street, Wolverhampton
WV1 1LY

University College Warrington
1964
Padgate Campus
Crab Lane
Warrington WA2 0DB
01925 821336

Hon. Secretary & Fixture Secretary
Mr C Smith
University College Warrington
Athletics Union
Padgate Campus, Crab Lane
Warrington, Cheshire WA2 0DB

University of Central Lancashire
1969
c/o Fylde RUFC
The Woodlands Memorial Ground
Blackpool Rd, Lytham St Annes
01253 734733

Hon. Secretary
Mr J Brown
University of Central Lancashire
Students Union, University of
Central Lancashire
Fylde Rd, Preston PR1 2TQ

Hon. Fixture Sec.
Ms B Woodruff
University of Central Lancashire
c/o The Students Union
UCLSU
Fylde Road, Preston PR1 2TQ

University of Luton
1952
Luton RFC
Newlands Road
Bedfordshire LU1 4BQ
01582 20355

Hon. Secretary
Mr J Harris
University of Luton,
Students Union, Europa House,
Vicarage Street, Luton, Beds.
LU1 3HZ

Hon. Fixture Sec.
Mr N Butler
University of Luton
82 Reginald Street, Luton, Beds

University of Northumbria
1969
Bullockstead Sports Ground
off Ponteland Road, Kingston
Park, Newcastle-upon-Tyne
NE13 8AH
0191 286 0088

Hon. Secretary
Mr B Lucas
University of Northumbria
c/o Athletic Union Office
Sports Centre, Ellison Place,
Newcastle Upon Tyne NE1 8ST

Hon. Fixture Sec.
Mr I Smith
University of Northumbria
University Athletic Union
Wynne Jones Centre, Northumbria
University, Newcastle-on-Tyne
NE1 8ST

University of Aston
1992
Recreation Ground
Birmingham Road
Walsall
0121 357 3675

Hon. Secretary
Mr Gareth Davies
University of Aston
37 Gadwell Croft
Erdington
Birmingham B23 7RN

Hon. Fixture Sec.
Mr William Wilson
University of Aston Athletic Union
Aston Students Guild
Aston University B4 7ET

University College Chester
1890
Chester College
Cheyney Road
Chester CH1 4BJ
01244 375444(373379 Fax)

Hon. Secretary & Fixture Secretary
Mr Jane Hodson
University College Chester
Sports Administrator
Chester Student Union
Chester College, Cheyney Rd
CH1 4BJ

University College Of St Martin
1968
Univ College of St Martin
Bowerham Rd
Lancaster LA1 3JD
01524 65827

Hon. Secretary & Fixture Secretary
Mr A D Baron
University College Of St Martin
Student Union
St Martins College
Bowerham, Lancaster L41 3JO

University Of East England
1990
c/o The Gymnasium
University of East England
East Road, Cambridge
CB1 1PT

Hon. Secretary & Fixture Secretary
Mr D Cosnett
University Of East England
30 King Edgar Close
Ely, Cambridge CB6 1DP

Univ Of Lincs & Humberside
1993
Haworth Park
Emmott Road
Hull HU6 7AB
01522 882000 (S Union)

Hon. Secretary & Fixture Secretary
Miss C Bingham
Univ Of Lincs & Humberside
Student Union,Barnston House
Inglemire Avenue
Hull HU6 7LU

West Hertfordshire College
1968
Watford Fullerians
Newfield, Connesibury Drive
Watford WD1 3EZ
01923 224483

Hon. Secretary & Fixture Secretary
Mr Roy Hughes
West Hertfordshire College
14 Trowley Rise
Abbots Langley WD5 0LW

Writtle College
1967
Lordship Road
Writtle
Chelmsford CM1 3RR
01245 424200

Hon. Secretary & Fixture Secretary
Mr M Rawlinson
Writtle College
27 Melba Court
Writtle
Chelmsford, Essex CM1 3EW

Wye College
1937
Wye
Nr Ashford, Kent TN25 5AH
01233 812401

Hon. Secretary
For Attention Of: Hon. Secretary
Wye College
Wye
Nr Ashford, Kent TN25 5AH

Hon. Fixture Sec.
Mr D Wells, Wye College, c/o JCR,
Wye College,
Nr Ashford, Kent, TN25 5AH

HMS CALEDONIA
Hilton Rd, Rosyth, Fife KY11 2XH.
Chairman CPO I Binks
Secretary/Fixtures LPT J Forwell
Treasurer Supply Officer, HMS
Caledonia.
Ground Fleet Sports
Ground, Rosyth.
Colours Red shirts, blue shorts &
socks.

HMS CARDIFF BFPO 249
Chairman Capt Fraser,
Rugby Officer Lt Tilden,
Secretary POPT Quirke,
Treasurer CPO Pearce,
Fixtures POPT Quirke,
Ground Burnaby Rd / Eastney,
Colours Blue with White.

HMS CHATHAM BFPO 253
Chairman Capt Moll,
Rugby Officer Lt Gillmore,
Secretary LPT Wain,
Treasurer LMEM Dash,
Fixtures LPT Wain,
Ground Military Sports Ground,
Colours Blue.

CDO LOGS REGT
RMB Chivenor,
Barnstaple, EX31 1AZ.
Chairman Lt Col Arding,
Rugby Officer WO2 Trantham,
Treasurer WO2 Sowerby,
Fixtures Sgt Cureton,
Ground Sports Pavillion,
Colours Red/White/Blue,
alternate Green.

HMS COLLINGWOOD
Newgate Lane,
Fareham, PO14 1AS.
Chairman Lt Cdr Cass,
Rugby OfficerLt Paulson,
Secretary POPT McConville,
Treasurer Lt Lee,
Ground Main Field,
Colours Home Green/Black
Away Blue

HMS CORNWALL BFPO 256
Chairman Lt Barret,
Rugby Officer Lt Barret,
Secretary POPT Murphy,
Treasurer CPO Overvoode,
Fixtures POPT Murphy,
Colours Black/Gold.

HMS COVENTRY BFPO 259
Chairman Lt Cdr Brown,
Rugby Officer PO Jones,
Treasurer Lt Cdr Rea,
Fixtures LPT Parcell,
Ground Bullpoint,
Colours 1st Blue/White, 2nd Gold.

BRNC DARTMOUTH,
Devon, TQ6 0HJ.
Secretary LPT Childs,
Fixtures LPT Childs, Groud
Britannia College,
Colours Blue/White

HMS DRYAD
Southwick, Fareham,
Hants, PO17 6EJ.
Chairman Lt Cdr Woollven,
Rugby Officer WO Scott,
Treasurer CPO Honey,
Ground HMS Dryad,
Colours Yellow/Black.

HMS EDINBURGH BFPO 277
Chairman Lt Cdr Sailabury,
Rugby Officer CPO Peachey,
Secretary POPT Barton,
Treasurer WTR Evans,
Fixtures POPT Barton,
Colours Blue.

HMS EXCELLENT
Whale Island,
Portsmouth, PO2 8ER.
Chairman Cdr Wrightson,
Rugby Officer Lt Col Bruce-Jones,
Secretary LPT Newcombe,
Treasurer CWRT David,
Fixtures LPT Newcombe, Gorund
Whale Island,
Colours Black with Gold stripe.

HMS EXETER BFPO 278
Chairman Cdr Richards,
Rugby Officer S/Lt Pollard,
Secretary Lpt Patilla,
Treasurer CPO Brewer,
Ground Burnaby Road,
Colours Green/White.

HMS GLASGOW BFPO 287
Chairman PO Robertson,
Rugby Officer Lt Cdr Adlam,
Secretary RS Gibson,
Treasurer RS Gibson,
Fixtures LPT Wilson,
Ground Burnably Road,
Colours Black.

HMS GLOUCESTER BFPO 289
Chairman Lt Cdr Deacon,
Rugby Officer Lt Cdr Deacon,
Secretary LPT Leeman,
Treasurer CCMEA Benford,
Fixtures LPT Leeman,
Ground Burnaby Road,
Colours Red/White.

HMS GRAFTON BFPO 007
Chairman Lt Cdr Watson,
Rugby Officer WO Loveday,
Secretary LPT Perry,
Treasurer Lt Wren,
Fixtures LPT Perry,
Ground Burnaby Road,
Colours Black/White.

HMS HERON
Ilchester, Somerset, BA22 8HT.
Chairman Lt Cdr Coomer,
Rugby Officer Lt Cdr Coomer,
Secretary LPT Gay,
Treasurer Lt Tutchings,
Fixtures LPT Gay, Coaching AEM,
Ground HMS Heron,
Colours Green/Black.

HMS ILLUSTRIOUS BFPO 305
Chairman Cdr Eskine,
Rugby Officer Lt Cdr McCue,
Secretary CPOPT Harris,
Treasurer Lt Hooper,
Fixtures CPOPT Harris,
Ground Burnaby Road,
Colours 1st Green/Yellow 2nd Blue.

HMS INVINCIBLE BFPO 308
Chairman Lt Millman,
Rugby Officer CPO Hand,
Secretary CPO Concannon,
Treasurer Lt Finch,
Ground Burnaby Road,
Colours Green/Blue.

HMS IRON DUKE BFPO 309,
Chairman PO Hillan,
Rugby Officer S/Lt Hocking,
Secretary LPT Scales,
Treasurer PO Bamford,
Fixtures LPT Scales,
Ground Burnaby Road,
Colours Black/White.

JSU NORTHWOOD
Sandy Lane, Northwood,
Middlesex, HA6 3HP.
Chairman Capt Oden,
Rugby Officer CPO Moody,
Secretary CPL Ball,
Fixtures CPL Ball,
Ground Bushey Metropolitan Police
Sports
Ground,
Colours Green/Blue.

HMS KENT BFPO 318
Chairman Lt Carroll,
Secretary LPT Howe,
Treasurer LCH Munday,
Fixtures LPT Howe,
Ground Burnaby Road,
Colours Red/Black.

HMS LANCASTER BFPO 323
Chairman Lt Cdr Tebbet,
Rugby Officer Lt Donaldson,
Secretary LPT Smith,
Treasurer POCA Grayson,
Fixtures LPT Smith,
Ground Burnaby Road/Eastney,
Colours Red/Blue.

HMS LIVERPOOL BFPO 327
Chairman Captain R Twitchen,
Chairman Lt Hassall,
Secretary/Fixtures POPT A Rose,
Treasurer S/Lt O Smith,
Ground Eastney, Portsmouth.
Colours Red/Blue hooped shirts &
socks, Navy shorts.

HMS MARLBOROUGH BFPO 333
Chairman Capt Potts,
Rugby Officer Lt Allen,
Secretary LPT Wright,
Treasurer LCH Oliver,
Fixtures LPT Wright,
Ground Burnaby Road,
Colours Red/Black.

HMS MONMOUTH   BFPO 338
Chairman Cdr Stockings,
Rugby Officer Lt Sullivan,
Secretary LPT Jones,
Treasurer Lt Richards,
Fixtures LPT Jones,
Ground Bullpoint,
Colours Black.

HMS MONTROSE   BFPO 339
Chairman Capt Johnstone,
Rugby Officer S/Lt Dumbleton,
Secretary LPT Armstrong,
Treasurer Lt Cdr Lewis,
Fixtures LPT Armstrong,
Ground Bullpoint,
Colours Red/Black.

HMS NELSON
Queens Street, Portsmouth.
Rugby Officer WO Penfold,
Secretary LPT Holl,
Colours Yellow/Green.

HMS NEWCASTLE   BFPO 343
Chairman Cdr Pearson,
Rugby Officer Lt Cdr Williams,
Secretary LPT Murray,
Treasurer PO Milner,
Fixtures LPT Murray,
Colours Black/White.

HMS OCEAN   BFPO 350
Chairman Cdr Lloyd,
Secretary LPT Matthews,
Treasurer Lt Cdr Watt,
Ground Bullpoint/Keyham,
Colours Red/Black.

HMS RALEIGH
Torpoint, Cornwall, PL11 2PD.
Chairman Cdr Westbrook,
Rugby Officer Lt Reed,
Secretary LPT Davies,
Treasurer Lt Carter,
Fixtures LPT Davies,
Ground Trevol Pitches,
Colours Blue/White.

HMS RICHMOND   BFPO 375
Chairman Lt Cdr West,
Rugby Officer CPO Walker,
Secretary LPT Edwards,
Treasurer LWEM Stevens,
Fixtures LPT Edwards, Grund
Burnaby Road,
Colours Black/Red.

HMS SEAHAWK
RNAS Culdrose, Helston,
Cornwall, TR12 7RH.
Chairman Lt Cdr Pryde,
Rugby Officer Lt Cdr Chittick,
Secretary LPT Kind,
Treasurer Lt Cordone,
Fixtures LPT Kind,
Ground Upper Sports Field,
Colours Red/Black & Yellow.

HMS SHEFFIELD   BFPO 383
Chairman Commander T Lowe,
Secretary/Fixtures LPY Mynett,
Treasurer L/Cdr Dodd,
Ground Bulpoint, Plymouth.
Colours Red/White/Blue hoops,
Blue shorts.

HMS SOMERSET   BFPO 395
Chairman Cdr Blount,
Rugby Officer Lt Murphy,
Secretary LPT Cavanagh,
Fixtures LPT Cavanagh, Groung
Bullpoint,
Colours 1st Sky Blue 2nd
Orange/Yellow.

HMS SOUTHAMPTON   BFPO 389
Chairman Cdy Doyle,
Rugby Officer Ensign McCaw,
Secretary LPT Jones,
Treasurer PO Simpson,
Fixtures LPT Jones,
Ground Burnaby Road/Eastney,
Colours Red/Blue.

RMB STONEHOUSE
Durmford Street,
Plymouth PL1 3QS.
Chairman WO1 CORP RSM
Tinson,
Rugby Officer Capt Stocker,
Secretary SGT Melbourne,
Ground Brickfields, Plymouth.
Colours Black/Gold.

HMS SULTAN
Military Road, Gosport, PO12 3BY.
Chairman Lt Penketh,
Rugby Officer Lt Cdr Knight,
Secretary LPT Jones,
Treasurer CPO Tweddie,
Fixtures LPT Cherrington,
Ground Main Sports
Ground,
Colours Maroon/Sky Blue.

HMS YORK   BFPO 430
Chairman Cdr Porter,
Rugby Officer Lt Cdr Cryer,
Secretary LPT New,
Treasurer ME Beattie,
Colours Black/Yellow.

HMS WESTMINSTER.
Chairman L/Cdr F Cunningham,
Secretary/Fixtures LPT Bowen,
Treasurer PO G Rule,
Rugby Officer L/Cdr D George,
Ground Burnaby Road, Portsmouth.
Colours All Black.

ROYAL MARINES POOLE.
Hamworthy, Poole, Dorset, BH15
4NQ. President Colonel Heaver,
Chairman WO2 Burns,
Secretary/Fixtures Cpl Costiff,
Treasurer WO2 Burns,
Ground RM Fields, Hamworthy,
Colours Dark & Light Blue Hoops.

40 COMMANDO
RM Norton Manor Camp, Taunton,
Somerset, TA2 6PF.
Tel : 01823 337966 Ext 4281.
Chairman Capt P Lynch,
Secretary/Fixtures Sgt D Silvester,
Treasurer C/Sgt Brookes,
Rugby Officer Lieutenant Morgan,
Ground Norton Manor Camp,
Colours Shirt - upper Red, lower
Yellow, Black Shorts.

ASSOCIATE MEMBERS

ANTI-ASSASSINS
Hon. Secretary   Ms S B Gardiner, Blossoms Farm, Blossoms Lane, Woodford, Cheshire SK7 1RF
Hon. Fixture Sec.   Mr P E Hughes, Height Top Smithy, Higham, Burnley, Lancashire BB12 9BU

BARBARIAN   1890
Hon. Secretary   Mr G Windsor-Lewis, Wilcote Place, Ramsden, Oxfordshire OX7 3BA

BRISTOL AND DISTRICT COMBINATION   1909
Headquarters   Bristol FC, Memorial Ground, Filton Avenue, Bristol BS7 0AG Tel: 0117 908 5500
Hon. Secretary   Mr A J Weaver, 8 Lower Chapel Lane, Frampton Cotterell, Bristol BS36 2RL
Hon. Fixture Sec.   Mr T Webb, 50 Monks Park Avenue, Filton, Bristol BS7 0UH

CHELTENHAM AND DISTRICT COMBINATION   1963
Hon. Secretary   Mr B F Didlick, 15 Stoneville Street, Cheltenham, Glos. GL51 8PH
Hon. Fixture Sec.   Mr M Kedward, 35 Bishops Cleeve, Cheltenham, Glos. GL52 4NU

COMBINED BIRMINGHAM OLD BOYS   1951
Hon. Secretary & Hon. Fixture Sec.
                     Mr C W Hayward, 6 Princethorpe Close, Shirley, Solihull, West Midlands B90 2LP

DERBYSHIRE COUNTY UNION   1922
Hon. Secretary   Mr P Fuller, Ednaston Lodge Farm, Ednaston, Ashbourne, Derbyshire DE6 3BA
Hon. Fixture Sec.   Mr G Morgan, 55 Lower Market Street, Broadbottom, Hyde SK14 6AA

FOREST OF DEAN COMBINATION   1923
Hon. Secretary   Mr G Ward, Willow Brae, Gorsley, Ross-on-Wye, Herefordshire HR9 7SH
Hon. Fixture Sec.   Mr C Edwards, Windbourne, High Beech Road, Bream, Nr Lydney, Glos. GL15 6JG

GREATER BIRMINGHAM   1936
Hon. Secretary   Mr C Humphreys, 75 Loxley Avenue, Shirley, Solihull, West Midlands B90 2QL
Hon. Fixture Sec.   Mr K Jordan, 74 William Road, Warley, West Midlands B67 6LW

LEICESTER THURSDAY   1888
Hon. Secretary   Mr R Mitchell, 8 Begonia Close, Leicester Forest Close, Leicester LE3 3QY
Hon. Fixture Sec.   Mr M Higgins, 36 Beechwood Avenue, Leicester Forest East, Leicester LE3 3PL

LINCOLNSHIRE COUNTY UNION   1947
Hon. Secretary   Mr M A Ross, Blacksmith's House, 26 Lincoln Road, Branston, Lincoln LN4 1PA
Hon. Fixture Sec.   Mr C Moon, 5 Manor Close, Welton, Lincoln LN2 3TQ

LONDON   1911
Hon. Secretary   Mr D S Straw, London, 161 High Street, Hampton Hill, Middlesex TW12 1NL

NORTH GLOUCESTER COMBINATION   1912
Hon. Secretary   Mr M S Slatter, 135 Grange Road, Tuffley, Gloucester GL4 0PR
Hon. Fixture Sec.   Mr D L Howell, 255c Stroud Road, Gloucester GL1 5JZ

NOTTINGHAMSHIRE COUNTY UNION   1920
Hon. Secretary   Mr D Sutton, 22 Vernon Avenue, Wilford Village, Nottingham HG11 7AE
Hon. Fixture Sec.   Mr V P Williams, 1 Carisbrooke Drive, Mapperley Park, Nottingham NG3 5DS

PENGUIN INTERNATIONAL   1959
Hon. Secretary   Mr A G L Wright, 11 Little St James's Street, London SW1A 1DP
Hon. Fixture Sec.   Mr I M Bullerwell, Duncombe Heights, Avenue Farm Lane, Wilden, Beds, MK44 2PY

PLYMOUTH & DISTRICT RUGBY COMBINATION   1901
Hon. Secretary   Mr S Reeves, 129 York Road, Weston Mill, Plymouth PL5 1AU

SHROPSHIRE   1959
Hon. Secretary   Mr I B Roberts, 2 Mount Cottages, Knighton, Adbaston, Stafford ST20 0QQ

STROUD AND DISTRICT COMBINATION   1974
Hon. Secretary   Mr R Edmonds, Woodlands Cottage, 205 Slad Road, Stroud, Glos. GL5 1RJ

THE WANDERERS (PSW)   1940
Hon. Secretary   Mrs J G Lowe, 46 Kingston Lane, Shoreham by Sea, West Sussex BN43 6YB
Hon. Fixture Sec.   Brigadier R N R P James CBE, 3 Upper Court, Old Church Rd, Colwall, Malvern, Worcs WR13 6ET

WORCESTERSHIRE AND HEREFORDSHIRE   1923
Hon. Secretary   Mr J P Hartley, Nightingate House, Bishampton, Worcs WR10 2NH
Hon. Fixture Sec.   Mr D S Price, Uplands Farm, Wellington Heath, Ledbury HR8 1NF

ITINERARY

Sat, 9th June 2001	Western Australia	Perth	W	116-10
Tue, 12th June 2001	Queensland President's XV	Townsville	W	83- 6
Sat, 16th June 2001	Queensland Reds	Brisbane	W	42- 8
Tue, 19th June 2001	Australia 'A'	Gosford	L	25-28
Sat, 23rd June 2001	New South Wales Waratahs	Sydney Football Stadium	W	41-24
Tue, 26th June 2001	New South Wales Country Cockatoos	Coff's Harbour	W	46- 3
Sat, 30th June 2001	AUSTRALIA (First Test)	Brisbane	W	29-13
Tue, 3rd July 2001	Australian Capital Territory Brumbies	Canberra	W	30-28
Sat, 7th July 2001	AUSTRALIA (Second Test)	Melbourne	L	14-35
Sat, 14th July 2001	AUSTRALIA (Third Test)	Stadium Australia, Sydney	L	23-29

Summary: Played 10, won 7, lost 3, points for 449, against 184.

TOUR PARTY

Coach: Graham Henry
Assistant Coach: Andy Robinson
Manager: Donal Lenihan
Captain: Martin Johnson

ENGLAND
RUGBY

TEAM (England unless stated):
* Replacement during tour.

BACKS:

I Balshaw (Bath), M Perry (Bath), B Cohen (Nortampton),
D Jones (Llanelli/Wales), D Luger (Saracens), J Robinson (Sale),
*T Howe (Dungannon/Ireland), M Catt (Bath), W Greenwood (Harlequins),
R Henderson (Wasps/Ireland), B O'Driscoll (Leinster/Ireland), M Taylor (Swansea/Wales),
*S Gibbs (Swansea/Wales), N Jenkins (Cardiff/Wales), R O'Gara (Munster/Ireland),
*A Nicol (Glasgow Ca\ledonians), J Wilkinson (Newcastle), M Dawson (Northampton),
A Healey (Leicester), R Howley (Cardiff/Wales).

SCOTTISH
RUGBY UNION

FORWARDS:

M Johnson (Leicester)(captain), J Leonard (Harlequins), D Morris (Swansea/Wales),
T Smith (Brive/Scotland), P Vickery (Gloucester), D Young (Cardiff/Wales),
*G Bulloch (Glasgow Caledonians/Scotland), P Greening (Wasps), R McBryde (Llanelli/Wales),
K Wood (Harlequins/Ireland), J Davidson (Castres/Ireland), D Grewcock (Saracens),
S Murray (Saracens/Scotland), M O'Kelly (Leinster/Ireland), N Back (Leicester),
C Charvis (Swansea/Wales), *M Corry (Leicester), L Dallaglio (Wasps),
R Hill (Saracens), S Quinnell (Llanelli/Wales), S Taylor (Edinburgh Reivers/Scotland),
M Williams (Cardiff/Wales).

WRU

Friday, 8th June 2001
In Perth.

Attendance: 20,695
Half-time: 0-57

WESTERN AUSTRALIA 10-116 BRITISH ISLES

WESTERN AUSTRALIA: S Apaapa; M Gardiner, A Broughton, H Waldin, B Becroft; T Feather, M Fleet; T Stevens, C Duff, A New, H Grace, N Hollis, T Thomas (captain), R Coney, A Brain. Replacements: P Noriega for New 15 mins., D McRae for Feather 20 mins., P Barugh for Fleet 53 mins., R Cameron for Holis 61 mins., R Kellam for Duff 64 mins., G Plimmer for Coney 68 mins., Feather for Apaapa 72 mins., Coney for Brain 72 mins.. Scorers: Tries: Becroft, Barugh.
BRITISH ISLES: B O'Driscoll; B Cohen, W Greenwood, M Taylor, D Luger; R O'Gara, R Howley; D Morris, K Wood (captain), P Vickery, R Hill, D Grewcock, M O'Kelly, N Back, S Quinnell. Replacements: S Taylor for Hill 40 mins., A Healey for Howley 57 mins., I Balshaw for Greenwood 59 mins., J Leonard for Vickery 60 mins., J Davidson for Grewcock 71 mins., R McBryde for Wood 71 mins., Howley for Balshaw 79 mins.. Temp. replacements: Davidson for Quinnell 42-46 mins..Scorers: Tries: Luger (3), Quinnell (3), Back (2), Howley (2), Balshaw (2), Greenwood, M Taylor, Grewcock, S Taylor, Healey, O'Driscoll. Cons: O'Gara (13).
Referee: W Erickson, Australia. .

Tuedsay, 12th June 2001
In Townsville

Attendance: 18,653
Half-time: 6-10

QUEENSLAND PRESIDENT'S XV 6-83 BRITISH ISLES

QUEENSLAND PRESIDENT'S XV: N Williams; D McCallum, J Pelesasa, J Ramsamy, S Barton; S Drahm, B Wakely; R Tyrell, S Hardman, F Dyson (captain), S Fava, M Mitchell, R Vedelago, T McVerry, J Roe. Replacements: S Kerr for Dyson 10 mins., M Tabrett for Williams 40 mins., A Scotney for Drahm 55 mins., Williams for Barton 70 mins., S Berry for Wakely 73 mins.. Scorer: Pens: Drahm (2).
BRITISH ISLES: M Perry; D James, W Greenwood, R Henderson, J Robinson; N Jenkins, M Dawson; T Smith. R McBryde, D Young (captain), C Charvis, J Davidson, S Murray, M Corry, M Williams. Replacements: G Bulloch for McBryde 9 mins., J Leonard for Smith 59 mins., A Healey for Jenkins 65 mins., M Taylor for Greenwood 65 mins., M O'Kelly for Davidson 68 mins..
Scorers: Tries: Robinson (5), Henderson (3), Charvis (2), Young, O'Kelly, pen.-try. Cons: Jenkins (5), Perry (4).
Referee: G Ayoub, Australia

Saturday, 16th June 2001
At Ballymore, Brisbane

Attendance: 27,000
Half-time: 3-33

QUEENSLAND REDS 8-42 BRITISH ISLES

QUEENSLAND REDS: N Tabrett; J Pelesasa, D Herbert (captain), S Kefu, D McCallum; E Flatley, S Cordingley; N Stiles, M Foley, G Panoho, M Cockbain, N Sharpe, M Connors, D Croft, T Kefu. Replacements: A Scotney for Flatley 40 mins., J Ramsamy for Kefu 53 mins., S Hardman for Foley 64 mins., S Kerr for Stiles 66 mins., M Mitchell for Sharpe 71 mins., J Roe for Cockbain 80 mins., B Wakely for Cordingley 83 mins.. Scorers: Try: Cordingley. Pen: Flatley.
BRITISH ISLES: I Balshaw; D James, B O'Driscoll, R Henderson, D Luger; J Wilkinson, R Howley; T Smith, K Wood, P Vickery, R Hill, M Johnson (captain), D Grewcock, N Back, S Quinnell. Replacements: M Dawson for Howley 48 mins., J Robinson for O'Driscoll 60 mins., C Charvis for Back 77 mins., S Murray for Johnson 83 mins.. Scorers: Tries: Luger, Henderson, James, Hill, O'Driscoll. Pens: Wilkinson (3). Cons; Wilkinson (4).
Referee: S Dickinson, Australia

Tuesday, 19th June 2001
In Gosford (New South Wales)

Attendance: 20,000
Half-time: 15-6

AUSTRALIA 'A' 28-25 BRITISH ISLES

AUSTRALIA 'A': R Graham; M Bartholomeusz, G Bond, N Grey, S Staniforth; M Edmonds, C Whitaker; C Blades, B Cannon, R Moore, D Lyons, T Bowman, J Harrison, P Waugh (captain), J Williams. Replacements: J Holbeck for Graham 25 mins., S Payne for Whitaker 59 mins., P Noriega for Blades 61 mins., J West for Bowman 66 mins., T Murphy for Cannon 75 mins. Temp. replacement: P Ryan for Williams 38-47 mins..
Scorers: Try: Staniforth. Pens: Edmonds (7). Con: Edmonds.
BRITISH ISLES: M Perry; B Cohen, W Greenwood, M Catt, J Robinson; N Jenkins, A Healey; J Leonard, R McBryde, D Young (captain), L Dallaglio, S Murray, M O'Kelly, M Williams, S Quinnell. Replacements: M Taylor for Catt 39 mins., G Bulloch for McBryde 54 mins., J Davidson for O'Kelly 54 mins., M Dawson for Jenkins 59 mins., D Morris for Young 69 mins.. Temporary replacement: C Charvis for Quinnell 29-38 mins.. Yellow card: Dallaglio 74-80+4 mins..
Scorers: Tries: Taylor, Perry, Robinson. Pens: Jenkins (2). Cons: Dawson (2).
Referee: P Honiss, New Zealand.

Saturday, 23rd June 2001
At Sydney Football Stadium

Attendance: 40,128
Half-time: 5-24

NEW SOUTH WALES WARATAHS 24-41 BRITISH ISLES

NEW SOUTH WALES WARATAHS: D McRae; F Cullimore, L Inman, S Harris, S Qau Qau; M Edmonds, S Payne; C Blades, R Cannon, R Moore, S Pinkerton, J West, T Bowman, P Waugh (captain), F Finau.
Replacements: P Besseling for Bowman 40 mins., D Hickey for Finau 62 mins., R Tombs for Inman 66 mins., E Carter for Pinkertson 68 mins.,P Noriega for Moore 69 mins., L Green for Harris 73 mins., J Mutton for Harris 73 mins..
Temporary replacement: S Pinkerton for West 83-87 mins.
Yellow cards: Bowman 1-11 mins., Blades 57-67 mins., Cannon 57-67 mins.. Sent off: McRae 56 mins..
Scorers: Pinkerton, Cullimore (10, Harris, Edmonds. Cons: Edmonds (2).
BRITISH ISLES: I Balshaw; D James, B O'Driscoll, W Greenwood, J Robinson; J Wilkinson, M Dawson; D Morris, K Wood, P Vickery, L Dallaglio, M Johnson (captain), D Grewcock, N Back, S Quinnell.
Replacements: R O'Gara for Greenwood 22 mins., M Perry for O'Gara 57 mins., T Smith for Vickery 66 mins., R Hill for Back 72 mins., A Healey for Wilkinson 74 mins., R McBryde for Wood 77 mins..
Yellow cards: Vickery 57-67 mins., Grewcock 57-67 mins..
Scorers:Tries: Robinson (2), O'Driscoll, Wilkinson, James. Pens: Wilkinson (2). Cons: Wilkinson (4), Dawson.
Referee: S Young, Queensland. .

Tuesday, 26th June 2001
In Coffs Harbour

Attendance: 10,000
Half-time: 3-29

NEW SOUTH WALES COUNTRY COCKATOOS 3-48 BRITISH ISLES

NEW SOUTH WALES COUNTRY COCKATOOS: N Croft; V Tailasa, R Macdougal, K Shepherd, W Crosby; C Doyle, R Petty; A Baldwin, J McCormack, M Bowman, B Dale, D Lubans, B Wright, C Taylor, B Klasen. Replacements: D Dimmock for Taylor 57 mins., G Refshuage for Wright 60 mins., D Banovich for McDougal 64 mins., J Vaalotu for McCormack 66 mins., M Brown for Shepherd 68 mins., M Ellis for Doyle 70 mins., D thomas for Baldwin 70 mins., Baldwin for Bowman 80-5 mins..
Scorer: Pen: Croft.

BRITISH ISLES: I Balshaw; B Cohen, M Taylor, S Gibbs, T Howe; N Jenkins, A Healey; J Leonard, G Bulloch, D Young (captain), C Charvis, J Davidson, M O'Kelly, M Williams, M Corry. Replacements: D Wallace for Corry 57 mins., D Morris for Leonard 58 mins., S Murray for O'Kelly 72 mins.. Temporary replacement: R O'Gara for Gibbs 49-58 mins..
Scorers: Tries: Cohen (2), Charvis, Gibbs, Healey, Young. Pens: Jenkins (2). Cons: Jenkins (5).
Referee: G Hinton, New South Wales. .

1st Test

Saturday, 30th June 2001
In The Gabba, Brisbane

Attendance: 37,500
Half-time: 3-12

AUSTRALIA 13-29 BRITISH ISLES

AUSTRALIA (Australian Capital Territory unless stated): C Latham (Queensland); A Walker, D Herbert (Queensland), N Grey (New South Wales), J Roff; S Larkham, G Gregan; N Stiles (Queensland), J Paul, G Panoho (Queensland), O Finegan, D Giffin, J Eales (Queensland)(captain), G Smith, T Kefu (Queensland).
Replacements: M Burke (New South wales) for Latham 40 mins., M Foley (Queensland) for Paul 55 mins., E Flatley (Queensland) for Larkham 55 mins., M Cockbain (Queensland) for Eales 73 mins., D Lyons (New South Wales) for Finegan 82 mins.,
Scorers: Tries: Walker, Grey. Pen: Grey.

BRITISH ISLES (England unless stated): M Perry (Bath); D James (Bridgend/Wales), B O'Driscoll (Blackrock College/Ireland), R Henderson (Young Munster/Ireland), J Robinson (Sale); J Wilkinson (Newcastle); R Howley (Cardiff/Wales); T Smith (Northampton/Scotland), K Wood (Harlequins/Ireland), P Vickery (Gloucester), M Corry (Leicester), M Johnson (Leicester)(captain), D Grewcock (Bath), R Hill (Saracens), S Quinnell (Llanelli/Wales).
Replacements: I Balshaw (Bath) for Perry 40 mins., C Charvis (Swansea/Wales) for Quinnell 70 mins., J Leonard (Harlequins) for Smith 82 mins.. Temporary replacement: G Bulloch (Glasgow Caledonians/Scotland) for Wood 74-81 mins.. Yellow cards: Corry 62-72 mins., Vickery 75 mins. to finish.
Scorers: Tries: Robinson, James, O'Driscoll, Quinnell. Pen: Wilkinson. Cons: Wilkinson (3).
Referee: A Watson, South Africa

Tuesday, 4th July 2001
At Bruce Stadium, Canberra

Attendance: 23,000
Half-time: 22-10

AUSTRALIAN CAPITAL TERRITORY BRUMBIES 28-30 BRITISH ISLES

AUSTRALIAN CAPITAL TERRITORY BRUMBIES: M Bartholomeusz; D McInally, G Bond, J Holbeck, W Gordon; P Howard, T Hall; A Scott, A Freier, M Weaver, D Tuiavaii, J Harrison, D Vickerman, P Ryan, J Williams (captain). Replacements: D Pusey for Vickerman 47 mins., R Samo for Williams 52 mins., C Pither for Gordon 71 mins., J Huxley for Holbeck 79 mins.. Yellow card: Ryan 59-69 mins..
Scorers: Tries: Bartholomewsz, Gordom. Tuiavaii. Pens: Hall (3). Cons: Hall (2).
BRITISH ISLES: I Balshaw; B Cohen, M Taylor, S Gibbs, A Healey; R O'Gara, M Dawson; D Morris, D West, D Young (captain), D Wallace, J Davidson, S Murray, M Williams, M Corry. Replacment: J Leonard for Young 71 mins.. Temp. replacement: D James for Taylor 17-23 mins..Yellow card: Balshaw 57-67 mins..
Scorers: Tries: Healey (2), Wallace. Pens: Dawson (3). Cons: Dawson (3).
Referee: P Marshall, Queensland

2nd Test

Saturady, 7th July 2001
At Colonial Stadium, Melbourne

Attendance: 56,605
Half-time: 6-11

AUSTRALIA 35-14 BRITISH ISLES

AUSTRALIA (Australian Capital Territory unless stated): M Burke (New South Wales); J Roff, N Grey (New South Wales), D Herbert (Queensland), A Walker; S Larkham, G Gregan; N Stiles (Queensland), M Foley (Queensland), R Moore (New South Wales), O Finegan, D Giffin, J Eales (Queensland)(captain), G Smith, T Kefu (Queensland). Replacements: M Cockbain (Queensland) for Giffin 42-45 mins. (Temporary) and 71 mins., C Latham (Queensland) for Walker 47 mins., E Flatley (Queensland) for Laekham 82 mins., B Cannon (New South Wales) for Foley 89 mins.. Scorers: Tries: Roff (2), Burke. Pens: Burke (6). Con: Burke.

BRITISH ISLES (England unless stated): M Perry (Bath); D James (Bridgend/Wales), B O'Driscoll (Blackrock College/Ireland), R Henderson (Young Munster/Ireland), J Robinson (Sale); J Wilkinson (Newcastle), R Howley (Cardiff/Wales); T Smith (Northampton/England), K Wood (Harlequins/Ireland), P Vickery (Gloucester), R Hill (Saracens), M Johnson (Liecester) (captain), D Grewcock (Saracens), N Back (Leicester), S Quinnell (Llanelli/Wales). Replacements: M Corry (Leicester) for Hill 34-36 mins. (temporary) and 40 mins., I Balshaw (Bath) for Perry 52 mins., J Leonard (Harlequins) for Vickery 66 mins., N Jenkins (Cardiff/Wales) for Wilkinson 75 mins., M Dawson (Northampton/England) for Howley 85 mins.).
Scorers: Try: Back. Pens: Wilkinson (3).
Referee: J Kaplan, South Africa.

3rd Test

Saturday, 14th July 2001
At Stadium Australia, Sydney

Attendance: 84,188
Half-time: 16-13

AUSTRALIA 29-23 BRITISH ISLES

AUSTRALIA (Australian Capital Territory unless stated): M Burke (New South Wales); J Roff, N Grey (New South Wales), D Herbert (Queensland), A Walker; E Flatley (Queensland), G Gregan; N Stiles (Queensland), M Foley (Queensland), R Moore (New South Wales), O Finegan, J Harrison, J Eales (Queensland)(captain), G Smith, T Kefu (Queensland). New cap: Harrison. Replacements: M Cockbain (Queensland) for Finegan 75 mins., J Holbeck for Grey 77 minuters. Yellow card: Herbert 52-62 mins..
Scorers: Tries: Herbert (2). Pens: Burke (5). Cons: Burke (2).

BRITISH ISLES (England unless stated): M Perry (Bath); D James (Llanelli/Wales), B O'Driscoll (Blackrock College/Ireland), R Henderson (Young Munster/Ireland), J Robinson (Sale); J Wilkinson (Newcastle), M Dawson (Northampton); T Smith (Northampton/Scotland), K Wood (Harlequins/Ireland), P Vickery (Gloucester), M Corry (Leicester), M Johnson (Leicester)(captain), D Grewcock (Saracens), N Back (Leicester), S Quinnell (Llanelli/Wales). Replacements: C Charvis (Swansea/Wales) for Quinnell 40 mins., D Morris (Swansea/Wales) for Smith 73 mins., I Balshaw (Bath) for James 74 mins..
Scorers: Tries: Robinson, Wilkinson. Pens: Wilkinson (3). Cons: Wilkinson (2).
Referee: P O'Brien, New Zealand.

LEADING POINTS SCORERS:

72	J Wilkinson (2 tries, 12 pens, 13 cons)
50	J Robinson (10 tries)
32	N Jenkins (4 pens, 10 cons)
26	R O'Gara (13 cons)
21	M Dawson (3 pens, 6 cons)
20	A Healey (4 tries)
	R Henderson (4 tries)
	D Luger (4 tries)
	B O'Driscoll (4 tries)
	S Quinnell (4 tries)
15	N Back (3 tries)
	C Charvis (3 tries)
	D James (3 tries)
13	M Perry (1 try, 4 cons)
10	I Balshaw (2 tries)
	B Cohen (2 tries)
	R Howley (2 tries)
	M Taylor (2 tries)
	D Young (2 tries)
5	S Gibbs
	W Greenwood
	D Grewcock
	R Hill
	M O'Kelly
	S Taylor
	D Wallace(one try each),
	plus one penalty try.

No dropped goals were scored during the tour.

John Eales by reaching 80 test appearances for Australia equalled the record for a lock held by W J McBride.

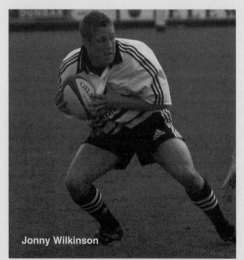

Jonny Wilkinson

MOST APPEARANCES
Test appearances in brackets
Replacement appearances marked with 'r'
and temporary replacements marked with 't')

M Corry	6+1r	(2+1r)
J Robinson	6+1r	(3)
D Grewcock	6	(3)
D James	6+1t	(3)
B O'Driscoll	6	(3)
S Quinnell	6+1r	(3)
P Vickery	6	(3)
K Wood	6	(3)
N Back	5	(2)
R Henderson	5	(3)
M Johnson	5	(3)
M Perry	5+1r	(3)
T Smith	5+1r	(3)
J Wilkinson	5	(3)
I Balshaw	3+4r	(0+3r)
J Leonard	2+5r	(0+2r)
J Davidson	3+3r	
M Taylor	3+3r	
A Healey	3+3r	
D Morris	2+4r	(0+1r)
C Charvis	2+3r+1t	(0+2r)
N Jenkins	3+1r+1t	(0+1r)
G Bulloch	1+3r+1t	(0+1t)
R Howley	4	(2)
B Cohen	4	
R Hill	4	(2)
D Young	4	
M Williams	4	
R O'Gara	2+1r+1t	
M O'Kelly	3+1r	
R McBryde	2+2	
S Murray	2+2	
W Greenwood	3	
D Luger	2	
L Dallaglio	2	
S Gibbs	2	
D Wallace	1+1	
M Catt	1	
T Howe	1	
D West	1	
S Taylor	0+1	

P Greening dropped out injured before the tour started and A Nicol was on the replacements bench for the Third Test against Australia but did not play.

HEINEKEN CUP 2000-01

POOL I

Friday, 6th October 2000
Edinburgh Reivers 29 Leinster 21
Saturday, 7th October 2000
Biarritz 37 Northampton 30
Friday, 13th October 2000
Leinster 35 Biarritz 9
Saturday, 14th October 2000
Northampton 22 Edinburgh Reivers 23
Saturday, 21st October 2000
Northampton 8 Leinster 14
Biarritz 29 Edinburgh Reivers 18
Friday, 27th October 2000
Edinburgh Reivers 27 Biarritz 35
Leinster 40 Northampton 31
Friday, 12th January 2001
Leinster 34 Edinburgh Reivers 34
Saturday, 13th January 2001
Northampton 32 Biarritz 24
Friday, 19th January 2001
Edinburgh Reivers 18 Northampton 15
Saturday, 20th January 2001
Biarritz 30 Leinster 10

	P	W	D	L	F	A	Ts	Pts
Biarritz	6	4	0	2	164	152	11	8
Edinburgh Reivers	6	3	1	2	149	156	13	7
Leinster	6	3	1	2	154	141	16	7
Northampton	6	1	0	5	140	156	17	2

Biarritz qualify.for Quarter Finals

POOL II

Saturday, 7th October 2000
Swansea 54 Wasps 28
Stade Francais 92 L'Aquila 7
Saturday, 14th October 2000
Swansea 18 Stade Francais 16
Sunday, 15th October 2000
L'Aquila 10 Wasps 39
Saturday, 21st October 2000
Stade Francais 40 Wasps 10
Sunday, 22nd October 2000
L'Aquila 6 Swansea 70
Saturday, 28th October 2000
Swansea 73 L'Aquila 3
Sunday, 29th October 2000
Wasps 28 Stade Francais 31
Saturday, 13th January 2001
L'Aquila 9 Stade Francais 76
Sunday, 14th January 2001
Wasps 28 Swansea 16
Saturday, 20th January 2001
Stade Francais 42 Swansea 13
Sunday, 21st January 2001
Wasps 42 L'Aquila 5

	P	W	D	L	F	A	Ts	Pts
Stade Francais	5	6	0	1	297	85	36	10
Swansea	6	4	0	2	244	123	28	8
Wasps	6	3	0	3	175	156	20	6
L'Aquila	6	0	0	6	40	392	3	0

Stade Francais and Swansea (on tries scored) qualify.

POOL III

Friday, 6th October 2000
Ulster 32 Cardiff 26
Saturday, 7th October 2000
Toulouse 22 Saracens 32
Saturday, 14th October 2000
Cardiff 26 Toulouse 17
Sunday, 15th October 2000
Saracens 55 Ulster 25
Saturday, 21st October 2000
Saracens 23 Cardiff 32
Sunday, 22nd October 2000
Toulouse 35 Ulster 35
Friday, 27th October 2000
Cardiff 24 Saracens 14
Ulster 25 Toulouse 29
Friday, 12th January 2001
Cardiff 42 Ulster 16
Sunday, 14th January 2001
Saracens 37 Toulouse 30
Friday, 19th January 2001
Ulster 13 Saracens 21
Saturday, 20th January 2001
Toulouse 38 Cardiff 27

	P	W	D	L	F	A	Ts	Pts
Cardiff	6	4	0	2	167	140	12	8
Saracens	6	4	0	2	172	146	18	8
Toulouse	6	2	1	3	171	182	15	5
Ulster	6	1	1	4	136	205	11	3

Cardiff qualify.

POOL IV

Saturday, 7th October 2000
Munster 26 Newport 18
Bath 25 Castres 13
Friday, 13th October 2000
Newport 28 Bath 17
Saturday, 14th October 2000
Castres 29 Munster 32
Saturday, 21st October 2000
Munster 31 Bath 9
Newport 21 Castres 20
Saturday, 28th October 2000
Bath 18 Munster 5
Castres 44 Newport 21
Saturday, 13th January 2001
Castres 19 Bath 32

Newport 24 Munster 39
Saturday, 20th January 2001
Munster 21 Castres 11
Tuesday, 23rd January 2001
Bath 38 Newport 10

	P	W	D	L	F	A	Ts	Pts
Munster	6	5	0	1	154	109	13	10
Bath	6	4	0	2	139	106	14	8
Newport	6	2	0	4	122	183	10	4
Castres	6	1	0	5	135	152	13	1*

* One point deducted for fielding an inegible player.
Munster qualify.

POOL V

Friday, 6th October 2000
Llanelli 20 Gloucester 27
Saturday, 7th October 2000
Roma 5 Colomiers 15
Saturday, 14th October 2000
Colomiers 6 Llanelli 19
Sunday, 15th October 2000
Gloucester 52 Roma 12
Saturday, 21st October 2000
Llanelli 46 Roma 0
Gloucester 22 Colomiers 22
Saturday, 28th October 2000
Roma 21 Llanelli 41
Saturday, 13th January 2001
Colomiers 55 Roma 21
Gloucester 28 Llanelli 27
Friday, 19th January 2001
Llanelli 34 Colomiers 21
Saturday, 20th January 2001
Roma 29 Gloucester 38 (Tre Fontaine)

	P	W	D	L	F	A	Ts	Pts
Gloucester	6	4	1	1	186	140	13	9
Llanelli	6	4	0	2	187	103	18	8
Colomiers	6	3	1	2	148	120	14	7
Roma	6	0	0	6	88	246	7	0

Gloucester qualify.

POOL VI

Saturday, 7th October 2000
Leicester 46 Pau 18
Pontyprid 40 Glasgow Caledonians 25
Saturday, 14th October 2000
Pau 12 Pontypridd 9
Sunday, 15th October 2000
Glasgow Caledonians 21 Leicester 33
Friday, 20th October 2000
Pontypridd 18 Leicester 11
Sunday, 22nd October 2000
Glasgow Caledonians 24 Pau 46
Saturday, 28th October 2000
Pau 44 Glasgow Caledonians 16
Leicester 27 Pontypridd 19
Saturday, 13th January 2001
Pau 3 Leicester 20

Sunday, 14th January 2001
Glasgow Caledonians 25 Pontypridd 23
Saturday, 20th January 2001
Leicester 41 Glasgow Caledonians 26
Sunday, 21st January 2001
Pontypridd 27 Pau 31

	P	W	D	L	F	A	Ts	Pts
Leicester	6	5	0	1	178	105	15	10
Pau	6	4	0	1	154	142	16	8
Pontypridd	6	2	0	4	136	131	8	4
Glasgow Caley	6	1	0	5	137	227	12	2

Leicester and Pau (on tries scored) qualify.

QUARTER-FINALS

Saturday, 27th January 2001

At Kingsholm, Gloucester.   Attendance: 11,800.
GLOUCESTER 21-15 CARDIFF
Half-time: 9-3

GLOUCESTER: C Catling; J Ewens, T Fanolua, J Little, T Beim; S Mannix, E Moncrieff; T Woodman, O Azam, P Vickery, J Boer, R Fidler, I Jones, K Jones (captain), J Paramore. Replacements: A Gomarsall for Moncrieff 41 mins., B Hayward for Mannix 65 mins., A Hazell for Paramore 69 mins., C Fortey for Azam 74 mins., A Deacon for Vickery 76 mins., C Yates for Ewens 79 mins.. Scorers: Pens: Mannix (6), Hayward.
CARDIFF: R Williams; N Walne, J Robinson, P Muller, G Thomas; N Jenkins, R Howley; S John, J Humphreys, P Young (captain), O Williams, C Quinnell, J Tait, M Williams, E Lewis. Replacements: G Kacala for O Wiliams 58 mins., P Rogers for Young 61 mins.. Scorers: Tries: Walne, G Thomas. Pen: Jenkins. Con: Jenkins.
Referee: J Jutge, France.

At Stade Jean Bouin, Paris.   Attendance: 8,000
STADE FRANCAIS 36-19 PAU
Half-time: 17-10

STADE FRANCAIS: C Dominici; A Gomes, F Comba, C Mytton, R Poulain; D Dominguez, C Laussucq; S Marconnet, F Landreau, P de Villiers, C Moni, D Auradou, M James, R Pool-Jones, C Juillet (captain). Replacements: M Blin for Landreau 31 mins., P Tabacco for Moni 57 mins., T Lombard for Mytton 70 mins., P Lemoine for Marconnet 70 mins., H Chaffardon for Auradou 79 mins., D George for James 79 mins..
Scorers: Tries: Poulain, Laussucq, Combes. DG: Dominguez (2). Pens: Dominguez (3). Cons: Dominguez (3).
PAU: D Arieta; P Bomati, J-C Cistacq, C Paille, L Arbo; D Aucagne, P Carbonneau; P Triep-Capdeville, M Dal Maso, S Bria, G Combes, A Charron (captain), A Lagouarde, L Maillier, I Harinordoquy. Replacements: J Espag for Bria 40 mins., G Chasseriau for Lagouarde 40 mins., J Rey for Dal Masso 60 mins., A Agueb for Maillier 61 mins., T Cleda for Harinordoquy 61 mins., D Traille for Paille 70 mins.. Scorers: Try: Paille. DG: Aucagne. Pens: Aucagne (3). Con: Aucagne.
Referee: N Whitehouse, Wales. .

Sunday, 28th January 2001

SEMI-FINALS

At Welford Road, Leicester.   Attendance: 14,000

LEICESTER 41-10 SWANSEA
Half-time: 19-3

LEICESTER: T Stimpson; F Tuilagi, L Lloyd, P Howard, G Murphy; A Goode, A Healey; G Rowntree, D West, D Garforth, W Johnson, L Deacon, B Kay, N Back (captain), M Corry. Replacements: G Gelderbloum for Lloyd 45 mins., J Hamilton for Healey 52 mins., P freshwater for Rowntree 62 mins., L Moody for Back 66 mins., R Cockerill for West 67 mins., R Nebbett for Garforth 73 mins.. Scorers: Tries: Murphy (2), Healey, Goode. DG: Goode.Pens: Stimpson (4). Cons: Stimpson (3).
SWANSEA: K Morgan; S Payne, M Taylor, S Gibbs (captain), M Robinson; A Thomas, S Martens; D Morris, G Jenkins, B Evans, G Lewis, J Griffiths, A Moore, C Charvis, L Jones. Replacements: C Anthony for B Evans 59 mins., G Smith for L Jones 62 mins., D Thomas for Charvis 67 mins., C Rees for A Thomas 70 mins., R Jones for Martens 70 mins., P Moriarty for L Jones 71 mins.. Temporary replacement: G Smith for L Jones 62-71 mins.. Yellow cards: G Jenkins, Griffiths. Scorers: Try: Moriarty. Pen: A Thomas. Con: C Rees.
Referee: A Lewis, Ireland.

At Thomond, Park, Limerick.   Attendance: 14,000

MUNSTER 38-29 BIARRITZ
Half-time: 17-15

MUNSTER: D Crotty; J Kelly, M Mullins, J Holland, A Horgan; R O'Gara, P Stringer; P Clohessy, F Sheahan, J Hayes, A Quinlan, M Galwey (captain), J Langford, D Wallace, A Foley. Scorers: Tries: Foley (3). Pens: O'Gara (7). Con: O'Gara.
BIARRITZ: S Bonetti; P Bernat-Salles, F Bidabe, N Couttet, S Legg; F Botica, S Bonnet; E Menieu, J-M Gonzalez (captain), D Avril, S Betsen, J-P Versailles, O Roumat, O Nauroy, C Milheres. Replacements: T Lievremont for Roumat 48 mins., M Lefevre for Versailles 53 mins., M Lievremont for Betsen 66 mins., M DFitzgerald for Menieu 75 mins.. Temporary replacement: Fitzgerald for Milheres 61-70 mins.. Yellow card: Avril. Scorers: Tries: Milheres (2), Legg, Bonnet. Pen: Botica. Cons: Botica (3).
Referee: E Morrison, England.

Saturday, 21st April 2001

At Stadium Lille Metropole, Lille.

STADE FRANCAIS 16-15 MUNSTER
Half-time: 16-6
Attendance: 20,400.

STADE FRANCAIS: C Dominici; T Lombard, F Comba, C Mytton, R Poulain; D Dominguez, A Laussucq; C Marconnet, M Williams, P de Villiers, C Moni, D Auradou, M James, R Pool-Jones, C Juillet (captain). Replacements: A Gomes for Juillet 70 mins.. Yellow card: Dominici 67-77 mins.. Scorers: Try: Mytton. Pens: Dominguez (3). Con: Dominguez.
MUNSTER: D Crotty; J O'Neill, M Mullins, J Holland, A Horgan; R O'Gara, P Stringer; P Clohessy, F Sheahan, J Hayes, D O'Callaghan, M Galwey (captain), J Langford, D Wallace, A Foley. Replacements: D O'Cuinneagain for O'Callaghan 70 mins., M Horan for Clohessy 80 mins.. Scorer: Pens: O'Gara (5).
Referee: C White, England

At Vicarage Road, Watford.

GLOUCESTER 15-19 LEICESTER
Half-time: 6-16.
Attendance: 14,010.

GLOUCESTER: B Hayward; R Greenslade-Jones, T Fanolua, J Little, J Simpson-Danielson; S Mannix, A Gomarsall; A Deacon, O Azam, P Vickery (captain), J Boer, R Fidler, I Jones, K Jones, J Paramore. Replacements: A Hazell temporary for Jones 28-33 mins. & 57 for Jones, C Fortey for Deacon 63 mins., M Cornwell 63 for Fidler, C Yates for Hayward 73 mins., S Ojomoh for Paramore 78 mins.. Yellow card: Paramore 55-65 mins.. Scorer: Pens: Mannix (5).
LEICESTER: G Murphy; T Stimpson, L Lloyd, P Howard, W Stanley; A Goode, A Healey; G Rowntree, D West, D Garforth, W Johnson, M Johnson (captain), B Kay, N Back, M Corry. Replacements: R Cockerill for West 39 mins.. P Gustard for Corry 80 mins.. Scorers: Try: Lloyd. Pens: Stimpson (4). Con: Stimpson.
Referee: J Dume, France.

FINAL

At Parc des Princes, Paris.   Attendance: 45,000

STADE FRANCAIS 30-34 LEICESTER
Referee: D McHugh, Ireland   Half-time: 15-9.

STADE FRANCAIS: C Dominici; T Lombard, F Comba, C Mytton, A Gomes; D Dominguez, M Williams; S Marconnet, F Landreau, P de Villiers, C Moni, D Auradou, M James, R Pool-Jones, C Juillet (captain).
Replacements: P Tabacco for Moni 65 mins., D Venditti for Mytton 75 mins.. Temp. replacement: M Blin for Juillet 5-15 mins.. Yellow card: Landreau 6-16 mins..
Scorer: DG: Dominguez. Pens: Dominguez (9).

LEICESTER: P Stimpson; G Murphy, L Lloyd, P Howard, W Stanley; A Goode, A Healey; G Rowntree, D West, D Garforth, W Johnson, M Johnson (captain), B Kay, N Back, M Corry.
Replacements: P Gustard for W Johnson 37 mins., J Hamilton for Goode 72 mins., G Gelderbloom for Murphy 76 mins.. Yellow card: M Johnson 48-58 mins..
Scorers: Tries: Lloyd (2), Back. Pens: Stimpson (5). Cons: Stimpson (2)

TABLE (after 8.4.01) (three matches involving Ireland postponed)

	P	W	D	L	F	A	Pts
England	4	4	0	0	215	60	8
Wales	4	2	1	1	119	130	5
Ireland	2	2	0	0	63	37	4
France	5	2	0	3	115	138	4
Scotland	4	1	1	2	60	106	3
Italy	5	0	0	5	106	207	0

1st Round:

Italy 22 Ireland 41   Wales 15 England 44   France 16 Scotland 6.

2nd Round:

England 80 Italy 23   Ireland 22 France 15   Scotland 28 Wales 28.

3rd Round:

England 43 Scotland 3   Italy 19 France 30   Wales v Ireland   (postponed)

4th Round:

France 35 Wales 43   Ireland v England postponed   Scotland 23 Italy 19.

5th Round:

England 48 France 19   Italy 23 Wales 33   Scotland v Ireland postponed.

FIRST ROUND

Saturday, 3rd April 2000

ITALY 22-41 IRELAND

Attendance: 42,000   Half-time: 14-19

ITALY: C Stoica (Narbonne); C Pilat (Treviso), L Martin (Northampton), G Raineri (Roma), D Dallan (Treviso); R Pez (Roma), A Troncon (Montferrand); A Lo Cicero (Roma), A Moscardi (Treviso)(captain), A Muraro (Padova), C Caione (Roma), W Visser (Treviso), C Checchinato (Treviso), M Bergamasco (Treviso), D Dal Maso (Rovigo). Replacements: E Galon (Bourgoin) for Pilat 30 mins., G De Carli (Roma) for Muraro 59 mins., W Pozzebon (Treviso) for Martin 60 mins., G Lanzi (Calvisano) for Checchinato 71 mins., F Frati (Parma) for Dal Maso 79 mins.. Temporary replacement: De Carli for Dal maso 39-41 mins.. Yellow card: Muraro 39-49 mins.. Sent-off: Troncon 76 mins..
Scorers: Tries: Tries: Pilat, Checchinato, Bergamasco. Pen: Pilat. Cons: Pez (2).

IRELAND: G Dempsey (Terenure College); S Horgan (lansdowne), M Mullins (Young Munster), R Henderson (Wasps), T Howe (Ballymena); R O'Gara (Cork Constitution), P Stringer (Shannon); P Clohessy (Young Munster), K Wood (Harlequins)(captain), J Hayes (Shannon), A Quinlan (Shannon), M Galwey (Shannon), M O'Kelly (St Mary's College), D Wallace (Garryowen), A Foley (Shannon). Replacements: J Davidson (Castres) for Galwey 65 mins., A Ward (Ballynahinch) for Foley 66 mins., D Humphreys (Dungannon) for Howe 71 mins., F Sheahan (Cork Constitution) for Quinlan 73 mins., B O'Meara (Cork Constitution) for Stringer 76 mins.. Yellow card: Clohessy 70-80 mins.. .
Scorers: Tries: Henderson (3), Horgan, O'Gara. Pens: O'Gara (4). Cons: O'Gara (2). .
Referee: J Kaplan, South Africa.

NB: A Troncon (Italy) became the first scrum-half to be sent off in the Five Nations or Six Nations tournament.

WALES 15-44 ENGLAND

Attendance: 72,500   Half-time: 8-29

WALES: S Jones (Llanelli); G Thomas (Cardiff), M Taylor (Swansea), S Gibbs (Swansea), D James (Llanelli); N Jenkins (Cardiff), R Howley (Cardiff); D Morris (Swansea), R McBryde (Lnaelli), D Young (Cardiff)(captain), M Williams (Cardiff), I Gough (Newport), C Wyatt (Llanelli), C Charvis (Swansea), S Quinnell (Llanelli). Replacements: A Moore (Swansea) for Wyatt 46 mins., M Jones (Llanelli) for A Thomas 54 mins., A Bateman (Northampton) for Taylor 64 mins., S John (Cardiff) for Morris 66 mins., R Moon (Llanelli) for Howley 80 mins.. New cap: M Jones.
Scorers: Tries: Howley, S Quinnell. Pen: N Jenkins. Con: N Jenkins.
ENGLAND: I Balshaw (Bath); B Cohen (Northampton), W Greenwood (Harlequins), M Catt (Bath), D Luger (Saracens); J Wilkinson (Newcastle), M Dawson (Northampton); J Leonard (Harlequins), D West (Leicester), P Vickery (Gloucester), R Hill (Saracens), M Johnson (Leicester)(captain), D Grewcock (Saracens), N Back (Leicester), L Dallaglio (Wasps). Replacements: A Healey (Leicester) for Luger seven mins., M Perry (Bath) for Balshaw 58 mins., T Woodman (Gloucester) for Leonard 62 mins., M Corry (Leicester) for Dallaglio 69 mins., M Tindall (Bath) for Catt 70 mins..
Scorers: Tries: Greenwood (3), Dawson (2), Cohen. Pens: Wilkinson (2). Cons: Wilkinson (4).
Referee: J Dume, France.
N Jenkins became the first player to reach 1,000 points in international rugby.

Sunday, 4th February 2001

FRANCE 16-6 SCOTLAND

Half-time: 6-6

FRANCE: X Garbajosa (Toulouse); P Bernat-Salles (Biarritz), F Comba (Stade Francais), R Dourthe (Beziers), D Bory (Montferrand); C Lamaison (Agen), F Galthie (Colomiers); S Marconnet (Stade Francais), R Ibanez (Castres), P de Villiers (Stade Francais), C Moni (Stade Francais), A Auradou (Stade Francais), F Pelous (Toulouse)(captain), O Magne (Montferrand), D Juillet (Stade Francais). Replacements: S Betsen (Biarritz) for Moni 51 mins., A Benazzi (Agen) for Auradou 51 mins., C Califano (Toulouse) for Marconnet 51 mins., G Merceron (Montferrand) for Dourthe 71 mins..
Scorers: Try: Bernat-Salles. Pens: Lamaison (3). Con: Lamaison.
SCOTLAND: C Paterson (Edinburgh Reivers); C Murray (Edinburgh Reivers), J McLaren (Glasgow Caledonians), J Leslie (Newcastle Falcons), K Logan (Wasps); G Townsend (Castres), A Nicol (Glasgow Caledonians)(captain); T Smith (Brive), G Bulloch (Glasgow Caledonians), M Stewart (Northampton), M Leslie (Edinburgh Reivers), S Murray (Saracens), R Metcalfe (Edinburgh Reivers), B Pountney (Northampton), J Petrie (Glasgow Caledonians). Replacements: D Hodge (Edinburgh Reivers) for Townsend four mins., S Grimes (Newcastle Falcons) for Metcalfe 22 mins., G McIlwham (Glasgow Caledonians) for Stewart 53 mins., B Redpath (Edinburgh Reivers) for Nicol 67 mins., R Russell (Saracens) for G Bulloch 67 mins., A Bulloch (Glasgow Caledonians) for McLaren 69 mins., J White (Glasgow Caledonians) for Petrie 76 mins.. Yellow card: M Leslie 40-50 mins..   Scorer: Pens: Logan (2).
Referee: S Dickinson, Australia.

SECOND ROUND

Saturday, 17th February 2001

ENGLAND 80-23 ITALY

Attendance: 73,500   Half-time: 33-23

ENGLAND: I Balshaw (Bath); A Healey (Leicester), W Greenwood (Harlequins), M Catt (Bath), B Cohen (Northampton); J Wilkinson (Newcastle), M Dawson (Northampton); J Leonard (Harlequins), D West (Leicster), P Vickery (Gloucester), R Hill (Saracens), M Johnson (Leicester)(captain), D Grewcock (Saracens), N Back (Leicester), L Dallaglio (Wasps). Replacements: M Regan (Bath) for West 50 mins., J Worsley (Wasps) for Back 50 mins., J Robinson (Sale) for Cohen 50 mins., K Bracken (Saracens) for Dawson 57 mins., T Woodman (Gloucester) for Leonard 68 mins., M Corry (Leicester) for Grewcock 73 mins.. New cap: Robinson.
Scorers: Tries: Healey (2), Balshaw (2), Cohen, Regan, Worsley, Greenwood, Wilkinson, Dallaglio. Pens: Wilkinson (4), Cons: Wilkinson (9).
ITALY: A Scanavaca (Roma); L Martin (Northampton), C Stoica (Narbonne), W Pozzebon (Treviso), D Dallan (Treviso); G Raineri (Roma), J-M Queirolo (Viadana); A Io Cicero (Roma), A Moscardi (Treviso)(captain), A Muraro (Padova), C Caione (Roma), A Gritti (Treviso), W Visser (Treviso), M Bergamasco (Treviso), C Checchinato (Treviso). Replacements: G de Carli (Roma) for Muraro 47 mins., M Rivaro (Bedford) for Pozzebon 66 mins., T Paoletti (La Rochelle) for Io Cicero 68 mins., D Dal Maso (Rovigo) for Caione 68 mins..
Scorers: Tries: Dallan, Checchinato. Pens: Scanavaca (3). Cons: Scanavaca (2).
Referee: S Dickinson, Australia.
England's 80 points were a record score for the competition as was J Wilkinson's personal contribution of 35 points.

IRELAND 22-15 FRANCE

Attendance: 49,000   Half-time: 9-3

IRELAND: G Dempsey (Terenure College); D Hickie (St Mary's College), B O'Driscoll (Blackrock College), R Henderson (Wasps), T Howe (Ballymena); R O'Gara (Cork Constitution), P Stringer (Shannon); P Clohessy (Young Munster), K Wood (Harlequins)(captain), J Hayes (Shannon), A Quinlan (Shannon), M Galwey (Shannon), M O'Kelly (St Mary's College), D Wallace (Garryowen), A Foley (Shannon). Replacements: E Byrne (St Mary's College) for Clohessy 71 mins., G Longwell (Ballymena) for Galwey 71 mins., A Ward (Ballynahinch) for Quinlan 71 mins., K Maggs (Bath) for Henderson 72 mins..

Scorers: Try: O'Driscoll. Pens: O'Gara (5). Con: O'Gara.

FRANCE: X Garbajosa (Toulouse); P Bernat-Salles (Biarritz), F Comba (Stade Francais), R Dourthe (Beziers), D Bory (Montferrand); C Lamaison (Agen), P Carbonneau (Brive); S Marconnet (Stade Francais), R Ibanez (Castres), P de Villiers (Stade Francais), C Moni (Stade Francais), D Auradou (Stade Francais), F Pelous (Toulouse)(captain), O Magne (Montferrand), D Juillet (Stade Francais). Replacements: C Califano (Toulouse) for Marconnet 63 mins., A Benazzi (Agen) for Auradou 63 mins., S Betsen (Biarritz) for Moni 70 mins., C Dominici (Stade Francais) for Bori 70 mins..

Yellow card: Lamaison - first half.

Scorers: Tries: Pelous, Bernat-Salles. Pen: Lamaison. Con: Lamaison.

Referee: S Young, Australia.

NB: This was Ireland's first victory over France in Dublin since 1983 and their first back-to-back success in the same fixture since 1952 and 1953.

SCOTLAND 28-28 WALES

Attendance: 67,500   Half-time: 6-18.

SCOTLAND: C Paterson (Edinburgh Reivers); C Murray (Edinburgh Reivers), J McLaren (Glasgow Caledonians), J Leslie (Northampton), K Logan (Wasps); D Hodge (Edinburgh Reivers), A Nicol (Glasgow Caledonians)(captain); T Smith (Brive), G Bulloch (Glasgow Caledonians), M Stewart (Northampron), M Leslie (Edinburgh Reivers), S Murray (Saracens), R Metcalfe (Edinburgh Reivers), B Pountney (Northampton), J Petrie (Glasgow Caledonians). Replacements: G McIlwham (Glasgow Caledonians) for Stewart 50 mins., S Grimes (Newcastle Falcons) for Metcalfe 68 mins., J Craig (Glasgow Caledonians) for C Murray 68 mins.. No new caps. Yellow card: Metcalfe 28-38 mins..

Scorers: Tries: Paterson, McLaren, Smith. Pens: Logan (3). Cons: Logan, Hodge.

WALES: R Williams (Neath); M Jones (Llanelli), M Taylor (Swansea), S Gibbs (Swansea), D James (Llanelli); N Jenkins (Cardiff), R Howley (Cardiff); D Morris (Swansea), R McBryde (Llanelli), D Young (Cardiff)(captain), C Charvis (Swansea), I Gough (Newport), A Moore (Swansea), M Williams (Cardiff), S Quinnell (Llanelli). Replacements: C Quinnell (Cardiff) for Gough 62 mins., R Moon (Llanelli) for Howley 62 mins., S John (Cardiff) for Young 80 mins.. No new caps.

Scorers: Try: Taylor. DGs Jenkins (3). Pens: Jenkins (4).Con: Jenkins.

Referee: S Lander, England.

THIRD ROUND

Saturday, 3rd March 2001

ENGLAND 43-3 SCOTLAND

ENGLAND: I Balshaw (Bath); A Healey (Leicester), W Greenwood (Harlequins), M Catt (Bath), B Cohen (Northampton); J Wilkinson (Newcastle), M Dawson (Northampton); J Leonard (Harlequins), D West (Leicester), P Vickery (Gloucester), R Hill (Saracens), M Johnson (Leicester)(captain), D Grewcock (Saracens), N Back (Leicester), L Dallaglio (Wasps). Replacements: M Regan (Bath) for West 40 mins., J Robinson (Sale) for Catt 62 mins., J Worsley (Wasps) for Back 67 mins., K Bracken (Saracens) for Dawson 73 mins.. No new caps.

Scorers: Tries: Dallaglio (2), Balshaw (2), Hill, Greenwood. Pen: Wilkinson. Cons: Wilkinson (5).

SCOTLAND: C Paterson (Edinburgh Reivers); C Murray (Edinburgh Reivers), A Bulloch (Glasgwo Caledonians), J Leslie (Northampton), K Logan (Wasps); D Hodge (Edinburgh Reivers); A Nicol (Glasgow Caledonians)(captain); T Smith (Brive), G Bulloch (Glasgow Caledonians), M Stewart (Northampton), M Leslie (Edinburgh Reivers), S Murray (Saracens), R Metcalfe (Edinburgh Reivers), B Pountney (Northampton), S Taylor (Edinburgh Reivers). Replacements: C McIlwhan (Glasgow Caledonians) for Stewart 45 mins., S Grimes (Newcastle) for Metcalfe 46 mins., B Redpath (Sale) for Nicol 60 mins., J Craig (Glasgow Caledonians) for C Murray 70 mins., J McLaren (Glasgow Caledonians) for A Bulloch 75 mins.. Yellow card: Pountney 51-61 mins.. No new caps.

Scorer: Pen: Hodge. Half-time: 22-3.

Referee: R Davies, Wales. Attendance: 73,500.

ITALY 19-30 FRANCE

Attendance: 24,937   Half-time: 9-14

ITALY (Treviso unless stated): C Stoica (Narbonne); M Perziano, W Pozzebon, M Dallan, D Dallan; D Dominguez (Stade Francais), A Troncon (Montferrand); A Lo Cicero (Roma), A Moscardi (captain), T Paoletti (La Rochelle), A Perisco (Viadana), A Gritti, W Visser, M Bergamasco, C Checchinato.
Replacements: F Properzi Curti for Paoletti 46 mins., J-M Queirolo (Viadana) for Troncon 66 mins..
Scorers: Try: Perziano. Pens: Dominguez (4). Con: Dominguez.
FRANCE: J-L Sadourny (Colomiers); P Bernat-Salles (Biarritz), S Bonetti (Biarritz), T Lombard (Stade Francais), C Dominici (Stade Francais); C Lamaison (Agen), F Galthie (Colomiers); C Califano (Toulouse), R Ibanez (Castres), P de Villiers (Stade Francais), C Moni (Stade Francais), D Auradou (Stade Francais), F Pelous (Toulouse)(captain), O Magne (Montferrand), C Juillet (Stade Francais). Replacements: S Betsen (Biarritz) for Moni 40 mins., S Marconnet (Stade Francais) for Califano 52 mins.. New cap: Bonetti.
Scorers: Tries: Sadourny, Bernat-Salles, Bonetti. Pens: Lamaison (3). Cons: Lamaison (3). .
Referee: C White, England.

Match postponed   **WALES v IRELAND**
(Selected teams)
WALES: S Jones (Llanelli); G Thomas (Cardiff), M Taylor (Swansea), S Gibbs (Swansea), D James (Llanelli); N Jenkins (Cardiff), R Howley (Cardiff); D Morris (Swansea), R McBryde (Llanelli), D Young (Cardiff)(captain), C Charvis (Swansea), I Gough (Newport), A Moore (Swansea), M Williams (Cardiff), S Quinnell (Llanelli).
IRELAND: G Dempsey (Terenure College); D Hickie (St Mary's College), B O'Driscoll (Blackrock College), R Henderson (Wasps), T Howe (Dungannon); R O'Gara (Cork Constitution), P Stringer (Shannon); P Clohessy (Young Munster), K Wood (Harlequins)(captain), J Hayes (Shannon), A Quinlan (Shannon), M Galwey (Shannon), M O'Kelly (St Mary's College), D Wallace (Garryowen), A Foley (Shannon).

FOURTH ROUND

Saturday, 17th March 2001

FRANCE 35-43 WALES

Attendance: 80,000   Half-time: 19-16

FRANCE: J-L Sadourny (Colomiers); P Bernat-Salles (Biarritz), S Bonetti (Biarritz), T Lombard (Stade Francais), C Dominici (Stade Francais); C Merceron (Montferrand), F Galthie (Colomiers); C Califano (Toulouse), R Ibanez (Castres), P de Villiers (Stade Francais), C Moni (Stade Francais), D Auradou (Stade Francais), F Pelous (Toulouse)(captain), O Magne (Montferrand), C Juillet (Stade Francais). Replacements: C Lamaison (Agen) for Merceron 42 mins., S Betsen (Biarritz) for Moni 61 mins., S Marconnet (Stade Francais) for Califano 72 mins.. No new caps.
Scorers: Tries: Bonetti, Bernat-Salles. Pens: Merceron (4), Lamaison (3). Cons: Merceron, Lamaison.
WALES: R Williams (Cardiff); G Thomas (Cardiff), M Taylor (Swansea), S Gibbs (Swansea), D James (Llanelli); N Jenkins (Cardiff), R Howley (Cardiff); D Morris (Swansea), R McBryde (Llanelli), D Young (Cardiff)(captain), C Charvis (Swansea), I Gough (Newport), A Moore (Swansea), M Williams (Cardiff), S Quinnell (Llanelli). Replacements: S Jones (Llanelli) for Gibbs 52 mins., G Lewis (Pontypridd) for Charvis 64 mins., A Lewis (Cardiff) for Morris 73 mins., C Quinnell (Cardiff) Gough 75 mins.. No new caps.
Scorers: Tries: Howley, S Quinnell, James, Jenkins. DGs: Jenkins (2). Pens: Jenkins (3). Cons: Jenkins (4).

SCOTLAND 23 - 19 ITALY

Attendance: 60,708   Half-time: 6-10

SCOTLAND: C Paterson (Edinburgh Reivers), J Craig (Glasgow Caledonians), G Twonsend (Castres), J Leslie (Newcastle Falcons), K Logan (Wasps); D Hodge (Edinburgh Reivers), B Redpath (Edinburgh Reivers); T Smith (Brive), G Bulloch (Glasgow Caledonians), B Stewart (Northampton), M Leslie (Edinburgh Reivers), S Murray (Saracens), S Grimes (Newcastle Falcons), B Pountney (Northampton)(captain), S Taylor (Edinburgh Reivers). Replacements: G McIlwham (Glasgow Caledonians) for Stewart 40 mins., C Murray (Edinburgh Reivers) for Craig 45 mins., J Petrie (Glasgow Caledonians) for Taylor 74 mins., S Scott (Edinburgh Reivers) for Bulloch 77 mins..
Scorers: Try: Smith. DG: Hodge. Pens: Hodge (5).
ITALY (Treviso unless stated): C Stoica (Narbonne); M Perziano, W Pozzebon, M Dallan, L Martin (Northampton); D Dominguez (Stade Francais), F Prati (Parma); A Lo Cicero (Roma), A Moscardi (captain), F Properzi Curti, A Persico (Vaidana), W Visser, A Gritti, M Bergamasco, C Checchinato.
Replacements: M Mazzantini for Prati 30 mins., S Perugini (L'Aquila) for Properzi Curti 40 mins., G Raineri (Roma) for Dallan 43 mins., C Caione (Roma) for Gritti 58 mins.. Yellow card: Checchinato 48-58 mins..
Scorers: Try: Bergamasco. Pens: Dominguez (4). Con: Dominguez.
Referee: J Dume, France. .

FIFTH ROUND

Saturday, 7th April 2001

ENGLAND 48-19 FRANCE

Attendance: 75,000
Half-time: 13-16
ENGLAND: I Balshaw (Bath); A Healey (Leicester), W Greenwood (Leicester), M Catt (Bath), B Cohen (Northampton); J Wilkinson (Newcastle), M Dawson (Northampton); J Leonard (Harlequins), P Greening (Wasps), J White (Saracens), R Hill (Saracens), M Johnson (Leicester)(captain), S Borthwick (Bath), N Back (Leicester), L Dallaglio (Wasps). Replacements: J Robinson (Sale) for Cohen 56 mins., J Worsley (Wasps) for Hill 77 mins., M Perry (Bath) for Balshaw 77 mins., K Bracken (Saracens) for Dawson 80 mins.. Temporary replacements: D West (Leicester) for Greening 19-28 mins., M Corry (Leicester) for Borthwick 30-78 mins., D Flatman (Saracens) for Leonard 41-46 mins.. New cap: Borthwick.
Scorers: Tries: Greenwood, Hill, Balshaw, Greening, Catt, Perry. Pens: Wilkinson (2). Cons: Wilkinson (6).
FRANCE: J-L Sadourny (Colomiers); P Bernat-Salles (Biarritz), X Garbajosa (Toulouse), S Glas (Bourgoin), C Dominici (Stade Francais); G Merceron (Montferrand), F Galthie (Colomiers); S Marconnet (Stade Francais), R Ibanez (Castres), P de Villiers (Stade Francais), C Milheres (Biarritz), L Naillet (Bourgoin), A Benazzi (Agen), O Magne (Montferrand), F Pelous (Toulouse)(captain). Replacements: D Auradou (Stade Francais) for Nallet 45 mins., T Lievremont (Biarritz) for Benazzi 45 mins., F Landreau (Stade Francais) for Ibanez 56 mins., A Galasson (Montferrand) for de Villiers 77 mins.. New cap: Milheres.
Scorers: Try: Bernat-Salles. DG: Merceron. Pens: Merceron (3). Con: Merceron. .
Referee: T Henning, South Africa (replaced by D McHugh, Ireland, after 45 mins..
By scoring 18 points J Wilkinson set a new England record of 407 in internationals on his 27th appearance.

Sunday, 8th April 2001

ITALY 23-33 WALES

Attendance: 25,000
Half-time: 12-18
ITALY (Treviso unless stated): C Stoica (Narbonne); M Perziano, W Pozzebon, G Raineri (Roma), D Dallan; D Dominguez (Stade Francais), M Mazzantini; A Lo Cicero (Roma), A Moscardi (captain), F Properzi-Curti, A Persico (Viadana), W Visser, A Gritti, M Bergamasco, C Checchinato. Replacements: S Perugini (L'Aquila) for Properzi-Curti 47 mins., C Pilat (Roma) for Raineri 50 mins., M Zaffiri (L'Aquila) for Gritti 63 mins., G de Carli (Roma) for Lo Cicero 76 mins., L Martin (Northampton) for Pozzebon 80 mins.. Yellow card: Stoica 72 mins..
Scorers: Try: Checchinato. DG: Dominguez. Pens: Dominguez (5).
WALES: R Williams (Cardiff); G Thomas (Cardiff), M Taylor (Swansea), S Gibbs (Swansea), D James (Llanelli); N Jenkins (Cardiff), G Cooper (Bath); D Morris (Swansea), R McBryde (Llanelli), D Young (Cardiff)(captain), C Charvis (Swansea), U Gough (Newport), A Moore (Swansea), M Williams (Cardiff), S Quinnell (Llanelli). Replacement: C Quinnell (Cardiff) for Gough 50 mins.. Temp. replacement: A Bateman (Northampton) for Taylor 35-40 mins.. Yellow card: C Quinnell 74 mins..
Scorers: Tries: Gibbs (2), Cooper. Pens: N Jenkins (4). Cons: N Jenkins (3).
Referee: P Honiss, New Zealand.

CLUB INDEX

CLUB INDEX

CLUB INDEX

CLUB INDEX

725

CLUB INDEX

CLUB INDEX

CLUB INDEX

731

Southampton Institute	Hampshire 3	L - 581-622
Southend	London 2 North	L - 581-622
Southgate	Herts/Middlesex 4 North	L - 581-622
*Southmead	Gloucester 2	SW - 641-670
Southport	South Lancs/Cheshire 2	N - 477-508
*Southwell	NLD/Leics 1 East	M - 525-558
Southwold	Eastern Counties 3 North	L - 581-622
Spalding	Midlands 2 East	M - 525-558
*Spartans (Midlands)	Warwickshire 1	M - 525-558
*Spartans	Gloucester Premier	SW - 641-670
St Agnes	Cornwall 1	SW - 641-670
*St Albans	London 4 North West	L - 581-622
St Austell	Western Counties West	SW - 641-670
*St Benedict's	North Lancs/Cumbria	N - 477-508
*St Bernadettes Old Boys	Somerset Premier	SW - 641-670
*St Brendans Old Boys	Gloucester 2	SW - 641-670
*St Columba & Torpoint	Devon 3	SW - 641-670
St Day	Cornwall 2	SW - 641-670
*St Edward's O.B.	South Lancs/Cheshire 1	N - 477-508
St Francis	Sussex 1	L - 581-622
St Ives (Midlands)	East Midlands 1	M - 525-558
St Ives (SW)	Cornwall & Devon	SW - 641-670
*St Just	Western Counties West	SW - 641-670
St Mary's O.B. (Lancs)	South Lancs/Cheshire 2	N - 477-508
*St Mary's O.B. (SW)	Western Counties North	SW - 641-670
*St Neots	East Midlands 2	M - 525-558
St Nicholas O.B.	Herts/Middlesex 3 South	L - 581-622
Stafford	Midlands 2 West	M - 525-558
Staines	London 1	563-6
Stamford	NLD/Leics 1 East	M - 525-558
Stamford College	NLD/Leics 2 East	M - 525-558
Standard	Warwickshire 1	M - 525-558
Stanford Le Hope	Eastern Counties 1	L - 581-622
Stanley Rodillians	Yorkshire 4	N - 477-508
Stevenage Town	Herts/Middlesex 1	L - 581-622
Stewarts & Lloyds	Midlands 3 East (South)	M - 525-558
*Stithians	Cornwall 2	SW - 641-670
Stockwood Park	Midlands 3 East (South)	M - 525-558
Stockport	North 2 West	N - 477-508
Stocksbridge	Yorkshire 3	N - 477-508
Stockton	North 2 East	N - 477-508
Stoke Old Boys	Warwickshire 1	M - 525-558
Stoke on Trent	Midlands 2 West	M - 525-558
*Stone	Staffordshire 2	M - 525-558
*Stoneygate	Midlands 3 East (North)	M - 525-558
Stothert & Pitt	Somerset 1	SW - 641-670
STOURBRIDGE	National 2	289
Stourport	Midlands 4 West (South)	M - 525-558
Stowmarket	Eastern Counties 2 North	L - 581-622
Stow-on-the-Wold	South West 2 East	SW - 641-670
Stratford-Upon-Avon	Midlands 2 West	M - 525-558
*Streatham-Croydon	Surrey 2	L - 581-622
Stroud	South West 1	627-30
Sudbury	London 2 North	L - 581-622
Sudbury and London Springboks	Herts/Middlesex 4 South	L - 581-622
Sunderland	Durham/Northumberland 2	N - 477-508
*Supermarine	Dorset & Wilts 2 North	SW - 641-670
*Sussex Police	Sussex 1	L - 581-622
Sutton & Epsom	London 1	563-6
Sutton Coldfield	Midlands 2 West	M - 525-558

Uttoxeter	Staffordshire 1	M - 525-558
Uxbridge	Herts/Middlesex 1	L - 581-622
Vagabonds (I.O.M.)	South Lancs/Cheshire 1	N - 477-508
*Vale of Lune	North 2 West	N - 477-508
Vauxhall Motors	East Midlands 2	M - 525-558
*Ventnor	Hampshire 2	L - 581-622
Veor	Cornwall 2	SW - 641-670
Verwood	Hampshire 3	L - 581-622
Veseyans	North Midlands 1	M - 525-558
Vickers Sports	Cumbria	N - 477-508
Vigo	Kent 3	L - 581-622
Vipers	Midlands 3 East (South)	M - 525-558
Vulcan	South Lancs/Cheshire 4	N - 477-508
Wadebridge Camels	Cornwall & Devon	SW - 641-670
WAKEFIELD	National 1	195
*Wakefield Cougars	Yorkshire 4	N - 477-508
Walcot Old Boys	Western Counties North	SW - 641-670
Walkington Rovers	Yorkshire 6	N - 477-508
Wallasey	South Lancs/Cheshire 2	N - 477-508
Wallingford	Berks/Bucks & Oxon 1	SW - 641-670
Wallsend	Durham/Northumberland 2	N - 477-508
*Walsall	Midland 1	513-6
Wandsworthians	Surrey 3	L - 581-622
Wanstead	Eastern Counties 2 South	L - 581-622
Ware	Herts/Middlesex 4 North	L - 581-622
*Warley	North Midlands 1	M - 525-558
Warlingham	London 4 South West	L - 581-622
Warminster	Dorset & Wilts 2 South	SW - 641-670
Warrington	North 2 West	N - 477-508
Warwick	Warwickshire 2	M - 525-558
Wasps	Herts/Middlesex 3 South	L - 581-622
WATERLOO	National 2	295
*Waterloo Vikings	South Lancs/Cheshire 5	N - 477-508
Watford	Herts/Middlesex 3 North	L - 581-622
*Wath on Dearne	Yorkshire 3	N - 477-508
Wearside	Durham/Northumberland 3	N - 477-508
Wednesbury	Midlands 4 West (North)	M - 525-558
Wellingborough	Midlands 2 East	M - 525-558
Wellingborough O.G.	East Midlands 1	M - 525-558
*Wellington	Cornwall & Devon	SW - 641-670
Wells	Somerset Premier	SW - 641-670
Welwyn	London 4 North West	L - 581-622
Wembley & Kodak	Herts/Middlesex 3 South	L - 581-622
Wensleydale	Durham/Northumberland 3	N - 477-508
Wessex	Cornwall & Devon	SW - 641-670
*West Bridgford	NLD/Leics 1 East	M - 525-558
WEST HARTLEPOOL	National 3 North	369
*West Hartlepool Amateurs	Durham/Northumberland 3	N - 477-508
West Hartlepool TDSOB	Durham/Northumberland 1	N - 477-508
West Leeds	Yorkshire 2	N - 477-508
*West London	London 3 North West	L - 581-622
West Norfolk	London 4 North East	L - 581-622
West Park Bramhope	Yorkshire 1	N - 477-508
West Park St Helens	North 1	463-7
West Park Warriors	North Lancs 2	N - 477-508
Westbury	Dorset & Wilts 1	SW - 641-670
Westbury on Severn	Gloucester 1	SW - 641-670
WESTCOMBE PARK	National 3 South	443
Westcliff	Eastern Counties 2 South	L - 581-622
*Westoe	North 2 East	N - 477-508
Weston-Super-Mare	South West 1	627-30

CLUB INDEX

736